W9-CBE-459

The H. S. for Law Enforcement & Public Safety
116-25 Guy Brewer Boulevard
Jamaica, NY 11434

NYSTL

NEW YORK
LIVING ENVIRONMENT

Prentice Hall

Biology
NEW YORK STATE

Kenneth R. Miller, Ph.D.
Professor of Biology
Brown University
Providence, Rhode Island

Joseph Levine, Ph.D.
Science Writer and Producer
Concord, Massachusetts

Prentice Hall

Upper Saddle River, New Jersey
Glenview, Illinois
Needham, Massachusetts

Print Components

New York Student Edition
New York Teacher's Edition
New York Teaching and Planning Guide
Laboratory Manual A
Laboratory Manual A,
  Annotated Teacher's Edition
Laboratory Manual B
Laboratory Manual B,
  Annotated Teacher's Edition
Teaching Resources
Guided Reading and Study Workbook
Cuaderno de orientación al estudio y
  a la lectura
Guided Reading and Study Workbook,
  Annotated Teacher's Edition
Chapter Tests: Levels A and B
Pruebas de los capítulos
Computer Test Bank
Biotechnology Manual
Prentice Hall Assessment System
Laboratory Assessment With
  Scoring Guide
Issues and Decision Making

Technology

Presentation Assistant Plus
  Teaching Transparencies Package
  Prentice Hall Presentation Pro CD-ROM
Biology iText CD-ROM
Biology iText Web Site
BioDetectives Videotapes With BioDetectives:
  Investigations in Forensics
Prentice Hall Web Site With *Science News*®
Resource Pro® CD-ROM
Computer Test Bank CD-ROM
ABC Videotapes

Acknowledgments appear on page 1110, which constitutes an extension of this copyright page.

ISBN 0-13-063163-9
5 6 7 8 9 10   07 06 05 04 03

Kenneth R. Miller grew up in Rahway, New Jersey, attended the local public schools, and graduated from Rahway High School in 1966. Miller attended Brown University on a scholarship and graduated with honors. He was awarded a National Defense Education Act fellowship for graduate study, and earned his Ph.D. in Biology at the University of Colorado. Miller is Professor of Biology at Brown University in Providence, Rhode Island, where he teaches courses in general biology and cell biology.

Miller's research specialty is the structure of biological membranes. He has published more than 70 research papers in journals such as *CELL, Nature,* and *Scientific American.* In 1999, he wrote the popular trade book *Finding Darwin's God.*

Miller lives with his wife, Jody, on a small farm in Rehoboth, Massachusetts. He is the father of two daughters, one of whom is a wildlife biologist. He swims competitively in the masters' swimming program and umpires high school and collegiate softball.

Joseph S. Levine was born in Mount Vernon, New York, where he attended public schools. He earned a B.S. in Biology at Tufts University, a master's degree from the Boston University Marine Program, and a Ph.D. at Harvard University. His research has been published in scientific journals ranging from *Science* to *Scientific American,* and in several academic books. He taught introductory biology, marine ecology, and neurobiology for six years at Boston College.

After receiving a Macy Fellowship in Science Broadcast Journalism at WGBH-TV, Levine dedicated himself to improving public understanding of science. His popular scientific writing has appeared in five trade books and in magazines such as *Smithsonian, GEO,* and *Natural History.* He has produced science features for National Public Radio and has designed exhibit programs for state aquarium projects in Texas, New Jersey, and Florida.

Since 1987, Levine has served as scientific advisor at WGBH, where he worked on *NOVA* programs and on projects including the film *Cocos: Island of Sharks* and the series *The Secret of Life.* Most recently, he served as Science Editor for *The Evolution Project.*

Levine and his family live in Concord, Massachusetts, a short distance from Thoreau's Walden Pond.

John Bartsch

Bartsch, a biology teacher for 34 years, has been a consultant to the New York State Education Department for the development of The Living Environment Core Curriculum, and currently works with their Office of State Assessment.

Mary Colvard

Colvard is an award-winning New York high school biology educator and has served on a number of State and National panels. Currently she is a consultant to the New York State Education Department, and served as a member of the writing team for The Living Environment Core Curriculum.

Elise Russo

Russo was an associate at the New York State Education Department, where she coordinated the development of The Living Environment Core Curriculum documents. In addition, she was the content specialist for The Living Environment Regents Exam in the Office of State Assessment.

Reading Consultant

Bonnie Armbruster, Ph.D.
Department of Curriculum
and Instruction
University of Illinois
Champaign, IL

Kathy Laney
Hicksvillle HS
Hicksville, OH

Neo/SCI
Rochester, NY

Safety Consultant

Douglas Mandt
Lab Safety Consultant
Edgewood, WA

Lab Activity Consultant

Paul C. Johnson
University of New Hampshire
Durham, NH

Activity Writers

Patsye Peebles
Louisiana State University
Lab School
Baton Rouge, LA

Herbert L. Saxon, Ed.D.
Ball State University
Muncie, IN

Content Reviewers

J. David Archibald, Ph.D.
Professor of Biology
Curator of Mammals
San Diego State University
San Diego, CA

David M. Armstrong
Professor
Environmental, Population,
and Organismic Biology
University of Colorado
Boulder, CO

Katharine Atkinson
Associate Professor
of Cell Biology
Department of Cell Biology
and Neuroscience
University of California
Riverside, CA

David L. Brautigan
Director, Center for
Cell Signaling
Professor, Microbiology and
Medicine (Endocrinology)
University of Virginia
Charlottesville, VA

Elizabeth Coolidge-Stolz, MD
Medical Writer
North Reading, MA

Dr. Darleen A. DeMason
Botany and Plant Sciences
University of California,
Riverside
Riverside, CA

Elizabeth De Stasio
Raymond H. Herzog
Professor of Science and
Associate Professor of
Biology
Lawrence University
Appleton, WI

Betsey Dyer
Professor of Biology
Wheaton College
Norton, MA

Milton Fingerman
Professor of Biology
Department of Ecology
and Evolutionary Biology
Tulane University
New Orleans, LA

Katherine Glew
Assistant Professor
University of Puget Sound
Tacoma, WA

Deborah L. Gumucio, Ph.D.
Associate Professor
Department of Cell and
Developmental Biology
University of Michigan
Medical School
Ann Arbor, MI

Paul R. Haberstroh, Ph.D.
Assistant Professor of
Chemical Oceanography
Department of Marine Science
University of Hawaii at Hilo
Hilo, HI

Evan B. Hazard, Ph.D.
Professor Emeritus of Biology
Bemidji State University
Bemidji, MN

Donald C. Jackson
Professor of Physiology
Brown University
Providence, RI

Jeremiah N. Jarrett
Assistant Professor
Department of Biological
Sciences
Central Connecticut State
University
New Britain, CT

Kirk Johnson
Curator of Paleontology
Denver Museum of
Nature and Science
Denver, CO

Ted Johnson, Ph.D.
Professor of Biology
St. Olaf College
Northfield, MN

Joe Leverich, Ph.D.
Professor
Biology Department
St. Louis University
St. Louis, MO

Martin K. Nickels, Ph.D.
Professor of Physical
Anthropology
Illinois State University
Normal, IL

Gerald P. Sanders, Sr.
Biology Publishing Consultant
Former Biology Instructor at
Grossmont College
El Cajon, CA

Ronald L. Sass, Ph.D.
Professor of Biology,
Chemistry, and Education
Department of Ecology and
Evolutionary Biology
Rice University
Houston, TX

David Scholnick
Assistant Professor
Eckerd College
St. Petersburg, FL

Dr. Dilbagh Singh
Professor of Biology
Blackburn College
Carlinville, IL

Bruce A. Wilcox
Affiliate Faculty
University of Hawaii
Kailua, HI

Alan C. Yen
Research Fellow
Harvard University
Cambridge, MA

Bruce A. Young
Professor of Biology
Department of Biology
Lafayette College
Easton, PA

Edward J. Zalisko
Professor of Biology
Illinois Professor of
the Year, 2000
Blackburn College
Carlinville, IL

High School Reviewers and Contributing Writers

Dr. William C. Alexander
So. Carolina Governor's School
  for Science and Mathematics
Hartsville, SC

Myron E. Blosser
Harrisonburg High School
Harrisonburg, VA

James Boal
Natrona County High School
Casper, WY

Jan Bowersox
Nathan Hale High School
Seattle, WA

LouEllen Parker Brademan
Potomac Senior High School
Dumfries, VA

Heidi Busa
Marcellus High School
Marcellus, NY

Dr. Charles E. Campbell
Burbank High School
Burbank, CA

Robert Campbell
Wilson Classical High School
Long Beach, CA

Beverly Cea
Grimsley High School
Greensboro, NC

Bob Culler
Avon Lake High School
Avon Lake, OH

Don Morris Curry
Silverado High School
Las Vegas, NV

Liz Dann
Phoenix Country Day School
Paradise Valley, AZ

Bob Demmink
East Kentwood High School
Kentwood, MI

Eloise Farmer
Torrington High School
Torrington, CT

Dale Faughn
Caldwell County High School
Princeton, KY

Steve Ferguson
Lee's Summit High School
Lee's Summit, MO

Diedre Galvin
Ridgewood High School
Ridgewood, NJ

Dennis Glasgow
Little Rock School District
Little Rock, AR

Ruth Gleicher
Niles West High School
Skokie, IL

John E. Gonzales
Temescal Canyon High School
Lake Elsinore, CA

Betsy Halpern
South Eugene High School
Eugene, OR

Dick Jordan
Timberline High School
Boise, ID

Marion LaFemina
Ridgewood High School
Ridgewood, NJ

Janice Lagatol
Fort Lee High School
Fort Lee, NJ

Leon Lange
Fort Campbell High School
Fort Campbell, KY

Michael I. Lopatka
Edgewater High School
Orlando, FL

Sue Madden
Chippewa Valley High School
Clinton Township, MI

Lora L. Marschall
Nathan Hale High School
Tulsa, OK

Gregory W. McCurdy
Salem High School
Salem, IN

Lynne M. McElhaney
LeFlore High School
Mobile, AL

Tamsen Knowlton Meyer
Boulder High School
Boulder, CO

Francis K. Mustapha
Snider High School
Fort Wayne, IN

Duane Nichols
Alhambra High School
Alhambra, CA

Joe E. Nunley, Jr.
Riverdale High School
Murfreesboro, TN

Richard K. Orgeron
Carencro High School
Lafayette, LA

Charlotte M. Parnell
Lakeside High School
Hot Springs, AR

Wendy Peterson
Velva High School
Velva, ND

Amelia Quillen
Smyrna High School
Smyrna, DE

Tracy Rader
Fulton Jr. High School
Indianapolis, IN

Debbie Richards
Bryan High School
Bryan, TX

Kathey A. Roberts
Lakeside High School
Hot Springs, AR

Dr. Thomas P. Rooney
Father Judge High School
Philadelphia, PA

Linda S. Samuels
Dana Hall School
Wellesley, MA

Jorge E. Sanchez
Green Valley High School
Henderson, NV

Sheila Smith
Terry High School
Terry, MS

Bob Sprang
Mitchell Public High School
Mitchell, SD

Tracy Swedlund
Medford Area Senior High
Medford, WI

Frank Tworek
Omaha North High School
Omaha, NE

Brenda Waldon
Clayton County Public
  Schools
Morrow, GA

Adam Weiss
Essex High School
Essex Junction, VT

Audra J. Williams
Sprayberry High School
Marietta, GA

Activity Testers

Diane Clark
Monticello High School
Charlottesville, VA

Lucy M. Fern
Ridgewood High School
Ridgewood, NJ

Laine Gurley, Ph.D.
Rolling Meadows High School
Rolling Meadows, IL

Patricia Anne Johnson
Ridgewood High School
Ridgewood, NJ

Wade Mercer
Fairhill School
Dallas, TX

Dwight Taylor
Goldenview Middle School
Anchorage, AK

Contents

UNIT 3   Cells   166–259

UNIT 4   Genetics   260–365

UNIT 5 Evolution 366–467

UNIT 6 Microorganisms and Fungi 468–547

UNIT 7 Plants 548–653

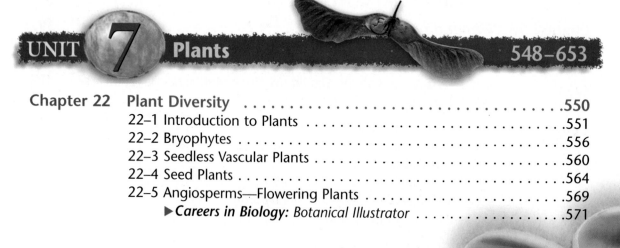

UNIT 8 Invertebrates   654–763

UNIT 9   Chordates   764–887

UNIT 10 — The Human Body — 888–1053

Labs and Activities

Inquiry Activity

**Opportunities for exploration
and inquiry before reading**

Quick Lab

**Activities that reinforce
key biological concepts**

Real-World Lab

Labs that demonstrate everyday applications of biological concepts

Design an Experiment

Labs that build key science skills

Exploration

Labs that provide in-depth exploration of biological concepts

Analyzing Data

Activities that provide students opportunities to interpret data and draw conclusions

Threats to Coral Reefs

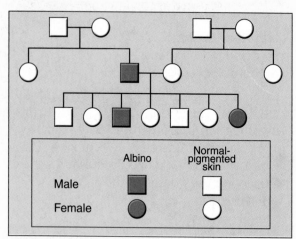

Albino   Normal-pigmented skin

Male

Female

Problem Solving

Activities that build critical-thinking skills

Features

Features that relate content to current issues

Features that relate content to current technological advances

Biology and History

Time lines that place biology in a social and historical context

Careers in Biology

Relates biology to actual occupations

Dear Student

Joe Levine and I wrote this book for a very simple reason: We wanted to let you in on a secret. Biology isn't just a "subject" in school. Biology is the science of life itself. Biology is the study of what makes an eagle fly, a flower bloom, or a caterpillar turn into a butterfly. It's the study of ourselves—of how our bodies grow and change and respond to the outside world, and it's the study of our planet, a world transformed by the actions of living things. Of course, you might have known some of this already. So, what's the secret?

The secret is that you've come along at just the right time. In all of human history, there has never been a moment like the present, a time when we stood so close to the threshold of answering the most fundamental questions about the nature of life. You belong to the first generation of students who can read the human genome almost as your parents might have read a book or a newspaper. You are the first students who will grow up in a world that has a chance to use that information for the benefit of humanity, and you are the very first to bear the burden of using that knowledge wisely.

If all of this seems like heavy stuff, it is. But there is another reason we wrote this book, and we hope that is not a secret at all. Science is fun! Biologists aren't a bunch of serious, grim-faced, middle-aged folks in lab coats who think of nothing but work. In fact, most of the people we know in science would tell you honestly, with broad grins on their faces,

that they have the best jobs in the world. They would say there's nothing that compares to the excitement of doing scientific work, and that the beauty and variety of life make every day a new adventure.

We agree, and we hope that you'll keep something in mind as you begin the study of biology. You don't need a lab coat or a degree or a laboratory to be a scientist. What you do need is an inquiring mind, the patience to look at nature carefully, and the willingness to figure things out. We've filled this book with some of the latest and most important discoveries about living things, but we hope we've also filled it with something else: our wonder, our amazement, and our sheer delight in the variety of life itself. Come on in, and enjoy the journey!

Sincerely,

Dear Student

What do you think about biology? Are you interested in the natural world and the workings of your body? Or could you care less, and do you find yourself wondering "What's in it for me?" However you think, Ken and I wrote this book to convince you that biology is exciting, fascinating—and important to you. In fact, biology is more important to the daily lives of all humans today than it has ever been.

Why? You could answer in three words: "We are one." Now, this is a science text, so this statement isn't meant in any kind of "touchy-feely" or "New Age" way. "We" means all living things on earth. And "are one" means that all of us are tied together more tightly, in more different ways, than anyone ever dreamed of until recently. That's what biology tells us.

All forms of life—from bacteria to palm trees to humans—are based on information written in a single, universal code carried in our genes. As biologists "read" those genes, they find nearly identical instructions directing life's processes in all of us. That's why medical researchers can learn about human diseases—diseases that may strike you or your family—by studying yeast. We are one on the molecular level.

All organisms interact with one another and with the environment in ways that create our planet's web of life. Organisms make tropical rain forests and coral reefs, prairies and swamps—and farms and cities. Our interactions involve not only each other—but also the winds and ocean currents that tie our planet together. Human activity can change, and is changing, local and global environments in ways that alter our ability to produce food and protect ourselves from diseases. We are one on the global ecological level.

All organisms change over time as they adapt to their surroundings. If humans alter the environment, we encourage other organisms to change. When we deploy antibiotics against bacteria, they develop resistance to our drugs. If we use pesticides against insects, they become immune to our poisons. We are one in our ability to evolve over time.

Those are the kinds of connections you will find in this book. Microscopic. Enormous. Amusing. Threatening. But always fascinating. That's why—no matter where you start off in your attitude about biology—we think you are in for some surprises!

Sincerely,

Joe Levine

New York State Living Environment
Core Curriculum

The state of New York has established standards describing science knowledge and skills you will learn this year. At first glance, learning all this information may seem overwhelming. In the following pages, however, we provide examples of how this book will help you gain the knowledge and skills you need to be successful. Listed below are the seven learning standards for mathematics, science, and technology that your curriculum is based on. Standards 2, 6, and 7 address the interconnectedness between biology, math, and other science disciplines. Your book will cover these three standards by teaching how current technologies affect biology, and by providing real-world examples of how biology,

math, chemistry, and other disciplines are used. Standards 1 and 4 outline the inquiry skills and biology content that you are expected to learn. You will find a review of these two standards in depth in the following pages.

To check your mastery of your new skills and knowledge, you may use the Preparing for the Living Environment Exam section at the end of each chapter. Also, don't forget to make use of our Take It to the Net feature located at: **www.phschool.com**

Learning Standards for Mathematics, Science, and Technology

STANDARD 1
Students will use mathematical analysis, scientific inquiry, and engineering design, as appropriate, to pose questions, seek answers, and develop solutions.

STANDARD 2
Students will access, generate, process, and transfer information using appropriate technologies.

STANDARD 3
Students will understand mathematics and become mathematically confident by communicating and reasoning mathematically, by applying mathematics in real-world settings, and by solving problems through the integrated study of number systems, geometry, algebra, data analysis, probability, and trigonometry.

STANDARD 4
Students will understand and apply scientific concepts, principles, and theories pertaining to the physical setting and living environment and recognize the historical development of ideas in science.

STANDARD 5
Students will apply technological knowledge and skills to design, construct, use, and evaluate products and systems to satisfy human and environmental needs.

STANDARD 6
Students will understand the relationships and common themes that connect mathematics, science, and technology and apply the themes to these and other areas of learning.

STANDARD 7
Students will apply the knowledge and thinking skills of mathematics, science, and technology to address real-life problems and make informed decisions.

STANDARD 1
Students will use mathematical analysis, scientific inquiry, and engineering designs, as appropriate, to pose questions, seek answers, and develop solutions.

Key Idea 1

The central purpose of scientific inquiry is to develop explanations of natural phenomena in a continuing and creative process.

1.1 Elaborate on basic scientific and personal explanations of natural phenomena, and develop extended visual models and mathematical formulations to represent one's thinking.

Example: You will build a model of the food chain to explain why pesticides accumulate in certain animals. (Chapter 6)

1.2 Hone ideas through reasoning, library research, and discussion with others, including experts.

Example: You will discuss controversial topics challenging biologists today, such as the safety of herbal drugs. (Chapter 25)

1.3 Work toward reconciling competing explanations; clarify points of agreement and disagreement.

Example: You will discover that all scientific explanations are tentative and subject to change or improvement. (Section 15–2)

1.4 Coordinate explanations at different levels of scale, points of focus, and degrees of complexity and specificity, and recognize the need for such alternative representations of the natural world.

Example: You will learn how a theory develops and becomes well accepted. (Section 1–1)

Key Idea 2

Beyond the use of reasoning and consensus, scientific inquiry involves the testing of proposed explanations involving the use of conventional techniques and procedures and usually requiring considerable ingenuity.

2.1 Devise ways of making observations to test proposed explanations.

Example: You will design an experiment to determine the effects of temperature on enzyme activity. (Chapter 2)

2.2 Refine research ideas through library investigations, including electronic information retrieval and reviews of the literature, and through peer feedback obtained from review and discussion.

Example: You will visit the Prentice Hall Web site (www.phschool.com) for extended learning opportunities. (each chapter)

2.3 Develop and present proposals including formal hypotheses to test explanations; i.e., predict what should be observed under specific conditions if the explanation is true.

Example: You will develop a hypothesis on how a lack of light effects photosynthesis. (Chapter 8)

2.4 Carry out a research plan for testing explanations, including selecting and developing techniques, acquiring and building apparatus, and recording observations as necessary.

Example: You will design an experiment to investigate homeostasis in fishes and amphibians. (Chapter 30)

Key Idea 3

The observations made while testing explanations, when analyzed using conventional and invented methods, provide new insights into natural phenomena.

3.1 Use various methods of representing and organizing observations (e.g. diagrams, tables, charts, graphs, equations, matrices) and insightfully interpret the organized data.

Example: You will build a chart that allows you to examine how hydra respond to stimuli. (Chapter 26)

Standard 1, Key Ideas and Performance Indicators (cont'd.)

3.2 Apply statistical analysis techniques when appropriate to test if chance alone explains the results.

Example: You will study the ban on CFCs and determine whether the ban has helped the environment. (Section 6–4)

3.3 Assess correspondence between the predicted result contained in the hypothesis and actual result, and reach a conclusion as to whether the explanation on which the prediction was based is supported.

Example: You will learn how to test whether a hypothesis is true or false. (Chapter 1)

3.4 Based on the results of the test and through public discussion, revise the explanation and contemplate additional research.

Example: You will learn that claims should be questioned if fact and opinion are intermingled. (Chapter 25)

3.5 Develop a written report for public scrutiny that describes the proposed explanation, including a literature review, the research carried out, its results, and suggestions for further research.

Example: You will write lab reports detailing your discoveries. (Chapter 18)

Standard 4, Key Ideas and Performance Indicators

STANDARD 4: Students will understand and apply scientific concepts, principles, and theories pertaining to the physical setting and living environment and recognize the historical development of ideas in science.

Key Idea 1

Living things are both similar to and different from each other and from nonliving things.

1.1 Explain how diversity of populations within ecosystems relates to the stability of ecosystems.

Example: You will learn that an ecosystem is shaped by weather and climate, as well as by its interacting species. (Section 4–1)

1.2 Describe and explain the structures and functions of the human body at different organizational levels (e.g. systems, tissues, cells, organelles.)

Example 1: You will examine the human body's complex systems in depth. (Chapters 35–40)

Example 2: You will delve into great detail about the reproductive, digestive, circulatory, nervous systems, and more. (Chapters 35–40)

1.3 Explain how a one-celled organism is able to function despite lacking the levels of organization present in more complex organisms.

Example: You will learn how a cell moves material through its membrane by active transport. (Section 7–3)

Key Idea 2

Organisms inherit genetic information in a variety of ways that result in continuity of structure and function between parents and offspring.

2.1 Explain how the structure and replication of genetic material result in offspring that resemble their parents.

Example: You will build a model of cell division to better understand heredity. (Section 11–4)

2.2 Explain how the technology of genetic engineering allows humans to alter genetic makeup of organisms.

Example 1: You will study bacteria cell transformation. (Section 13–3)

Example 2: You will learn how selective breeding is used to obtain desirable traits in certain animals. (Section 13–1)

Key Idea 3

The observations made while testing explanations, when analyzed using conventional and invented methods, provide new insights into natural phenomena.

3.1 Explain the mechanisms and patterns of evolution.

Example: You will build a model civilization to understand how changes in the environment affect survival. (Section 15–3)

Key Idea 4

The continuity of life is sustained through reproduction and development.

4.1 Explain how organisms, including humans, reproduce their own kind.

Example: You will investigate the human reproductive system. (Section 39–3)

Key Idea 5

Organisms maintain a dynamic equilibrium that sustains life.

5.1 Explain the basic biochemical processes in living organisms and their importance in maintaining dynamic equilibrium.

Example: You will learn how a cell's membrane regulates what enters and leaves the cell. (Section 7–3)

5.2 Explain disease as a failure of homeostasis.

Example: You will learn how the human body's immune system functions. (Chapter 40)

5.3 Relate processes at the system level to the cellular level in order to explain dynamic equilibrium in multicelled organisms.

Example: You will examine how kidneys help maintain a chemical balance inside the human body. (Section 38–3)

Key Idea 6

Plants and animals depend on each other and their physical environment.

6.1 Explain factors that limit growth of individuals and populations.

Example: You will study how human population has changed through the years. (Section 5–3)

6.2 Explain the importance of preserving diversity of species and habitats

Example: You will learn strategies for conservation. (Section 6–3)

6.3 Explain how the living and nonliving environments change over time and respond to disturbances.

Example: You will learn how geology effects evolution. (Section 16–3)

Key Idea 7

Human decisions and activities have had a profound impact on the physical and living environment.

7.1 Describe the range of interrelationships of humans with the living and nonliving environment.

Example: You will conduct an experiment to understand the effects of acid rain. (Section 6–4)

7.2 Explain the impact of technological development and growth in the human population on the living and nonliving environment.

Example: You will learn how antibiotics have affected human health. (Section 19–2)

7.3 Explain how individual choices and societal actions can contribute to improving the environment.

Example: You will learn the importance of renewable resources. (Section 6–2)

Use This Book for Success

See the book as a whole.

Knowing the chapter organization makes studying easier.

Contents

The table of contents, glossary, and index help you find specific topics.

Read for mastery.

 Key Concepts are clearly identified.

Guide for Reading

Key Concept
• What factors limit population growth?

Vocabulary
limiting factor
density-dependent limiting factor
density-independent limiting factor
predator-prey relationship

Reading Strategy: Predicting Before you read, preview the diagram in **Figure 5–5.** Predict how each factor might limit the growth of a population. As you read, note whether your predictions were correct or incorrect.

Use concrete strategies for active learning.

level. These factors operate most strongly when a population is large and dense, and do not usually affect small, scattered populations. **Density-dependent limiting factors include competition, predation, parasitism, and disease.**

✔CHECKPOINT *What is a density-dependent limiting factor?*

5–2 Section Assessment

1. **Key Concept** List three density-dependent factors and three density-independent factors that can limit the growth of a population.
2. What is the relationship between competition and population size?
3. If an entire lynx population disappears, what is likely to happen to the hare population on which it preys?

4. **Critical Thinking Applying Concepts** Give an example of a density-independent limiting factor that has affected a human population. Describe how this factor changed the human population.

iTEXT Assessment Use iText to review the important concepts in Section 5–2.

MAKING CONNECTIONS

Biotic and Abiotic Factors Study the factors that limit population growth in **Figure 5–5.** Classify each factor as either biotic or abiotic. (*Hint:* Refer to the information on biotic and abiotic factors in Section 4–2.)

Monitor your progress.

Visualize the content.

Photographs
Photographs of real-world examples make topics memorable.

The eastern meadowlark (left) and western meadowlark (right) have overlapping ranges. They do not interbreed, however, because they have different mating songs.
Applying Concepts *What type of reproductive isolation does this situation illustrate?*

Caption questions reinforce knowledge and deepen understanding.

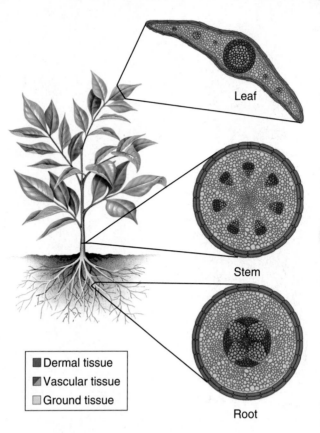

Leaf

Stem

Root

- ■ Dermal tissue
- ▨ Vascular tissue
- ☐ Ground tissue

Diagrams
Diagrams break down complex ideas and demonstrate abstract processes.

Prepare for the Living Environment Exam.

Review each chapter with test questions similar to the ones found on the New York Living Environment Regents Exam.

Measure your knowledge with self-administered tests.

UNIT 1

Chapters

The Nature of Life

▶ The ocean floor off the coast of New Guinea is home to many forms of life. Small fish called basslets swim gracefully among the rocks and coral, while yellow feather star crinoids grow out of plate corals. Feather star crinoids are relatives of sea stars.

What do we know about science and the nature of life?

- All life is based on a universal genetic code written in DNA. That's why we can learn about human cancer by studying yeast and mice!

- Scientific tools such as computers, gene-sequencing machines, and satellites provide more information about the living world than we ever dreamed possible.

- Science enables us to understand the natural world and offers the power to predict or influence natural events. That power gives us awesome responsibility.

What discoveries lie in the future?

- Can new tools and techniques for studying genes help biomedical researchers combat diseases such as diabetes and cancer?

- How will individuals, businesses, and politicians respond to new information about humanity's complicated effects on the living world?

- How will studies of life's smallest systems (molecules) affect our understanding of the largest biological systems (ecosystems and the biosphere)?

Chapter 1 The Science of Biology

Researchers paired this wood ant and microchip to show their relative sizes. A scanning electron microscope was used to make this image, which has been artificially colored.

Inquiry Activity

Can your procedure be replicated?

Procedure

1. Behind a screen, assemble 10 blocks into an unusual structure. Write directions that others can use to replicate that structure without seeing it.

2. Exchange directions with another team. Replicate the team's structure by using its directions.

3. Compare each replicated and original structure. Identify which parts of the directions were clear and accurate, and which were unclear or misleading.

Think About It

1. **Evaluating and Revising** How could you have written better directions?

2. **Inferring** Why is it important that scientists write procedures that can be replicated?

1–1 What Is Science?

One ancient evening, lost in the mists of time, someone looked into the sky and wondered for the first time: What are those lights? Where did plants and animals come from? How did I come to be? Since then, humans have tried to answer those questions. At first, the answers our ancestors came up with involved tales of magic or legends like the one that inspired the art in **Figure 1–1.** Then, slowly, humans began to explore the natural world using a scientific approach.

What Science Is and Is Not

What does it mean to say that an approach to a problem is scientific? **The goal of science is to investigate and understand nature, to explain events in nature, and to use those explanations to make useful predictions.**

Science has several features that make it different from other human endeavors. First, science deals only with the natural world. Second, scientists collect and organize information in a careful, orderly way, looking for patterns and connections between events. Third, scientists propose explanations that can be tested by examining evidence. In other words, **science** is an organized way of using evidence to learn about the natural world. The word *science* also refers to the body of knowledge that scientists have built up after years of using this process.

Guide for Reading

🔑 **Key Concept**
• What is the goal of science?

Vocabulary
science
observation
data
inference
hypothesis

Reading Strategy:
Making Comparisons As you read, list steps that scientists use to solve problems. After you read, compare the methods you use to solve problems with those used by scientists.

◀ **Figure 1–1** A Navajo artist, Harrison Begay, produced this painting called *Creation of North Sacred Mountain.* It shows the first woman and man interacting with nature.

▲ **Figure 1–2** ⊙ The goal of science is to investigate and understand nature. The first step in this process is making observations. This researcher is observing the behavior of a manatee in Florida.

Evidence Based on Observation

Science starts with observation. **Observation** involves using one or more of the senses—sight, hearing, touch, smell, and sometimes taste—to gather information. The information gathered from observations, such as those being made in **Figure 1–2,** is called evidence, or **data.**

Observations can be classified into two types. Quantitative observations involve numbers, for example, counting or measuring objects. An example of a quantitative observation is *There are seven birds at the feeder.* Qualitative observations involve characteristics that cannot be easily measured or counted, such as color or texture. A qualitative observation could be *One of the birds has a red head.* As scientists make observations, they try to be objective and avoid bias, which is a preference for a particular, predetermined point of view.

Interpreting the Evidence

An observation alone has little meaning in science, because the goal is to understand what was observed. Scientists usually follow observations with inferences. An **inference** is a logical interpretation based on prior knowledge and experience. For example, researchers might sample water from a reservoir, as shown in **Figure 1–3.** If samples collected from different parts of the reservoir are all clean enough to drink, the researchers may infer that all the water in the reservoir is safe to drink.

◀ **Figure 1–3** Researchers testing water for lead pollution cannot test every drop, so they check small amounts, called samples. **Inferring** *How might a local community use such scientific information?*

Explaining the Evidence

Suppose a group of people became ill with an unknown kind of infectious disease after attending a large public event. Health professionals would want to know how the people contracted the disease. They might form several hypotheses. A **hypothesis** is a possible explanation for a set of observations or an answer to a scientific question. In everyday settings, a hypothesis can be stated about any topic or idea. In science, a hypothesis is useful only if it can be tested.

In the infectious disease example, health professionals might propose several competing hypotheses: (1) The disease was spread by human contact. (2) The disease was spread through insect bites. (3) The disease was spread through contaminated air, water, or food. Evidence could be gathered to test each of these hypotheses. The incorrect hypotheses would be ruled out, and the correct explanation would eventually be found.

Scientific hypotheses may be developed and tested in different ways, often by researchers working in teams like the one in **Figure 1–4.** Hypotheses may arise from prior knowledge, logical inferences, or imaginative guesses. The testing may sometimes be done by making further observations or through careful questioning. Discovering how infected individuals contracted a disease, for instance, might require surveying what they did before developing the disease symptoms. Often, however, a hypothesis is tested through a controlled experiment, a procedure you'll learn about in the next section. The tests of a hypothesis may support it, or suggest that the hypothesis is partly true but needs to be revised. The tests may even prove that the hypothesis is wrong. No matter what the outcome, a tested hypothesis has value in science because it helps researchers advance scientific knowledge.

CHECKPOINT *How do scientists develop hypotheses?*

KEEP CURRENT WITH . . .
SCIENCE NEWS®

To find out more about the topics in this chapter, go to:
www.phschool.com

◀ **Figure 1–4** Researchers often work in teams, combining imagination and logic to develop and test hypotheses. **Applying Concepts** *How do scientists decide whether to accept or reject a hypothesis?*

A Scientific View of the World

People often think about everyday events in a scientific way. Suppose a car won't start. Perhaps it's out of gas. A glance at the fuel gauge tests that idea. Perhaps the battery is dead. An auto mechanic can use an instrument to test that idea. A logical person would continue to look for a mechanical explanation, testing one possible explanation after another until the cause of the problem was identified.

All scientists, including the researcher in **Figure 1–5,** bring the same kind of problem-solving attitude to their work. They consider the whole universe a system in which basic rules apply to all events, small or large. Scientists assume that those rules can be discovered through scientific inquiry. They collect data as a means of achieving their goal—a better understanding of nature. For scientists, science is an ongoing process, not the discovery of an unchanging, absolute truth. Scientific findings are always subject to revision as new evidence is developed.

In keeping with this approach to pursuing knowledge, certain qualities are desirable in a scientist: curiosity, honesty, open-mindedness, skepticism, and the recognition that science has limits. An open-minded person is ready to give up familiar ideas if the evidence demands it. A skeptical person continues to ask questions and looks for alternative explanations. Scientists are persuaded by logical arguments that are supported by evidence. Despite recognizing the power of science, scientists know that science has definite limits. Science cannot help you decide whether a painting is beautiful or cheating on a test is wrong.

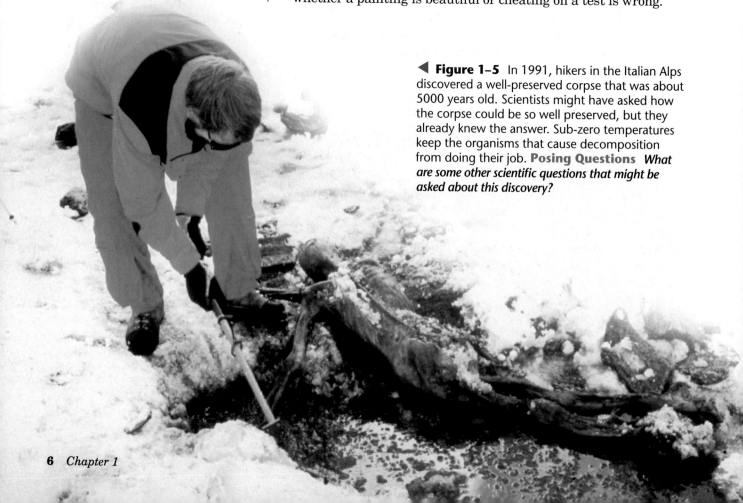

◀ **Figure 1–5** In 1991, hikers in the Italian Alps discovered a well-preserved corpse that was about 5000 years old. Scientists might have asked how the corpse could be so well preserved, but they already knew the answer. Sub-zero temperatures keep the organisms that cause decomposition from doing their job. **Posing Questions** *What are some other scientific questions that might be asked about this discovery?*

Science and Human Values

Most of this textbook deals with the workings of biological science. The importance of science, however, reaches far beyond the scientific world. Today, scientists contribute information to discussions about health and disease, and about the relationship between human beings and the rest of the living world.

Make a list of things that you need to understand to protect your life and the lives of others close to you. Chances are that your list will include drugs and alcohol, smoking and lung disease, AIDS, cancer, and heart disease. Other questions focus on public health and the environment. How can we best use antibiotics to make sure that those "wonder drugs" keep working for a long time? How much of the information in your genes should you be able to keep private? Should communities produce electricity using fossil fuels, nuclear power, or hydroelectric dams? How should chemical wastes be disposed of? Who should be responsible for their disposal? The people in **Figure 1–6** are expressing their concern about the effect of pollution on Earth.

All of these questions involve scientific information. For that reason, an understanding of science and the scientific approach is essential to making intelligent decisions about them. None of these questions, however, can be answered by science alone. They involve the society in which we live and the economy that provides jobs, food, and shelter. They may require us to consider laws and moral principles. In our society, scientists alone do not make final decisions—they make recommendations. Who makes the decisions? We, the citizens of our democracy do—when we vote to express our opinions to elected officials. That is why it is more important than ever that everyone understand what science is, what it can do, and what it cannot do.

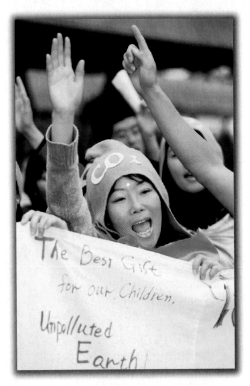

▲ **Figure 1–6** How people treat the environment is an issue involving science and human values. This protester shows her concern about the amount of carbon dioxide in the atmosphere. **Applying Concepts** *How is science involved in this discussion? How are values involved?*

1–1 Section Assessment

1. **Key Concept** What does science study? What does it not study?

2. What does it mean to describe a scientist as skeptical? Why is skepticism considered a valuable quality in a scientist?

3. What is the main difference between qualitative and quantitative observations?

4. Is a scientific hypothesis accepted if there is no way to prove that the hypothesis is wrong? Explain your answer.

5. **Critical Thinking Making Judgments** Suppose a community proposes a law to require the wearing of seatbelts in all moving vehicles. How could science play a role in the decision?

TEXT **Assessment** Use iText to review the important concepts in Section 1–1.

ALTERNATIVE ASSESSMENT

Making a Table
List the five main senses—vision, hearing, smell, taste, and touch—and give an example of an observation that can be made using each sense. Then, add at least one inference that could be made from each observation.

1–2 How Scientists Work

Guide for Reading

🔑 **Key Concepts**
- How do scientists test hypotheses?
- How does a scientific theory develop?

Vocabulary
spontaneous generation
controlled experiment
manipulated variable
responding variable
theory

Reading Strategy:
Outlining As you read, make an outline of the main steps in a controlled experiment.

▼ **Figure 1–7** About 2000 years ago, a Roman poet wrote these directions for producing bees. **Inferring** *Why do you think reasonable individuals once accepted the ideas behind this recipe?*

Recipe for Bees

1. Kill a bull during the first thaw of winter.

2. Build a shed.

3. Place the dead bull on branches and herbs inside the shed.

4. Wait for summer. The decaying body of the bull will produce bees.

Have you ever noticed what happens to food that is left in an open trash can for a few days in summer? Creatures that look like worms appear on the discarded food. These creatures are called maggots. For thousands of years people have been observing maggots on food that is not protected. The maggots seem to suddenly appear out of nowhere. Where do they come from?

Designing an Experiment

People's ideas about where some living things come from have changed over the centuries. Exploring this change can help show how science works. Remember that what might seem obvious now was not so obvious thousands of years ago.

About 2300 years ago, the Greek philosopher Aristotle made extensive observations of the natural world. He tried to explain his observations through reasoning. During and after his lifetime, people thought that living things followed a set of natural rules that were different from those for nonliving things. They also thought that special "vital" forces brought some living things into being from nonliving material. These ideas, exemplified by the directions in **Figure 1–7,** persisted for many centuries. About 400 years ago, some people began to challenge these established ideas. They also began to use experiments to answer their questions about life.

Stating the Problem For many years, observations seemed to indicate that some living things could just suddenly appear: Maggots showed up on meat; mice were found on grain; and beetles turned up on cow dung. Curious about what they saw, people wondered how these events happened. They were, in their own everyday way, identifying a problem to be solved: How do new living things, or organisms, come into being?

Forming a Hypothesis For centuries, people accepted the prevailing explanation for the sudden appearance of some organisms, that some life somehow "arose" from nonliving matter. The maggots arose from the meat, the mice from the grain, and the beetles from the dung. Scholars of the day even gave a name to the idea that life could arise from nonliving matter—**spontaneous generation.** In today's terms, the idea of spontaneous generation can be considered a hypothesis.

In 1668, Francesco Redi, an Italian physician, proposed a different hypothesis for the appearance of maggots. Redi had observed that these organisms appeared on meat a few days after flies were present. He considered it likely that the flies laid eggs too small for people to see. Thus, Redi was proposing a new hypothesis—flies produce maggots. Redi's next step was to test his hypothesis.

Setting Up a Controlled Experiment In science, testing a hypothesis often involves designing an experiment. The factors in an experiment that can change are called variables. Examples of variables include equipment used, type of material, amount of material, temperature, light, and time.

Suppose you want to know whether an increase in water, light, or fertilizer can speed up plant growth. If you change all three variables at once, you will not be able to tell which variable is responsible for the observed results. **Whenever possible, a hypothesis should be tested by an experiment in which only one variable is changed at a time. All other variables should be kept unchanged, or controlled.** This type of experiment is called a **controlled experiment.** The variable that is deliberately changed is called the **manipulated variable.** The variable that is observed and that changes in response to the manipulated variable is called the **responding variable.**

Based on his hypothesis, Redi made a prediction that keeping flies away from meat would prevent the appearance of maggots. To test this hypothesis, he planned the experiment shown in **Figure 1–8.** Notice that Redi controlled all variables except one—whether or not there was gauze over each jar. The gauze was important because it kept flies off the meat.

CHECKPOINT *What was the responding variable in Redi's experiment?*

▼ **Figure 1–8** In a controlled experiment, only one variable is tested at a time. Redi designed an experiment to determine what caused the sudden appearance of maggots (photograph, below). In his experiment, the manipulated variable was the presence or absence of the gauze covering. The results of this experiment helped disprove the hypothesis of spontaneous generation.

Redi's Experiment on Spontaneous Generation

OBSERVATIONS: Flies land on meat that is left uncovered. Later, maggots appear on the meat.

HYPOTHESIS: Flies produce maggots.

PROCEDURE

Controlled Variables: jars, type of meat, location, temperature, time

Manipulated Variable: gauze covering that keeps flies away from meat

Responding Variable: whether maggots appear

Uncovered jars

Covered jars

Several days pass.

Maggots appear

No maggots appear

CONCLUSION: Maggots form only when flies come in contact with meat. Spontaneous generation of maggots did not occur.

Ein cötrafact Anatomy d̄ innerē glidern des
mẽschẽ durch dē hochgelertē phyficū vñ medicīne doctoz Wedelinū hack võ Bra
ckenā zū Straß. declariert in beiwefē viler fcherer wūdartzt grūtlich durchfucht

▲ Figure 1–9 For centuries, the workings of the human body remained a mystery. Gradually, scientists observed the body's structures and recorded their work in drawings like this. **Comparing and Contrasting** *How does this drawing compare with the modern illustrations in Unit 10?*

Recording and Analyzing Results

Scientists usually keep written records of their observations, or data. In the past, data were usually recorded by hand, often in notebooks or personal journals. Sometimes, drawings recorded certain kinds of observations more completely and accurately than a verbal description could. The drawing in **Figure 1–9** was made in Austria in the fifteenth century. Today, researchers may record their work on computers. Online storage often makes it easier for researchers to review the data at any time and, if necessary, offer a new explanation for the data. Scientists know that Redi recorded his data because copies of his work were available to later generations of scientists. His investigation showed that maggots appeared on the meat in the control jars. No maggots appeared in the jars covered with gauze.

Drawing a Conclusion Scientists use the data from an experiment to evaluate the hypothesis and draw a conclusion. That is, they use the evidence to determine whether the hypothesis was supported or refuted. In Redi's case, his results supported his hypothesis. He therefore concluded that the maggots were indeed produced by flies.

As scientists look for explanations for specific observations, they assume that the patterns in nature are consistent. Thus, Redi's results could be viewed not only as an explanation about maggots and flies but also as a refutation of the hypothesis of spontaneous generation.

Publishing and Repeating Investigations

A key assumption in science is that experimental results can be reproduced because nature behaves in a consistent manner. When one particular variable is manipulated in a given set of variables, the result should always be the same. In keeping with this assumption, scientists expect to test one another's investigations. Thus, publishing a description of an experiment is an essential part of science. Today's researchers often report their work in a scientific journal. Other scientists review the experimental procedures to make sure that the design was without flaws. They often repeat experiments to be sure that the results match those already obtained. In Redi's day, scientific journals were not common, but he wrote about his work in a book that included a description of his investigation and its results.

Needham's Test of Redi's Findings Some later tests of Redi's work were influenced by an unexpected discovery. About the time Redi was carrying out his experiment, Anton van Leeuwenhoek (LAY-vun-hook) of the Netherlands was preparing lenses that let him magnify tiny objects. He was not trying to discover new types of life, but that is what he found—a world of tiny moving objects in rainwater, pond water, and dust. Inferring that these objects were alive, he called them "animalcules," or tiny animals. He made drawings of his observations and shared them with other scientists. This discovery had a major effect on the arguments about spontaneous generation. For the next 200 years or so, scientists could not agree on whether the animalcules were alive or how they came to exist.

In the mid-1700s, John Needham, an English scientist, used an experiment involving animalcules to attack Redi's work. Needham claimed that spontaneous generation could occur under the right conditions. To prove his claim, he sealed a bottle of gravy and heated it. He claimed that the heat had killed any living things that might be in the gravy. After several days, he examined the contents of the bottle and found it swarming with activity. "These little animals," he inferred, "can only have come from juice of the gravy."

Spallanzani's Test of Redi's Findings
An Italian scholar, Lazzaro Spallanzani, read about Redi's and Needham's work. Spallanzani thought that Needham had not heated his samples enough and decided to improve upon Needham's experiment. **Figure 1–10** shows that Spallanzani boiled two containers of gravy, assuming that the boiling would kill any tiny living things, or microorganisms, that were present. He sealed one jar immediately and left the other jar open. After a few days, the gravy in the open jar was teeming with microorganisms. The sealed jar remained free of microorganisms.

✓ CHECKPOINT *How did Spallanzani's investigation improve upon Needham's work?*

Gravy is boiled.   Gravy is boiled.

Flask is open.   Flask is sealed.

Gravy is teeming with microorganisms.   Gravy is free of microorganisms.

▶ **Figure 1–10** Spallanzani's experiment showed that microorganisms will not grow in boiled and sealed gravy but will grow in boiled gravy that is left open to the air. **Interpreting Graphics** *What variable was controlled in this experiment?*

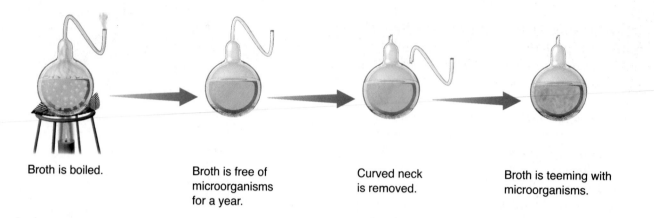

Broth is boiled.

Broth is free of microorganisms for a year.

Curved neck is removed.

Broth is teeming with microorganisms.

▲ **Figure 1–11** Pasteur's experiment showed that boiled broth would remain free of microorganisms even if air was allowed in, as long as dust and other particles were kept out. **Inferring** *Why did microorganisms grow after Pasteur broke the neck of the flask?*

Spallanzani concluded that nonliving gravy did not produce living things. The microorganisms in the unsealed jar were offspring of microorganisms that had entered the jar through the air. This experiment and Redi's work supported the hypothesis that new organisms are produced only by existing organisms.

Pasteur's Test of Spontaneous Generation Well into the 1800s, scientists continued to argue for the spontaneous generation hypothesis. Some supporters of the hypothesis argued that air was a necessary factor in the process of generating life because air contained the "life force" needed to produce new life. They pointed out that Spallanzani's experiment was not a fair test because air had been excluded from the sealed jar.

Biology and History

Major Discoveries

The history of biology includes discoveries about the structure of the human body, the nature of cells, how species evolve, ways to fight deadly diseases, and what molecule determines hereditary traits. You will learn about these discoveries as you study this textbook.

Anton van Leeuwenhoek
Van Leeuwenhoek perfects the simple microscope and observes cells and microorganisms. Four years later, he discovers protozoa.

Suleiman I becomes sultan of the Ottoman Empire
1520

Charles I of England is executed by Parliament
1649

1673

1500   1600   1700

1543

Andreas Vesalius
Vesalius publishes *On the Structure of the Human Body*, the first accurate and detailed study of human anatomy.

1628

William Harvey
Harvey is the first scholar to describe the circulation of blood. He shows how blood pumped through blood vessels returns to the heart and is recirculated.

In 1864, an ingenious French scientist, Louis Pasteur, found a way to settle the argument. He designed a flask that had a long curved neck, as shown in **Figure 1–11.** The flask remained open to the air, but microorganisms from the air did not make their way through the neck into the flask. Pasteur showed that as long as the broth was protected from microorganisms, it remained free of living things. About a year after the experiment began, Pasteur broke the neck of the flask, and the broth quickly became filled with microorganisms. His work convinced other scientists that the hypothesis of spontaneous generation was not correct. In other words, Pasteur showed that all living things come from other living things. This change in thinking represented a major shift in the way scientists viewed living things.

The Impact of Pasteur's Work During his lifetime, Pasteur made many discoveries related to microorganisms. He saved the French wine industry, which was troubled by unexplained souring of wine, and the silk industry, which was endangered by a silkworm disease. Moreover, he began to uncover the very nature of infectious diseases, showing that they were not inexplicable events but the result of microorganisms entering the bodies of the victims. Pasteur is considered one of biology's most remarkable problem solvers.

✓ CHECKPOINT **What improvement did Pasteur make to Redi's experiment?**

Writing Activity

Find out more about one of these discoveries. Research the person or people who made the discovery and how they did it. Write a one-page report detailing your findings.

Louis Pasteur
Pasteur develops the first vaccine against anthrax, a deadly bacterial disease that affects both animals and humans.

Napoleon is defeated at Waterloo

Germany invades Belgium; World War I begins

Soviet Union is dissolved

1815
1800

1881
1900

1914

1992
2000

1859

1953

Charles Darwin
Darwin publishes *On the Origin of Species,* stating that all forms of life have evolved into their present state over the course of millions of years.

James Watson and Francis Crick
Watson and Crick determine the structure of DNA. They, along with fellow scientist Maurice Wilkins, win the Nobel Prize, in 1962, for their discovery.

▲ **Figure 1–12** In animal field studies, such as the observation of wild elephants, scientists usually try to work without making the animals aware that humans are present.
Comparing and Contrasting
How do animal field studies differ from controlled experiments?

When Experiments Are Not Possible

It is not always possible to do an experiment to test a hypothesis. For example, to learn how animals in the wild interact with others in their group, researchers carry out field studies. It is necessary to observe the animals without disturbing them, as shown in **Figure 1–12.** Ethical considerations prevent certain experiments, such as determining the effect on people of a chemical suspected of causing cancer. In such cases, medical researchers may choose volunteers who have already been exposed to the chemical. For comparison, they would study a group of people who have not been exposed to the chemical.

When researchers design such alternative investigations, they try to maintain the rigorous thinking associated with a controlled experiment. They often study large groups of subjects so that small differences do not produce misleading results. They try to identify as many relevant variables as possible so that most variables are controlled. For example, in a study of a cancer-causing chemical, they might exclude volunteers who have other serious health problems. By exerting great care in planning these kinds of investigations, scientists can discover reliable patterns that add to scientific knowledge.

✓ CHECKPOINT **Why are controlled experiments sometimes impossible?**

How a Theory Develops

As evidence from numerous investigations builds up, a particular hypothesis may become so well supported that scientists consider it a **theory.** That is what happened with the hypothesis that new organisms come from existing organisms. This idea is now considered one of the major ideas in science. It is called biogenesis, meaning "generating from life."

You may have heard the word *theory* used in everyday conversations as people discuss ideas. Someone might say, "Oh, that's just a theory," to criticize an idea that is not supported by evidence. **In science, the word *theory* applies to a well-tested explanation that unifies a broad range of observations.** A theory enables scientists to make accurate predictions about new situations.

Figure 1–13 A theory is a well-tested explanation that unifies a broad range of observations. The theories of plate tectonics and evolution help explain why marsupials such as the koala (top) and kangaroo (below) can be found only in Australia and some nearby islands.

Sometimes, more than one theory is needed to explain a particular circumstance. For example, why are the marsupial mammals in **Figure 1–13** found only in Australia and some nearby islands? An answer lies with the theories of plate tectonics and evolution. Millions of years ago, when marsupials were evolving, Australia, Antarctica, and South America were joined as a single land mass. That land mass began to break apart, and Australia became a separate continent. Its marsupials were thus separated from other kinds of mammals, and they evolved as a unique group. You will study the theory of evolution in Unit 5.

A useful theory may become the dominant view among the majority of scientists, but no theory is considered absolute truth. As new evidence is uncovered, a theory may be revised or replaced by a more useful explanation. Sometimes, scientists resist a new way of looking at nature, but over time new evidence determines which ideas survive and which are replaced. Thus, science is characterized by both continuity and change.

1–2 Section Assessment

1. **Key Concept** Why is Redi's experiment on spontaneous generation considered a controlled experiment?

2. **Key Concept** How does a scientific theory compare with a scientific hypothesis?

3. Explain the hypothesis of spontaneous generation.

4. How did the design of Pasteur's flask help him successfully refute the hypothesis of spontaneous generation?

5. **Critical Thinking Applying Concepts** What problem might arise if a researcher fails to control the relevant variables in an experiment?

Assessment Use iText to review the important concepts in Section 1–2.

ALTERNATIVE ASSESSMENT

Making a Table Compare the experiments done by Redi, Spallanzani, and Pasteur. Identify the problem each experiment was designed to solve. State the conclusion of each experiment.

1–3 Studying Life

Guide for Reading

Key Concepts
- What are some characteristics of living things?
- How can life be studied at different levels?

Vocabulary
biology
cell
sexual reproduction
asexual reproduction
metabolism
homeostasis
evolve

Reading Strategy:
Summarizing As you read, make a list of the properties of living things. Write one sentence describing each property.

B eneath the sparkling waves near a South Pacific island, divers carry cameras and underwater notepads as they crisscross a coral reef. Outside an Antarctic research station, a lone figure searches the ice around her for signs of life. In a high-security facility in Atlanta, a man dressed like an astronaut passes through a double airlock into a sterile laboratory. Sweltering in the heat and humidity of sub-Saharan Africa, volunteers collect blood samples from women and children with AIDS. What do these people have in common? They are biologists.

The word *biology* means the study of life. (The Greek word *bios* means "life," and *-logy* means "study of.") **Biology** is the science that seeks to understand the living world. A biologist is someone who uses a scientific method to study living things. The work of biologists can be quite varied, because organisms are complex and vary so greatly.

Characteristics of Living Things

Are the firefly and the fire in **Figure 1–14** alive? They are both giving off energy. Describing what makes something alive is not easy. No single characteristic is enough to describe a living thing. Also, some nonliving things share one or more traits with living things. Mechanical toys, automobiles, and clouds move around, for example, whereas mushrooms and trees live their lives in one spot. Other things, such as viruses, exist at the border between organisms and nonliving things. (You'll read more about viruses in Chapter 19.)

Despite these difficulties, it is possible to describe what most living things have in common. **Living things share several characteristics. These characteristics include the following:**

- **Living things are made up of units called cells.**
- **Living things reproduce.**
- **Living things are based on a universal genetic code.**
- **Living things grow and develop.**
- **Living things obtain and use materials and energy.**
- **Living things respond to their environment.**
- **Living things maintain a stable internal environment.**
- **Taken as a group, living things change over time.**

Figure 1–14 A Colorado firefly beetle (top) has all of the characteristics of living things. Even though fire (bottom) uses materials and can grow as living things do, fire is not alive because it does not have other characteristics of living things.

Made Up of Cells Living things, or organisms, are made up of small, self-contained units called cells. A **cell** is a collection of living matter enclosed by a barrier that separates the cell from its surroundings. Cells are the smallest units of an organism that can be considered alive. Cells can grow, respond to their surroundings, and reproduce. Despite their small size, cells are complex and highly organized.

Many living things consist of only a single cell and are therefore called unicellular organisms. (The Latin prefix *uni-* means "one," so *unicellular* means "single-celled.") Many of the microorganisms involved in Spallanzani's and Pasteur's experiments were unicellular organisms.

The organisms you are most familiar with—for example, animals and plants—are multicellular. You can see one type of multicellular organism in **Figure 1–15.** (The Latin prefix *multi-* means "many." Thus, *multicellular* means "many-celled.") Multicellular organisms contain hundreds, thousands, or even trillions of cells. The cells in these organisms are often remarkably diverse, existing in a variety of sizes and shapes. In some multicellular organisms, each type of cell is specialized to perform a different function. The human body alone is made up of at least 85 different cell types. You will learn more about cells in Chapter 7.

▲ **Figure 1–15** ◯ **Living things are made of cells.** Cats and most other familiar organisms are made of many cells. The inset shows cells from a cat's stomach (magnification: 500×).

Reproduction All organisms produce new organisms through a process called reproduction. There are two basic kinds of reproduction: sexual and asexual. The vast majority of multicellular organisms—from maple trees to birds and humans—reproduce sexually. In **sexual reproduction,** two cells from different parents unite to produce the first cell of the new organism. In **asexual reproduction,** the new organism has a single parent. In some forms of asexual reproduction, a single-celled organism divides in half to form two new organisms. In the type of asexual reproduction shown in **Figure 1–16,** a portion of an organism splits off to form a new organism.

✔CHECKPOINT *What is sexual reproduction?*

Based on a Genetic Code Offspring usually resemble their parents. With asexual reproduction, offspring and their parents have the same traits. With sexual reproduction, offspring differ from their parents in some ways. However, there are limits to these differences. Flies produce flies, dogs produce dogs, and seeds from maple trees produce maple trees.

Explaining how organisms inherit traits is one of the greatest achievements of modern biology. Biologists now know that the directions for inheritance are carried by a molecule called deoxyribonucleic acid, or DNA. With minor exceptions, the DNA genetic code determines the inherited traits of every organism on Earth. You will learn how this is possible in Unit 4.

▲ **Figure 1–16** ◯ **All living things reproduce.** Here, one hydra is being formed from another through a type of asexual reproduction called budding. Shortly, the new organism will break away from the parent and live independently.

The Science of Biology **17**

Figure 1–17 All living things grow and develop. These photographs show how a spicebush swallowtail butterfly develops from an egg into a caterpillar (larva), a pupa, and, finally, an adult butterfly.

Growth and Development Each type of organism has a distinctive life cycle—a particular pattern of growth and change that occurs over the organism's lifetime. For some microorganisms, the main change that occurs is growth, an increase in size. All organisms grow during at least part of their lives.

Another type of change may occur, however. The life cycle of many kinds of multicellular organisms involves a process called development. The flies you read about earlier in Redi's experiment started life as eggs and became maggots (larvae) before becoming the familiar adult flies. **Figure 1–17** shows how a spicebush swallowtail butterfly changes before it becomes an adult. These changes are examples of development. During this process, the cells in an organism not only increase in number but also become different, or differentiate.

Need for Materials and Energy Think of what an organism needs as it grows and develops. Just as a building grows taller because workers use energy to assemble new materials, an organism uses energy and a constant supply of materials to grow, develop, and reproduce. The chameleon in **Figure 1–18**, for example, gets the materials it needs by eating smaller animals. Organisms also need materials and energy just to stay alive. The combination of chemical reactions through which an organism builds up or breaks down materials as it carries out its life processes is called **metabolism.**

All organisms take in selected materials that they need from their surroundings, or environment, but the way they obtain energy varies. Plants, some bacteria, and most algae obtain their energy directly from sunlight. Through a process called photosynthesis, these organisms convert light into a form of energy that is stored in certain molecules. That stored energy is ready to be used when needed.

Most other organisms rely on the energy stored during photosynthesis. Some organisms, such as grasshoppers and sheep, obtain their energy by eating plants and other photosynthesizing organisms. Other organisms, such as birds and wolves, get energy by eating the grasshoppers or sheep. And some organisms, called decomposers, obtain energy from the remains of organisms that have died.

CHECKPOINT *What is metabolism?*

▲ **Figure 1–18** Living things obtain and use materials and energy. This chameleon has captured a large grasshopper, whose body will provide energy and a supply of materials needed for growth.

Response to the Environment Organisms live in constantly changing environments. Variables such as the amount of light and the temperature change from day to day and from season to season. Other nearby living and nonliving things may change. An organism may make changes to its environment as well. Each organism responds to these changes in its own way.

A plant seed, for example, can germinate only when there is sufficient water and the ground is warm enough. The new leaves and stems that develop grow up toward light. The roots respond to gravity and grow down into the soil. Meanwhile, the plant takes in water and certain materials from the soil. It takes other materials from the air. The plant may provide shelter for insects and food for rabbits. Even after the plant dies, its remains become part of the very environment in which it once lived.

Maintaining Internal Balance The changes that happen in an organism are complex. A plant, for example, may take in water at one time and give off water at another. The plant may even take in and give off water at the same time. It may need large amounts of energy at one moment and have extra energy to store at another. Yet, while the plant lives, it maintains a certain internal consistency. The process by which organisms keep their internal conditions relatively stable is called **homeostasis** (hoh-mee-oh-STAY-sis). The condition of homeostasis is constantly being threatened by changes in the environment, such as shifting temperatures and changing light. The bird in **Figure 1–19** maintains a fairly constant body temperature during cold winters and hot summers. If homeostasis is disrupted in a major way, an organism cannot survive.

▲ **Figure 1–19** ⬤ **Living things maintain an internal stability.** Despite the cold temperatures of this robin's environment, its body temperature remains fairly constant, partly because its feathers provide a layer of insulation and partly because of body heat it produces.

Quick Lab

What are the characteristics of living things?

Materials hand lens, unknown objects (dry), same objects soaked in water

Procedure

1. Examine the dry unknown object your teacher provides. Record your observations.
2. **Predicting** In step 3, you will observe the same kind of object after it has been soaked in water. Write a prediction describing what you expect to see.
3. Examine one of the objects that has been soaking in water for a period of time. Record your observations. Wash your hands when you have finished.

Analyze and Conclude
1. **Evaluating** Was the prediction you made in step 2 correct? Explain your answer.
2. **Inferring** Were the objects you observed in step 1 living or nonliving? Were the objects you observed in step 3 living or nonliving? Use the observations you made as supporting evidence for your answers.
3. **Formulating Hypotheses** Suggest one or more ways to explain the differences between the dry and wet objects.
4. **Formulating Hypotheses** In what kind of natural environment might the objects you observed in this lab be found?

Figure 1–20 👁 Taken as a group, all living things change over time. If you suddenly moved most plants to this Namibian desert (left), they would be killed by the heat and lack of water. But a few types of plants have become adapted to these hot and dry conditions, surviving periods of drought to grow and flower after a rainfall (right).

Evolution Although individual organisms experience many changes during their lives, the basic traits they inherited from their parents usually do not change. As a group, however, any given kind of organism can **evolve**, or change over time.

Over a few generations, the changes in a group may not seem significant. But over hundreds of thousands or even millions of years, the changes can be dramatic. The ability of certain plants, such as those in **Figure 1–20**, to survive periods without water is one example. Another example concerns fishes. Scientists study deposits containing the remains of animals that lived long ago to learn about the evolution of organisms. From the study of very early deposits, scientists know that at one time there were no fishes in Earth's waters. Yet, in more recent deposits, the remains of fishes and other animals with backbones are abundant. The ability of a group of organisms to change over time is invaluable for survival in a world that is always changing. You will read about the processes of evolution in Unit 5.

Branches of Biology

The diversity of life is so great that no biologist can study everything, so biology is often organized into branches, or divisions. Some divisions are based on the type of organism being studied. Zoologists study animals. (The prefix *zoo-* means "animal.") Botanists study plants. (*Botanikos* means "plants.") Others study life from a particular perspective. Ethologists study animal behavior. (*Ethos-* means "custom.") Paleontologists study life as it was in the past. (*Paleo-* means "ancient.")

The study of biology can also be approached based on the idea that life can be studied at different levels of organization. Each level is a system made up of smaller parts. Each system may, in turn, be part of a larger system. The levels can differ in both size and complexity. 🔑 **The many levels at which life can be studied include molecules, cells, organisms, populations of a single organism, communities of populations living in the same area, and the biosphere.** Some of the levels of organization of interest to biologists are summarized in the table in **Figure 1–21**.

Levels of Organization

Biosphere	The part of Earth that contains all ecosystems	Biosphere
Ecosystem	Community and its nonliving surroundings	Hawk, snake, bison, prairie dog, grass, stream, rocks, air
Community	Populations that live together in a defined area	Hawk, snake, bison, prairie dog, grass
Population	Group of organisms of one type that live in the same area	Bison herd
Organism	Individual living thing	Bison
Groups of Cells	Tissues, organs, and organ systems	Nervous tissue Brain Nervous system
Cells	Smallest functional unit of life	Nerve cell
Molecules	Groups of atoms; smallest unit of most chemical compounds	Water DNA

Figure 1–21 ⬤ **Living things may be studied on many different levels.** The largest and most complex level is the biosphere. The smallest level is the molecules that make up living things.

▲ **Figure 1–22** Progress in biology has meant huge improvements in health not just for you and your family but, in some societies, for pets as well. **Predicting** *How do you expect advances in biology to change health care during your lifetime?*

Biology in Everyday Life

As you begin studying biology, you may be thinking of it as just another course, with a textbook to read plus labs, homework, and tests. It's also a *science* course, so you may worry that it will be too difficult. But you will see that more than any other area of study, biology touches your life every day. In fact, it's hard to think of anything you do that isn't affected by it. It helps you understand and appreciate every other form of life, from pets such as the dog in **Figure 1–22** to dinosaurs no longer present on Earth. It provides information about the food you need and the methods for sustaining the world's food supplies. It describes the conditions of good health and the behaviors and diseases that can harm you. It is used to diagnose and treat medical problems. It identifies environmental factors that might threaten you, such as disposal of wastes from human activities. More than any other science, biology helps you understand what affects the quality of your life.

Biologists do not make the decisions about most matters affecting human society or the natural world; citizens and governments do. In just a few years, you will be able to exercise the rights of a voting citizen, influencing public policy by the ballots you cast and the messages you send public officials. With others, you will make decisions based on many factors, including customs, values, ethical standards, and scientific knowledge. Biology can provide decision makers with useful information and analytical skills. It can help them envision the possible effects of their decisions. Biology can help people understand that humans are capable of predicting and trying to control their future and that of the planet.

1–3 Section Assessment

1. 🔑 **Key Concept** Describe five characteristics of living things.
2. 🔑 **Key Concept** What topics might biologists study at the community level of organization?
3. Compare sexual reproduction and asexual reproduction.
4. What biological process includes chemical reactions that break down materials?
5. What happens to an organism if its homeostasis is disrupted and not restored?

6. **Critical Thinking Applying Concepts** Try to think of a nonliving thing that satisfies each characteristic of living things. Does any nonliving thing have all the characteristics of life?

i **TEXT** Assessment Use iText to review the important concepts in Section 1–3.

MAKING CONNECTIONS

Making Observations
List some observations that could be made to determine whether an object that is not moving is living or nonliving. Refer to Section 1–1.

When Scientists Have a Conflict of Interest

Science Advisors Were Paid Industry Consultants Two scientists testifying at a public hearing about the safety of a new pesticide today admitted that they had once worked for the pesticide's manufacturer. Both researchers denied that their testimony was influenced by the company. However, neither scientist had disclosed the relationship before giving a recommendation.

Scientists are expected to be completely honest about their investigations. Doctors are expected to place the welfare of their patients first. Yet, conflicts of interest can often threaten the credibility of a researcher. A conflict of interest exists when a person's work can be influenced by personal factors such as financial gain, fame, future work, or favoritism.

The Viewpoints

Regulation Is Necessary

Some scientists argue that, because the public must be able to trust the work of science, some rules are essential for preserving scientific integrity. Every profession should regulate its members, and every science publication should have strict rules about avoiding conflicts of interest. In any published work, announcements of potential conflicts should be required. In some cases, scientists should avoid or be forbidden to do work that involves personal gain in addition to the usual payment for doing the work. Some form of government regulation may be needed.

Regulation Is Unnecessary

Other scientists insist that conflict-of-interest regulations are unnecessary for the majority of researchers, who are honest and objective about their work. It is unfair to assume that a researcher's discoveries would be different because a particular organization has paid for an investigation. In fact, without additional funding from some organizations, new drugs or new techniques would never have been developed. So, it is important that scientists be allowed to investigate any topic, especially when it would help others.

You Decide

1. **Defining the Issue** When might scientists have a conflict of interest? Are financial incentives more dangerous to a scientist's objectivity than other conflicts of interest? Explain.
2. **Analyzing the Viewpoints** How might the views about a possible conflict of interest differ among a group of scientists, a science journal editor deciding to publish a scientist's work, the company employing a scientist, and people seeking information from a scientist?
3. **Forming Your Opinion** How do you think this problem of possible conflicts of interest should be decided? Include information or reasoning that answers people with the opposite view.
4. **Role-Playing** Suppose doctors who own a company developing a new medicine want their patients to help test the medicine. Let one person represent a doctor, a second person a patient, and a third person a medical reporter asking: Should the patients take part in the tests?

1–4 Tools and Procedures

Guide for Reading

 Key Concepts
- What measurement system do most scientists use?
- How are light microscopes and electron microscopes similar? How are they different?

Vocabulary
metric system
microscope
compound light microscope
electron microscope
cell culture
cell fractionation

**Reading Strategy:
Using Graphic Organizers**
As you read, create a table that lists the procedures discussed in this section. List one example of what biologists can accomplish using each procedure.

I magine being one of the first people to see living things through a magnifying glass. How surprised you would have been to discover a a whole new realm of life! Could there still be other types of life that remain undiscovered today because the right tools are not available?

Tools play a major role in science. Electronic balances measure the mass of objects with great precision. Microscopes and telescopes make it possible to observe objects that are very small or very far away. With powerful computers, scientists can store and analyze vast collections of data. Biologists have even devised procedures that help them unlock the information stored in the DNA of different organisms.

A Common Measurement System

Because researchers need to replicate each other's experiments and most experiments involve measurements, scientists need a common system of measurement. **Most scientists use the metric system when collecting data and performing experiments.** The **metric system** is a decimal system of measurement whose units are based on certain physical standards and are scaled on multiples of 10. A revised version of the original metric system is called the International System of Units, or SI. The abbreviation SI comes from the French *Le Système International d'Unités.*

Because the metric system is based on multiples of 10, it is easy to use. Notice in **Figure 1–23** how the basic unit of length, the meter, can be multiplied or divided to measure objects and distances much larger or smaller than a meter. The same process can be used when measuring volume and mass. You can learn more about the metric system in Appendix C.

▶ **Figure 1–23**
🔑 **Scientists usually use the metric system in their work.** This system is easy to use because it is based on multiples of 10.

Common Metric Units	
Length	**Mass**
1 meter (m) = 100 centimeters (cm) 1 meter = 1000 millimeters (mm) 1000 meters = 1 kilometer (km)	1 kilogram (kg) = 1000 grams (g) 1 gram = 1000 milligrams (mg) 1000 kilograms = 1 metric ton (t)
Volume	**Temperature**
1 liter (L) = 1000 milliliters (mL) 1 liter = 1000 cubic centimeters (cm^3)	0˚C = freezing point of water 100˚C = boiling point of water

Water Released and Absorbed by Tree				
Time	Absorbed by Roots (g/h)	Released by Leaves (g/h)		
8 AM	1	2		
10 AM	1	5		
12 PM	4	12		
2 PM	6	17		
4 PM	9	16		
6 PM	14	10		
8 PM	10	3		

Analyzing Biological Data

When scientists collect data, they are often trying to find out whether certain factors changed or remained the same. Often, the simplest way to do that is to record the data in a table and then make a graph. Although you may be able to detect a pattern of change from a data table like the one in **Figure 1–24**, a graph of the data can make a pattern much easier to recognize and understand.

In science today, the amount of data being produced by biologists is so huge that no individual can look at more than a tiny fraction of it. To make sense of the data, biologists often turn to computers. For example, computers help determine the structure of molecules. They also allow biologists to search through DNA sequences, find significant regions of the molecule, and discover how organisms are affected by that region. At the opposite end of the scale, computers are essential to every step of data gathering by satellite, including analyzing satellite data and presenting the results. Analyses of satellite data are used to make predictions about complex phenomena such as global climate changes.

CHECKPOINT *How can a graph help biologists analyze data?*

Microscopes

When people think of scientific tools, one of the first tools that comes to mind is the microscope. **Microscopes** are devices that produce magnified images of structures that are too small to see with the unaided eye. 🔑 **Light microscopes produce magnified images by focusing visible light rays. Electron microscopes produce magnified images by focusing beams of electrons.** Since the first microscope was invented, microscope manufacturers have had to deal with two problems: What is the instrument's magnification—that is, how much larger can it make an object appear compared to the object's real size? And how sharp an image can the instrument produce?

▲ **Figure 1–24** One way to record data from an experiment is by using a data table. Then, the data may be plotted on a graph to make it easier to interpret. **Interpreting Graphics** *At what time of day is the rate of water released by leaves equal to the rate of water absorbed by roots?*

Word Origins

Microscope comes from the Greek words *micro-*, meaning "small," and *skop-*, meaning "see." So, *microscope* means an instrument for looking at very small objects. **What do you think the word *microorganism* means?**

▲ Figure 1–25 🔵 Light microscopes produce magnified images by focusing visible light rays. The tick shown in the inset is magnified about 10 times.

Light Microscopes

The most commonly used microscope is the light microscope. Light microscopes can produce clear images of objects at a magnification of about 1000 times. **Figure 1–25** shows a compound light microscope similar to those in many high school laboratories. **Compound light microscopes** allow light to pass through the specimen and use two lenses to form an image. In addition to studying specimens of dead organisms or their parts, light microscopes make it possible to observe some tiny organisms and cells while they are still alive. You can refer to Appendix D to learn how to use a compound light microscope.

Biologists have developed techniques and procedures to make light microscopes more useful. Chemical stains, also called dyes, can show specific structures in the cell. Fluorescent dyes have been combined with video cameras and new optical techniques to produce moving three-dimensional images of processes such as cell movement. Computer processing of the video signals from such microscopes even makes it possible to follow the movements of cell parts and materials within the cell in real time.

Electron Microscopes

Light microscopes can produce sharp images of objects only when the objects are larger than 0.2 micrometers, or about $\frac{1}{50}$ the diameter of a typical cell. To study smaller objects, biologists developed electron microscopes in the 1950s. **Electron microscopes** focus beams of electrons on specimens. These microscopes can form images of objects 1000 times smaller than those visible under a light microscope. Because light from the visible spectrum is not involved, untouched electron microscope images have no color.

Biologists use two main types of electron microscopes. Transmission electron microscopes (TEMs) shine a beam of electrons through a thin specimen. Scanning electron microscopes (SEMs) run a pencil-like beam of electrons back and forth across the surface of a specimen. SEMs produce realistic—and often dramatic—three-dimensional images of the surfaces of objects. The image of the ant in **Figure 1–26** was produced by a scanning electron microscope. Despite their power, however, electron microscopes cannot be used to study live specimens. Samples for TEM and SEM work must be completely dried out before they are placed in the vacuum inside the microscope. This means that only dead and preserved cells can be observed. Living specimens would be killed by the processes that are used to prepare the sample.

✓ **CHECKPOINT** *What are microscopes used for?*

◄ Figure 1–26 🔵 Electron microscopes produce images by focusing beams of electrons. This image of an ant on a blade of grass was created using a scanning electron microscope. The color, not part of the original image, was added artificially.

Bacterial Reproduction

Bacteria are tiny microorganisms that can reproduce by dividing into two. The graph shows the results of an experiment on the effect of temperature on bacterial reproduction. At the beginning, three populations of bacteria, all of the same type, were of equal size. Each population was kept at a different temperature for 4 days.

1. **Classifying** What variable did the researcher change during this experiment?

2. **Inferring** What do the shapes of the curves tell you about the changes in population size?

3. **Calculating** For the bacteria kept at 15°C, how did population size change during the experiment?

4. **Drawing Conclusions** What effect did the different temperatures have on the growth of the bacterial populations?

Bacterial Growth and Temperature

5. **Going Further** Suppose some bacteria used in this experiment were kept at a temperature of 100°C (the temperature of boiling water). Would you expect the population sizes to increase even faster than at 15°C? Explain your reasoning.

Laboratory Techniques

Biologists use a variety of techniques to study cells. Two common laboratory techniques are cell culturing and cell fractionation.

Cell Cultures To obtain enough material to study, biologists like the one in **Figure 1–27** sometimes place a single cell into a dish containing a nutrient solution. The cell is able to reproduce so that a group of cells, called a **cell culture,** develops from the single original cell. Cell cultures can be used to test cell responses under controlled conditions, to study interactions between cells, and to select specific cells for further study.

Cell Fractionation Suppose you want to study just one part of a cell. How could you separate that one part from the rest of the cell? Biologists often use a technique known as **cell fractionation** to separate the different cell parts. First, the cells are broken into pieces in a special blender. Then, the broken cell bits are added to a liquid and placed in a tube. The tube is inserted into a centrifuge, which is an instrument that can spin the tube up to 20,000 times per minute. Spinning causes the cell parts to separate, with the most dense parts settling near the bottom of the tube and the least dense parts rising toward the top. A biologist can then remove the specific part of the cell to be studied by selecting the appropriate layer.

▼ **Figure 1–27** This researcher is preparing a cell culture by transferring bacteria to a solid that contains nutrients, which will enable the bacteria to reproduce. **Comparing and Contrasting** *How do the results of a cell culture differ from the products of cell fractionation?*

Working Safely in Biology

Scientists working in a laboratory or in the field like those in **Figure 1–28** are trained to use safe procedures when carrying out investigations. Laboratory work may involve flames or heating elements, electricity, chemicals, hot liquids, sharp instruments, and breakable glassware. Laboratory or field work may involve contact with living or dead organisms—not just the plants, animals, and other living things you can see but other organisms you cannot see without a microscope.

Whenever you work in your biology laboratory, it's important for you to follow safety precautions as well. Before performing any activity in this course, study the safety rules in Appendix B. Before you start any activity, read all the steps, and make sure that you understand the entire procedure, including any safety precautions that must be followed. The single most important rule for your safety is simple: Always follow your teacher's instructions and the textbook directions exactly. If you are in doubt about any part of an activity, always ask your teacher for an explanation. And, because you may be in contact with organisms you cannot see, it is essential that you wash your hands thoroughly after every scientific activity. Remember, you are responsible for your own safety and that of your teacher and classmates. If you are handling live animals, you are responsible for their safety as well.

▼ **Figure 1–28** These workers are cleaning up Rocky Flats, a Colorado site once used for producing nuclear weapons. **Applying Concepts** *Why must they wear heavy protective gear?*

1–4 Section Assessment

1. 🔑 **Key Concept** Why do scientists use a common system of measurement?

2. 🔑 **Key Concept** What is the difference in the way light microscopes and electron microscopes produce images?

3. Describe the technique and purpose of cell fractionation.

4. What types of objects can be studied with a light microscope? What types can be studied with an electron microscope?

5. **Critical Thinking Applying Concepts** It has been said that many great discoveries lie in wait for the tools needed to make them. What does this statement mean to you? If possible, include an example in your answer.

iTEXT Assessment Use iText to review the important concepts in Section 1–4.

Take It to the NET

Construct a time line of the early types of microscopes. Include photographs or drawings of the microscopes. Use the links provided in the Biology area at the Prentice Hall Web site for help in completing this activity: **www.phschool.com**

Using a Compound Microscope

Microscopes are widely used in biology. In this investigation, you will use a compound microscope to determine the positions and sizes of objects. Before you begin, read Appendix D on pages 1064–1065 and practice the procedures described there.

Problem What kinds of information can a compound microscope provide?

Materials

- compound microscope
- microscope slide
- newspaper or other small-print text
- scissors
- dropper pipette
- coverslips
- prepared slide of crossed fibers
- transparent 15-cm plastic ruler
- prepared slide of root or stem
- prepared slide of bacteria

Skills Observing, Measuring, Calculating

Procedure

1. Use scissors to cut out a square of printed text approximately 1 cm wide. Place the paper square on a microscope slide. **CAUTION:** *Be careful when handling sharp instruments.*

2. Use a dropper pipette to place a drop of water on the paper square. Add a coverslip. Place the slide on the stage of a compound microscope. Use the stage clips to hold the slide in place.

3. Use the low-power objective to bring the letters on the paper square into focus. Slowly move the slide in different directions along the stage. Record how the image changes when you move the slide.

4. Observe a prepared slide of crossed fibers through the low-power objective. Use the fine adjustment to focus up and down through the area where the fibers cross. Record the order of the fibers, from top to bottom.

5. Observe a transparent ruler through the low-power objective. Use the ruler to measure the diameter of your field of view. Record this distance and the magnification of the low-power objective.

6. Calculate and record the diameter of the field of view through the other objectives. For example, if a 4× objective has a field of 2 mm (2000 micrometers), then a 10× objective will have a field of (4 ÷ 10) × 2 mm = 0.8 mm (800 micrometers).

7. Examine a prepared slide of a plant stem or root at low and high powers. The small round shapes you see are cells. Use the field diameters you calculated in step 6 to estimate and record the size of a typical plant cell. For example, if 4 cells fit across an 800-micrometer field, then each cell is 200 micrometers long.

8. Repeat step 7 with a prepared slide of bacteria.

Analyze and Conclude

1. **Applying Concepts** What are the advantages of using the high-power objective? What are the disadvantages?

2. **Inferring** Some plant diseases are caused by bacteria. Could bacteria injure plants by consuming plant cells? By entering plant cells? Explain.

3. **Drawing Conclusions** In what ways did the microscope alter the image in step 3? How did moving the slide affect the image?

4. **Drawing Conclusions** In what order were the fibers arranged on the slide you observed in step 4?

Go Further

Measuring With your teacher's permission, use the microscope to observe one of your hairs and estimate its width.

1–1 What Is Science?

 Key Concept

- The goal of science is to investigate and understand nature, to explain events in nature, and to use those explanations to make useful predictions.

Vocabulary
science, p. 3
observation, p. 4
data, p. 4
inference, p. 4
hypothesis, p. 5

1–2 How Scientists Work

 Key Concepts

- Whenever possible, a hypothesis should be tested by an experiment in which only one variable is changed at a time. All other variables should be kept unchanged, or controlled.
- In science, the word *theory* applies to a well-tested explanation that unifies a broad range of observations.

Vocabulary
spontaneous generation, p. 8
controlled experiment, p. 9
manipulated variable, p. 9
responding variable, p. 9
theory, p. 14

1–3 Studying Life

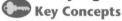 **Key Concepts**

- Living things share characteristics including cellular organization, reproduction, a universal genetic code, growth and development, use of materials and energy, response to their environment, and maintaining an internal stabiity.
- Living things can be studied at different levels of organization, from the molecular level to the biosphere.

Vocabulary
biology, p. 16
cell, p. 17
sexual reproduction, p. 17
asexual reproduction, p. 17
metabolism, p. 18
homeostasis, p. 19
evolve, p. 20

1–4 Tools and Procedures

 Key Concepts

- Most scientists use the metric system when collecting data and doing experiments.
- Light microscopes produce magnified images by focusing visible light rays. Electron microscopes produce images by focusing beams of electrons.

Vocabulary
metric system, p. 24
microscope, p. 25
compound light microscope, p. 26
electron microscope, p. 26
cell culture, p. 27
cell fractionation, p. 27

Thinking Visually

Make a concept map that shows some ways scientists think and work. You can start with the partial concept map shown below or create your own. Recalling how scientists investigated spontaneous generation may help you identify important ideas to include.

Chapter 1

Part A

Multiple Choice
For each statement or question, select the number of the word or expression that, of those given, best completes the statement or answers the question.

1 Which statement about the image shown below is *not* an observation?
(1) The insect has three legs on the left side.
(2) The insect has a pattern on its back.
(3) The insect's pattern shows that it is poisonous.
(4) The insect is green, white, and black.

2 The statement "the worm is 2 cm long" is a(an)
(1) quantitative observation
(2) qualitative observation
(3) inference
(4) hypothesis

3 An inference is
(1) the same as an observation
(2) a logical interpretation of an observation
(3) a statement involving numbers
(4) the best way to avoid bias

4 To be useful in science, a hypothesis must be
(1) measurable   (3) testable
(2) observable   (4) correct

5 The term *spontaneous generation* means that
(1) living things can arise from nonliving matter
(2) living things arise from other living things
(3) a maggot is part of the life cycle of a fly
(4) living things evolve over time

6 Which statement about a controlled experiment is true?
(1) All the variables must be kept the same.
(2) Only one variable is changed at a time.
(3) Scientists always use controlled experiments.
(4) Controlled experiments cannot be performed on living things.

7 A scientific theory is
(1) another word for hypothesis
(2) a well-tested explanation that unifies a broad range of observations
(3) the same as the conclusion of an experiment
(4) established when the conclusions of two separate experiments are the same

8 The process in which two cells from different parents unite to produce the first cell of a new organism is called
(1) homeostasis
(2) development
(3) asexual reproduction
(4) sexual reproduction

9 Which process is used by organisms to keep their internal conditions relatively stable?
(1) metabolism
(2) reproduction
(3) evolution
(4) homeostasis

10 An instrument that produces images by focusing light rays is called a(an)
(1) light microscope
(2) transmission electron microscope
(3) scanning electron microscope
(4) electronic balance

For questions 11 and 12, complete each analogy by selecting the correct number. In analogies, A : B :: C : means "A is to B as C is to ___?___."

11 Sexual reproduction : two parents :: asexual reproduction :
(1) two parents
(2) two cells
(3) one parent
(4) one cell

12 One gram : 1000 milligrams :: one meter :
(1) 1000 millimeters
(2) 1 millimeter
(3) 1000 meters
(4) 1 milliliter

Test-Taking Tip Before taking a standardized test, it helps to become familiar with the format of the test, including the different question types. One helpful method is to complete practice tests, such as this one.

Parts B and C

Multiple Choice and Extended Response
For those questions that ask you to select a response, choose the one that best completes the statement or answers the question. For all others follow the directions given.

13 How does an observation about an object differ from an inference about that object?

Base your answer to questions 14 and 15 on the information and graph below and on your knowledge of biology.

A researcher investigated two groups of fruit flies. Population A was kept in a 0.5-L container. Population B was kept in a 1-L container.

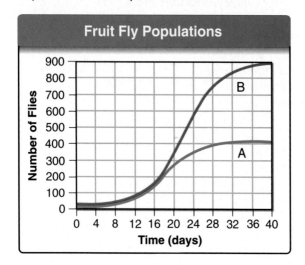

Fruit Fly Populations

14 The manipulated (independent) variable was the
   (1) number of flies
   (2) number of groups studied
   (3) time in days
   (4) size of the containers

15 Which is a scientific inference based on the contents of the graph?
   (1) The flies in Population B were healthier than those in Population A.
   (2) A fly population with more available space will grow larger than a population with less space.
   (3) In 40 more days, the sizes of both populations would decrease at the same rate.
   (4) The pattern shown in this graph is true only for fruit flies.

16 At one time, people believed in spontaneous generation—the idea that new life can arise from nonliving matter. Explain why we no longer believe in spontaneous generation.

17 How does a hypothesis that is not supported by experimental data help scientists understand the natural world?

18 In a controlled experiment, there is one variable that is changed at a time. This is the manipulated (independent) variable. The experimental data can then show a difference between the way the experimental and control groups responded. The variable that is measured during the experiment is referred to as the responding (dependent) variable. Identify both the manipulated (independent) variable and the responding (dependent) variable in Redi's experiment and in Spallanzani's experiment. (*Hint:* Refer to pages 9 and 11.)

19 Why is it important for scientists to test only one variable at a time during an experiment?

Base your answer to questions 20 and 21 on the information below and on your knowledge of biology.

A scientist adds an equal quantity of a new fertilizer he is testing to each of the pots in which 50 tomato plants are growing. He then measures the growth of the plants over a 3-week period, records his results, and draws a conclusion about the benefit of the new fertilizer.

20 Is this a controlled experiment? Support your answer with an explanation.

21 Explain why it was important to use 50 plants rather than one plant for the experiment.

22 Why is publishing the design and results of an experiment considered an essential part of science?

23 A scientist does an experiment and draws a conclusion. How does this conclusion differ from a theory?

24 Describe one way unicellular and multicellular organisms are alike. Describe one way they are different.

25 State three characteristics of all living things.

26 Explain how a graph of data can be more informative than a table of the same data.

27 Use a metric ruler to find the length and width of this book. Record you answer in both millimeters and centimeters.

28 An animal has a mass of 1.5 kilograms. State its mass in grams.

29 A scientist wants to study the way a microscopic, unicellular organism moves. State two reasons that the scientist should choose a compound light microscope rather than an electron microscope for making his or her observations.

30 The following graphs show the sizes of four different populations over a period of time. Write a sentence summarizing what each graph shows.

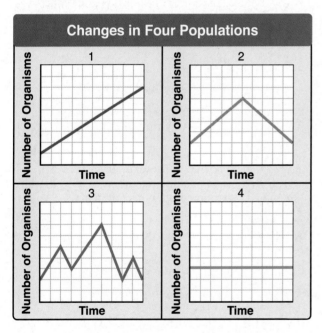

Changes in Four Populations

31 Graphs that represent two entirely different situations can have the same appearance. Select one of the graphs from question 30 and explain how the shape of the graph you choose could apply to something other than population change.

32 Suggest an experiment that could be carried out to test the hypothesis that mosquitoes are attracted to people wearing light-colored clothing.

33 Explain why you cannot draw a conclusion about the effect of one variable in an investigation when the other key variables are not controlled.

34 What is a cell culture? Explain how a cell culture can be useful to biologists.

35 Each of the following safety symbols might appear in a laboratory activity in this book. Describe what each symbol stands for. (*Hint:* Refer to Appendix B.)

A   B   C   D   E   F

36 A drug company has developed a new antibiotic that is effective against a strain of *Staphylococcus aureus* that has become resistant to most of the currently available antibiotics. The new antibiotic has been tested successfully on animals and will soon be tested on humans. The company claims that results so far indicate that the antibiotic could be a cure for what have often been lethal *Staphylococcus* infections.

In conducting the research on human subjects, several questions need to be answered. Summarize some of the important aspects of the research on humans. In your summary, be sure to explain

• how the experimental and control groups will be treated differently

• why it would be important to use a large number of people in this research

• how the researcher will be able to conclude that the new antibiotic is effective in curing *Staphylococcus* infections in humans

Take It to the NET

Where can you learn about different careers in biology? Visit the Prentice Hall Web site at **www.phschool.com** to find out. Then, answer the following questions:

• List five different careers in biology and describe what skills are needed for those careers.

• For each of the five careers, list the training and education that is needed.

• Choose one career that you would be interested in pursuing. Write down three questions that you have about that career. How might you go about finding the answers to those questions?

Chapter 2 The Chemistry of Life

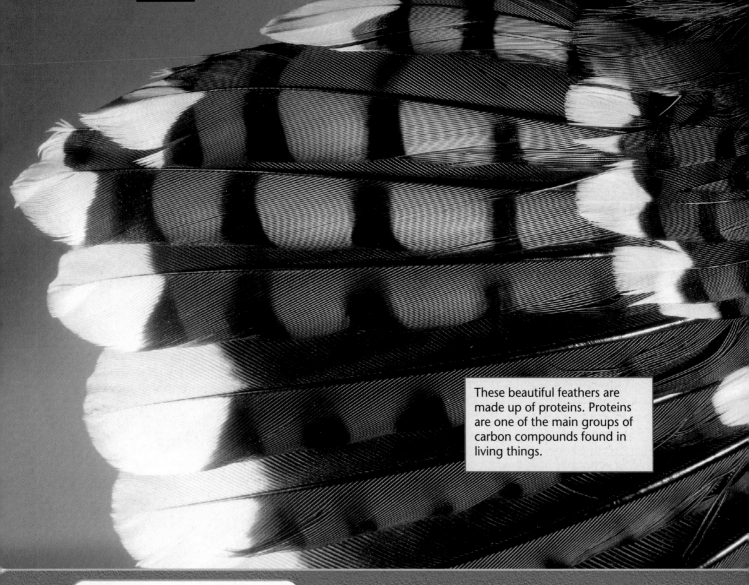

These beautiful feathers are made up of proteins. Proteins are one of the main groups of carbon compounds found in living things.

Inquiry Activity

Do large and small molecules behave exactly alike?

Procedure

1. Label six test tubes as follows: tofu, soy sauce, butter, soap, starch, and sugar. Place a tiny amount of each sample in the appropriate test tube.

2. Half-fill each test tube with water. Stopper the test tubes. Shake each test tube for 2 minutes. Record your observations of each test tube.

Think About It

1. **Observing** Which substances dissolved easily in water?

2. **Drawing Conclusions** Tofu, starch, and butter consist mostly of large molecules (protein, starch, and fat, respectively). Soy sauce, sugar, and soap contain smaller molecules that are related to the large molecules. Are the large molecules more or less soluble than the smaller molecules?

2–1 The Nature of Matter

Life depends on chemistry. When you eat food or inhale oxygen, your body uses these materials in chemical reactions that keep you alive. Just as buildings are made from bricks, steel, glass, and wood, living things are made from chemical compounds. If the first task of an architect is to understand building materials, then the first job of a biologist is to understand the chemistry of life.

Atoms

The study of chemistry begins with the basic unit of matter, the **atom.** The Greek word *atomos,* which means "unable to be cut," was first used to refer to matter by the Greek philosopher Democritus nearly 2500 years ago. Democritus asked a simple question: If you take an object like a stick of chalk and break it in half, are both halves still chalk? The answer, of course, is yes. But what happens if you go on? Suppose you break it in half again and again and again. Can you continue to divide without limit, or does there come a point at which you cannot divide the fragment of chalk without changing it into something else? Democritus thought that there had to be a limit. He called the smallest fragment the atom, a name scientists still use today.

Atoms are incredibly small. Placed side by side, 100 million atoms would make a row only about 1 centimeter long—about the width of your pinkie! Despite its extremely small size, an atom contains subatomic particles that are even smaller.

Figure 2–1 shows the subatomic particles in a helium atom. **The subatomic particles that make up atoms are protons, neutrons, and electrons.** Protons and neutrons have about the same mass. However, protons are positively charged particles (+) and neutrons carry no charge. Their name is a reminder that they are neutral particles. Strong forces bind protons and neutrons together to form the **nucleus,** which is at the center of the atom.

The **electron** is a negatively charged particle (–) with 1/1840 the mass of a proton. Electrons are in constant motion in the space surrounding the nucleus. They are attracted to the positively charged nucleus but remain outside the nucleus because of the energy of their motion. Because atoms have equal numbers of electrons and protons, and because these subatomic particles have equal but opposite charges, atoms are neutral.

Guide for Reading

Key Concepts
- What three subatomic particles make up atoms?
- How are all of the isotopes of an element similar?
- What are the two main types of chemical bonds?

Vocabulary
atom
nucleus
electron
element
isotope
compound
ionic bond
ion
covalent bond
molecule
van der Waals forces

**Reading Strategy:
Using Prior Knowledge**
Before you read, write down what you already know about atoms, elements, and compounds. As you read, note the main new concepts you learn.

+ Proton
 Neutron
− Electron

Helium
Atomic number = 2
Mass number = 4

▶ **Figure 2–1** Helium atoms contain protons, neutrons, and electrons. The positively charged protons and uncharged neutrons are bound together in the dense nucleus, while the negatively charged electrons move in the space around the nucleus.

Elements and Isotopes

A chemical **element** is a pure substance that consists entirely of one type of atom. More than 100 elements are known, but only about two dozen are commonly found in living organisms. Elements are represented by a one- or two-letter symbol. C, for example, stands for carbon, H for hydrogen, and Na for sodium. The number of protons in an atom of an element is the element's atomic number. Carbon's atomic number is 6, meaning that each atom of carbon has six protons and, consequently, six electrons.

Isotopes Atoms of an element can have different numbers of neutrons. For example, some atoms of carbon have six neutrons, some have seven, and a few have eight. Atoms of the same element that differ in the number of neutrons they contain are known as **isotopes.** The sum of the protons and neutrons in the nucleus of an atom is called its mass number. Isotopes are identified by their mass numbers. **Figure 2–2** shows the subatomic composition of carbon-12, carbon-13, and carbon-14 atoms. The weighted average of the masses of an element's isotopes is called its atomic mass. "Weighted" means that the abundance of each isotope in nature is considered when the average is calculated. 🔑 **Because they have the same number of electrons, all isotopes of an element have the same chemical properties.**

Radioactive Isotopes Some isotopes are radioactive, meaning that their nuclei are unstable and break down at a constant rate over time. The radiation these isotopes give off can be dangerous, but radioactive isotopes have a number of important scientific and practical uses.

For example, geologists can determine the ages of rocks and fossils by analyzing the isotopes found in them. Radiation from certain isotopes can be used to treat cancer and to kill bacteria that cause food to spoil. Radioactive isotopes can also be used as labels or "tracers" to follow the movements of substances within organisms.

▼ **Figure 2–2** 🔑 Because they have the same number of electrons, these isotopes of carbon have the same chemical properties. The difference among the isotopes is the number of neutrons in their nuclei.

Isotopes of Carbon		
Nonradioactive carbon-12	**Nonradioactive carbon-13**	**Radioactive carbon-14**
6 electrons	6 electrons	6 electrons
6 protons	6 protons	6 protons
6 neutrons	7 neutrons	8 neutrons

Careers in Biology

Forensic Scientist

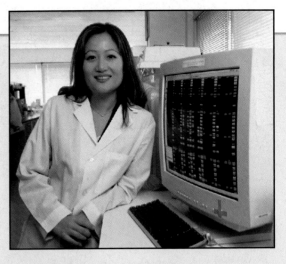

Job description: work as a forensic scientist for local, state, or federal investigative agencies in order to conduct scientific forensic examinations in criminal investigations

Education: a bachelor's degree in science—biology, physics, chemistry, metallurgy; some states require several years of forensic laboratory experience

Skills: analytical, computer literate, detail oriented, capable of taking meticulous notes, logical, and capable of preparing evidence for presentation in court as well as testifying as an expert witness

Highlights: You have the opportunity to use logic and science to solve unique or unusual problems in criminal investigations.

Kelly Yi, who is pictured here, chose forensic science when DNA analysis was just beginning to be accepted as evidence in court. "Everything in forensic science deals with basic principles," she explains.

To find out more about forensic science, view the videotape "History's Mystery: An Introduction to Forensic Science."

Chemical Compounds

In nature, most elements are found combined with other elements in compounds. A chemical **compound** is a substance formed by the chemical combination of two or more elements in definite proportions. Scientists show the composition of compounds by a kind of shorthand known as a chemical formula. Water, which contains two atoms of hydrogen for each atom of oxygen, has the chemical formula H_2O. The formula for table salt, NaCl, indicates that the elements from which table salt forms—sodium and chlorine—combine in a 1 : 1 ratio.

The physical and chemical properties of a compound are usually very different from those of the elements from which it is formed. For example, hydrogen and oxygen, which are gases at room temperature, can combine explosively and form liquid water. Sodium is a silvery metal that is soft enough to cut with a knife. It reacts explosively with cold water. Chlorine is very reactive, too. It is a poisonous, greenish gas that was used to kill many soldiers in World War I. Sodium and chlorine combine to form sodium chloride (NaCl), or table salt. Sodium chloride is a white solid that dissolves easily in water. As you know, sodium chloride is not poisonous. In fact, it is essential for the survival of most living things.

 CHECKPOINT *What information is contained in a chemical formula?*

Sodium atom (Na)		Chlorine atom (Cl)		Sodium ion (Na⁺)		Chloride ion (Cl⁻)	
Protons	+11	Protons	+17	Protons	+11	Protons	+17
Electrons	−11	Electrons	−17	Electrons	−10	Electrons	−18
Charge	0	Charge	0	Charge	+1	Charge	−1

Transfer of electron

▲ **Figure 2–3** The chemical bond in which electrons are transferred from one atom to another is called an ionic bond. The compound sodium chloride forms when sodium loses its valence electron to chlorine.

Water Molecule

▲ **Figure 2–4** The chemical bond in which electrons are shared between atoms is called a covalent bond. In a water molecule, each hydrogen atom shares two electrons with the oxygen atom.

Chemical Bonds

The atoms in compounds are held together by chemical bonds. Much of chemistry is devoted to understanding how and when chemical bonds form. Bond formation involves the electrons that surround each atomic nucleus. The electrons that are available to form bonds are called valence electrons. **The main types of chemical bonds are ionic bonds and covalent bonds.**

Ionic Bonds An **ionic bond** is formed when one or more electrons are transferred from one atom to another. Recall that atoms are electrically neutral because they have equal numbers of protons and electrons. An atom that loses electrons has a positive charge. An atom that gains electrons has a negative charge. These positively and negatively charged atoms are known as **ions.**

Figure 2–3 shows how ionic bonds form between sodium and chlorine in table salt. A sodium atom easily loses its one valence electron and becomes a sodium ion (Na⁺). A chlorine atom easily gains an electron and becomes a chloride ion (Cl⁻). In a salt crystal, there are trillions of sodium and chloride ions. These oppositely charged ions have a strong attraction. The attraction between oppositely charged ions is an ionic bond.

Covalent Bonds Sometimes electrons are shared by atoms instead of being transferred. What does it mean to "share" electrons? It means that the moving electrons are located in a region between the atoms where the orbitals of the atoms overlap. A **covalent bond** forms when electrons are shared between atoms. When the atoms share two electrons, the bond is called a single covalent bond. Sometimes the atoms share four electrons and form a double bond. In a few cases, atoms can share six electrons and form a triple bond.

The structure that results when atoms are joined together by covalent bonds is called a molecule. The **molecule** is the smallest unit of most compounds. The diagram of a water molecule in **Figure 2–4** shows that each hydrogen atom forms a single covalent bond with the oxygen atom.

Van der Waals Forces Because of their structures, atoms of different elements do not all have the same ability to attract electrons. Some atoms have a stronger attraction for electrons than do other atoms. Therefore, when the atoms in a covalent bond share electrons, the sharing is not always equal. Even when the sharing is equal, the rapid movement of electrons can create regions on a molecule that have a tiny positive or negative charge.

When molecules are close together, a slight attraction can develop between the oppositely charged regions of nearby molecules. Chemists call such intermolecular forces of attraction **van der Waals forces,** after the scientist who discovered them. Although van der Waals forces are not as strong as ionic bonds or covalent bonds, they can hold molecules together, especially when the molecules are large.

People who keep geckos as pets have already seen van der Waals forces in action. These remarkable little lizards can climb up vertical surfaces, even smooth glass walls, and then hang on by a single toe despite the pull of gravity. How do they do it? No, they do not have some sort of glue on their feet and they don't have suction cups.

A gecko foot like the one shown in **Figure 2–5** is covered by as many as half a million tiny hairlike projections. Each projection is further divided into hundreds of tiny, flat-surfaced fibers. This design allows the gecko's foot to come in contact with an extremely large area of the wall at the molecular level. Van der Waals forces form between molecules on the surface of the gecko's foot and molecules on the surface of the wall. The combined strength of all the van der Waals forces allows the gecko to balance the pull of gravity. When the gecko needs to move its foot, it peels the foot off at an angle and reattaches it at another location on the wall.

▼ **Figure 2–5** Van der Waals forces help geckos to grip smooth, vertical surfaces. **Applying Concepts** *Explain why a similar technique could not work for humans.*

2–1 Section Assessment

1. 🔑 **Key Concept** Describe the structure of an atom.
2. 🔑 **Key Concept** Why do all isotopes of an element have the same chemical properties? In what way do isotopes of an element differ?
3. 🔑 **Key Concept** What is a covalent bond? An ionic bond?
4. What is a compound? How are compounds related to molecules?
5. How do van der Waals forces hold molecules together?
6. **Critical Thinking Comparing and Contrasting** How are ionic bonds and van der Waals forces similar? How are they different?

iTEXT Assessment Use iText to review the important concepts in Section 2–1.

Take It to the NET

Read about elements in the periodic table. Then, choose two elements and create a two-column chart to compare them. Use the links provided in the Biology area at the Prentice Hall Web site for help in completing this activity: **www.phschool.com**

2–2 Properties of Water

Guide for Reading

Key Concepts
- Why are water molecules polar?
- What are acidic solutions? What are basic solutions?

Vocabulary
cohesion
adhesion
mixture
solution
solute
solvent
suspension
pH scale
acid
base
buffer

**Reading Strategy:
Using Visuals** Before you read, preview **Figure 2–7** and **Figure 2–9.** As you read, note how these two figures are related.

After several days in space, one of the first astronauts to travel to the moon looked back longingly at Earth and marveled at its distant beauty. If there are other beings who have seen Earth, he said, they must surely call it "the blue planet." The astronaut was referring to the blue appearance of the water in the oceans, which cover three fourths of Earth's surface. Water is also the single most abundant compound in most living things.

Water is one of the few compounds that is a liquid at the temperatures found over much of Earth's surface. Unlike most substances, water expands as it freezes. Thus, ice is less dense than liquid water, which explains why ice floats on the surface of lakes and rivers. If the ice sank to the bottom, the situation would be disastrous for fish and plant life in regions with cold winters, to say nothing of the sport of ice skating!

The Water Molecule

Like all molecules, a water molecule (H_2O) is neutral. The positive charges on its 10 protons balance out the negative charges on its 10 electrons. However, there is more to the story.

Polarity With 8 protons in its nucleus, an oxygen atom has a much stronger attraction for electrons than does the hydrogen atom with a single proton in its nucleus. Thus, at any moment, there is a greater probability of finding the shared electrons near the oxygen atom than near the hydrogen atom. Because the water molecule has a bent shape, as shown in **Figure 2–6,** the oxygen atom is on one end of the molecule and the hydrogen atoms are on the other. As a result, the oxygen end of the molecule has a slight negative charge and the hydrogen end of the molecule has a slight positive charge.

A molecule in which the charges are unevenly distributed is called a polar molecule because the molecule is like a magnet with poles. **A water molecule is polar because there is an uneven distribution of electrons between the oxygen and hydrogen atoms.** The negative pole is near the oxygen atom and the positive pole is between the hydrogen atoms.

◄ **Figure 2–6** ◔ The unequal sharing of electrons causes the water molecule to be polar. The hydrogen end of the molecule is slightly positive and the oxygen end is slightly negative.

Hydrogen Bonds Because of their partial positive and negative charges, polar molecules such as water can attract each other, as shown in **Figure 2–7.** The charges on a polar molecule are written in parentheses, (–) or (+), to show that they are weaker than the charges on ions such as Na^+ and Cl^-. The attraction between the hydrogen atom on one water molecule and the oxygen atom on another water molecule is an example of a hydrogen bond. Hydrogen bonds are not as strong as covalent or ionic bonds, but they are the strongest of the bonds that can form between molecules.

A single water molecule may be involved in as many as four hydrogen bonds at the same time. The ability of water to form multiple hydrogen bonds is responsible for many of water's properties. **Cohesion** is an attraction between molecules of the same substance. Because of hydrogen bonding, water is extremely cohesive. Water's cohesion causes molecules on the surface of water to be drawn inward, which is why drops of water form beads on a smooth surface. Cohesion also explains why some insects and spiders can walk on a pond's surface, as shown in **Figure 2–8.**

Adhesion is an attraction between molecules of different substances. Have you ever been told to read the volume in a graduated cylinder at eye level? The surface of the water in the graduated cylinder dips slightly in the center because the adhesion between water molecules and glass molecules is stronger than the cohesion between water molecules. Adhesion between water and glass also causes water to rise in a narrow tube against the force of gravity. This effect is called capillary action. Capillary action is one of the forces that draw water out of the roots of a plant and up into its stems and leaves. Cohesion holds the column of water together as it rises.

✓ **CHECKPOINT** How are cohesion and adhesion similar? Different?

Solutions and Suspensions

Water is not always pure—it is often found as part of a mixture. A **mixture** is a material composed of two or more elements or compounds that are physically mixed together but not chemically combined. Salt and pepper stirred together constitute a mixture. So do sugar and sand. Earth's atmosphere is a mixture of gases. Living things are in part composed of mixtures involving water. Two types of mixtures that can be made with water are solutions and suspensions.

▲ **Figure 2–7** The illustration shows the hydrogen bonds that form between water molecules. **Applying Concepts** *Why are water molecules attracted to one another?*

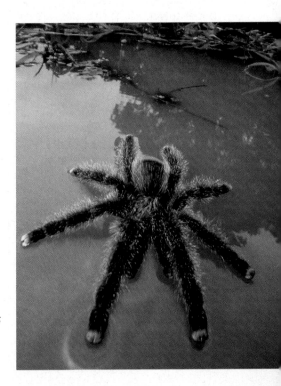

▶ **Figure 2–8** Cohesion is responsible for enabling this tarantula to rest on the water's surface. **Observing** *How does the tarantula's physical structure help it to stay afloat?*

▶ **Figure 2–9** When an ionic compound such as sodium chloride is placed in water, water molecules surround and separate the positive and negative ions. **Interpreting Graphics** *What happens to the sodium ions and chloride ions in the solution?*

Solutions If a crystal of table salt is placed in a glass of warm water, sodium and chloride ions on the surface of the crystal are attracted to the polar water molecules. Ions break away from the crystal and are surrounded by water molecules, as illustrated in **Figure 2–9.** The ions gradually become dispersed in the water, forming a type of mixture called a solution. All the components of a **solution** are evenly distributed throughout the solution. In a salt–water solution, table salt is the **solute**—the substance that is dissolved. Water is the **solvent**—the substance in which the solute dissolves. Water's polarity gives it the ability to dissolve both ionic compounds and other polar molecules, such as sugar. Without exaggeration, water is the greatest solvent on Earth.

Suspensions Some materials do not dissolve when placed in water but separate into pieces so small that they do not settle out. The movement of water molecules keeps the small particles suspended. Such mixtures of water and nondissolved material are known as **suspensions.** Some of the most important biological fluids are both solutions and suspensions. The blood that circulates through your body is mostly water, which contains many dissolved compounds. However, blood also contains cells and other undissolved particles that remain in suspension as the blood moves through the body.

Acids, Bases, and pH

A water molecule can react to form ions. This reaction can be summarized by a chemical equation in which double arrows are used to show that the reaction can occur in either direction.

$$H_2O \rightleftharpoons H^+ + OH^-$$

water $\rightleftharpoons$ hydrogen ion + hydroxide ion

How often does this happen? In pure water, about 1 water molecule in 550 million reacts and forms ions. Because the number of positive hydrogen ions produced is equal to the number of negative hydroxide ions produced, water is neutral.

The pH scale Chemists devised a measurement system called the **pH scale** to indicate the concentration of H^+ ions in solution. As **Figure 2–10** shows, the pH scale ranges from 0 to 14. At a pH of 7, the concentration of H^+ ions and OH^- ions is equal. Pure water has a pH of 7. Solutions with a pH below 7 are called acidic because they have more H^+ ions than OH^- ions. The lower the pH, the greater the acidity. Solutions with a pH above 7 are called basic because they have more OH^- ions than H^+ ions. The higher the pH, the more basic the solution. Each step on the pH scale represents a factor of 10. For example, a liter of a solution with a pH of 4 has 10 times as many H^+ ions as a liter of a solution with a pH of 5.

Acids Where do all those extra H^+ ions in a low-pH solution come from? They come from acids. An **acid** is any compound that forms H^+ ions in solution. 🔑 **Acidic solutions contain higher concentrations of H^+ ions than pure water and have pH values below 7.** Strong acids tend to have pH values that range from 1 to 3. The hydrochloric acid produced by the stomach to help digest food is a strong acid.

Bases A **base** is a compound that produces hydroxide ions (OH^- ions) in solution. 🔑 **Basic, or alkaline, solutions contain lower concentrations of H^+ ions than pure water and have pH values above 7.** Strong bases, such as lye, tend to have pH values ranging from 11 to 14.

Buffers The pH of the fluids within most cells in the human body must generally be kept between 6.5 and 7.5. If the pH is lower or higher, it will affect the chemical reactions that take place within the cells. Thus, controlling pH is important for maintaining homeostasis. One of the ways that the body controls pH is through dissolved compounds called buffers. **Buffers** are weak acids or bases that can react with strong acids or bases to prevent sharp, sudden changes in pH.

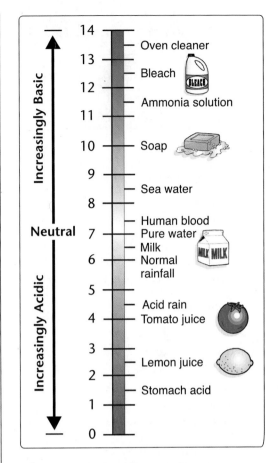

▲ **Figure 2–10** 🔑 The concentration of H^+ ions determines whether solutions are acidic or basic. The most acidic material on this pH scale is stomach acid. The most basic material on this scale is oven cleaner.

2–2 Section Assessment

1. 🔑 **Key Concept** Use the structure of a water molecule to explain why it is polar.

2. 🔑 **Key Concept** Compare acidic and basic solutions in terms of their H^+ ion and OH^- ion concentrations.

3. What is the difference between a solution and a suspension?

4. What does pH measure?

5. **Critical Thinking Predicting** The strong acid hydrogen fluoride (HF) can be dissolved in pure water. Will the pH of the solution be greater or less than 7.0?

iTEXT Assessment Use iText to review the important concepts in Section 2–2.

2–3 Carbon Compounds

Guide for Reading

🔑 **Key Concept**
• What are the functions of each group of organic compounds?

Vocabulary
monomer
polymer
carbohydrate
monosaccharide
polysaccharide
lipid
nucleic acid
nucleotide
ribonucleic acid (RNA)
deoxyribonucleic acid (DNA)
protein
amino acid

Reading Strategy:
Summarizing As you read, find the key ideas. Write down a few key words from each main idea. Then, use the key words in your summary. Reread your summary, keeping only the most important ideas.

Until the early 1800s, many chemists thought that compounds created by organisms—organic compounds—were distinctly different from compounds in nonliving things. In 1828, a German chemist was able to synthesize the organic compound urea from a mineral called ammonium cyanate. Chemists soon realized that the principles governing the chemistry of nonliving things could be applied to living things. Scientists still use the term *organic chemistry,* but now it describes something a little different. Today, organic chemistry is the study of all compounds that contain bonds between carbon atoms.

The Chemistry of Carbon

Is carbon so interesting that a whole branch of chemistry should be set aside just to study carbon compounds? It is indeed, for two reasons. First, carbon atoms have four valence electrons. Each electron can join with an electron from another atom to form a strong covalent bond. Carbon can bond with many elements, including hydrogen, oxygen, phosphorus, sulfur, and nitrogen.

Even more important, a carbon atom can bond to other carbon atoms, which gives carbon the ability to form chains that are almost unlimited in length. These carbon-carbon bonds can be single, double, or triple covalent bonds. Chains of carbon atoms can even close upon themselves to form rings, as shown in **Figure 2–11.** Carbon has the ability to form millions of different large and complex structures. No other element even comes close to matching carbon's versatility.

▼ **Figure 2–11** Carbon can form single, double, or triple bonds with other carbon atoms. Each line between atoms in a molecular drawing represents one covalent bond. **Observing** *How many covalent bonds are there between the carbon atoms in acetylene?*

Methane   **Acetylene**   **Butadiene**   **Benzene**   **Isooctane**

Macromolecules

Many of the molecules in living cells are so large that they are known as macromolecules, which means "giant molecules." Macromolecules are made from thousands or even hundreds of thousands of smaller molecules.

Macromolecules are formed by a process known as polymerization (pah-lih-mur-ih-ZAY-shun), in which large compounds are built by joining smaller ones together. The smaller units, or **monomers,** join together to form **polymers.** The monomers in a polymer may be identical like the links on a metal watch band, or the monomers may be different like the beads in a multicolored necklace. **Figure 2–12** illustrates the formation of a polymer from more than one type of monomer.

It would be difficult to study the millions of organic compounds if they were not classified into groups. 🔑 **Four groups of organic compounds found in living things are carbohydrates, lipids, nucleic acids, and proteins.**

✓CHECKPOINT *What is polymerization?*

Carbohydrates

Carbohydrates are compounds made up of carbon, hydrogen, and oxygen atoms, usually in a ratio of $1 : 2 : 1$. 🔑 **Living things use carbohydrates as their main source of energy. Plants and some animals also use carbohydrates for structural purposes.** The breakdown of sugars, such as glucose, supplies immediate energy for all cell activities. Living things store extra sugar as complex carbohydrates known as starches. As shown in **Figure 2–13,** the monomers in starch polymers are sugar molecules.

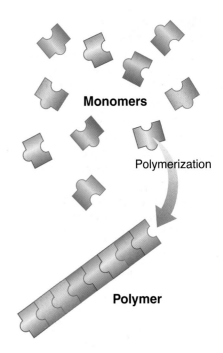

▲ **Figure 2–12** When small molecules called monomers join together, they form polymers, or large molecules. **Using Analogies** *How are monomers similar to links in a chain?*

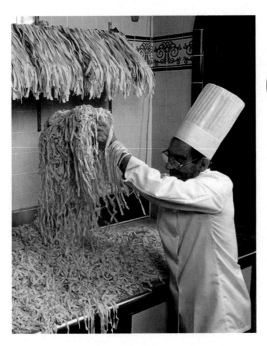

Figure 2–13 👁 Starches and sugars are examples of carbohydrates that are used by living things as a source of energy. Starches form when sugars join together in a long chain.

Monomer comes from the Greek words *monos*, meaning "single," and *meros*, meaning "part." *Monomer* means "single part." The prefix *poly-* comes from the Greek word *polus*, meaning "many," so *polymer* means "many parts." **The word *saccharide* comes from the Latin word *saccharum*, meaning "sugar." What do you think the terms *monosaccharide* and *polysaccharide* mean?**

Single sugar molecules are also called **monosaccharides** (mahn-oh-SAK-uh-rydz). Besides glucose, monosaccharides include galactose, which is a component of milk, and fructose, which is found in many fruits.

The large macromolecules formed from monosaccharides are known as **polysaccharides.** Many animals store excess sugar in a polysaccharide called glycogen, or animal starch. When the level of glucose in your blood runs low, glycogen is released from your liver. The glycogen stored in your muscles supplies the energy for muscle contraction and, thus, for movement.

Plants use a slightly different polysaccharide, called plant starch, to store excess sugar. Plants also make another important polysaccharide called cellulose. Tough, flexible cellulose fibers give plants much of their strength and rigidity. Cellulose is the major component of both wood and paper, so you are actually looking at cellulose as you read these words!

Lipids

Lipids are a large and varied group of biological molecules that are generally not soluble in water. **Lipids** are made mostly from carbon and hydrogen atoms. The common categories of lipids are fats, oils, and waxes. **Lipids can be used to store energy. Some lipids are important parts of biological membranes and waterproof coverings.** Steroids are lipids as well. Many steroids serve as chemical messengers.

Many lipids are formed when a glycerol molecule combines with compounds called fatty acids, as shown in **Figure 2–14.** If each carbon atom in a lipid's fatty acid chains is joined to another carbon atom by a single bond, the lipid is said to be saturated. The term *saturated* is used because the fatty acids contain the maximum possible number of hydrogen atoms.

▼ **Figure 2–14** Lipids are used to store energy. Lipid molecules are made up of fatty acids and glycerol. Liquid lipids, such as olive oil, contain mainly unsaturated fatty acids.

Lipid

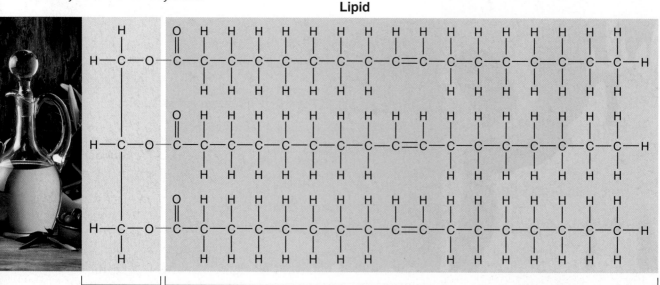

Glycerol   Fatty acids

If there is at least one carbon-carbon double bond in a fatty acid, the fatty acid is said to be unsaturated. Lipids whose fatty acids contain more than one double bond are said to be polyunsaturated. If the terms *saturated* and *polyunsaturated* seem familiar, you have probably seen them on food package labels. Lipids such as olive oil, which contains unsaturated fatty acids, tend to be liquid at room temperature. Cooking oils, such as corn oil, sesame oil, and peanut oil, contain polyunsaturated lipids.

Nucleic Acids

Nucleic acids are macromolecules containing hydrogen, oxygen, nitrogen, carbon, and phosphorus. Nucleic acids are polymers assembled from individual monomers known as nucleotides. **Nucleotides** consist of three parts: a 5-carbon sugar, a phosphate group, and a nitrogenous base, as shown in **Figure 2–15**. Individual nucleotides can be joined by covalent bonds to form a polynucleotide, or nucleic acid.

⬤ **Nucleic acids store and transmit hereditary, or genetic, information.** There are two kinds of nucleic acids: **ribonucleic acid (RNA)** and **deoxyribonucleic acid (DNA)**. As their names indicate, RNA contains the sugar ribose and DNA contains the sugar deoxyribose.

✓ CHECKPOINT *What are the three parts of a nucleotide?*

Proteins

Proteins are macromolecules that contain nitrogen as well as carbon, hydrogen, and oxygen. Proteins are polymers of molecules called **amino acids.** Amino acids are compounds with an amino group (–NH$_2$) on one end and a carboxyl group (–COOH) on the other end.

Figure 2–16 shows one reason why proteins are among the most diverse macromolecules. More than 20 different amino acids are found in nature. All amino acids are identical in the regions where they may be joined together by covalent bonds. This uniformity allows any amino acid to be joined to any other amino acid—by bonding an amino group to a carboxyl group.

▲ **Figure 2–15** ⬤ Nucleic acids store and transmit genetic information. The monomers that make up a nucleic acid are nucleotides. Each nucleotide has a 5-carbon sugar, a phosphate group, and a nitrogenous base.

▶ **Figure 2–16** Amino acids are the monomers of proteins. All amino acids have an amino group at one end and a carboxyl group at the other end. What distinguishes one amino acid from another is the R-group section of the molecule. **Comparing and Contrasting** *How are proteins and carbohydrates similar? How are they different?*

Amino Acids

General structure

Alanine

Serine

▲ **Figure 2–17** 🔑 Proteins help to carry out chemical reactions, transport small molecules in and out of cells, and fight diseases. Proteins are made up of chains of amino acids folded into complex structures.

The portion of each amino acid that is different is a side chain called an R-group. Some R-groups are acidic and some are basic. Some are polar and some are nonpolar. Some contain carbon rings. The instructions for arranging amino acids into many different proteins are stored in DNA. Each protein has a specific role. 🔑 **Some proteins control the rate of reactions and regulate cell processes. Some are used to form bones and muscles. Others transport substances into or out of cells or help to fight disease.**

Proteins can have up to four levels of organization. The first level is the sequence of amino acids in a protein chain. Second, the amino acids within a chain can be twisted or folded. Third, the chain itself is folded. If a protein has more than one chain, they have a specific arrangement in space as illustrated by the red and blue structures in **Figure 2–17.** Van der Waals forces and hydrogen bonds help maintain a protein's shape. In the next section, you will learn why a protein's shape is so important.

2–3 Section Assessment

1. 🔑 **Key Concept** Name four groups of organic compounds found in living things.

2. 🔑 **Key Concept** Describe at least one function of each group of organic compounds.

3. What properties of carbon explain carbon's ability to form many different macromolecules?

4. **Critical Thinking Applying Concepts** Explain why proteins are polymers but lipids are not.

i **TEXT** Assessment Use iText to review the important concepts in Section 2–3.

MAKING CONNECTIONS

Levels of Organization
Use what you learned about levels of organization in Section 1–3 to discuss the levels of organization in macromolecules.

2–4 Chemical Reactions and Enzymes

Living things, as you have seen, are made of chemical compounds—some simple and some complex. The influence of chemistry doesn't stop, however, with the study of the composition of living organisms. To get the whole story, you have to look further. Chemistry isn't just what life is made of—chemistry is also what life does. Everything that happens in an organism—its growth, its interaction with the environment, its reproduction, and even its movement—is based on chemical reactions.

Chemical Reactions

A **chemical reaction** is a process that changes one set of chemicals into another set of chemicals. Some chemical reactions occur slowly, such as the combination of iron and oxygen to form an iron oxide called rust, shown in **Figure 2–18.** Other reactions occur quickly. When hydrogen gas is ignited in the presence of oxygen, the reaction is rapid and explosive. The elements or compounds that enter into a chemical reaction are known as **reactants.** The elements or compounds produced by a chemical reaction are known as **products.** **Chemical reactions always involve the breaking of bonds in reactants and the formation of new bonds in products.**

One example of an important chemical reaction that occurs in your body involves carbon dioxide. Your cells constantly produce carbon dioxide as a normal part of their activity. This carbon dioxide is carried to your lungs through the bloodstream, and then is eliminated as you exhale. However, carbon dioxide is not very soluble in water. The bloodstream could not possibly dissolve enough carbon dioxide to carry it away from your tissues were it not for a chemical reaction. As it enters the blood, carbon dioxide reacts with water to produce a highly soluble compound called carbonic acid, H_2CO_3.

$$CO_2 + H_2O \longrightarrow H_2CO_3$$

This reaction enables the bloodstream to carry carbon dioxide to the lungs. In the lungs, the reaction is reversed.

$$H_2CO_3 \longrightarrow CO_2 + H_2O$$

This reverse reaction produces carbon dioxide gas, which is released as you exhale.

▶ **Figure 2–18** Chemical reactions always involve changes in chemical bonds. The iron in these chain links gradually combined with oxygen to produce a compound known as rust.

Guide for Reading

Key Concepts
• What happens to chemical bonds during chemical reactions?
• How do energy changes affect whether a chemical reaction will occur?
• Why are enzymes important to living things?

Vocabulary
chemical reaction
reactant
product
activation energy
catalyst
enzyme
substrate

**Reading Strategy:
Building Vocabulary** After you read, write a phrase or sentence using your own words to define or describe each boldfaced word in the section.

Energy in Reactions

Energy is released or absorbed whenever chemical bonds form or are broken. Because chemical reactions involve breaking and forming bonds, they involve changes in energy.

Energy Changes Some chemical reactions release energy, and other reactions absorb energy. Energy changes are one of the most important factors in determining whether a chemical reaction will occur. 🔑 **Chemical reactions that release energy often occur spontaneously. Chemical reactions that absorb energy will not occur without a source of energy.** An example of an energy-releasing reaction is hydrogen gas burning, or reacting, with oxygen to produce water vapor.

$$2H_2 + O_2 \longrightarrow 2H_2O$$

The energy is released in the form of heat, and sometimes—when hydrogen gas explodes—light and sound.

The reverse reaction, in which water is changed into hydrogen and oxygen gas, absorbs so much energy that it generally doesn't occur by itself. In fact, the only practical way to reverse the reaction is to pass an electrical current through water to decompose water into hydrogen gas and oxygen gas. Thus, in one direction the reaction produces energy, and in the other direction the reaction requires energy.

What significance do these energy changes have for living things? In order to stay alive, organisms need to carry out reactions that require energy. Thus, every organism must have a source of energy to carry out chemical reactions. Plants get their energy by trapping and storing the energy from sunlight in energy-rich compounds. Animals get their energy when they consume plants or other animals. Humans release the energy needed to grow tall, to breathe, to think, and even to dream through the chemical reactions that occur when humans metabolize, or break down, digested food.

Activation Energy Even chemical reactions that release energy do not always occur spontaneously. That's a good thing because if they did, the pages of this book might burst into flames. The cellulose in paper burns in the presence of oxygen and releases heat and light. However, the cellulose will burn only if you light it with a match, which supplies enough energy to get the reaction started. Chemists call the energy that is needed to get a reaction started the **activation energy.** As **Figure 2–19** shows, activation energy is a factor in whether the overall chemical reaction releases energy or absorbs energy.

CHECKPOINT *What is activation energy?*

▼ **Figure 2–19** 🐭 Chemical reactions that release energy often occur spontaneously. Chemical reactions that absorb energy will occur only with a source of energy. The peak of each graph represents the energy needed for the reaction to go forward. The difference between this required energy and the energy of the reactants is the activation energy.

Energy-Absorbing Reaction

Energy-Releasing Reaction

How does pH affect an enzyme?

Catalase is an enzyme that helps decompose the toxic hydrogen peroxide that is produced during normal cell activities. The products of this reaction are water and oxygen gas. The pressure of the oxygen gas in a closed container increases as oxygen is produced. Any increase in the rate of the reaction will cause an increase in the pressure of the oxygen.

The purple line on the graph represents the normal rate of the reaction in a water solution of hydrogen peroxide and catalase. The red line represents the rate of reaction when an acid is added to the solution. The blue line represents the rate of reaction when a base is added to the solution.

1. **Applying Concepts** What variable is plotted on the x-axis? What variable is plotted on the y-axis?

2. **Interpreting Graphics** How did the rate of reaction change over time in the control reaction?

3. **Inferring** Suggest an explanation for the change in the control reaction at about 40 seconds.

4. **Interpreting Graphics** How does the presence of a base affect the rate of the reaction? How does the presence of an acid affect the rate?

5. **Drawing Conclusions** What effect do acids and bases have on the enzyme catalase?

6. **Going Further** Predict what would happen if vinegar were added to a water solution of hydrogen peroxide and catalase.

Enzymes

Some chemical reactions that make life possible are too slow or have activation energies that are too high to make them practical for living tissue. These chemical reactions are made possible by a process that would make any chemist proud—cells make catalysts. A **catalyst** is a substance that speeds up the rate of a chemical reaction. Catalysts work by lowering a reaction's activation energy.

Enzymes are proteins that act as biological catalysts. 🔑 **Cells use enzymes to speed up chemical reactions that take place in cells.** Like other catalysts, enzymes act by lowering the activation energies, as illustrated by the graph in **Figure 2–20.** Lowering the activation energy has a dramatic effect on how quickly the reaction is completed. How big an effect? Remember the reaction in which carbon dioxide combines with water to produce carbonic acid.

$$CO_2 + H_2O \longrightarrow H_2CO_3$$

▼ **Figure 2–20** 🔑 **Cells use enzymes to speed up chemical reactions that take place in cells.** Notice how the addition of an enzyme lowers the activation energy in this reaction. This action speeds up the reaction.

KEEP CURRENT WITH . . .
SCIENCE NEWS®

To find out more about the
topics in this chapter, go to:
www.phschool.com

Left to itself, this reaction is so slow that carbon dioxide might build up in the body faster than the bloodstream could remove it. Your bloodstream contains an enzyme called carbonic anhydrase that speeds up the reaction by a factor of 10 million. With carbonic anhydrase on the job, the reaction takes place immediately and carbon dioxide is removed from the blood quickly.

Enzymes are very specific, generally catalyzing only one chemical reaction. For this reason, part of an enzyme's name is usually derived from the reaction it catalyzes. Carbonic anhydrase gets its name because it catalyzes the reaction that removes water from carbonic acid.

Enzyme Action

How do enzymes do their jobs? For a chemical reaction to take place, the reactants must collide with enough energy so that existing bonds will be broken and new bonds will be formed. If the reactants do not have enough energy, they will be unchanged after the collision.

The Enzyme-Substrate Complex Enzymes provide a site where reactants can be brought together to react. Such a site reduces the energy needed for reaction. The reactants of enzyme-catalyzed reactions are known as **substrates.**

▼ **Figure 2–21** The enzyme hexokinase converts the substrates glucose and ATP into glucose-6-phosphate and ADP. **Predicting** *What happens to the hexokinase after the products are released?*

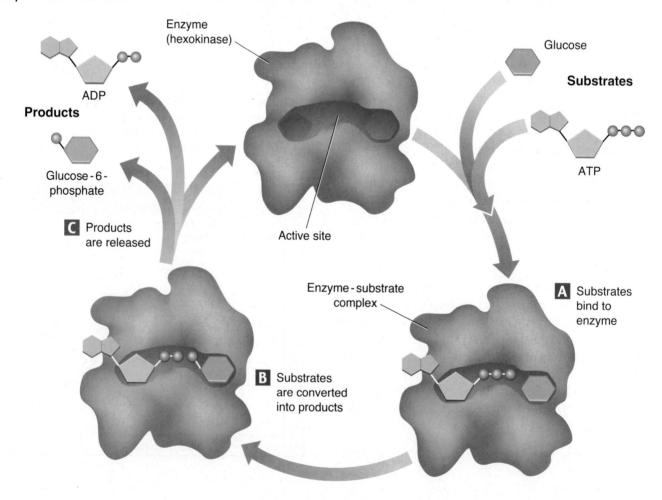

Enzyme (hexokinase)

Glucose

Substrates

ATP

Products

ADP

Glucose - 6 - phosphate

Active site

C Products are released

Enzyme - substrate complex

A Substrates bind to enzyme

B Substrates are converted into products

Figure 2–21 provides an example of an enzyme-catalyzed reaction. The enzyme is hexokinase. The substrates are glucose and ATP. During the reaction, a phosphate group is transferred from ATP to the glucose molecule. Recall that each protein has a specific, complex shape. The substrates bind to a site on the enzyme called the active site. The active site and the substrates have complementary shapes. The fit is so precise that the active site and substrates are often compared to a lock and key.

Figure 2–22 shows a substrate fitting into an active site on an enzyme. The enzyme and substrate are bound together by intermolecular forces and form an enzyme-substrate complex. They remain bound together until the reaction is done. Once the reaction is over, the products of the reaction are released and the enzyme is free to start the process again.

Regulation of Enzyme Activity Because they are catalysts for reactions, enzymes can be affected by any variable that influences a chemical reaction. Enzymes, including those that help digest food, work best at certain pH values. Many enzymes are affected by changes in temperature. Not surprisingly, those enzymes produced by human cells generally work best at temperatures close to 37°C, the human body's core temperature.

Cells can regulate the activities of enzymes in a variety of ways. Most cells contain proteins that help to turn key enzymes "on" or "off" at critical stages in the life of the cell. Enzymes play essential roles in regulating chemical pathways, making materials that cells need, releasing energy, and transferring information.

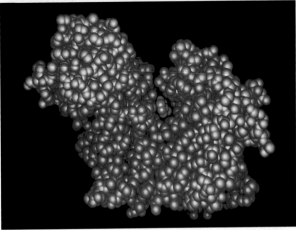

▲ **Figure 2–22** This space-filling model shows how a substrate binds to an active site on an enzyme. **Interpreting Graphics** *What happens after the substrate binds to the enzyme?*

2–4 Section Assessment

1. 🔑 **Key Concept** What happens to chemical bonds during chemical reactions?

2. 🔑 **Key Concept** Describe the role of energy in chemical reactions.

3. 🔑 **Key Concept** What are enzymes, and how are they important to living things?

4. Describe how enzymes work, including the role of the enzyme-substrate complex.

5. **Critical Thinking Applying Concepts** A change in pH can change the shape of a protein. How might a change in pH affect the function of an enzyme such as hexokinase?

📱**TEXT** Assessment Use iText to review the important concepts in Section 2–4.

Investigating the Effect of Temperature on Enzyme Activity

Almost all chemical reactions that occur in living organisms are catalyzed by enzymes. Many factors in a cell's environment affect the action of an enzyme. In this investigation, you will design an experiment to determine the effect of temperature on an enzyme-catalyzed reaction.

Problem
How does temperature affect the rate of an enzyme-catalyzed reaction?

Materials
- raw liver
- petri dish
- dropper pipette
- 1% hydrogen peroxide solution
- liver puree
- 25-mL graduated cylinder
- 5 50-mL beakers
- filter-paper disks
- forceps
- glass-marking pencil
- ice bath
- 3 thermometers
- warm water bath
- clock or watch with second hand

Skills
Formulating Hypotheses, Predicting

Design Your Experiment

Part A: Observe the Catalase Reaction

1. Place a small piece of raw liver in an open petri dish. Use a dropper pipette to put a drop of hydrogen peroxide solution on the liver. **CAUTION:** *Hydrogen peroxide can be irritating to skin and eyes. If you spill any on yourself or your clothes, wash it off immediately and tell your teacher.* Observe what happens. Liver contains the enzyme catalase, which breaks down hydrogen peroxide (H_2O_2) formed in cells to water (H_2O) and oxygen gas (O_2). When hydrogen peroxide is broken down by catalase, bubbles of oxygen gas are released.

2. To measure the activity of catalase, use a graduated cylinder to place 25 mL of hydrogen peroxide solution in a 50-mL beaker.

3. Use forceps to dip a filter-paper disk in liver puree. Place the filter-paper disk on a paper towel for 4 seconds to remove any excess liquid.

4. Use the forceps to place the filter-paper disk at the bottom of the beaker of hydrogen peroxide solution. Observe the filter-paper disk and record the number of seconds it takes to float to the top of the liquid.

Part B: Design an Experiment

5. **Formulating Hypotheses** Develop a hypothesis about how temperature will affect the rate at which catalase breaks down hydrogen peroxide. Record your hypothesis.

6. **Designing Experiments** Design an experiment to test your hypothesis. Your experimental plan should include a prediction of the result based on your hypothesis, and any appropriate controls and replications (repetitions). Be sure to identify all manipulated, responding, and controlled variables in your experimental plan.

7. Construct a data table in which to record the results of your experiment. Perform your experiment only after you have obtained your teacher's approval of your plan.

8. Make a graph of the results of your experiment. Plot temperature on the *x*-axis and the variable by which you measured catalase activity on the *y*-axis.

Analyze and Conclude

1. **Inferring** How does the time required for a catalase-soaked, filter-paper disk to float reflect the amount of catalase activity in the solution?

2. **Evaluating and Revising** How did temperature affect catalase activity? Was your prediction confirmed?

3. **Drawing Conclusions** Many mammals, including cattle and pigs, have body temperatures close to 37°C. Does your graph indicate that catalase is most active close to the temperature at which it exists in a living animal?

Go Further

Design an Experiment Catalase is also found in potatoes. Design an experiment using potato puree instead of liver puree to determine the temperature at which potato catalase is most active.

2–1 The Nature of Matter
Key Concepts

- The subatomic particles that make up atoms are protons, neutrons, and electrons.
- Because they have the same numbers of electrons, all isotopes of an element have the same chemical properties.
- The main types of chemical bonds are covalent bonds and ionic bonds.

Vocabulary
- atom, p. 35 • nucleus, p. 35 • electron, p. 35
- element, p. 36 • isotope, p. 36
- compound, p. 37 • ionic bond, p. 38
- ion, p. 38 • covalent bond, p. 38
- molecule, p. 38 • van der Waals forces, p. 39

2–2 Properties of Water
Key Concepts

- A water molecule is polar because there is an uneven distribution of electrons between the oxygen and hydrogen atoms.
- Acidic solutions contain higher concentrations of H^+ ions than pure water and have pH values below 7.
- Basic, or alkaline, solutions contain lower concentrations of H^+ ions than pure water and have pH values above 7.

Vocabulary
- cohesion, p. 41 • adhesion, p. 41 • mixture, p. 41
- solution, p. 42 • solute, p. 42 • solvent, p. 42
- suspension, p. 42 • pH scale, p. 43 • acid, p. 43
- base, p. 43 • buffer, p. 43

2–3 Carbon Compounds
Key Concepts

- Four groups of organic compounds found in living things are carbohydrates, lipids, nucleic acids, and proteins.
- Living things use carbohydrates as their main source of energy. Plants and some animals also use carbohydrates for structural purposes.
- Lipids can be used to store energy. Some lipids are important parts of biological membranes and waterproof coverings.
- Nucleic acids store and transmit hereditary, or genetic, information.
- Some proteins control the rate of reactions and regulate cell processes. Some proteins build tissues such as bone and muscle. Others transport materials or help to fight disease.

Vocabulary
- monomer, p. 45 • polymer, p. 45
- carbohydrate, p. 45 • monosaccharide, p. 46
- polysaccharide, p. 46 • lipid, p. 46
- nucleic acid, p. 47 • nucleotide, p. 47
- ribonucleic acid (RNA), p. 47
- deoxyribonucleic acid (DNA), p. 47
- protein, p. 47 • amino acid, p. 47

2–4 Chemical Reactions and Enzymes
Key Concepts

- Chemical reactions always involve the breaking of bonds in reactants and the formation of new bonds in products.
- Chemical reactions that release energy often occur spontaneously. Chemical reactions that absorb energy will not occur without a source of energy.
- Cells use enzymes to speed up chemical reactions that take place in cells.

Vocabulary
- chemical reaction, p. 49 • reactant, p. 49
- product, p. 49 • activation energy, p. 50
- catalyst, p. 51 • enzyme, p. 51 • substrate, p. 52

Thinking Visually
Create a cycle diagram that shows how enzymes work. Use the following terms in your cycle diagram: *enzyme, substrate, enzyme-substrate complex, active site, reactants, products.*

Chapter 2

Part A

Multiple Choice

For each statement or question, select the number of the word or expression that, of those given, best completes the statement or answers the question.

1 Two or more different elements are chemically combined in definite proportions in any
(**1**) symbol   (**3**) element
(**2**) isotope   (**4**) compound

2 A covalent bond is formed by the
(**1**) transfer of electrons
(**2**) sharing of electrons
(**3**) gaining of electrons
(**4**) losing of electrons

3 Examples of large, complex molecules formed by joining together many smaller molecules include
(**1**) proteins and amino acids
(**2**) carbohydrates and monosaccharides
(**3**) DNA and proteins
(**4**) mitochondria and vacuoles

4 Which formula represents an amino acid?
(**1**) formula A   (**3**) formula C
(**2**) formula B   (**4**) formula D

5 When you shake sugar and sand together in a test tube, you cause them to form a
(**1**) compound   (**3**) solution
(**2**) mixture   (**4**) suspension

6 Proteins are large, organic molecules formed from
(**1**) fats   (**3**) amino acids
(**2**) carbohydrates   (**4**) simple sugars

7 A protein that acts as a biological catalyst is a(an)
(**1**) enzyme   (**3**) hormone
(**2**) fat   (**4**) simple sugar

8 In humans, carbon dioxide and water quickly combine to form carbonic acid in the presence of a particular enzyme. Most likely, this same enzyme
(**1**) helps in the breakdown of acidic foods in the stomach
(**2**) is not involved in other types of reactions because enzymes are specific
(**3**) is involved in other reactions where the temperature and pH are the same
(**4**) helps in the synthesis of sugars during photosynthesis

9 Which is *not* an organic molecule found in living organisms?
(**1**) protein   (**3**) sugar
(**2**) water   (**4**) carbohydrate

10 Which combination of particle and charge is correct?
(**1**) proton: positively charged
(**2**) electron: positively charged
(**3**) neutron: negatively charged
(**4**) electron: no charge

11 In which way do isotopes of the same element differ?
(**1**) in number of neutrons, only
(**2**) in number of protons, only
(**3**) in number of protons and in mass
(**4**) in number of neutrons and in mass

Test-Taking Tip   As you briefly scan the questions, mark those that may require pure guesswork on your part and save them for last. (Do not write in this book.) Use whatever time you have left for those questions to eliminate as many answers as possible through reasoning.

Parts B and C

Multiple Choice and Extended Response

For those questions that ask you to select a response, choose the one that best completes the statement or answers the question. For all others follow the directions given.

For questions 12 through 14, select the best choice among those listed below. A choice may be used once, more than once, or not at all.

A Cohesion   D Reactants
B Adhesion   E Products
C Catalysts

12 An attraction between different substances

13 Lowers a chemical reaction's activation energy

14 The elements or compounds that enter into a chemical reaction

---

15 How is an enzyme related to a catalyst?

16 Describe some factors that may influence enzyme activity.

17 Suppose you wanted to decrease the pH of a solution. What could you add to the solution to decrease the pH? Support your prediction.

18 Why is it important that energy-releasing reactions take place in living organisms?

19 The bar graph below shows the total amount of product from a chemical reaction performed at three different temperatures. The same enzyme was involved in each case.

Effect of Temperature on a Reaction

• Describe the results of each reaction.

• How can you explain these results?

Base your answers to questions 20 and 21 on the information and graph below and on your knowledge of biology.

The enzyme catalase speeds up the chemical reaction that changes hydrogen peroxide into oxygen and water. The amount of oxygen given off is an indication of the rate of the reaction.

Concentration of Catalase and Amount of Oxygen Given Off

20 Based on the graph, what can you conclude about the relationship between enzyme concentration and reaction rate?
  (1) Reaction rate decreases with increasing enzyme concentration.
  (2) Reaction rate increases with decreasing enzyme concentration.
  (3) Reaction rate increases with increasing enzyme concentration.
  (4) The variables are not related.

21 Which concentration of catalase will produce the fastest reaction rate?
  (1) 0%   **(3)** 15%
  (2) 10%   **(4)** 20%

Base your answers to questions 22 and 23 on the information below and on your knowledge of biology.

Often a model referred to as a "lock and key" model is used to describe the way an enzyme works.

22 Why is comparing the way a key and a lock work together a good analogy for explaining how an enzyme works?

23 In what ways is the analogy *not* perfect?

Base your answers to questions 24 and 25 on the reading passage below and on your knowledge of biology.

Molecular Modeling

The way a molecule behaves chemically, along with its physical characteristics, provides information about the numbers and kinds of atoms making it up. For centuries chemists and biologists have been working to find out more about chemical bonds and molecular structure. Recently, high-speed computers have provided another way of learning more about the shape of molecules through a process called molecular modeling.

Molecular modeling allows scientists to build and visualize molecules. With this information, scientists have the ability to design new and more potent drugs to use in the fight against various diseases. For example, based on experimental evidence, researchers proposed that the outer protein shell of most viruses is composed of small, repeating subunits. They thought these subunits were packed together in such a way that all sides of a virus are provided with an identical environment. Through the use of modern electron microscopes and molecular modeling, these ideas have been confirmed. Learning more about the structure of viruses may make it easier to combat viral diseases.

Molecular modeling has become important in designing medications and in learning more about biological structures. Recently, the structural arrangement and bonding patterns of several proteins important in the process of photosynthesis were discovered. Scientists will be able to use this knowledge to develop systems that can carry out artificial photosynthesis. Think of the impact this could have on atmospheric oxygen and carbon dioxide levels and on space travel!

24 Molecular modeling involves the use of
(1) attractive lab assistants wearing the latest laboratory fashions
(2) modeling clay and other materials to construct representations of viruses
(3) high-speed computers in learning more about the shape of molecules
(4) powerful computers in carrying out photo-synthesis in space

25 State two ways molecular modeling can improve our lives.

26 In living organisms, the millions of organic compounds are classified into groups. For example, lipids are a large and varied group of organic compounds that include fats, oils, and waxes. Name three other groups of organic compounds and explain why each is important.

27 Design an experiment to determine if pH affects the rate at which an enzyme found in potatoes breaks down hydrogen peroxide. In your design, be sure to include
• a hypothesis, list of materials, and a procedure to be followed (*Hint:* Refer to page 54.)
• what variables must be kept the same for all setups
• what the manipulated (independent) variable and the responding (dependent) variable is

28 How are acids and bases different? How do their pH values differ?

29 Identify three major roles of proteins.

30 Suggest one or two simple experiments to determine whether a solid white substance is a protein or a carbohydrate. What evidence would you need to support each hypothesis?

31 Changing the temperature or pH can change an enzyme's ability to function. Describe why changing the temperature or pH might affect the function of the enzyme in Figure 2–21 on page 52.

 Take It to the NET

Amino acids are the monomers in proteins. Visit the Prentice Hall Web site at **www.phschool.com** to find out more about the chemistry of amino acids. Then, answer the following questions:
• Which element is in the center of an amino acid?
• What is the difference between D-amino acids and L-amino acids?
• What is a peptide bond?
• What do the primary and secondary structures of a protein refer to?

▶ Like all living things, alligators such as this one are involved in interactions with other living things (trees and vines) and with their physical surroundings (water, air, and climate).

What do we know about ecology?

- Biologists have discovered entire ecosystems living in the total darkness of the ocean floor, 1.6 kilometers beneath the surface.

- Global temperatures are rising. Plants and animals on land and in the sea are already responding to these warmer temperatures.

- Ecosystems around the world are under stress from human activities and from the introduction of "weed" species that have been introduced far from their natural ranges.

What discoveries lie in the future?

- What effects will rising temperatures have on the environment? Can humans take any actions to stop the trends of global warming?

- Can humans learn how to produce the food and energy that they need while preserving the environment?

- What steps can be taken to preserve biodiversity?

Chapter 3 The Biosphere

A tawny owl prepares to seize a mouse. The mouse is carrying a berry in its mouth as it runs along a fallen, moss-covered tree trunk. The owl, the mouse, the tree trunk, and the moss are all members of this forest ecosystem.

Inquiry Activity

How do organisms affect one another's survival?

Procedure

1. Make a list of all the types of organisms, including plants, humans, insects, and so on, that you have seen near your home or school.
2. Make a diagram that shows how the organisms on your list interact with one another.

Think About It

1. **Classifying** Which organisms on your list provide energy or nutrients to the others?
2. **Predicting** What would you expect to happen if all the plants on your diagram died? Explain your answer.
3. **Posing Questions** Why is it difficult to make accurate predictions about changes in communities of organisms?

3–1 What Is Ecology?

The stories flash across television screens, radios, newspapers, and the Internet nearly every day. "Floods hit the Midwest!" "Southwest wildfires char thousands of acres!" "Florida's Everglades faces drought!" "Great Lakes battle marine invaders!" What do floods, raging wildfires, and droughts have in common? What are "marine invaders," and why do they pose problems in lakes? Every one of these headline-grabbing events involves interactions between organisms and their environment. To understand the changes that occur as a result of such interactions, scientists turn to a branch of biology called ecology.

Interactions and Interdependence

Ecology (ee-KAHL-uh-jee) is the scientific study of interactions among organisms and between organisms and their environment, or surroundings. The word *ecology* was coined in 1866 by the German biologist Ernst Haeckel. Haeckel based this term on the Greek word *oikos,* meaning house, which is also the root of the word *economy.* Haeckel saw the living world as a household with an economy in which each organism plays a role.

Nature's "houses" come in many sizes—from single cells to the entire planet. The largest of these houses is called the biosphere. The **biosphere** contains the combined portions of the planet in which all of life exists, including land, water, and air or atmosphere. It extends from about 8 kilometers above Earth's surface to as far as 11 kilometers below the surface of the ocean.

Interactions within the biosphere produce a web of interdependence between organisms and the environment in which they live. Whether it occurs on top of a glacier, in a forest like the one in **Figure 3–1,** or deep within an ocean trench, the interdependence of life on Earth contributes to an ever-changing, or dynamic, biosphere.

Guide for Reading

Key Concepts
- What different levels of organization do ecologists study?
- What methods are used to study ecology?

Vocabulary
ecology
biosphere
species
population
community
ecosystem
biome

Reading Strategy:
Asking Questions Before you read, rewrite the headings in this section as *how, what,* or *why* questions about ecology. Then, as you read, write brief answers to your questions.

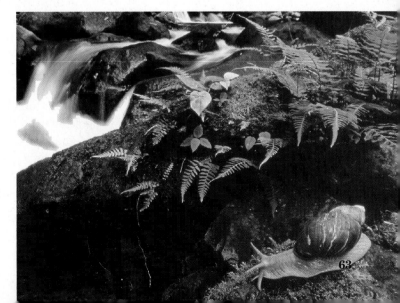

▶ **Figure 3–1** Organisms and their environment are interdependent. This giant land snail could not survive without plants and algae to eat, and the plants and algae could not grow unless bacteria and other organisms helped recycle nutrients in the water and soil. **Classifying** *List the organisms that you see in the photograph. Then list the nonliving parts of the environment with which the organisms interact.*

63

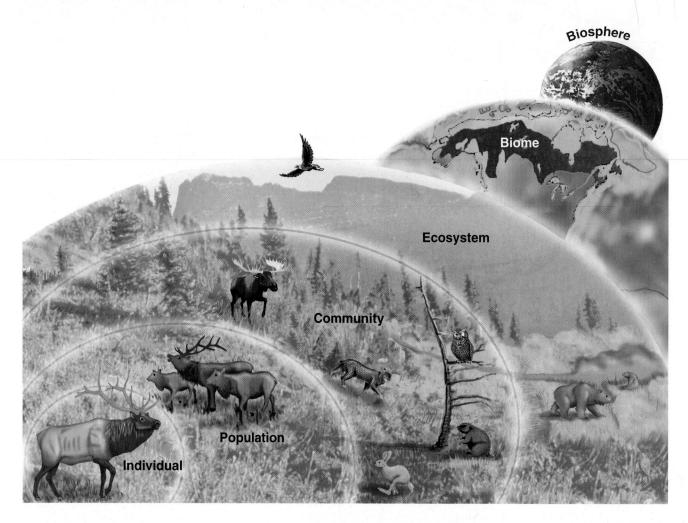

▲ Figure 3–2 🔈 The study of ecology ranges from the study of an individual organism to populations, communities, ecosystems, biomes—and finally, to the entire biosphere. The information that ecologists gain at each level contributes to our understanding of natural systems.

KEEP CURRENT WITH . . .

To find out more about the topics in this chapter, go to: **www.phschool.com**

Levels of Organization

🔈 **To understand relationships within the biosphere, ecologists ask questions about events and organisms that range in complexity from a single individual to the entire biosphere.** The many levels of organization that ecologists study are shown in **Figure 3–2.**

Some ecologists study interactions between a particular kind of organism and its surroundings. Such studies focus on the species level. A **species** is a group of organisms so similar to one another that they can breed and produce fertile offspring. Other ecologists study **populations,** or groups of individuals that belong to the same species and live in the same area. Still other ecologists study **communities,** or assemblages of different populations that live together in a defined area.

Ecologists may study a particular ecosystem. An **ecosystem** is a collection of all the organisms that live in a particular place, together with their nonliving, or physical, environment. Larger systems called biomes are also studied by teams of ecologists. A **biome** is a group of ecosystems that have the same climate and similar dominant communities. The highest level of organization that ecologists study is the entire biosphere itself.

✓ **CHECKPOINT** *What is an ecosystem?*

Ecological Methods

Ecologists use a wide range of tools and techniques to study the living world. Some, like the scientists in **Figure 3–3**, use binoculars and field guides to assess changes in plant and wildlife communities. Others use studies of DNA to identify bacteria in the mud of coastal marshes. Still others use radio tags to track migrating wildlife or use data gathered by satellites. Regardless of the tools they use, scientists conduct modern ecological research using three basic approaches: observing, experimenting, and modeling. All of these approaches rely on the application of scientific methods to guide ecological inquiry.

Observing Observing is often the first step in asking ecological questions. Some observations are simple: What species live here? How many individuals of each species are there? Other observations are more complex and may form the first step in designing experiments and models.

Experimenting Experiments can be used to test hypotheses. An ecologist may set up an artificial environment in a laboratory to imitate and manipulate conditions that organisms would encounter in the natural world. Other experiments are conducted within natural ecosystems.

Modeling Many ecological phenomena occur over long periods of time or on such large spatial scales that they are difficult to study. Ecologists make models to gain insight into complex phenomena such as the effects of global warming on ecosystems. Many ecological models consist of mathematical formulas based on data collected through observation and experimentation. The predictions made by ecological models are often tested by further observations and experiments.

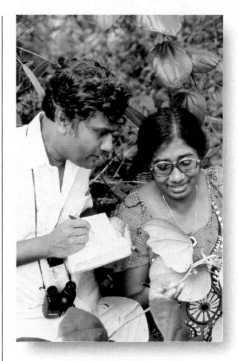

▲ **Figure 3–3** The three fundamental approaches to ecological research involve observing, experimenting, and modeling. These ecologists are studying a rain forest ecosystem in Sri Lanka. They are using field observations to collect data on vines and other plants.

3–1 Section Assessment

1. **Key Concept** List the six different levels of organization that ecologists study, in order from smallest to largest.

2. **Key Concept** Describe the three basic methods of ecological research.

3. Identify two ways in which you interact with each of the three parts of the biosphere—land, water, and air—every day.

4. **Critical Thinking Applying Concepts** Suppose you wanted to know if the water in a certain stream is safe to drink. Which ecological method(s) would you choose, and why?

iTEXT Assessment Use iText to review the important concepts in Section 3–1.

Take It to the NET

Visit three different ecological institutions on the Web. Then, make a table that shows the level of organization, location, and method(s) of study that each group uses. Use the links provided in the Biology area at the Prentice Hall Web site for help in completing this activity: **www.phschool.com**

Exploring Ecology From Space

Modern research in global ecology would not be possible if all its tools were earthbound. Studies on a planetary scale require enormous data-gathering networks. Through a process called remote sensing, satellites extend the range of information that ecologists can collect within the biosphere.

Remote-sensing satellites are fitted with optical sensors that can scan several bands of the electromagnetic spectrum and convert those bands into electrical signals. The signals are run through a computer and converted into digital values, which are used to construct an image.

Remote sensing provides detailed images of essentially every square meter of Earth's surface. How else could scientists view all the world's lakes and oceans to see where concentrations of algae are the highest? Or view areas of destroyed forests in places like the Amazon Basin or northern Russia?

Global Change

The false-color image below was assembled from data gathered by NASA's Sea-viewing Wide Field-of-view Sensor (SeaWiFS) Project. The project's goal is to study factors that affect global change and to assess the oceans' role in the global carbon cycle, as well as other chemical cycles. The different ocean colors indicate varying concentrations of microscopic algae. Blue represents the least amount of algae, and red the highest amount. On land, the dark green areas have the most vegetation, while gold land areas have the least.

Rain Forest Destruction

Remote sensing is a powerful tool for ecologists monitoring the destruction of the world's rain forests. The two satellite images above show one tract of land in Brazil's rain forest. The image on the right was taken 11 years after the one on the left. Red areas show healthy vegetation, while light blue areas show urban areas and deforested land—land where forests have been cut down. Notice the feathered or fishbone pattern of deforestation in the right-hand photo. This pattern typically occurs because the cutting of forests begins along roads and then fans out.

Satellite images like these allow ecologists to estimate the rate at which rain forest destruction is occurring. They also add to scientists' understanding of the complex issues involved in this global problem. This information can help ecologists in their work with local governments to slow the destruction of these vital ecosystems.

On Your Own

Find out more about the use of satellites in ecological studies. Log on to the Prentice Hall Web site at **www.phschool.com**.

3–2 Energy Flow

At the core of every organism's interaction with the environment is its need for energy to power life's processes. Consider, for example, the energy that ants use to carry objects many times their size, or the energy that birds use to migrate thousands of miles. Think about the energy that you need to get out of bed in the morning! The flow of energy through an ecosystem is one of the most important factors that determines the system's capacity to sustain life.

Producers

Without a constant input of energy, living systems cannot function. **Sunlight is the main energy source for life on Earth.** Of all the sun's energy that reaches Earth's surface, only a small amount—less than 1 percent—is used by living things. This seemingly small amount is enough to produce as much as 3.5 kilograms of living tissue per square meter a year in some tropical forests.

In a few ecosystems, some organisms obtain energy from a source other than sunlight. **Some types of organisms rely on the energy stored in inorganic chemical compounds.** For instance, mineral water that flows underground or boils out of hot springs and undersea vents is loaded with chemical energy.

Only plants, some algae, and certain bacteria can capture energy from sunlight or chemicals and use that energy to produce food. These organisms are called **autotrophs.** Autotrophs use energy from the environment to fuel the assembly of simple inorganic compounds into complex organic molecules. These organic molecules combine and recombine to produce living tissue. Because they make their own food, autotrophs, like the kelp in **Figure 3–4,** are also called **producers.** Both types of producers—those that capture energy from sunlight and those that capture chemical energy—are essential to the flow of energy through the biosphere.

Guide for Reading

Key Concepts
- Where does the energy for life processes come from?
- How does energy flow through living systems?
- How efficient is the transfer of energy among organisms in an ecosystem?

Vocabulary
- autotroph • producer
- photosynthesis
- chemosynthesis • heterotroph
- consumer • herbivore
- carnivore • omnivore
- detritivore • decomposer
- food chain • food web
- trophic level
- ecological pyramid • biomass

Reading Strategy:
Building Vocabulary As you read, make notes about the meaning of each term in the list above and how it relates to energy flow in the biosphere. Then, draw a concept map to show the relationships among the new terms in this section.

▼ **Figure 3–4** Sunlight falls on a dense kelp forest off the coast of California. **Kelp is an autotroph that uses energy from the sun to produce living tissue.**

PHOTOSYNTHESIS IN PLANTS

CHEMOSYNTHESIS IN SULFUR BACTERIA

▲ **Figure 3–5** Sunlight is the main energy source for life on Earth. Some types of organisms rely on the energy stored in inorganic chemical compounds. Plants use the energy from sunlight to carry out the process of photosynthesis. Other autotrophs, such as sulfur bacteria, use the energy stored in chemical bonds for chemosynthesis. In both cases, energy-rich carbohydrates are produced.

Energy From the Sun The best-known autotrophs are those that harness solar energy through a process known as photosynthesis. During **photosynthesis,** these autotrophs use light energy to power chemical reactions that convert carbon dioxide and water into oxygen and energy-rich carbohydrates such as sugars and starches. This process, shown in **Figure 3–5,** is responsible for adding oxygen to—and removing carbon dioxide from—Earth's atmosphere. In fact, were it not for photosynthetic autotrophs, the air would not contain enough oxygen for you to breathe!

On land, plants are the main autotrophs. In freshwater ecosystems and in the sunlit, upper layers of the ocean, algae are the principal autotrophs. Photosynthetic bacteria, the most common of which are called cyanobacteria (sy-an-oh-bak-TEER-ee-uh), are important in certain wet ecosystems such as tidal flats and salt marshes.

Life Without Light Although plants are the most visible and best-known autotrophs, some autotrophs can produce food in the absence of light. Such autotrophs rely on energy within the chemical bonds of inorganic molecules such as hydrogen sulfide. When organisms use chemical energy to produce carbohydrates, the process is called **chemosynthesis** (kee-moh-SIN-thuh-sis). This process is performed by several types of bacteria. Surprisingly, these bacteria represent a large proportion of living autotrophs. Some chemosynthetic bacteria live in very remote places on Earth, such as volcanic vents on the deep-ocean floor and hot springs in Yellowstone Park. Others live in more common places, such as tidal marshes along the coast.

CHECKPOINT *What is the difference between photosynthesis and chemosynthesis?*

Consumers

Many organisms—including animals, fungi, and many bacteria—cannot harness energy directly from the physical environment as autotrophs do. The only way these organisms can acquire energy is from other organisms. Organisms that rely on other organisms for their energy and food supply are called **heterotrophs** (HET-ur-oh-trohfs). Heterotrophs are also called **consumers.**

There are many different types of heterotrophs. **Herbivores** obtain energy by eating only plants. Some herbivores are cows, caterpillars, and deer. **Carnivores,** including snakes, dogs, and owls, eat animals. Humans, bears, crows, and other **omnivores** eat both plants and animals. **Detritivores** (dee-TRYT-uh-vawrz), such as mites, earthworms, snails, and crabs, feed on plant and animal remains and other dead matter, collectively called detritus. Another important group of heterotrophs, called **decomposers,** breaks down organic matter. Bacteria and fungi such as the one in **Figure 3–6** are decomposers.

Feeding Relationships

What happens to the energy in an ecosystem when one organism eats another? That energy moves along a one-way path. 🔑 **Energy flows through an ecosystem in one direction, from the sun or inorganic compounds to autotrophs (producers) and then to various heterotrophs (consumers).** The relationships between producers and consumers connect organisms into feeding networks based on who eats whom.

Food Chains The energy stored by producers can be passed through an ecosystem along a **food chain,** a series of steps in which organisms transfer energy by eating and being eaten. For example, in a prairie ecosystem, a food chain might consist of a producer—such as grass—that is fed upon by an herbivore—such as a grazing antelope. The herbivore is in turn fed upon by a carnivore—such as a coyote. In this situation, the carnivore is only two steps removed from the producer.

In some marine food chains, such as the one in **Figure 3–7,** the producers are microscopic algae that are eaten by very small organisms called zooplankton (zoh-oh-PLANK-tun). The zooplankton, in turn, are eaten by small fish, such as herring. The herring are eaten by squid, which are ultimately eaten by large fish, such as sharks. In this food chain, the top carnivore is four steps removed from the producer.

▲ **Figure 3–6** This fungus, growing on the forest floor, is a decomposer that obtains nutrients by breaking down dead and decaying plants and animals. It is called a coral fungus because of its color and shape. **Classifying** *Is the fungus a producer or a consumer?*

▼ **Figure 3–7** 🔑 Food chains show the one-way flow of energy in an ecosystem. In this marine food chain, energy is passed from the producers (algae) to four different groups of consumers.

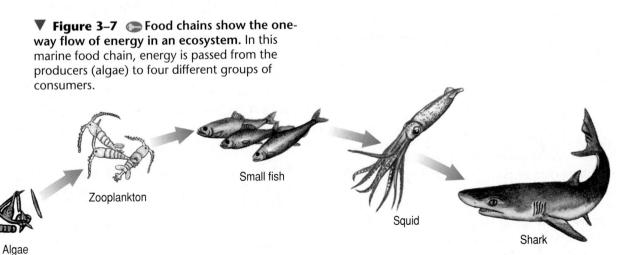

Algae

Zooplankton

Small fish

Squid

Shark

Quick Lab

How is a food chain organized?

Materials 2 wide-mouth jars, 2 pieces of flexible screening, 2 rubber bands, 2 bean seedlings in small pots or paper cups, pea aphids, ladybird beetles

Procedure
1. Place a potted bean seedling in each of the two jars.
2. Add 20 aphids to one jar and cover the jar with screening to prevent the aphids from escaping. Use a rubber band to attach the screening to the jar.
3. Add 20 aphids and 4 ladybird beetles to the second jar. Cover the second jar as you did the first one.
4. **Formulating Hypotheses** Record your hypothesis about how the presence of the ladybird beetles will affect the survival of the aphids and the bean seedling. Also, record your prediction of what will happen to the organisms in each jar during the next week.

5. Place both jars in a sunny location. Observe the jars each day for one week and record your observations each day. Water the seedlings as needed.

Analyze and Conclude
1. **Observing** What happened to the aphids and the seedling in the jar without the ladybird beetles? In the jar with the ladybird beetles? How can you explain this difference?
2. **Classifying** Identify each organism in the jars as a producer or a consumer.

Food Webs In most ecosystems, feeding relationships are more complex than can be shown in a food chain. Consider, for example, the relationships in a salt marsh. Although some producers—including marsh grass and other salt-tolerant plants—are eaten by water birds, grasshoppers, and other herbivores, most producers complete their life cycles, then die and decompose. Decomposers convert the dead plant matter to detritus, which is eaten by detritivores, such as sandhoppers. The detritivores are in turn eaten by smelt and other small fish. Some of those consumers will also eat detritus directly. Add mice, larger fish, and hawks to the scenario, and feeding relationships can get very confusing!

When the feeding relationships among the various organisms in an ecosystem form a network of complex interactions, ecologists describe these relationships as a **food web.** A food web links all the food chains in an ecosystem together. The food web in **Figure 3–8,** for example, shows the feeding relationships in a salt-marsh community.

Trophic Levels Each step in a food chain or food web is called a **trophic level** (TRAHF-ik). Producers make up the first trophic level. Consumers make up the second, third, or higher trophic levels. Each consumer depends on the trophic level below it for energy.

Word Origins

Trophic originates from the Greek word *trophe,* which means "food or nourishment." **What do you think are the original meanings of the words *heterotroph* and *autotroph*?**

✓**CHECKPOINT** *What is a food web?*

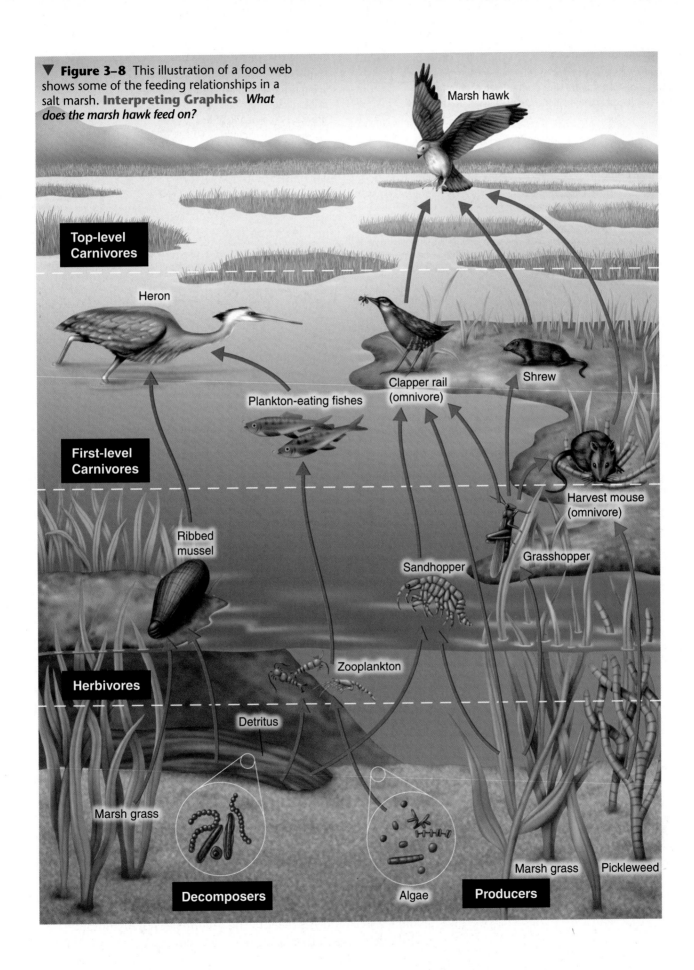

▼ **Figure 3–8** This illustration of a food web shows some of the feeding relationships in a salt marsh. **Interpreting Graphics** *What does the marsh hawk feed on?*

Marsh hawk

Top-level Carnivores

Heron

Clapper rail (omnivore)

Shrew

Plankton-eating fishes

First-level Carnivores

Harvest mouse (omnivore)

Grasshopper

Ribbed mussel

Sandhopper

Zooplankton

Herbivores

Detritus

Marsh grass

Decomposers

Algae

Marsh grass

Pickleweed

Producers

Energy Pyramid
Shows the relative amount of energy available at each trophic level. Organisms use about 10 percent of this energy for life processes. The rest is lost as heat.

0.1% Third-level consumers
1% Second-level consumers
10% First-level consumers
100% Producers

Light or chemical energy

HEAT

Biomass Pyramid
Represents the amount of living organic matter at each trophic level. Typically, the greatest biomass is at the base of the pyramid.

50 grams of human tissue
500 grams of chicken
1500 grams of grain

Ecological Pyramids

The amount of energy or matter in an ecosystem can be represented by an ecological pyramid. An **ecological pyramid** is a diagram that shows the relative amounts of energy or matter contained within each trophic level in a food chain or food web. Ecologists recognize three different types of ecological pyramids: energy pyramids, biomass pyramids, and pyramids of numbers. **Figure 3–9** shows an example of each type.

Energy Pyramid Theoretically, there is no limit to the number of trophic levels that a food chain can support. But there is one hitch. Only part of the energy that is stored in one trophic level is passed on to the next level. This is because organisms use much of the energy that they consume for life processes, such as respiration, movement, and reproduction. Some of the remaining energy is released into the environment as heat. 🔑 **Only about 10 percent of the energy available within one trophic level is transferred to organisms at the next trophic level.** For instance, one tenth of the solar energy captured by grasses ends up stored in the tissues of cows and other grazers. Only one tenth of that energy—10 percent of 10 percent, or 1 percent total—is transferred to the humans that eat the cows. Thus, the more levels that exist between a producer and a top-level consumer in an ecosystem, the less energy that remains from the original amount.

Biomass Pyramid The total amount of living tissue within a given trophic level is called **biomass.** Biomass is usually expressed in terms of grams of organic matter per unit area. A biomass pyramid represents the amount of potential food available for each trophic level in an ecosystem.

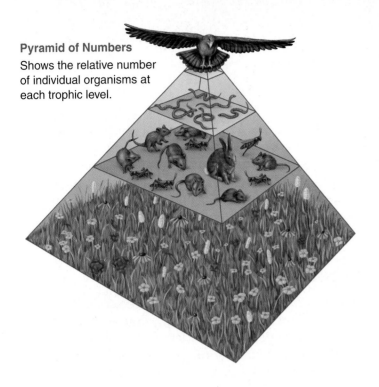

Pyramid of Numbers
Shows the relative number of individual organisms at each trophic level.

◀ **Figure 3–9** Ecological pyramids show the decreasing amounts of energy, living tissue, or number of organisms at successive feeding levels. The pyramid is divided into sections that represent each trophic level. The area of each level symbolizes the amount of energy or matter remaining at that level. ⬤ **Because each trophic level harvests only about one tenth of the energy from the level below, it can support only about one tenth the amount of living tissue.**

Pyramid of Numbers Ecological pyramids can also be based on the numbers of individual organisms at each trophic level. For some ecosystems, such as the meadow shown in **Figure 3–9** above, the shape of the pyramid of numbers is the same as that of the energy and biomass pyramids. This, however, is not always the case. In most forests, for example, there are fewer producers than there are consumers. A single tree has a large amount of energy and biomass, but it is only one organism. Many insects live in the tree, but they have less energy and biomass. Thus, a pyramid of numbers for a forest ecosystem would not resemble a typical pyramid at all!

3–2 Section Assessment

1. ⬤ **Key Concept** What are the two main forms of energy that power living systems?

2. ⬤ **Key Concept** Briefly describe the flow of energy among organisms in an ecosystem.

3. ⬤ **Key Concept** What proportion of energy is transferred from one trophic level to the next in an ecosystem?

4. Show the following as a food chain: omnivore, autotroph, herbivore.

5. **Critical Thinking Calculating** Draw an energy pyramid for a five-step food chain. If 100 percent of the energy is available at the first trophic level, what percentage of the total energy is available at the highest trophic level?

🧍**TEXT** **Assessment** Use iText to review the important concepts in Section 3–2.

MAKING CONNECTIONS
Characteristics of Living Things Review what you learned in Chapter 1 about an organism's needs for materials and energy. Then describe how the following organisms meet their energy needs: a caterpillar, a plant, a snake, and a fungus.

3–3 Cycles of Matter

Guide for Reading

🔑 Key Concepts
- How does matter move among the living and nonliving parts of an ecosystem?
- How are nutrients important in living systems?

Vocabulary
biogeochemical cycle
evaporation
transpiration
nutrient
nitrogen fixation
denitrification
primary productivity
limiting nutrient
algal bloom

Reading Strategy:
Using Visuals Before you read, preview the cycles shown in **Figures 3–11, 3–13, 3–14,** and **3–15.** Notice how each diagram is similar to or different from the others. As you read, take notes on how each chemical moves through the biosphere.

▼ **Figure 3–10** 🔄 Matter moves through an ecosystem in biogeochemical cycles. In this Alaskan wetland, matter is recycled through the air, the shrubs, the pond, and the caribou—as it is used, transformed, moved, and reused.

Energy is crucial to an ecosystem. But all organisms need more than energy to survive. They also need water, minerals, and other life-sustaining compounds. In most organisms, more than 95 percent of the body is made up of just four elements: oxygen, carbon, hydrogen, and nitrogen. Although these four elements are common on Earth, organisms cannot use them unless the elements are in a chemical form that cells can take up.

Recycling in the Biosphere

Energy and matter move through the biosphere very differently. 🔑 **Unlike the one-way flow of energy, matter is recycled within and between ecosystems.** Elements, chemical compounds, and other forms of matter are passed from one organism to another and from one part of the biosphere to another through **biogeochemical cycles.** As the long word suggests, biogeochemical cycles connect *bio*logical, *geo*logical, and *chemi*cal aspects of the biosphere.

Matter can cycle through the biosphere because biological systems do not use up matter, they transform it. The matter is assembled into living tissue or passed out of the body as waste products. Imagine, for a moment, that you are a carbon atom in a molecule of carbon dioxide floating in the air of a lowland marsh like the one in **Figure 3–10.** The leaf of a blueberry bush absorbs you during photosynthesis. You become part of a carbohydrate molecule and are used to make fruit. The fruit is eaten by a caribou, and within a few hours, you are passed out of the animal's body. You are soon swallowed by a dung beetle, then combined into the body tissue of a hungry shrew, which is then eaten by an owl. Finally, you are released into the atmosphere once again when the owl exhales. Then, the cycle starts again.

Simply put, biogeochemical cycles pass the same molecules around again and again within the biosphere. Just think—with every breath you take, you inhale hundreds of thousands of oxygen atoms that might have been inhaled by dinosaurs millions of years ago!

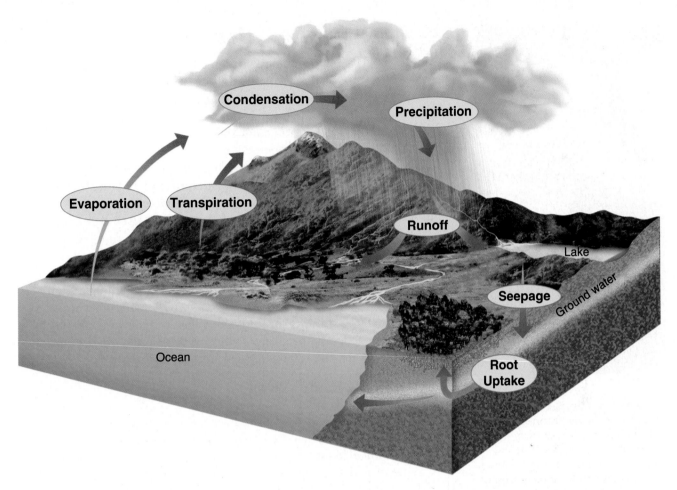

Condensation

Precipitation

Evaporation

Transpiration

Runoff

Lake

Seepage

Ground water

Ocean

Root Uptake

▲ **Figure 3–11** This diagram shows the main processes involved in the water cycle. Scientists estimate that it can take a single water molecule as long as 4000 years to complete one cycle. **Interpreting Graphics** *What happens to the water that evaporates from oceans and lakes?*

The Water Cycle

All living things require water to survive. Where does all this water come from? It moves between the ocean, atmosphere, and land. As **Figure 3–11** shows, water molecules enter the atmosphere as water vapor, a gas, when they evaporate from the ocean or other bodies of water. The process by which water changes from liquid form to an atmospheric gas is called **evaporation** (ee-vap-uh-RAY-shun). Water can also enter the atmosphere by evaporating from the leaves of plants in the process of **transpiration** (trans-puh-RAY-shun).

During the day, the sun heats the atmosphere. As the warm, moist air rises, it cools. Eventually, the water vapor condenses into tiny droplets that form clouds. When the droplets become large enough, the water returns to Earth's surface in the form of precipitation—rain, snow, sleet, or hail.

On land, much of the precipitation runs along the surface of the ground until it enters a river or stream that carries the runoff back to an ocean or lake. Rain also seeps into the soil, some of it deeply enough to become ground water. Water in the soil enters plants through the roots, and the water cycle begins anew.

✓ CHECKPOINT **How are evaporation and transpiration related?**

Nutrient Cycles

The food you eat contains energy, but it also contains important chemicals that sustain you. Together, all the chemical substances that an organism, like the owl monkey in **Figure 3–12**, requires to live are called **nutrients.** You can think of nutrients as the body's building blocks.

🔑 **Every living organism needs nutrients to grow and carry out essential life functions. Like water, nutrients are passed between organisms and the environment through biogeochemical cycles.** In many ecosystems, nutrients are often in short supply. Thus, recycling nutrients is essential for these ecosystems to keep functioning. Nutrient cycling also prevents many chemicals from reaching concentrations that would otherwise be toxic, or harmful, to organisms. Three nutrient cycles play especially prominent roles in the biosphere: the carbon cycle, the nitrogen cycle, and the phosphorus cycle.

✓ CHECKPOINT *What is a nutrient?*

▲ **Figure 3–12** 🔑 Like all living organisms, the owl monkey needs nutrients to grow and carry out essential life functions. This monkey, which is found in Central and South America, obtains most of its nutrients by eating plants.

The Carbon Cycle Carbon is especially important to living systems because it is the key ingredient in all living organisms. Carbon is also found in the oceans, in the air, and in certain types of rocks. However, of all the carbon on Earth, less than 1 percent actively circulates within the biosphere.

Like water, carbon cycles between the various components of the biosphere. There are four different kinds of processes involved in the carbon cycle:

- biological processes, such as photosynthesis, respiration, and decomposition of plants and animals;

- geochemical processes, such as the release of carbon dioxide (CO_2) gas to the atmosphere by volcanoes;

- mixed biogeochemical processes, such as the burial of carbon-rich remains of organisms and their conversion into coal and petroleum (fossil fuels) by the pressure of the overlying earth; and

- human activity, including mining, the burning of fossil fuels, and the cutting and burning of forests.

Scientists identified these processes decades ago. Now we face an urgent need to know more about them. For example, how much carbon is released into the atmosphere by human activity? How do other components of the carbon cycle respond to changes in atmospheric carbon levels? What is the capacity of the ocean to absorb excess carbon dioxide? You will learn more about the effects of human activity on the carbon cycle later in this unit.

Figure 3–13 shows how these processes move carbon through the biosphere. In the atmosphere, carbon is present as carbon dioxide gas. Carbon dioxide is released into the atmosphere by volcanic activity, by respiration, by human activities such as the burning of fossil fuels, and by the decomposition of organic matter. Plants take in carbon dioxide and use the carbon to build carbohydrates during photosynthesis. The carbohydrates are passed along food webs to animals and other consumers. In the ocean, carbon is also found, along with calcium and oxygen, in calcium carbonate, which is formed by many marine organisms. Calcium carbonate can also be formed chemically in certain marine environments. This chalky, carbon-based compound accumulates in marine sediments and in the bones and shells of organisms. Eventually these compounds break down and the carbon returns to the atmosphere.

▼ **Figure 3–13** Carbon is found in several large reservoirs in the biosphere. In the atmosphere, it is found as carbon dioxide gas; in the oceans as dissolved carbon dioxide; on land in organisms, rocks, and soil; and underground as coal, petroleum, and calcium carbonate rock. **Interpreting Graphics** *What are the main sources of carbon dioxide in the ocean?*

The Nitrogen Cycle All organisms require nitrogen to make amino acids, which in turn are used to build proteins. Many different forms of nitrogen occur naturally in the biosphere. Nitrogen gas (N_2) makes up 78 percent of Earth's atmosphere. Nitrogen-containing substances such as ammonia (NH_3), nitrate ions (NO_3^-), and nitrite ions (NO_2^-) are found in the wastes produced by many organisms and in dead and decaying organic matter. Nitrogen also exists in several forms in the ocean and other large water bodies. Human activity adds nitrogen to the biosphere in the form of nitrate—a major component of plant fertilizers.

Figure 3–14 shows how the different forms of nitrogen cycle through the biosphere. Although nitrogen gas is the most abundant form of nitrogen on Earth, only certain types of bacteria can use this form directly. Such bacteria, which live in the soil and on the roots of plants called legumes, convert nitrogen gas into ammonia in a process known as **nitrogen fixation.** Other bacteria in the soil convert ammonia into nitrates and nitrites. Once these products are available, producers can use them to make proteins. Consumers then eat the producers and reuse the nitrogen to make their own proteins.

When organisms die, decomposers return nitrogen to the soil as ammonia. The ammonia may be taken up again by producers. Other soil bacteria convert nitrates into nitrogen gas in a process called **denitrification.** This process releases nitrogen into the atmosphere once again.

▼ **Figure 3–14** The atmosphere is the main reservoir of nitrogen in the biosphere. Nitrogen also cycles through the soil and through the tissues of living organisms. **Interpreting Graphics** *What are the main nitrogen-containing nutrients in the biosphere?*

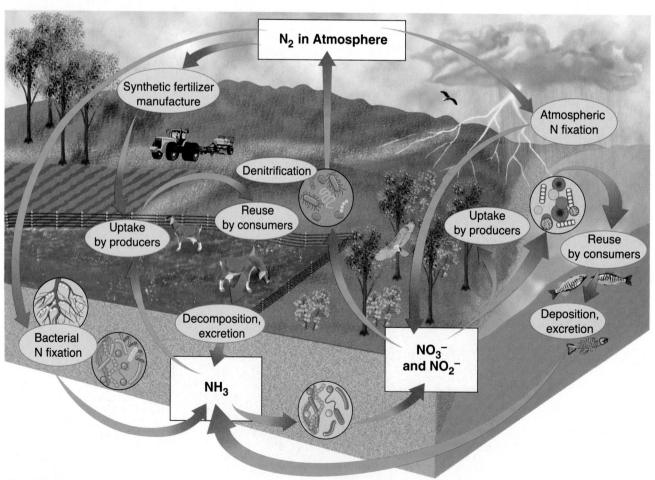

Farming in the Rye

Sometimes, farmers grow crops of rye and other grasses and then plow them under the soil to decay. This practice helps to increase crop yields of other plants. Farmers may also plow under legumes such as peas, vetch, and lentils. Legumes are plants that have colonies of nitrogen-fixing bacteria living in nodules on the plant roots.

In an effort to determine which practice produces the best crop yields, scientists performed an experiment in Georgia. They grew corn on land that had previously received one of five treatments. Three fields had previously been planted with three different legumes. A fourth field had been planted with rye. The fifth field was left bare before the corn was planted. None of the fields received fertilizer while the corn was growing. The table shows how much corn was produced per hectare of land (kg/ha) in each field. One hectare is equivalent to 10,000 square meters.

Corn Production	
Previous Crop	**Average Yield of Corn (kg/ha)**
Monantha vetch	2876
Hairy vetch	2870
Austrian peas	3159
Rye	1922
None	1959

1. **Using Tables and Graphs** Use the data in the table to create a bar graph.

2. **Comparing and Contrasting** Compare the effect of growing legumes to that of growing grass on the yield of corn. How do the yields differ from the yield on the field that had received no prior treatment?

3. **Analyzing Data** Which treatment produced the best yield of corn? The worst yield?

4. **Applying Concepts** Based on your knowledge of the nitrogen cycle, how can you explain these results?

The Phosphorus Cycle Phosphorus is essential to living organisms because it forms part of important life-sustaining molecules such as DNA and RNA. Although phosphorus is of great biological importance, it is not very common in the biosphere. Unlike carbon, oxygen, and nitrogen, phosphorus does not enter the atmosphere. Instead, phosphorus remains mostly on land in rock and soil minerals, and in ocean sediments. There, phosphorus exists in the form of inorganic phosphate. As the rocks and sediments gradually wear down, phosphate is released. On land, some of the phosphate washes into rivers and streams, where it dissolves. The phosphate eventually makes its way to the oceans, where it is used by marine organisms.

As **Figure 3–15** shows, some phosphate stays on land and cycles between organisms and the soil. When plants absorb phosphate from the soil or from water, the plants bind the phosphate into organic compounds. Organic phosphate moves through the food web, from producers to consumers, and to the rest of the ecosystem.

CHECKPOINT *Where is most of the phosphorus stored in the biosphere?*

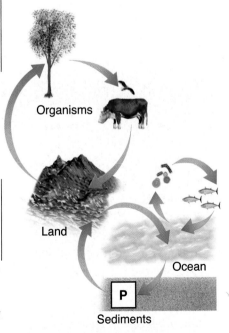

Organisms

Land

Ocean

P

Sediments

▶ **Figure 3–15** Phosphorus in the biosphere cycles among the land, ocean sediments, and living organisms. **Inferring** *How is phosphorus important to living organisms?*

Nutrient Limitation

Ecologists are often interested in the **primary productivity** of an ecosystem, which is the rate at which organic matter is created by producers. One factor that controls the primary productivity of an ecosystem is the amount of available nutrients. If a nutrient is in short supply, it will limit an organism's growth. When an ecosystem is limited by a single nutrient that is scarce or cycles very slowly, this substance is called a **limiting nutrient.**

Farmers, who are well aware of this phenomenon, apply fertilizers to their crops to boost their productivity. Fertilizers usually contain three important nutrients—nitrogen, phosphorus, and potassium. These nutrients help plants grow larger and more quickly than they would in unfertilized soil.

The open oceans of the world can be considered nutrient-poor environments compared to the land. Sea water contains at most only 0.00005 percent nitrogen, or 1/10,000 of the amount typically found in soil. In the ocean and other saltwater environments, nitrogen is often the limiting nutrient. In some areas of the ocean, however, silica or even iron can be the limiting nutrient. In streams, lakes, and freshwater environments, phosphorus is typically the limiting nutrient.

When an aquatic ecosystem receives a large input of a limiting nutrient—for example, runoff from heavily fertilized fields—the result is often an immediate increase in the amount of algae and other producers. This result is called an **algal bloom**. Why do algal blooms occur? There are more nutrients available, so the producers can grow and reproduce more quickly. If there are not enough consumers to eat the excess algae, conditions can become so favorable for growth that algae cover the surface of the water. Algal blooms, like the one shown in **Figure 3–16**, can sometimes upset the health of an ecosystem.

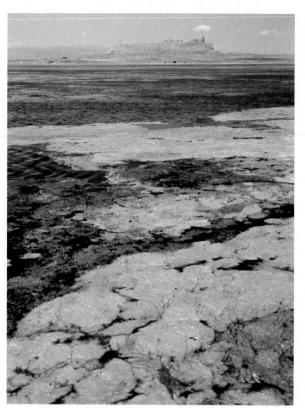

▲ **Figure 3–16** When an aquatic ecosystem receives a large input of a limiting nutrient, the result is often an increase in the number of producers. Here, an extensive algal bloom covers the shoreline of Tule Lake in California. **Using Analogies** *How is this situation similar to the one that occurs in a fish tank in which the fish have been overfed?*

3–3 Section Assessment

1. 🔑 **Key Concept** How does the way that matter flows through an ecosystem differ from the way that energy flows?

2. 🔑 **Key Concept** Why do living organisms need nutrients?

3. Describe the path of nitrogen through its biogeochemical cycle.

4. Explain how a nutrient can be a limiting factor in an ecosystem.

5. **Critical Thinking Predicting** Based on your knowledge of the carbon cycle, what do you think might happen if vast areas of forests are cleared?

ITEXT **Assessment** Use iText to review the important concepts in Section 3–3.

Identifying a Limiting Nutrient

Limiting nutrients control the growth of organisms in many ecosystems. Excess nutrients can promote the growth of weeds, disease-causing bacteria, and other undesirable organisms. In this investigation, you will determine whether phosphate is a limiting nutrient for the growth of algae.

Problem Does the supply of phosphate limit the growth of algae?

Materials
- dropper pipette
- algae culture
- 2 test tubes with stoppers
- test-tube rack
- 50-mL graduated cylinder
- pond water
- glass-marking pencil
- 10% trisodium phosphate solution

Skills Formulating Hypotheses, Predicting

Procedure

1. Put on your safety goggles, apron, and plastic gloves. Use a dropper pipette to place 20 drops of algae culture in each of two test tubes.

2. Use a 30-mL graduated cylinder to add 19 mL of pond water to each test tube.

3. Use the glass-marking pencil to label one test tube "control" and the other test tube "phosphate." Use a dropper pipette to add 2 drops of trisodium phosphate to the "phosphate" test tube. **CAUTION:** *Trisodium phosphate can injure your skin. Do not get it on your skin or touch your face after handling it.*

4. Stopper both test tubes and place them in a sunny place.

5. **Formulating Hypotheses** Record your hypothesis of how phosphate will affect the growth of the algae if it is a limiting nutrient. Also, record your prediction of how the two test tubes will appear after 7 days.

6. Observe the two test tubes each day for the next week. Record your observations each day, including a labeled sketch of each test tube.

Analyze and Conclude

1. **Observing** How did the added phosphate affect the growth of the algae?

2. **Drawing Conclusions** Do your results indicate that phosphate is a limiting nutrient for algae?

3. **Evaluating and Revising** Do your results support your hypothesis? If not, how would you revise your hypothesis?

4. **Predicting** Some detergents are labeled as environmentally safe because they contain little or no phosphate. What might you expect to see in a river or lake that contains high levels of phosphate detergents?

Go Further

Designing Experiments Select another nutrient and design an experiment to determine whether it is a limiting nutrient for the growth of algae. With your teacher's permission, conduct the experiment and share your findings with the class.

To find out more about how scientists investigate algal blooms, view the videotape *"Pfiesteria: A Killer in the Water."*

3–1 What Is Ecology?
Key Concepts

- To understand the various relationships within the biosphere, ecologists ask questions about events and organisms that range in complexity from a single individual to a population, community, ecosystem, or biome, or to the entire biosphere.

- Scientists conduct modern ecological research according to three basic approaches: observing, experimenting, and modeling. All of these approaches rely on the application of scientific methods to guide ecological inquiry.

Vocabulary
ecology, p. 63
biosphere, p. 63
species, p. 64
population, p. 64
community, p. 64
ecosystem, p. 64
biome, p. 64

3–2 Energy Flow
Key Concepts

- Sunlight is the main energy source for life on Earth. In a few ecosystems, some organisms rely on the energy stored in inorganic chemical compounds.

- Energy flows through an ecosystem in one direction, from the sun or inorganic compounds to autotrophs (producers) and then to various heterotrophs (consumers).

- Only about 10 percent of the energy available within one trophic level is transferred to organisms at the next trophic level.

Vocabulary
autotroph, p. 67
producer, p. 67
photosynthesis, p. 68
chemosynthesis, p. 68
heterotroph, p. 68
consumer, p. 68
herbivore, p. 69
carnivore, p. 69
omnivore, p. 69
detritivore, p. 69
decomposer, p. 69
food chain, p. 69
food web, p. 70
trophic level, p. 70
ecological pyramid, p. 72
biomass, p. 72

3–3 Cycles of Matter
Key Concepts

- Unlike the one-way flow of energy, matter is recycled within and between ecosystems.

- Every living organism needs nutrients to grow and carry out essential life functions. Like water, nutrients are passed between organisms and the environment through biogeochemical cycles.

Vocabulary
biogeochemical cycle, p. 74
evaporation, p. 75
transpiration, p. 75
nutrient, p. 76
nitrogen fixation, p. 78
denitrification, p. 78
primary productivity, p. 80
limiting nutrient, p. 80
algal bloom, p. 80

Thinking Visually
Using information from this chapter, complete the following flowchart:

Chapter 3

Part A

Multiple Choice

For each statement or question, select the number of the word or expression that, of those given, best completes the statement or answers the question.

1 All of life on Earth interacts with the nonliving environment and exists in a region known as
(1) an ecosystem (3) the biosphere
(2) a niche (4) a food web

2 Groups of different species that live together in a defined area make up a(an)
(1) population (3) ecosystem
(2) community (4) biosphere

3 Autotrophs are organisms that
(1) rely on other organisms for their energy and food supply
(2) consume plant and animal remains and other dead matter
(3) use energy they take in from the environment to convert inorganic molecules into complex organic molecules
(4) obtain energy by eating plants

4 The series of steps in which a large fish eats a small fish that has eaten algae is a(an)
(1) food web (3) cyclic change
(2) food chain (4) energy pyramid

5 Which organism is a decomposer?

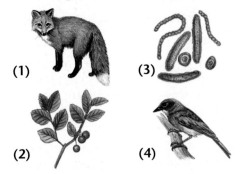

(1)   (3)

(2)   (4)

6 The relative amount of energy available at each trophic level can be shown in a(an)
(1) energy pyramid
(2) recycling diagram
(3) heterotrophic plan
(4) nutrient cycle

7 Nutrients are combined and recombined in different ways as they move through an ecosystem in
(1) water cycles
(2) energy pyramids
(3) food webs
(4) cellular cycles

8 Phosphorus is an element essential to living things. Based on the diagram below, living things obtain the phosphorus they need from
(1) the atmosphere
(2) sunlight
(3) the food chain
(4) ATP

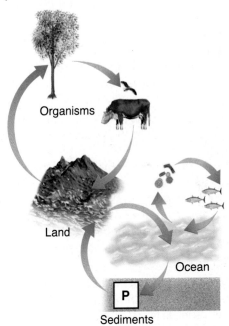

Organisms

Land

Ocean

P

Sediments

9 Which group of organisms is most likely found at the base of a food chain or food web?
(1) viruses (3) insects
(2) plants (4) fungi

Test-Taking Tip As you briefly scan the questions, identify those that may require pure guesswork on your part and save them for last. (Do not write in this book.) Then, use your time on those questions to reason through them and eliminate incorrect choices.

Parts B and C

Multiple Choice and Extended Response

For those questions that ask you to select a response, choose the one that best completes the statement or answers the question. For all others follow the directions given.

10 Which is *not* true about matter in the biosphere?
(1) Matter is recycled in the biosphere.
(2) Oxygen and nitrogen cycles transform and reuse molecules.
(3) The total amount of matter decreases over time.
(4) The lack of a specific nutrient can reduce productivity in an ecosystem.

11 In any particular environment, growth and survival of organisms depends on physical conditions such as
(1) competition
(2) amount of minerals
(3) members of the food chain
(4) type of microorganisms

12 Native Americans taught European settlers to bury pieces of fish with the seeds of corn they planted. Why might this practice ensure a good harvest?
(1) Corn grows best by the ocean where fish are plentiful.
(2) The nutrients from decomposing fish can be used by corn plants.
(3) Fish bones should be recycled.
(4) Fish provide water that is essential for plants to grow.

13 Human activities, such as the burning of fossil fuels, cycle carbon through the carbon cycle. Which other process(es) also participate(s) in the carbon cycle?
(1) nitrogen fixation by bacteria on legume roots
(2) evaporation of water vapor into the atmosphere
(3) movement of organic phosphates through the food web
(4) biological processes such as photosynthesis

14 Two ways in which water enters the atmosphere in the water cycle are
(1) evaporation and transpiration
(2) respiration and runoff
(3) precipitation and condensation
(4) osmosis and diffusion

15 The graph below shows the effect of annual rainfall on the rate of plant productivity in an ecosystem. What happens to productivity as rainfall increases? What factors other than water might affect plant growth?

16 Classify each of the following as a producer, a primary consumer, a secondary consumer, or a decomposer: crow, bear, corn plant, cow, fungus, owl.

17 One theory attributes the extinction of dinosaurs to a collision with an asteroid, which created a huge dust cloud on Earth. How would blocking the sun's rays cause dinosaurs and other organisms to die?

18 Describe how the carbon cycle provides organisms with the raw materials necessary to synthesize complex organic compounds.

19 Create flowcharts that show four different food chains in the food web shown below.

Base your answers to questions 20 through 22 on Figure 3–7 on page 69 and Figure 3–8 on page 71.

20 Food chains and food webs show how energy flows through ecosystems. Which type of model —a food chain or food web—is a better representation of how energy flows through ecosystems in the natural world? Support your answer with an explanation.

21 In Figure 3–7 on page 69, identify which group of organisms is missing from the diagram. What function does this group of organisms serve in the flow of energy?

22 If there were a disease that reduced the zooplankton population shown in Figure 3–7 on page 69, how would the squid be affected?

Base your answers to questions 23 through 25 on the information below and on your knowledge of biology.

Along the mid-ocean ridge at a depth of about 2200 meters, are chimney-like structures called "black smokers." They form when hot, mineral-rich water flows out of undersea volcanoes. Black smokers support the only communities on Earth whose immediate energy source is not sunlight. Tiny microbes, called *Archaea,* form the basis of the food chain by using sulfide instead of sunlight to produce food.

23 *Archaea* belong to a group of organisms called "chemoautotrophs." Their name describes the niche they fill. Based on their name, how are *Archaea* different from plants?

24 What abiotic factors are present in the black smoker ecosystem that differ from abiotic factors present in more familiar ecosystems on land?

25 *Archaea* need oxygen to make organic compounds from inorganic ones. Where does the oxygen come from?

Base your answers to questions 26 through 29 on the information below and on your knowledge of biology.

Coyotes have managed to survive for thousands of years because they are very adaptable. They can run fast and jump high, they are not fussy about what they eat, and they can hide from most predators except humans. Coyotes feed on small rodents and help to keep rodent populations under control. They also feed on the remains of large herbivores that have died. Because coyotes often kill livestock, some ranchers might try to poison them.

26 Draw a food chain that includes producers, coyotes, and the coyotes' prey.

27 Why must coyotes kill several sheep to satisfy their own nutritional needs?

28 What might happen to a rancher's livestock population if coyotes did not limit the size of rodent populations?

29 What effect would humans have on the ecosystem if they succeeded in killing all coyotes?

Take It to the NET

What does ecology have to do with you? Visit the Prentice Hall Web site at **www.phschool.com** to learn about ecology's role in human society. Then, answer the following questions:

- What are two examples of how ecological knowledge has helped improve the environment?

- What are three ways in which ecological knowledge helps to protect human health?

- What are four ways that we can use ecological knowledge to help manage natural resources?

4 Ecosystems and Communities

In a tropical rain forest in Belize, Central America, a jaguar drinks from a pool.

Inquiry Activity

What relationships exist in an ecosystem?

Procedure

1. Observe a terrarium, aquarium, or other small ecosystem that your teacher provides.

2. Use your observations to construct a diagram (similar to a concept map) showing all the relationships that exist among the parts of the ecosystem.

3. Indicate on your diagram which relationships involve nonliving parts of the ecosystem.

Think About It

1. **Classifying** What types of relationships did you find among the organisms? What types of relationships did you find between the organisms and the nonliving parts of their environment?

2. **Predicting** How might your diagram change if the ecosystem were in the dark for a week?

4–1 The Role of Climate

If you live in Michigan, you know better than to try to grow banana trees in your backyard. Bananas are tropical plants that need plenty of water and heat. They cannot survive in freezing temperatures. It may not be as obvious, however, that cranberries will not grow in the Rio Grande Valley of Texas. Cranberries need plenty of water and a cold rest period. They cannot tolerate the months of very hot weather that frequently occur in the Rio Grande Valley.

Bananas and cranberries, like many other organisms, require a specific set of environmental conditions in order to grow. Bananas need warm temperatures, and cranberries thrive in cool temperatures. What produces the wide range of environmental conditions that shapes the communities in which organisms live?

What Is Climate?

In the atmosphere, temperature, precipitation, and other environmental factors combine to produce weather and climate. **Weather** is the day-to-day condition of Earth's atmosphere at a particular time and place. The weather where you live may be clear and sunny one day but cloudy and cold the next. **Climate,** on the other hand, refers to the average, year-after-year conditions of temperature and precipitation in a particular region.

Climate is caused by the interplay of many factors, including the trapping of heat by the atmosphere, the latitude, the transport of heat by winds and ocean currents, and the amount of precipitation that results. The shape and elevation of landmasses also contribute to global climate patterns.

The energy of incoming sunlight drives Earth's weather and helps determine climate. As you might expect, solar energy has an important effect on the temperature of the atmosphere. At the same time, the presence of certain gases in the atmosphere also has an effect on its temperature.

The Greenhouse Effect

Temperatures on Earth remain within a range suitable for life as we know it because the biosphere has a natural insulating blanket—the atmosphere. **Carbon dioxide, methane, water vapor, and a few other atmospheric gases trap heat energy and maintain Earth's temperature range.** These gases perform a function similar to that of the glass windows of a greenhouse. Just as the glass keeps the greenhouse plants warm, so these gases trap the heat energy of sunlight inside Earth's atmosphere. The natural situation in which heat is retained by this layer of greenhouse gases is called the **greenhouse effect,** shown in **Figure 4–1.**

Guide for Reading

Key Concepts
- How does the greenhouse effect maintain the biosphere's temperature range?
- What are Earth's three main climate zones?

Vocabulary
- weather • climate
- greenhouse effect • polar zone
- temperate zone • tropical zone

Reading Strategy: Outlining Before you read, use the headings in this section to make an outline about climate. As you read, fill in the subtopics and smaller topics. Then, add phrases or a sentence after each subtopic to provide key information.

▼ **Figure 4–1** Carbon dioxide, water vapor, and several other gases in the atmosphere allow solar radiation to enter the biosphere but slow down the loss of heat to space. These greenhouse gases cause the greenhouse effect, which helps maintain Earth's temperature range.

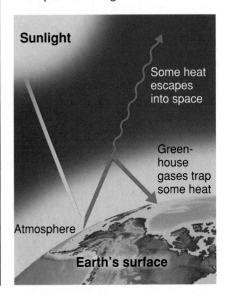

Sunlight

Some heat escapes into space

Greenhouse gases trap some heat

Atmosphere

Earth's surface

Greenhouse gases allow solar energy to penetrate the atmosphere in the form of sunlight. Much of the sunlight that hits the surface of our planet is converted into heat energy and then radiated back into the atmosphere. However, those same gases do not allow heat energy to pass out of the atmosphere as readily as light energy enters it. Instead, the gases trap heat inside Earth's atmosphere. If these gases were not present in the atmosphere, Earth would be 30 Celsius degrees cooler than it is today.

The Effect of Latitude on Climate

Because Earth is a sphere that is tilted on its axis, solar radiation strikes different parts of Earth's surface at an angle that varies throughout the year. At the equator, the sun is almost directly overhead at noon all year. At the North and South poles, however, the sun is much lower in the sky for months at a time. Look at **Figure 4–2,** and you will see that differences in the angle of sunlight directed at different latitudes result in the delivery of more heat to the equator than to the poles. The difference in heat distribution with latitude has important effects on Earth's climate zones.

As a result of differences in latitude and thus the angle of heating, Earth has three main climate zones: polar, temperate, and tropical. The **polar zones** are cold areas where the sun's rays strike Earth at a very low angle. These zones are located in the areas around the North and South poles, between 66.5° and 90° North and South latitudes. The **temperate zones** sit between the polar zones and the tropics. Because temperate zones are more affected by the changing angle of the sun over the course of a year, the climate in these zones ranges from hot to cold, depending on the season. The **tropical zone,** or tropics, is near the equator, between 23.5° North and 23.5° South latitudes. The tropics thus receive direct or nearly direct sunlight year-round, making the climate almost always warm. **Figure 4–2** shows Earth's main climate zones.

✓CHECKPOINT **What effect does latitude have on climate?**

▶ **Figure 4–2** Earth has three main climate zones. These climate zones are caused by the unequal heating of Earth's surface. Near the equator, energy from the sun strikes Earth almost directly. Near the poles, the sun's rays strike Earth's surface at a lower angle. The same amount of solar energy is spread out over a larger area, heating the surface less than at the equator.

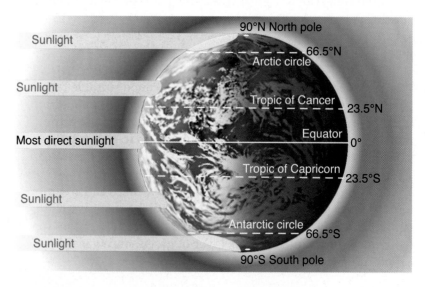

Heat Transport in the Biosphere

The unequal heating of Earth's surface drives winds and ocean currents, which transport heat throughout the biosphere. Winds form because warm air tends to rise and cool air tends to sink. Consequently, air that is heated near the equator rises. At the same time, cooler air over the poles sinks toward the ground. The upward movement of warm air and the downward movement of cool air create air currents, or winds, that move heat throughout the atmosphere, from regions of sinking air to regions of rising air. The prevailing winds, shown in **Figure 4–3,** bring warm or cold air to a region, affecting its climate.

Similar patterns of heating and cooling occur in Earth's oceans. Cold water near the poles sinks and then flows parallel to the ocean bottom, eventually rising again in warmer regions through a process called upwelling. Meanwhile, surface water is moved by winds. In both cases, the water flow creates ocean currents. Like air currents, ocean currents transport heat energy within the biosphere. Surface ocean currents warm or cool the air above them, thus affecting the weather and climate of nearby landmasses.

Continents and other landmasses can also affect winds and ocean currents. Landmasses can interfere with the movement of air masses. For example, a mountain range causes a moist air mass to rise. As this happens, the air mass cools and moisture condenses, forming clouds that bring precipitation to the mountains. Once the air mass reaches the far side of the mountains, it has lost much of its moisture. The result is a rain shadow—an area with a dry climate—on the far side of the mountains.

OCEAN CURRENTS

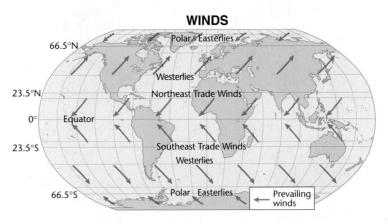

WINDS

▲ **Figure 4–3** Earth's ocean currents (top) and winds (bottom) interact to help produce Earth's climates. The curved paths of some currents and winds are the result of Earth's rotation. **Interpreting Maps** *In what direction do cold currents in Earth's oceans generally move?*

4–1 Section Assessment

1. 🔑 **Key Concept** What is the greenhouse effect?

2. 🔑 **Key Concept** Describe Earth's three main climate zones.

3. What are the main factors that determine Earth's climate?

4. Describe two ways in which heat is transported in the biosphere.

5. **Critical Thinking Applying Concepts** What might conditions on Earth be like without the greenhouse effect?

🧍**iTEXT** **Assessment** Use iText to review the important concepts in Section 4–1.

4–2 What Shapes an Ecosystem?

Guide for Reading

 Key Concepts
• How do biotic and abiotic factors influence an ecosystem?
• What interactions occur within communities?
• What is ecological succession?

Vocabulary
biotic factor
abiotic factor
habitat
niche
resource
competitive exclusion principle
predation
symbiosis
mutualism
commensalism
parasitism
ecological succession
primary succession
pioneer species
secondary succession

Reading Strategy:
Building Vocabulary Before you read, preview new vocabulary terms by skimming the section and making a list of the boldfaced terms. Leave space to make notes as you read.

If you ask an ecologist where a particular organism lives, that person might say the organism lives on a Caribbean coral reef, or in an Amazon rain forest, or in a desert in the American Southwest. Those answers provide a kind of ecological address not unlike a street address in a city or town. An ecological address, however, tells you more than where an organism lives. It tells you about the climate the organism experiences and what neighbors it is likely to have. But what shapes the ecosystem in which an organism lives?

Biotic and Abiotic Factors

Ecosystems are influenced by a combination of biological and physical factors. The biological influences on organisms within an ecosystem are called **biotic factors.** These include the entire living cast of characters with which an organism might interact, including birds, trees, mushrooms, and bacteria—in other words, the ecological community. Biotic factors that influence a bullfrog, for example, might include the tiny plants it eats as a tadpole, the herons that eat the adult frog, and other species that compete with the bullfrog for food or space.

Physical, or nonliving, factors that shape ecosystems are called **abiotic factors** (ay-by-AHT-ik). For example, the climate of an area includes abiotic factors such as temperature, precipitation, and humidity. Other abiotic factors are wind, nutrient availability, soil type, and sunlight. For example, the bullfrog in **Figure 4–4** is affected by abiotic factors such as the availability of water and the temperature of the air. **Together, biotic and abiotic factors determine the survival and growth of an organism and the productivity of the ecosystem in which the organism lives.** The area where an organism lives is called its **habitat.** A habitat includes both biotic and abiotic factors.

✓CHECKPOINT **Give an example of an abiotic factor.**

◀ **Figure 4–4** Like all ecosystems, this pond is shaped by a combination of biotic and abiotic factors. The bullfrog, plants, and other organisms in the pond are biotic factors. The water, air, and the rock on which the bullfrog sits are abiotic factors.

How do abiotic factors affect different plant species?

Materials presoaked rye and rice seeds, sand, potting soil, 4 paper cups

Procedure

1. Use a pencil to punch three holes in the bottom of each cup. Fill 2 cups with equal amounts of sand and 2 cups with the same amount of potting soil.
2. Plant 5 rice seeds in one sand-filled cup and 5 rice seeds in one soil-filled cup. Plant 5 rye seeds in each of the other 2 cups. Label each cup with the type of seeds and soil it contains.
3. Place all the cups in a warm, sunny location. Each day for 2 weeks, water the cups equally and record your observations of any plant growth. **CAUTION:** *Wash your hands well with soap and warm water after handling plants or soil.*

Analyze and Conclude

1. **Analyzing Data** In which medium did the rice grow best—sand or soil? Which was the better medium for the growth of rye?
2. **Inferring** Soil retains more water than sand, providing a moister environment. What can you infer from your observations about the kind of environment that favors the growth of rice? The growth of rye?
3. **Drawing Conclusions** Which would compete more successfully in a dry environment—rye or rice? In a moist environment?

The Niche

If an organism's habitat is its address, its niche is its occupation. A **niche** (NITCH) is the full range of physical and biological conditions in which an organism lives and the way in which the organism uses those conditions. For instance, part of the description of an organism's niche includes its place in the food web. Another part of the description might include the range of temperatures that the organism needs to survive. The combination of biotic and abiotic factors in an ecosystem often determines the number of different niches in that ecosystem.

A niche includes the type of food the organism eats, how it obtains this food, and which other species use the organism as food. For example, a mature bullfrog catches insects, worms, spiders, small fish, or even mice. Predators such as herons, raccoons, and snakes prey on bullfrogs.

The physical conditions that the bullfrog requires to survive are part of its niche. As amphibians, bullfrogs spend their lives in or near the water of ponds, lakes, and slow-moving streams. A bullfrog's body temperature varies with that of the surrounding water and air. As winter approaches, bullfrogs burrow into the mud of pond or stream bottoms to hibernate.

The bullfrog's niche also includes when and how it reproduces. Female bullfrogs lay their eggs in water during the warmer months of the year. The young frogs, called tadpoles, live in the water until their legs and lungs develop.

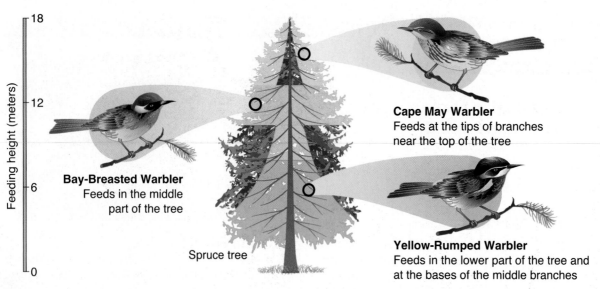

Cape May Warbler
Feeds at the tips of branches near the top of the tree

Bay-Breasted Warbler
Feeds in the middle part of the tree

Spruce tree

Yellow-Rumped Warbler
Feeds in the lower part of the tree and at the bases of the middle branches

Feeding height (meters)

▲ **Figure 4–5** Each of these warbler species has a different niche in its spruce tree habitat. By feeding in different areas of the tree, the birds avoid competing with one another for food. **Inferring** *What would happen if two of the warbler species occupied the same niche?*

As you will see, no two species can share the same niche in the same habitat. However, different species can occupy niches that are very similar. For instance, the three species of North American warblers shown in **Figure 4–5** live in the same spruce trees but feed at different elevations and in different parts of those trees. The species are similar, yet each warbler has a different niche within the forest.

✓**CHECKPOINT** *What is a niche?*

Community Interactions

When organisms live together in ecological communities, they interact constantly. These interactions help shape the ecosystem in which they live. 🔑 **Community interactions, such as competition, predation, and various forms of symbiosis, can powerfully affect an ecosystem.**

Competition Competition occurs when organisms of the same or different species attempt to use an ecological resource in the same place at the same time. The term **resource** refers to any necessity of life, such as water, nutrients, light, food, or space. In a forest, for example, broad-leaved trees such as oak or hickory may compete for sunlight by growing tall, spreading out their leaves, and blocking the sunlight from shorter trees. Similarly, two species of lizards in a desert might compete by attempting to eat the same type of insect.

Direct competition in nature often results in a winner and a loser—with the losing organism failing to survive. A fundamental rule in ecology, the **competitive exclusion principle,** states that no two species can occupy the same niche in the same habitat at the same time. Look again at the distribution of the warblers in **Figure 4–5.** Can you see how this distribution avoids direct competition among the different warbler species?

Predation An interaction in which one organism captures and feeds on another organism is called **predation** (preh-DAY-shun). The organism that does the killing and eating is called the predator (PRED-uh-tur), and the food organism is the prey. Cheetahs are active predators with claws and sharp teeth. Their powerful legs enable them to run after prey. Other predators, such as anglerfishes, are more passive. An anglerfish has a fleshy appendage that resembles a fishing lure, which it uses to draw unsuspecting prey close to its mouth.

Symbiosis Any relationship in which two species live closely together is called **symbiosis** (sim-by-OH-sis), which means "living together." Biologists recognize three main classes of symbiotic relationships in nature: mutualism, commensalism, and parasitism. Examples of these three relationships are shown in **Figure 4–6.**

In **mutualism** (MYOO-choo-ul-iz-um), both species benefit from the relationship. Many flowers, for example, depend on certain species of insects to pollinate them. The flowers provide the insects with food in the form of nectar, pollen, or other substances, and the insects help the flowers reproduce.

In **commensalism** (kuh-MEN-sul-iz-um), one member of the association benefits and the other is neither helped nor harmed. Small marine animals called barnacles, for example, often attach themselves to a whale's skin. The barnacles perform no service to the whale, nor do they harm it. Yet, the barnacles benefit from the constant movement of water past the swimming whale, because the water carries food particles to them.

In **parasitism** (PAR-uh-sit-iz-um), one organism lives on or inside another organism and harms it. The parasite obtains all or part of its nutritional needs from the other organism, called the host. Generally, parasites weaken but do not kill their host, which is usually larger than the parasite. Tapeworms, for example, are parasites that live in the intestines of mammals. Fleas, ticks, and lice live on the bodies of mammals, feeding on the blood and skin of the host.

Figure 4–6 Mutualism—both species benefit (top): The ant cares for the aphids and protects them from predators. The aphids produce a sweet liquid that the ant drinks. Commensalism—one species benefits; the other is neither helped nor harmed (center): The orchid benefits from its perch in the tree as it absorbs water and minerals from rainwater and runoff, but the tree is not affected. Parasitism—one species benefits while the other is harmed (bottom): A flea feeds on the blood of its host, which can be harmed by diseases the flea carries. **Predicting** *What would happen to the aphids if the ant died?*

Ecological Succession

On the time scale of a human life, some ecosystems may seem stable. The appearance of stability is often misleading, because ecosystems and communities are always changing. Sometimes, an ecosystem changes in response to an abrupt disturbance, such as a severe storm. At other times, change occurs as a more gradual response to natural fluctuations in the environment.

🔑 **Ecosystems are constantly changing in response to natural and human disturbances. As an ecosystem changes, older inhabitants gradually die out and new organisms move in, causing further changes in the community.** This series of predictable changes that occurs in a community over time is called **ecological succession.** Sometimes succession results from slow changes in the physical environment. A sudden natural disturbance from human activities, such as clearing a forest, may also be a cause of succession.

Primary Succession   On land, succession that occurs on surfaces where no soil exists is called **primary succession.** For example, primary succession occurs on the surfaces formed as volcanic eruptions build new islands or cover the land with lava rock or volcanic ash. Primary succession also occurs on bare rock exposed when glaciers melt.

In **Figure 4–7,** you can follow the stages of primary succession after a volcanic eruption. When primary succession begins, there is no soil, just ash and rock. The first species to populate the area are called **pioneer species.** The pioneer species on volcanic rocks are often lichens (LY-kunz). A lichen is made up of a fungus and an alga and can grow on bare rock. As lichens grow, they help break up the rocks. When they die, the lichens add organic material to help form soil in which plants can grow.

✓CHECKPOINT   *What are pioneer species?*

▼ **Figure 4–7** Primary succession occurs on newly exposed surfaces, such as this newly deposited volcanic rock and ash. A volcanic eruption destroys the previous ecosystem (1). The first organisms to appear are lichens (2). Mosses soon appear, and grasses take root in the thin layer of soil (3). Eventually, tree seedlings and shrubs sprout among the plant community (4). **Predicting** *What types of animals would you expect to appear at each stage, and why?*

Secondary Succession When a disturbance of some kind changes an existing community without removing the soil, then **secondary succession** can follow. Secondary succession occurs when land cleared and plowed for farming is abandoned. It also occurs when wildfire burns woodlands. **Figure 4–8** shows a wildfire in Yellowstone National Park that led to secondary succession after the fire. Fires set by lightning occur naturally in many ecosystems. Certain plants have adapted to a regular cycle of fire and regrowth. Their seeds will not sprout unless exposed to fire.

Ecologists used to think that the process of succession in a given area always proceeded in certain specific and predictable stages and ended with a mature, stable community that did not undergo further succession. This stage was referred to as a "climax community." Old-growth forests in the Pacific Northwest and ancient cypress swamps in Alabama, Georgia, Louisiana, and Arkansas were considered climax communities. Although these communities may appear to be permanent, they too undergo change. Long-term climate change and introduction of nonnative species can profoundly affect these communities.

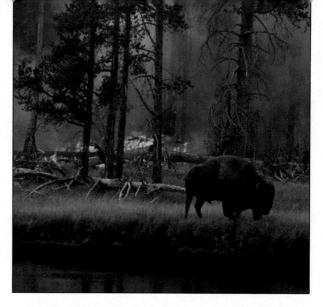

▲ **Figure 4–8** Wildfires in Yellowstone National Park in 1988 quickly led to secondary succession. **Observing** *What are some characteristics of the ecosystem in the photograph that might help to explain the occurrence of the Yellowstone fires?*

Careers in Biology

Forestry Technician

Job description: work outdoors to help maintain, protect, and develop forests (by planting trees, fighting insects and diseases that attack trees, and controlling soil erosion)

Education: two- or four-year college degree in forestry, wildlife, or conservation; summer work in parks, state and national forests; and private industry provides on-the-job training

Skills: knowledge of the outdoors and basic safety precautions; communication skills for working with the public; keen observational skills; physical fitness for jobs that require walking long distances through forests

Highlights: help to manage and conserve forest biomes by analyzing data, planting trees, and managing fires when necessary; contribute to people's enjoyment of outdoor recreation

Belva Fry said this about seeing grown trees she planted: "I love tree planting—working physically hard, then going back later to where you planted and seeing trees about 20 feet tall on the hillside. You know you really did something."

 Take It to the NET

For more career information, visit the Prentice Hall Web site at **www.phschool.com**.

Figure 4–9 Ecosystems are constantly changing in response to disturbances. In natural environments, succession occurs in stages. A dead whale that falls to the ocean floor is soon covered with scavengers, including tiny crustaceans called amphipods (inset), hagfish, crabs, and shrimp. After a time, only bare bones are left. The bones contain oil that supports several types of deep-sea bacteria. In the next stage of succession, the bacteria provide energy and nutrients for a different community of organisms, such as limpets, marine worms, and marine snails (inset), that live on the bones and in the surrounding sediments.

Succession in a Marine Ecosystem Succession can occur in any ecosystem—even in the permanently dark, deep ocean. In 1987, scientists found an unusual community of organisms living on the remains of a dead whale in the deep waters off the coast of southern California. At first, ecologists did not know what to make of this extraordinary community. After several experiments and hours of observation, the ecologists found that the community represented a stage in succession amid an otherwise stable and well-documented deep-sea ecosystem. Since that discovery, several more whale carcasses have been found in other ocean basins with similar organisms surrounding them. **Figure 4–9** illustrates three stages in the succession of a whale-fall community.

1 The disturbance that causes this kind of succession begins when a large whale, such as a blue or fin whale, dies and sinks to the normally barren ocean floor. The whale carcass attracts a host of scavengers and decomposers, including amphipods (inset), hagfishes, and sharks, that feast on the decaying meat.

2 Within a year, most of the whale's tissues have been eaten. The carcass then supports only a much smaller number of fishes, crabs, marine snails (inset), and other marine animals. The decomposition of the whale's body, however, enriches the surrounding sediments with nutrients, forming an oasis of sediment dwellers, including many different species of marine worms.

3 When only the whale's skeleton remains, a third community moves in. Heterotrophic bacteria begin to decompose oils inside the whale bones. In doing so, they release chemical compounds that serve as energy sources for other bacteria that are chemosynthetic autotrophs. The chemosynthetic bacteria, in turn, support a diverse community of mussels, limpets, snails, worms, crabs, clams, and other organisms that live on the bones and within the nearby sediments.

4–2 Section Assessment

1. **Key Concept** What is the difference between a biotic factor and an abiotic factor?

2. **Key Concept** Name three types of community interactions that can affect an ecosystem.

3. **Key Concept** What is the difference between primary succession and secondary succession?

4. How is an organism's niche determined?

5. **Critical Thinking Comparing and Contrasting** How are the three types of symbiotic relationships different? How are they similar?

iTEXT Assessment Use iText to review the important concepts in Section 4–2.

ALTERNATIVE ASSESSMENT

Creative Writing
Use the information from this section to write a short story about an ecosystem that is disturbed and undergoes succession. Include a flowchart with your story to show the main stages of change.

4–3 Land Biomes

Guide for Reading

🔑 **Key Concept**
• What are the unique characteristics of the world's major land biomes?

Vocabulary
• biome • microclimate
• canopy • understory
• deciduous • coniferous
• humus • taiga
• permafrost

Reading Strategy:
Using Visuals Before you read, preview **Figure 4–11.** Write down the names of the different biomes. As you read, examine the photographs and list the main characteristics of each biome.

Our planet is home to an amazing diversity of organisms that live in many different ecosystems—from frozen, treeless expanses near the North Pole to steaming tropical forests with trees that tower higher than the Statue of Liberty. Sometimes, it is useful to classify the bewildering variety of ecosystems into a manageable number of categories. To do this, ecologists may use the concept of biomes. A **biome** is a particular physical environment that contains a characteristic assemblage of plants and animals.

For example, the temperate grassland biome occupies large areas of flat or rolling land in regions with dry, temperate climates on several continents. This biome generally receives too little rainfall for forests to grow, but does support grasses and wildflowers and large herds of herbivores.

Climate and Microclimate

Climate is especially important in determining the characteristics of a biome. The two main factors that determine a region's climate—temperature and precipitation—can be summarized on a graph called a climate diagram. Study the general climate diagram in **Figure 4–10,** because you will encounter similar diagrams on the next few pages.

Climate conditions can vary over much smaller distances than you might imagine. Mountains, forests, oceans, lakes, and other natural features can influence the climate in a small area within a biome. The climate within a small area that differs significantly from the climate around it is called a **microclimate.** In California, for example, certain streets within the city of San Francisco are often blanketed with thick fog, yet the sun shines just a few blocks away. Parts of California's northern coast are covered with lush redwood forests, while areas a short distance inland are desertlike, spotted with cacti and other drought-resistant plants. Even a small park, if it is usually sunnier or windier than nearby areas, can have its own microclimate.

✔ **CHECKPOINT** *What is a microclimate?*

New Orleans, Louisiana

[Climate diagram: Average Temperature (°C) plotted as a line ranging approximately from 12 in January rising to about 28 in July–August and back to about 14 in December; Average Precipitation (mm) shown as vertical bars. Months J F M A M J J A S O N D along the x-axis.]

◀ **Figure 4–10** Climate diagrams show the average temperature and precipitation at a given location during each month of the year. In this graph, and the others to follow, temperature is plotted as a red line. Precipitation is shown as vertical bars. **Interpreting Graphics** *What is the approximate average temperature and precipitation in New Orleans during the month of July?*

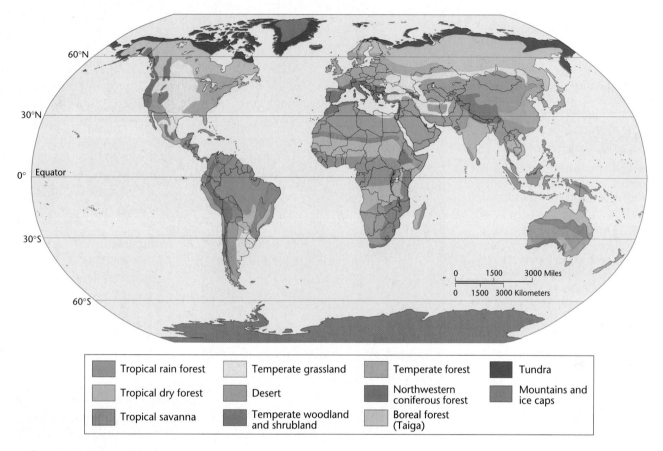

Tropical rain forest

Tropical dry forest

Tropical savanna

Temperate grassland

Desert

Temperate woodland and shrubland

Temperate forest

Northwestern coniferous forest

Boreal forest (Taiga)

Tundra

Mountains and ice caps

The Major Biomes

Ecologists recognize at least ten different biomes. **The world's major land biomes include tropical rain forest, tropical dry forest, tropical savanna, desert, temperate grassland, temperate woodland and shrubland, temperate forest, northwestern coniferous forest, boreal forest, and tundra. Each of these biomes is defined by a unique set of abiotic factors—particularly climate—and has a characteristic ecological community.** The map in **Figure 4–11** shows the natural geographic distribution of these major biomes. Be aware, however, that this is just one of many different systems that are used to classify biomes. The map does not take into account changes made by human activity, which you will read about in a later chapter.

The boundaries between the biomes may appear to be sharp on the map. On the ground, however, there are often transitional areas between biomes. In these transitional areas, one biome's plants and animals gradually become less frequent, while the organisms characteristic of the adjacent biome become more frequent. In addition, the community structure of a particular biome will differ slightly, depending on location and elevation above sea level. For this survey, you will study an example of each major biome from a specific location and elevation. You will begin in the tropics and finish at the poles.

▲ **Figure 4–11** This map shows the locations of the world's major land biomes. Other parts of Earth's surface are classified as mountains or ice caps. **Each biome has a characteristic climate and community of organisms.** These characteristics are shown in the pages that follow.

Tropical Rain Forest

Tropical rain forests are home to more species than all other land biomes combined. The leafy tops of tall trees—extending up to 70 meters above the forest floor—form a dense covering called a **canopy**. In the shade below the canopy, a second layer of shorter trees and vines forms an **understory**. Organic matter that falls to the forest floor quickly decomposes and the nutrients are recycled.

▶ **Abiotic factors:** hot and wet year-round; thin, nutrient-poor soils

▶ **Dominant plants:** broad-leaved evergreen trees; ferns; large woody vines and climbing plants; orchids and bromeliads

▶ **Dominant wildlife:** herbivores such as sloths, tapirs, and capybaras; predators such as jaguars; anteaters; monkeys; birds such as toucans, parrots, and parakeets; insects such as butterflies, ants, and beetles; piranhas and other freshwater fishes; reptiles such as caymans, boa constrictors, and anacondas

▶ **Geographic distribution:** parts of South and Central America, Southeast Asia, parts of Africa, southern India, and northeastern Australia

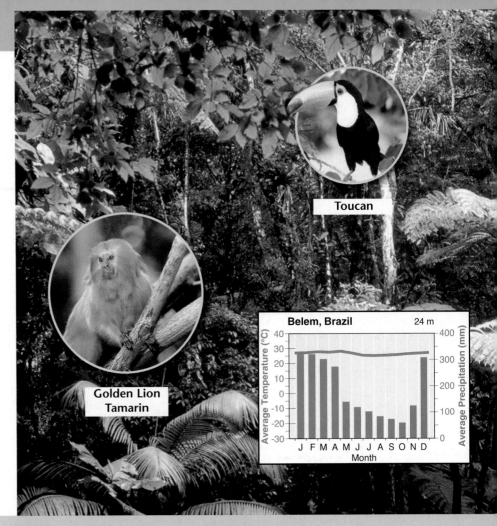

Toucan

Golden Lion Tamarin

Tropical Dry Forest

Tropical dry forests grow in places where rainfall is highly seasonal rather than year-round. During the dry season, nearly all the trees drop their leaves to conserve water. A tree that sheds its leaves during a particular season each year is called **deciduous**.

▶ **Abiotic factors:** generally warm year-round; alternating wet and dry seasons; rich soils subject to erosion

▶ **Dominant plants:** tall, deciduous trees that form a dense canopy during the wet season; drought-tolerant orchids and bromeliads; aloes and other succulents

▶ **Dominant wildlife:** tigers; monkeys; herbivores such as elephants, Indian rhinoceros, hog deer; birds such as great pied hornbill, pied harrier, and spot-billed pelican; insects such as termites; reptiles such as snakes and monitor lizards

▶ **Geographic distribution:** parts of Africa, South and Central America, Mexico, India, Australia, and tropical islands

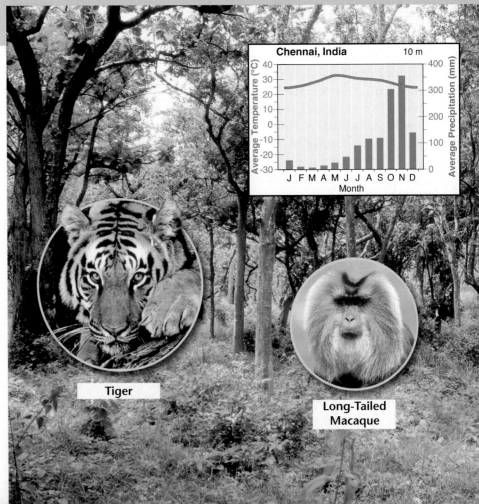

Tiger

Long-Tailed Macaque

Tropical Savanna

Receiving more seasonal rainfall than deserts but less than tropical dry forests, tropical savannas, or grasslands, are characterized by a cover of grasses. Savannas are spotted with isolated trees and small groves of trees and shrubs. Compact soils, fairly frequent fires, and the action of large animals such as rhinoceros prevent some savanna areas from turning into dry forest.

◀ **Abiotic factors:** warm temperatures; seasonal rainfall; compact soil; frequent fires set by lightning

◀ **Dominant plants:** tall, perennial grasses; sometimes drought-tolerant and fire-resistant trees or shrubs

◀ **Dominant wildlife:** predators such as lions, leopards, cheetahs, hyenas, and jackals; aardvarks; herbivores such as elephants, giraffes, antelopes, and zebras; baboons; birds such as eagles, ostriches, weaver birds, and storks; insects such as termites

◀ **Geographic distribution:** large parts of eastern Africa, southern Brazil, northern Australia

Nubian Vulture

White Rhinoceros

Mombasa, Kenya 57 m

Desert

All deserts are dry—in fact, a desert biome is defined as having annual precipitation of less than 25 centimeters. Beyond that, deserts vary greatly, depending on elevation and latitude. Many undergo extreme temperature changes during the course of a day, alternating between hot and cold. The organisms in this biome can tolerate the extreme conditions.

◀ **Abiotic factors:** low precipitation; variable temperatures; soils rich in minerals but poor in organic material

◀ **Dominant plants:** cacti and other succulents; creosote bush and other plants with short growth cycles

◀ **Dominant wildlife:** predators such as mountain lions, gray foxes, and bobcats; herbivores such as mule deer, pronghorn antelope, desert bighorn sheep, and kangaroo rats; bats; birds such as owls, hawks, and roadrunners; insects such as ants, beetles, butterflies, flies, and wasps; reptiles such as tortoises, rattlesnakes, and lizards

◀ **Geographic distribution:** Africa, Asia, the Middle East, United States, Mexico, South America, and Australia

Yuma, Arizona 60 m

Golden Eagle

Desert Hairy Scorpion

Ecosystems and Communities **101**

Temperate Grassland

Characterized by a rich mix of grasses and underlaid by some of the world's most fertile soils, temperate grasslands—such as plains and prairies—once covered vast areas of the midwestern United States. Since the development of the steel plow, however, most have been converted to agricultural fields. Periodic fires and heavy grazing by large herbivores maintain the characteristic plant community.

▶ **Abiotic factors:** warm to hot summers; cold winters; moderate, seasonal precipitation; fertile soils; occasional fires

▶ **Dominant plants:** lush, perennial grasses and herbs; most are resistant to drought, fire, and cold

▶ **Dominant wildlife:** predators such as coyotes and badgers—historically included wolves and grizzly bears; herbivores such as mule deer, pronghorn antelope, rabbits, prairie dogs, and introduced cattle—historically included bison; birds such as hawks, owls, bobwhite, prairie chicken, mountain plover; reptiles such as snakes; insects such as ants and grasshoppers

▶ **Geographic distribution:** central Asia, North America, Australia, central Europe, and upland plateaus of South America

Black-Tailed Prairie Dog

Prairie Chicken

Omaha, Nebraska 400 m

Temperate Woodland and Shrubland

This biome is characterized by a semiarid climate and a mix of shrub communities and open woodlands. In the open woodlands, large areas of grasses and wildflowers such as poppies are interspersed with oak trees. Communities that are dominated by shrubs are also known as chaparral. The growth of dense, low plants that contain flammable oils makes fires a constant threat.

▶ **Abiotic factors:** hot, dry summers; cool, moist winters; thin, nutrient-poor soils; periodic fires

▶ **Dominant plants:** woody evergreen shrubs with small, leathery leaves; fragrant, oily herbs that grow during winter and die in summer

▶ **Dominant wildlife:** predators such as coyotes, foxes, bobcats, and mountain lions; herbivores such as blacktailed deer, rabbits, squirrels, and mice; birds such as hawks, California quail, western scrub jay, warblers and other songbirds; reptiles such as lizards and snakes; butterflies; spiders

▶ **Geographic distribution:** western coasts of North and South America, areas around the Mediterranean Sea, South Africa, and Australia

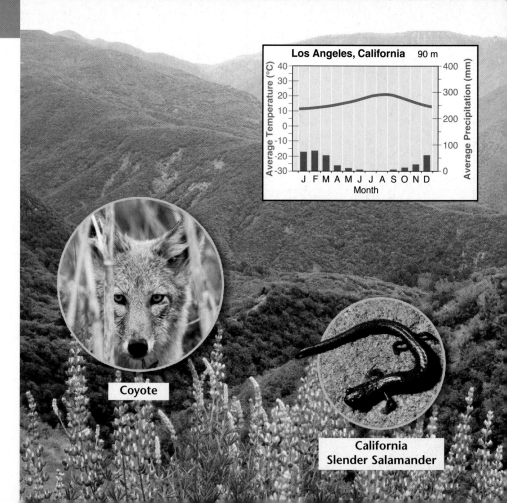

Los Angeles, California 90 m

Coyote

California Slender Salamander

Temperate Forest

Temperate forests contain a mixture of deciduous and coniferous (koh-NIF-ur-us) trees. **Coniferous** trees, or conifers, produce seed-bearing cones and most have leaves shaped like needles. These forests have cold winters that halt plant growth for several months. In autumn, the deciduous trees shed their leaves. In the spring, small plants burst out of the ground and flower. Soils of temperate forests are often rich in **humus** (HYOO-mus), a material formed from decaying leaves and other organic matter that makes soil fertile.

◄ **Abiotic factors:** cold to moderate winters; warm summers; year-round precipitation; fertile soils

◄ **Dominant plants:** broadleaf deciduous trees; some conifers; flowering shrubs; herbs; a ground layer of mosses and ferns

◄ **Dominant wildlife:** Deer; black bears; bobcats; nut and acorn feeders, such as squirrels; omnivores such as raccoons and skunks; numerous songbirds; turkeys

◄ **Geographic distribution:** eastern United States; southeastern Canada; most of Europe; and parts of Japan, China, and Australia

Tiger Beetle

Whitetail Deer

Philadelphia, Pennsylvania 4 m

Northwestern Coniferous Forest

Mild, moist air from the Pacific Ocean provides abundant rainfall to this biome. The forest is made up of a variety of conifers, ranging from giant redwoods along the coast of northern California to spruce, fir, and hemlock farther north. Moss often covers tree trunks and the forest floor. Flowering trees and shrubs such as dogwood and rhododendron are also abundant. Because of its lush vegetation, the northwestern coniferous forest is sometimes called a "temperate rain forest."

◄ **Abiotic factors:** mild temperatures; abundant precipitation during fall, winter, and spring; relatively cool, dry summer; rocky, acidic soils

◄ **Dominant plants:** Douglas fir, Sitka spruce, western hemlock, redwood

◄ **Dominant wildlife:** bears; large herbivores such as elk and deer; beavers; predators such as owls, bobcats, and members of the weasel family

◄ **Geographic distribution:** Pacific coast of northwestern United States and Canada, from northern California to Alaska

Seattle, Washington 150 m

Black Bear

Flying Squirrel

Boreal Forest

Along the northern edge of the temperate zone are dense evergreen forests of coniferous trees. These biomes are called boreal forests, or **taiga** (TY-guh). Winters are bitterly cold, but summers are mild and long enough to allow the ground to thaw. The word *boreal* comes from the Greek word for "north," reflecting the fact that boreal forests occur mostly in the Northern Hemisphere.

▶ **Abiotic factors:** long, cold winters; short, mild summers; moderate precipitation; high humidity; acidic, nutrient-poor soils

▶ **Dominant plants:** needleleaf coniferous trees such as spruce and fir; some broadleaf deciduous trees; small, berry-bearing shrubs

▶ **Dominant wildlife:** predators like lynx and timberwolves and members of the weasel family; small herbivorous mammals; moose and other large herbivores; beavers; songbirds and migratory birds

▶ **Geographic distribution:** North America, Asia, and northern Europe

Lynx

Moose

Fairbanks, Alaska 133 m

Tundra

The tundra is characterized by **permafrost**, a layer of permanently frozen subsoil. During the short, cool summer, the ground thaws to a depth of a few centimeters and becomes soggy and wet. In winter, the topsoil freezes again. This cycle of thawing and freezing, which rips and crushes plant roots, is one reason that tundra plants are small and stunted. Cold temperatures, high winds, the short growing season, and humus-poor soils also limit plant height.

▶ **Abiotic factors:** strong winds; low precipitation; short and soggy summers; long, cold, and dark winters; poorly developed soils; permafrost

▶ **Dominant plants:** ground-hugging plants such as mosses, lichens, sedges, and short grasses

▶ **Dominant wildlife:** a few resident birds and mammals that can withstand the harsh conditions; migratory waterfowl, shore birds, musk ox, Arctic foxes, and caribou; lemmings and other small rodents

▶ **Geographic distribution:** northern North America, Asia, and Europe

Snowy Owl

Caribou

Barrow, Alaska 8 m

Other Land Areas

Some areas of land on Earth do not fall neatly into the major biome categories described on the previous pages. These areas include mountain ranges and polar ice caps.

Mountain Ranges Mountain ranges can be found on all continents. On mountains like the one in **Figure 4–12**, the abiotic and biotic conditions vary with elevation. As you move up from base to summit, temperatures become colder and precipitation increases. Therefore, the types of plants and animals also change. If you were to climb the Rocky Mountains in Colorado, for example, you would begin in a grassland. Then, you would pass through an open woodland of pines. Next, you would hike through a forest of spruce and other conifers. Near the summit, you would reach open areas of wildflowers and stunted vegetation resembling tundra. In the Canadian Rockies, ice fields occur at the peaks of some ranges.

Polar Ice Caps The icy polar regions that border the tundra are cold year-round. Outside of the ice and snow, plants and algae are few but do include mosses and lichens. In the north polar region, the Arctic Ocean is covered with sea ice, and a thick ice cap covers most of Greenland. Polar bears, seals, insects, and mites are the dominant animals. In the south polar region, the continent of Antarctica is covered by a layer of ice that is nearly 5 kilometers thick in some places. There, the dominant wildlife includes penguins and marine mammals.

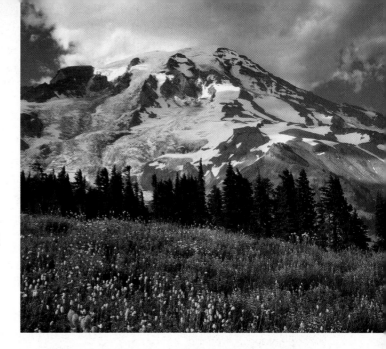

▲ **Figure 4–12** Washington's Mount Rainier towers above the tree line. **Applying Concepts** *Based on what you have seen in the previous pages, which biome lies at the base of this mountain?*

4–3 Section Assessment

1. **Key Concept** List the major land biomes and give one characteristic feature of each.

2. How are biomes classified?

3. What are the two types of tropical forest? How do they differ?

4. How might the presence of a mountain range affect the types of plants and animals found in an area?

5. **Critical Thinking Inferring** What characteristics would you expect tundra animals to have?

Assessment Use iText to review the important concepts in Section 4–3.

4–4 Aquatic Ecosystems

Guide for Reading

 Key Concepts
- What are the main factors that govern aquatic ecosystems?
- What are the two types of freshwater ecosystems?
- What are the characteristics of the different marine zones?

Vocabulary
- plankton • phytoplankton
- zooplankton • wetland
- estuary • detritus • salt marsh
- mangrove swamp
- photic zone • aphotic zone
- zonation • coastal ocean
- kelp forest • coral reef
- benthos

**Reading Strategy:
Making Comparisons** As you read, write down statements about similarities and differences among the different types of aquatic ecosystems.

▼ **Figure 4–13** The Menominee River in Michigan is a flowing-water ecosystem. ⊂• **Like all aquatic ecosystems, this river's communities are determined by the depth, flow, and chemistry of the water.**

Nearly three fourths of Earth's surface is covered with water, so it is not surprising that many organisms make their home in aquatic habitats. Oceans, streams, lakes, and marshes—indeed, nearly any body of water—contain a wide variety of communities. These aquatic communities are governed by biotic and abiotic factors, including light, nutrient availability, and oxygen. ⊂• **Aquatic ecosystems are determined primarily by the depth, flow, temperature, and chemistry of the overlying water.** In contrast to land biomes, which are grouped geographically, aquatic ecosystems are often grouped according to the abiotic factors that affect them. One such factor is the depth of water, or distance from shore. The depth of water, in turn, determines the amount of light that organisms receive. Water chemistry refers primarily to the amount of dissolved chemicals—especially salts, nutrients, and oxygen—on which life depends. For example, communities of organisms found in shallow water close to shore can be very different from the communities that occur away from shore in deep water. One abiotic factor that is important both to land biomes and aquatic ecosystems is latitude. Aquatic ecosystems in polar, temperate, and tropical oceans all have distinctive characteristics.

Freshwater Ecosystems

It may surprise you to know that only 3 percent of the surface water on Earth is fresh water. ⊂• **Freshwater ecosystems can be divided into two main types: flowing-water ecosystems and standing-water ecosystems.**

Flowing-Water Ecosystems Rivers, streams, creeks, and brooks are all freshwater ecosystems that flow over the land. Organisms that live there are well adapted to the rate of flow. Some insect larvae have hooks that allow them to take hold of aquatic plants. Certain catfish have suckers that anchor them to rocks. Trout and many other fishes have streamlined bodies that help them move with or against the current.

Flowing-water ecosystems like the river in **Figure 4–13** originate in mountains or hills, often springing from an underground water source. Near the source, the turbulent water has plenty of dissolved oxygen but little plant life. As the water flows downhill, sediments build up and enable plants to establish themselves. Farther downstream, the water may meander more slowly through flat areas, where turtles, beavers, or river otters make their homes.

Standing-Water Ecosystems Lakes and ponds are the most common standing-water ecosystems. In addition to the net flow of water in and out of these systems, there is usually water circulating within them. This circulation helps to distribute heat, oxygen, and nutrients throughout the ecosystem.

The relatively still waters of lakes and ponds provide habitats for many organisms, such as plankton, that would be quickly washed away in flowing water. **Plankton** is a general term for the tiny, free-floating or weakly swimming organisms that live in both freshwater and saltwater environments. See **Figure 4–14** for examples. Single-celled algae, or **phytoplankton** (FYT-oh-plank-tun), are supported by nutrients in the water and form the base of many aquatic food webs. Planktonic animals, or **zooplankton** (ZO-oh-plank-tun), feed on the phytoplankton.

✓ CHECKPOINT *What are phytoplankton?*

Freshwater Wetlands A **wetland** is an ecosystem in which water either covers the soil or is present at or near the surface of the soil for at least part of the year. The water in wetlands may be flowing or standing, or fresh, salty, or brackish—a mixture of fresh and salt water. Many wetlands are very productive ecosystems that serve as breeding grounds for insects, fishes and other aquatic animals, amphibians, and migratory birds.

The three main types of freshwater wetlands are bogs, marshes, and swamps. Bogs typically form in depressions called "kettle holes" left by ice sheets that melted thousands of years ago. Thick mats of sphagnum moss grow in bogs, where the water tends to be very acidic. Marshes are shallow wetlands along rivers. Marshes may be under water for all or part of the year. Marshes often contain cattails, rushes, and other tall, grasslike plants. Water flows slowly through swamps, which often look like flooded forests. The presence of trees and shrubs is what distinguishes a swamp from a marsh.

Some wetlands, such as the swamp shown in **Figure 4–15**, are wet year-round. Other kinds of wetlands, however, may not always be covered in standing water. Such areas may be classified as wetlands because they have certain kinds of soils and are wet enough to support a specific community of water-loving plants and animals.

▲ **Figure 4–14** Both freshwater and saltwater ecosystems often include plankton. This photograph shows phytoplankton, zooplankton, and larger animals called water fleas. **Predicting** *What might happen to an aquatic food web if phytoplankton were removed from the ecosystem?*

▼ **Figure 4–15** ⬤ Freshwater ecosystems can be divided into two main types: flowing-water ecosystems and standing-water ecosystems. Although this swamp along the Loxahatchee River in Florida appears stagnant, water actually flows through it slowly. The swamp is home to turtles, otters, alligators, and herons that live among the bald cypress trees.

Estuaries

Estuaries (ES-tyoo-ehr-eez) are wetlands formed where rivers meet the sea. Estuaries thus contain a mixture of fresh water and salt water, and are affected by the rise and fall of ocean tides. Many are shallow, so sufficient sunlight reaches the bottom to power photosynthesis. Primary producers include plants, algae, and both photosynthetic and chemosynthetic bacteria. Estuary food webs differ from those of more familiar ecosystems because most primary production is not consumed by herbivores. Instead, much of that organic material enters the food web as detritus. **Detritus** is made up of tiny pieces of organic material that provide food for organisms at the base of the estuary's food web. Organisms that feed on detritus include clams, worms, and sponges.

Estuaries support an astonishing amount of biomass, although they usually contain fewer species than freshwater or marine ecosystems. Estuaries serve as spawning and nursery grounds for commercially important fishes and for shellfish such as shrimps and crabs. Many young animals feed and grow in estuaries, then head out to sea to mature, and return to reproduce. Many waterfowl use estuaries for nesting, feeding, and resting during migrations.

Salt marshes are temperate-zone estuaries dominated by salt-tolerant grasses above the low-tide line, and by seagrasses under water. Salt marshes like the one shown in **Figure 4–16** (left) are (or were once) found along great stretches of Eastern North America from Southern Maine to Georgia. One of the largest systems of connected salt marshes in America surrounds the Chesapeake Bay estuary in Maryland.

Mangrove swamps, shown in **Figure 4–16** (right), are coastal wetlands that are widespread across tropical regions, including southern Florida and Hawaii. Here, the dominant plants are several species of salt-tolerant trees, collectively called mangroves. Seagrasses are also common below the low-tide line. Like salt marshes, mangrove swamps are valuable nurseries for fish and shellfish. The largest mangrove area in the continental United States is Florida's Everglades National Park.

Figure 4–16 Salt marshes occur in estuaries along seacoasts in the temperate zone. Salt-tolerant grasses are the dominant plants in this salt marsh (left) along the coast of Mount Desert Island in Maine. Mangrove swamps (right) occur in bays and estuaries along tropical coasts. The stiltlike roots of mangrove trees trap sediment that accumulates as mud behind the trees. This allows other plants to take root and helps to build the mangrove forest out from the shoreline. **Predicting** *Would you expect to find mangrove swamps or salt marshes on a coast exposed to large ocean waves? Explain.*

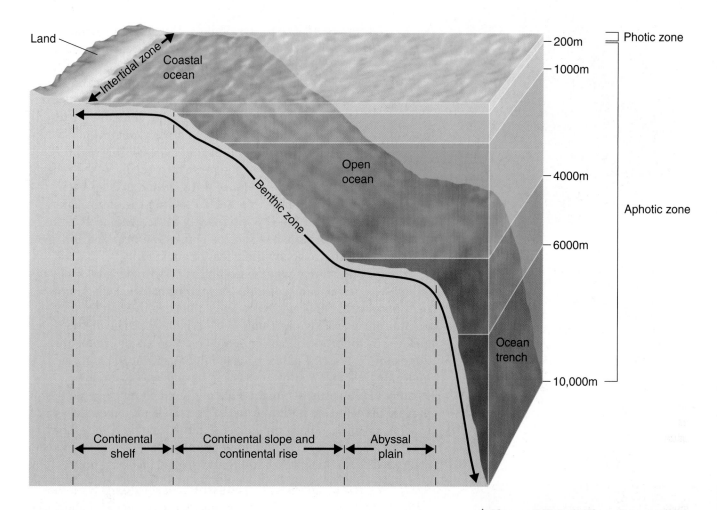

Labels on diagram:
Land
Intertidal zone
Coastal ocean
Benthic zone
Open ocean
Ocean trench
Continental shelf
Continental slope and continental rise
Abyssal plain
200m
1000m
4000m
6000m
10,000m
Photic zone
Aphotic zone

▲ **Figure 4–17** The ocean can be divided into zones based on light penetration and into zones based on depth and the distance from shore. Each zone contains a characteristic assemblage of organisms.

Marine Ecosystems

Unless you are an avid diver or snorkeler, it takes some imagination to picture what life is like in the vast, three-dimensional ocean. Sunlight penetrates only a relatively short distance through the surface of the water. Photosynthesis is limited to this well-lit upper layer known as the **photic zone** (FOH-tihk). Only in this relatively thin surface layer—typically down to a depth of about 200 meters—can algae and other producers grow. Below the photic zone is the **aphotic zone** (ay-FOH-tihk), which is permanently dark. Chemosynthetic autotrophs are the only producers that can survive in the aphotic zone.

There are several different classification systems that scientists use to describe marine ecosystems. **In addition to the division between the photic and aphotic zones, marine biologists also divide the ocean into zones based on the depth and distance from shore: the intertidal zone, the coastal ocean, and the open ocean.** Each of these zones supports distinct ecological communities. The benthic zone covers the ocean floor and is, therefore, not exclusive to any of the other marine zones. **Figure 4–17** shows a generalized diagram of the marine zones.

✔ CHECKPOINT *What factor is absent in the aphotic zone?*

▲ **Figure 4–18** ◯ The main divisions in the ocean based on depth and distance from shore are the intertidal zone, the coastal ocean, and the open ocean. Along the coast of Vancouver Island in Canada, low tide reveals sea stars, seaweed, and other organisms adapted to life in the intertidal zone.

Intertidal Zone Organisms that live in the intertidal zone are exposed to regular and extreme changes in their surroundings. Once or twice a day, they are submerged in sea water. The remainder of the time, they are exposed to air, sunlight, and temperature changes. Often, organisms in this zone are battered by waves and sometimes by strong currents.

There are many different types of intertidal communities. One of the most interesting is the rocky intertidal, shown in **Figure 4–18,** which exists in temperate regions where exposed rocks line the shore. There, barnacles and seaweed permanently attach themselves to the rocks. Other organisms, such as snails, sea urchins, and sea stars, cling to the rocks by their feet or suckers.

Competition among organisms in the rocky intertidal zone often leads to zonation (zoh-NAY-shun). **Zonation** is the prominent horizontal banding of organisms that live in a particular habitat. In the rocky intertidal zone, each band can be distinguished by differences in color or shape of the major organisms. For example, a stripe of black algae might grow at the highest high-tide line, followed by encrusting barnacles. Lower down, clusters of blue mussels might stick out amid clumps of green algae. This zonation is similar to the pattern that you might observe as you climb up a mountain. In the intertidal zone, however, zonation exists on a smaller vertical scale—just a few meters compared to the kilometers you would ascend on a mountain.

Coastal Ocean The **coastal ocean** extends from the low-tide mark to the outer edge of the continental shelf, the relatively shallow border that surrounds the continents. The continental shelf is often shallow enough to fall mostly or entirely within the photic zone, so photosynthesis can usually occur throughout its depth. As a result, the coastal ocean is often rich in plankton and many other organisms.

One of the most productive coastal ocean communities is the kelp forest. **Kelp forests** are named for their dominant organism: a giant brown algae that can grow at extraordinary rates—as much as 50 centimeters a day. Huge forests of this seaweed are found in cold-temperate seas around the world, including those along the coasts of California and the Pacific Northwest. Kelp forests, like the one shown in **Figure 4–19,** support a complex food web that includes snails, sea urchins, sea otters, a variety of fishes, seals, and whales.

✔CHECKPOINT **What is the coastal ocean?**

◀ **Figure 4–19** Kelp forests are ecosystems that occur in coastal oceans swept by cold-water currents. The long strands of giant kelp create a habitat that shelters a variety of fishes and other organisms. This kelp forest off the coast of California is part of a larger zone of kelp forests found along the western coast of North America from Alaska to Mexico. **Comparing and Contrasting** *How is a kelp forest like a forest on land?*

Coral Reefs In the warm, shallow water of coastal, tropical oceans are coral reefs, among the most diverse and productive environments on Earth. **Coral reefs** are named for the coral animals whose hard, calcium carbonate skeletons make up their primary structure. As you can see in **Figure 4–20**, an extraordinary diversity of organisms flourishes in these spectacular habitats.

Coral animals are tiny relatives of jellyfish that live together in vast numbers. Most coral animals are the size of your fingernail, or even smaller. Each one looks like a small sack with a mouth surrounded by tentacles. These animals use their tentacles to capture and eat microscopic creatures that float by. Coral animals cannot grow in cold water or water that is low in salt.

Coral animals live in symbiosis with algae contained within the body of each coral animal. The algae carry out photosynthesis, supplying nutrients to the corals. In turn, the coral animals provide a framework on which the algae grow. Below 40 meters, not enough light penetrates the water for algae to grow. For this reason, almost all growth in a coral reef occurs within 40 meters of the surface.

▶ **Figure 4–20** This coral reef off the island of New Britain in the Pacific Ocean supports a dazzling variety of corals and fishes. Some coral reefs in the Pacific have been damaged by crown-of-thorns starfish, which prey on corals. Reefs are most abundant around islands and along the eastern coasts of continents. In the United States, only the coasts of southern Florida and Hawaii have coral reefs. **Applying Concepts** *In what types of community interactions are coral animals involved?*

Analyzing Data

Ecosystem Productivity

The data table on the right compares the primary productivity of some of the world's ecosystems. Use the data table to answer the following questions.

1. **Using Tables and Graphs** Construct a bar graph to display the data. Use different colors to distinguish aquatic and land ecosystems.

2. **Analyzing Data** According to your graph, which ecosystem is most productive? Use what you know to explain that fact.

3. **Inferring** Although the open ocean is among the least productive ecosystems, it contributes greatly to the overall productivity of the biosphere. How can this situation be explained?

4. **Applying Concepts** What are two abiotic factors that might account for the differences in productivity among the land ecosystems in the table? (*Hint:* Review the relevant biomes on pages 100–104.)

Productivity of Aquatic and Land Ecosystems	
Ecosystem	**Average Primary Productivity (grams of organic matter produced per sq. meter per year)**
Aquatic Ecosystems:	
Coral reef	2500
Estuary	1800
Lake	500
Open ocean	125
Land Ecosystems:	
Tropical rain forest	2200
Temperate forest	1250
Tropical savanna	900
Tundra	90

▲ Figure 4–21 🔑 The main divisions in the ocean based on depth and distance from shore are the intertidal zone, the coastal ocean, and the open ocean. In the open ocean, the swordfish (top) can sometimes be seen swimming near the surface, yet these fish can also dive to more than 600m to prey on fishes of the deep ocean. Some types of octopus (bottom) live in the depths of the open ocean, although other types live in shallow coastal waters.

Open Ocean The open ocean, often referred to as the oceanic zone, begins at the edge of the continental shelf and extends outward. It is the largest marine zone, covering more than 90 percent of the surface area of the world's oceans. The open ocean ranges from about 500 meters deep along continental slopes to more than 11,000 meters at the deepest ocean trench. Organisms in the deep ocean are exposed to high pressure, frigid temperatures, and total darkness.

Typically, the open ocean has very low levels of nutrients and supports only the smallest producers. Productivity is generally low. Still, because of the enormous area, most of the photosynthetic activity on Earth occurs in the part of the open ocean within the photic zone. Fishes of all shapes and sizes dominate the open ocean. The swordfish and the octopus in **Figure 4–21** are just two examples of the organisms found in this zone. Marine mammals such as dolphins and whales also live there but must stay close to the surface to breathe.

Benthic Zone The ocean floor contains organisms that live attached to or near the bottom, such as sea stars, anemones, and marine worms. Scientists refer to these organisms as the **benthos.** That is why the ocean floor is called the benthic zone. This zone extends horizontally along the ocean floor from the coastal ocean through the open ocean.

Benthic ecosystems often depend on food from organisms that grow in the photic zone, particularly the producers. Animals that are attached to the bottom or do not move around much, such as clams and sea cucumbers, feed on pieces of dead organic material, or detritus, that drift down from the surface waters. Near deep-sea vents, where superheated water boils out of cracks on the ocean floor, dwell chemosynthetic primary producers that support life without light and photosynthesis.

4–4 Section Assessment

1. 🔑 **Key Concept** List three characteristics that determine the structure of aquatic ecosystems.

2. 🔑 **Key Concept** How are standing-water ecosystems similar to flowing-water ecosystems? How are they different?

3. 🔑 **Key Concept** List six distinct ecological zones that can be found in the ocean. Give two abiotic factors for each zone.

4. Define a wetland and an estuary.

5. **Critical Thinking Predicting** How might the damming of a river affect an estuary at the river's mouth?

💻 **Assessment** Use iText to review the important concepts in Section 4–4.

Take It to the NET

Read about the productivity of the world's oceans. Then, print out a map of the oceans and color-code the regions of highest productivity. Use the links provided in the Biology area at the Prentice Hall Web site for help in completing this activity: **www.phschool.com**

Observing Succession

The most obvious examples of succession involve large organisms, such as plants and animals, that are easily seen. In this investigation, you will determine whether succession also occurs in a community of microorganisms.

Problem What changes occur in a microscopic community over time?

Materials

- 1000-mL beaker or large jar
- soil
- grass clippings
- dried leaves
- 600-mL aged water
- 4 coverslips
- 4 glass slides
- 4 dropper pipettes
- microscope
- reference book or chart for identifying common microorganisms

Skills Using Graphs, Analyzing Data

Procedure

1. Place enough soil in the 1000-mL beaker to cover the bottom. Fill the beaker with a loosely packed mixture of grass clippings and dried leaves and add the aged water.

2. Set the beaker aside in a cool place where it can remain undisturbed for 24 hours.

3. After 24 hours, check the water for signs of life. For example, a strong odor or cloudy water is evidence of bacterial growth; fuzzy growths or threads indicate the presence of mold; and a green tint is due to algae. Record your observations.

4. Use a dropper pipette to transfer a drop of water from the beaker to a microscope slide. Add a coverslip.

5. Examine the slide under the low-power objective of the microscope to locate any microorganisms. Then, switch to high power. Use a reference book or chart to identify the organisms. Record the date and your observations, including labeled drawings, the number of each type of organism in your field of view, and the magnification.

6. Repeat steps 4 and 5 with water samples from several different areas of the beaker.

7. Repeat steps 3 through 6 every day for 2 weeks. Note any changes in the number or types of organisms in the beaker.

Analyze and Conclude

1. **Using Graphs** Make a graph of the population of each type of organism. Plot time on the *x*-axis and number of organisms per field of view on the *y*-axis.

2. **Observing** How did the number and variety of organisms in the beaker change over the 2-week period?

3. **Analyzing Data** What kinds of organisms appeared first in the microscopic water community? Which appeared last? How can you explain these changes?

4. **Drawing Conclusions** Do your observations support the idea that succession occurs in communities of microorganisms? Explain your answer.

Go Further

Analyzing Data With your teacher's approval, set up a simple community of only a few known species of microorganisms. Observe the community for two weeks and try to explain any evidence of succession that you observe.

4–1 The Role of Climate
 Key Concepts

- Carbon dioxide, methane, water vapor, and a few other atmospheric gases trap heat energy and maintain Earth's temperature range.
- As a result of differences in latitude and thus the angle of heating, Earth has three main climate zones: polar, temperate, and tropical.

Vocabulary
- weather, p. 87 • climate, p. 87
- greenhouse effect, p. 87 • polar zone, p. 88
- temperate zone, p. 88 • tropical zone, p. 88

4–2 What Shapes an Ecosystem?
Key Concepts

- Together, biotic and abiotic factors determine the survival and growth of an organism and the productivity of the ecosystem in which the organism lives.
- Community interactions, such as competition, predation, and various forms of symbiosis, can powerfully affect an ecosystem.
- Ecosystems are constantly changing in response to natural and human disturbances. As an ecosystem changes, older inhabitants gradually die out and new organisms move in, causing further changes in the community.

Vocabulary
- biotic factor, p. 90 • abiotic factor, p. 90
- habitat, p. 90 • niche, p. 91 • resource, p. 92
- competitive exclusion principle, p. 92
- predation, p. 93 • symbiosis, p. 93
- mutualism, p. 93 • commensalism, p. 93
- parasitism, p. 93 • ecological succession, p. 94
- primary succession, p. 94 • pioneer species, p. 94
- secondary succession, p. 95

4–3 Land Biomes
Key Concept

- The world's major land biomes include tropical rain forest, tropical dry forest, tropical savanna, temperate grassland, desert, temperate woodland and shrubland, temperate forest, northwestern coniferous forest, boreal forest, and tundra. Each of these biomes is defined by a unique set of abiotic factors—particularly climate—and has a characteristic ecological community.

Vocabulary
- biome, p. 98 • microclimate, p. 98
- canopy, p. 100 • understory, p. 100
- deciduous, p. 100 • coniferous, p. 103
- humus, p. 103 • taiga, p. 104
- permafrost, p. 104

4–4 Aquatic Ecosystems
Key Concepts

- Aquatic ecosystems are determined primarily by the depth, flow, temperature, and chemistry of the overlying water.
- Freshwater ecosystems can be divided into two main types: flowing-water ecosystems and standing-water ecosystems.
- In addition to the division between the photic and aphotic zones, marine biologists also divide the ocean into zones based on the depth and distance from shore: the intertidal zone, coastal ocean, and the open ocean.

Vocabulary
- plankton, p. 107 • phytoplankton, p. 107
- zooplankton, p. 107 • wetland, p. 107
- estuary, p. 108 • detritus, p. 108
- salt marsh, p. 108 • mangrove swamp, p. 108
- photic zone, p. 109 • aphotic zone, p. 109
- zonation, p. 110 • coastal ocean, p. 110
- kelp forest, p. 110 • coral reef, p. 111
- benthos, p. 112

Thinking Visually
Using information from this chapter, create a concept map that includes the following terms: *abiotic factors, biotic factors, community interactions, predation, competition, symbiosis, nutrients, ecosystems, light, oxygen.*

Chapter 4

Part A

Multiple Choice

For each statement or question, select the number of the word or expression that, of those given, best completes the statement or answers the question.

1 The average, year-after-year conditions of temperature and precipitation in a particular region are its
  (1) weather   (3) biotic factors
  (2) climate   (4) biome

2 Generally, which has the greatest effect on determining the climate of a region?
  (1) longitude
  (2) dominant plant species
  (3) distance from the equator
  (4) month of the year

3 Which factors define an organism's niche?
  (1) abiotic factors, only
  (2) biotic factors, only
  (3) abiotic factors and place in the food web only
  (4) abiotic and biotic factors and place in the food web

4 In which marine zone are you likely to find algae growing?
  (1) intertidal zone
  (2) photic zone
  (3) aphotic zone
  (4) benthic zone

5 The burning of fossil fuels causes an increase in the air of
  (1) oxygen   (3) carbon dioxide
  (2) water   (4) silicon dioxide

6 All of the biotic and abiotic factors in a pond form a(an)
  (1) biosphere   (3) community
  (2) ecosystem   (4) niche

7 Tapeworms can live inside a dog's intestines and prevent the dog from getting all the nutrients it needs. In this relationship, the tapeworms are
  (1) producers   (3) scavengers
  (2) parasites   (4) decomposers

8 Natural disturbances, such as forest fires or hurricanes, can result in changes in the ecosystem that are called
  (1) competition   (3) succession
  (2) stability   (4) interdependence

9 Which biome would you expect to find in a region with an average monthly temperature of 25°C and high year-round rainfall?
  (1) tropical rain forest
  (2) tropical dry forest
  (3) desert
  (4) tundra

10 Which biome is correctly paired with a factor or organism that is found there?
  (1) boreal forest—moss
  (2) tundra—permafrost
  (3) temperate forest—prairie dog
  (4) grassland—bear

11 Which sequence best describes primary succession?
  (1) soil—shrubs—lichens—mosses
  (2) shrubs—mosses—lichens—soil
  (3) lichens—soil—mosses—shrubs
  (4) mosses—soil—shrubs—lichens

12 The photic zone in marine ecosystems is important because
  (1) it provides a habitat for chemosynthetic organisms
  (2) it is the layer where photosynthesis takes place
  (3) it is an area free from predator-prey relationships
  (4) all organisms in this layer are consumers

13 Wetland areas are under government protection because they are
  (1) inexpensive building sites
  (2) very limited in number
  (3) important for shipping companies
  (4) breeding grounds for many organisms

14 The water in an estuary is
  (1) salt water, only
  (2) poor in nutrients
  (3) fresh water, only
  (4) a mixture of fresh water and salt water

Test-Taking Tip When you are asked to analyze a graph showing experimental data, first look at the shape of the curve. Identify the variables and try to determine how they are related. Then, read and answer the questions about the graph.

Preparing for the
Living Environment Exam

Parts B and C

Multiple Choice and Extended Response

For those questions that ask you to select a response, choose the one that best completes the statement or answers the question. For all others follow the directions given.

15 In a tropical rain forest, the leafy tops of tall trees get more sunlight than the shorter trees and vines that form the understory. How can all the plants in this ecosystem survive?

Base your answers to questions 16 and 17 on the information below and on your knowledge of biology.

A monkey from a rain forest was switched with squirrel from a temperate forest.

16 Copy the chart below and fill in the characteristics of the two biomes. (Do not write in this book.)

Characteristics	Rain Forest	Temperate Forest
Abiotic factors		
Dominant plants		
Dominant wildlife		

17 Based on the characteristics of each biome, predict how successful the squirrel would be in the rain forest and how successful the monkey would be in the temperate forest.

18 List the major abiotic factors that shape ecosystems.

19 A windstorm blows down the large trees in one part of a forest. Soon, sun-loving plants sprout in the new clearing. What type of succession is this? What might this area look like in five years? In 50 years?

20 How does the photic zone differ from the aphotic zone?

21 How do freshwater ecosystems differ from marine ecosystems? Give an example of each type of ecosystem.

22 What is the difference between an organism's habitat and its niche? Give an example.

23 The table below lists the average monthly temperature and precipitation for Lillehammer, Norway. Using graph paper or a computer graphing program, construct a climate diagram for Lillehammer. Model your diagram on the ones for biomes in this chapter. After you have completed the diagram, identify the biome that is most likely to occur in Lillehammer.

Climate Data for Lillehammer, Norway

Month	Average Temperature (°C)	Precipitation (mm)
Jan.	-8.1	38.1
Feb.	-6.2	27.9
Mar.	-3.9	30.5
Apr.	3.3	35.6
May	8.9	45.7
June	13.9	63.5
July	16.4	81.3
Aug.	14.2	88.9
Sept.	9.5	58.4
Oct.	3.9	63.5
Nov.	-3.8	50.8
Dec.	-6.1	48.3

24 On a separate sheet of paper, draw the chart below. Then, fill in the chart with the following organisms in their correct marine zone(s): sea star, phytoplankton, dolphin, sea otter, clam, kelp, coral. (Do not write in this book.)

Zone	Organism(s)
Intertidal	
Costal ocean	
Open ocean	
Benthic	

Base your answers to questions 25 through 29 on the information below and on your knowledge of biology.

As cattle graze in the grasslands of East Africa, they stir up insects living in the grass. This is why birds known as cattle egrets can capture more insects when they hunt near cattle than when they hunt on their own. Some scientists want to design an experiment to determine if the relationship between the cattle and egrets is one of mutualism, parasitism, or commensalism.

25 Distinguish between mutualism, parasitism, and commensalism.

26 The egrets obviously benefit from their relationship with the cattle. The scientists hypothesize that the behavior of the cattle is not affected by the egrets. What type of relationship would this be?

27 How could the scientists test their hypothesis?

28 What type of data should the scientists collect?

29 The scientists observed two herds of cattle repeatedly. Then, they averaged their data and displayed it in the table below.

Relationship Between Cattle and Egrets				
Behavior	Herd 1		Herd 2	
	Birds	No birds	Birds	No birds
Grazing (hours/day)	4.5	4.25	5.25	5
Visits to pond	4	4	3	3
No. in shade (measured at noon each day)	5	4	8	8
Resting (hours/day)	2.5	2.5	4	4.25

Based on the data, the scientists concluded that the relationship between the cattle and egrets could be classified as commensalism. Why did they come to this conclusion?

30 State the competitive exclusion principle. Give an example.

31 A developer has proposed filling in a salt marsh to create a coastal resort. You have been asked by the local residents to prepare a report that will help them decide whether or not the proposal should be supported. Your report should include the following
  • definitions of wetlands and salt marshes
  • examples of organisms found in salt marshes
  • description of the role of salt marshes in the lives of insects, fishes, birds, and other organisms
  • description of the role of salt marshes in the water cycle
  • your opinion about whether the resort should be built

32 State two abiotic factors that cause deciduous trees to shed their leaves.

33 How are salt marshes and mangrove swamps alike? How are they different?

34 Although the amount of precipitation is low, most parts of the tundra biome are very wet during the summer. What would explain this apparent contradiction?

35 The cowbird lays its eggs in other birds' nests. When the cowbird egg hatches, the "parents" feed the cowbird along with their own young, which the young cowbird then pushes out of the nest. Is this an example of mutualism, parasitism, or commensalism? Support your answer with an explanation.

Take It to the NET

Are biomes distinct enough to be seen from space? Visit the Prentice Hall Web Site at **www.phschool.com** to find out how biomes can be differentiated from space. Then, answer the following questions:
  • What two factors are used to differentiate biomes from space? Explain.
  • What is a climograph?
  • Obtain temperature and rainfall data for your area and construct your own climograph.

5 Populations

This trio of sea otters is part of the population that lives near Monterey, California. Sea otters often rest by wrapping themselves in kelp to keep from drifting away.

Inquiry Activity

How do populations grow?

Procedure

1. Suppose that one mated pair of rabbits in a park can produce a litter of 6 offspring each year. Assume that all the members of one generation reproduce each year and that no rabbits die. Calculate how many offspring would be produced each year for 5 years.
2. Construct a graph of your data. Plot time on the *x*-axis and population on the *y*-axis.

Think About It

1. **Analyzing Data** Describe the shape of your graph.
2. **Using Graphs** Use your graph to predict the population of rabbits in 10 years and in 20 years.
3. **Predicting** What would eventually happen to the population of rabbits if they were not able to leave the park?
4. **Formulating Hypotheses** How can you explain the fact that Earth is not covered by rabbits?

5–1 How Populations Grow

Sea otters are important members of the kelp forest community of America's Pacific Northwest coast. This "forest" is made up of algae called giant kelp, which have stalks up to 30 meters long, as well as smaller types of kelp. The kelp forest provides habitat for a variety of animals. Sea otters need lots of energy to stay warm in cold water, so they eat lots of their favorite food: sea urchins. Sea urchins, in turn, feed on the kelp.

The relationships along this food chain set the stage for a classic tale of population growth and decline. A century ago, otters were nearly eliminated by hunting. Sea urchin populations increased greatly, and kelp forests nearly disappeared. Why? Because the kelp was eaten down to the bare rock by hordes of sea urchins! The future of the kelp forests looked grim. Then sea otters were declared an endangered species and were protected from hunting. With hunters out of the picture, otter populations recovered. Sea urchin numbers dropped dramatically. Kelp grew back. But now, some otter populations are shrinking again because otters are being eaten by killer whales. To better understand why populations such as these change as they do, we turn to the study of population biology.

Characteristics of Populations

Several terms can be used to describe a population in nature. **Three important characteristics of a population are its geographic distribution, density, and growth rate.** A fourth characteristic, the population's age structure, will be discussed later in this chapter. Geographic distribution, or range, is a term that describes the area inhabited by a population. The range can vary in size from a few cubic centimeters occupied by bacteria in a rotting apple to the millions of square kilometers occupied by migrating whales in the Pacific Ocean.

Population density is the number of individuals per unit area. This number can vary tremendously depending on the species and its ecosystem. The population of saguaro cactus in the desert plant community shown in **Figure 5–1,** for example, has a low density, whereas other plants in that community have a relatively high density.

Guide for Reading

🔑 **Key Concepts**
- What characteristics are used to describe a population?
- What factors affect population size?
- What are exponential and logistic growth?

Vocabulary
population density
immigration
emigration
exponential growth
logistic growth
carrying capacity

Reading Strategy:
Asking Questions Before you read, rewrite the headings in the section as *how, why,* or *what* questions about populations. As you read, write down the answers to your questions.

▶ **Figure 5–1** The tall saguaro cactuses in this Arizona desert have a low population density compared to the smaller desert plants. ⚭**Density is one of the main characteristics that describe a natural population. Other characteristics of populations are their geographic distribution and growth rate.**

Immigration is formed from the Latin prefix *in-,* meaning "in," and *migrare,* meaning "to move from one place to another." **If the Latin prefix *e-* means "out," then what does *emigration* mean?**

Population Growth

Natural populations may stay the same size from year to year. But a population can grow rapidly, as sea otter populations did when they were first protected from hunting. Populations can also decrease in size, as otter populations are doing now because of predation by killer whales. But just how do interacting factors such as these influence population growth?

🔑 **Three factors can affect population size: the number of births, the number of deaths, and the number of individuals that enter or leave the population.** Simply put, a population will increase or decrease in size depending on how many individuals are added to it or removed from it.

Generally, populations grow if more individuals are born than die in any period of time. For some organisms, such as the penguins in **Figure 5–2,** being born may actually mean hatching. Plants can add new individuals as seeds sprout and begin to grow.

A population can grow when its birthrate is greater than its death rate. If the birthrate equals the death rate, the population stays more or less the same size. If the death rate is greater than the birthrate, the population shrinks. Sea otter populations grew when hunting stopped, because their death rate dropped. Those same otter populations are shrinking now because killer whales have raised the death rates of otters again.

Immigration (im-uh-GRAY-shun), the movement of individuals into an area, is another factor that can cause a population to grow. **Emigration** (em-uh-GRAY-shun), the movement of individuals out of a population, can cause a population to decrease in size. Wildlife biologists studying changes in populations of animals such as grizzly bears and wolves must consider immigration and emigration. For example, emigration can occur when young animals approaching maturity leave the area where they were born, find mates, and establish new territories. A shortage of food in one area may also lead to emigration. On the other hand, populations can increase by immigration as animals in search of mates or food arrive from outside.

▼ **Figure 5–2** This king penguin population has grown in size due to the recent births of chicks, recognizable by their downy brown feathers. 🔑 **Population size is affected by the number of births, the number of deaths, and the number of individuals that enter or leave the population.**

Exponential Growth

If a population has abundant space and food, and is protected from predators and disease, then organisms in that population will multiply and the population size will increase. Let's conduct an imaginary investigation to understand how growth under ideal conditions might occur. Suppose you put a single bacterium in a petri dish. Supply it with enough nutrients and incubate the culture with the right amount of heat, moisture, and light. How will the population change over time?

Bacteria reproduce by splitting in half. If the bacteria have a doubling time of 20 minutes, then within 20 minutes the first bacterium will divide to produce 2 bacteria. Twenty minutes later, the 2 bacteria will divide to produce 4. After another 20 minutes, there will be 8 bacteria. In another hour, there will be 64 bacteria, and in two more hours there will be 512. And in just one day, this colony of bacteria will grow to an astounding size of 4,720,000,000,000,000,000,000. What would happen if this growth pattern continued for several days without slowing down? Bacteria would cover the planet!

Figure 5–3 shows a graph with the size of the bacterial population plotted against time. As you can see, the pattern of growth is a J-shaped curve. The J-shaped curve indicates that the population is undergoing exponential (eks-poh-NEN-shul) growth. **Exponential growth** occurs when the individuals in a population reproduce at a constant rate. At first, the number of individuals in an exponentially growing population increases slowly. Over time, however, the population becomes larger and larger until it approaches an infinitely large size. 🔑 **Under ideal conditions with unlimited resources, a population will grow exponentially.**

With a doubling time of 20 minutes, some bacteria have the fastest rates of reproduction among living things. Populations of other species grow more slowly. For example, a female elephant can produce an infant only every 2 to 4 years, then the offspring take about 10 years to mature. But as you can see in **Figure 5–3,** in the unlikely event that all the offspring of a single pair of elephants survived and reproduced for 750 years, there would be more than 20 million elephants!

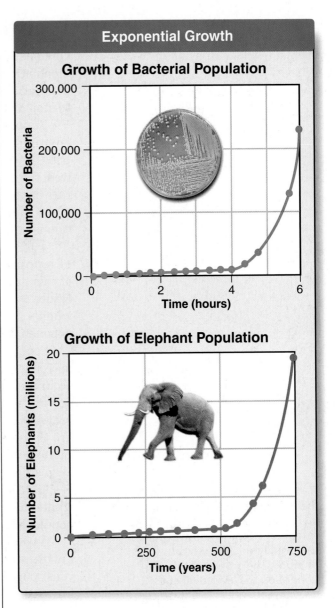

Exponential Growth

Growth of Bacterial Population

Growth of Elephant Population

▲ **Figure 5–3** 🔄 In the presence of unlimited resources, and in the absence of predation and disease, a population will grow exponentially. Both of these hypothetical graphs show the characteristic J-shape of exponential population growth. Of course, there are many reasons why populations—whether bacteria or elephants—do not usually grow exponentially for very long.

✓ **CHECKPOINT** *What is exponential growth?*

Logistic Growth

Obviously, neither bacteria nor elephants cover the planet. This means that exponential growth does not continue in natural populations for very long. What might cause population growth to stop or to slow down?

Suppose that a few animals are introduced into a new environment. At first, as the animals begin to reproduce, the population increases slowly. Then, because resources are unlimited, the population grows exponentially. In time, however, the rate of population growth begins to slow down. This does not mean that the size of the population has dropped. The population is still growing, but at a much slower rate.

As resources become less available, the growth of a population slows or stops. The general, S-shaped curve of this growth pattern, called logistic growth, is shown in **Figure 5–4** in a yeast population. **Logistic growth** occurs when a population's growth slows or stops following a period of exponential growth. How might this happen?

Population growth may slow down when the birthrate decreases, when the death rate increases, or when both events occur at the same rate. Similarly, population growth may slow down when the rate of immigration decreases, the rate of emigration increases, or both. When the birthrate and death rate are the same, or when the rate of immigration is equal to the rate of emigration, then population growth will slow down or even stop for a time. Note that even when the population growth is said to stop, the population is still rising and falling somewhat, but the ups and downs average out around a certain population size.

If you look again at **Figure 5–4,** you will see a horizontal line through the region of the graph where the growth of the yeast population has leveled off. The point at which that line intersects the y-axis tells you the size of the population when the average growth rate reaches zero. That number, in turn, represents the largest number of individuals—in this case, yeast cells—that a given environment can support. Ecologists call this number the **carrying capacity** of the environment for a particular species.

If you examine natural populations of familiar plant and animal species, you will find that many of them follow a logistic growth curve. In the natural world there are many factors that can slow the growth of a population. The factors that limit population growth are discussed in the next section.

▼ **Figure 5–4** This graph shows the S-shaped curve of logistic growth in a population of yeast cells. **As resources become less available, the population growth rate slows or stops.** The growth of this yeast population has leveled off at its carrying capacity.

Logistic Growth of Yeast Population

Carrying capacity

Number of Yeast Cells

Time (hours)

Population Trends

Do fruit flies and rabbits show similar trends in population growth?

1. **Tables and Graphs** Make a graph using the data in each data table. One graph will show the growth rate of a fruit fly population. The other graph will show the growth rate of a population of rabbits.

2. **Analyzing Data** What type of growth pattern is exhibited by the fruit fly population? Is it the same type of growth as in the rabbit population? Explain.

3. **Drawing Conclusions** Does either graph indicate that there is a carrying capacity for the population? If so, when does the population reach its carrying capacity? What is the maximum number of individuals that can be supported at that time?

4. **Predicting** Animals such as foxes and cats often prey on rabbits. Based on the growth curve of the rabbit population, what might have happened if a group of predators moved into the rabbits' habitat during the tenth generation and began eating the rabbits?

Fruit Fly Population Growth	
Days	**Number of Fruit Flies**
5	10
10	50
15	100
20	200
25	300
30	310
35	320
40	320

Rabbit Population Growth	
Generations	**Number of Rabbits**
1	100
2	105
25	1000
37	1600
55	2400
72	3350
86	8000
100	13,150

5–1 Section Assessment

1. **Key Concept** List three characteristics that are used to describe a population.

2. **Key Concept** What factors can change a population's size?

3. **Key Concept** What is the difference between exponential growth and logistic growth?

4. What is meant by population density?

5. Define carrying capacity.

6. **Critical Thinking Inferring** What factors might cause the carrying capacity of a population to change?

iTEXT Assessment Use iText to review the important concepts in Section 5–1.

5–2 Limits to Growth

Guide for Reading

🔑 Key Concept
• What factors limit population growth?

Vocabulary
limiting factor
density-dependent limiting
    factor
predator-prey relationship
density-independent limiting
    factor

Reading Strategy:
Predicting Before you read, preview the diagram below. Predict how each factor might limit the growth of a population. As you read, note whether your predictions were correct.

Now that you know a few things about population growth, think again about the sea otter example in the beginning of the previous section. When a sea otter population declines, something has changed the relationship between the birthrate and the death rate, or between the rates of immigration and emigration. For instance, in part of the sea otter's range, the death rate of sea otters is increasing because killer whales are eating the otters. Predation by killer whales creates a situation that reduces the growth of the sea otter population.

Limiting Factors

Recall from Chapter 3 that the primary productivity of an ecosystem can be reduced when there is an insufficient supply of a particular nutrient. Ecologists call such substances limiting nutrients. A limiting nutrient is an example of a more general ecological concept: a limiting factor. In the context of populations, a **limiting factor** is a factor that causes population growth to decrease.

Some of the limiting factors that can affect a population are shown in **Figure 5–5.** Those limiting factors that affect a population more strongly as the population grows larger are shown with purple arrows. Factors that limit a population's growth regardless of the population's size are shown with green arrows.

▼ **Figure 5–5** Many different factors can limit population growth. **Inferring** *How might each of these factors increase the death rate in a population?*

Competition

Predation

Parasitism
and disease

Drought and other
climate extremes

Human
disturbances

Population
Size

Density-Dependent Factors

A limiting factor that depends on population size is called a **density-dependent limiting factor.** Density-dependent factors become limiting only when the population density—the number of organisms per unit area—reaches a certain level. These factors operate most strongly when a population is large and dense. They do not affect small, scattered populations as greatly. **Density-dependent limiting factors include competition, predation, parasitism, and disease.** An example of competition can be seen in **Figure 5–6.**

Competition When populations become crowded, organisms compete, or struggle, with one another for food, water, space, sunlight, and other essentials of life. It is easy to see why competition among members of the same species is a density-dependent limiting factor. The more individuals that live in an area, the sooner they will use up the available resources. Likewise, the fewer the number of individuals, the more resources that are available to them, and the less they must compete with one another.

Competition can also occur between members of different species. This type of competition is a major force behind evolutionary change. When two species compete for the same resources, both species are under pressure to change in ways that decrease their competition. Over time, the species may evolve to occupy separate niches. That is because, as you may recall, no two species can occupy the same niche in the same place at the same time.

✓ **CHECKPOINT** *What is a density-dependent limiting factor?*

◀ **Figure 5–6** The Atlantic puffin lives in large colonies along the coast of eastern North America from Maine north into the Arctic. Puffins nest in burrows dug into the sides of cliffs. Because nesting sites are limited, puffins must compete for space. **Competition is a density-dependent limiting factor. Other density-dependent factors are predation, parasitism, and disease.**

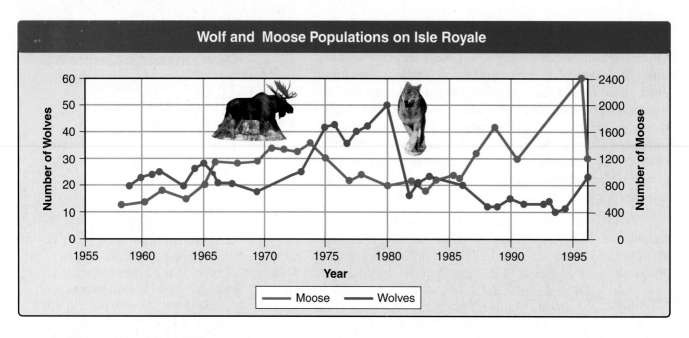

Wolf and Moose Populations on Isle Royale

Number of Wolves (left axis: 0, 10, 20, 30, 40, 50, 60)
Number of Moose (right axis: 0, 400, 800, 1200, 1600, 2000, 2400)
Year (1955, 1960, 1965, 1970, 1975, 1980, 1985, 1990, 1995)

— Moose — Wolves

▲ **Figure 5–7** The relationship between moose and wolves on Isle Royale illustrates how predation can affect population growth. Other factors can come into play. In this example, the moose population was affected by changes in food supply, and the wolf population was affected by disease. **Interpreting Graphics** *How are the increases and decreases in the moose population related to the changes in the wolf population?*

Predation Populations in nature are often controlled by predation. The regulation of a population by predation takes place within a **predator-prey relationship,** one of the best-known mechanisms of population control. The relationships between sea otters and sea urchins and between sea otters and killer whales are examples of predator-prey interactions that affect population growth.

A well-documented example of a predator-prey relationship is the interaction between wolves and moose on Isle Royale, an island in Lake Superior. The graph in **Figure 5–7** shows how periodic increases in the moose population—the prey—on Isle Royale are quickly followed by increases in the wolf population—the predators. As the wolves prey on the moose, the moose population falls. The decline in the moose population is followed, sooner or later, by a decline in the wolf population because there is less for the wolves to feed upon. A decline in the wolf population means that the moose have fewer enemies, so the moose population rises again. This cycle of predator and prey populations can be repeated indefinitely.

Parasitism and Disease Parasites can also limit the growth of a population. Parasitic organisms range in size from microscopic, disease-causing bacteria to tapeworms 30 centimeters or more in length. These organisms are similar to predators in many ways. Like predators, parasites take nourishment at the expense of their hosts, often weakening them and causing disease or death. The wasp cocoons in **Figure 5–8,** for example, can weaken or kill many caterpillars.

◄ **Figure 5–8** This larval sphinx moth has been attacked by a parasitic wasp. The wasp inserted its eggs beneath the moth's skin. After hatching, the wasp larvae fed on their host internally until they appeared as white cocoons on its back. **Predicting** *How might the wasp larvae affect the sphinx moth population?*

Density-Independent Factors

Density-independent limiting factors affect all populations in similar ways, regardless of the population size. Unusual weather, natural disasters, seasonal cycles, and certain human activities—such as damming rivers and clear-cutting forests—are all examples of density-independent limiting factors. In response to such factors, many species show a characteristic crash in population size. After the crash, the population may build right up again or it may stay low for some time.

For some species, storms or hurricanes can nearly extinguish a population. For example, thrips, aphids, and other insects that feed on plant buds and leaves might be washed out by a heavy rainstorm. Extremes of cold or hot weather also can take their toll on a population, regardless of the population's density. A severe winter frost, for example, can kill giant saguaro cacti in the Arizona desert. In some areas, periodic droughts can affect entire populations of grasses. Such events can, in turn, affect the populations of consumers within the food web.

Environments are always changing, and most populations can adapt to a certain amount of change. Populations often grow and shrink in response to such changes. Major upsets in an ecosystem, however, can lead to long-term declines in certain populations. Human activities have caused some of these major upsets, as you will soon read.

▶ **Figure 5–9** A drought can result in the abrupt decrease of a population, regardless of its size. **Droughts and other natural disasters are density-independent limiting factors. So are many human activities, such as clear-cutting forests.**

5–2 Section Assessment

1. **Key Concept** List three density-dependent factors and three density-independent factors that can limit the growth of a population.

2. What is the relationship between competition and population size?

3. If an entire lynx population disappears, what is likely to happen to the hare population on which it preys?

4. **Critical Thinking Applying Concepts** Give an example of a density-independent limiting factor that has affected a human population. Describe how this factor changed the human population.

iTEXT **Assessment** Use iText to review the important concepts in Section 5–2.

MAKING CONNECTIONS

Biotic and Abiotic Factors Study the factors that limit population growth in **Figure 5–5.** Classify each factor as either biotic or abiotic. (*Hint:* Refer to the information on biotic and abiotic factors in Section 4–2.)

Does the Gray Wolf Population Need Protection?

Feds Reconsider Status of Gray Wolf The federal government is preparing to announce that the gray wolf, which was once nearly extinct in the United States, is abundant enough in some states that it no longer needs the strict protection required under the Endangered Species Act. The change would mean that wolves that pose a threat to human affairs could be chased away or legally shot by government agents.

Wolves were once widely distributed around the world, occupying almost every habitat except tropical jungles. Today, however, wolves occupy only a fraction of their former range. In 1973, the Endangered Species Act was passed by the United States Congress to protect declining populations of gray wolves from becoming extinct. At the time, there were only about 400 wolves in the lower 48 states. By 1999, the population had swelled to an estimated 3500 individuals scattered mostly throughout the Rocky Mountains and Great Lakes areas.

Classifying the status of animals is a judgment call. In some cases, the judgment is easy. For instance, the California condor population now includes only a few remaining members and is clearly in great danger. With other species, such as the gray wolf, the situation is much more complex. How should the gray wolf be classified—and therefore managed—in the United States?

The Viewpoints

Keep the Endangered Classification

People who want to keep the gray wolf's status as an endangered species say that most of its former habitat in the 48 contiguous states is unsuitable due to human encroachment. Proponents of this view cite the fact that only after wolves were given protection under the Endangered Species Act did the wolf population in the United States begin to increase. There is concern that human persecution and loss of habitat will restrict gray wolves to more remote areas, or reduce their habitat even further, unless federal protection continues.

Reclassify the Wolf and Remove Federal Protection

Opponents of the endangered species classification counter that in states like Minnesota, the gray wolf population is growing at a rate of 4 to 5 percent each year. These people are confident that, because the populations are increasing at a healthy rate, the wolves no longer need federal protection. Ranchers are concerned that, at the current growth rate, wolves will encroach on their livestock. Many feel strongly that landowners should have the right to protect themselves from potential losses. The protection of wolves currently costs the United States government over $200,000 per year. If the wolves could be legally hunted and trapped, the money that would be saved could be used to help protect other, more endangered species.

You Decide

1. **Defining the Issue** In your own words, explain the issues surrounding the classification and management of the gray wolf in the United States.
2. **Analyzing the Viewpoints** List the pros and cons of each option as they relate to both humans and wolves. Consider the different perspectives of landowners, conservationists, and other stakeholders.
3. **Forming Your Opinion** Should the federal status of the gray wolf change? Why or why not?

5–3 Human Population Growth

How quickly is the world's human population growing? In the United States and other developed countries, the current growth rate is very low. In some developing countries, the human population is growing at a rate of nearly 3 people per second. Because of this bustling growth rate, the human population is well on its way to reaching 9 billion within your lifetime.

Historical Overview

 Like the populations of many other living organisms, the size of the human population tends to increase with time. For most of human existence, the population grew slowly. Life was harsh, and limiting factors kept population sizes low. Food was scarce. Incurable diseases were rampant. Until fairly recently, only half the children in the world survived to adulthood. Because death rates were so high, families had many children, just to make sure that some would survive.

About 500 years ago, the human population began growing more rapidly. Agriculture and industry made life easier and safer. The world's food supply became more reliable, and essential goods could be shipped around the globe. Improved sanitation, medicine, and health care dramatically reduced the death rate and increased longevity. At the same time, birthrates in most places remained high. With these advances, the human population experienced exponential growth, as shown in **Figure 5–10.**

Guide for Reading

Key Concepts
- How has the size of the human population changed over time?
- Why do population growth rates differ in countries throughout the world?

Vocabulary
demography
demographic transition
age-structure diagram

Reading Strategy: Asking Questions Before you read, preview the graphs in **Figures 5–10**, **5–12**, and **5–13.** Make a list of questions about the graphs. As you read, write down the answers to your questions.

▼ **Figure 5–10** The size of the human population has increased over time. After a long, slow start, the worldwide population grew exponentially following improvements in medicine, sanitation, agriculture, energy use, and technology.

Figure 5–11 Medical advances can lead to a dramatic drop in a population's death rate. Dr. Leila Denmark (left), the oldest known practicing physician in the United States, helped invent the whooping cough vaccine in 1936. A health-care worker in Rwanda (right) vaccinates an infant. **Applying Concepts** *What other advancements can reduce a population's death rate?*

Patterns of Population Growth

The human population cannot keep growing exponentially forever, because Earth and its resources are limited. The question is, when and how will our population growth slow? Two centuries ago, English economist Thomas Malthus observed that human populations were growing rapidly. Malthus predicted that such growth would not continue indefinitely. Instead, according to Malthus, war, famine, and disease would limit human population growth.

Today, scientists have identified a variety of other social and economic factors that can affect human populations. The scientific study of human populations is called **demography** (duh-MAH-gruh-fee). Demography examines the characteristics of human populations and attempts to explain how those populations will change over time. ⬤ **Birthrates, death rates, and the age structure of a population help predict why some countries have high growth rates while other countries grow more slowly.**

The Demographic Transition Over the past century, population growth in the United States, Japan, and much of Europe has slowed dramatically. Demographers have developed a hypothesis to explain this shift. According to this hypothesis, these countries have completed the **demographic transition,** a dramatic change in birth and death rates.

Throughout most of history, human societies have had high death rates and equally high birthrates. As countries modernize, however, advances in nutrition, sanitation, and medicine result in more children surviving to adulthood and more adults living to old age. These changes lower the death rate and begin the demographic transition.

As you can see in **Figure 5–12,** when the death rate first begins to fall, birthrates remain high. During this phase of the demographic transition, births greatly exceed deaths, and population increases rapidly. This was the situation in the United States from 1790 to about 1910. Many parts of South America, Africa, and Asia are still in this phase.

As societies continue to modernize, however, families have fewer children. As the birthrate falls, population growth slows. The demographic transition is complete when the birthrate falls to meet the death rate, and population growth stops.

The Demographic Transition

Birth/death rates

A

C

B

Time (years)

—— Birthrate —— Death rate

▲ **Figure 5–12** ⬤ **Birthrates, death rates, and the age structure of a population help predict why some countries have high growth rates while other countries grow more slowly.** Birthrates and death rates fall during the demographic transition. Initially, both rates are high (A). Then, the death rate drops while the birthrate remains high (B). Finally, the birth rate also decreases (C).

So far, the demographic transition has happened in only a few countries. Despite the trend in the United States, Europe, and Japan, the worldwide human population is still growing exponentially. Most people live in countries that have not yet completed the demographic transition. Much of the population growth today is contributed by only 10 countries, with India and China in the lead, where birthrates remain high.

Age Structure Population growth depends, in part, on how many people of different ages make up a given population. Demographers can predict future growth using models called **age-structure diagrams,** or population profiles, which graph the numbers of people in different age groups in the population.

Consider **Figure 5–13,** which compares the age structure of the United States population with that of Rwanda. In the United States, there are nearly equal numbers of people in each age group. This age structure predicts a slow but steady growth rate for the near future. In Rwanda, on the other hand, there are many more young children than teenagers, and many more teenagers than adults. This age structure predicts a population that will double in about 30 years.

✔CHECKPOINT   *What are age-structure diagrams?*

▼ **Figure 5–13** These graphs compare the age structure of the U.S. population with the population of Rwanda. Each bar in the age-structure diagram represents individuals within a 5-year group. Males are to the left of the center line, and females are to the right.
Analyzing Data *How do the United States and Rwanda differ in the percentages of 10- to 14-year-olds in the population?*

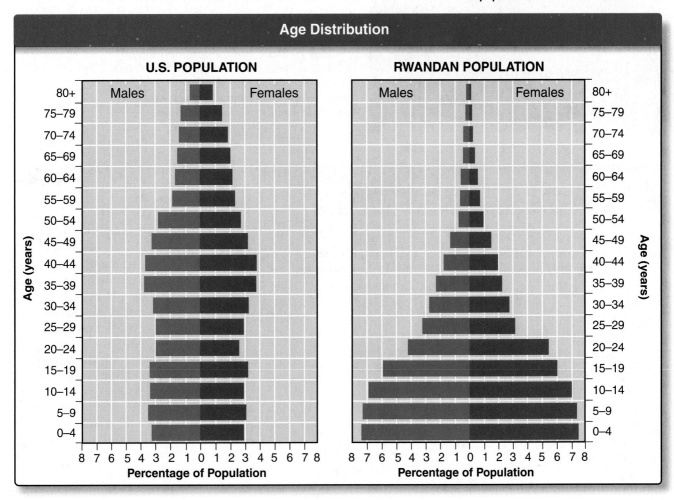

Age Distribution

U.S. POPULATION — Males / Females

RWANDAN POPULATION — Males / Females

Age (years): 80+, 75–79, 70–74, 65–69, 60–64, 55–59, 50–54, 45–49, 40–44, 35–39, 30–34, 25–29, 20–24, 15–19, 10–14, 5–9, 0–4

Percentage of Population

Future Population Growth

To predict how the worldwide human population will grow in the near future, demographers must take into account the age structures of every country. Current projections suggest that by the year 2025, the world's population will reach 7.8 billion. By 2050, the population may reach more than 9 billion people. There is evidence, however, that the growth rate may level off, or even slow down, by that time. This may happen if countries that are currently growing rapidly move toward the demographic transition. One such country, India, is shown in **Figure 5–14**.

Will human population growth continue at its current rate, or will it level out to a logistic growth curve and become stable? Many ecologists suggest that if the growth of the human population does not slow down, there could be serious and lasting damage to the environment as well as to the global economy. On the other hand, many economists assert that science, technology, and positive changes in society will help to control those negative impacts.

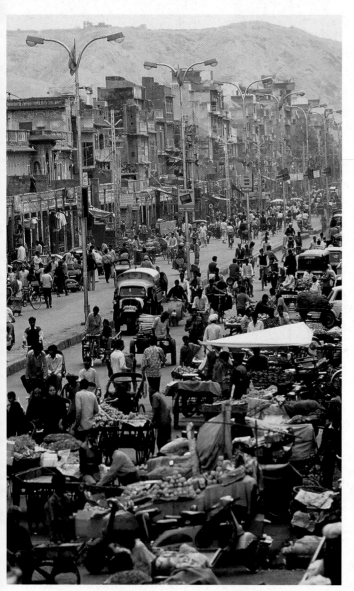

◄ **Figure 5–14** This photograph shows a bustling street in a city in India, which has one of the world's fastest growing populations. **Inferring** *What would you expect an age-structure diagram for India to look like?*

5–3 Section Assessment

1. **Key Concept** Describe the general trend of human population growth that has occurred over time.

2. **Key Concept** What factors explain why populations in different countries grow at different rates?

3. What is demography?

4. Describe the demographic transition and explain how it might affect a country's population growth rate.

5. **Critical Thinking Evaluating** Why do you think age-structure diagrams can help predict future population trends?

iTEXT Assessment Use iText to review the important concepts in Section 5–3.

Take It to the NET

Read about world population growth. Then, create a bar graph comparing the world's population in 2000 and projections for 2025 and 2050. Use the links provided in the Biology area at the Prentice Hall Web site for help in completing this activity:
www.phschool.com

Investigating the Growth of a Population of Bacteria

Bacteria are convenient for laboratory studies of populations because they are small in size and reproduce rapidly. In this investigation, you will examine the growth of a bacterial culture.

Problem What happens to a population that depends on limited resources?

Materials

- 2 lima beans
- 2 dropper pipettes
- 100-mL beaker
- coverslips
- microscope slides
- 10-mL graduated cylinder
- 100-mL graduated cylinder
- methylene blue stain
- microscope
- test-tube rack
- 4 test tubes
- aluminum foil

Skills Calculating, Using Tables and Graphs

Procedure

1. Before you begin, review the rules for sterile procedure with your teacher.

2. Wash your hands. Put on your plastic gloves. Then, to start a bacterial culture, put 2 lima beans into a 100-mL beaker. Add 50 mL of water. Allow this mixture to sit for 48 hours.

3. Construct a data table with four columns and five blank rows. At the top of the table, label the columns "Day," "Bacteria Observed," "Dilution Factor," and "Bacteria Present."

4. After 48 hours, use a dropper pipette to place a drop of the culture on a microscope slide. Add a coverslip. Place a drop of methylene blue stain on the slide next to the coverslip. Lightly touch a paper towel on the opposite side of the coverslip to draw the stain under the coverslip.

5. Use the high-power objective of a microscope to locate some bacteria. If you can count the bacteria in your field of view, go to step 7. If there are too many bacteria to count, go to step 6.

6. Use a dropper pipette to put 1 mL of the culture into a 10-mL graduated cylinder. Add 9 mL of water to the graduated cylinder. Empty the graduated cylinder into a test tube. This procedure dilutes the culture by a factor of 10. Examine the diluted sample under the microscope as in step 5. If there are still too many bacteria to count, dilute the sample again in the same way. Stop diluting when you can count the bacteria. Each time you dilute, multiply the dilution by 10.

7. Record the number of bacteria and the dilution factor in your data table. If you did not dilute, the dilution factor is 1. To determine the number of bacteria present, multiply the number of bacteria you observed by the dilution factor.

8. Cover the beaker with aluminum foil and set it aside overnight. Wash your hands when you are finished.

9. **Predicting** Record a prediction of how the population of bacteria will change.

10. Repeat steps 5 through 8 every day for 5 days.

Analyze and Conclude

1. **Using Tables and Graphs** Make a graph of the data from your data table. When did the population grow most quickly? Most slowly?

2. **Drawing Conclusions** How can you explain the changes in population growth?

3. **Inferring** What caused the changes in the population growth rate?

Go Further

Designing Experiments Design an experiment to investigate how a change in the food supply affects the growth of a bacterial population. With your teacher's approval, carry out your experiment.

Chapter 5 Study Guide

5–1 How Populations Grow
 Key Concepts

- Three important characteristics of a population are its geographic distribution, density, and growth rate.

- Three factors affect population size: the number of births, the number of deaths, and the number of individuals that enter or leave the population.

- Under ideal conditions and unlimited resources, a population will continue to grow in a pattern called exponential growth. As resources are used up and population growth slows or stops, the population exhibits logistic growth.

Vocabulary

population density, p. 119
immigration, p. 120
emigration, p. 120
exponential growth, p. 121
logistic growth, p. 122
carrying capacity, p. 122

5–2 Limits to Growth
Key Concepts

- Density-dependent limiting factors include competition, predation, parasitism, and disease.

- Unusual weather, natural disasters, seasonal cycles, and certain human activities—such as damming rivers and clear-cutting forests—are all examples of density-independent limiting factors.

Vocabulary

limiting factor, p. 124
density-dependent limiting factor, p. 125
predator-prey relationship, p. 126
density-independent limiting factor, p. 127

5–3 Human Population Growth
Key Concepts

- Like the populations of many other living organisms, the size of the human population tends to increase with time.

- The characteristics of populations, and the social and economic factors that affect them, explain why some countries have high population growth rates while populations of other countries grow slowly or not at all.

Vocabulary

demography, p. 130
demographic transition, p. 130
age-structure diagram, p. 131

Thinking Visually
Using information from this chapter, complete the following concept map:

Chapter 5

Part A

Multiple Choice

For each statement or question, select the number of the word or expression that, of those given, best completes the statement or answers the question.

1 The movement of individuals into an area occupied by an existing population is called
(1) demography   (3) carrying capacity
(2) immigration   (4) emigration

2 The area occupied by a population is its
(1) growth rate
(2) geographic distribution
(3) age structure
(4) population density

3 What portion of the graph below is most similar to a graph representing human population growth during this century?
(1) A   (3) C
(2) B   (4) E

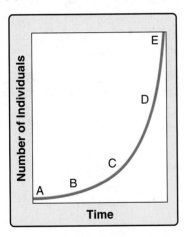

4 The maximum number of organisms of a particular species that can be supported by an environment is called
(1) growth rate
(2) carrying capacity
(3) food chain
(4) ecological succession

5 If a population grows larger than the carrying capacity of its environment, the
(1) death rate may rise
(2) birthrate may rise
(3) death rate may fall
(4) immigration rate may increase

6 A limiting factor that depends on abiotic components of the ecosystem is
(1) predation   (3) hurricanes
(2) competition   (4) parasitism

7 The limiting factor that depends most on population size is
(1) amount of competition
(2) soil and rock type
(3) amount of precipitation
(4) air temperature

8 The scientific study of human populations is called
(1) immigration
(2) emigration
(3) geography
(4) demography

9 The demographic transition is complete when
(1) population growth stops
(2) the birthrate is greater than the death rate
(3) the death rate begins to fall
(4) the death rate is greater than the birthrate

10 The number of individuals of a single species per unit area is known as
(1) carrying capacity
(2) logistic growth
(3) population density
(4) population growth rate

11 Density-independent limiting factors include
(1) predation
(2) drought
(3) competition
(4) parasitism

12 What is the major environmental factor limiting the number of autotrophs at great depths in the ocean?
(1) type of seafloor
(2) amount of light
(3) availibility of minerals
(4) absence of biotic factors

Test-Taking Tip To answer questions that have different combinations of Roman numerals as answer choices, you must evaluate each Roman numeral separately in relation to the question. Then, look to see which answer choice corresponds to the numerals you have selected.

Parts B and C

Multiple Choice and Extended Response

For those questions that ask you to select a response, choose the one that best completes the statement or answers the question. For all others follow the directions given.

13 Distinguish between immigration and emigration.

14 Sketch the growth curve of the human population over the last 2000 years.

15 Is the carrying capacity of a field the same for both grasshoppers and foxes? Explain your answer.

Base your answers to questions 16 through 19 on the information below and on your knowledge of biology.

A student designed an experiment to determine if the type of food present in a yeast culture influenced the growth rate of the population. He set up one culture with table sugar and the other with an equal mass of molasses. The student examined the cultures through a microscope each day for four days. The illustrations below show the number of yeast cells observed each day.

Observed Yeast Cells

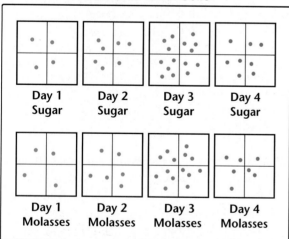

16 Describe the growth trend illustrated by both cultures.

17 Describe two factors that could cause the change observed in the molasses culture between Day 3 and Day 4.

18 How will the populations change between Day 4 and Day 5? Support your answer.

19 Did the type of food available to the yeast make a significant difference in population growth? Use data from the experiment to support your answer.

Base your answers to questions 20 and 21 on the information below and on your knowledge of biology.

A farm field is used year after year to grow the same crop. Slowly, the amount of potassium in the soil decreases. All the other nutrients the crop requires are present in adequate levels.

20 How would the decrease in potassium eventually affect the ability of the crop to grow?

21 How is potassium in this field an example of a limiting factor?

22 Explain how the introduction of a limiting nutrient such as phosphorus into a pond ecosystem would affect the carrying capacity of the pond.

23 Study the age-structure diagram for Sweden that is shown below. Then, predict how Sweden's rate of population growth is likely to change over the next 50 years. Use data from the age-structure diagram to support your answer.

Base your answers to questions 24 and 25 on the graph below and on your knowledge of biology.

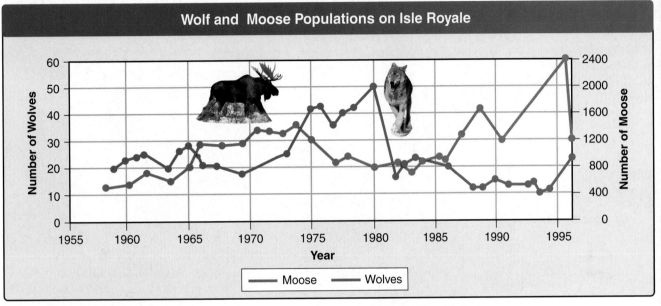

Wolf and Moose Populations on Isle Royale

(Graph showing Number of Wolves on left axis (0–60) and Number of Moose on right axis (0–2400) versus Year (1955–1995), with separate lines for Moose and Wolves.)

24 The relationship between wolf and moose populations can best be described as
(1) parasite-host
(2) scavenger-decomposer
(3) predator-prey
(4) producer-consumer

25 How might an increase in the rabbit population on Isle Royale affect the size of the moose population? Support your answer.

26 Describe the long-term effects of competition on populations of two different species competing for the same resources.

27 Describe how a predator-prey relationship can be a mechanism of population control.

28 How do parasites serve as a limiting factor?

29 Explain how factors such as atmospheric changes and soil erosion act as limiting factors on the growth of populations.

30 How does the age structure of a population affect its growth rate?

31 Why might a contagious virus that causes a fatal disease be considered a density-dependent limiting factor?

32 What will happen to a population of predators if there is a sudden increase in food for the prey? Support your answer with an explanation.

33 What questions would a demographer need to answer in order to determine whether a country is approaching the demographic transition?

34 Nitrogen is a limiting factor in aquatic ecosystems. Suppose that runoff from a field washes nitrogen-rich fertilizer into a pond containing a population of algae. Predict how the fertilizer will affect the carrying capacity of the pond for algae. (*Hint:* Refer to the information on limiting nutrients in Section 3–3.)

Take It to the NET

How is population growth similar to the growth of your savings account? Visit the Prentice Hall Web site at **www.phschool.com** to learn more about how populations grow. Then answer the following questions:

• How does population growth compare to the way money grows when interest is left to compound over time?

• What is the most crucial difference between compound interest and population growth?

• Why is it easier to interpret population data in graphs than data presented in table format?

Chapter 6

Humans in the Biosphere

This hang glider soars above the coast of Oahu, one of the Hawaiian Islands. Over the past 1500 years, human activities have changed the islands' ecosystems.

Inquiry Activity

What happens to household trash?

Procedure

1. Examine the contents of a bag containing roughly the amount of dry trash produced per person each day in the United States.

2. Sort the trash into items that can be reused, items that can be recycled, items that can be composted, and items that must be discarded because they cannot be recycled or composted.

Think About It

1. **Analyzing Data** Which materials make up most of the trash? Does this reflect the amount and types of trash you produce?

2. **Predicting** What do you think happens to the trash you produce? What effect does trash have on the environment?

3. **Evaluating** List three ways you can reduce the amount of trash you produce.

6–1 A Changing Landscape

About 1600 years ago, human settlers from Polynesia began arriving on the island chain called Hawaii. As an island people, they were accustomed to living in limited space. Their farming and fishing practices were guided by centuries of accumulated wisdom. To cut down a coconut palm, a person had to plant two palm trees to take its place. Laws prohibited fishing for certain species during spawning season.

Even though their customs taught respect for the land, these early settlers changed the ecology of the Hawaiian Islands. From the forested mountaintops to the ocean's fringing reefs, a wide range of ecosystems and many unique species were used for basic needs such as food, medicine, wood, and fiber. Pigs and other nonnative species that the Polynesians brought to Hawaii altered many native communities. By the time Captain Cook came ashore in 1778, about 60 species of native birds were already extinct. The arrival of Europeans changed the islands even more, introducing ranching, predators, and disease.

The Hawaii of today is very different from what it was long ago. Vast tracts of land have been cleared to grow pineapples and sugar cane. Large areas have been paved for housing, schools, and industry. Ground water has been tapped for irrigation, depleting water resources in many places. In addition to the reduction—by two thirds—of native bird species, like the one in **Figure 6–1,** an enormous number of land snails, plants, insects, and hundreds of other native Hawaiian species are gone. Imported plants and animals have crowded out many of the remaining native species.

Earth as an Island

The history of humans in Hawaii offers an important lesson for the twenty-first century. In a sense, Earth, too, is an island. All of the organisms—including humans—that live on Earth share a limited resource base. We all depend on the natural ecological processes that sustain these resources. The human population is still growing, but the planet we live on is not. Along with this growing population come increasing demands on Earth's air, water, land, and living things.

Understanding how humans interact with the biosphere is crucial to protecting these resources. It requires you to remember all that you have learned about energy flow, chemical cycling, climate, and population-limiting factors. You must also understand how scientific models can be used to make predictions about complex systems. It is also important to realize why studies of islands like Hawaii are important to people who don't live on an island—or don't think they do.

Guide for Reading

 Key Concept
- What types of human activities can affect the biosphere?

Vocabulary
subsistence hunting
agriculture
green revolution
monoculture

**Reading Strategy:
Finding Main Ideas**
As you read, make a list of facts that support the statement "The spreading influence of humans can and does affect the biosphere."

▼ **Figure 6–1** The iiwi, or Hawaiian honeycreeper, is one of the most beautiful birds in Hawaii. Like many native species in Hawaii, the iiwi is becoming scarce. Disease, habitat loss, and predation by introduced animals have taken their toll on the species. **Drawing Conclusions** *Based on the photograph, what can you conclude about the iiwi's niche?*

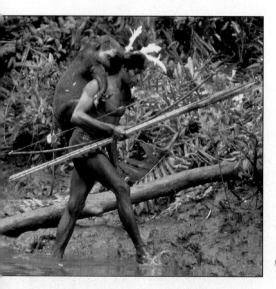

▲ Figure 6–2 People of the Paleolithic, or Stone Age, relied on hunting and gathering for their existence. This cave painting from Northern Spain shows ancient hunters slaying a herd of deer with bows and arrows. ⬤ Hunting and gathering are among the many human activities that have changed the biosphere.

▼ Figure 6–3 Like his Stone Age predecessors, this modern subsistence hunter from the Asmat tribe in New Guinea uses bows and spears. Other subsistence hunters may use modern tools like guns or motorized vehicles. **Predicting** *What effects might subsistence hunters have on the environment in which they live?*

Human Activities

Industry and technology give humans a strong advantage in competing with other species for limited resources such as food, energy, and space. According to a recent study, human activity uses as much energy as all of Earth's other multicellular species combined. Today, humans are the most important source of environmental change on the planet.

Because humans take part in local and global food webs and chemical cycles within the biosphere, human activities can change the flow of energy in an ecosystem and reduce the ability of ecosystems to recycle nutrients. ⬤ **Among the human activities that have transformed the biosphere are hunting and gathering, agriculture, industry, and urban development.**

Hunting and Gathering

For most of human history, hunting and gathering was the primary means of survival. Early humans hunted birds and other animals and fished in rivers and oceans. They gathered wild seeds, fruits, and nuts. Some peoples were nomadic, traveling great distances to take advantage of movements and cycles of natural plant and animal populations.

Hunters and gatherers lived in small groups. Yet, even prehistoric hunter-gatherers, like the ones who created the cave painting in **Figure 6–2**, changed the environment. They built dams to divert water and burned grasslands to encourage the growth of certain plants. Some scientists hypothesize that when human hunters arrived in North America about 12,000 years ago, they caused one of the major mass extinctions of large animals— including woolly mammoths, giant ground sloths, and sabertooth cats. Even species you wouldn't think of as living in North America—cheetahs, zebras, and yaks, for example—disappeared within one or two thousand years of human arrival there.

Today, groups of people in scattered parts of the world, from the Arctic to Central Africa, still follow the hunter-gatherer way of life to some degree. These groups supplement their diet with the meat of wild animals through **subsistence hunting.** Modern subsistence hunters, like the one in **Figure 6–3,** make relatively few demands on the environment. However, nearly all modern subsistence hunters use some form of technology, such as guns, snowmobiles, or manufactured tools.

✓**CHECKPOINT** *What is subsistence hunting?*

Agriculture

During thousands of years of foraging, early hunter-gatherers learned how plants grew and ripened and discovered which ones were useful for food and medicines. They then began planting seeds near human settlements. By the end of the last ice age—about 11,000 years ago—humans began the practice of farming, or **agriculture.** Soon, villagers in different regions of the world were growing wheat, rice, and millet in nearby fields. From these regions, agriculture spread in many directions as people planted other varieties of seeds.

The spread of agriculture was an important event in human history because it provided people with one of their most basic needs—a dependable supply of food. With a stable and predictable food source, humans began to gather in larger settlements, such as towns and cities, and to develop elements of civilization such as government, laws, and writing.

Domestication of Animals Over the next few thousand years, as crops improved and farming methods became more reliable, farmers began to keep herds of domesticated animals, including sheep, goats, cows, pigs, horses, and dogs. These animals supplied humans with milk, meat, hides, wool, companionship, and the energy to do work. With the cultivation of both plants and animals, however, came many ecological changes. Overgrazing by goats, cows, and other herbivores changed grassland ecosystems to scrub, eroded soils, and put large demands on water supplies.

From Traditional to Modern Agriculture Historical farming practices continued successfully for thousands of years. Between 1450 and 1700, world exploration and discovery led to an exchange of foods that greatly influenced farming and nutrition around the globe. In the 1800s, advancements in science and technology set the stage for a remarkable change in agriculture. Large-scale watering, or irrigation; new crop varieties; and the invention of farm machines—like the seed drill shown in **Figure 6–4**—for plowing, planting, and harvesting helped farmers to increase their yields tremendously.

Word Origins

Agriculture is a combination of the Latin words *ager,* meaning "a field," and *cultura,* meaning "care." *Agriculture* is the science and art of farming, which includes the cultivation of field soils, production of crops, and the raising of livestock. **If the prefix *agro-* has the same meaning as *agri-*, what do you think the definition of the noun *agrochemical* is?**

▼ **Figure 6–4** By the 1700s, most Europeans relied on simple tools and animal-drawn plows and vehicles to work the land. This illustration shows a farmer guiding a four-wheeled seed drill as his horse pulls it across a field. The seed drill was invented to help farmers plant seeds in straight lines. **Applying Concepts** *How were such inventions linked to human population growth?*

The Green Revolution By the 1950s, the fast-growing human population was overstraining the world's food supply. In a global effort to increase food production, governments and scientists introduced new, intensive farming practices that greatly increased yields of rice, wheat, and other crops. This effort is now known as the **green revolution.**

The green revolution depended on several strategies to increase crop yields. The central strategy was the development of new, highly productive varieties of major food crops. Crop breeders developed new plant varieties called "miracle strains" that improved harvests. Another strategy was to use a method called **monoculture.** This method called for large fields to be cleared, plowed, and planted with a single crop year after year. To support these fields, farmers relied on irrigation to provide needed water, chemical fertilizers to boost plant growth, and pesticides to control unwanted species. Farmers also replaced human and animal power with heavy equipment and machinery, as shown in **Figure 6–5.**

The benefits of the green revolution to human society were enormous. The new farming practices increased food production in many places and helped to prevent food shortages worldwide. For the first time in years, densely populated countries such as China and India were able to feed their populations. Within 20 years, Mexican farmers increased the production of wheat tenfold. Because of the green revolution, global food production has more than doubled in the past 50 years.

In many places, green revolution techniques continue to be successful. However, the constant use of these techniques has also caused problems. Intensive farming can deplete energy and water supplies. Monoculture allows many pest species, such as the cabbage white butterfly, to reproduce on a vast scale. In turn, farmers spray their crops with pesticides that carry potentially harmful chemicals. The application of fertilizers can interfere with food webs and biogeochemical cycles. Clearly, other techniques are needed to supply the world with food while protecting the biosphere from further harm.

CHECKPOINT *What was the green revolution?*

▼ **Figure 6–5** Modern agriculture relies on heavy equipment and mechanized systems of irrigation. This farmer is using a tractor to cultivate a field of soybeans. **Comparing and Contrasting** *In what ways do modern farming methods affect the biosphere more than historical practices did?*

Industrial Growth and Urban Development

Human society and its impact on the biosphere were transformed by the Industrial Revolution, which added machines and factories to civilization during the 1800s. That revolution led to the combination of industrial productivity and scientific know-how that provides us with most of the conveniences of modern life, from the homes we live in and the clothes we wear to the electronic devices we use in work and play. Mass-produced farm machinery makes efficient, large-scale agriculture possible. Automobiles give us mobility. Of course, to produce and power these machines, we need energy. We obtain most of this energy from fossil fuels—coal, oil, and natural gas.

For years, our cities and industries could grow rapidly and cheaply because they discarded wastes from manufacturing and energy production into the air, water, and soil. Meanwhile, as urban centers became crowded, many people moved from the cities to the suburbs. The result was the growth of suburbs and suburban sprawl, or the spread of suburban communities across the American landscape, as shown in **Figure 6–6**. Industrial development and the growth of cities and suburbs are closely tied to the high standard of living that so many Americans enjoy.

Many ecologists, however, are concerned about the effects of human activity on both local and global environments. Certain kinds of industrial processes pollute air, water, and soil. Dense human communities produce wastes that must be disposed of. Suburban sprawl consumes farmland and natural habitats, placing additional stress on plant and animal populations and on the biosphere's life-support systems. Can we learn to control these harmful effects of human activity while preserving—or even improving—our standard of living? This is the enormous challenge that you and your children face.

Figure 6–6 In the United States today, most people live and work either in cities or in the suburbs that surround them. The continued spread of suburbs is now referred to as suburban sprawl. **Problem Solving** *List some ways that problems associated with suburban sprawl can be prevented.*

6–1 Section Assessment

1. **Key Concept** List three types of human activities that can affect the biosphere. For each activity, give one environmental cost and one benefit.

2. What is the difference between early hunter-gatherers and modern subsistence hunters?

3. What did agriculture provide that changed the course of human history?

4. Name three results of the Industrial Revolution.

5. **Critical Thinking Predicting** How might improved agricultural practices in a developing nation affect that nation's human population?

*i***TEXT** Assessment Use iText to review the important concepts in Section 6–1.

6-2 Renewable and Nonrenewable Resources

Guide for Reading

🔑 Key Concepts
- How are environmental resources classified?
- What effects do human activities have on natural resources?

Vocabulary
- renewable resource
- nonrenewable resource
- sustainable use
- soil erosion • desertification
- deforestation • aquaculture
- smog • pollutant • acid rain

Reading Strategy: Building Vocabulary

As you read, make notes about the meaning of each new term in the list above. Then, draw a concept map to show the relationships among the terms in this section.

A few hundred years ago, villagers in England grazed their cattle on a pasture in the town center called the *commons,* which the king provided free. The villagers were quick to realize that whoever grazed the most cattle on the commons would reap the biggest reward. People added more and more cattle to their herds, and soon, there were too many animals eating the grass in the commons. People did not remove their cattle because those who did sacrificed personal profits while others continued to gain. The herders were locked into a system that eventually led to their ruin. They kept adding cattle until, eventually, the commons was destroyed. Was this a lesson for the modern world?

The Tragedy of the Commons

Generally speaking, a resource is something that can be drawn upon to take care of a need. When an environmental resource is owned by many people in common, or by no one, it is called a common resource. In 1968, environmentalists spoke about the *tragedy of the commons.* What was the tragedy? It was the notion that any resource that is open to everyone—such as the air or parts of the oceans—will eventually be destroyed because everyone can use the resource, but no one is responsible for preserving it. When people are not compelled to preserve resources for the welfare of future generations, the tragedy of the commons occurs.

🔑 **Regardless of whether they are held in common, environmental resources can be classified into two types: renewable and nonrenewable.** A tree is an example of a renewable resource, because a new tree can grow in place of an old tree. **Renewable resources** can regenerate and are therefore replaceable. However, a renewable resource is not necessarily unlimited. Fresh water, for example, is a renewable resource that can easily become limited by drought or overuse.

A **nonrenewable resource** is one that cannot be replenished by natural processes. The fossil fuels coal, oil, and natural gas are nonrenewable resources. Fossil fuels formed over hundreds of millions of years from deeply buried organic materials. When these fuels are depleted, they are gone forever.

The classification of a resource as renewable or nonrenewable depends on its context. Although a single tree is renewable, a population of trees in a forest ecosystem—on which a community of organisms depends—may not be renewable, because that ecosystem may change forever once those trees are gone.

✓ CHECKPOINT *What is the "tragedy of the commons"?*

▼ **Figure 6–7** 🔑 Natural resources can be classified as renewable or nonrenewable. The grass growing in these pastures is a renewable resource—as long as the number of sheep grazing there is limited.

Sustainable Use

How can people be sure that renewable resources will be available for future generations? The concept of sustainable use is one answer to this question. **Sustainable use** is a way of using natural resources at a rate that does not deplete them. 🔑 **Human activities affect the supply and the quality of renewable resources, including resources such as land, forests, ocean resources, air, and water.** A sustainable system operates without causing long-term harm to the ecological resources on which it depends. Unless sustainable strategies are used, human activities can damage or deplete these resources.

Sustainable practices are based on principles of ecology as well as economics. Those principles can be applied to agriculture, fisheries, land development, and other human activities. One example of sustainable use in agriculture is the management of unwanted species by understanding their interactions with other organisms and the environment. The ladybug in **Figure 6–8** is used in biological pest control in place of pesticides.

Land Resources

Land is a resource that provides space for cities and suburbs and raw materials for industry. Land is also important for the soils in which crops are grown. If managed properly, soil is a renewable resource. Soil, however, can be permanently damaged if it is mismanaged.

Food crops grow best in fertile soil, which is a mixture of humus, sand, clay, and rock particles. Most of the humus that makes soil fertile is in the uppermost layer of the soil, called topsoil. Good topsoil absorbs and retains moisture yet allows excess water to drain. It is rich in nutrients but low in salts. Such soil is produced by long-term interactions between the soil and plants growing in it. Much agricultural land in the American Midwest, for example, was once covered by prairie ecosystems that produced and maintained a meter or more of very fertile topsoil. Deep roots of long-lived grasses held soil in place against rain and wind.

Plowing the land removes the roots that hold the soil in place. This increases the rate of **soil erosion**—the wearing away of surface soil by water and wind. A typical field on the High Plains of the Midwest loses roughly 47 metric tons of topsoil per hectare every year! In certain parts of the world with dry climates, a combination of farming, overgrazing, and drought has turned once productive areas into deserts—a process called **desertification.** There are, however, a variety of sustainable-use practices that can guard against these problems. One practice is contour plowing, in which fields are plowed across the slope of the land to reduce erosion. Other strategies include leaving the stems and roots of the previous year's crop in place to help hold the soil and planting a field with rye rather than leaving it unprotected from erosion.

▲ **Figure 6–8** Alternative methods of pest control, such as the use of beneficial insects, are often an appropriate choice in sustainable agriculture. The ladybug in this photograph is eating an unwanted pest—a black aphid. **Applying Concepts** *Why is biological pest control preferable to the use of pesticides?*

▼ **Figure 6–9** 🌐 Human activities affect the supply and the quality of renewable resources, including resources such as land, forests, ocean resources, air, and water. In dry regions, human activities, such as farming practices that fail to protect the soil, can contribute to desertification.

145

Forest Resources

Earth's forests are an important resource for the products they provide and for the ecological functions they perform. People use the wood from forests to make products ranging from homes to paper. In many parts of the world, wood is still burned as fuel for cooking and heating. But living forests also provide a number of important ecological services. Forests have been called "lungs of the Earth" because they remove carbon dioxide and produce oxygen. Forests also store nutrients, provide habitats and food for organisms, moderate climate, limit soil erosion, and protect freshwater supplies.

Whether a forest can be considered a renewable resource depends partly on the type of forest. For example, the temperate forests of the northeastern United States can be considered renewable. Most of these forests have been logged at least once in the past and have grown back naturally. However, today's forests differ somewhat in species composition from the forests they replaced.

Other forests, such as those in Alaska and the Pacific Northwest, are called old-growth forests because they have never before been cut. Worldwide, about half of the area originally covered by forests and woodlands has been cleared. Only about one fifth of the world's original old-growth forests remain. Because it takes many centuries to produce old-growth forests, they are in effect nonrenewable resources. Old-growth forests often contain a rich variety of species. When logging occurs in these forests, the irreplaceable species they contain are lost.

Loss of forests, or **deforestation,** has several effects. Deforestation can lead to severe erosion as soil is exposed to heavy rains. Erosion also can wash away nutrients in the topsoil. Grazing or plowing after deforestation can cause permanent changes to local soils and microclimates that in turn prevent the regrowth of trees—even after human disturbance has stopped. For example, certain tropical soils exposed by deforestation have changed chemically to a hard, bricklike material called laterite.

There are a variety of sustainable-use strategies for forest management. In some forests, mature trees can be harvested selectively to promote the growth of younger trees and preserve the forest ecosystem. Increasingly, foresters plant, manage, harvest, and replant tree farms in places where forests have already been cut, as shown in **Figure 6–10.** Tree farms can now be planted and harvested efficiently, making them fully renewable resources. Tree geneticists are also breeding new, faster-growing tree varieties that produce high-quality wood.

✓ **CHECKPOINT** *What is deforestation?*

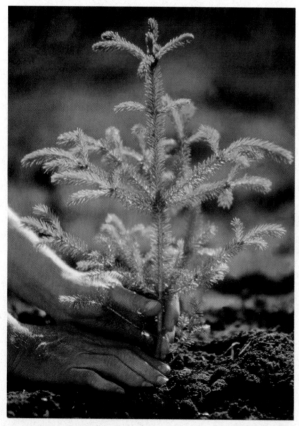

▼ **Figure 6–10** Planting new trees is one way to counteract the effects of deforestation. **Applying Concepts** *What are two ways in which reforestation might affect the biosphere?*

Ocean Resources

Earth's oceans are particularly valuable for the food resources they contain. People depend on the ocean as a major source of protein, both from finfish (such as cod) and from shellfish (such as shrimp). Yet, despite modern technology, people still obtain most food from the sea by hunting and gathering!

Throughout the second half of the twentieth century, larger fishing boats with better gear for locating and catching fish were deployed around the world. As you can see in **Figure 6–11,** the annual world fish catch grew from about 20 million tons to more than 90 million tons between 1950 and 1990. This growth led many to believe that the oceans' food supply was endless. But by the 1970s, more effort was needed to catch the same amount of fish. More sophisticated equipment, and many more boats, were put to work. Fish catches kept rising—for a time.

As fishing has increased, however, fish stocks in many fisheries are being harvested faster than they can reproduce. This situation, called overfishing, can destroy a fishery. For example, Peru's anchovy fishery was once one of the most productive in the world. At the fishery's peak, overfishing stressed the system so much that fish populations collapsed. Decades later, the fishery has still not recovered. Other important species, including halibut, cod, salmon, Atlantic herring, and Alaskan king crab, have also been overfished.

One approach to sustainable use of fisheries is to limit the catch of fish populations stressed by overfishing. To prevent population collapse, portions of Georges Banks and other Atlantic fishing grounds have been closed temporarily. Researchers hope to give fish populations a chance to recover. One problem with this approach is that open ocean waters and their animals lie in international waters, outside the legal control of any single country. For that reason, they are a good example of a common resource that everyone wants but no one has the incentive to manage properly.

As wild-caught fishes become scarce, people have turned to another sustainable-use strategy: **aquaculture,** or the farming of aquatic organisms. Aquaculture can be an efficient way to produce animal protein. If not properly managed, aquaculture can pollute water with fish wastes and can damage local aquatic ecosystems. However, more environment-friendly aquaculture techniques are steadily being developed.

Figure 6–11 Despite the increase in the total amount of fish caught each year, the supply of fish per person has stayed the same. Stocks of fishes like the Atlantic cod (below) are nearly depleted. **Predicting** *If the world's total fish catch levels off but the human population keeps growing, what might happen to the amount of fish per person?*

Codfish

Emissions to Atmosphere
Nitrogen oxides
Sulfur dioxide

Chemical Transformation
Nitric acid
Sulfuric acid

Condensation

Dry Fallout
Particulates, gases

Precipitation
Acid rain, fog,
snow, and mist

Industry   Transportation   Ore smelting   Power generation

Figure 6–12 Acid rain results from the chemical transformation of nitrogen and sulfur products that come from human activities. The face of the statue (below) shows damage from acid rain.
Interpreting Graphics *What pathways do the chemicals in atmospheric emissions take on their way to becoming acid rain?*

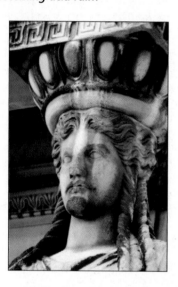

Air Resources

Air is a common resource that we use every time we breathe. Although it's easy to take air for granted, preserving air quality remains a challenge for modern society.

If you live in a large city, you have probably seen **smog,** a mixture of chemicals that occurs as a gray-brown haze in the atmosphere. Smog is primarily due to automobile exhausts and industrial emissions. Because it threatens the health of people and animals with asthma or respiratory conditions, smog is considered a pollutant. A **pollutant** is a harmful material that can enter the biosphere through the land, air, or water.

The burning of fossil fuels can release pollutants that cause smog and other problems in the atmosphere. Potentially toxic chemicals, like nitrates, sulfates, and particulates (pahr-TIK-yoo-lits), are especially troublesome in large concentrations. Particulates are microscopic particles of ash and dust that can enter the nose, mouth, and lungs, causing health problems over the long term. Today, most industries use technology to control emissions from factory smokestacks. Strict automobile emission standards and clean-air regulations have improved air quality in many American cities, but air pollution is an ongoing problem in other parts of the world.

Many combustion processes, such as the burning of fossil fuels, release acidic gases containing nitrogen and sulfur compounds into the atmosphere. When these gases combine with water vapor in the air, they form drops of nitric and sulfuric acids. These strong acids can drift for miles before they fall as **acid rain.** Acid rain can kill plants by damaging their leaves and changing the chemistry of soils and standing-water ecosystems. Acid rain may also dissolve and release toxic elements, such as mercury, from the soil, freeing those elements to enter other portions of the biosphere. **Figure 6–12** shows the processes that lead to the formation of acid rain.

✓**CHECKPOINT** *What is a pollutant?*

Water Resources

Americans use billions of gallons of fresh water daily for everything from drinking and washing to watering crops and making steel. Although water is a renewable resource, the total supply of fresh water is limited. For this reason, protecting water supplies from pollution and managing society's ever-growing demand for water are major priorities.

Pollution such as the oil spill in **Figure 6–13** threatens water supplies in several ways. Improperly discarded chemicals can enter streams and rivers. Wastes discarded on land can seep through soil and enter underground water supplies that we tap with wells. Domestic sewage, which is the wastewater from sinks and toilets, contains nitrogen and phosphorous compounds that can encourage the growth of algae and bacteria in aquatic habitats. Sewage can also contain microorganisms that can spread disease among humans and animals. In this country, most cities and towns now treat their sewage to make it environmentally safer.

One way of ensuring the sustainable use of water resources is to protect the natural systems involved in the water cycle. For example, wetlands such as swamps can help to purify the water passing through them. As water flows slowly through a swamp, densely growing plants filter certain pollutants out of the water. Similarly, forests and other vegetation not only hold soil in place but help to purify the water that seeps into the ground or runs off into rivers and lakes.

As demand for water grows rapidly in many parts of the United States, water conservation is becoming an increasingly important aspect of sustainable use. There are many strategies for conserving water—in homes, industry, and agriculture. More than three quarters of all water consumed in this country is used in agriculture, so conservation in this area can save large amounts of water. For example, drip irrigation delivers water directly to plant roots. This reduces the amount of water lost through evaporation.

▲ **Figure 6–13** Trawlers clean up an oil spill caused by a disaster at sea. A system of floats called booms helps keep the oil from spreading during the cleanup process. **Formulating Hypotheses** *What factors might improve the cleanup of an oil spill at sea?*

6–2 Section Assessment

1. 🔑 **Key Concept** What is the difference between a renewable and a nonrenewable resource?

2. 🔑 **Key Concept** List two human activities that affect land resources, and explain the changes that can result. Do the same for air and water resources.

3. How does the decline in world fisheries represent a "tragedy of the commons"?

4. **Critical Thinking Applying Concepts** Describe sustainable-use strategies to manage forests as a renewable resource.

📱 **TEXT** **Assessment** Use iText to review the important concepts in Section 6–2.

Take It to the NET

Choose a concept of sustainable use that is not described in this section. Explain how the features of sustainable use apply to the activity. If you need help, use the links provided in the Biology area at the Prentice Hall Web site: **www.phschool.com**

6–3 Biodiversity

Guide for Reading

Key Concepts
- What is the value of biodiversity?
- What are the current threats to biodiversity?
- What is the goal of conservation biology?

Vocabulary
biodiversity
ecosystem diversity
species diversity
genetic diversity
extinction
endangered species
habitat fragmentation
biological magnification
invasive species
conservation

**Reading Strategy:
Asking Questions** Before you read, rewrite the headings in the section as *how, why,* or *what* questions about biodiversity. As you read, write brief answers to your questions.

Those of us who love nature find much to admire in the many forms of life that surround us. We marvel at the soaring flight of an eagle, the majestic movements of a whale, and the colors of spring wildflowers. "Variety," the saying goes, "is the spice of life." But variety in the biosphere gives us more than just interesting things to look at. Human society takes part in local and global food webs and energy cycles, and depends on both the physical and biological life-support systems of our planet. For that reason, our well-being is closely tied to the well-being of a great variety of other organisms—including many that are neither majestic nor beautiful to our eyes.

The Value of Biodiversity

Another word for variety is diversity. Therefore, biological diversity, or **biodiversity,** is the sum total of the genetically based variety of all organisms in the biosphere. **Ecosystem diversity** includes the variety of habitats, communities, and ecological processes in the living world. **Species diversity** refers to the number of different species in the biosphere. So far, biologists have identified and named about 1.5 million species and estimate that millions more may be discovered in the future. **Genetic diversity** refers to the sum total of all the different forms of genetic information carried by all organisms living on Earth today. Within each species, genetic diversity refers to the total of all different forms of genes present in that species. You will read about genetic information later in the book.

Biodiversity is one of Earth's greatest natural resources. Species of many kinds have provided us with foods, industrial products, and medicines—including painkillers, antibiotics, heart drugs, antidepressants, and anticancer drugs. For example, the rosy periwinkle plant in **Figure 6–14** is the source of substances used to treat certain cancers. The biodiversity represented by wild plants and animals is a kind of "library" of genetic information upon which humans can draw for future use. For example, most crop plants have wild relatives with useful traits such as resistance to disease or pests. When biodiversity is lost, potential sources of material with significant value to the biosphere and to humankind may be lost with it.

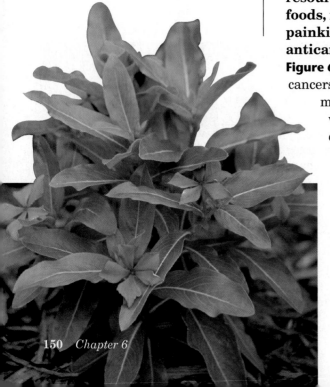

◀ **Figure 6–14** Biodiversity is one of Earth's greatest natural resources. Species of many kinds have provided us with foods, industrial products, and medicines. The rosy periwinkle is a pink-petaled flowering plant native only to an island off the coast of Africa. The substances produced by this plant are used in modern medicine.

Threats to Biodiversity

🔑 **Human activity can reduce biodiversity by altering habitats, hunting species to extinction, introducing toxic compounds into food webs, and introducing foreign species to new environments.** As human activities alter ecosystems, this may lead to the extinction of species. **Extinction** occurs when a species disappears from all or part of its range. A species whose population size is declining in a way that places it in danger of extinction is called an **endangered species.** As the population of an endangered species declines, the species loses genetic diversity—an effect that can make it even more vulnerable to extinction.

Habitat Alteration and Fragmentation

When land is developed, natural habitats may be destroyed. As habitats disappear, the species that live in those habitats vanish. In addition, development often splits ecosystems into pieces, a process called **habitat fragmentation.** As a result, remaining pieces of habitat become biological "islands." We usually think of islands as bits of land surrounded by water. But a biological island can be any patch of habitat surrounded by a different habitat. New York's Central Park is an island of trees and grass in a sea of concrete. In suburbs, patches of forest can be surrounded by farms, houses, and shopping malls. Habitat islands are very different from large, continuous ecosystems. The smaller the "island," the fewer species can live there, the smaller their populations can be, and the more vulnerable they are to further disturbance or climate change.

✓CHECKPOINT **What is habitat fragmentation?**

Demand for Wildlife Products

Throughout history, humans have pushed some animal species to extinction by hunting them for food or other products. During the 1800s, hunting caused the extinction of species such as the Carolina parakeet, shown in **Figure 6–15,** and the passenger pigeon.

Today, in the United States, endangered species are protected from hunting. Hunting, however, still threatens populations of rare animals in parts of Africa, South America, and Southeast Asia. Some species are hunted for meat, fur, or hides. Others are hunted because people think that their body parts such as horns or gall bladders have medicinal properties. The Convention on International Trade in Endangered Species, often referred to as CITES, bans international trade in products derived from an agreed-upon list of endangered species. It is, however, often difficult to enforce laws in remote wilderness areas.

▲ **Figure 6–15** 🔑Human activity can reduce biodiversity by altering habitats, hunting species to extinction, introducing toxic compounds into food webs, and introducing foreign species to new environments. The Carolina parakeet was once common in the southeastern United States. This colorful bird was hunted to extinction by the early twentieth century because its feathers were in demand to decorate hats.

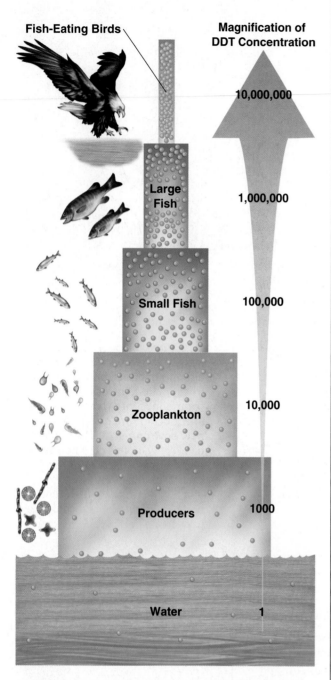

Fish-Eating Birds

Magnification of DDT Concentration

	10,000,000
Large Fish	1,000,000
Small Fish	100,000
Zooplankton	10,000
Producers	1000
Water	1

▲ **Figure 6–16** In the process of biological magnification, the concentration of a pollutant such as DDT—represented here by orange dots—is multiplied as it passes up the food chain from producers to consumers. By the time it reaches the top-level consumers, shown here as fish-eating birds, the amount of DDT in biological tissues can be magnified nearly 10 million times. **Calculating** *By what number is the concentration of DDT multiplied at each successive trophic level?*

Pollution

Many forms of pollution can threaten biodiversity, but one of the most serious problems occurs when toxic compounds accumulate in the tissues of organisms. The history of DDT, one of the first widely used pesticides, explains the situation well. At first, DDT seemed to be a perfect pesticide. It remains active for a long time, kills many different insects, and is cheap enough to be sprayed widely to control agricultural pests and disease-carrying mosquitoes.

When DDT was sprayed, it drained into rivers and streams at low concentrations that seemed harmless. But DDT has two properties that make it hazardous. First, DDT is nonbiodegradable, which means that it is not broken down by metabolic processes in bacteria, plants, or animals. Second, when DDT is picked up by organisms, they do not eliminate it from their bodies. As a result, something unexpected happens. DDT is picked up, concentrated, and stored by aquatic plants and algae. When herbivores eat those plants, they concentrate DDT to levels ten times higher than levels found in plants! When carnivores eat herbivores, the toxic substance is concentrated further, as shown in **Figure 6–16.** In this process, called **biological magnification,** concentrations of a harmful substance increase in organisms at higher trophic levels in a food chain or food web. Biological magnification affects the entire food web, although top-level carnivores are at highest risk.

In 1962, biologist Rachel Carson wrote a book called *Silent Spring* that alerted people to the dangers of biological magnification. The widespread spraying of DDT over many years had threatened populations of many animals—especially fish-eating birds like the osprey, brown pelican, and bald eagle—with extinction. One effect of DDT was to make eggs of these birds so fragile that the eggs could not survive intact. By the early 1970s, DDT was banned in the United States and in most other industrialized countries. In the years since, scientists have noted a marked recovery in the populations of birds that had been affected. Bald eagles, for example, can once again be seen around rivers, lakes, and estuaries in the lower 48 states.

✓ CHECKPOINT **What is biological magnification?**

How does biological magnification occur?

Materials paper cups (3 small, 1 medium, and 1 large); 1-L beaker; sand; 12 beads; masking tape

Procedure

1. Use a pencil to punch five holes in the bottom of each paper cup. Place tape over the outsides of the holes. The small cups represent grasshoppers, the medium-sized cup represents an insect-eating lizard, and the large cup represents a hawk.
2. Half-fill each small cup with sand and 4 beads. The sand represents food. The beads represent a chlorinated pesticide.

3. Hold each small cup over a beaker to catch the sand and remove the tape. The sand that flows out of the cup represents digested food. Record the number of beads in each cup.
4. To model the effects of biological magnification on the lizard, empty the contents of the three small cups into the medium-sized cup. Repeat step 3 with the medium-sized cup.
5. With two classmates, empty the three medium-sized cups into a large cup to model a hawk eating the lizard. Repeat step 3 with the large cup.

Analyze and Conclude

1. **Inferring** Which animals accumulated the most pesticide?
2. **Predicting** Which level of the food chain is most affected by biological magnification?

Introduced Species

One of the most important threats to biodiversity today comes from an unexpected source: apparently harmless plants and animals that humans transport around the world either accidentally or intentionally. Introduced into new habitats, these organisms often become **invasive species** that reproduce rapidly. Invasive species increase their populations because their new habitat lacks the parasites and predators that control their population "back home."

Hundreds of invasive species, including the one in **Figure 6–17,** are already causing ecological problems in the United States. Zebra mussels, an aquatic pest, were imported from Europe during the 1980s. They spread through the Great Lakes and several major rivers. These mussels reproduce and grow so quickly that they cause major ecological changes and are driving several native species close to extinction. There are also many examples on land. One European weed, the leafy spurge, now infests millions of hectares of grasslands across the Northern Great Plains, where it displaces native plants.

▶ **Figure 6–17** 🌐 **Human activity can reduce biodiversity by introducing foreign species to new environments.** Native to South America, nutrias have become pests in coastal areas of the southeastern United States. These furry rodents eat water plants that protect fragile shorelines from erosion. This destroys the habitats of species native to those ecosystems.

Conserving Biodiversity

Most people would like to preserve Earth's biodiversity for future generations. In ecology, the term **conservation** is used to describe the wise management of natural resources, including the preservation of habitats and wildlife. The modern science of conservation biology seeks to protect biodiversity. To do so requires detailed information about ecological relationships—such as the way natural populations use their habitats—and integrates information from other scientific disciplines, such as genetics, geography, and natural resource management.

Strategies for Conservation Many conservation efforts are aimed at managing individual species to keep them from becoming extinct. Some zoos, for example, have established captive breeding programs, in which young animals are raised in protected surroundings until the population is stable, then are later returned to the wild. This strategy has succeeded with a few species, including the black-footed ferret.

 Today, conservation efforts focus on protecting entire ecosystems as well as single species. Protecting an ecosystem will ensure that the natural habitats and the interactions of many different species are preserved at the same time. This effort is a much bigger challenge. Governments and conservation groups worldwide are working to set aside land, or expand existing areas, as parks and reserves.

Biology and History

Success in Conservation

Human activity can have a dramatic impact on the biosphere, to the point where other forms of life are threatened. Many efforts have been made to protect and preserve Earth's natural environments.

Harriet Hemenway
Hemenway and her cousin, Minna Hall, petition in Boston for legislation to prevent the extinction of birds due to unregulated hunting. By refusing to buy or wear plumed hats, the two cousins are among the first founders of the conservation movement.

Yellowstone becomes the world's first national park.
1872

1896

1850

1900

1854

Henry David Thoreau
Thoreau recommends the preservation of wildlife. In his book *Walden,* he cautions against seeking to dominate nature and suggests living in harmony with it.

1900

Lacey Act
Enacted by the U.S. Congress, the Lacey Act is the first major national conservation law. Transporting illegally killed animals across state borders becomes a federal crime.

The United States has an extensive system of national parks, forests, and other protected areas. Few of these, however, were designed with ecological principles in mind. As a result, these areas may not be large enough, or contain the right resources, to protect biodiversity. Marine sanctuaries are being designated to protect marine resources, such as coral reefs and marine mammals. Ecologists are realizing, however, that even these areas may not be enough to conserve the world's biodiversity.

Challenges in Conservation Sometimes, the need to protect biodiversity is greatest in countries that are least able to do so. The destruction of tropical rain forests, for example, is the single greatest threat to biodiversity on land. Most rain forests are located in developing countries, where conservation goals must be weighed against the survival needs of the human population.

Protecting species and ecosystem diversity in many places around the world is an enormous challenge. As part of the effort to locate problem areas and set up a list of priorities, conservation biologists often identify "hot spots," 25 of which are shown in **Figure 6–18** on page 156. Each hot spot is a place where significant numbers of habitats and species are in immediate danger of extinction as a result of human activity. The hot-spot strategy may help scientists and governments to focus their efforts to make and enforce laws that protect habitats and prevent or regulate hunting.

✓ CHECKPOINT *What do conservation biologists mean by a "hot spot"?*

Writing Activity

Choose and research a specific endangered species and its habitat. Then, write a letter to the editor of your local newspaper stating the problem and offering one or more possible conservation efforts for that species.

Endangered Species Preservation Act
This act allows for the identification of and research on endangered species. Seven years after passing, the act was expanded to protect plants and to prohibit threats to endangered species.

Earth Summit
A United Nations conference in Brazil seeks international solutions for environmental issues, including the worldwide loss of species.

Benny Goodman brings new style to jazz music.

1938

1966

1992

1950

2000

1933

1970

1972

Civilian Conservation Corps
President Roosevelt establishes the CCC, providing work in reforestation, prevention of soil erosion, and park and flood control projects. The "tree army" renews the nation's forests by planting an estimated 3 billion trees.

Earth Day
The first celebration takes place in New York to rally against pollution and population overgrowth.

National Marine Sanctuaries Act
The Secretary of Commerce is empowered to designate marine ecosystems as preservation or conservation areas.

Rhinoceros iguana
Caribbean

Red colobus monkey
Tanzania/Kenya

Jumping spider
Western Ghats and Sri Lanka

Asian elephant
Indo-Burma

Baobab tree
Madagascar

Orangutan
Sundaland

Butterfly orchid
Philippines

Giant anteater
Brazil's Atlantic Forest

Figure 6–18 Many conservation biologists are focusing on "biodiversity hot spots," where the biodiversity of these unique ecosystems is threatened. The 25 identified hot spots are shown in orange on the map. By focusing on protecting specific ecosystems, biologists hope to preserve global biodiversity.

6–3 Section Assessment

1. **Key Concept** Why is biodiversity worth preserving?

2. **Key Concept** List four different ways in which humans are decreasing biodiversity.

3. **Key Concept** What is the current focus of conservation biologists worldwide?

4. Explain the relationship between habitat size and species diversity.

5. **Critical Thinking Predicting** What problems could result if an endangered species were introduced into a nonnative habitat?

iTEXT Assessment Use iText to review the important concepts in Section 6–3.

MAKING CONNECTIONS

Exploring Biomes
Review biomes in Chapter 4. Then, choose one of the hot spots shown above. Find out about the biome in which these unique ecosystems and endangered species occur. Report on your findings and suggest specific actions that can be taken to preserve the biome's biodiversity.

6–4 Charting a Course for the Future

For most of human history, environmental change was a local affair. For example, many animals in the Hawaiian islands became extinct after humans arrived there. Yet, the effect of these extinctions on the biosphere at large was negligible. Since your parents and grandparents were born, however, global human population has grown from around 2.5 billion to more than 6.1 billion! Today, much of Earth's land surface has been altered by human activity. What's more, our species now uses as much energy and transports almost as much material as all of Earth's other multicellular species combined. We have become the most important source of environmental change.

As we enter the twenty-first century, many biologists are concerned about the biological effects of two types of global change: the thinning, or depletion, of the ozone layer and global warming. Understanding these phenomena requires that you remember what you have learned about global climate and weather, energy flow, nutrient cycling, population growth, and factors that limit population size. It also requires that you understand how scientific models make predictions about the complex systems that make up the biosphere. One such system is Earth's atmosphere.

Ozone Depletion

Between 20 and 50 kilometers above Earth's surface, the atmosphere contains a concentration of ozone gas—the **ozone layer.** Molecules of ozone consist of three oxygen atoms. Although ozone at ground level is a pollutant, the naturally occurring ozone layer serves an important function. It absorbs a good deal of harmful ultraviolet, or UV, radiation from sunlight before it reaches Earth's surface. You may know that overexposure to UV radiation is the principal cause of sunburn. You may not know that exposure to UV can also cause cancer, damage eyes, and decrease organisms' resistance to disease. Intense UV radiation can also damage tissue in plant leaves and even phytoplankton in the oceans. Thus, by shielding the biosphere from UV light, the ozone layer serves as a global sunscreen.

Beginning in the 1970s, scientists found evidence from satellite data and other measurements that the ozone layer was in trouble. The first problem sign was a gap or "hole" in the ozone layer over Antarctica during winter. Over the past 20 years, that hole has been growing larger and lasting longer, as shown in **Figure 6–19.** A similar ozone hole has also appeared over the Arctic. By 1995, that northern ozone hole had grown enough to expose parts of the United States to higher-than-normal levels of UV.

Guide for Reading

 Key Concept
• What are two types of global change of concern to biologists?

Vocabulary
ozone layer
global warming

**Reading Strategy:
Summarizing** As you read, find the key concept in the section. Write down a few words or phrases from the key concept, then use them in a summary of Section 6–4.

▼ **Figure 6–19** Many biologists are concerned about the thinning, or depletion, of the ozone layer. This image, taken by satellite in October 1999, shows the thinning of the ozone layer in the Southern Hemisphere. The image is color-coded, with yellow being the area with the highest concentration of ozone and blue the lowest. The ozone hole is the bright blue area surrounding Antarctica.

Ozone hole

Antarctica

◀ **Figure 6–20** The ultraviolet light that causes sunburn is known to be a cause of skin cancer. The thinning of the ozone layer resulting from ozone depletion could lead to higher rates of this disease. **Using Analogies** *State an analogy that explains the similarity between sunblock and the ozone layer.*

We now know that this problem is caused by compounds called chlorofluorocarbons (klawr-oh-FLAWR-uh-kar-bunz), or CFCs. CFCs were once widely used as propellants in aerosol cans, in the production of plastic foams, and as coolants in refrigerators, freezers, and air conditioners. In the intense cold of the polar atmosphere, CFCs act as catalysts that enable UV light to break apart ozone molecules. The United States has joined many other nations in an international agreement to phase out the use of CFCs. Those already present in the atmosphere will linger for some time. Even in temperate latitudes, it is still important for people to protect themselves from overexposure to UV light, as shown in **Figure 6–20.**

CHECKPOINT *What is ozone depletion?*

Analyzing Data

Banning CFCs

A layer of ozone is normally present in Earth's upper atmosphere, or stratosphere. The ozone layer prevents much of the ultraviolet light emitted by the sun from reaching Earth's surface. In the 1970s, scientists discovered an ozone hole over the Southern Hemisphere, which was caused by the introduction of chlorofluorocarbons into the atmosphere.

In the lower atmosphere, CFCs are stable. However, when CFCs are carried into the stratosphere, UV rays bombard them and break them apart. This process causes a series of chemical reactions that break down the ozone molecules into ordinary oxygen, which offers no protection from UV light at all.

In 1987, environmental experts from around the world met to address the problem of Earth's changing ozone layer. Forty-six nations signed an agreement called the Montreal Protocol, which called for an immediate reduction in production and use of CFCs. The following year, the United States passed a law to phase out the use of CFCs in aerosol cans by 2000. The members of the Montreal Protocol met again in 1990 and agreed to end the use of all CFCs by the year 2000.

The graph shows the rise and predicted fall of the amount of chlorine from CFCs in Earth's stratosphere for three different scenarios of CFC use. Use the graph to answer the questions that follow.

1. **Inferring** In the years that immediately followed the signing of the Montreal Protocol, chlorine levels continued to rise. What might have caused the rise?

2. **Predicting** Explain the three different future scenarios shown on the graph.

Global Warming

Any change in Earth's climate can have a profound effect on the biosphere. That's why many ecologists and biologists are concerned about evidence of an increase in the temperature of Earth's atmosphere and oceans.

The term used to describe this increase in the average temperature of the biosphere is **global warming.** Over the past 120 years, global temperatures have risen 0.5 degrees Celsius. Scientists have evidence that temperatures between 1980 and 2000 rose at a faster rate than during the previous 100 years. The 1990s were the hottest decade ever recorded, and each year of that decade was among the hottest 15 years since record keeping began in 1880. Global warming has even affected Earth's ice caps, as shown in **Figure 6–21.**

What is the cause of global warming? The most widely accepted hypothesis is that human activities have caused global warming by adding carbon dioxide and other greenhouse gases such as methane to the atmosphere. As a result, the global atmospheric greenhouse is retaining more heat. Atmospheric concentrations of carbon dioxide have been rising for 200 years. During this period, the burning of fossil fuels, combined with the cutting down and burning of forests, has been adding carbon dioxide to the atmosphere faster than the carbon cycle can remove it.

Not everyone agrees about the causes of global warming. Some scientists think that the rise in global temperature may be part of natural variations in climate. Even scientists who do accept that global warming is a result of human activities admit that it is difficult to predict just how global temperatures will change in the future. The most recent computer models suggest that average global surface temperature will increase by about 1 to 2 degrees Celsius by the year 2050.

Scientists around the world are trying to model the possible effects of global warming on the biosphere. If global warming continues at current rates, the polar ice caps will continue to melt and sea levels could rise enough to flood some low-lying coastal areas. Storms and other weather disturbances could become more frequent and more severe. Several climate models also suggest that parts of North America may experience more serious droughts during the summer growing season.

All these changes in climate and weather are abiotic factors that affect ecosystems and the geographic distributions of species. Environmental change favors certain species of both plants and animals—such as weeds, insects, and rodents—that flourish in a wide range of conditions and reproduce and spread relatively quickly. At the same time, other species with very specific requirements for heat and moisture might be unable to survive. In addition, health scientists are concerned that warmer temperatures could increase the geographic distribution and abundance of some species that carry diseases, such as the mosquitoes that transmit malaria.

▼ **Figure 6–21** Biologists are also concerned about global warming. This map of the Arctic is based on images taken by satellites in 1979 and 1999. Sea ice in the Arctic Ocean has receded so quickly that some scientists suggest that, within the next 50 years, the ice could disappear completely.

☐ Multiyear ice, 1999
▨ Melting of multiyear ice since 1979

Ecosystem Services	
Solar energy	
Production of oxygen	
Storage and recycling of nutrients	
Regulation of climate	
Purification of water and air	
Storage and distribution of fresh water	
Food production	
Nursery habitats for wildlife	
Detoxification of human and industrial waste	
Natural pest and disease control	
Management of soil erosion and runoff	

▲ **Figure 6–22** Human society depends on healthy, diverse, and productive ecosystems because of the environmental and economic benefits they provide. **Classifying** *Should the ecosystem services in the chart be considered renewable or nonrenewable resources? Explain.*

The Value of a Healthy Biosphere

A healthy biosphere provides us with many valuable goods and services. The goods include the raw materials for foods, medicines, and many other products. The services include temperature control, water purification, soil formation, and other services listed in **Figure 6–22.**

Is there any way that people can help maintain the health of the biosphere without drastically changing their lifestyles? The answer is yes. People can make wise choices in the use of resources and in the disposal or recycling of materials. Energy conservation is probably the most important shift that a society can make. Most people, without seriously affecting their quality of life, could better insulate their homes and offices, purchase cars that are more fuel-efficient, and recycle. Collectively, the actions of individuals can make a difference in the health of the biosphere.

You will face a great challenge as you come of age in America in the twenty-first century. It will be your responsibility to help build a sustainable global economy—one that can improve the living conditions of people worldwide without harming the global environment. Understanding that humans are part of the ecosystems they inhabit is only the first step in charting that course for the future. Each of us affects the biosphere with everything we do, from driving a car or eating hamburgers to heating or air-conditioning our houses.

Studies examining the impact of our choices are not about predicting disaster. The biosphere is strong. Humans are clever. We have great ability to deal with change. But we do need to pay attention to what we are doing. The results of your choices in these matters will affect life on Earth for generations to come.

6–4 Section Assessment

1. 🔑 **Key Concept** What are two major global changes affecting the biosphere today?

2. Why is the ozone layer important to living things?

3. How could a worldwide increase in temperature affect organisms?

4. What actions can people take in their daily lives to help preserve a healthy biosphere?

5. **Thinking Critically Predicting** Ultraviolet light is known to have a harmful effect on phytoplankton. Given this fact, how might depletion of the ozone layer affect an aquatic ecosystem?

📱 **TEXT** Assessment Use iText to review the important concepts in Section 6–4.

ALTERNATIVE ASSESSMENT

Comparing Media
Locate five print, radio, television, or Internet sources about global warming or the ozone hole. What attitudes and opinions are expressed in these sources? Compare them with the information in this section.

Observing the Effects of Acid Rain

Acid rain is formed when the combustion of fossil fuels releases gases containing nitrogen and sulfur compounds into the atmosphere. It can damage crops, forests, soil, and buildings. In this investigation, you will design and perform an experiment to simulate and test the effect of acid rain on the germination of seeds.

Problem   How does acid rain affect the germination of seeds?

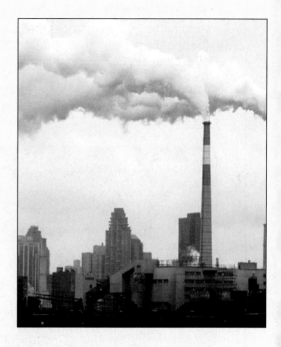

Materials

- diluted sulfuric acid
- filter paper
- glass-marking pencil
- 2 petri dishes
- 100-mL graduated cylinder
- 100 seeds (mustard or radish)
- pH paper
- 2 100-mL beakers
- hand lens

Skills   Designing Experiments, Controlling Variables

Design Your Experiment

1. **Formulating Hypotheses** Use your knowledge of acid rain to develop a hypothesis about its effect on plant growth and development. Record your hypothesis.

2. **Predicting** Record a prediction about how acid rain will affect seed germination.

3. Design an experiment to test your prediction. It is not practical in the classroom to expose some plants to acid rain and others to nonacid rain. You will need to choose a way to simulate acid rain.

4. Check your experimental design to make sure you are testing only one variable and have included any necessary controls. Construct any data tables you will need to use for recording the results of your experiment. With your teacher's approval, carry out your experiment.

Analyze and Conclude

1. **Analyzing Data** What percentage of your control seeds germinated? What percentage of your acid-treated seeds germinated?

2. **Drawing Conclusions** What do your results imply about the short-term effects of acid rain?

3. **Predicting** Would you expect acid rain to injure plants after they have completed germination? Explain your answer.

Go Further

Problem Solving Conduct research and report to the class on the various methods used in industry to reduce the amounts of sulfur dioxide and nitrogen oxides being emitted into the atmosphere.

Chapter 6 Study Guide

6–1 A Changing Landscape
 Key Concept

- Among the human activities that have transformed the biosphere are hunting and gathering, agriculture, industry, and urban development.

Vocabulary
- subsistence hunting, p. 140 • agriculture, p. 141
- green revolution, p. 142 • monoculture, p. 142

6–2 Renewable and Nonrenewable Resources
Key Concepts

- Regardless of whether they are held in common, environmental resources can be classified into two types: renewable and nonrenewable.
- Human activities affect the supply and the quality of renewable resources, including resources such as land, forests, ocean resources, air, and water.

Vocabulary
- renewable resource, p. 144
- nonrenewable resource, p. 144
- sustainable use, p. 145 • soil erosion, p. 145
- desertification, p. 145 • deforestation, p. 146
- aquaculture, p. 147 • smog, p. 148
- pollutant, p. 148 • acid rain, p. 148

6–3 Biodiversity
Key Concepts

- Biodiversity is one of Earth's greatest natural resources. Many species have provided us with foods, industrial products, and medicines—including painkillers, antibiotics, heart drugs, antidepressants, and anticancer drugs.

- Human activity can reduce biodiversity by altering habitats, hunting species to extinction, introducing toxic compounds into food webs, and introducing foreign species to new environments.

- Today, conservation efforts focus on protecting entire ecosystems as well as single species. Protecting an ecosystem will ensure that the natural habitats and interactions of many different species are preserved at the same time.

Vocabulary
- biodiversity, p. 150 • ecosystem diversity, p. 150
- species diversity, p. 150 • genetic diversity, p. 150
- extinction, p. 151 • endangered species, p. 151
- habitat fragmentation, p. 151
- biological magnification, p. 152
- invasive species, p. 153 • conservation, p. 154

6–4 Charting a Course for the Future
Key Concept

- Many biologists are concerned about the biological effects of two types of global change: the thinning, or depletion, of the ozone layer and global warming.

Vocabulary
ozone layer, p. 157
global warming, p. 159

Thinking Visually
Using information from this chapter, complete the following concept map:

Chapter 6

Part A

Multiple Choice

For each statement or question, select the number of the word or expression that, of those given, best completes the statement or answers the question.

1 Which human activity has had the *least* effect on the biosphere?
   (1) agriculture
   (2) industry
   (3) urban development
   (4) aquaculture

2 A resource that cannot be replenished by natural processes is called
   (1) common   (3) renewable
   (2) nonrenewable (4) conserved

3 The burning of fossil fuels may cause all effects *except*
   (1) acid rain
   (2) smog
   (3) global warming
   (4) the ozone hole

4 The sum total of the genetically based variety of all organisms on Earth is referred to as
   (1) the biosphere
   (2) species diversity
   (3) biodiversity
   (4) genetic diversity

5 When land development divides a habitat into isolated "islands" of the original area, the result is likely to be
   (1) fewer species
   (2) greater diversity
   (3) increased water pollution
   (4) reduced global warming

6 A species that enters an environment where it has not lived before
   (1) always goes extinct
   (2) mates with other species living there
   (3) may not have natural enemies there
   (4) will have no effect on the new environment

7 A species whose population size is declining in a way that places it in danger of extinction is called a(an)
   (1) fragmented species
   (2) endangered species
   (3) biodiverse species
   (4) invasive species

8 Ozone depletion is to CFCs as deforestation is to
   (1) ozone
   (2) soil erosion
   (3) suburban sprawl
   (4) pollution

9 Endangered species is to extinction as soil erosion is to
   (1) monoculture
   (2) desertification
   (3) fertilizer use
   (4) acid rain

10 The sustainable use of natural resources
   (1) causes long-term harm to resources
   (2) leads to depletion of resources
   (3) involves the use of pesticides
   (4) is based on principles of ecology as well as economics

11 Which is *not* an effect of deforestation?
   (1) global warming
   (2) loss of soil nutrients
   (3) soil erosion
   (4) the ozone hole

12 Ozone is made up of
   (1) water
   (2) oxygen
   (3) hydrogen
   (4) chlorine

13 The conversion of a previously soil-rich area to a sandy desert is called
   (1) habitat fragmentation
   (2) deforestation
   (3) desertification
   (4) acid rain

14 Which resource is *not* a renewable resource?
   (1) the wind
   (2) a fossil fuel
   (3) freshwater
   (4) a tree

Test-Taking Tip When evaluating multiple choice answers, be sure to read all of the answer choices, even if the first choice seems to be the correct one. By doing so, you can make sure that the answer you chose is the best one.

Parts B and C

Multiple Choice and Extended Response

For those questions that ask you to select a response, choose the one that best completes the statement or answers the question. For all others follow the directions given.

15 Based on the map below, which statement is correct?

   (1) Earth's ice caps are increasing in size.
   (2) Earth's ice caps are decreasing in size.
   (3) Global warming has not affected Earth's ice caps.
   (4) The changes shown are due to acid rain.

☐ Multiyear ice, 1999
■ Melting of multiyear ice since 1979

Base your answers to questions 16 through 21 on the graph below and on your knowledge of biology.

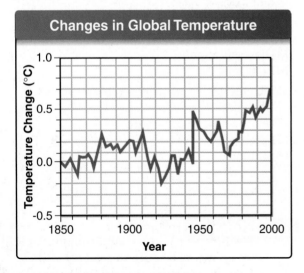

Changes in Global Temperature

16 What is plotted on the y-axis? What does the value 0.0 represent?

17 How much higher was global temperature in 2000 than in 1850?

18 Describe the trend in global temperature between 1970 and 2000.

19 Does the graph predict the pattern of global temperature change in the future? Support your answers with an explanation.

20 What atmospheric changes caused the rise in global temperature?

21 What led to these atmospheric changes?

- -

22 Australian koalas eat only the leaves of eucalyptus trees. If all the eucalyptus trees were destroyed, what might happen to the koalas?
   (1) Koalas would increase in number.
   (2) Many koalas would leave Australia.
   (3) Some koalas might survive by eating other kinds of leaves.
   (4) Koalas would become meat eaters.

23 Describe the process by which chlorofluoro-carbons deplete the ozone layer.

24 In the food web below, which organism would accumulate the highest level of a chlorinated pesticide?
   (1) hawk   **(3)** frog
   (2) rabbit   **(4)** grasses

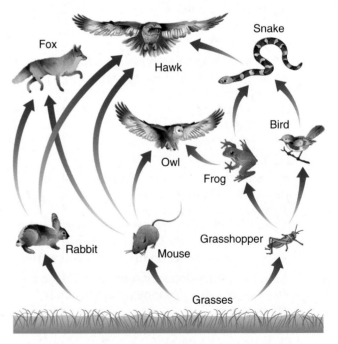

Base your answers to questions 25 through 28 on the information and maps below and on your knowledge of biology.

Fire ants first arrived in the United States in 1918, probably on a ship traveling from South America to Alabama. The maps below show the location of the United States fire ant population in 1953 and 1994.

1953

1994

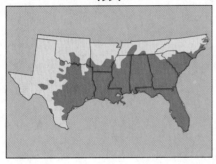

25 What can you conclude about fire ants in the United States?
(1) They reproduce slowly.
(2) They are a native species of the United States.
(3) They are an invasive species.
(4) Their numbers are declining.

26 By 2010, fire ants are likely to
(1) occupy Florida only
(2) have reached their carrying capacity
(3) die out
(4) have spread to cover a larger area

27 What can you conclude about the natural enemies of fire ants in the southeastern United States? Support your answer.

28 Some wildlife managers have suggested introducing fire anteaters from South America into Florida. What information should they obtain about these predators before they are introduced?

Base your answers to questions 29 through 31 on the reading passage below and on your knowledge of biology.

Deforestation: New Term, Old Technique

The clearing of tropical rain forests has been going on for centuries. The clearing is done in order to create areas for grazing cattle or planting crops, to harvest trees for lumber or papermaking, or to build dams or towns. When the trees are cut and burned, the carbon stored in them is released into the atmosphere, increasing levels of carbon dioxide and adding to the greenhouse effect and global warming. With fewer trees, there is also a lower rate of evaporation of moisture from the tree canopy. This leads to less cloud cover and higher temperatures. In addition, more than half of all the species alive today live in tropical rain forests. When the trees are cleared, habitats are destroyed and species risk extinction. Finally, soils of tropical rain forests are low in nutrients, which are quickly depleted when the forests are cleared and the land is used to grow crops. As a result, farmers soon move on to clear and farm other parts of the forest.

29 What are some of the consequences of clearing tropical rain forests?

30 In what ways does deforestation affect the carbon-oxygen cycle?

31 How might a program to teach tropical farmers agricultural techniques, such as the rotation of crops and the use of fertilizers, help the deforestation problem?

Take It to the NET

What kinds of organisms are invading your region? Visit the Prentice Hall Web site at **www.phschool.com** to find out about invasive species in the United States. Then, answer the following questions:
• How much do invasive species cost taxpayers each year?
• What is the main way that invasive species are transported and introduced to nonnative areas?
• Choose three invasive species and describe the nature of the problems they are causing today.

Cells

▶ This color-enhanced photograph shows two long cell nuclei (colored blue and yellow) from a human sarcoma, or cancer of the connective tissue. Cancer occurs when cells multiply uncontrollably and destroy healthy tissue. The round, orange structure near the middle of each nucleus is the nucleolus, or little nucleus.

What do we know about cells?

- All living things are made of cells, and there are just two basic types of cells—those with nuclei and those without nuclei.

- Cells can store, transform, and use energy. These transformations are at the very heart of what makes life possible.

- Living things grow, change, and develop as a result of cell growth and division.

What discoveries lie in the future?

- Can we discover the precise signals that determine whether cells develop into bones, muscles, nerves, or other tissues in the body?

- Can we use our understanding of photosynthesis and cellular respiration to improve the productivity of crop plants and feed more people on less agricultural land?

- Can we learn how to regulate cell division so that we can stop the spread of cancer and other diseases that are caused by abnormal cell growth and division?

KEEP CURRENT WITH . . .

SCIENCE NEWS®

Find out more about topics in this unit:
www.phschool.com

7 Cell Structure and Function

This is an artificially colored electron micrograph of a neutrophil, a cell found in bone marrow. The colored regions are organelles that perform various functions within the cell (magnification: 27,500×).

Inquiry Activity

What is a cell?

Procedure

1. Look through a microscope at a slide of a plant leaf or stem cross section. **CAUTION:** *Handle the microscope and slide carefully to avoid breaking them.* Sketch one or more cells. Record a description of their features, such as shape and internal parts.

2. Repeat step 1 with slides of nerve cells, bacteria, and paramecia.

3. Make a list of characteristics that all of the cells have in common. List some differences among the cells.

Think About It

1. **Forming Operational Definitions** Use your observations to write a definition of "cell."

2. **Classifying** Classify the cells you observed into two or more groups. Explain what characteristics you used to put each cell in a particular group.

7–1 Life Is Cellular

Look closely at a part of a living thing, and what do you see? Hold a blade of grass up against the light, and you see tiny lines running the length of the blade. Examine the tip of your finger, and you see the ridges and valleys that make up finger-prints. Place an insect under a powerful dissecting microscope, and you see the intricate structures of its wings and the spikes and bristles that protect its body. As interesting as these close-up views may be, however, they're only the beginning of the story. Look closely at **Figure 7–1,** and you'll see that there is a common structure that makes up every living thing—the cell.

The Cell Theory

The first lenses were used in Europe in the late 1500s by merchants who needed to determine the quality of cloth. They used their magnifying lenses to examine the quality of the thread and the precision of the weave in a bolt of cloth. From these simple glass lenses, combinations of lenses were put together. In Holland in the early 1600s, two useful instruments were constructed: the telescope and the microscope. In the 1600s, Dutch businessman Anton van Leeuwenhoek (LAY-vuhn-hook) became one of the first people to use a microscope to study nature. Using only a single powerful lens, van Leeuwenhoek crafted instruments that could produce magnified images of very small objects. His simple microscope enabled him to see things that no one had ever seen before. He was the first person, for example, to see tiny living organisms in a drop of water. Van Leeuwenhoek carefully observed the living things in pond water and made detailed drawings of each kind of organism.

Guide for Reading

 Key Concepts
- What is the cell theory?
- What are the characteristics of prokaryotes and eukaryotes?

Vocabulary
cell
cell theory
cell membrane
cell wall
nucleus
cytoplasm
prokaryote
eukaryote
organelle

**Reading Strategy:
Finding Main Ideas**
As you read, look for evidence to support the statement "The cell theory revolutionized how biologists thought about living things."

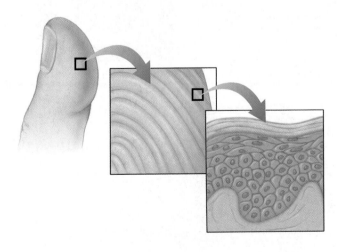

◄ **Figure 7–1** Like all living things, you are made up of cells. This illustration shows that even a portion of your thumb contains cells. **Using Analogies** *How is a cell in an organism similar to a brick in a building? How is it different?*

(magnification: 12,000×)

▲ **Figure 7–2** 🔑 The cell theory states that cells are the basic units of all living things. This cell is from a plant leaf.

In 1665, English physicist Robert Hooke used one of the first light microscopes to look at thin slices of plant tissues. One of these, a slice of cork, especially caught his eye. Under the microscope, cork seemed to be made of thousands of tiny chambers. Hooke called these chambers "cells," because they reminded him of a monastery's tiny rooms, which were also known as cells. The term *cell* is used to this day. Hooke's discovery stimulated other scientists to search for cells in other living things. Before long, it became apparent that **cells** were the basic units of all forms of life. **Figure 7–2** shows a typical plant cell.

In 1838, German botanist Matthias Schleiden (SHLY-dun) concluded that all plants are made of cells. The next year, another German scientist, Theodor Schwann, concluded that animals are also made of cells. Rudolf Virchow (FUR-koh), a German physician, studied cell reproduction. In 1855, he summarized years of research by stating, "Where a cell exists, there must have been a preexisting cell. . . ."

The discoveries of these and other biologists are summarized in the **cell theory,** one of the fundamental concepts of biology. 🔑 **The cell theory states the following:**

• **All living things are composed of cells.**

• **Cells are the basic units of structure and function in living things.**

• **New cells are produced from existing cells.**

Biology and History

A History of the Cell

The observations and conclusions of many scientists helped to develop the current understanding of the cell.

English settlers found colony at Jamestown, Virginia

1607

1600

Anton van Leeuwenhoek
Leeuwenhoek observes tiny living organisms in drops of pond water through his simple microscope.

1674

1700

1665

Robert Hooke
Hooke publishes his book *Micrographia,* which contains his drawings of sections of cork as seen through one of the first microscopes.

Basic Cell Structures

Cells come in many shapes and sizes. Although typical cells range from 5 to 50 micrometers in diameter, the tiniest bacteria are only 0.2 micrometers across. These bacteria are so small that they are difficult to see, even with the aid of the most powerful light microscope. In contrast, the giant amoeba, *Chaos chaos,* may reach 1000 micrometers in diameter—large enough to be seen without a microscope.

Despite differences in cell size and shape, certain structures are common to most cells. All cells have a cell membrane and cytoplasm. The **cell membrane** is a thin, flexible barrier around the cell. Many cells also have a strong layer around the cell membrane known as a **cell wall.** Cell walls and cell membranes support and protect cells, while allowing them to interact with their surroundings.

Some cells also have a **nucleus** (plural: nuclei), a large structure that contains the cell's genetic material and controls the cell's activities. The material inside the cell membrane—but not including the nucleus—is called the **cytoplasm.** The cytoplasm contains many important structures. You will read about these structures, as well as more about the cell membrane, cell wall, and nucleus, in the next section.

CHECKPOINT *What is the cytoplasm?*

KEEP CURRENT WITH . . .
SCIENCE NEWS®

To find out more about the topics in this chapter, go to:
www.phschool.com

Writing Activity

Use the library or the Internet to find more information about new discoveries concerning the cell or its structures. Then, present the discovery to your classmates in the form of an oral report.

Lynn Margulis
Margulis proposes the theory that certain organelles, tiny structures within some cells, were once free-living cells themselves.

Theodor Schwann
Schwann concludes that all animals are made up of cells.

Janet Plowe
Plowe demonstrates that the cell membrane is a physical structure, not an interface between two liquids.

1839

1931

1970

1800

1900

2000

1838

1855

1945

Matthias Schleiden
Schleiden concludes that all plants are made up of cells.

Rudolph Virchow
Virchow proposes that all cells come from existing cells, completing the cell theory.

World War II ends

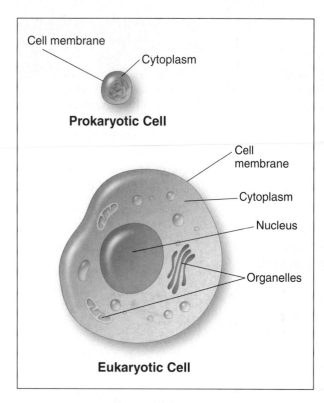

Cell membrane
Cytoplasm

Prokaryotic Cell

Cell membrane
Cytoplasm
Nucleus
Organelles

Eukaryotic Cell

▲ **Figure 7–3** 🔑 Biologists divide cells into two categories: eukaryotes and prokaryotes. The cells of eukaryotes have a nucleus, but the cells of prokaryotes do not.

Prokaryotes and Eukaryotes

🔑 **Biologists divide cells into two categories: eukaryotes and prokaryotes. The cells of eukaryotes have a nucleus, but the cells of prokaryotes do not.** The differences between the cells of prokaryotes and those of eukaryotes are shown in **Figure 7–3.**

Prokaryotes The cells of prokaryotes (proh-KAR-ee-ohts) are generally smaller and simpler than the cells of eukaryotes. **Prokaryotes** have cell membranes and cytoplasm but do not contain nuclei. All bacteria are prokaryotes. Examples of prokaryotes include *Escherichia coli,* which live in your intestines, and *Staphylococcus aureus,* which can cause skin infections.

Even though they are relatively simple, prokaryotes carry out every activity associated with life. They grow, reproduce, and respond to changes in the environment. Some even move by gliding along surfaces or swimming through liquids!

Eukaryotes Unlike the cells of prokaryotes, the cells of **eukaryotes** (yoo-KAR-ee-ohts) do contain nuclei. In addition to a nucleus, a cell membrane, and cytoplasm, most cells of eukaryotes contain dozens of other specialized structures, called **organelles,** that perform important cellular functions. Although some eukaryotes live solitary lives as single-celled organisms, many are large, multicellular organisms. All plants, animals, and fungi, and many microorganisms, are eukaryotes.

7–1 Section Assessment

1. 🔑 **Key Concept** What three statements describe the cell theory?

2. 🔑 **Key Concept** What is the main characteristic that distinguishes eukaryotes from prokaryotes?

3. When Hooke first used the term *cell,* did he intend to have it apply to living material? Explain your answer.

4. Name two structures that all cells have.

5. **Critical Thinking Inferring** If microscopes had not been invented, do you think the cell theory would have been developed? Explain your answer.

*i*TEXT **Assessment** Use iText to review the important concepts in Section 7–1.

ALTERNATIVE ASSESSMENT

Constructing a Chart
Make a two-column chart comparing prokaryotes with eukaryotes. In the first column, list the features of prokaryotes. In the second column, list the features of eukaryotes.

7-2 Cell Structures

At first look, the image of a cell as seen by the electron microscope seems chaotic, as shown in **Figure 7-4.** The cell is filled with membranes, granules, fibers, and other structures. Look closely, however, and patterns begin to emerge. To see the patterns more clearly, let's look, one at a time, at some structures that are common to eukaryotic cells, such as those of plants and animals.

Cell Wall

Cell walls are found in many organisms, including plants, algae, fungi, and nearly all prokaryotes. Animal cells, however, do not contain cell walls. The cell wall lies outside the cell membrane. Most cell walls allow water, oxygen, carbon dioxide, and other substances to pass through them. **The main function of the cell wall is to provide support and protection for the cell.**

Most cell walls are made from fibers of carbohydrate and protein. The cell produces these substances, which are then released at the surface of the cell membrane. There, they are assembled to form the wall. Plant cell walls are made mostly of cellulose, a tough carbohydrate fiber. Cellulose is the principal component of both wood and paper. Every time you pick up a sheet of paper, you are holding the stuff of cell walls in your hands.

Guide for Reading

🔑 **Key Concept**
• What are the functions of the major cell structures?

Vocabulary
chromatin
chromosome
nucleolus
nuclear envelope
cytoskeleton
microtubule
microfilament
ribosome
endoplasmic reticulum
Golgi apparatus
lysosome
vacuole
chloroplast
mitochondrion

**Reading Strategy:
Building Vocabulary**
Before you read, preview new vocabulary by skimming the section and making a list of the boldfaced terms. Leave space to make notes as you read.

(magnification: 1500×)

◄ **Figure 7–4** This electron micrograph of a plant cell shows the different types of structures that are found in cells. The cell has been artificially colored so that you can distinguish one structure from another. The green structure encircling the cell is the cell wall. 🔑 **The cell wall supports and protects the cell.**

FIGURE 7–5 PLANT AND ANIMAL CELLS

Both plant and animal cells contain a variety of organelles. Some structures are specific to either plant or animal cells. Others are found in both types of cells. **Interpreting Graphics** *What structures do plant cells have that animal cells do not?*

Plant Cell

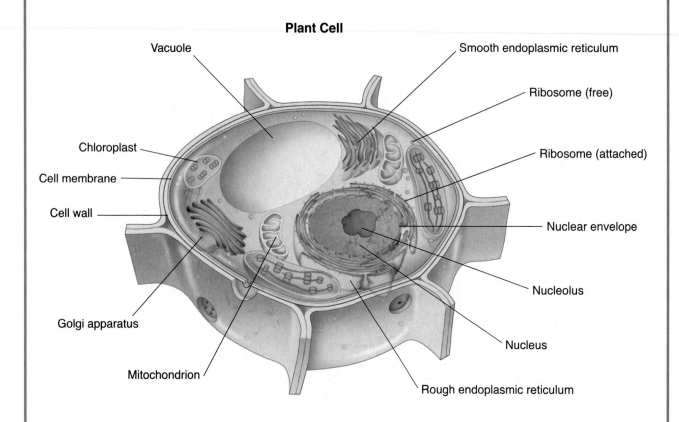

Vacuole
Smooth endoplasmic reticulum
Ribosome (free)
Chloroplast
Ribosome (attached)
Cell membrane
Cell wall
Nuclear envelope
Golgi apparatus
Nucleolus
Mitochondrion
Nucleus
Rough endoplasmic reticulum

Animal Cell

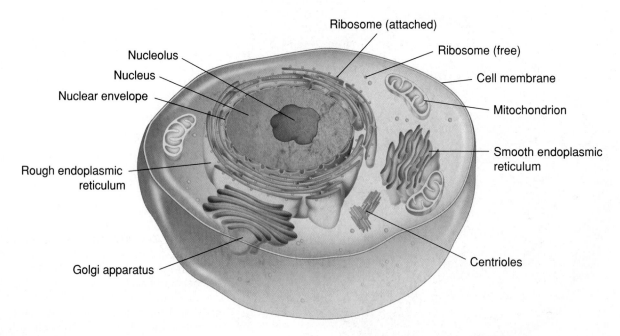

Ribosome (attached)
Ribosome (free)
Nucleolus
Nucleus
Cell membrane
Nuclear envelope
Mitochondrion
Smooth endoplasmic reticulum
Rough endoplasmic reticulum
Golgi apparatus
Centrioles

FIGURE 7-6 THE NUCLEUS

🔑 **The nucleus controls most cell processes and contains the hereditary information of DNA.** The DNA combines with protein to form chromatin, which is found throughout the nucleus. The small, dense region in the nucleus is the nucleolus.

Nucleolus

Chromatin

Nuclear envelope

Nuclear pores

(magnification: 10,000×)

Nucleus

When the Scottish botanist Robert Brown first identified the nucleus in 1831, he immediately had a sense that this organelle was doing something important. Today, biologists know that Brown was right. 🔑 **The nucleus controls most cell processes and contains the hereditary information of DNA (deoxyribonucleic acid).** Almost all eukaryotic cells, including the plant and animal cells shown in **Figure 7–5,** contain a nucleus.

The structure of the nucleus is shown in **Figure 7–6.** The nucleus contains nearly all of the cell's DNA. This substance holds the coded instructions for making proteins and other important molecules. The nucleus is important because making proteins is one of the main functions of cells.

Chromatin and Chromosomes The granular material visible within the nucleus is called **chromatin.** It consists of DNA bound to protein. Most of the time, chromatin is spread throughout the nucleus. When a cell divides, however, chromatin condenses to form **chromosomes** (KROH-muh-sohms). These are distinct, threadlike structures containing the genetic information that is passed from one generation of cells to the next.

✓CHECKPOINT *What kind of information do chromosomes hold?*

Nucleolus Most nuclei also contain a small, dense region known as the **nucleolus** (noo-KLEE-uh-lus). For many years, the function of the nucleolus was a mystery. Scientists now know, however, that this is where the assembly of ribosomes begins. Ribosomes aid in the production of proteins within the cell.

Nuclear Envelope The nucleus is surrounded by a double-membrane layer called the **nuclear envelope.** The nuclear envelope is dotted with thousands of nuclear pores, which allow material to move into and out of the nucleus. The nucleus sends a steady stream of RNA and other information-carrying molecules to the rest of the cell through the nuclear pores.

Cytoskeleton

Some cells have a structure—the **cytoskeleton**—that helps to support the cell. 🔑 **The cytoskeleton is a network of protein filaments that helps the cell to maintain its shape. The cytoskeleton is also involved in many forms of cell movement.**

The cytoskeleton is made up of a number of important structures, including microtubules and microfilaments, as **Figure 7–7** shows. **Microtubules** are hollow tubes of protein about 25 nanometers in diameter. They maintain cell shape and can also serve as "tracks" along which organelles are moved.

Microtubules are especially important in cell division, in which they help to separate chromosomes. In animal cells, microtubules form a pair of structures known as centrioles. Plant cells do not have centrioles.

In some cells, bundles of microtubules form hairlike projections from the cell surface known as cilia and flagella that enable cells to swim rapidly through liquids. Cilia and flagella can produce considerable force; in some cells, cilia move almost like the oars of a boat, pulling or pushing cells through the water.

The cytoskeleton also includes microfilaments. **Microfilaments** are long, thin fibers that function in the movement and support of the cell. Microfilaments are about 7 nanometers in diameter—much narrower than microtubules. Like microtubules, microfilaments form extensive networks in some cells. Microfilaments also produce a tough, flexible framework that supports the cell.

Another function performed by the cytoskeleton is moving organelles within the cell. The cell contains scores of motor proteins that can attach to organelles and generate force to move them along microtubules or microfilaments.

✓ **CHECKPOINT** *What are microtubules and microfilaments?*

(magnification: 1000×)

Cell membrane

Endoplasmic reticulum

Microtubule

Microfilament

Ribosomes

Mitochondrion

▲ **Figure 7–7** 🔑 The cytoskeleton is a network of protein filaments that helps the cell to maintain its shape and is involved in many forms of cell movement. The photograph shows the microtubules of kidney cells. Microtubules are part of the cytoskeleton and maintain cell shape.

FIGURE 7–8 ENDOPLASMIC RETICULUM

The endoplasmic reticulum is the organelle in which components of the cell membrane are assembled and some proteins are modified. The endoplasmic reticulum illustrated is called rough endoplasmic reticulum because of the ribosomes on its surface.

Ribosomes
(magnification: 160,000×)

Ribosomes

Endoplasmic reticulum
(magnification: 20,000×)

Organelles in the Cytoplasm

The cytoplasm contains many important structures. Because many of these structures act almost as though they were specialized organs in their own right, they are known as organelles, or "little organs."

Ribosomes One of the most important jobs carried out in the cell is making proteins. Proteins are assembled on **ribosomes,** small particles made of RNA (ribonucleic acid) and protein. Ribosomes are about 0.025 micrometers in diameter. Ribosomes produce proteins following coded instructions that come from the nucleus.

Endoplasmic Reticulum Eukaryotic cells also contain an internal membrane system known as the **endoplasmic reticulum** (en-doh-PLAZ-mik rih-TIK-yuh-lum), or ER. The endoplasmic reticulum is the organelle in which components of the cell membrane are assembled and some proteins are modified.

The part of the endoplasmic reticulum that is involved in the synthesis of proteins is called rough endoplasmic reticulum (rough ER). The rough endoplasmic reticulum has this name because of the ribosomes that stud its surface, as shown in **Figure 7–8.** Newly made proteins move directly from these ribosomes into the rough endoplasmic reticulum, where they may be chemically modified.

FIGURE 7–9 GOLGI APPARATUS

Enzymes in the Golgi apparatus attach carbohydrates and lipids to proteins. Notice the stacklike membranes that make up the Golgi apparatus in this scanning electron micrograph of an olfactory bulb cell.

(magnification: 25,000×)

Proteins that will be released from the cell are modified in the rough endoplasmic reticulum, as are many membrane proteins. Other cellular proteins are made by "free" ribosomes, which are not attached to any membrane.

The other part of the endoplasmic reticulum, the smooth endoplasmic reticulum (smooth ER), does not have ribosomes on its surface. In many cells, the smooth endoplasmic reticulum contains collections of enzymes that perform specialized tasks, such as the synthesis of lipids.

✓ CHECKPOINT *What distinguishes rough ER from smooth ER?*

Golgi Apparatus Proteins produced by the rough endoplasmic reticulum move into a stack of membranes called the **Golgi apparatus,** shown in **Figure 7–9.** The Golgi apparatus was named after the Italian biologist Camillo Golgi, who discovered it. **Enzymes in the Golgi apparatus attach carbohydrates and lipids to proteins.** From the Golgi apparatus, proteins are then sent to their final destinations.

Lysosomes Lysosomes (LY-suh-sohmz) are small organelles filled with enzymes. One function of lysosomes is to break down lipids, carbohydrates, and proteins from food into particles that can be used by the rest of the cell.

Quick Lab

How can you make a model of a cell?

Materials variety of craft supplies, index cards

Procedure
1. Your class is going to make a model of a plant cell using the whole classroom. Either with a partner or in a small group, decide what cell part or organelle you would like to model.
2. Using materials of your choice, make a three-dimensional model of the cell part or organelle you chose. Make the model as complete and as accurate as you can.
3. Label an index card with the name of your cell part or organelle and list its main features and functions. Attach the card to your model.
4. Attach your model to an appropriate place in the room. If possible, attach your model to another related cell part or organelle.

Analyze and Conclude
1. **Inferring** Why does a plant cell have so many different organelles?
2. **Calculating** Assume that a typical plant cell is 50 micrometers wide. Calculate the scale of your classroom cell model. (*Hint:* Divide the width of the classroom by the width of a cell, making sure to use the same units.)
3. **Comparing and Contrasting** How is your model cell part or organelle similar to the real cell part or organelle? How is it different?

Lysosomes also help break down organelles that have outlived their usefulness. Lysosomes perform the vital function of removing debris that might otherwise accumulate and clutter up the cell.

Vacuoles Cells often store materials such as water, salts, proteins, and carbohydrates in saclike structures known as **vacuoles** (VAK-yoo-ohlz). Many plant cells have a single large, central vacuole filled with liquid, as shown in **Figure 7–10.** Pressure in these central vacuoles makes it possible for plants to support heavy structures such as leaves and flowers. Vacuoles are also found in single-celled organisms and in animals. Smaller vacuoles, especially those involved in transporting substances within the cell, are often also called vesicles.

✓ CHECKPOINT **What are two functions of vacuoles?**

▶ **Figure 7–10** The large blue structure in the center of this *Coleus* plant cell is a vacuole. Vacuoles store water, salts, proteins, and carbohydrates. **Applying Concepts** *How do vacuoles help to support plant structures?*

(magnification: about 3000×)

FIGURE 7–11 CHLOROPLAST

Chloroplasts use the energy from sunlight to make energy-rich food molecules. The cells of plants and some other organisms contain chloroplasts, whereas animal and fungal cells do not. The photograph shows a chloroplast from a *Phleum pratense* plant.

Envelope membranes

Photosynthetic membranes

(magnification: 9000×)

Chloroplasts The **chloroplasts** (KLAWR-uh-plasts) are found in plants and some other organisms. Animal and fungal cells do not contain chloroplasts. **Chloroplasts use the energy from sunlight to make energy-rich food molecules in a process known as photosynthesis.**

As **Figure 7–11** shows, chloroplasts are bounded by two envelope membranes and contain large stacks of photosynthetic membranes. The green pigment chlorophyll is located in the photosynthetic membranes.

CHECKPOINT *What types of cells contain chloroplasts?*

Mitochondria The **mitochondria** (myt-oh-KAHN-dree-uh; singular: mitochondrion) are organelles that release energy from stored food molecules. **Mitochondria use energy from food to make high-energy compounds that the cell can use to power growth, development, and movement.**

Like chloroplasts, mitochondria are enclosed by two envelope membranes, an outer membrane and an inner membrane. The inner membrane is folded, as shown in **Figure 7–12.** Mitochondria are found in nearly all eukaryotic cells, including those of plants and algae.

FIGURE 7–12 **MITOCHONDRION**

⊙Mitochondria use energy from food to make high-energy compounds that the cell can use to power growth, development, and movement. Note that mitochondria, such as the one shown here from an intestinal cell, have two membranes. The inner membrane, which is folded, is the place where the high-energy compounds are produced.

Inner membrane

Outer membrane

(magnification: about 1000×)

Organelle DNA

Unlike other organelles, chloroplasts and mitochondria contain some of their own genetic information in the form of DNA. These small DNA molecules contain information that is essential for the normal function of both organelles. The American biologist Lynn Margulis has suggested that mitochondria and chloroplasts are actually the descendants of ancient prokaryotes. Her idea is that the prokaryotic ancestors of these organelles formed relationships with early eukaryotic cells that benefited both cells. As these relationships developed, DNA in the cell nucleus took over more and more of the genetic information of each organelle. Mitochondrial DNA, according to this idea, is just the remnant of the genetic information of the bacteria from which mitochondria are descended.

Whether Margulis's idea is correct or not, one of the most interesting aspects of mitochondria is the way in which they are inherited. In humans, all or nearly all of our mitochondria come from the cytoplasm of the ovum, or egg cell. This means that when your relatives are discussing which side of the family should take credit for your best characteristics, you can tell them that you got your mitochondria from Mom!

The Cell as a Factory

Now that you have read about how each part of the cell functions, let's look at how the cell as a whole works. In some respects, a eukaryotic cell is very much like a factory. Although cells perform many different functions, one of the most important jobs carried out in the cellular "factory" is making proteins. **Figure 7–13** shows how manufacturing proteins in the cell is like manufacturing a product in a factory.

The walls and roof of a factory building are supported by steel or concrete beams and columns. Some cells also have a supporting structure—the cytoskeleton. A factory needs a transportation system to move parts and machines from one end of the building to the other, and so does a cell. This is another function performed by the cytoskeleton.

In the same way that the main office controls a large factory, the nucleus is the control center of the cell. In a factory, the main office sends instructions out to the factory floor. In a cell, the nucleus sends a steady stream of RNA and other information-carrying molecules to the rest of the cell. RNA contains instructions that tell the cell what type of protein to make. The instructions travel to ribosomes. Each ribosome is like a factory machine turning out proteins on orders that come from its "boss"—the nucleus.

From the ribosomes, proteins that will be released from the cell move to the Golgi apparatus, which attaches carbohydrates and lipids to them to prepare the proteins for their roles. The Golgi apparatus is a bit like a factory's customization shop, where the finishing touches are put on products before they are ready to leave the factory. From the Golgi apparatus, proteins are then "shipped" to their final destinations.

Only one thing remains to complete the picture of the cell as a busy factory— a source of energy. Cells cannot be hooked up to the local power company, of course, so they get their energy from two organelles: mitochondria and chloroplasts. Some cells contain chloroplasts, which use energy from the sun to make food molecules. Thus, chloroplasts are the biological equivalents of solar power plants. Mitochondria then use these molecules to produce high-energy compounds that the cell can use immediately. In this way, the mitochondria are like a factory's oil-burning furnace.

✓**CHECKPOINT** How is the nucleus like the main office of a factory?

▼ **Figure 7–13** The way in which proteins are made in cells is similar to the way products are made in factories. Like a cell, a factory has a control center, support structures, an assembly area, and a power supply. **Interpreting Graphics** *What part of a factory corresponds to the mitochondria of a cell?*

Golgi apparatus

Mitochondrion

Protein being exported

Ribosomes

FUEL

Rough endoplasmic reticulum

Chloroplast

Nucleus

A Comparison of Cells			
Structure	Prokaryotic Cells	Eukaryotic Cells	
		Animal	Plant
Cell Membrane	Yes	Yes	Yes
Cell Wall	Yes	No	Yes
Nucleus	No	Yes	Yes
Ribosomes	Yes	Yes	Yes
Endoplasmic Reticulum	No	Yes	Yes
Golgi Apparatus	No	Yes	Yes
Lysosomes	No	Yes	No
Vacuoles	No	Small or none	Yes
Mitochondria	No	Yes	Yes
Chloroplasts	No	No	Yes
Cytoskeleton	No	Yes	Yes

Comparing Cells

Figure 7–14 summarizes the main differences among cells. The greatest distinction among types of cells is between prokaryotes and eukaryotes. Prokaryotic cells have cell membranes but do not have nuclei. Eukaryotic cells are much larger than prokaryotic cells and contain nuclei. They also contain more highly specialized organelles, including the endoplasmic reticulum, Golgi apparatus, and mitochondria. There are also large differences between plant and animal cells. Plant cells contain cell walls, large vacuoles, and chloroplasts. Animal cells do not have cell walls or chloroplasts.

▲ **Figure 7–14** This table shows the main similarities and differences among different types of cells. **Comparing and Contrasting** *How are prokaryotic and eukaryotic cells similar? How are they different?*

7–2 Section Assessment

1. **Key Concept** Describe the functions of the endoplasmic reticulum, Golgi apparatus, chloroplast, and mitochondrion.
2. What does the cell wall provide for a cell?
3. Describe the role of the nucleus in the cell.
4. What are two functions of the cytoskeleton?
5. How is a cell like a factory?

6. **Critical Thinking Inferring** If you examine an unknown cell under the microscope and discover that the cell contains chloroplasts, what could you infer about the organism from which the cell came?

iTEXT **Assessment** Use iText to review the important concepts in Section 7–2.

ALTERNATIVE ASSESSMENT

Creating Artwork
Create a work of art—such as a painting or sculpture—depicting a plant or animal cell in cross section. Include all the different organelles described in this section that would be found in that type of cell. Label each organelle in your artwork.

7–3 Movement Through the Membrane

Guide for Reading

Key Concepts
- What are the main functions of the cell membrane?
- What happens during diffusion?
- What is osmosis?

Vocabulary
- lipid bilayer
- concentration • diffusion
- selective permeability
- osmosis • facilitated diffusion
- active transport • endocytosis
- phagocytosis • exocytosis

Reading Strategy:
Summarizing As you read, make a list of the ways in which substances can move through the cell membrane. Write one sentence describing each process.

When you begin to study a country, one of the first things you may do is draw a map of the country's borders. Before you can learn anything about a nation, it's important to understand where it begins and where it ends. The same principle applies to cells. Among the most important parts of a cell are its borders, which separate the cell from its surroundings. The boundary of the cell is the cell membrane.

Cell Membrane

The cell membrane regulates what enters and leaves the cell and also provides protection and support. The cell takes in food and water and eliminates wastes through the cell membrane.

The core of nearly all cell membranes is a double-layered sheet called a **lipid bilayer.** Lipid bilayers form by themselves when certain kinds of lipids are dissolved in water. The bilayer gives cell membranes a tough, flexible structure that forms a strong barrier between the cell and its surroundings.

In addition to lipids, most cell membranes contain protein molecules that run through the lipid bilayer. Carbohydrate molecules form chains that are attached to the outer surfaces of these proteins. There are so many kinds of molecules attached to most cell membranes that scientists call the membrane a "mosaic" of different molecules. A mosaic is a work of art made of individual tiles or other pieces assembled to form a picture or design.

The structure of a cell membrane is shown in **Figure 7–15.** As you will see, some of the proteins form channels and pumps that help to move material across the cell membrane. Many of the carbohydrates act like chemical identification cards, allowing cells to identify one another.

▼ **Figure 7–15** ◔The cell membrane regulates what enters and leaves the cell and also provides protection and support to the cell. This illustration of the cell membrane shows that it is made up of a lipid bilayer in which proteins are embedded.

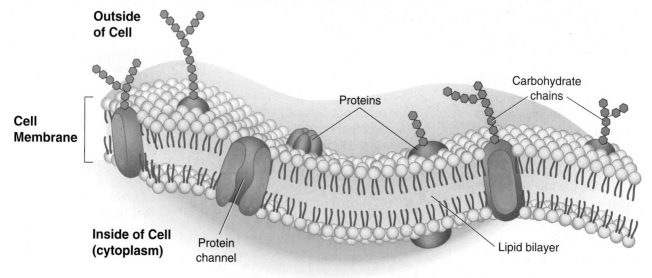

Diffusion

Every living cell contains a liquid interior and is surrounded by liquid. Even in the dust and heat of a desert, the cells of cactus plants, scorpions, and vultures are bathed in liquid. The cell membrane separates the solution that surrounds the cell from the solution within the cell. One of the most important functions of the cell membrane is to regulate the movement of molecules from one side of the membrane to the other.

The cytoplasm of a cell is a solution of many different substances in water. Recall that a solution is a liquid mixture of two or more substances in which the molecules of the substances are evenly mixed. The substances dissolved in the liquid are called solutes. The **concentration** of a solution is the mass of solute in a given volume of solution, or mass/volume. For example, if you dissolved 12 grams of salt in 3 liters of water, the concentration of the solution would be 12 g/3 L, or 4 g/L (grams per liter).

In a solution, molecules move constantly. They collide with one another and tend to spread out randomly through space. As a result, the molecules tend to move from an area where they are more concentrated to an area where they are less concentrated, a process known as **diffusion** (dih-FYOO-zhun). When the concentration of the solute is the same throughout a solution, the system has reached equilibrium. ⚷ **Diffusion causes many substances to move across a cell membrane but does not require the cell to use energy.**

What do diffusion and equilibrium have to do with biological membranes? Suppose two substances are present in unequal concentrations on either side of a membrane, as shown in **Figure 7–16.** The substance that can cross the membrane will tend to move toward the area where it is less concentrated until equilibrium is reached. Then, the concentration of the substance on both sides of the membrane will be the same. Even after equilibrium is reached, individual molecules continue to move rapidly across the membrane in both directions. Roughly equal numbers of molecules move in each direction, however, so there is no further change in concentration on either side.

✓ CHECKPOINT　*When is equilibrium reached in a solution?*

Solute

High Concentration

Cell Membrane

Low Concentration

▶ **Figure 7–16** Diffusion is the process by which molecules of a substance move from areas of higher concentration to areas of lower concentration. ⚷ Diffusion is also responsible for the movement of some materials across cell membranes.

Osmosis

Not all substances can cross biological membranes. If a substance is able to diffuse across a membrane, the membrane is permeable (PER-mee-uh-bul) to that substance. A membrane is said to be impermeable to those things that cannot pass across it. Most biological membranes are **selectively permeable,** meaning that some substances can pass across them and others cannot.

A process called **osmosis** allows water molecules to pass easily through most biological membranes. **Osmosis is the diffusion of water through a selectively permeable membrane.**

How Osmosis Works Like the cell membrane, the membrane in **Figure 7–17** is permeable to water but impermeable to sugar. There is a concentrated sugar solution on one side of the membrane and a dilute sugar solution on the other side. Although water molecules move in both directions across the membrane, there is a net movement of water into the compartment containing the concentrated sugar solution. That means more water is moving into this compartment than out of it. Why? Water, like other substances, tends to diffuse from a region where it is highly concentrated to one where it is less concentrated. The compartment with the dilute sugar solution starts out with the highest concentration of water.

Water will move across the membrane until equilibrium is reached. At that point, the concentrations of water and sugar will be the same on both sides of the membrane. When this happens, the two solutions will be isotonic, which means "same strength." When the experiment began, the more concentrated sugar solution was hypertonic, which means "above strength." The dilute sugar solution was hypotonic, or "below strength."

Word Origins

Hypotonic comes from the Greek word *hupo,* meaning "under" and the New Latin word *tonicus,* meaning "tension" or "strength." So a hypotonic solution is less strong, or less concentrated, than another solution. **If *hyper* means "over," how would you describe a hypertonic solution?**

▼ **Figure 7–17** Osmosis is the diffusion of water through a selectively permeable membrane. In this illustration, there is a higher concentration of water outside the cell than inside it. As a result, water molecules move across the membrane into the cell.

Higher Concentration of Water

Water molecules

Cell Membrane

Lower Concentration of Water

Sugar molecules

	Animal Cell		Plant Cell	
The Effects of Osmosis on Cells				
Solution	**Before**	**After**	**Before**	**After**
Isotonic				
Hypotonic				
Hypertonic				

Osmotic Pressure Osmosis exerts a pressure known as osmotic pressure on the hypertonic side of a selectively permeable membrane. Osmotic pressure can cause serious problems for a cell. Because the cell is filled with salts, sugars, proteins, and other molecules, it will almost always be hypertonic to fresh water. That means that osmotic pressure should produce a net movement of water into a typical cell that is surrounded by fresh water. If this happens, the volume of a cell will increase until the cell becomes swollen, as shown in **Figure 7–18.** Eventually, it may burst like an overinflated balloon.

Fortunately, cells in large organisms are not in danger of bursting. Most cells in such organisms do not come in contact with fresh water. Instead, the cells are bathed in fluids, such as blood, that are isotonic. These isotonic fluids have concentrations of dissolved materials roughly equal to those in the cells themselves.

Other cells, such as plant cells and bacteria, which do come into contact with fresh water, are surrounded by tough cell walls. The cell walls prevent the cells from expanding, even under tremendous osmotic pressure. However, the increased osmotic pressure makes the cells extremely vulnerable to injuries to their cell walls.

Still other cells use a mechanism to pump out the water that is forced in by osmosis. For example, some single-celled organisms have a structure called a contractile vacuole. By contracting rhythmically, the contractile vacuole pumps excess water out of the cell. This process is an example of homeostasis, the maintenance of a controlled internal environment.

▲ **Figure 7–18** Cells placed in an isotonic solution neither gain nor lose water. In a hypotonic solution, animal cells swell and burst. The vacuoles of plant cells swell, pushing the cell contents out against the cell wall. In a hypertonic solution, animal cells shrink, and plant cell vacuoles collapse. **Predicting** *What would happen to the animal cell in the hypertonic solution if it were placed in pure water?*

✓ CHECKPOINT *How do cell walls protect cells from osmotic pressure?*

Crossing the Cell Membrane

The cell membrane regulates what enters and leaves the cell and also provides protection and support. The core of nearly all cell membranes is a double-layered sheet called a lipid bilayer. Most materials entering the cell pass across this membrane by diffusion. The graph shows the sizes of several molecules that can diffuse across a lipid bilayer.

1. **Predicting** Which substances do you think will diffuse across the lipid bilayer most quickly? Most slowly? Explain your answers.

2. **Formulating Hypotheses** Formulate a hypothesis about the relationship between molecule size and rate of diffusion.

3. **Designing Experiments** Design an experiment to test your hypothesis.

4. **Going Further** What other factors do you think might affect the rate of diffusion? (*Hint:* Review Chapter 2.)

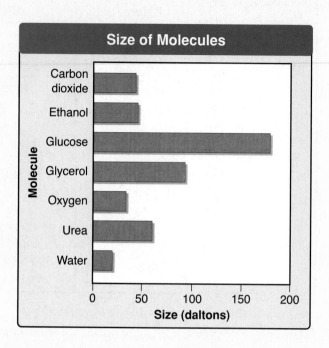

Size of Molecules

Molecule: Carbon dioxide, Ethanol, Glucose, Glycerol, Oxygen, Urea, Water

Size (daltons): 0, 50, 100, 150, 200

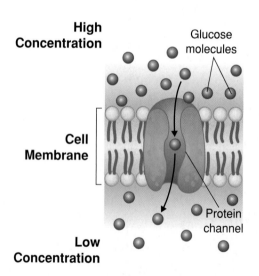

High Concentration

Glucose molecules

Cell Membrane

Low Concentration

Protein channel

▲ **Figure 7–19** During facilitated diffusion, molecules such as glucose that cannot cross the cell membrane's lipid bilayer directly move through protein channels instead. **Applying Concepts** *Why does facilitated diffusion not require the cell to use energy?*

Facilitated Diffusion

Some molecules, including alcohol, water, and small lipids, can move through the lipid bilayer and diffuse directly across the cell membrane. Other molecules cannot cross the lipid bilayer but do diffuse across the membrane. How do they do this?

Many membranes have protein channels that allow molecules to cross the membrane. In red blood cells, for example, a specific protein that spans the membrane has an internal channel that allows glucose to pass right through it. Only glucose can pass through this channel, and it can move through in either direction. This membrane protein is said to facilitate, or help, the diffusion of glucose across the membrane. The process, which is shown in **Figure 7–19**, is known as **facilitated diffusion** (fuh-SIL-uh-tayt-ud dih-FYOO-zhun). Hundreds of different protein channels have been found that allow ions, sugars, and salts to cross various membranes.

Although facilitated diffusion is fast and specific, it is still diffusion. Therefore, a net movement of molecules across a cell membrane will occur only if there is a higher concentration of the molecules on one side than on the other side. This movement does not require the addition of energy.

Active Transport

Often, material moves across a cell membrane against a concentration difference, as shown in **Figure 7–20.** The material moves from an area of lower concentration to an area of greater concentration, in a process called **active transport.** Active transport requires the input of energy, hence the term "active."

Active transport of small molecules is often compared to a pump. Most animal cells, for example, have membrane proteins that pump sodium ions (Na^+) out of the cell and pump potassium ions (K^+) in. Like any pump, these transport proteins require energy to move ions against the forces of diffusion. Because of the sodium-potassium pump, the insides of most animal cells have a low concentration of sodium but a high concentration of potassium.

In another type of active transport, large amounts of material are transported through movements of the cell membrane. One of these movements, called **endocytosis** (en-doh-sy-TOH-sis), is the process of taking material into the cell by means of infoldings, or pockets, of the cell membrane. The pocket that results breaks loose from the outer portion of the cell membrane and forms a vacuole within the cytoplasm. Large molecules, clumps of food, and even whole cells can be taken up by endocytosis.

When large particles are taken into the cell by endocytosis, the process is called **phagocytosis** (fag-oh-sy-TOH-sis). In phagocytosis, extensions of cytoplasm surround and engulf large particles.

As you might expect, cells are also able to send material out of the cell. The removal of large amounts of material from a cell is known as **exocytosis** (ek-soh-sy-TOH-sis). During exocytosis, the membrane of the vacuole surrounding the material fuses with the cell membrane, forcing the contents out of the cell.

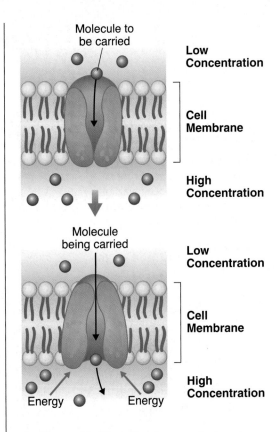

▲ **Figure 7–20** Active transport of molecules and ions against a concentration difference requires transport proteins and energy. **Interpreting Graphics** *What is happening in the illustration?*

7–3 Section Assessment

1. 🔑 **Key Concept** What processes are made possible by the cell membrane?

2. 🔑 **Key Concept** How does diffusion affect cells?

3. 🔑 **Key Concept** Describe how water moves during osmosis.

4. What is the basic structure of a cell membrane?

5. **Critical Thinking Comparing and Contrasting** How does active transport differ from diffusion?

TEXT Assessment Use iText to review the important concepts in Section 7–3.

Take It to the NET

As a graphic designer, you are asked to create an animation that shows osmosis and the selective permeability of a membrane. Make a storyboard that shows the main steps in your animation. Use the links provided in the Biology area at the Prentice Hall Web site for help in completing this activity: **www.phschool.com**

7-4 The Diversity of Cellular Life

Guide for Reading

 Key Concepts
- What is cell specialization?
- What are the four levels of organization in multicellular organisms?

Vocabulary
cell specialization
tissue
organ
organ system

Reading Strategy:
Using Visuals Before you read, preview **Figure 7–23.** As you read, note the different levels of organization in the body.

E arth is sometimes called a living planet, and for good reason. Living things are found in every corner of the globe—above and below its surface, and deep within its seas. The diversity of life is so great that you might have to remind yourself just how similar the different forms of life really are. All cells, no matter how different they may seem, use the same basic chemistry. This does not, however, mean that all living things are the same. Cells are specialized to perform certain tasks, either as individuals or as parts of larger organisms.

Unicellular Organisms

Cells are the basic living units of all organisms, but sometimes a single cell is a little more than that. Sometimes, a cell *is* the organism. A single-celled organism is also called a unicellular organism. Unicellular organisms do everything that you would expect a living thing to do. They grow, respond to the environment, and reproduce. In some ways, unicellular organisms dominate life on Earth. Some examples of unicellular organisms are shown in **Figure 7–21.**

Unicellular organisms include both prokaryotes and eukaryotes. Prokaryotes, especially bacteria, are remarkably adaptable. Bacteria live almost everywhere—in the soil, on leaves, in the ocean, in the air, and even within the human body.

Many eukaryotes also spend their lives as single cells. Some types of algae, which contain chloroplasts and are found in oceans, lakes, and streams around the world, are single-celled. Yeasts, or unicellular fungi, are also widespread. Yeasts play an important role in breaking down complex nutrients, which makes them available for other organisms. People use yeasts in making bread and other foods.

A few organisms stretch the concept of unicellularity. Some species of protists and algae are colonial. Colonial organisms live in groups of individuals of the same species that are attached to one another but have few specialized structures.

Figure 7–21 Yeasts are unicellular fungi often used in breadmaking. The *Volvox aureus* cells shown are actually individual alga cells that live together in a colony. The spiral-shaped bacterium *Leptospira interrogans* causes a serious disease in humans.

Yeast (magnification: 34,000×)   ***Volvox aureus*** (magnification: 250×)   ***Leptospira interrogans***
(magnification: 27,000×)

FIGURE 7–22 CELL SPECIALIZATION

Cells in multicellular organisms are specialized to perform particular functions within the organism. Red blood cells transport oxygen throughout the body. Pancreatic cells produce compounds such as insulin that the body needs. Nerve cells transmit information from one part of the body to another. Muscle cells contract and relax to move parts of the body.

Red Blood Cells (magnification: 13,000×)

Pancreatic Cell (magnification: 4000×) **Nerve Cells** (magnification: 8900×) **Muscle Cells** (magnification 90×)

Multicellular Organisms

The cells of multicellular organisms, such as human beings, do not live on their own. They are interdependent, like the members of a baseball team. Each player has a function that contributes to the success of the team. Organisms that are made up of many cells that work together are called multicellular organisms. Multicellular organisms have **cell specialization,** or separate roles for each type of cell. **Cells in multicellular organisms are specialized to perform particular functions within the organism.** Some cells are specialized to move, others to react to the environment, and still others to produce substances that the organism needs. The human body contains scores of different cell types. Look at **Figure 7–22** to get an idea of specialized cells in the human body.

Pancreatic cells are a good example of cell specialization. These cells are specialized to produce protein enzymes that make it possible to digest food. To perform this function, these cells contain enormous amounts of the organelles involved in protein synthesis—rough endoplasmic reticulum, Golgi apparatus, and clusters of storage vacuoles loaded with protein.

Careers in Biology

Histotechnologist

Job Description: work in a hospital laboratory, research institution, industrial laboratory, or government agency to prepare slides of body tissues for microscopic examination using special dyes and more advanced techniques, such as an electron microscope

Education: a bachelor's degree from a certified histotechnology program or a bachelor's degree with emphasis in biology and chemistry and one year's experience under a board-certified pathologist to become eligible for national certification exam, leading to a histotechnologist (HTL) certification

Skills: background in biology, anatomy, pathology, and/or chemistry; manual dexterity; attention to detail; good organizational skills; strong writing skills; computer literacy

Highlights: "There are many sides to histo-technology that make the field wide open for people with a variety of interests and skills," says Tim Morken. You will have the opportunity to learn new techniques and use cutting-edge technology as the field is changing. "One hospital I have heard about has no pathologists of its own and instead puts microscope slides on a robotic microscope with a video camera, all controlled and viewed by a pathologist in a distant city!"

"In our laboratory we deal with the most unusual (and deadly) infectious agents on the planet," says Tim Morken. "We are diagnosing and investigating these organisms with cutting-edge molecular biology technology."

 Take It to the NET

For more career information, visit the Prentice Hall Web site at **www.phschool.com**.

Levels of Organization

Biologists have identified levels of organization that make it easier to classify and describe the cells within an organism. 🔑 **The levels of organization in a multicellular organism are individual cells, tissues, organs, and organ systems.** These levels of organization are shown in **Figure 7–23.**

Cells The organization of the cells of the body creates a division of labor among those cells that makes multicellular life possible. Specialized cells such as nerve and muscle cells are able to exist because other cells are specialized to obtain the food and oxygen that those cells need.

This specialization and interdependence is one of the remarkable attributes of living things. Appreciating this is an important step in understanding the nature of living things.

Tissues In multicellular organisms, cells—the first level of organization—are organized in specialized groups called tissues. A **tissue** is a group of similar cells that perform a particular function. The collection of cells that produce digestive enzymes in the pancreas makes up one kind of tissue. This also applies to cells in the eye that respond to light and the contractile cells in muscle.

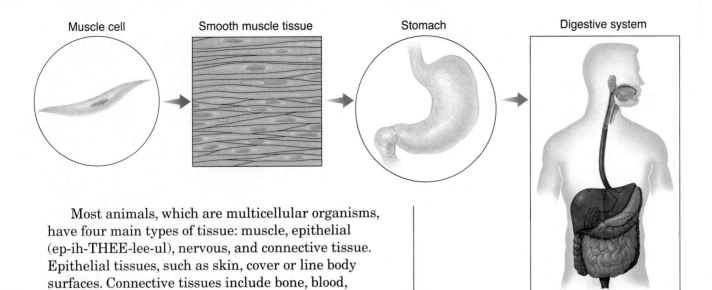

Muscle cell   Smooth muscle tissue   Stomach   Digestive system

Most animals, which are multicellular organisms, have four main types of tissue: muscle, epithelial (ep-ih-THEE-lee-ul), nervous, and connective tissue. Epithelial tissues, such as skin, cover or line body surfaces. Connective tissues include bone, blood, cartilage, and lymph.

✓ CHECKPOINT *What is a tissue?*

Organs Many tasks within the body are too compli-cated to be carried out by just one type of tissue. In these cases, many groups of tissues work together as an **organ.** For example, each muscle in your body is an individual organ. Within a muscle, however, there is much more than muscle tissue. There is nerve tissue, and there is connective tissue, which connects different parts of the body. Each tissue performs an essential task to help the organ function.

Organ Systems In most cases, organs must com-plete a series of specialized tasks. A group of organs that work together to perform a specific function is called an **organ system.** There are 11 major organ systems in the human body, including the muscular, skeletal, circulatory, and nervous systems. You will discover more about organ systems in the human body in Unit 10.

▲ **Figure 7–23** The levels of organization in a multicellular organism are individual cells, tissues, organs, and organ systems. In this example, muscle cells make up smooth muscle tissue, which, along with other tissues, makes up the stomach, an organ. The stomach in turn is part of an organ system, the digestive system.

7–4 Section Assessment

1. 🔑 **Key Concept** In what kinds of organisms is cell special-ization a characteristic?

2. 🔑 **Key Concept** List the levels of biological organization from most simple to most complex.

3. Which level of organization is represented by the eye?

4. Give two examples of an organ system.

5. **Critical Thinking Predicting** Muscle cells have a large number of which organelle?

🧍**iTEXT Assessment** Use iText to review the important con-cepts in Section 7–4.

ALTERNATIVE ASSESSMENT

Using Analogies
There are different levels of organization in many areas, for example, school and government. Use an area of your life such as school, sports, or extracurricular activities as an example to construct an analogy to explain the levels of organization in living organisms.

Observing Cell Parts and Processes

A cell's structures affect how it responds to changes in its environment. In this investigation, you will observe the differences between plant and animal cells. You will then determine how plant and animal cells are affected by hypertonic and hypotonic solutions and relate those effects to the cells' structures.

Problem
How do the differences in structure between plant and animal cells affect how they are affected by hypertonic and hypotonic solutions?

Materials
- forceps
- piece of red onion
- scalpel
- 4 glass slides
- dropper pipette

- 4 coverslips
- iodine solution
- paper towel
- microscope
- plastic gloves

- prepared slide of human cheek cells
- concentrated salt solution
- distilled water
- treated animal blood

Skills
Observing, Comparing and Contrasting, Drawing Conclusions

Procedure

Part A: Plant and Animal Cell Structures

1. Put on safety goggles and a lab apron. Using forceps, peel a thin layer from the inner surface of a piece of a red onion, as shown in the photograph.

2. Use a scalpel to cut a small piece out of the layer you removed. **CAUTION:** *The scalpel is very sharp. Handle it carefully and make sure to cut away from yourself.*

3. Place the piece of onion in the center of a glass slide. Add a drop of water to the piece of onion and cover it with a coverslip.

4. Use a dropper pipette to place a drop of iodine solution at one end of the coverslip. **CAUTION:** *Iodine can stain skin and clothing. Be careful not to spill it on yourself.* Hold a piece of paper towel near the opposite edge of the coverslip, as shown in the diagram. This will draw the iodine under the coverslip, where it will stain the onion cells.

5. Examine your slide under the low-power objective of the microscope. **CAUTION:** *Microscopes and slides are fragile. Handle them carefully.* Sketch one cell and label any structures you recognize.

6. Carefully switch to high power and observe the cell again. Try to identify other cell structures and add them to your sketch with appropriate labels.

7. Repeat steps 5 and 6 using prepared slides of human cheek cells.

Part B: Effects of Hypertonic and Hypotonic Solutions

8. Repeat steps 1 to 3 to prepare another onion cell wet mount. Using the same method as in step 4, add a drop of concentrated salt solution to the slide and use a paper towel to draw it under the coverslip.

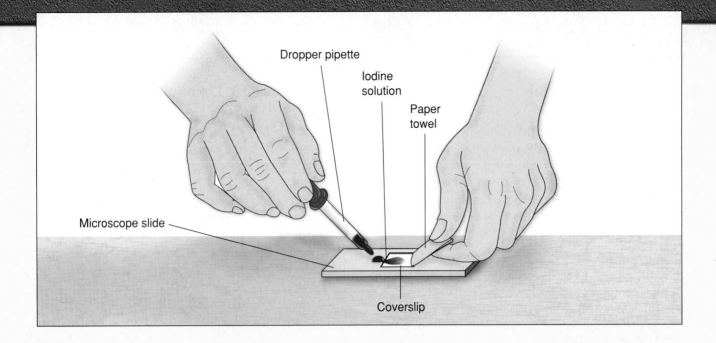

Dropper pipette

Iodine solution

Paper towel

Microscope slide

Coverslip

9. Observe the onion cells under the microscope under both low power and high power. Record your observations.

10. Put on your plastic gloves. Prepare a wet-mount slide using treated animal blood. **CAUTION:** *Use only blood samples provided by your teacher.* Do not add water as you did with the onion cells.

11. Observe the blood cells under the microscope under low power and high power. Sketch one cell and label any structures you recognize.

12. Using the same method as in step 4, add a drop of concentrated salt solution to the slide and use a paper towel to draw it under the coverslip.

13. Observe the blood cells under the microscope under both low power and high power. Record your observations. Rinse out the dropper pipette with distilled water.

14. Prepare another wet-mount slide of blood cells. This time, add a drop of distilled water to the slide and draw it under the coverslip.

15. Observe the blood cells under the microscope under both low power and high power. Record your observations.

16. Remove the plastic gloves and discard them according to your teacher's instructions. Wash your hands thoroughly with warm water and soap.

Analyze and Conclude

1. **Applying Concepts** Describe the general shapes of the onion cells and the cheek cells you observed in Part A. What structures did you see in the onion cells? The cheek cells? Describe the functions of each of the structures you saw.

2. **Comparing and Contrasting** How are plant and animal cells similar in structure? How are they different?

3. **Drawing Conclusions** Explain your observations in step 9 in terms of osmosis.

4. **Drawing Conclusions** Explain your observations in steps 13 and 15 in terms of osmosis.

5. **Applying Concepts** What part of the cell is involved in the processes you observed in steps 9, 13, and 15? Explain your answer.

6. **Comparing and Contrasting** Why don't onion cells burst when they are in distilled water? Relate your answer to the differences between plant and animal cells.

Go Further

Designing Experiments Design one or more experiments to test the effects of hypotonic and hypertonic solutions on other cells. Make sure to write a hypothesis for each experiment and control all variables. Get your teacher's permission before carrying out your experiments.

Chapter 7 Study Guide

7–1 Life Is Cellular
 Key Concepts

- The cell theory states that all living things are composed of cells, cells are the basic units of structure and function in living things, and new cells are produced from existing cells.

- Biologists divide cells into two categories: eukaryotes and prokaryotes. The cells of eukaryotes have a nucleus; the cells of prokaryotes do not.

Vocabulary
- cell, p. 170 • cell theory, p. 170
- cell membrane, p. 171 • cell wall, p. 171
- nucleus, p. 171 • cytoplasm, p. 171
- prokaryote, p. 172 • eukaryote, p. 172
- organelle, p. 172

7–2 Cell Structures
Key Concepts

- The main function of the cell wall is to provide support and protection for the cell.

- The nucleus controls most cell processes and contains the hereditary information of DNA.

- The cytoskeleton is a network of protein filaments that helps the cell to maintain its shape. The cytoskeleton is also involved in many forms of cell movement.

- The endoplasmic reticulum is the organelle in which components of the cell membrane are assembled and some proteins are modified.

- Enzymes in the Golgi apparatus attach carbohydrates and lipids to proteins.

- Chloroplasts use the energy from sunlight to make energy-rich food molecules, a process known as photosynthesis.

- Mitochondria use energy from food to make high-energy compounds that the cell can use to power growth, development, and movement.

Vocabulary
- chromatin, p. 175 • chromosome, p. 175
- nucleolus, p. 176 • nuclear envelope, p. 176
- cytoskeleton, p. 176 • microtubule, p. 176
- microfilament, p. 176 • ribosome, p. 177
- endoplasmic reticulum, p. 177
- Golgi apparatus, p. 178 • lysosome, p. 178
- vacuole, p. 179 • chloroplast, p. 180
- mitochondrion, p. 180

7–3 Movement Through the Membrane
Key Concepts

- The cell membrane regulates what enters and leaves the cell and also provides protection and support.

- Diffusion causes many substances to move across a cell membrane but does not require the cell to use energy.

- Osmosis is the diffusion of water through a selectively permeable membrane.

Vocabulary
lipid bilayer, p. 184
concentration, p. 185
diffusion, p. 185
selective permeability, p. 186
osmosis, p. 186
facilitated diffusion, p. 188
active transport, p. 189
endocytosis, p. 189
phagocytosis, p. 189
exocytosis, p. 189

7–4 The Diversity of Cellular Life
Key Concepts

- Cells in multicellular organisms are specialized to perform particular functions within the organism.

- The levels of organization in a multicellular organism are individual cells, tissues, organs, and organ systems.

Vocabulary
cell specialization, p. 191
tissue, p. 192
organ, p. 193
organ system, p. 193

Thinking Visually
Use the information in this chapter to create a concept map about the ways substances can move into and out of cells. Use the following terms in your concept map: *diffusion, osmosis, facilitated diffusion, active transport, phagocytosis, endocytosis, exocytosis.*

Chapter 7

Part A

Multiple Choice
For each statement or question, select the number of the word or expression that, of those given, best completes the statement or answers the question.

1 Which structure in most cells controls the cell's activities?
  (1) cell membrane   **(3)** ribosome
  (2) mitochondrion   **(4)** nucleus

2 Despite differences in size and shape, all cells must have cytoplasm and a
  (1) cell wall   **(3)** mitochondrion
  (2) nucleus   **(4)** cell membrane

3 Distinct threadlike structures containing genetic information are called
  (1) ribosomes   **(3)** nuclei
  (2) chromosomes   **(4)** mitochondria

4 Which organelle makes energy stored in high-energy compounds available for the cell?
  (1) ribosome   **(3)** mitochondrion
  (2) chromosome   **(4)** chloroplast

5 Cell membranes are constructed mainly of
  (1) lipid bilayers   **(3)** carbohydrate gates
  (2) protein pumps   **(4)** free-moving proteins

6 A substance that moves across a cell membrane without using the cell's energy tends to move
  (1) away from the area of equilibrium
  (2) away from the area where it is less concentrated
  (3) away from the area where it is more concentrated
  (4) toward the area where it is more concentrated

7 Which cell is best suited to transmit information through the human body?

  (1)   **(3)**

  (2)   **(4)**

8 A tissue is composed of a group of
  (1) similar cells
  (2) related organelles
  (3) organ systems
  (4) related organs

9 Which structure is *not* associated with animal cells?
  (1) mitochondrion   **(3)** nucleus
  (2) chloroplast   **(4)** cell membrane

10 The nucleus consists of all structures *except*
  (1) cytoplasm
  (2) chromatin
  (3) genetic material
  (4) a nuclear envelope

11 Which statement best describes the expected result when a typical cell is placed into fresh water?
  (1) There would be a net movement of water out of the cell.
  (2) There would be a net movement of water into the cell.
  (3) Active transport of water into the cell would begin.
  (4) No change in the cell's water content would occur.

12 Which cell structure is sometimes found attached to the endoplasmic reticulum?
  (1) chloroplast   **(3)** nucleus
  (2) mitochondrion   **(4)** ribosome

For questions 13 and 14, complete each analogy by selecting the correct number. In analogies, A : B :: C : means "A is to B as C is to __?__ ."

13 Chloroplast : energy transfer :: nucleus :
  (1) mitochondrion   **(3)** protein manufacture
  (2) DNA   **(4)** information storage

14 Factory : assembly-line workers :: cell :
  (1) vacuoles   **(3)** ribosomes
  (2) nuclei   **(4)** mitochondria

Test-Taking Tip When you answer a question based on experimental data, read the description of the experiment carefully to determine the steps followed. Then, try to see if there are any trends in the data. For example, "if *x* increases, what happens to *y*"?

Cell Structure and Function   **197**

Parts B and C

Multiple Choice and Extended Response
For those questions that ask you to select a response, choose the one that best completes the statement or answers the question. For all others follow the directions given.

Base your answers to questions 15 and 16 on the information and graph below and on your knowledge of biology.

In an experiment, plant cells were placed in sucrose solutions of varying concentrations. The rate at which the plant cells absorbed sucrose from the solution was then measured for the different concentrations. The results are summarized in the graph.

Sucrose Uptake

15 Which statement is best supported by information in the graph?
 (1) The rate of sucrose uptake increases at a constant rate from 0 to 30 mmol/L.
 (2) The rate of sucrose uptake decreases at a varying rate from 0 to 30 mmol/L.
 (3) The rate of sucrose uptake is less at 25 mmol/L than at 5 mmol/L.
 (4) The rate of sucrose uptake is constant between 30 and 40 mmol/L.

16 The graph shows that as the concentration of sucrose increases from 10 to 30 mmol/L, the plant cells
 (1) take in sucrose more slowly
 (2) take in sucrose more quickly
 (3) secrete sucrose more slowly
 (4) secrete sucrose more quickly

17 Create a two-column table to summarize the contributions made to the cell theory by Robert Hooke, Matthias Schleiden, Theodor Schwann, and Rudolf Virchow.

18 Many cells produce proteins that are secreted from the cell. State the two cell structures that cooperate to produce these specific proteins and describe the role of each in the process.

19 Chloroplasts and mitochondria are each involved in the transfer of energy. State how these two organelles work together in plant cells to take care of the plant's energy needs.

20 Other than the nucleus, which two cell structures contain their own DNA? What hypothesis has Lynn Margulis proposed to account for the DNA in these structures?

21 State one function of the protein molecules that are located in cell membranes.

22 State what is meant by the concentration of a solution. Give a specific example of concentration involving volume and mass.

23 Describe the process of diffusion. Name and describe the condition that exists when the diffusion of a particular substance is complete.

24 As waste chemicals build up in a cell, homeostasis is threatened. State how diffusion helps cells maintain low levels of waste chemicals.

25 Name and describe the cell structure that helps prevent damage to certain cells when they are subjected to high osmotic pressure.

26 State why it is necessary for most foods to be broken down into smaller molecules before they can be used within the body's cells.

27 The beaker in the diagram has a selectively permeable membrane separating two solutions. Assume that the salt molecules can pass freely through the membrane. Will the water level on either side of the membrane change?

28 Diffusion and active transport are processes that are important to the maintenance of homeostasis in organisms. Compare the two processes, including examples that describe how they are important to living organisms. In your answer be sure to
- state two ways in which active transport differs from diffusion
- state one way the two processes are similar
- state an example of each process as used by a living organism

29 Make a copy of the chart below on your answer paper, and then fill in the names of the appropriate cell structures.

Cell Structure Function	
Cell Structure	**Function**
	Fluid that transports materials within the cell
	Extracts energy from nutrients
	Uses amino acids to build proteins
	Disposes of cell wastes
	Stores cell materials
	Stores the critical information for the cell

30 State what would happen to a sample of your red blood cells if it were placed into distilled water. Support your answer with an explanation.

31 Would skin cells normally contain more or fewer mitochondria than muscle cells? Support your answer with an explanation.

32 Single-celled organisms do not have the tissues, organs, or organ systems that multicellular organisms have. State what features of most single-celled organisms enable them to carry on their life activities and maintain homeostasis.

Base your answers to questions 33 and 34 on the information below and on your knowledge of biology.

In an investigation to test the effects of varying salt concentrations on potato cells, a student placed a slice of raw potato into each of three beakers. Different solutions were added to the beakers, and the beakers were sealed. After 24 hours, the condition of each potato slice was observed. The results are summarized in the table below.

Experiment Results		
Beaker	**Contents of Beaker**	**Condition of Potato Slice After 24 Hours**
A	Pure water	Very firm
B	2% salt solution	Near normal firmness
C	4% salt solution	Very flexible—not firm

33 Based on the results above, predict the approximate concentration of water in the cytoplasm of normal potato cells. Support your answer.

34 Predict how the cells of the potato slice in Beaker A would differ in appearance from normal potato cells when viewed with a compound microscope. Support your answer.

35 The body's immune system has the ability to recognize cells that are "foreign" to the body. State how the carbohydrate chains attached to proteins in the cell membrane might protect body cells from attack.

Take It to the NET

How do illustrations of cell organelles compare to the real things? Visit the Prentice Hall Web site at **www.phschool.com** to find out more about the parts of a plant cell. Then, answer the following questions:
- What are the indentations in the inner mitochondrial membrane called? What is the inner space called? What processes occur in each location?
- What is a thylakoid? Use the "zoom" action for a closer look. Describe the difference, if any, between the illustration and the electron micrograph of the thylakoids.
- Compare the nuclear pores in the illustration of the nucleus with those in the photograph taken through an electron micrograph.

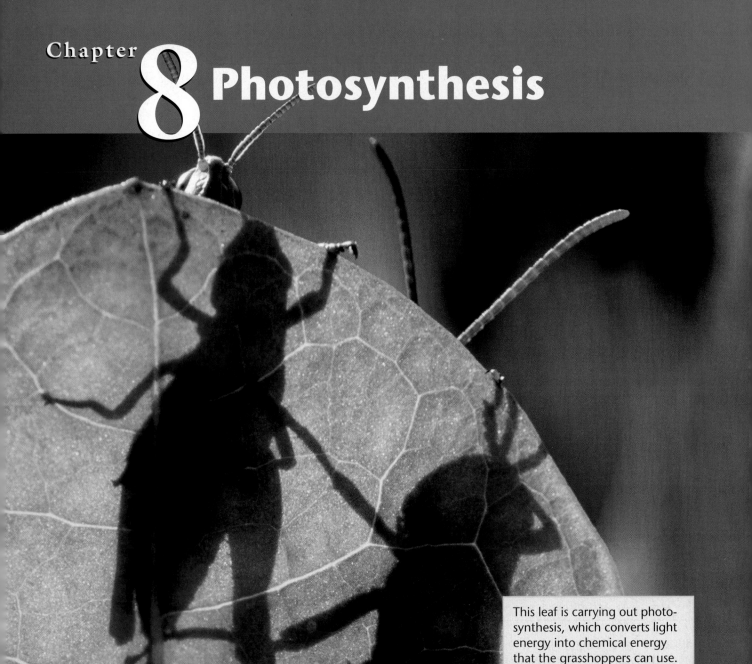

Chapter 8 Photosynthesis

This leaf is carrying out photo-synthesis, which converts light energy into chemical energy that the grasshoppers can use.

Inquiry Activity

How do organisms capture and use energy?

Procedure

1. Obtain two test tubes wrapped in foil. Note the hole in the foil surrounding one test tube.
2. **Predicting** The test tubes contain *Euglena,* photosynthetic microorganisms that have chloroplasts and can move. Record your prediction of where in each test tube you will find *Euglena.*
3. Without shaking or disturbing the contents of the test tubes, carefully remove the foil. Record where *Euglena* are located in each test tube.

Think About It

1. **Observing** What pattern did you observe in the distribution of the *Euglena?* Why do you think they behave this way?
2. **Inferring** What is the source of energy that powers the *Euglena's* swimming?

8–1 Energy and Life

Energy is the ability to do work. Nearly every activity in modern society depends on one kind of energy or another. When a car runs out of fuel—more precisely, out of the chemical energy in gasoline—it comes to a sputtering halt. Without electrical energy, lights, appliances, and computers stop working.

Living things depend on energy, too. Sometimes, the need for energy is easy to see. It is obvious that energy is needed to play soccer or other sports. However, there are times when that need is less obvious. For example, when you are sleeping, your cells are busy using energy to build new proteins and amino acids. Clearly, without the ability to obtain and use energy, life would cease to exist.

Autotrophs and Heterotrophs

Where does the energy that living things need come from? The simple answer is that it comes from food. Originally, though, the energy in most food comes from the sun. **Plants and some other types of organisms are able to use light energy from the sun to produce food.** Organisms such as plants, which make their own food, are called **autotrophs** (AW-toh-trohfs).

Other organisms, such as animals, cannot use the sun's energy directly. These organisms, known as **heterotrophs** (HET-uh-roh-trohfs), obtain energy from the foods they consume. Impalas, for example, eat grasses, which are autotrophs. Other heterotrophs, such as the leopard shown in **Figure 8–1,** obtain the energy stored in autotrophs indirectly by feeding on animals that eat autotrophs. Still other heterotrophs—mushrooms, for example—obtain food by decomposing other organisms. To live, all organisms, including plants, must release the energy in sugars and other compounds.

Guide for Reading

Key Concepts
- Where do plants get the energy they need to produce food?
- What is the role of ATP in cellular activities?

Vocabulary
autotroph
heterotroph
adenosine triphosphate (ATP)

**Reading Strategy:
Asking Questions** Before you read, study the diagram in **Figure 8–3.** Make a list of questions about the diagram. As you read, write down the answers to your questions.

Figure 8–1 Autotrophs use light energy from the sun to produce food. These impalas get their energy by eating grass, while this leopard gets its energy by eating impalas and other animals. Impalas and leopards are both heterotrophs.

Chemical Energy and ATP

Energy comes in many forms, including light, heat, and electricity. Energy can be stored in chemical compounds, too. For example, when a candle burns, carbon and hydrogen in the wax combine with oxygen from the air to produce water and carbon dioxide. This process releases energy in the form of light and heat.

ATP and ADP The activities of the cell are powered by chemical fuels. One of the principal chemical compounds that living things use to store energy is **adenosine triphosphate** (uh-DEN-uh-seen try-FAHS-fayt), abbreviated **ATP.** As **Figure 8–2** shows, an ATP molecule consists of a nitrogen-containing compound called adenine, a 5-carbon sugar called ribose, and three phosphate groups.

Adenosine diphosphate (ADP) has a structure that is similar to ATP but with one important difference: ADP has two phosphate groups instead of three. This difference is the key to the way in which cells store energy. When a cell has energy available, it can store small amounts of energy by adding a phosphate group to ADP molecules, producing ATP molecules, as shown in **Figure 8–3.** In a way, ATP is like a fully charged battery, ready to power the machinery of the cell.

CHECKPOINT *What is the difference between ATP and ADP?*

Releasing Energy From ATP The energy stored in ATP is released when ATP is converted into ADP and a phosphate group. Because a cell can add and subtract a third phosphate group, it has a way of storing and releasing energy as needed. ATP carries just enough energy to power a variety of cellular activities. **The characteristics of ATP make it an exceptionally useful molecule that is used by all types of cells as their basic energy source.**

Using Biochemical Energy Cells use the energy provided by ATP in a number of ways. One way is active transport. Many cell membranes contain a sodium-potassium pump that moves sodium ions (Na$^+$) out of the cell and potassium ions (K$^+$) into it. A single ATP molecule provides enough energy to cause the pump to move three sodium ions and two potassium ions in different directions.

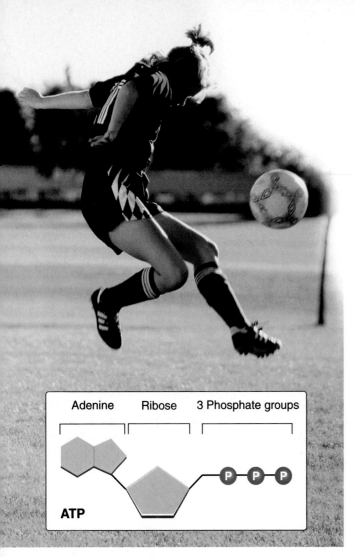

Adenine   Ribose   3 Phosphate groups

P P P

ATP

▲ **Figure 8–2** ATP is used by all types of cells as their basic energy source. The energy needed by the cells of this soccer player comes from ATP.

ADP

ATP

Adenosine Diphosphate (ADP) + Phosphate → Energy → Adenosine Triphosphate (ATP)

Partially charged battery

Fully charged battery

ATP also powers movement within the cell. Cell organelles are moved along microtubules by motor proteins that use the energy of ATP to generate force. When enough ATP is available, the organelle moves quickly along the microtubule.

ATP and Glucose

Most cells have only a small amount of ATP, enough to last for only a few seconds of activity. Why is this? Even though ATP is very efficient at transferring energy, it is not very good for storing large amounts of energy over the long term. In fact, a single molecule of the sugar glucose stores more than 90 times the chemical energy of a molecule of ATP. Therefore, it is more efficient for cells to keep only a small supply of ATP on hand. Cells can regenerate ATP from ADP as needed by using the energy in carbohydrates like glucose.

▲ **Figure 8–3** ATP can be compared to a fully charged battery because both contain stored energy, whereas ADP resembles a partially charged battery. **Predicting** *What happens when a phosphate group is removed from ATP?*

8–1 Section Assessment

1. **Key Concept** What is the ultimate source of energy for plants?

2. **Key Concept** What is ATP and what is its role in the cell?

3. Describe cellular activities that use the energy released by ATP.

4. How do autotrophs obtain energy? How do heterotrophs obtain energy?

5. **Critical Thinking Comparing and Contrasting** With respect to energy, how are ATP and glucose similar? How are they different?

TEXT **Assessment** Use iText to review the important concepts in Section 8–1.

ALTERNATIVE ASSESSMENT

Making a Poster
Find an area near your school with several types of plants. Without disturbing any of the organisms, identify any relationships between the autotrophs and the heterotrophs. Create a poster showing these relationships that are present in your community.

8–2 Photosynthesis: An Overview

Guide for Reading

 Key Concepts
- What did the experiments of van Helmont, Priestley, and Ingenhousz reveal about how plants grow?
- What is the overall equation for photosynthesis?
- What is the role of light and chlorophyll in photosynthesis?

Vocabulary
photosynthesis
pigment
chlorophyll

Reading Strategy:
Summarizing As you read, find the key ideas under each blue head. Write down a few key words from each key idea. Then, use the key words in your summary.

The study of energy capture and use begins with photosynthesis. In the process of **photosynthesis,** plants use the energy of sunlight to convert water and carbon dioxide into oxygen and high-energy carbohydrates—sugars and starches. The experiments of many scientists have contributed to the modern understanding of the process of photosynthesis.

Investigating Photosynthesis

Research into photosynthesis began centuries ago with a simple question: When a tiny seedling grows into a tall tree with a mass of several tons, where does the tree's increase in mass come from? From the soil? From the water? From the air?

Van Helmont's Experiment In the 1600s, the Belgian physician Jan van Helmont devised an experiment to find out if plants grew by taking material out of the soil. Van Helmont determined the mass of a pot of dry soil and a small seedling. Then, he planted the seedling in the pot of soil. He watered it regularly. At the end of five years, the seedling, which by then was a small tree, had gained about 75 kg. The mass of the soil,

Biology and History

Understanding Photosynthesis

 Many scientists have contributed to understanding how plants carry out photosynthesis. Early research focused on the overall process. Later researchers investigated the detailed chemical pathways.

Peter the Great becomes czar of Russia

1689

1600

1700

Joseph Priestley
Using a bell jar, a candle, and a plant, Priestley finds that the plant releases a substance that keeps the candle burning—a substance that we now know is oxygen.

1771

United States Declaration of Independence signed

1776

1643

Jan van Helmont
After careful measurements of a plant's water intake and weight increase, van Helmont concludes that trees gain most of their mass from water.

1779

Jan Ingenhousz
Ingenhousz finds that aquatic plants produce oxygen bubbles in the light but not in the dark. He concludes that plants need sunlight to produce oxygen.

however, was almost unchanged. Van Helmont concluded that most of the mass the plant gained had come from water, because that was the only thing that he had added to the pot.

Van Helmont's experiment accounts for the "hydrate," or water, portion of the carbohydrate produced by photosynthesis. But where does the carbon of the "carbo-" portion come from? Although van Helmont did not realize it, carbon dioxide in the air made a major contribution to the mass of his tree. The carbon in carbon dioxide is used to make sugars and other carbohydrates in photosynthesis. Van Helmont had only part of the story, but he had made a major contribution to science.

Priestley's Experiment

More than 100 years after van Helmont's experiment, the English minister Joseph Priestley performed an experiment that would give another insight into the process of photosynthesis. Priestley took a candle, placed a glass jar over it, and watched as the flame gradually died out. Something in the air, Priestley reasoned, was necessary to keep a candle flame burning. When that substance was used up, the candle went out. That substance was oxygen.

Priestley then found that if he placed a live sprig of mint under the jar and allowed a few days to pass, the candle could be relighted and would remain lighted for a while. The mint plant had produced the substance required for burning. In other words, it released oxygen.

✓ **CHECKPOINT** *What did Priestley discover about photosynthesis?*

Julius Robert Mayer
Mayer proposes that plants convert light energy into chemical energy.

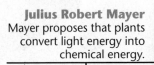

1845

Melvin Calvin
Calvin traces the chemical path that carbon follows to form glucose. These light-independent reactions are also known as the Calvin cycle.

1948

1800   1900   2000

1836
Republic of Texas formed after Texans defeat Mexico at the Battle of San Jacinto

1941
Samuel Ruben Martin Kamen
Ruben (pictured) and Kamen use isotopes to determine that the oxygen liberated in photosynthesis comes from water.

1992
Rudolph Marcus
Marcus wins the Nobel Prize in chemistry for describing the process by which electrons are transferred from one molecule to another in the electron transport chain.

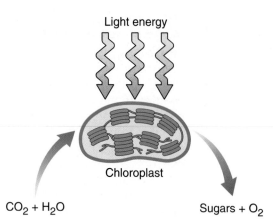

Light energy

Chloroplast

$CO_2 + H_2O$

Sugars + O_2

▲ **Figure 8–4** Photosynthesis is a series of reactions that uses energy from the sun to convert water and carbon dioxide into sugars and oxygen. Photosynthesis takes place in a plant organelle called the chloroplast.

Jan Ingenhousz Later, the Dutch scientist Jan Ingenhousz showed that the effect observed by Priestley occurred only when the plant was exposed to light. The results of Priestley's and Ingenhousz's experiments showed that light is necessary for plants to produce oxygen.

The experiments performed by van Helmont, Priestley, Ingenhousz, and other scientists reveal that in the presence of light, plants transform carbon dioxide and water into carbohydrates and release oxygen.

The Photosynthesis Equation

Because photosynthesis usually produces 6-carbon sugars ($C_6H_{12}O_6$) as its final products, the overall equation for photosynthesis can be shown as follows:

$$6CO_2 + 6H_2O \xrightarrow{\text{light}} C_6H_{12}O_6 + 6O_2$$

carbon dioxide + water $\xrightarrow{\text{light}}$ sugar + oxygen

Photosynthesis uses the energy of sunlight to convert water and carbon dioxide into oxygen and high-energy sugars. Plants then use the sugars to produce complex carbohydrates such as starches. Plants obtain carbon dioxide from the air or water in which they grow. The overall process of photosynthesis is shown in **Figure 8–4.**

Quick Lab

What colors of light does chlorophyll absorb?

Materials spectroscope, test tube of chlorophyll solution, colored pencils or markers

Procedure

1. **Predicting** Write a prediction about which colors of light chlorophyll absorbs.
2. Observe a lamp through a spectroscope. Use colored pencils to draw the spectrum that you see.
3. As you observe the spectrum, hold a test tube of chlorophyll solution in front of the spectroscope. Draw the spectrum and mark the differences from the spectrum you observed in step 2. **CAUTION:** *Be careful when handling glassware.*

Analyze and Conclude

1. **Observing** Which colors of light does chlorophyll absorb most effectively? Was your prediction correct?
2. **Inferring** How do chlorophyll and light interact to produce a green color?
3. **Drawing Conclusions** Which part of the visible spectrum do you think is most important in photosynthesis? Explain the reasons for your answer.

Light and Pigments

Although the equation tells you that water and carbon dioxide are required for photosynthesis, it does not tell you how plants use these low-energy raw materials to produce high-energy sugars. To answer that question, you have to know how plants capture the energy of sunlight. **In addition to water and carbon dioxide, photosynthesis requires light and chlorophyll, a molecule in chloroplasts.**

Energy from the sun travels to Earth in the form of light. Sunlight, which your eyes perceive as "white" light, is actually a mixture of different wavelengths of light. Many of these wavelengths are visible to your eyes and make up what is known as the visible spectrum. Your eyes see the different wavelengths of the visible spectrum as different colors.

Plants gather the sun's energy with light-absorbing molecules called **pigments.** The plants' principal pigment is **chlorophyll** (KLAWR-uh-fil). There are two main types of chlorophyll: chlorophyll *a* and chlorophyll *b*.

As **Figure 8–5** shows, chlorophyll absorbs light very well in the blue and red regions of the visible spectrum. However, chlorophyll does not absorb light well in the green region of the spectrum, which is why plants are green. Plants also contain red and orange pigments such as carotene that absorb light in other regions of the spectrum.

Because light is a form of energy, any compound that absorbs light also absorbs the energy from that light. When chlorophyll absorbs light, much of the energy is transferred directly to electrons in the chlorophyll molecule, raising the energy levels of these electrons. These high-energy electrons make photosynthesis work.

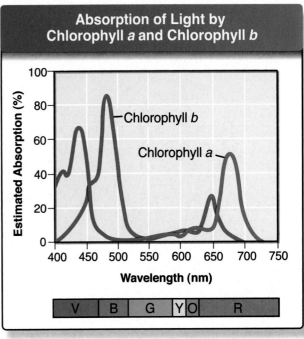

Absorption of Light by Chlorophyll *a* and Chlorophyll *b*

▲ **Figure 8–5** Photosynthesis **requires light and chlorophyll, which absorbs light energy.** In the graph, notice how chlorophyll *a* absorbs light in the violet and red regions of the visible spectrum, while chlorophyll *b* absorbs light in the blue and red regions of the visible spectrum.

8–2 Section Assessment

1. **Key Concept** What did van Helmont, Priestley, and Ingenhousz discover about plant growth?

2. **Key Concept** Describe the process of photosynthesis, including the reactants and products.

3. **Key Concept** Why are light and chlorophyll needed for photosynthesis?

4. Why are plants green?

5. **Critical Thinking Predicting** How well would a plant grow under pure yellow light? Explain your answer.

Assessment Use iText to review the important concepts in Section 8–2.

Take It to the NET

Read about the various pigments, such as chlorophyll and carotenoids, found in plants. Then, create a table listing these pigments and the colors of light they absorb. Use the links provided in the Biology area at the Prentice Hall Web site for help in completing this activity: **www.phschool.com**

8-3 The Reactions of Photosynthesis

Guide for Reading

🔑 **Key Concepts**
• What happens in the light-dependent reactions?
• What is the Calvin cycle?

Vocabulary
thylakoid
stroma
NADP⁺
light-dependent reactions
ATP synthase
Calvin cycle

Reading Strategy:
Using Visuals Before you read, preview **Figures 8–7, 8–10,** and **8–11.** As you read, notice where in the chloroplast each stage of photosynthesis takes place.

The requirements of photosynthesis were discovered in the 1800s. It was not until the second half of the 1900s, however, that biologists unraveled the complex reactions that allow plants to use the energy of sunlight to produce carbohydrates.

Inside a Chloroplast

In plants and other photosynthetic eukaryotes, photosynthesis takes place inside chloroplasts. The chloroplasts, shown in **Figure 8–6,** contain saclike photosynthetic membranes called **thylakoids** (THY-luh-koydz). Thylakoids are arranged in stacks known as grana (singular: granum). Thylakoids contain clusters of chlorophyll and other pigments and protein known as photosystems that are able to capture the energy of sunlight.

To understand photosynthesis, scientists break the reaction into two stages: the light-dependent reactions and the light-independent reactions, or Calvin cycle. The relationship between these two sets of reactions is shown in **Figure 8–7.** The light-dependent reactions take place within the thylakoid membranes. The Calvin cycle takes place in the **stroma,** the region outside the thylakoid membranes.

Figure 8–6 In plants, photosynthesis takes place inside chloroplasts. **Observing** *What color are the thylakoids, and why?*

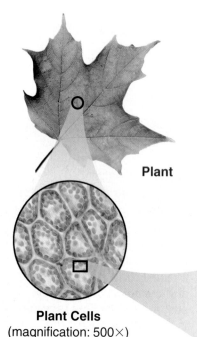

Plant

Plant Cells
(magnification: 500×)

Chloroplast

The stroma is the space outside the thylakoid membranes.

A granum is a stack of thylakoids.

Photosystems, clusters of pigment and protein that absorb light energy, are found in saclike photosynthetic membranes called thylakoids.

Chloroplast
(magnification: 10,000×)

FIGURE 8–7 **PHOTOSYNTHESIS: AN OVERVIEW**

The process of photosynthesis includes the light-dependent reactions as well as the Calvin cycle. **Interpreting Graphics** *What are the products of the light-dependent reactions?*

Chloroplast

NADPH

When sunlight excites electrons in chlorophyll, the electrons gain a great deal of energy. These high-energy electrons require a special carrier. Think of a high-energy electron as being similar to a red-hot coal from a fireplace or campfire. If you wanted to move the coal from one place to another, you wouldn't pick it up in your hands. You would use a pan or bucket—a carrier—to transport it, as shown in **Figure 8-8.** Cells treat high-energy electrons in the same way. Instead of a pan or bucket, they use electron carriers to transfer high-energy electrons from chlorophyll to other molecules. A carrier molecule is a compound that can accept a pair of high-energy electrons and transfer them along with most of their energy to another molecule.

One of these carrier molecules is a compound known as **NADP$^+$** (nicotinamide adenine dinucleotide phosphate). The name is complicated, but the job that NADP$^+$ has is simple. NADP$^+$ accepts and holds 2 high-energy electrons along with a hydrogen ion (H$^+$). This converts the NADP$^+$ into NADPH. The conversion of NADP$^+$ into NADPH is one way in which some of the energy of sunlight can be trapped in chemical form.

The NADPH can then carry high-energy electrons produced by light absorption in chlorophyll to chemical reactions elsewhere in the cell. These high-energy electrons are used to help build a variety of molecules the cell needs, including carbohydrates like glucose.

▲ **Figure 8–8** When NADP$^+$ accepts a pair of high-energy electrons, it becomes NADPH. **Making Analogies** *How are the electrons similar to the hot coals?*

Light-Dependent Reactions

As you might expect from their name, the **light-dependent reactions** require light. That is why plants like the one in **Figure 8–9** need light to grow. The light-dependent reactions use energy from light to produce ATP and NADPH. 🔑 **The light-dependent reactions produce oxygen gas and convert ADP and NADP⁺ into the energy carriers ATP and NADPH.** Look at **Figure 8–10** to see what happens at each step of the process.

A Photosynthesis begins when pigments in photosystem II absorb light. The first photosystem in the light-dependent reactions is called photosystem II because it was discovered after photosystem I. Energy from the light is absorbed by electrons, increasing their energy level. These high-energy electrons are passed on to the electron transport chain.

As light continues to shine, does the chlorophyll run out of electrons? No, it does not. The thylakoid membrane contains a system that provides new electrons to chlorophyll to replace the ones it has lost. These new electrons come from water molecules (H_2O). Enzymes on the inner surface of the thylakoid membrane break up each water molecule into 2 electrons, 2 H^+ ions, and 1 oxygen atom. The 2 electrons replace the high-energy electrons that chlorophyll has lost to the electron transport chain. The oxygen is eventually released into the air as oxygen gas (O_2). The 2 H^+ ions are released inside the thylakoid membrane.

B High-energy electrons move through the electron transport chain from photosystem II to photosystem I. Energy from the electrons is used by the molecules in the electron transport chain to transport H^+ ions from the stroma into the inner thylakoid.

C Pigments in photosystem I use energy from light to reenergize the electrons. NADP⁺ then picks up these high-energy electrons at the outer surface of the thylakoid membrane, plus a H^+ ion, and becomes NADPH.

D As a result of the H^+ ions released during water-splitting and electron transport, the inside of the thylakoid membrane becomes positively charged and the outside becomes negatively charged. The difference in charges across the membrane provides the energy to make ATP.

E H^+ ions cannot cross the membrane directly. However, the membrane contains a protein called **ATP synthase** (SIN-thays) that allows H^+ ions to pass through it. As H^+ ions pass through this protein, the protein rotates like a turbine being spun by water in a hydroelectric power plant. As it rotates, ATP synthase binds ADP and a phosphate group together to produce ATP.

✔CHECKPOINT *What are the roles of the two photosystems?*

▲ **Figure 8–9** Like all plants, this seedling needs light to grow. **Applying Concepts** *What stage of photosynthesis requires light?*

FIGURE 8–10 LIGHT-DEPENDENT REACTIONS

The light-dependent reactions use energy from sunlight to produce ATP, NADPH, and oxygen. The light-dependent reactions take place within the thylakoid membranes of chloroplasts.

Chloroplast

A Photosystem II

Light is absorbed by chlorophyll or other pigments in photosystem II. The energy from this light is transferred to electrons, which are then passed on to the electron transport chain. Separately, enzymes break up water molecules into electrons, hydrogen ions (H$^+$), and oxygen.

D Hydrogen Ion Movement

The inside of the thylakoid membrane fills up with positively charged hydrogen ions. This action makes the outside of the thylakoid membrane negatively charged and the inside positively charged.

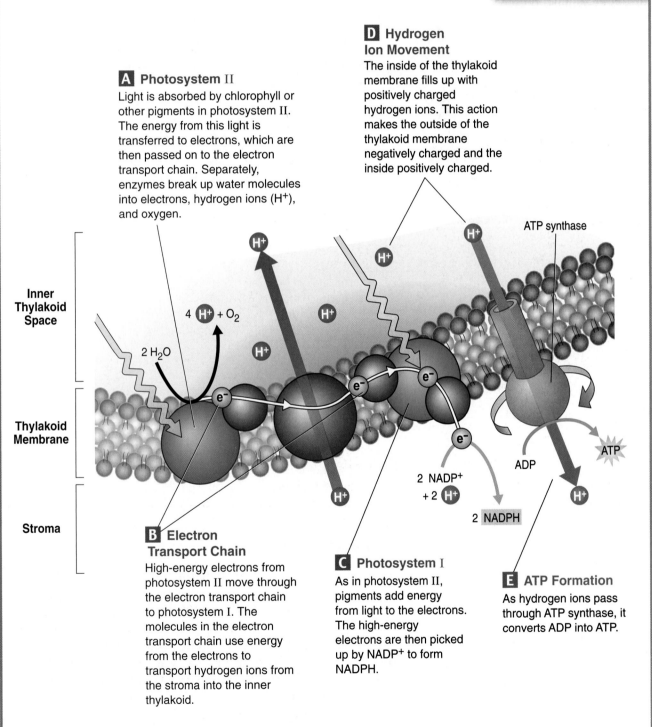

Inner Thylakoid Space

Thylakoid Membrane

Stroma

ATP synthase

4 H$^+$ + O$_2$

2 H$_2$O

2 NADP$^+$ + 2 H$^+$

2 NADPH

ADP

ATP

B Electron Transport Chain

High-energy electrons from photosystem II move through the electron transport chain to photosystem I. The molecules in the electron transport chain use energy from the electrons to transport hydrogen ions from the stroma into the inner thylakoid.

C Photosystem I

As in photosystem II, pigments add energy from light to the electrons. The high-energy electrons are then picked up by NADP$^+$ to form NADPH.

E ATP Formation

As hydrogen ions pass through ATP synthase, it converts ADP into ATP.

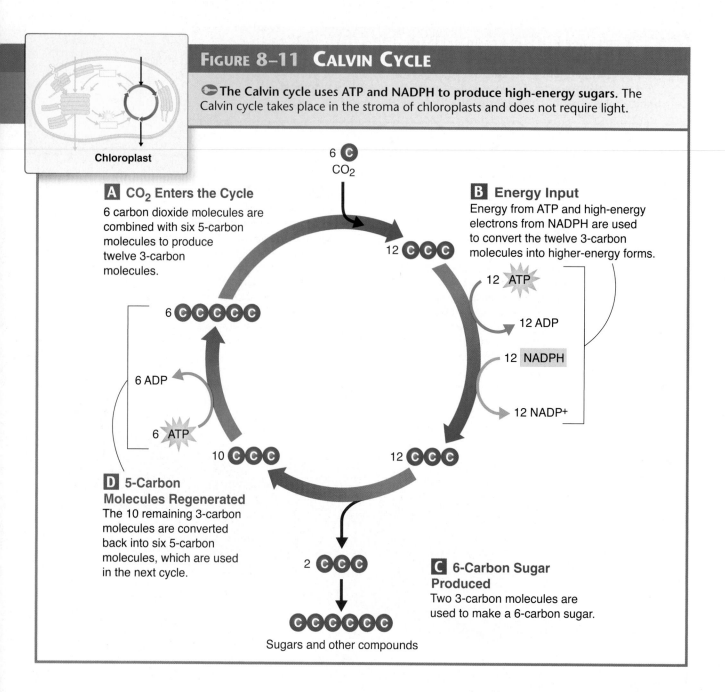

FIGURE 8–11 CALVIN CYCLE

The Calvin cycle uses ATP and NADPH to produce high-energy sugars. The Calvin cycle takes place in the stroma of chloroplasts and does not require light.

Chloroplast

6 C
CO_2

A CO₂ Enters the Cycle
6 carbon dioxide molecules are combined with six 5-carbon molecules to produce twelve 3-carbon molecules.

B Energy Input
Energy from ATP and high-energy electrons from NADPH are used to convert the twelve 3-carbon molecules into higher-energy forms.

12 C C C

12 ATP
12 ADP
12 NADPH
12 NADP+

6 C C C C C

6 ADP

6 ATP

10 C C C

12 C C C

D 5-Carbon Molecules Regenerated
The 10 remaining 3-carbon molecules are converted back into six 5-carbon molecules, which are used in the next cycle.

2 C C C

C 6-Carbon Sugar Produced
Two 3-carbon molecules are used to make a 6-carbon sugar.

C C C C C C
Sugars and other compounds

The Calvin Cycle

The ATP and NADPH formed by the light-dependent reactions contain an abundance of chemical energy, but they are not stable enough to store that energy for more than a few minutes. During the **Calvin cycle,** plants use the energy that ATP and NADPH contain to build high-energy compounds that can be stored for a long time. **The Calvin cycle uses ATP and NADPH from the light-dependent reactions to produce high-energy sugars.** The Calvin cycle is named after the American scientist Melvin Calvin, who worked out the details of this remarkable cycle. Because the Calvin cycle does not require light, these reactions are also called the light-independent reactions. Follow **Figure 8–11** to see how the Calvin cycle works.

A Six carbon dioxide molecules enter the cycle from the atmosphere. The carbon dioxide molecules combine with six 5-carbon molecules. The result is twelve 3-carbon molecules.

B The twelve 3-carbon molecules are then converted into higher-energy forms. The energy for this conversion comes from ATP and high-energy electrons from NADPH.

C Two of the twelve 3-carbon molecules are converted into two similar 3-carbon molecules. These 3-carbon molecules are used to form various 6-carbon sugars and other compounds.

D The remaining ten 3-carbon molecules are converted back into six 5-carbon molecules. These molecules combine with six new carbon dioxide molecules to begin the next cycle.

The Calvin cycle uses six molecules of carbon dioxide to produce a single 6-carbon sugar molecule. As photosynthesis proceeds, the Calvin cycle works steadily, turning out energy-rich sugars and removing carbon dioxide from the atmosphere. The plant uses the sugars for energy and to build more complex carbohydrates such as starches and cellulose, which it needs for growth and development. When other organisms eat plants, they can also use the energy stored in carbohydrates.

✓**CHECKPOINT** *What are the main products of the Calvin cycle?*

KEEP CURRENT WITH . . .

SCIENCE NEWS®

To find out more about the topics in this chapter, go to:
www.phschool.com

Analyzing Data

Rates of Photosynthesis

The rate at which a plant carries out photosynthesis depends in part on its environment. Plants that grow in the shade, for example, carry out photosynthesis at low levels of light. Plants that grow in the sun, such as desert plants, typically carry out photosynthesis at much higher levels of light.

The graph compares the rates of photosynthesis between plants that grow in the shade and plants that grow in the sun. It shows how the rate of photosynthesis changes with the number of micromoles of photons per square meter per second (μmol photons/m²/s), a standard unit of light intensity.

1. **Interpreting Graphics** When light intensity is below 200 μmol photons/m²/s, do sun plants or shade plants have a higher rate of photosynthesis?

2. **Drawing Conclusions** Does the relationship in question 1 change when light intensity increases above 400 μmol photons/m²/s? Explain your answer.

3. **Inferring** The average light intensity in the Sonoran Desert is about 400 μmol photons/m²/s. According to the graph, what would be the approximate rate of photosynthesis for sun plants that grow in this environment?

4. **Going Further** Suppose you transplant a sun plant to a shaded forest floor that receives about 100 μmol photons/m²/s. Do you think this plant will grow and thrive? Why or why not? How does the graph help you answer this question?

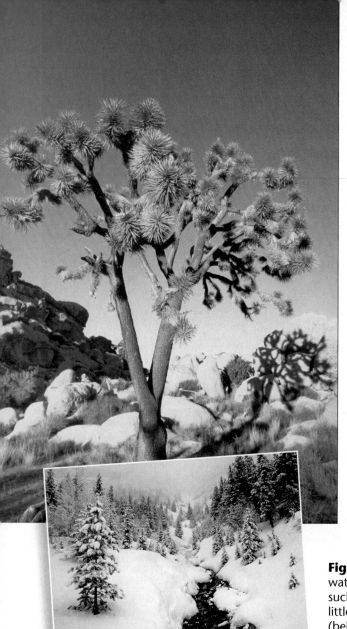

Factors Affecting Photosynthesis

Many factors affect the rate at which photosynthesis occurs. Because water is one of the raw materials of photosynthesis, a shortage of water can slow or even stop photosynthesis. Plants that live in dry conditions, such as desert plants and conifers, have a waxy coating on their leaves that reduces water loss.

Temperature is also a factor. Photosynthesis depends on enzymes that function best between 0°C and 35°C. Temperatures above or below this range may damage the enzymes, slowing down the rate of photosynthesis. At very low temperatures, photosynthesis may stop entirely. The conifers shown in **Figure 8–12** can carry out photosynthesis only on sunny days.

The intensity of light also affects the rate at which photosynthesis occurs. As you might expect, increasing light intensity increases the rate of photosynthesis. After the light intensity reaches a certain level, however, the plant reaches its maximum rate of photosynthesis. The level at which light intensity no longer affects photosynthesis varies from plant type to plant type.

Figure 8–12 Both temperature and the availability of water can affect rates of photosynthesis. Desert plants such as this Joshua tree (above) are adapted to survive with little water. During the cold winter months these conifers (below) may only occasionally carry out photosynthesis. **Comparing and Contrasting** *What do both plants shown have that helps them conserve water?*

8–3 Section Assessment

1. **Key Concept** Summarize the light-dependent reactions.
2. **Key Concept** What reactions make up the Calvin cycle?
3. What is the function of NADPH?
4. How is light energy converted into chemical energy during photosynthesis?

5. **Critical Thinking Inferring** Can the complete process of photosynthesis take place in the dark? Explain your answer.

iTEXT **Assessment** Use iText to review the important concepts in Section 8–3.

ALTERNATIVE ASSESSMENT

Making a Flowchart
Construct a flowchart that illustrates the steps of photosynthesis. Begin with the energy of sunlight and end with the production of sugars. Include as much detail as possible in the numerous steps.

Investigating Photosynthesis

If only part of a leaf receives light, does the whole leaf perform photo-synthesis? What if a leaf receives only light of one color? You are going to design an experiment to test the effects of colored light on photosynthesis.

Problem **How do different colors of light affect the process of photosynthesis?**

Materials

- scissors
- black construction paper
- potted plant
- tape
- blue, red, and green cellophane
- 5 large test tubes
- glass-marking pencil
- forceps
- 400-mL beaker
- 5 petri dishes
- iodine solution
- paper towels

Skills Predicting, Formulating Hypotheses

Design Your Experiment

1. **Predicting** During photosynthesis, starch accumulates in leaves. Record your prediction of how keeping part of a leaf in darkness will affect starch accumulation.

2. Cut two pieces of black construction paper large enough to cover half of one leaf of the plant.

3. Sandwich half of the leaf between the two squares of black paper and tape the paper in place as shown.

4. **Formulating Hypotheses** Develop a hypothe-sis that predicts how the color of light will affect photosynthesis. Record your hypothesis.

5. Design an experiment to test your hypothesis. Have your teacher check your plan. Set up your experiment using leaves from the same plant as in step 3.

6. Leave your plant in a sunlit area for 2 days.

7. Cut off each experimental leaf and one leaf that was not treated. Roll up each leaf and put it in a large test tube. Label each tube and petri dish with the treatment the leaf received.

8. Before you test the leaves for starch, the chloro-phyll must be removed from the leaves. Your teacher will add alcohol to your test tubes and heat them in hot water. **CAUTION:** *Alcohol is toxic and flammable, and its fumes are irritating.* When the color has disappeared from each leaf, use forceps to swirl each leaf in a beaker of water. Place it in a labeled petri dish.

9. Cover each leaf with iodine solution. Iodine solution stains starch blue or black. **CAUTION:** *Iodine is corrosive and irritating to the skin and can stain clothes and skin.*

10. After 1 minute, use forceps to gently swirl each leaf in the beaker of water and lay the leaf flat on a paper towel.

11. Observe each leaf and record your observations.

Analyze and Conclude

1. **Observing** Which leaves contained starch? Which did not? Was your prediction about the leaf covered in black paper correct? Explain your answer.

2. **Evaluating** What effect did each color of light have on the leaves? Was your hypothesis correct?

3. **Drawing Conclusions** Use your knowledge of chlorophyll to explain your results.

Go Further

Designing an Experiment Where is starch found in the multicolored leaves of a coleus plant? With your teacher's approval, perform an experiment to find out. Explain your results.

8–1 Energy and Life
Key Concepts

- Plants and some other types of organisms are able to use light energy from the sun to produce food.
- The characteristics of ATP make it an exceptionally useful molecule that is used by all types of cells as their basic energy source.

Vocabulary
autotroph, p. 201
heterotroph, p. 201
adenosine triphosphate (ATP), p. 202

8–2 Photosynthesis: An Overview
Key Concepts

- The experiments performed by van Helmont, Priestley, Ingenhousz, and other scientists reveal that in the presence of light, plants transform carbon dioxide and water into carbohydrates and release oxygen as a byproduct.
- Photosynthesis uses the energy of sunlight to convert water and carbon dioxide into oxygen and high-energy sugars.
- In addition to water and carbon dioxide, photosynthesis requires light and chlorophyll, a molecule found in chloroplasts.

Vocabulary
photosynthesis, p. 204
pigment, p. 207
chlorophyll, p. 207

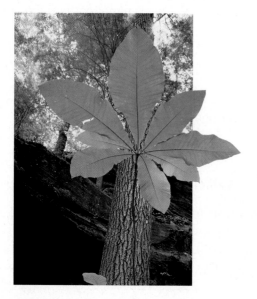

8–3 The Reactions of Photosynthesis
Key Concepts

- The process of photosynthesis includes the light-dependent reactions as well as the Calvin cycle.
- The light-dependent reactions produce oxygen gas and convert ADP and $NADP^+$ into ATP and NADPH. The light-dependent reactions occur in different areas of the thylakoid, called photosystem I and photosystem II.
- The Calvin cycle uses ATP and NADPH from the light-dependent reactions to produce high-energy sugars. The Calvin cycle is also known as the light-independent reactions.

Vocabulary
thylakoid, p. 208
stroma, p. 208
$NADP^+$, p. 209
light-dependent reactions, p. 210
ATP synthase, p. 210
Calvin cycle, p. 212

Thinking Visually
Using the information in this chapter, complete the following flowchart about photosynthesis:

Chapter 8

Part A

Multiple Choice

For each statement or question, select the number of the word or expression that, of those given, best completes the statement or answers the question.

1 Maple trees, algae, and wheat are all
   (1) autotrophs   (3) heterotrophs
   (2) decomposers   (4) scavengers

2 One of the principal chemical compounds that living things use to store energy is
   (1) DNA   (3) ATP
   (2) H_2O (4) CO_2

3 Van Helmont placed a known mass of soil in a large container. He then planted a small tree with a known mass in the container of soil. For five years, he watered and observed the tree. At the conclusion of his experiment, he discovered that the tree had gained 75 kilograms, while the mass of the soil was almost unchanged. A reasonable conclusion van Helmont could make based on his data is that
   (1) plants obtain food from the soil
   (2) plants convert soil compounds into new plant cells
   (3) plants obtain their food from a source other than water
   (4) plants may use water as a source of building materials

4 In addition to light and chlorophyll, photosynthesis requires
   (1) water and oxygen
   (2) water and sugars
   (3) oxygen and carbon dioxide
   (4) water and carbon dioxide

5 The leaves of a plant appear green because chlorophyll
   (1) reflects blue and orange light
   (2) absorbs blue and orange light
   (3) reflects green light
   (4) absorbs green light

6 The products of photosynthesis are
   (1) sugars and oxygen
   (2) sugars and carbon dioxide
   (3) water and carbon dioxide
   (4) hydrogen and oxygen

7 Which organelle contains chlorophyll?

(1)

(3)

(2)

(4)

8 The first process in the light-dependent reactions of photosynthesis is
   (1) light absorption
   (2) electron transport
   (3) oxygen production
   (4) ATP formation

9 The light-independent reactions of photosynthesis are also known as the
   (1) Calvin cycle   (3) Ingenhousz cycle
   (2) Priestley cycle   (4) van Helmont cycle

10 Energy for use in cells is stored in the form of
   (1) chemical-bond energy
   (2) solar energy
   (3) heat energy
   (4) mechanical energy

For questions 11 and 12, complete each analogy by selecting the correct number. In analogies, A : B :: C : means "A is to B as C is to ___?___ ."

11 Oak tree : autotroph :: human :
   (1) parasite   (3) autotroph
   (2) producer   (4) heterotroph

12 Light-dependent reactions : oxygen :: Calvin cycle :
   (1) sugar   (3) carbon dioxide
   (2) NADPH   (4) ADP

Test-Taking Tip   In tests, analogies compare pairs of items, such as *kitten : cat :: puppy ___?___*. Before looking at the possible answers, identify how the first pair is related. For example, since a kitten is a young cat, the relationship is *baby : adult*, so the correct answer is *puppy : dog*.

Parts B and C

Multiple Choice and Extended Response

For those questions that ask you to select a response, choose the one that best completes the statement or answers the question. For all others follow the directions given.

13 How do heterotrophs and autotrophs differ in the way they obtain energy?

Base your answers to questions 14 through 19 on the information below and on your knowledge of biology.

The activities of the cell are powered by chemical fuels. One of the principal chemical compounds that living organisms use to store energy is ATP.

14 Make a copy of the chart below on your answer paper and complete the comparison of ATP and ADP. (Do not write in this book.)

Comparison of ATP and ADP		
Name of Part	Number in ATP	Number in ADP
Adenine		
Ribose		
Phosphate groups		

15 What is the primary difference between ATP and ADP?

16 How is this difference important in the way a cell stores energy?

17 Use the analogy of a battery to explain how energy is stored in and released from ATP.

18 Compare the amounts of energy stored by ATP and glucose.

19 Which compound is used by the cell as an immediate source of energy?

20 Without light and chlorophyll, photosynthesis in green plants could not occur. Explain why each of these is important in the process of photosynthesis.

21 Expain how Priestley's and Ingenhousz's discoveries about photosynthesis are related.

22 How do the events in the Calvin cycle depend on the light-dependent reactions?

Base your answers to questions 23 through 25 on the illustration below and on your knowledge of biology.

23 Identify the structures labeled A, B, C, and D.

24 In which structure(s) does the light-dependent reactions occur?

25 In which structure(s) does the Calvin cycle take place?

26 Explain the role of $NADP^+$ as an energy carrier in photosynthesis.

27 State three factors that affect the rate at which photosynthesis occurs.

28 Some plant leaves contain yellow and red pigments as well as chlorophyll. In the fall, those leaves may become red or yellow. Suggest an explanation for such color changes.

Base your answers to questions 29 through 33 on the information below and on your knowledge of biology.

A water plant placed in a bright light gives off bubbles of oxygen. In the laboratory, you notice that if the light is placed at different distances from the plant, the rate at which the plant produces bubbles changes. Your data are shown in the following table.

Oxygen Production	
Distance From Light (cm)	Bubbles Produced per Minute
10	39
20	22
30	8
40	5

29 Using the information in the data table, make a line graph on a piece of graph paper. As you make your graph, be sure you
- mark an appropriate scale on each axis
- label each axis
- provide the graph with a title
- plot the data for "Bubbles Produced per Minute" on the grid. Surround each point with a small circle, and connect the points

30 Describe the trend you observe on the graph.

31 When the light was farther from the plant, did the number of bubbles produced increase or decrease? Support your answer with an explanation.

32 At what distance is gas production at its highest?
(1) 10 cm   (3) 30 cm
(2) 20 cm   (4) 40 cm

33 What relationship exists between the distance from the plant to the light and the number of bubbles produced? Support your answer with an explanation.

34 Examine the photograph of the Indian pipe plant shown below. What can you conclude about the ability of the Indian pipe plant to make its own food? Support your answer with an explanation.

35 The Calvin cycle is sometimes described as the light-independent reactions. Study Figure 8–11 on page 212 and give evidence to support the idea that the Calvin cycle does not depend on light.

36 Many of the sun's rays may be blocked by dust or clouds formed by volcanic eruptions or pollution. Explain one possible short-term effect and one possible long-term effect of this on photosynthesis.

37 Recall what you learned about the flow of energy through an ecosystem. Explain how photosynthesis relates to that flow.

38 Write an equation that summarizes the process of photosynthesis. Use the following terms in your equation: light, sugars, oxygen, water, carbon dioxide.

39 Design an experiment that uses pond water and algae to demonstrate the importance of light energy to pond life. In your answer be sure to
- identify the variables you will control
- identify the manipulated (independent) variable
- identify the responding (dependent) variable
- list the materials you will use
- detail the procedure you will follow

40 Suppose you water a potted plant and place it by a window in an airtight jar. Predict when photosynthesis might occur over the next few days. Would you expect the pattern to change if the plant were left for several weeks? Support your answer with an explanation.

Take It to the NET

Why is it important to study photosynthesis? Visit the Prentice Hall Web site at **www.phschool.com** to find out some of the ways in which the study of photosynthesis is important. Then, answer the following questions:
- In what ways do people use the products of photosynthesis in their everyday lives?
- How might research into photosynthesis help scientists increase the amount of food that farmers are able to produce?
- How can we use the products of photosynthesis to help reduce levels of harmful pollutants?

9 Cellular Respiration

Athletes get the energy they need from the breakdown of glucose during cellular respiration.

Inquiry Activity

How do living things release energy?

Procedure

1. Draw a table with 5 rows and 4 columns. Label the columns from left to right: Item, Activities, Energy Source, and How Energy Is Released.

2. Fill in each row of your table for every item your teacher provides.

3. Complete your table, using yourself for the last item.

Think About It

1. **Using Tables and Graphs** Was it easier to describe how organisms use energy or how nonliving devices use energy?

2. **Using Tables and Graphs** What is the most common energy source for organisms?

3. **Formulating Hypotheses** How do you think organisms release the energy they need?

9–1 Chemical Pathways

When you are hungry, how do you feel? If you are like most people, your stomach may seem empty, you might feel a little dizzy, and above all, you feel weak. The sensations produced by hunger vary from one person to the next, but the bottom line is always the same. Our bodies have a need for food, and they have their own ways of telling us when we need it.

Food provides living things with the chemical building blocks they need to grow and reproduce. Food serves as a source of raw materials from which the cells of the body can synthesize new molecules. Most of all, food serves as a source of energy.

Chemical Energy and Food

How much energy is actually present in food? Quite a lot. One gram of the sugar glucose ($C_6H_{12}O_6$), when burned in the presence of oxygen, releases 3811 calories of heat energy. A **calorie** is the amount of energy needed to raise the temperature of 1 gram of water 1 Celsius degree. The Calorie (capital "C") that is used on food labels is a kilocalorie, or 1000 calories. Cells, of course, don't "burn" glucose. Instead, they gradually release the energy from glucose and other food compounds.

This process begins with a pathway called **glycolysis** (gly-KAHL-ih-sis). Glycolysis releases only a small amount of energy. If oxygen is present, glycolysis leads to two other pathways that release a great deal of energy. If oxygen is not present, however, glycolysis is followed by a different pathway.

Guide for Reading

 Key Concepts
- What is cellular respiration?
- What happens during the process of glycolysis?
- What are the two main types of fermentation?

Vocabulary
calorie
glycolysis
cellular respiration
NAD+
fermentation
anaerobic

Reading Strategy:
Asking Questions Before you read this section, rewrite the headings as *how, why,* or *what* questions about releasing energy. Then, as you read, write brief answers to your questions.

Figure 9–1 Living things get the energy they need from food. Both plant and animal cells carry out the final stages of cellular respiration in the mitochondria.

Animal

Plant

Animal Cells
(magnification: 2500×)

Plant Cells (magnification: 500×)

Outer membrane

Intermembrane space

Inner membrane

Mitochondrion

Mitochondrion
(magnification: about 10,000×)

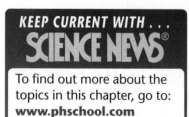
FIGURE 9–2 CELLULAR RESPIRATION: AN OVERVIEW

Cellular respiration is the process that releases energy by breaking down food molecules in the presence of oxygen. Glycolysis takes place in the cytoplasm. The Krebs cycle and electron transport take place inside the mitochondria.

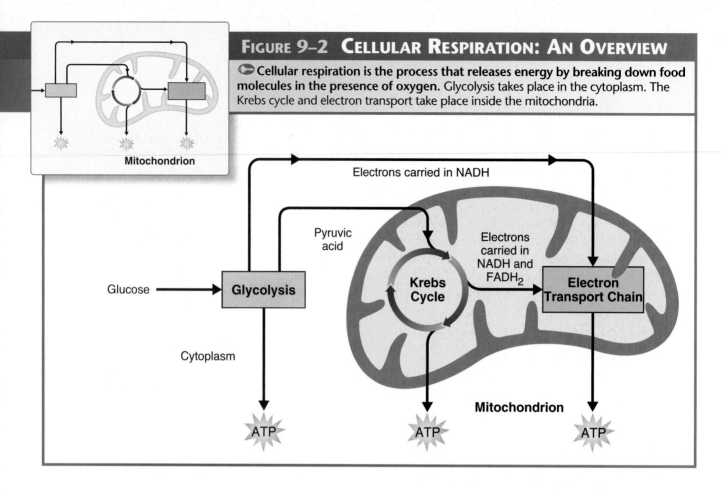

Overview of Cellular Respiration

In the presence of oxygen, glycolysis is followed by the Krebs cycle and the electron transport chain. Glycolysis, the Krebs cycle, and the electron transport chain make up a process called **cellular respiration.** Cellular respiration is the process that releases energy by breaking down food molecules in the presence of oxygen. The equation for cellular respiration is:

$$6O_2 + C_6H_{12}O_6 \longrightarrow 6CO_2 + 6H_2O + Energy$$

$$\text{oxygen + glucose} \longrightarrow \text{carbon dioxide + water + energy}$$

As you can see, cellular respiration requires a food molecule such as glucose and oxygen, and gives off carbon, water, and energy. Do not be misled, however, by the simplicity of this equation. If cellular respiration took place in just one step, all of the energy from glucose would be released at once, and most of it would be lost in the form of light and heat. Clearly, a living cell has to control that energy. It can't simply start a fire—it has to release the explosive chemical energy in food molecules a little bit at a time. The cell needs to find a way to trap those little bits of energy by using them to make ATP. As you will see, that is exactly what the cell does.

The three main stages of cellular respiration are shown in **Figure 9–2.** Each of the three stages captures some of the chemical energy available in food molecules and uses it to produce ATP.

Glycolysis

The first set of reactions in cellular respiration is glycolysis. 🔑 **Glycolysis is the process in which one molecule of glucose is broken in half, producing two molecules of pyruvic acid, a 3-carbon compound.** The process of glycolysis is shown in **Figure 9–3**.

ATP Production Even though glycolysis is an energy-releasing process, the cell needs to put in a little energy to get things going. At the pathway's beginning, 2 molecules of ATP are used up. In a way, those 2 ATP molecules are like an investment that pays back interest. In order to earn interest from a bank, first you have to put money into an account. Although the cell puts 2 ATP molecules into its "account" to get glycolysis going, when glycolysis is complete, 4 ATP molecules have been produced. This gives the cell a net gain of 2 ATP molecules.

NADH Production One of the reactions of glycolysis removes 4 high-energy electrons and passes them to an electron carrier called **NAD⁺,** or nicotinamide adenine dinucleotide. Like NADP⁺ in photosynthesis, each NAD⁺ accepts a pair of high-energy electrons. This molecule, known as NADH, holds the electrons until they can be transferred to other molecules. By doing this, NAD⁺ helps to pass energy from glucose to other pathways in the cell.

Although the energy yield from glycolysis is small, the process is so fast that cells can produce thousands of ATP molecules in just a few milliseconds. Besides speed, another advantage is that glycolysis itself does not require oxygen. This means that glycolysis can supply chemical energy to cells when oxygen is not available.

However, when a cell generates large amounts of ATP from glycolysis, it runs into a problem. In just a few seconds, all of the cell's available NAD⁺ molecules are filled up with electrons. Without NAD⁺, the cell cannot keep glycolysis going, and ATP production stops.

✓ CHECKPOINT *What does glycolysis break down?*

Word Origins

Glycolysis comes from the Greek word *glukus,* meaning "sweet," and the Latin word *lysis,* which indicates a process of loosening or decomposing. Thus, *glycolysis* means "breaking glucose." **If *hydro* means "water," what do you think the term *hydrolysis* means?**

▼ **Figure 9–3** Glycolysis is the first stage in cellular respiration. 🔑 During glycolysis, glucose is broken down into 2 molecules of pyruvic acid.

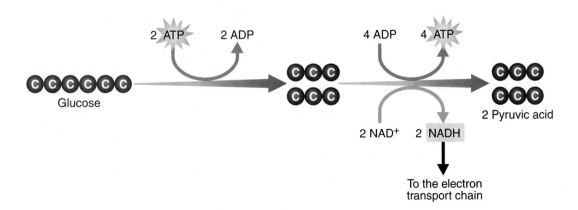

Glucose

2 ATP → 2 ADP

4 ADP → 4 ATP

2 NAD⁺ → 2 NADH

2 Pyruvic acid

To the electron transport chain

Fermentation

When oxygen is not present, glycolysis is followed by a different pathway. The combined process of this pathway and glycolysis is called fermentation. **Fermentation** releases energy from food molecules in the absence of oxygen.

During fermentation, cells convert NADH to NAD^+ by passing high-energy electrons back to pyruvic acid. This action converts NADH back into the electron carrier NAD^+, allowing glycolysis to continue producing a steady supply of ATP. Because fermentation does not require oxygen, it is said to be **anaerobic.** The term *anaerobic* means "not in air." 🗝 **The two main types of fermentation are alcoholic fermentation and lactic acid fermentation.**

Alcoholic Fermentation Yeasts and a few other microorganisms use alcoholic fermentation, forming ethyl alcohol and carbon dioxide as wastes. The equation for alcoholic fermentation after glycolysis is:

$$\text{pyruvic acid } + \text{ NADH} \longrightarrow \text{alcohol } + \text{ CO}_2 + \text{NAD}^+$$

Alcoholic fermentation produces carbon dioxide as well as alcohol. Alcoholic fermentation causes bread dough to rise. When yeast in the dough runs out of oxygen, it begins to ferment, giving off bubbles of carbon dioxide which form the air spaces you see in a slice of bread. The small amount of alcohol produced in the dough evaporates when the bread is baked.

Problem Solving

A Family Recipe

You have opened a bakery, selling bread made according to your family's favorite recipe. Unfortunately, most of your customers find your bread too heavy. You need to make your bread more appealing to your customers. Before bread is baked, yeast cells in the dough ferment some of the carbohydrate in the flour, producing bubbles of carbon dioxide. These bubbles cause the dough to rise and give bread its light, spongy structure. How can you make your bread lighter?

Define the Problem In your own words, write down what problem you are trying to solve.

Organizing Information The process of fermentation is a series of chemical reactions catalyzed by enzymes. Review what you've learned about such reactions. Make a list of factors, such as temperature and the amounts of yeast and flour in the dough, that might affect the process of fermentation. Predict how each factor will affect the rate of fermentation.

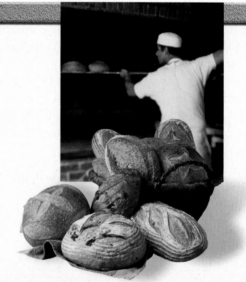

Creating a Solution Write a detailed description of an experiment that could determine if changing the conditions of the fermentation would make the bread lighter. Identify each of your variables. What controls and experimental treatments will you use?

Presenting Your Plan Make a poster showing the procedures in your proposed experiment and explain it to your classmates.

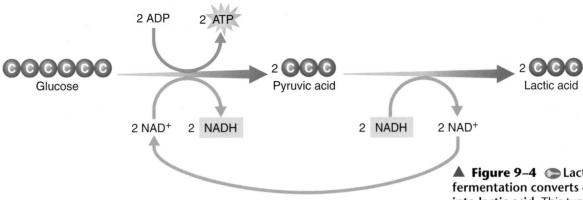

▲ **Figure 9–4** Lactic acid fermentation converts glucose into lactic acid. This type of fermentation occurs in human muscle cells during strenuous exercise when breathing cannot supply the cells with enough oxygen.

Lactic Acid Fermentation In many cells, the pyruvic acid that accumulates as a result of glycolysis can be converted to lactic acid. Because this type of fermentation produces lactic acid, it is called lactic acid fermentation. This process regenerates NAD$^+$ so that glycolysis can continue, as shown in **Figure 9–4**. The equation for lactic acid fermentation after glycolysis is:

$$\text{pyruvic acid } + \text{ NADH } \longrightarrow \text{ lactic acid } + \text{ NAD}^+$$

Lactic acid is produced in your muscles during rapid exercise when the body cannot supply enough oxygen to the tissues. Without enough oxygen, the body is not able to produce all of the ATP that is required. When you exercise vigorously by running, swimming, or riding a bicycle as fast as you can, the large muscles of your arms and legs quickly run out of oxygen. Your muscle cells rapidly begin to produce ATP by lactic acid fermentation. The buildup of lactic acid causes a painful, burning sensation. This is why muscles may feel sore after only a few seconds of intense activity.

9–1 Section Assessment

1. **Key Concept** Describe the process of cellular respiration.
2. **Key Concept** What are the products of glycolysis?
3. **Key Concept** Name the two main types of fermentation.
4. What is a calorie? A Calorie?
5. How is the function of NAD$^+$ similar to that of NADP$^+$?

6. **Critical Thinking Comparing and Contrasting** How are lactic acid fermentation and alcoholic fermentation similar? How are they different?

iTEXT Assessment Use iText to review the important concepts in Section 9–1.

Take It to the NET
Read about fermented foods that are consumed by humans. Then, make a data table that lists each food and its source (before fermentation). Use the links provided in the Biology area at the Prentice Hall Web site for help in completing this activity: **www.phschool.com**

9–2 The Krebs Cycle and Electron Transport

Guide for Reading

Key Concepts
• What happens during the Krebs cycle?
• How are high-energy electrons used by the electron transport chain?

Vocabulary
aerobic
Krebs cycle
electron transport chain

Reading Strategy:
Using Visuals Before you read, review **Figure 9–2** on page 222. Then preview **Figures 9–6** and **9–7.** As you read, notice where the Krebs cycle and electron transport take place.

At the end of glycolysis, about 90 percent of the chemical energy that was available in glucose is still unused, locked in the high-energy electrons of pyruvic acid. To extract the rest of that energy, the cell turns to one of the world's most powerful electron acceptors—oxygen. Oxygen is required for the final steps of cellular respiration. Because the pathways of cellular respiration require oxygen, they are said to be **aerobic.**

As you know, the word *respiration* is often used as a synonym for breathing. This is why we have used the term "cellular respiration" to refer to energy-releasing pathways within the cell. The double meaning of respiration points out a crucial connection between cells and organisms: The energy-releasing pathways within cells require oxygen, and that is the reason we need to breathe, to respire.

The Krebs Cycle

In the presence of oxygen, pyruvic acid produced in glycolysis passes to the second stage of cellular respiration, the **Krebs cycle.** The Krebs cycle is named after Hans Krebs, the British biochemist who demonstrated its existence in 1937. **During the Krebs cycle, pyruvic acid is broken down into carbon dioxide in a series of energy-extracting reactions.** Because citric acid is the first compound formed in this series of reactions, the Krebs cycle is also known as the citric acid cycle.

A The Krebs cycle begins when pyruvic acid produced by glycolysis enters the mitochondrion. One carbon atom from pyruvic acid becomes part of a molecule of carbon dioxide, which is eventually released into the air. Two of the 3 carbon atoms are joined to a compound called coenzyme A to form acetyl-CoA. (The acetyl part of acetyl-CoA is made up of 2 carbon atoms, 1 oxygen atom, and 3 hydrogen atoms.) Acetyl-CoA then adds the 2-carbon acetyl group to a 4-carbon molecule, producing a 6-carbon molecule called citric acid.

B As the cycle continues, citric acid is broken down into a 4-carbon molecule, more carbon dioxide is released, and electrons are transferred to energy carriers. Follow the reactions in **Figure 9–6,** and you will see how this happens. First, look at the 6 carbon atoms in citric acid. One is removed, and then another, releasing 2 molecules of carbon dioxide and leaving a 4-carbon molecule. This 4-carbon molecule is then ready to accept another 2-carbon acetyl group, which starts the cycle all over again.

Next, look for ATP. For each turn of the cycle, a molecule equivalent to ATP is produced. Finally, look at the electron carriers. For each turn of the cycle, 5 pairs of high-energy

▲ **Figure 9–5** Hans Krebs won the Nobel Prize in 1953 for his discovery of the citric acid cycle, or Krebs cycle.

FIGURE 9-6 THE KREBS CYCLE

⊂During the Krebs cycle, pyruvic acid from glycolysis is used to make carbon dioxide, NADH, ATP, and FADH$_2$.

Mitochondrion

A Citric Acid Production

As pyruvic acid enters the mitochondrion, a carbon is removed, forming CO$_2$, and electrons are removed, changing NAD$^+$ to NADH. Coenzyme A joins the 2-carbon molecule, forming acetyl-CoA. Acetyl-CoA then adds the 2-carbon acetyl group to a 4-carbon compound, forming citric acid.

B Energy Extraction

Citric acid is broken down into a 5-carbon compound, then into a 4-carbon compound. Along the way, two more molecules of CO$_2$ are released, and electrons join NAD$^+$ and FAD, forming NADH and FADH$_2$. In addition, one molecule of ATP is generated. The energy tally from one molecule of pyruvic acid is 4 NADH, 1 FADH$_2$, and 1 molecule of ATP.

electrons are captured by 5 carrier molecules: 4 NADH molecules and 1 FADH$_2$. FAD (flavine adenine dinucleotide) and FADH$_2$ are molecules similar to NAD$^+$ and NADH, respectively.

What happens to each of these Krebs cycle products? First, the carbon dioxide released is the source of all the carbon dioxide in your breath. Every time you exhale, you expel the carbon dioxide produced by the Krebs cycle. Next, the ATP produced directly in the Krebs cycle can be used for cellular activities. However, what does the cell do with all those high-energy electrons in carriers like NADH? In the presence of oxygen, those high-energy electrons can be used to generate huge amounts of ATP.

CHECKPOINT   *Why is the Krebs cycle also known as the citric acid cycle?*

FIGURE 9–7 ELECTRON TRANSPORT CHAIN

The electron transport chain uses high-energy electrons from the Krebs cycle to convert ADP into ATP.

Electron Transport

As we have just seen, the Krebs cycle spins round and round, generating high-energy electrons that are passed to NADH and FADH$_2$. What's next? The electrons are passed from those carriers to the **electron transport chain**. 🔑 **The electron transport chain uses the high-energy electrons from the Krebs cycle to convert ADP into ATP.** The beauty of the electron transport chain is the way in which it couples the movement of high-energy electrons with the production of ATP. Look at **Figure 9–7** to see how this happens.

A High-energy electrons from NADH and FADH$_2$ are passed into and along the electron transport chain. In eukaryotes, the electron transport chain is composed of a series of carrier proteins that is located in the inner membrane of the mitochondrion. In prokaryotes, the same chain is in the cell membrane. High energy electrons are passed from one carrier protein to the next. At the end of the electron transport chain is an enzyme that combines electrons from the electron chain with hydrogen ions and oxygen to form water. If you're still wondering why we need oxygen, here's why: oxygen serves as the final electron acceptor of the electron transport chain. Thus oxygen is essential for getting rid of low-energy electrons and hydrogen ions, the wastes of cellular respiration.

B Every time 2 high-energy electrons transport down the electron transport chain, their energy is used to transport hydrogen ions (H^+) across the membrane. During electron transport, H^+ ions build up in the intermembrane space, making it positively charged. The other side of the membrane, from which those H^+ ions have been taken, is now negatively charged.

C How does the cell use the charge differences that build up as a result of electron transport? The inner membranes of the mitochondria contain protein spheres called ATP synthases. As H^+ ions escape through channels into these proteins, the ATP synthases spin. Each time it rotates, the enzyme grabs a low-energy ADP and attaches a phosphate, forming high-energy ATP. On average, each pair of high-energy electrons that moves down the electron transport chain provides enough energy to convert 3 ADP molecules into 3 ATP molecules.

✓ CHECKPOINT *What is the role of ATP synthase?*

The Totals

How much chemical energy does cellular respiration yield from a single molecule of glucose? Recall that glycolysis produces just 2 ATP molecules per glucose. In the absence of oxygen, that is all the energy that a cell can extract from each molecule of glucose.

In the presence of oxygen, everything changes. As **Figure 9–8** shows, the Krebs cycle and electron transport enable the cell to produce 34 more ATP molecules per glucose molecule, in addition to the 2 ATP molecules obtained from glycolysis. This means that 18 times as much ATP can be generated from glucose in the presence of oxygen. The final wastes of cellular respiration are water and carbon dioxide.

How efficient is the process of cellular respiration? The 36 ATP molecules the cell makes per glucose represent about 38 percent of the total energy of glucose. That might not seem like much, but it means that the cell is actually more efficient at using food than the engine of a typical automobile is at burning gasoline. What happens to the remaining 62 percent? It is released as heat, which is one of the reasons your body feels warmer after vigorous exercise, and you do not freeze in winter.

▼ **Figure 9–8** The complete breakdown of glucose through cellular respiration, including glycolysis, results in the production of 36 molecules of ATP. **Interpreting Graphics** *How many molecules of ATP are produced during glycolysis?*

Total number of ATP molecules formed during cellular respiration — 36 ATP

▲ **Figure 9–9** During a race, runners rely on the energy supplied by ATP to make it to the finish line. **Applying Concepts** *When runners begin a race, how do their bodies obtain energy?*

Energy and Exercise

Bang! The starter's pistol goes off, and the runners push off their starting blocks and sprint down the track. The initial burst of energy soon fades, and the runners settle down to a steady pace. After the runners hit the finish line, they walk around slowly and breathe deeply to catch their breaths.

Let's look at what happens at each stage of the race in terms of the pathways the body uses to release energy. To obtain energy, the body uses ATP already in muscles and new ATP made by lactic acid fermentation and cellular respiration. At the beginning of a race, the body uses all three ATP sources, but stored ATP and lactic acid fermentation can only supply energy for a limited time.

Quick Energy What happens when your body needs lots of energy in a hurry? In response to sudden danger, quick actions might make the difference between life and death. To an athlete, a sudden burst of speed might win a race.

Cells normally contain small amounts of ATP produced during glycolysis and cellular respiration. When the starting gun goes off in a footrace, the muscles of the runners contain only enough of this ATP for a few seconds of intense activity. Before most of the runners have passed the 50-meter mark, that store of ATP is nearly gone. At this point, their muscle cells are producing most of their ATP by lactic acid fermentation. These sources can usually supply enough ATP to last about 90 seconds. In a 200- or 300-meter sprint, such as in **Figure 9–9,** this may be just enough to reach the finish line.

Fermentation produces lactic acid as a byproduct. When the race is over, the only way to get rid of lactic acid is in a chemical pathway that requires extra oxygen. For that reason, you can think of a quick sprint building up an oxygen debt that a runner has to repay after the race with plenty of heavy breathing.

Long-Term Energy What happens if a race is longer? How does your body generate the ATP it needs to run 2 kilometers or more, or to play in a soccer game that lasts more than an hour? For exercise longer than about 90 seconds, cellular respiration is the only way to generate a continuing supply of ATP. Cellular respiration releases energy more slowly than fermentation, which is why even well-conditioned athletes have to pace themselves during a long race or over the course of a game. Your body stores energy in muscle and other tissues in the form of the carbohydrate glycogen. These stores of glycogen are usually enough to last for 15 or 20 minutes of activity. After that, your body begins to break down other stored molecules, including fats, for energy. This is one reason why aerobic forms of exercise such as running, dancing, and swimming are so beneficial for weight control.

✓ CHECKPOINT *Why do runners breathe heavily after a race?*

Quick Lab

How does exercise affect cellular respiration?

Materials 2 small test tubes, glass marking pencil, 10-mL graduated cylinder, bromthymol blue solution, 2 straws, clock or watch with second hand

Procedure

1. **Predicting** Record your prediction of how exercise will affect your body's production of carbon dioxide.
2. Label two test tubes A and B. Put 10 mL of water and a few drops of bromthymol blue solution in each test tube. Carbon dioxide causes bromthymol blue to turn yellow or green.
3. Your partner will time you during this step. When your partner says "go," slowly blow air through a straw into the bottom of test tube A. **CAUTION:** *Do not inhale through the straw.*
4. When the solution changes color, your partner should say "stop," and then record how long the color change took.

5. Jog in place for 1 minute. **CAUTION:** *Do not do this if you have a medical condition that interferes with exercise. If you feel faint or dizzy, stop immediately and sit down.*
6. Repeat steps 3 and 4 using test tube B.
7. Trade roles with your partner. Repeat steps 2 to 6.

Analyze and Conclude

1. **Analyzing Data** How did exercise affect the time for the solution to change color?
2. **Inferring** What process in your body produces carbon dioxide? How does exercise affect this process?
3. **Drawing Conclusions** Was your hypothesis correct? Explain your answer.

▶ **Figure 9–10**
Photosynthesis and
cellular respiration can
be thought of as
opposite processes as
shown in the chart.
Using Analogies
*How is the chemical
energy in glucose similar
to money in a savings
account?*

Comparing Photosynthesis and Cellular Respiration

	Photosynthesis	Cellular Respiration
Function	Energy storage	Energy release
Location	Chloroplasts	Mitochondria
Reactants	CO_2 and H_2O	$C_6H_{12}O_6$ and O_2
Products	$C_6H_{12}O_6$ and O_2	CO_2 and H_2O
Equation	$6CO_2 + 6H_2O \longrightarrow C_6H_{12}O_6 + 6O_2$	$6O_2 + C_6H_{12}O_6 \longrightarrow 6CO_2 + 6H_2O$

Comparing Photosynthesis and Cellular Respiration

Photosynthesis and cellular respiration are almost opposite processes. Earlier in this chapter, the chemical energy in carbohydrates was compared to money in a savings account. Photosynthesis is the process that "deposits" energy. Cellular respiration is the process that "withdraws" energy. The equations for photosynthesis and cellular respiration are the reverse of each other.

Photosynthesis removes carbon dioxide from the atmosphere, and cellular respiration puts it back. Photosynthesis releases oxygen into the atmosphere, and cellular respiration uses that oxygen to release energy from food. As **Figure 9–10** shows, the products of photosynthesis are similar to the reactants of cellular respiration. The products of cellular respiration are the reactants of photosynthesis. Cellular respiration takes place in all eukaryotes and some prokaryotes. Photosynthesis, however, occurs only in plants, algae, and some bacteria.

9–2 Section Assessment

1. 🔑 **Key Concept** What happens to pyruvic acid during the Krebs cycle?

2. 🔑 **Key Concept** How does the electron transport chain use the high-energy electrons from the Krebs cycle?

3. Why is cellular respiration considered to be much more efficient than glycolysis alone?

4. How many molecules of ATP are produced in the entire breakdown of glucose?

5. **Critical Thinking Comparing and Contrasting** Compare photosynthesis and cellular respiration. How are they similar? How are they different?

🅘**TEXT** **Assessment** Use iText to review the important concepts in Section 9–2.

ALTERNATIVE ASSESSMENT

Organizing Information
Using **Figure 9–6** and **Figure 9–7** as guides, prepare a poster showing the main events of the process of cellular respiration. For each event, show the reactant and products and where in the mitochondrion the event occurs. Use your poster to explain cellular respiration to a classmate.

Should Creatine Supplements Be Banned?

Many athletes now use a dietary supplement called creatine to enhance their performance. Creatine may improve athletic performance but critics point to potentially serious side effects as a reason to control its use.

Although muscle cells contain only enough ATP for a few seconds of intense activity, most have a reserve nearly twice as large in the form of a molecule called creatine phosphate. When the muscle goes to work and starts to use up its available ATP, phosphates are transferred from creatine phosphate directly to ADP, regenerating ATP in a matter of milliseconds. The more creatine phosphate a muscle contains, the longer it can sustain intense activity. Hoping to increase their capacity for strong, short-term muscle contractions, many athletes have added creatine to their diets. Should athletes be allowed to use creatine supplements?

The Viewpoints

Creatine Supplements Should Be Allowed
Creatine is a natural substance found in human cells and in foods such as meat. Taken in recommended doses, creatine helps build muscle strength and performance, which can mean the difference between winning and losing. When athletes have followed instructions on container labels, no serious side effects have been reported. The risks are small and the rewards of winning are large enough to justify its use.

Creatine Supplements Should Be Banned
Like any natural substance, creatine can be abused. Creatine is known to cause water loss, putting the athletes who use it at risk for dehydration, muscle injury, diarrhea, kidney failure, and perhaps even death. Because creatine is considered a dietary supplement and not a drug, the Food and Drug Administration (FDA) has never determined its safety. Until a truly safe dose has been determined by careful scientific studies, athletes should not be allowed to use creatine.

You Decide

1. **Defining the Issue** In your own words, describe at least two major issues involved in the controversy surrounding the use of creatine to enhance athletic performance.
2. **Analyzing the Viewpoints** List the key arguments expressed by the proponents and critics of using creatine as a dietary supplement. What is known? What is not known? What are the benefits? What are the risks?
3. **Forming Your Opinion** Should athletes be allowed to take creatine to enhance performance? Weigh the pro and con arguments. Research to find out if some professional sports have banned the use of creatine by athletes. What were the reasons for this decision? Do some arguments outweigh others? Which arguments? Explain your answer.
4. **Writing an Editorial** Write an editorial for a sports magazine that takes a stand on creatine. Your editorial should persuade your readers that your opinion is justified.

Making Kimchi

In this investigation, you will make a popular Korean side dish known as kimchi. Kimchi is made by allowing microorganisms to ferment Chinese cabbage. The main microorganism involved is a bacterium called Lactobacillus. *This bacterium mainly carries out lactic acid fermentation. Some species of* Lactobacillus *and other microorganisms on the cabbage carry out alcoholic fermentation. All of these microorganisms occur naturally on the surface of the Chinese cabbage. As these microorganisms ferment the Chinese cabbage, turning it into kimchi, you will measure the chemical changes that occur during this process. You will use your knowledge of fermentation to explain the observations that you make.*

Problem How does fermentation affect pH?

Materials

- 2 resealable plastic sandwich bags
- chopped Chinese cabbage
- noniodized salt
- 2.5-mL (1/2 teaspoon) measuring spoon
- pH-indicator paper
- thermometer

Skills Predicting, Measuring, Drawing Conclusions

Procedure

1. **Formulating Hypotheses** Recall that pH is a measure of how acidic or basic a solution is. Bases have pH levels between 7 and 14, and acids have pH levels between 0 and 7. Formulate a hypothesis that explains how fermentation leads to changes in pH. Record your hypothesis and your prediction of how the pH of the kimchi will change as it ferments.

2. Put one resealable plastic bag inside the other. Half-fill the inner bag with chopped cabbage. Add 2.5 mL of salt. Seal both bags and turn them upside down several times to mix the ingredients.

3. Unseal the bags and press down on them to expel any air. Then, reseal the bags. Label the plastic bags containing the kimchi with your name and place them in a cool area where they will remain undisturbed. Copy the data table shown. Measure and record the air temperature in your copy of the data table.

4. Each day, observe the kimchi in the bags. Record your observations of any changes in the appearance of the kimchi or the bags in your data table. When a small amount of liquid appears in the bottom of the inner bag, open the bags. **CAUTION:** *Do not eat the kimchi.*

Data Table			
Day	pH	Temperature	Observations
1			
8			
15			
22			
29			

5. Use pH-indicator paper to measure the pH of the liquid. Record the pH in your data table.

6. Press out any gas in the bags and reseal them. Return the bags to the cool area and leave them undisturbed for a week.

7. One week after you first measured the pH, repeat steps 5 and 6. Then, move the bags containing the kimchi to a refrigerator. Record the temperature of the refrigerator in your data table. Continue to observe the kimchi and record its pH every week for 4 weeks.

Analyze and Conclude

1. **Using Tables and Graphs** Use your data table to construct a graph showing the relationship between pH and time. Describe how the pH of the kimchi changed over time.

2. **Inferring** What substance do you think was responsible for the change in pH? What process could have produced this substance?

3. **Evaluating and Revising** Was your prediction correct? What changes would you make in your hypothesis as a result of your observations?

4. **Inferring** Did you see any evidence that a gas was produced or consumed in the bags? If so, what was this gas? What process was responsible for this change? Explain the reasons for your answers.

Go Further

Designing an Experiment Yogurt is made from milk using microorganisms that carry out lactic acid fermentation. Describe an experiment you could do to determine how a factor, such as temperature or sugar concentration, affects the fermentation of yogurt. Your description should state your hypothesis; identify all variables; and explain how the outcome of the experiment could support or contradict your hypothesis.

Take It to the NET

Visit the Prentice Hall Web site at **www.phschool.com**. Enter your data on time, pH, and temperature. Look at the data entered by other students around the country. Basing your conclusion on the data, how do you think temperature affects the rate of fermentation by the microorganisms in the kimchi?

9–1 Chemical Pathways

 Key Concepts

- Cellular respiration is the process that releases energy by breaking down food molecules in the presence of oxygen.

- Glycolysis is the process in which one molecule of glucose is broken in half, producing two molecules of pyruvic acid, a 3-carbon compound.

- Glycolysis captures two pairs of high-energy electrons with the carrier NAD^+. Because glycolysis does not require oxygen, it supplies chemical energy to cells when oxygen is not available.

- The two main types of fermentation are alcoholic fermentation and lactic acid fermentation.

- In the absence of oxygen, yeast and a few other microorganisms use alcoholic fermentation, forming ethyl alcohol and carbon dioxide as wastes.

- Animals cannot perform alcoholic fermentation, but some cells, such as human muscle cells, can convert glucose into lactic acid. This is called lactic acid fermentation.

Vocabulary
calorie, p. 221
glycolysis, p. 221
cellular respiration, p. 222
NAD^+, p. 223
fermentation, p. 224
anaerobic, p. 224

9–2 The Krebs Cycle and Electron Transport

Key Concepts

- During the Krebs cycle, pyruvic acid is broken down into carbon dioxide in a series of energy-extracting reactions.

- The electron transport chain uses the high-energy electrons from the Krebs cycle to convert ADP into ATP.

- The products of photosynthesis are similar to the reactants of cellular respiration. The products of cellular respiration are the reactants of photosynthesis.

Vocabulary
aerobic, p. 226
Krebs cycle, p. 226
electron transport chain, p. 228

Thinking Visually
Using the information in this chapter, complete the following compare-and-contrast table about fermentation and cellular respiration:

Comparing Fermentation and Cellular Respiration		
Characteristic	**Fermentation**	**Cellular Respiration**
Starting reactants	1	2
Pathways involved	3	4
End products	5	6
Number of ATP molecules produced	7	8

Chapter 9

Part A

Multiple Choice

For each statement or question, select the number of the word or expression that, of those given, best completes the statement or answers the question.

1 In cells, the energy available in food is used to make an energy-rich compound called
   (1) water   (3) glucose
   (2) ATP   (4) ADP

2 The first step in releasing the energy of glucose in the cell is known as
   (1) alcoholic fermentation
   (2) Krebs cycle
   (3) glycolysis
   (4) electron transport

3 The process that releases energy from food in the presence of oxygen is
   (1) synthesis
   (2) cellular respiration
   (3) ATP synthase
   (4) photosynthesis

4 Which organism performs cellular respiration?

   (1) only C   (3) all of the organisms
   (2) only B and D   (4) only A and B

5 The net gain of energy from glycolysis is
   (1) 4 ATP molecules
   (2) 2 ATP molecules
   (3) 8 ADP molecules
   (4) 3 pyruvic acid molecules

6 Because fermentation takes place in the absence of oxygen, it is said to be
   (1) aerobic
   (2) anaerobic
   (3) cyclic
   (4) essential to oxygen production

7 In many organisms, cellular respiration is concluded within the
   (1) chloroplast   (3) mitochondrion
   (2) nucleus   (4) cytoplasm

8 The electron transport chain uses the high-energy electrons from the Krebs cycle to
   (1) produce glucose
   (2) convert ADP to ATP
   (3) produce acetyl-CoA
   (4) produce GTP

9 A total of 36 molecules of ATP is produced from 1 molecule of glucose as a result of
   (1) cellular respiration
   (2) glycolysis
   (3) alcoholic fermentation
   (4) lactic acid fermentation

10 During heavy exercise, the buildup of lactic acid in muscle cells results in
   (1) alcoholic fermentation
   (2) the Calvin cycle
   (3) oxygen debt
   (4) the Krebs cycle

11 What raw materials are needed for cellular respiration?
   (1) glucose and carbon dioxide
   (2) glucose and oxygen
   (3) carbon dioxide and oxygen
   (4) oxygen and lactic acid

12 Which substance is needed to begin the process of glycolysis?
   (1) ATP   (3) NADP
   (2) pyruvic acid   (4) carbon dioxide

13 The human body can use all as energy sources *except*
   (1) ATP in muscles
   (2) alcoholic fermentation
   (3) glycolysis
   (4) cellular respiration

14 Which best represents the waste products of cellular respiration?
   (1) O_2 (3) H_2O and O_2
   (2) CO_2 and H_2O (4) CO_2 and O_2

Test-Taking Tip When you are asked to analyze a graph showing experimental data, first look at the shape of the curve. Identify the variables and try to determine how they are related. Then, read and answer the questions about the graph.

Parts B and C

Multiple Choice and Extended Response

For those questions that ask you to select a response, choose the one that best completes the statement or answers the question. For all others follow the directions given.

15 Complete the following concept map showing the flow of energy in photosynthesis and cellular respiration. (Do not write in this book.)

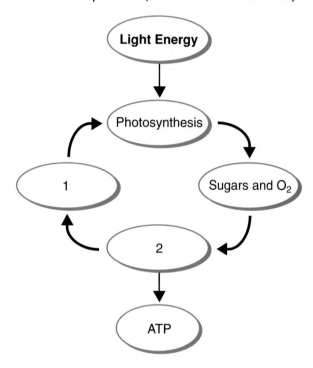

16 What is a calorie? How do cells use a high-calorie molecule such as glucose?

17 How is glucose changed during glycolysis?

18 What products are produced as a result of glycolysis?

19 What happens during the Krebs cycle?
(1) The cell releases a small amount of energy through fermentation.
(2) Each glucose molecule is broken down into two molecules of pyruvic acid.
(3) Hydrogen ions build up on one side of the mitochondrial membrane.
(4) Pyruvic acid is broken down into carbon dioxide in a series of reactions.

20 How is ATP synthase involved in making energy available to the cell?

21 Expand the analogy of deposits and withdrawals of money used in the chapter, or develop another analogy. Using the analogy, write a short paragraph to explain cellular respiration.

Base your answers to questions 22 through 24 on the graph below and on your knowledge of biology.

22 What is the relationship between the rate of fermentation and temperature?
(1) The rate of fermentation continually increases as temperature increases.
(2) The rate of fermentation continually decreases as temperature increases.
(3) The rate of fermentation increases with temperature, then it rapidly decreases.
(4) The rate of fermentation decreases with temperature, then it increases.

23 Which statement could explain the data shown in the graph?
(1) The molecules that regulate fermentation perform optimally at temperatures above 30°C.
(2) The yeast begins releasing carbon dioxide at 30°C.
(3) The yeast cannot survive at temperatures above 30°C.
(4) The molecules that regulate fermentation perform optimally at temperatures below 10°C.

24 What hypothesis do you think was most likely being investigated in the experiment that produced the data in the graph?

25 Certain types of bacteria thrive in conditions that lack oxygen. What does this fact indicate about the way they obtain energy?

26 Carbon monoxide (CO) molecules bring the electron transport chain in a mitochondion to a stop by binding to an electron carrier. Use this information to explain why carbon monoxide gas kills organisms.

27 When runners race for about 20 minutes, how do their bodies obtain energy?

28 In Chapter 3, you learned that certain substances are involved in chemical cycles. Draw a sketch showing how cellular respiration fits into one of those cycles.

Base your answers to questions 29 through 31 on the reading passage below and on your knowledge of biology.

The ABCs of Winemaking

Saccharomyces cerevisae is the variety of yeast used most often in winemaking. This yeast species lives in the soil and on the grape vines themselves. As soon as the grapes are harvested and crushed, the yeast goes to work using the sugar from the grapes for energy and, in the process, changing the juice to wine.

To get energy from the sugar, the yeast uses enzymes to catalyze the reaction and break molecular bonds. Energy is released along with carbon dioxide and alcohol.

There are bacteria that winemakers especially dread—*Acetobacter*. These bacteria consume the alcohol, turning the wine into vinegar. Fortunately, *Acetobacter* require oxygen to breathe, and the yeast *Saccharomyces* uses up oxygen in the process of producing the carbon dioxide.

29 Write equations to show the steps in fermentation of grape juice.

30 What is the name given to organisms like *Acetobacter* that require oxygen to survive?

31 Compare the site of fermentation in *Saccharomyces* with the site of cellular respiration of the *Acetobacter*.

32 Yeast cells can carry out both fermentation and cellular respiration, depending on whether oxygen is present. In which case would you expect yeast cells to grow more rapidly?

Base your answers to questions 33 through 35 on the reading passage below and on your knowledge of biology.

The Carbon Cycle

Atoms and molecules on Earth are cycled and recycled through living and nonliving parts of the environment. In this way, carbon, hydrogen, nitrogen, and oxygen are used and reused. Energy from the sun keeps this process going in biogeo-chemical cycles.

Carbon cycles through the environment during biological processes like photosynthesis, respiration, and decomposition of plants and animals.

33 Use formulas to write a chemical equation for cellular respiration. Label the formulas with the names of the compounds.

34 "Photosynthesis and respiration are reverse processes." Defend this statement by explaining what happens to oxygen and carbon dioxide in each process.

35 How are the sites of photosynthesis and respiration in the cell different?

Take It to the NET

Why is knowledge of cellular respiration and fermentation important to sports physiologists? Visit the Prentice Hall Web site at **www.phschool.com** to learn more about sports and cellular processes. Then, answer the following questions:

• Which three metabolic systems are important in understanding the limits of physical activity?

• Under optimal conditions, how many minutes of muscle activity can anaerobic metabolism produce?

• Which metabolic system provides you with the most endurance? Which system is most important for giving extra power during intermediate races, such as a 200-meter run?

• Which system functions almost exclusively in weight lifting? Tennis? Cross-country skiing?

Chapter 10 Cell Growth and Division

This liver cell has almost completed the process of cell division. During cell division, a cell splits into two roughly equal daughter cells (magnification: 11,500×).

Inquiry Activity

How do organisms grow?

Procedure

1. Use a microscope to compare the sizes of similar cells in large and small plants. For example, you might compare the leaf cells of grass to the leaf cells of a tree. Be sure to use the same magnification when comparing the sizes of the cells.

2. Use a microscope to compare the sizes of cells in similar tissues from small and large animals, such as muscle tissue from a frog and from a human.

Think About It

1. **Observing** Are the cells of the small plant larger or smaller than those of the large plant? Are the cells of the small animal larger or smaller than those of the large animal?

2. **Comparing and Contrasting** Make a general statement that compares the number and size of cells in small organisms to those in larger organisms.

10–1 Cell Growth

When a living thing grows, what happens to its cells? Does an animal get larger because each cell increases in size or because it produces more of them? In most cases, living things grow by producing more cells. On average, the cells of an adult animal are no larger than those of a young animal—there are just more of them.

Limits to Cell Growth

There are two main reasons why cells divide rather than continuing to grow indefinitely. **The larger a cell becomes, the more demands the cell places on its DNA and the more trouble the cell has moving enough nutrients and wastes across the cell membrane.**

DNA "Overload" As you may recall, the information that controls a cell's function is stored in a molecule known as DNA. In eukaryotic cells, DNA is found in the nucleus of the cell. When a cell is small, the information stored in that DNA is able to meet all of the cell's needs. But as a cell increases in size, it usually does not make extra copies of DNA. If a cell were to grow without limit, an "information crisis" would occur.

To help understand why a larger cell has a more difficult time functioning efficiently than a smaller cell, compare the cells to a growing town. Suppose a small town has a library with a few thousand books. If more people move into the town, the town will get larger. There will be more people borrowing books, and sometimes people may have to wait to borrow popular titles. Similarly, a larger cell would have to make greater demands on its available genetic "library." In time, the cell's DNA would no longer be able to serve the increasing needs of the growing cell.

Exchanging Materials There is another reason why the size of cells is limited. You may recall that food, oxygen, and water enter a cell through its cell membrane. Waste products leave in the same way. The rate at which this exchange takes place depends on the surface area of the cell, which is the total area of its cell membrane. However, the rate at which food and oxygen are used up and waste products are produced depends on the cell's volume. Understanding the relationship between a cell's volume and its surface area is the key to understanding why cells must divide as they grow.

Guide for Reading

Key Concept
• What problems does growth cause for cells?

Vocabulary
cell division

**Reading Strategy:
Asking Questions** Before reading this section, rewrite each blue heading as a *what, where,* or *how* question. Then, as you read, fill in the answer to each question.

▼ **Figure 10–1** Living things grow by producing more cells. Although the adult snail is larger than the young snail, the cells of both are the same size.

Ratio of Surface Area to Volume Imagine a cell that is shaped like a cube, like those in **Figure 10–2.** If this cell has a length of 1 cm, its surface area would be equal to length × width × number of sides, or 1 cm × 1 cm × 6 = 6 cm². The volume of the cell would be equal to length × width × height, or 1 cm × 1 cm × 1 cm = 1 cm³. To obtain the ratio of surface area to volume, divide the surface area by the volume. In this case, the ratio of surface area to volume would be 6 / 1, or 6 : 1.

If the length of the cell doubled, what would happen to the cell's surface area compared to its volume? The cell's surface area would be equal to 2 cm × 2 cm × 6 = 24 cm². The volume would be equal to 2 cm × 2 cm × 2 cm = 8 cm³. The cell's ratio of surface area to volume would be 24 / 8, or 3 : 1.

What if the length of the cell triples? The cell's surface area now would be 3 cm × 3 cm × 6 = 54 cm². The volume would be 3 cm × 3 cm × 3 cm = 27 cm³. The ratio of surface area to volume would be 54 / 27, or 2 : 1.

Note that the volume increases much more rapidly than the surface area, causing the ratio of surface area to volume to decrease. This decrease creates serious problems for the cell.

To use the town analogy again, suppose the small town has a two-lane main street. As the town grows, more people will use this street. The main street leading through town, however, has not increased in size. As a result, people will encounter more traffic as they enter and leave the town. A cell that continues to grow larger would experience similar problems. It would be more

Quick Lab

What limits the sizes of cells?

Materials 2 peeled hard-boiled eggs, blue food coloring, 150-mL beaker, scalpel, spoon, paper towels, metric ruler

Procedure

1. Place 100 mL of water in a beaker. Add 10 drops of blue food coloring, and stir with a spoon. **CAUTION:** *Food coloring may stain hands and clothing.*
2. Use the scalpel to cut through the middle of 1 hard-boiled egg. **CAUTION:** *Be careful with the scalpel.* Remove the yolk. Cut an 8-mm cube from the thickest part of the egg white.
3. Place the egg cube and a peeled hard-boiled egg gently into the beaker of food coloring and water. Allow the eggs to sit in the beaker for 10 minutes.

4. After 10 minutes, use a spoon to carefully remove the egg cube and the whole egg from the beaker, and place them on a paper towel. Cut the egg cube in half. Clean the scalpel blade and cut the whole egg in half. Measure how far the blue color penetrated the egg cube and the whole egg.

Analyze and Conclude

1. **Observing** How close to the centers of the egg cube and the whole egg did the color reach?
2. **Using Models** Compare the whole egg and the egg cube to cells to explain why a cell cannot continue to grow indefinitely.

Ratio of Surface Area to Volume in Cells

Cell Size	1 cm 1 cm 1 cm	2 cm 2 cm 2 cm	3 cm 3 cm 3 cm
Surface Area (length x width x 6)	1 cm x 1 cm x 6 = 6 cm^2	2 cm x 2 cm x 6 = 24 cm^2	3 cm x 3 cm x 6 = 54 cm^2
Volume (length x width x height)	1 cm x 1 cm x 1 cm = 1 cm^3	2 cm x 2 cm x 2 cm = 8 cm^3	3 cm x 3 cm x 3 cm = 27 cm^3
Ratio of Surface Area to Volume	6 / 1 = 6 : 1	24 / 8 = 3 : 1	54 / 27 = 2 : 1

difficult for a larger cell to get oxygen and nutrients in and waste products out. This problem is one reason why cells do not grow much larger even if the organism of which they are a part does.

Cell Division Before it becomes too large, a growing cell divides forming two "daughter" cells. The process by which a cell divides into two new daughter cells is called **cell division.**

Before cell division occurs, the cell replicates, or copies, all of its DNA. This replication of DNA solves the problem of information storage because each daughter cell gets one complete set of genetic information. Thus, each daughter cell receives its own genetic "library." Cell division also solves the problem of increasing size by reducing cell volume. Each daughter cell has an increased ratio of surface area to volume. This allows efficient exchange of materials with the environment.

▲ **Figure 10–2** As the length of a cell increases, its volume increases faster than its surface area. The resulting decrease in the cell's ratio of surface area to volume makes it more difficult for the cell to move needed materials in and waste products out.

10–1 Section Assessment

1. **Key Concept** Give two reasons why cells divide.
2. How is a cell's DNA like the books in a library?
3. What is the solution to the problems caused by cell growth?
4. As a cell increases in size, which increases more rapidly, its surface area or its volume?

5. **Critical Thinking Calculating** Calculate the surface area, volume, and ratio of surface area to volume of an imaginary cubic cell with a length of 4 cm.

TEXT Assessment Use iText to review the important concepts in Section 10–1.

MAKING CONNECTIONS

Stability and Equilibrium Select two cell organelles and describe how their functions might be impaired if the cell were to become too large. *Hint:* A review of Chapter 7 may help you with this task.

10–2 Cell Division

Guide for Reading

Key Concepts
- What are the main events of the cell cycle?
- What are the four phases of mitosis?

Vocabulary
chromatid
centromere
interphase
cell cycle
mitosis
prophase
centriole
spindle
metaphase
anaphase
telophase
cytokinesis

Reading Strategy:
Outlining As you read this section, outline the major events of the cell cycle. Write a few sentences to describe the activity of chromosomes as they progress through each part of the cell cycle.

What do you think would happen if a cell were simply to split into two, without any advance preparation? Would each daughter cell have everything it needed to survive? Because each cell has only one set of genetic information, the answer is no. Every cell must first copy its genetic information before cell division begins. Each daughter cell then gets a complete copy of that information.

In most prokaryotes, the rest of the process of cell division is a simple matter of separating the contents of the cell into two parts. Although eukaryotic cells divide in a similar way, their greater complexity makes eukaryotic cell division a more involved process.

Chromosomes

In eukaryotic cells, the genetic information that is passed on from one generation of cells to the next is carried by chromosomes. Chromosomes are made up of DNA—which carries the cell's coded genetic information—and proteins. The cells of every organism have a specific number of chromosomes. The cells of fruit flies, for example, have 8 chromosomes; human cells have 46 chromosomes; and carrot cells have 18 chromosomes.

Chromosomes are not visible in most cells except during cell division. This is because the DNA and protein molecules that make up the chromosomes are spread throughout the nucleus. At the beginning of cell division, however, the chromosomes condense into compact, visible structures that can be seen through a light microscope.

Well before cell division, each chromosome is replicated, or copied. Because of this, when they become visible at the beginning of cell division, each chromosome consists of two identical "sister" **chromatids** (KROH-muh-tidz), as shown in **Figure 10–3.** Each pair of chromatids is attached at an area called the centromere (SEN-troh-meer). **Centromeres** are usually located near the middle of the chromatids, although some lie near the ends. A human body cell entering cell division contains 46 chromosomes, each of which consists of two chromatids.

✓**CHECKPOINT** *When are chromosomes visible?*

Centromere

Sister chromatids

(magnification: 20,000×)

◀ **Figure 10–3** This is a human chromosome shown as it appears through an electron microscope. Each chromosome has two sister chromatids attached at the centromere. **Inferring** *Why are the sister chromatids identical?*

The Cell Cycle

At one time, biologists described the life of a cell as one cell division after another separated by an "in-between" period of growth called **interphase.** We now appreciate that a great deal happens in the time between cell divisions, and use a concept known as the cell cycle to represent recurring events in the life of the cell. The **cell cycle** is the series of events that cells go through as they grow and divide. ⚷ **During the cell cycle, a cell grows, prepares for division, and divides to form two daughter cells, each of which then begins the cycle again.** The main events of the cell cycle are shown in **Figure 10–4.**

The cell cycle consists of four phases. Two of these are so important that they are used as landmarks to define everything else. One of these phases is the M phase. During the M phase, **mitosis** (my-TOH-sis)—the division of the cell nucleus—and cytokinesis take place. The other important phase—the S phase—is the copying of the chromosomes. When the cell copies the chromosomes, it synthesizes, or makes, a duplicate set of DNA. Between the M and S phases are G_1 and G_2. The G in the names of these phases stands for "gap," but the G_1 and G_2 are definitely not periods when nothing takes place. They are actually periods of intense growth and activity.

Events of the Cell Cycle

During the normal cell cycle, interphase can be quite long, whereas the actual division of the cell takes place quickly. Interphase is divided into three phases: G_1, S, and G_2.

The G_1 phase is a period of activity in which cells do most of their growing. During this phase, cells increase in size and synthesize new proteins and organelles.

G_1 is followed by the S phase, in which chromosomes are replicated and the synthesis of DNA molecules takes place. Key proteins associated with the chromosomes are synthesized during the S phase. Usually, once a cell enters the S phase and begins the replication of its chromosomes, it completes the rest of the cell cycle including mitosis.

When the DNA replication is completed, the cell enters the G_2 phase. G_2 is usually the shortest of the three phases of interphase. During the G_2 phase, many of the organelles and molecules required for cell division are produced. When the events of the G_2 phase are complete, the cell is ready to enter the M phase and begin the process of cell division.

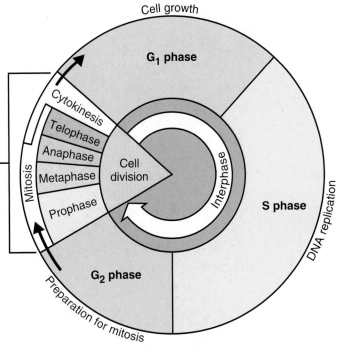

▼ **Figure 10–4** ⚷ During the cell cycle, the cell grows, replicates its DNA, and divides into two daughter cells.

Mitosis

🔑 **Biologists divide the events of mitosis into four phases: prophase, metaphase, anaphase, and telophase.** Depending on the type of cell, the four phases of mitosis may last anywhere from a few minutes to several days. As you read about each phase of mitosis, look at **Figure 10–5.**

Prophase The first and longest phase of mitosis, **prophase,** can take as much as 50 to 60 percent of the total time required to complete mitosis. During prophase, the chromosomes become visible. The **centrioles** (SEN-tree-ohlz), two tiny structures located in the cytoplasm near the nuclear envelope, separate and take up positions on opposite sides of the nucleus.

▼ **Figure 10–5** Most eukaryotic cells go through a regular cycle of interphase, mitosis, and cytokinesis. 🔑**Mitosis has four phases: prophase, metaphase, anaphase, and telophase.** The events shown here are typical of animal cells. The photographs shown are from a developing whitefish embryo (magnification: 625×).

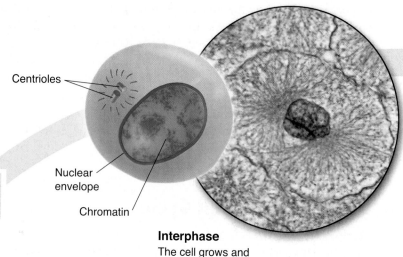

Centrioles

Nuclear envelope

Chromatin

Interphase
The cell grows and replicates its DNA and centrioles.

Cytokinesis
The cytoplasm pinches in half. Each daughter cell has an identical set of duplicate chromosomes.

Telophase
The chromosomes gather at opposite ends of the cell and lose their distinct shapes. Two new nuclear membranes form.

Nuclear envelope reforming

The centrioles lie in a region called the centrosome that helps to organize the **spindle,** a fanlike microtubule structure that helps separate the chromosomes. During prophase, the condensed chromosomes become attached to fibers in the spindle at a point near the centromere of each chromatid. Interestingly, plant cells do not have centrioles, but still organize their mitotic spindles from centrosomes.

Near the end of prophase, the chromosomes coil more tightly. In addition, the nucleolus disappears, and the nuclear envelope breaks down.

✓ CHECKPOINT) *What is the function of the spindle?*

KEEP CURRENT WITH . . .
SCIENCE NEWS®

To find out more about the topics in this chapter, go to:
www.phschool.com

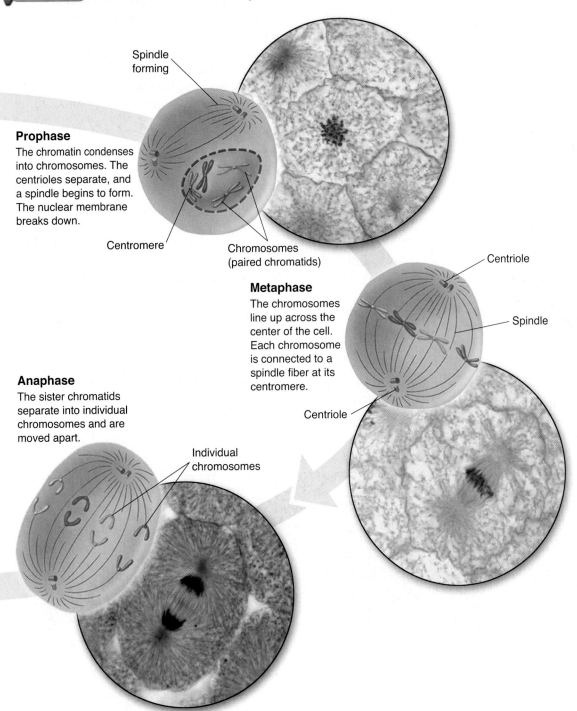

Spindle forming

Prophase
The chromatin condenses into chromosomes. The centrioles separate, and a spindle begins to form. The nuclear membrane breaks down.

Centromere

Chromosomes (paired chromatids)

Centriole

Metaphase
The chromosomes line up across the center of the cell. Each chromosome is connected to a spindle fiber at its centromere.

Spindle

Centriole

Anaphase
The sister chromatids separate into individual chromosomes and are moved apart.

Individual chromosomes

Cell Growth and Division **247**

Metaphase The second phase of mitosis, **metaphase,** often lasts only a few minutes. During metaphase, the chromosomes line up across the center of the cell. Microtubules connect the centromere of each chromosome to the poles of the spindle.

Anaphase **Anaphase** is the third phase of mitosis. During anaphase, the centromeres that join the sister chromatids separate, allowing the sister chromatids to separate and become individual chromosomes. The chromosomes continue to move until they have separated into two groups near the poles of the spindle. Anaphase ends when the chromosomes stop moving.

Telophase Following anaphase is **telophase,** the fourth and final phase of mitosis. In telophase, the chromosomes, which were distinct and condensed, begin to disperse into a tangle of dense material. A nuclear envelope re-forms around each cluster of chromosomes. The spindle begins to break apart, and a nucleolus becomes visible in each daughter nucleus. Mitosis is complete. However, the process of cell division is not complete.

✓ CHECKPOINT *What happens during anaphase?*

Cytokinesis

As a result of mitosis, two nuclei—each with a duplicate set of chromosomes—are formed, usually within the cytoplasm of a single cell. All that remains to complete the M phase of the cycle is **cytokinesis** (sy-toh-kih-NEE-sis), the division of the cytoplasm itself. Cytokinesis usually occurs at the same time as telophase.

Cytokinesis can take place in a number of ways. In most animal cells, the cell membrane is drawn inward until the cytoplasm is pinched into two nearly equal parts. Each part contains its own nucleus and cytoplasmic organelles. In plants, a structure known as the cell plate forms midway between the divided nuclei, as shown in **Figure 10–6.** The cell plate gradually develops into a separating membrane. A cell wall then begins to appear in the cell plate.

Word Origins

Cytokinesis comes from the Greek words *kytos,* meaning "hollow vessel," and *kinesis,* meaning "motion." The prefix *cyto-* refers to cells, so *cytokinesis* means movement within the cell. **What do you think the term *cytotoxic* means?**

▶ **Figure 10–6** During cytokinesis in plant cells, the cytoplasm is divided by a cell plate. The thin line you can see between the two dark nuclei in this electron micrograph of onion cells dividing is the cell plate forming. **Interpreting Graphics** *What structure forms between the divided nuclei?*

(magnification: 2200×)

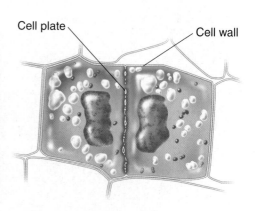

Cell plate

Cell wall

Life Spans of Human Cells

Like all organisms, cells have a given life span from birth to death. In multicellular organisms, such as humans, the health of the organism depends on cells not exceeding their life span. This is especially true of cells that tend to divide rapidly. If these cells did not die on schedule, overcrowding of cells would occur, causing uncontrolled growth that would be life-threatening.

The data table shows the life spans of various human cells. It also contains information about the ability of the cells to multiply through cell division.

1. **Inferring** White blood cells help protect the body from infection and disease-producing organisms. How might their function relate to their life span?

2. **Comparing and Contrasting** Based on the data, how are the consequences of injuries to the heart and spinal cord similar to each other? How are they different from the consequences of injuries to smooth muscle?

3. **Formulating Hypotheses** Propose a hypothesis to account for the data related to the cell life spans of the lining of the esophagus, small intestine, and large intestine.

Life Spans of Various Human Cells

Cell Type	Life Span	Cell Division
Lining of esophagus	2–3 days	Can divide
Lining of small intestine	1–2 days	Can divide
Lining of large intestine	6 days	Can divide
Red blood cells	Less than 120 days	Cannot divide
White blood cells	10 hours to decades	Cannot divide
Smooth muscle	Long-lived	Can divide
Cardiac (heart) muscle	Long-lived	Cannot divide
Skeletal muscle	Long-lived	Cannot divide
Neuron (nerve cell)	Long-lived	Most do not divide

4. **Going Further** Cancer is a disease related to cell life span and cell division. If cancer cells were added to the data table, predict what would be written under the columns headed "Life Span" and "Cell Division." Explain the reasoning underlying your predictions.

10–2 Section Assessment

1. **Key Concept** Name the main events of the cell cycle.

2. **Key Concept** Describe what happens during each of the four phases of mitosis.

3. Describe what happens during interphase.

4. What are chromosomes made of?

5. How do prokaryotic cells divide?

6. **Critical Thinking Comparing and Contrasting** How is cytokinesis in plant cells similar to cytokinesis in animal cells? How is it different?

iTEXT Assessment Use iText to review the important concepts in Section 10–2.

Take It to the NET

Read about the relationship between the enzyme telomerase and the process of cell division. Then, construct a time line of the scientists who contributed to this discovery. Use the links provided in the Biology area at the Prentice Hall Web site for help in completing this activity: **www.phschool.com**

10–3 Regulating the Cell Cycle

Guide for Reading

Key Concepts
- How is the cell cycle regulated?
- How are cancer cells different from other cells?

Vocabulary
cyclin
cancer

Reading Strategy:
Summarizing Summarizing helps you understand and remember what you read. Write a main-idea statement for each section. When you have finished the section, compare your statements with those in the study guide.

One of the most striking aspects of cell behavior in a multicellular organism is how carefully cell growth and cell division are controlled. Not all cells move through the cell cycle at the same rate. In the human body, most muscle cells and nerve cells do not divide at all once they have developed. In contrast, the cells of the skin and digestive tract, and cells in the bone marrow that make blood cells, grow and divide rapidly throughout life. Such cells may pass through a complete cycle every few hours. This process provides new cells to replace those that wear out or break down.

Controls on Cell Division

Scientists can observe the effects of controlled cell growth in the laboratory by placing some cells in a petri dish containing nutrient broth. The nutrient broth provides food for the cells. Most cells will grow until they form a thin layer covering the bottom of the dish, as shown in **Figure 10–7**. Then, the cells stop growing. When cells come into contact with other cells, they respond by not growing.

If cells are removed from the center of the dish, however, the cells bordering the open space will begin dividing until they have filled the empty space. These experiments show that the controls on cell growth and cell division can be turned on and off.

Something similar happens within the body. When an injury such as a cut in the skin or a break in a bone occurs, cells at the edges of the injury are stimulated to divide rapidly. This action produces new cells, starting the process of healing. When the healing process nears completion, the rate of cell division slows down, controls on growth are restored, and everything returns to normal.

▼ **Figure 10–7** Cells in a petri dish will continue to grow until they come into contact with other cells. **Applying Concepts** *What would happen if the cells continued to divide?*

Cell Cycle Regulators

For many years, biologists searched for a substance that might regulate the cell cycle—something that would "tell" cells when it was time to divide, duplicate their chromosomes, or enter another phase of the cycle. In the early 1980s, biologists found the substance.

Several scientists, including Tim Hunt of Great Britain and Mark Kirschner of the United States, discovered that cells in mitosis contained a protein that when injected into a nondividing cell, would cause a mitotic spindle to form. Such an experiment is shown in **Figure 10–8.** To their surprise, they discovered that the amount of this protein in the cell rose and fell in time with the cell cycle. They decided to call this protein **cyclin** because it seemed to regulate the cell cycle. Investigators have since discovered a family of closely related proteins known as cyclins. **Cyclins regulate the timing of the cell cycle in eukaryotic cells.**

The discovery of cyclins was just the beginning. More recently, dozens of other proteins have been discovered that also help to regulate the cell cycle. There are two types of regulatory proteins: internal regulators and external regulators.

✓ CHECKPOINT *What are cyclins?*

Internal Regulators Proteins that respond to events inside the cell are called internal regulators. For example, several regulatory proteins make sure that a cell does not enter mitosis until all its chromosomes have been replicated. Another regulatory protein prevents a cell from entering anaphase until all its chromosomes are attached to the mitotic spindle.

External Regulators Proteins that respond to events outside the cell are called external regulators. External regulators direct cells to speed up or slow down the cell cycle. Growth factors are among the most important external regulators. They stimulate the growth and division of cells, and are especially important during embryonic development and wound healing. Molecules found on the surfaces of neighboring cells often have an opposite effect, causing cells to slow down or stop their cell cycles. These signals prevent excessive cell growth and keep the tissues of the body from disrupting each other.

A sample of cytoplasm is removed from a cell in mitosis.

The sample is injected into a second cell in G_2 of interphase.

As a result, the second cell enters mitosis.

▲ **Figure 10–8** The timing of the cell cycle is regulated by cyclins. When cytoplasm from a cell in mitosis is injected into another cell, the second cell enters mitosis. The reason for this effect is a protein called cyclin, which triggers cell division.

(magnification: 6900×)

▲ **Figure 10–9** 🔑 **Cancer cells do not respond to the signals that would normally stop them from dividing.** Masses of cancer cells form tumors that can damage normal tissues. These cancer cells are from a cancer tumor in the large intestine.

To find out more about how scientists study cancer, view the videotape "Skin Cancer: Deadly Cells."

Uncontrolled Cell Growth

Why is cell growth regulated so carefully? The principal reason may be that the consequences of uncontrolled cell growth in a multicellular organism are very severe. **Cancer,** a disorder in which some of the body's own cells lose the ability to control growth, is one such example. 🔑 **Cancer cells do not respond to the signals that regulate the growth of most cells. As a result, they form masses of cells called tumors that can damage the surrounding tissues.** Cancer cells may break loose from tumors and spread throughout the body, disrupting normal activities and causing serious medical problems or even death. **Figure 10–9** shows typical cancer cells.

What causes the loss of growth control that results in cancer? The various forms of cancer have many causes, including smoking tobacco, radiation exposure, and even viral infection. All cancers, however, have one thing in common: The control over the cell cycle has broken down. Some cancer cells will no longer respond to external growth regulators, while others fail to produce the internal regulators that ensure orderly growth.

An astonishing number of cancer cells have a defect in a gene called p53, which normally halts the cell cycle until all chromosomes have been properly replicated. As a result, chromosome damage builds up in such cells. This damage causes the cells to lose the information needed to respond to signals that would normally control their growth.

Cancer is a serious disease. Understanding and combating cancer remains a major scientific challenge, but scientists at least know where to start. Cancer is a disease of the cell cycle, and conquering cancer will require a much deeper understanding of the processes that control cell division.

10–3 Section Assessment

1. 🔑 **Key Concept** What chemicals regulate the cell cycle? How do they work?

2. 🔑 **Key Concept** What happens when cells do not respond to the signals that normally regulate their growth?

3. How do cells respond to contact with other cells?

4. Why can cancer be considered a disease of the cell cycle?

5. **Critical Thinking Formulating Hypotheses** Write a hypothesis about what you think would happen if cyclin were injected into a cell that was in mitosis.

📱 **TEXT** **Assessment** Use iText to review the important concepts in Section 10–3.

Stem Cells: Promises and Problems

Every cell in the human body, including muscle cells, neurons, and blood cells, developed from a single fertilized cell. The cells that form during the first few divisions after fertilization can potentially become any type of cell in the body. During development before birth, however, most cells become differentiated, which means that some cells become bone cells, others become skin cells, and still others become cells in blood vessels.

Once a cell becomes a specific type of cell, it remains that way—it cannot be changed into another type of cell. Some cells, however, do not become specialized. These cells, called stem cells, can develop into any number of specialized cells. Stem cells are abundant in developing embryos, but adults also have stem cells. Stem cells in the bone marrow, for example, can produce more than a dozen types of blood cells that are used to replace those lost due to normal wear and tear.

Stem Cells in Medicine

Although your body produces billions of new cells every day, it is not always able to produce the right kind of cell to replace those damaged by injury or disease. For example, the body is not able to produce new neurons to repair spinal cord injuries, such as those that cause paralysis. Because of this, there is no way for doctors to restore movement and feeling to people who are paralyzed.

Stem cells may be the perfect solution to this problem. Recently, researchers have found that implants of stem cells can reverse the effects of brain injuries in mice. There is hope that the same will hold true for humans and that a similar technique can be used to reverse brain and spinal cord injuries in humans. It may also be possible to use stem cells to grow new liver tissue, to replace heart valves, and to reverse the effects of diabetes.

Sources of Stem Cells

Stem cells can easily be collected from embryonic tissue, but research with human embryos raises serious moral and ethical issues. The fact that embryonic tissue is genetically different from that of a person who might need a stem cell transplant presents a problem, too. The immune system of a transplant recipient might reject the stem cells, causing the transplant to fail. Is there any way to solve these problems?

A breakthrough in stem cell research may be at hand. Using stem cells from adults, researchers have shown that bone marrow stem cells can sometimes develop into nerve cells, and that brain stem cells can develop into blood cells. Experiments like these may usher in an era in which doctors literally grow new parts—replacement tissues—from a person's own cells.

On Your Own

Research the latest information on stem cell research by visiting the Prentice Hall Web site at **www.phschool.com**. Write a brief report of your findings.

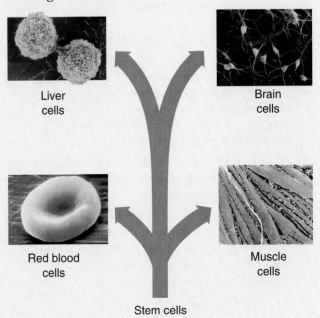

Liver cells

Brain cells

Red blood cells

Muscle cells

Stem cells

Observing the Phases of the Cell Cycle

In a growing root, the cells at the tip of the root are constantly dividing. Because each cell divides independently of the others, a root tip contains many cells at different phases of the cell cycle. This makes a root tip an excellent tissue in which to study the cell cycle. In this investigation, you will identify and describe the phases of the cell cycle in root tip cells.

Problem What do the phases of the cell cycle look like in a typical plant cell?

Materials

- microscope
- prepared slides of onion root tips
- scissors
- tape or glue
- craft materials such as beads, yarn, and pipe cleaners

Onion Root Tip
(magnification: 700×)

Skills Classifying, Using Models

Procedure

1. Obtain a prepared slide of an onion root tip. Hold the slide up to the light and find the pointed end of the root section. This is the root tip where cells were actively dividing.

2. Place the slide on the microscope stage with the root tip pointing away from you. Using the low-power objective, adjust the focus of the microscope until the root tip is clearly visible. Just above the root tip is a region that contains many new small cells. The larger cells of this region were in the process of dividing when the slide was made. These are the cells you will be observing.

3. Observe the boxlike cells that are arranged in rows. Scan across one row and down to the next row to compare the cells. The chromosomes of the cells have been stained to make them easily visible. Select one cell whose chromosomes are clearly visible. Switch to high power and sketch this cell.

4. Use the craft materials to make a model of the cell that you sketched, showing how its chromosomes are arranged.

5. Select at least four more cells whose internal appearances are different from the first cell you sketched. Switch to high power and sketch each of these cells. Repeat step 4 for each cell you sketch.

6. On a separate sheet of paper, make a copy of the data table shown. Choose 25 root tip cells at random and decide which phase of the cell cycle each is in. Record the number of cells in each phase in your copy of the data table. If you find that some cells appear to be between two phases, record those observations as well.

7. Look closely at your sketches and models. Arrange the models in order to represent the process of cell division.

8. Refer to **Figure 10–5** on pages 246 and 247 to determine whether you have ordered the phases of the cell cycle correctly. Correct the order of your models, if necessary, and label each of the models and sketches with the name of the phase it represents. Use the models to explain the process of cell division to another student.

Data Table	
Phase	**Number of Cells**
Interphase	
Prophase	
Metaphase	
Anaphase	
Telophase	

Analyze and Conclude

1. **Analyzing Data** Do your results indicate that there were more cells in some phases than in others? Identify the most common phase(s) and explain what these differences in numbers of cells might mean.

2. **Drawing Conclusions** What evidence did you observe that shows mitosis is a continuous process, not a series of separate events?

3. **Using Models** Describe what is happening in each phase of your cell models.

4. **Applying Concepts** Cells in the root divide many times as the root grows longer and thicker. With each cell division, the chromosomes are divided between two daughter cells, yet the number of chromosomes in each cell does not change. What process ensures that the normal number of chromosomes is restored after each cell division? During which part of the cell cycle does this process occur?

Go Further

Making Models In muscle cells, mitosis is not always followed by cell division. Instead, repeated cycles of mitosis result in long, tubular cells with many nuclei. These cells are called muscle fibers. Make a model that shows how mitosis occurs in a muscle fiber.

Take It to the NET Go to the Prentice Hall Web site at **www.phschool.com** and follow the links for this lab. Add your data to the pool of data from students across the country. Compare your numbers of cells in the various phases to those of other students. Why might they be different?

Chapter 10 Study Guide

10–1 Cell Growth
 Key Concept

- The larger a cell becomes, the more demands the cell places on its DNA and the more trouble the cell has moving enough nutrients and wastes across the cell membrane.

Vocabulary
cell division, p. 243

10–2 Cell Division
 Key Concepts

- During the cell cycle, a cell grows, prepares for division, and divides to form two daughter cells, each of which then begins the cycle again.
- Biologists divide the events of mitosis into four phases: prophase, metaphase, anaphase, and telophase.
- During prophase in animal cells, the centrioles separate and take up positions on opposite sides of the nucleus.
- During metaphase, the chromosomes line up across the center of the cell. Microtubules connect the centromere of each chromosome to the poles of the spindle.
- During anaphase, the centromeres that join the sister chromatids split, allowing the sister chromatids to separate and become individual chromosomes.
- In telophase, the chromosomes, which were distinct and condensed, begin to disperse into a tangle of dense material.
- Cytokinesis is the division of the cytoplasm.

Vocabulary
chromatid, p. 244
centromere, p. 244
interphase, p. 245
cell cycle, p. 245
mitosis, p. 245
prophase, p. 246
centriole, p. 246
spindle, p. 247
metaphase, p. 248
anaphase, p. 248
telophase, p. 248
cytokinesis, p. 248

10–3 Regulating the Cell Cycle
Key Concepts

- Cyclins regulate the timing of the cell cycle in eukaryotic cells.
- Cancer cells do not respond to the signals that regulate the growth of most cells. As a result, they form masses of cells called tumors that can damage the surrounding tissues.

Vocabulary
cyclin, p. 251
cancer, p. 252

Thinking Visually
Using the information in this chapter, complete the following cycle diagram of the cell cycle.

Chapter 10

Part A

Multiple Choice

For each statement or question, select the number of the word or expression that, of those given, best completes the statement or answers the question.

1 Normal cell division results in the production of
   (1) two daughter cells
   (2) double the number of chromosomes
   (3) two sex cells
   (4) half the number of chromosomes

2 Each pair of chromatids is attached at an area called the
   (1) centriole   **(3)** spindle
   (2) centromere   **(4)** chromosome

3 If a cell has 12 chromosomes, how many chromosomes will each of its daughter cells have after mitosis?
   (1) 4   **(3)** 12
   (2) 6   **(4)** 24

4 For a cell to divide successfully, it must first
   (1) duplicate its genetic information
   (2) increase its ratio of surface area to volume
   (3) increase its number of chromosomes
   (4) decrease its number of organelles

5 Which statement best describes the genetic information associated with the two chromatids of a chromosome?
   (1) Each of the two chromatids normally contains the same genetic information.
   (2) Each of the two chromatids normally contains different genetic information.
   (3) Each chromatid normally contains one-half of the chromosome's genetic information.
   (4) Only one chromatid normally carries the chromosome's genetic information.

6 In plant cells, what forms midway between the divided nuclei during cytokinesis?
   (1) nuclear membrane
   (2) centromere
   (3) cell membrane
   (4) cell plate

7 At one time, biologists called the period between cell divisions
   (1) interphase
   (2) the mitotic phase
   (3) the G3 phase
   (4) cytokinesis

8 Which of the illustrations below best represents metaphase of mitosis?

  (1)   **(3)**

  (2)   **(4)**

9 The timing of the cell cycle in eukaryotic cells is controlled by a group of closely related proteins known as
   (1) chromatids   **(3)** centromeres
   (2) cyclins   **(4)** centrioles

10 Which does *not* occur during mitosis?
   (1) duplication of cell DNA
   (2) formation of a new nuclear membrane
   (3) separation of "sister" chromatids
   (4) breakdown of the nuclear membrane

11 At the beginning of cell division, a chromosome consists of two chromatids. Which statement best describes what happens to these two chromatids as a result of mitotic division?
   (1) One daughter cell receives one chromatid, and the other chromatid is used to form the spindle.
   (2) One daughter cell receives both chromatids, and the other daughter cell receives neither.
   (3) One daughter cell receives one chromatid, and the other daughter cell receives the other chromatid.
   (4) Each daughter cell receives both chromatids, since the chromatids are copied first.

> **Test-Taking Tip** If after reading all of the answer choices you are not sure which one is correct, eliminate the choices that you know are wrong. Then, select your answer from the remaining choices.

Parts B and C

Multiple Choice and Extended Response

For those questions that ask you to select a response, choose the one that best completes the statement or answers the question. For all others follow the directions given.

For each description in questions 12 through 14, select the process or event, chosen from the list below, that is most closely associated with that process or event. Then, record its number on your answer paper.

Process or Event

(1) Interphase   (3) Cytokinesis
(2) Cell cycle   (4) Cancer

12 A process in which unregulated cell division occurs

13 A process by which the cytoplasm divides

14 A series of events that cells go through as they divide and grow

---

Base your answers to questions 15 through 18 on the information and illustration below and on your knowledge of biology.

The spindle fibers of a dividing cell were labeled with a fluorescent dye. At the beginning of anaphase, a laser beam was used to stop the dye from glowing on one side of the cell, thereby marking the fibers, as shown in the second diagram. The laser did not inhibit the normal function of the fibers.

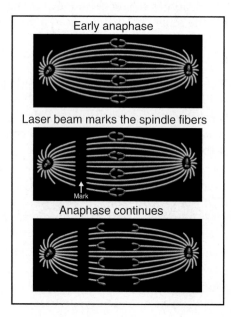

Early anaphase

Laser beam marks the spindle fibers

Mark

Anaphase continues

15 This experiment tests a hypothesis about
(1) how chromosomes migrate during cell division
(2) how fluorescent dyes work in the cell
(3) the effect of lasers on cells
(4) why cells divide

16 The diagram shows that the spindle fibers
(1) shorten on the chromosome side of the mark
(2) lengthen on the chromosome side of the mark
(3) shorten on the centriole side of the mark
(4) lengthen on the centriole side of the mark

17 A valid conclusion that can be drawn from this experiment is that
(1) centrioles pull chromosomes toward the poles of the cell
(2) chromosomes do not migrate in the presence of dye
(3) lasers inhibit the migration of chromosomes
(4) chromosomes travel along the fibers toward the poles of the cell

18 Would this experiment have provided the same information if the laser beam were focused on the fibers at the point where they contact the chromatids? Support your answer with an explanation.

---

19 Summarize what happens to a cell's genetic material both before and during the process of cell division. In your answer, be sure to
- explain the changes in chromosomes that occur before cell division and the process that brings about the change
- describe how chromosomes are arranged at the beginning of cell division
- describe specifically how the chromosomes change during cell division
- describe what happens to chromosomes at the end of cell division
- compare the amount of genetic material present in the cell with the amount present in the daughter (offspring) cells

20 Describe how a cell's chromosomes change as a cell prepares to divide.

21 Compare the quantity of DNA in a cell at the beginning of mitosis with the quantity of DNA in each of the two newly produced daughter cells.

22 How does the number of chromosomes in the two new cells compare with the number in the original cell at the end of cell division?

23 Laboratory Dish A contains 100 cells that completely cover the bottom of the dish. Laboratory Dish B, a larger dish, contains 100 cells that do not cover the bottom of the entire dish. Would cell division be likely to be observed in either or both dishes? Support your answer.

24 How do cancer cells differ from noncancerous cells?

25 Molecules found on the surfaces of cells might play a role in the process by which cells divide until they contact other cells. Explain how an alteration of a cell's DNA could produce cells that would continue to grow and divide even after coming into contact with other cells.

Base your answers to questions 26 and 27 on the illustration below and on your knowledge of biology.

26 The diagram shows a phase of mitosis. Identify the phase of cell division illustrated, and then indicate whether the cell most resembles that of a tree or a tiger. Support your answer.

27 The four chromosomes shown in the center of this cell each have two connected strands. Explain how the two strands on the same chromosome compare with regard to the genetic information they carry. Also, explain why this is important to the cell.

28 A classmate suggests that temperature might affect the rate of mitosis in plant cells. Describe an experiment that could be done to test this hypothesis.

29 Some cells have several nuclei within the cytoplasm of a single cell. Considering the events in a typical cell cycle, which phase of the cell cycle is not operating when this occurs?

30 State one similarity between the process of cell division in an animal cell and cell division in a plant cell.

31 The nerve cells in the human nervous system seldom undergo mitosis. Based on this information, explain why complete recovery from injuries to the nervous system may not occur.

For each description in questions 32 through 34, select the phase of mitosis, chosen from the list below, that is most closely associated with that process or event. Then, record its number on your answer paper.

Phase of Mitosis

(1) Anaphase   (3) Prophase
(2) Metaphase   (4) Telophase

32 The phase when chromosomes first become visible as distinct structures when viewed with a microscope

33 The phase when the genetic material has been fully divided and new nuclei begin to form

34 The phase when paired chromatids separate and move apart toward the poles of the cell

Take It to the NET

When the cell cycle goes awry, cancer can result. Visit the Prentice Hall Web site at **www.phschool.com** to find out more about cancer. Then, answer the following questions:

• Identify the four different categories of cancer.

• List four prefixes used in naming cancers and explain the meaning of each.

• Describe the two mechanisms by which cancers are spread through the body.

• What is the difference between a benign tumor and a malignant tumor?

Genetics

▶ Genetics is the study of heredity, or the transmission of characteristics from parent to offspring. Why didn't these normal-colored, white-tail fawns inherit the white fur from their albino mother? Read on to find out.

What do we know about genetics?

- The characteristics of living things are determined by genes that are passed from one generation to the next.

- Genes are written in molecular code in a molecule known as DNA. Scientists now know many of the rules by which this code can be read and understood by the cell.

- It is possible to change and transfer genes from one organism to another. Many biologists now work on the genetic engineering of plants, animals, and other organisms.

What discoveries lie in the future?

- Will we learn enough about genes to completely describe how they work together to produce a living organism?

- The Human Genome Project has already provided knowledge about the causes of many genetic diseases. Can we use that knowledge to cure genetic diseases?

- Will we apply the techniques of genetic engineering to help protect the living world and ensure our own survival?

11 Introduction to Genetics

The varied colors of these parakeets result from differences in their genetic makeup.

Inquiry Activity

Are traits inherited?

Procedure

1. Look at your classmates. Note how they vary in the shape of the front hairline, the space between the two upper front teeth, and the way in which the earlobes are attached.

2. Make a list of the different forms of these traits that you have observed in the class or among other people you know.

Think About It

1. **Inferring** Could these traits be inherited? From whom could they be inherited?

2. **Inferring** How is it possible that these traits could be found in a person and his or her biological grandparents but not in the biological parents?

11–1 The Work of Gregor Mendel

What is an inheritance? To most people, it is money or property left to them by a relative who has passed away. That kind of inheritance is important, of course. There is another form of inheritance, however, that matters even more. This inheritance has been with you from the very first day you were alive—your genes.

Every living thing—plant or animal, microbe or human being—has a set of characteristics inherited from its parent or parents. Since the beginning of recorded history, people have wanted to understand how that inheritance is passed from generation to generation. More recently, however, scientists have begun to appreciate that heredity holds the key to understanding what makes each species unique. As a result, **genetics,** the scientific study of heredity, is now at the core of a revolution in understanding biology.

Gregor Mendel's Peas

The work of an Austrian monk named Gregor Mendel was particularly important to understanding biological inheritance. Gregor Mendel was born in 1822 in what is now the Czech Republic. After becoming a priest, Mendel spent several years studying science and mathematics at the University of Vienna. He spent the next 14 years working in the monastery and teaching at the high school. In addition to his teaching duties, Mendel was in charge of the monastery garden. In this ordinary garden, he was to do the work that changed biology forever.

Mendel worked with garden peas. Like many plants, pea plants use parts of their flowers to reproduce. The male part of each flower produces pollen—which contains male sex cells. The female part of the flower produces eggs—female sex cells.

When pollen fertilizes an egg cell, a seed for a new plant is formed. Pea plants normally reproduce by self-pollination, in which pollen fertilizes the egg cells in the very same flower. Seeds that are produced by self-pollination inherit all of their characteristics from the single plant that bore them. In effect, they have only one parent.

When Mendel took charge of the monastery garden, he had several different stocks of pea plants. These peas were **true-breeding,** meaning that if they were allowed to self-pollinate, they would produce offspring identical to themselves. One stock of seeds would produce only tall plants, another only short plants. One stock produced only green seeds, another only yellow seeds. These true-breeding plants were the basis of Mendel's experiments.

Guide for Reading

 Key Concepts
- What is the principle of dominance?
- What happens during segregation?

Vocabulary
- genetics • true-breeding
- trait • hybrid • gene • allele
- segregation • gamete

Reading Strategy:
Finding Main Ideas As you read, find evidence to support the following statement: Mendel's ideas about genetics were the beginning of a new area of biology.

▲ **Figure 11–1** Gregor Mendel's experiments with pea plants laid the foundations of the science of genetics.

Pea Flower

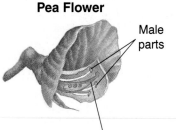

Male parts

Female part

◀ **Figure 11–2** To cross-pollinate pea plants, Mendel cut off the male parts of one flower and then dusted it with pollen from another flower. **Applying Concepts** *How did this procedure prevent self-pollination?*

Cross-Pollination

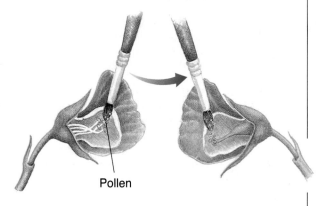

Pollen

▼ **Figure 11–3** When Mendel crossed plants with contrasting characters for the same trait, the resulting offspring had only one of the characters. ⬤ **From these experiments, Mendel concluded that some alleles are dominant and others are recessive.**

However, pea plants can also cross-pollinate. In cross-pollination, male sex cells in pollen from the flower on one plant fertilize the egg cells of a flower on another plant. The seeds produced from cross-pollination have two plants as parents.

To perform his experiments, Mendel had to select the pea plants that he would mate with each other. Therefore, he had to prevent the pea flowers from self-pollinating and control their cross-pollination. How did Mendel accomplish this task? First, he cut away the male parts of a flower. Then, he dusted that flower with pollen from a second flower, as shown in **Figure 11–2**. The resulting seeds were crosses between the two plants.

Genes and Dominance

Mendel studied seven different pea plant traits. A **trait** is a specific characteristic, such as seed color or plant height, that varies from one individual to another. Each of the seven traits Mendel studied had two contrasting characters, for example, green seed color and yellow seed color. Mendel crossed plants with each of the seven contrasting characters and studied their offspring. Mendel called each original pair of plants the P (parental) generation. He called the offspring the F_1, or "first filial," generation. *Filius* is the Latin word for "son." The off-spring of crosses between parents with different traits are called **hybrids.**

Mendel's Seven F_1 Crosses on Pea Plants							
	Seed Shape	Seed Color	Seed Coat Color	Pod Shape	Pod Color	Flower Position	Plant Height
P	Round X Wrinkled	Yellow X Green	Gray X White	Smooth X Constricted	Green X Yellow	Axial X Terminal	Tall X Short
F_1	Round	Yellow	Gray	Smooth	Green	Axial	Tall

What were those F_1 hybrid plants like? Did the characters of the parent plants blend in the offspring? Not at all. To Mendel's surprise, all of the offspring had the character of only one of the parents, as shown in **Figure 11–3**. In each cross, the character of the other parent seemed to have disappeared.

From this set of experiments, Mendel drew two conclusions. Mendel's first conclusion was that biological inheritance is determined by factors that are passed from one generation to the next. Today, scientists call the chemical factors that determine traits **genes.** Each of the traits Mendel studied was controlled by one gene that occurred in two contrasting forms. These contrasting forms produced the different characters of each trait. For example, the gene for plant height occurs in one form that produces tall plants and in another form that produces short plants. The different forms of a gene are called **alleles** (uh-LEELZ).

Mendel's second conclusion is called the principle of dominance. **The principle of dominance states that some alleles are dominant and others are recessive.** An organism with a dominant allele for a particular form of a trait will always have that form. An organism with a recessive allele for a particular form of a trait will have that form only when the dominant allele for the trait is not present. In Mendel's experiments, the allele for tall plants was dominant and the allele for short plants was recessive. The allele for yellow seeds was dominant, while the allele for green seeds was recessive.

Segregation

Mendel wanted the answer to another question: Had the recessive alleles disappeared, or were they still present in the F_1 plants? To answer this question, he allowed all seven kinds of F_1 hybrid plants to produce an F_2 (second filial) generation by self-pollination. In effect, he crossed the F_1 generation with itself to produce the F_2 offspring, as shown in **Figure 11–4.**

▼ **Figure 11– 4** When Mendel allowed the F_1 plants to reproduce by self-pollination, the traits controlled by recessive alleles reappeared in about one fourth of the F_2 plants in each cross. **Calculating** *What proportion of the F_2 plants had a trait controlled by a dominant allele?*

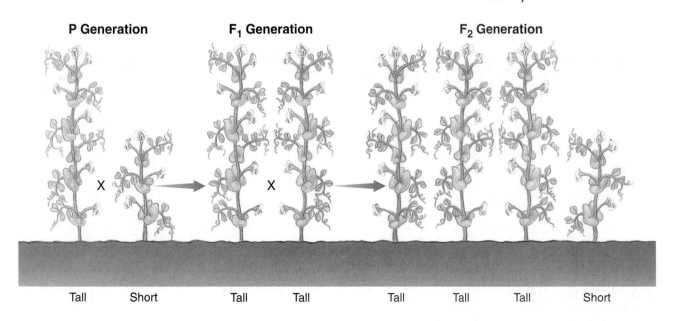

| **P Generation** | | **F₁ Generation** | | **F₂ Generation** | | | |

Tall   Short   Tall   Tall   Tall   Tall   Tall   Short

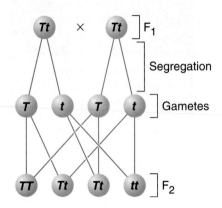

▲ **Figure 11–5** 🔑 During gamete formation, alleles are segregated from each other so that each gamete carries only a single copy of each gene. Each F₁ plant produces two types of gametes—those with the allele for tallness and those with the allele for shortness. The alleles are paired up again when gametes fuse during fertilization.

The F₁ Cross The results of the F₁ cross were remarkable. The traits controlled by the recessive alleles reappeared! Roughly one fourth of the F₂ plants showed the trait controlled by the recessive allele. Why did the recessive alleles seem to disappear in the F₁ generation and then reappear in the F₂ generation? To answer this question, let's take a closer look at one of Mendel's crosses.

Explaining the F₁ Cross To begin with, Mendel assumed that a dominant allele had masked the corresponding recessive allele in the F₁ generation. However, the trait controlled by the recessive allele showed up in some of the F₂ plants. This reappearance indicated that at some point the allele for short-ness had been separated from the allele for tallness. How did this separation, or **segregation,** of alleles occur? Mendel suggested that the alleles for tallness and shortness in the F₁ plants were segregated from each other during the formation of the sex cells, or **gametes** (GAM-eets). Did that suggestion make sense?

Let's assume, as perhaps Mendel did, that the F₁ plants inherited an allele for tallness from one parent and an allele for shortness from the other parent. Because the allele for tallness is dominant, all the F₁ plants are tall. 🔑 **When each F₁ plant flowers, the two alleles are segregated from each other so that each gamete carries only a single copy of each gene. Therefore, each F₁ plant produces two types of gametes—those with the allele for tallness and those with the allele for shortness.**

Look at **Figure 11–5** to see how alleles are separated during gamete formation and then paired up again in the F₂ genera-tion. A capital letter *T* represents a dominant allele. A lowercase letter *t* represents a recessive allele. The result of this process is an F₂ generation with new combinations of alleles.

11–1 Section Assessment

1. 🔑 **Key Concept** What are dominant and recessive alleles?

2. 🔑 **Key Concept** What is segregation? What happens to alleles during segregation?

3. What did Mendel conclude determines biological inheri-tance?

4. Describe how Mendel cross-pollinated pea plants.

5. **Critical Thinking Applying Concepts** Why were true-breeding pea plants important for Mendel's experiments?

🅘**TEXT** **Assessment** Use iText to review the important concepts in Section 11–1.

11–2 Probability and Punnett Squares

Whenever Mendel performed a cross with pea plants, he carefully counted the offspring. Every time Mendel repeated a particular cross, he obtained similar results. For example, whenever Mendel crossed two plants that were hybrid for stem height (*Tt*), about three fourths of the resulting plants were tall and about one fourth were short. Mendel realized that the principles of probability could be used to explain the results of genetic crosses.

Genetics and Probability

The likelihood that a particular event will occur is called **probability.** As an example of probability, consider an ordinary event like the coin flip shown in **Figure 11– 6.** There are two possible outcomes: The coin may land heads up or tails up. The chances, or probabilities, of either outcome are equal. Therefore, the probability that a single coin flip will come up heads is 1 chance in 2. This is 1/2 or 50 percent.

If you flip a coin three times in a row, what is the probability that it will land heads up? Because each coin flip is an independent event, the probability of each coin's landing heads up is 1/2. Therefore, the probability of flipping three heads in a row is:

$$\tfrac{1}{2} \times \tfrac{1}{2} \times \tfrac{1}{2} = \tfrac{1}{8}.$$

As you can see, you have 1 chance in 8 of flipping heads three times in a row. That the individual probabilities are multiplied together illustrates an important point—past outcomes do not affect future ones.

How is coin flipping relevant to genetics? The way in which alleles segregate is completely random, like a coin flip. **The principles of probability can be used to predict the outcomes of genetic crosses.**

✔CHECKPOINT **What is the probability that a tossed coin will come up tails twice in a row?**

Guide for Reading

🔑 **Key Concept**
• How do geneticists use the principles of probability?

Vocabulary
probability
Punnett square
homozygous
heterozygous
phenotype
genotype

Reading Strategy:
Building Vocabulary Before you read, preview the list of new vocabulary words. Predict the relationship between phenotype and genotype. As you read, check to see if your predictions were correct.

▶ **Figure 11–6** The mathematical concept of probability allows you to calculate the likelihood that a particular event will occur. **Predicting** *What is the probability that the coin will land heads up?*

How are dimples inherited?

Father's genotype is *dd* (2 even digits)

Mother's genotype is *Dd* (1 even digit and 1 odd digit)

4638

Materials copy of page from telephone book, calculator

Procedure

1. Write the last 4 digits of any telephone number. These 4 random digits represent the gene that determines whether a person will have dimples. Odd digits represent the allele for the dominant trait of dimples. Even digits stand for the allele for the recessive trait of no dimples.
2. Use the first 2 digits to represent a certain father's genotype. Use the symbols *D* and *d* to write his genotype, as shown in the example.
3. Use the last 2 digits the same way to find the mother's genotype. Write her genotype.

4. Use **Figure 11–7** as an example to construct a Punnett square for the cross of these parents. Then, using the Punnett square, determine the probability that their child will have dimples.
5. Determine the class average of the percent of children with dimples.

Analyze and Conclude

1. **Applying Concepts** How does the class average compare with the result of a cross of two heterozygous parents?
2. **Drawing Conclusions** What percentage of the children will be expected to have dimples if one parent is homozygous for dimples *(DD)* and the other is heterozygous *(Dd)*?

Punnett Squares

The gene combinations that might result from a genetic cross can be determined by drawing a diagram known as a **Punnett square.** The Punnett square in **Figure 11–7** shows one of Mendel's segregation experiments. The types of gametes produced by each F_1 parent are shown along the top and left sides of the square. The possible gene combinations for the F_2 offspring appear in the four boxes that make up the square. The letters in the Punnett square represent alleles: capital letters for dominant alleles and lowercase letters for recessive alleles. In this example, *T* represents the dominant allele for tallness and *t* represents the recessive allele for shortness.

Organisms that have two identical alleles for a particular trait—*TT* or *tt* in this example—are said to be **homozygous** (hoh-moh-ZY-gus). Organisms that have two different alleles for the same trait are **heterozygous** (het-er-oh-ZY-gus). Homozygous organisms are true-breeding for a particular trait. Heterozygous organisms are hybrid for a particular trait.

All of the tall plants have the same **phenotype,** or physical characteristics. They do not, however, have the same **genotype,** or genetic makeup. The genotype of one third of the tall plants is *TT,* while the genotype of two thirds of the tall plants is *Tt.* The plants shown in **Figure 11–8** have the same phenotype but different genotypes.

Tt

Tt

	T	t
T	TT 25%	Tt 25%
t	Tt 25%	tt 25%

▲ **Figure 11–7** ◉ **The principles of probability can be used to predict the outcomes of genetic crosses.** This Punnett square shows the probability of each possible outcome of a cross between hybrid tall *(Tt)* pea plants.

Probability and Segregation

Look again at **Figure 11–7.** One fourth (1/4) of the F_2 plants have two alleles for tallness *(TT)*; 2/4, or 1/2, of the F_2 plants have one allele for tallness and one allele for shortness *(Tt)*. Because the allele for tallness is dominant over the allele for shortness, 3/4 of the F_2 plants should be tall. Overall, there are 3 tall plants for every 1 short plant in the F_2 generation. Thus, the ratio of tall plants to short plants is 3 : 1. This assumes, of course, that Mendel's model of segregation is correct.

Did the data from Mendel's experiments fit his model? Yes. The predicted ratio—3 dominant to 1 recessive—showed up consistently, indicating that Mendel's assumptions about segregation had been correct. For each of his seven crosses, about 3/4 of the plants showed the trait controlled by the dominant allele. About 1/4 showed the trait controlled by the recessive allele. Segregation did indeed occur according to Mendel's model.

Probabilities Predict Averages

Probabilities predict the average outcome of a large number of events. However, probability cannot predict the precise outcome of an individual event. If you flip a coin twice, you are likely to get one head and one tail. However, you might also get two heads or two tails. To be sure of getting the expected 50 : 50 ratio, you would have to flip the coin many times.

The same is true of genetics. The larger the number of individuals, the closer the resulting offspring numbers will get to expected values. If an F_1 generation contains just three or four offspring, it may not match Mendelian predictions. When an F_1 generation contains hundreds or thousands of individuals, however, the ratios usually come very close to matching expectations.

TT
Homozygous

Tt
Heterozygous

▲ **Figure 11–8** Although these plants have different genotypes *(TT and Tt)*, they have the same phenotype (tall). **Predicting** *If you crossed these two plants, would their offspring be tall or short?*

11–2 Section Assessment

1. 🔑 **Key Concept** How are the principles of probability used to predict the outcomes of genetic crosses?

2. What is probability?

3. What is a Punnett square?

4. Define the terms *genotype* and *phenotype.*

5. **Critical Thinking Problem Solving** An F_1 plant that is homozygous for shortness is crossed with a heterozygous F_1 plant. What is the probability that a seed from the cross will produce a tall plant? Use a Punnett square to explain your answer.

iTEXT Assessment Use iText to review the important concepts in Section 11–2.

iTEXT Assessment Use iText to review the important concepts in Section 11–2.

ALTERNATIVE ASSESSMENT

Drawing Punnett Squares
Imagine that you came upon a tall pea plant similar to those Mendel used in his experiments. How could you determine the plant's genotype with respect to height? Draw two Punnett squares to show your answer.

11–3 Exploring Mendelian Genetics

Guide for Reading

 Key Concepts
- What is the principle of independent assortment?
- What inheritance patterns exist aside from simple dominance?

Vocabulary
independent assortment
incomplete dominance
codominance
multiple alleles
polygenic traits

Reading Strategy:
Finding Main Ideas Before you read, draw a line down the center of a sheet of paper. On the left side, write down the main topics of the section. On the right side, note supporting details and examples.

After showing that alleles segregate during the formation of gametes, Mendel wondered if they did so independently. In other words, does the segregation of one pair of alleles affect the segregation of another pair of alleles? For example, does the gene that determines whether a seed is round or wrinkled in shape have anything to do with the gene for seed color? Must a round seed also be yellow?

Independent Assortment

To answer these questions, Mendel performed an experiment to follow two different genes as they passed from one generation to the next. Mendel's experiment is known as a two-factor cross.

The Two-Factor Cross: F$_1$ First, Mendel crossed true-breeding plants that produced only round yellow peas (genotype *RRYY*) with plants that produced wrinkled green peas (genotype *rryy*). All of the F$_1$ offspring produced round yellow peas. This shows that the alleles for yellow and round peas are dominant over the alleles for green and wrinkled peas. A Punnett square for this cross, shown in **Figure 11–9**, shows that the genotype of each of these F$_1$ plants is *RrYy*.

This cross does not indicate whether genes assort, or segregate, independently. However, it provides the hybrid plants needed for the next cross—the cross of F$_1$ plants to produce the F$_2$ generation.

Figure 11–9 Mendel crossed plants that were homozygous dominant for round yellow peas with plants that were homozygous recessive for wrinkled green peas. All of the F$_1$ offspring were heterozygous dominant for round yellow peas.
Interpreting Graphics *How is the genotype of the offspring different from that of the homozygous dominant parent?*

The Two-Factor Cross: F$_2$ Mendel knew that the F$_1$ plants had genotypes of *RrYy*. In other words, the F$_1$ plants were all heterozygous for both the seed shape and seed color genes. How would the alleles segregate when the F$_1$ plants were crossed to each other to produce an F$_2$ generation? Remember that each plant in the F$_1$ generation was formed by the fusion of a gamete carrying the dominant *RY* alleles with another gamete carrying the recessive *ry* alleles. Did this mean that the two dominant alleles would always stay together? Or would they "segregate independently," so that any combination of alleles was possible?

In Mendel's experiment, the F$_2$ plants produced 556 seeds. Of these, 315 seeds were round and yellow and another 32 were wrinkled and green, the two parental phenotypes. However, 209 of the seeds had combinations of phenotypes—and therefore combinations of alleles—not found in either parent. This clearly meant that the alleles for seed shape segregated independently of those for seed color—a principle known as **independent assortment.** Put another way, genes that segregate independently—such as the genes for seed shape and seed color in pea plants—do not influence each other's inheritance. Mendel's experimental results were very close to the 9 : 3 : 3 : 1 ratio that the Punnett square shown in **Figure 11–10** predicts. Mendel had discovered the principle of independent assortment. 🔑 **The principle of independent assortment states that genes for different traits can segregate independently during the formation of gametes.**

F$_2$ Generation

▲ **Figure 11–10** 🔑 When Mendel crossed plants that were heterozygous dominant for round yellow peas, he found that the alleles segregated independently to produce the F$_2$ generation.

Problem Solving

Producing True-Breeding Seeds

Imagine that you work for a company that specializes in ornamental flowers. One spring, you find an ornamental tobacco plant with beautiful lavender flowers, a color you are sure will be in high demand. Knowing that tobacco plants are self-pollinating, you harvest seeds from it. A test plot of the seeds planted the following season fails to impress your boss. Of the 106 test plants, 31 have white flowers. Is there a way to develop seeds guaranteed to produce only lavender flowers?

Defining the Problem Describe the problem that must be solved to make the lavender-flowered plants a commercial success.

Organizing Information The first lavender flower produced offspring with both lavender and white flowers when allowed to self-pollinate. Use your knowledge of Mendelian genetics, including Punnett

squares, to draw conclusions about the nature of the allele for lavender flowers.

Creating a Solution Write a description of how you would begin with seeds from your test plot and produce seeds guaranteed to produce 100 percent lavender plants. Keep in mind that a single tobacco plant can produce as many as 1000 seeds.

Presenting Your Plan Prepare a step-by-step outline of your plan, including Punnett squares when appropriate. Present the procedure to your class as you would a business plan.

A Summary of Mendel's Principles

Mendel's principles form the base on which the modern science of genetics has been built. These principles can be summarized as follows:

- The inheritance of biological characteristics is determined by individual units known as genes. In organisms that reproduce sexually, genes are passed from parents to their offspring.
- In cases in which two or more forms of the gene for a single trait exist, some forms of the gene may be dominant and others may be recessive.
- In most sexually reproducing organisms, each adult has two copies of each gene—one from each parent. These genes are segregated from each other when gametes are formed.
- The alleles for different genes usually segregate independently of one another.

Beyond Dominant and Recessive Alleles

Despite the importance of Mendel's work, it would be a mistake to characterize the principles he discovered as "laws," because there are important exceptions to most of them. For example, not all genes show simple patterns of dominant and recessive alleles. In most organisms, genetics is more complicated, because the majority of genes have more than two alleles. In addition, many important traits are controlled by more than one gene. **Some alleles are neither dominant nor recessive, and many traits are controlled by multiple alleles or multiple genes.**

Incomplete Dominance A cross between two four o'clock (*Mirabilis*) plants shows one of these complications. The F_1 generation produced by a cross between red-flowered *(RR)* and white-flowered *(WW)* plants consists of pink-colored flowers *(RW)*, as shown in **Figure 11–11.** Which allele is dominant in this case? Neither one. Cases in which one allele is not completely dominant over another are called **incomplete dominance.** In incomplete dominance, the heterozygous phenotype is somewhere in between the two homozygous phenotypes.

Codominance A similar situation is **codominance,** in which both alleles contribute to the phenotype of the organism. For example, in cattle the allele for red hair is codominant with the allele for white hair. Cattle with both alleles are roan, or pinkish brown, because their coats are a mixture of both red and white hairs. In certain varieties of chickens, the allele for black feathers is codominant with the allele for white feathers. Heterozygous chickens appear speckled with black and white feathers.

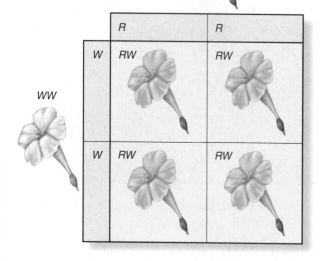

▲ **Figure 11–11** Some alleles are neither dominant nor recessive. In four o'clock plants, for example, the alleles for red and white flowers show incomplete dominance. Heterozygous *(RW)* plants have pink flowers—a mix of red and white coloring.

Figure 11–12 Coat color in rabbits is determined by a single gene that has at least four different alleles. Different combinations of alleles result in the four colors you see here. **Interpreting Graphics** *What allele combinations can a chinchilla rabbit have?*

Full color: CC, Cc^ch, Cc^h, or Cc

Chinchilla: c^ch c^h, c^ch c^ch, or c^ch c

Himalayan: c^h c or c^h c^h

Albino: cc

Key

C = full color; dominant to all other alleles

c^ch = chinchilla; partial defect in pigmentation; dominant to c^h and c alleles

c^h = Himalayan; color in certain parts of body; dominant to c allele

c = albino; no color; recessive to all other alleles

Multiple Alleles

Many genes have more than two alleles and are therefore said to have **multiple alleles.** This does not mean that an individual can have more than two alleles. It only means that more than two possible alleles exist in a population. One of the best-known examples is coat color in rabbits. A rabbit's coat color is determined by a single gene that has at least four different alleles. The four known alleles display a pattern of simple dominance that can produce four possible coat colors, as shown in **Figure 11–12.** Many other genes have multiple alleles, including the human genes for blood type.

Polygenic Traits

Many traits are produced by the interaction of several genes. Traits controlled by two or more genes are said to be **polygenic traits,** which means "having many genes." For example, at least three genes are involved in making the reddish-brown pigment in the eyes of fruit flies. Different combinations of alleles for these genes produce very different eye colors. Polygenic traits often show a wide range of phenotypes. For example, the wide range of skin color in humans comes about partly because more than four different genes probably control this trait.

CHECKPOINT *What are multiple alleles?*

Applying Mendel's Principles

Mendel's principles don't apply only to plants. At the beginning of the 1900s, the American geneticist Thomas Hunt Morgan decided to look for a model organism to advance the study of genetics. He wanted an animal that was small, easy to keep in the laboratory, and able to produce large numbers of offspring in a short period of time. He decided to work on a tiny insect that kept showing up, uninvited, in his laboratory. The insect was the common fruit fly, *Drosophila melanogaster,* shown in **Figure 11–13.**

Morgan grew the flies in small milk bottles stoppered with cotton gauze. Morgan found that he could breed a new generation of flies every 14 days. A single pair of flies could produce as many as 100 offspring. *Drosophila* was an ideal organism for genetics because it could produce plenty of offspring, and it did so quickly. Before long, Morgan and other biologists had tested every one of Mendel's principles and learned that they applied not just to pea plants but to other organisms as well.

Mendel's principles also apply to humans. The basic principles of Mendelian genetics can be used to study the inheritance of human traits and to calculate the probability of certain traits appearing in the next generation.

In 1900, Archibald Garrod, a British doctor, discovered that the pattern of inheritance of a rare disorder known as alkaptonuria fit the Mendelian pattern. Before long, a wide variety of human genes had been discovered. One of these is a gene for skin pigmentation. The gene's dominant allele *(A)* produces skin coloration. Individuals who are homozygous for the recessive form of the allele *(a)* have albinism, meaning that they lack the pigment melanin that gives human skin its color.

If two people with normal skin color have a child with albinism, what are the odds that a second child will also have albinism? By constructing a Punnett square, you can see that there is a 1 in 4 probability that their next child will also have albinism.

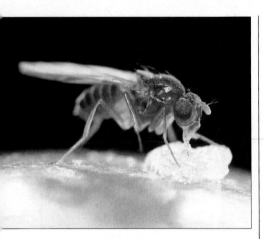

▲ **Figure 11–13** The common fruit fly is a popular organism for genetic research. **Inferring** *Why are fruit flies easier to use for genetic research than large animals, such as dogs?*

11–3 Section Assessment

1. 🔑 **Key Concept** Explain what *independent assortment* means.

2. 🔑 **Key Concept** Describe two inheritance patterns besides simple dominance.

3. What is the difference between incomplete dominance and codominance?

4. Why are fruit flies an ideal organism for genetic research?

5. **Critical Thinking Problem Solving** A geneticist crosses a pea plant that is true-breeding for round green seeds *(RRyy)* with one that is true-breeding for wrinkled yellow seeds *(rrYY).* Construct a Punnett square to show the results of this cross.

👤 **TEXT** Assessment Use iText to review the important concepts in Section 11–3.

ALTERNATIVE ASSESSMENT

Problem Solving
Construct a genetics problem to be given as an assignment to a classmate. The problem must test incomplete dominance, codominance, multiple alleles, or polygenic traits. Your problem must have an answer key that includes all of your work.

11–4 Meiosis

Gregor Mendel did not know where the genes he had discovered were located in the cell. Fortunately, his predictions of how genes should behave were so specific that it was not long before biologists were certain they had found them. Genes are located on chromosomes in the cell nucleus.

Mendel's principles of genetics require at least two things. First, each organism must inherit a single copy of every gene from both its "parents." Because each pea plant has two "parents," each plant must carry two complete sets of genes. Second, when an organism produces its own gametes, those two sets of genes must be separated from each other so that each gamete contains just one set of genes. This means that when gametes are formed, there must be a process that separates the two sets of genes so that each gamete ends up with just one set. Although Mendel didn't know it, gametes are formed through exactly such a process.

Chromosome Number

As an example of how this process works, let's consider the fruit fly, *Drosophila*. A body cell in an adult fruit fly has 8 chromosomes, as shown in **Figure 11–14.** Four of the chromosomes came from the fruit fly's male parent, and 4 came from its female parent. These two sets of chromosomes are **homologous** (hoh-MAHL-uh-guhs), meaning that each of the 4 chromosomes that came from the male parent has a corresponding chromosome from the female parent.

A cell that contains both sets of homologous chromosomes is said to be **diploid,** which means "two sets." The number of chromosomes in a diploid cell is sometimes represented by the symbol 2N. Thus for *Drosophila,* the diploid number is 8, which can be written 2N = 8. Diploid cells contain two complete sets of chromosomes and two complete sets of genes. This agrees with Mendel's idea that the cells of an adult organism contain two copies of each gene.

By contrast, the gametes of sexually reproducing organisms, including fruit flies and peas, contain only a single set of chromosomes, and therefore only a single set of genes. Such cells are said to be **haploid,** which means "one set." For *Drosophila,* this can be written as N = 4, meaning that the haploid number is 4.

Guide for Reading

 Key Concepts
- What happens during the process of meiosis?
- How is meiosis different from mitosis?

Vocabulary
homologous
diploid
haploid
meiosis
tetrad
crossing-over

Reading Strategy:
Using Visuals Before you read, preview **Figure 11–15.** As you read, note what happens at each stage of meiosis.

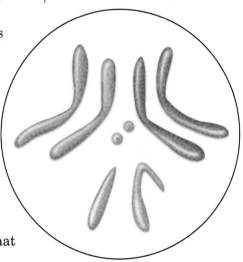

▶ **Figure 11–14** These chromosomes are from a fruit fly *(Drosophila).* Each of the fruit fly's body cells has 8 chromosomes.

Figure 11–15 During meiosis, the number of chromosomes per cell is cut in half through the separation of the homologous chromosomes. The result of meiosis is 4 haploid cells that are genetically different from one another and from the original cell.

MEIOSIS I

Interphase I
Cells undergo a round of DNA replication, forming duplicate chromosomes.

Prophase I
Each chromosome pairs with its corresponding homologous chromosome to form a tetrad.

Metaphase I
Spindle fibers attach to the chromosomes.

Anaphase I
The fibers pull the homologous chromosomes toward opposite ends of the cell.

Telophase I and Cytokinesis
Nuclear membranes form. The cell separates into two cells.

Phases of Meiosis

How are haploid (N) gamete cells produced from diploid (2N) cells? That's where **meiosis** (my-OH-sis) comes in. **Meiosis is a process of reduction division in which the number of chromosomes per cell is cut in half through the separation of homologous chromosomes in a diploid cell.**

Meiosis usually involves two distinct stages: the first meiotic division, called meiosis I, and the second meiotic division, called meiosis II. By the end of meiosis II, the diploid cell that entered meiosis has become 4 haploid cells. **Figure 11–15** shows the details of meiosis in an organism that has a diploid number of 4 (2N = 4).

CHECKPOINT *What is meiosis?*

Meiosis I Prior to meiosis I, each chromosome is replicated. The cells then begin to divide in a way that looks similar to mitosis. In mitosis, the 4 chromosomes line up individually in the center of the cell. The 2 chromatids that make up each chromosome then separate from each other.

In prophase of meiosis I, however, each chromosome pairs with its corresponding homologous chromosome to form a structure called a **tetrad.** There are 4 chromatids in a tetrad. This pairing of homologous chromosomes is the key to understanding meiosis.

◀ **Figure 11–16** During prophase I of meiosis, homologous chromosomes may cross over and exchange portions of their chromatids. **Interpreting Graphics** *How does crossing-over affect the alleles on a chromatid?*

MEIOSIS II

Prophase II

Meiosis I results in two haploid (N) daughter cells, each with half the number of chromosomes as the original cell.

Metaphase II

The chromosomes line up in a similar way to the metaphase stage of mitosis.

Anaphase II

The sister chromatids separate and move toward opposite ends of the cell.

Telophase II and Cytokinesis

Meiosis II results in four haploid (N) daughter cells.

As homologous chromosomes pair up and form tetrads in meiosis I, they may exchange portions of their chromatids in a process called **crossing-over.** Crossing-over, shown in **Figure 11–16,** results in the exchange of alleles between homologous chromosomes and produces new combinations of alleles.

What happens next? The homologous chromosomes separate, and two new cells are formed. Although each cell now has 4 chromatids (as it would after mitosis), something is different. Because each pair of homologous chromosomes was separated, neither of the daughter cells has the two complete sets of chromosomes that it would have in a diploid cell. Those two sets have been shuffled and sorted almost like a deck of cards. The two cells produced by meiosis I have sets of chromosomes and alleles that are different from each other and from the diploid cell that entered meiosis I.

Meiosis II The two cells produced by meiosis I now enter a second meiotic division. Unlike the first division, neither cell goes through a round of chromosome replication before entering meiosis II. Thus, each of the cell's chromosomes has 2 chromatids. During metaphase II of meiosis, 2 chromosomes line up in the center of each cell. In anaphase II, the paired chromatids separate. Each of the four daughter cells produced in meiosis II receives 2 chromatids. Those four daughter cells now contain the haploid number (N)—just 2 chromosomes each.

In Males

2N — Meiosis I

N   N — Meiosis II

N   N   N   N

Sperm

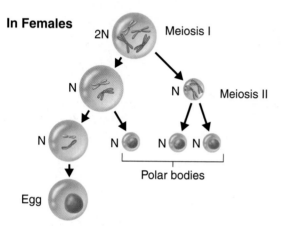

In Females

2N — Meiosis I

N   N — Meiosis II

N   N   N   N

Polar bodies

Egg

▲ **Figure 11–17** Meiosis produces four genetically different haploid cells. In males, meiosis results in four equal-sized gametes called sperm. In females, only one large egg cell results from meiosis. The other three cells, called polar bodies, usually are not involved in reproduction.

Gamete Formation

In male animals, the haploid gametes produced by meiosis are called sperm. In some plants, pollen grains contain haploid sperm cells. In female animals, generally only one of the cells produced by meiosis is involved in reproduction. This female gamete is called an egg in animals and an egg cell in some plants.

In many female animals, the cell divisions at the end of meiosis I and meiosis II are uneven, so the egg or egg cell receives most of the cytoplasm, as shown in **Figure 11–17**. The other three cells produced in the female during meiosis are known as polar bodies and usually do not participate in reproduction.

Comparing Mitosis and Meiosis

In a way, it's too bad that the words *mitosis* and *meiosis* sound so much like each other, because the two processes are very different. **Mitosis results in the production of two genetically identical diploid cells, whereas meiosis produces four genetically different haploid cells.**

A diploid cell that divides by mitosis gives rise to two diploid (2N) daughter cells. The daughter cells have sets of chromosomes and alleles that are identical to each other and to the original parent cell. Meiosis, on the other hand, begins with a diploid cell but produces four haploid (N) cells. These cells are genetically different from the diploid cell and from one another.

11–4 Section Assessment

1. **Key Concept** Describe the main results of meiosis.

2. **Key Concept** What are the principal differences between mitosis and meiosis?

3. What do the terms *diploid* and *haploid* mean?

4. What is crossing-over?

5. **Critical Thinking Applying Concepts** In human cells, 2N = 46. How many chromosomes would you expect to find in a sperm cell? In an egg cell? In a white blood cell? Explain.

TEXT **Assessment** Use iText to review the important concepts in Section 11–4.

MAKING CONNECTIONS

Modeling
Using materials found around the house, create a model that illustrates the difference between sister chromatids and homologous pairs of chromosomes. You may want to refer to Chapter 10 for help.

11–5 Linkage and Gene Maps

If you thought carefully about Mendel's principle of independent assortment as you analyzed meiosis, one question might have been bothering you. It's easy to see how genes located on different chromosomes assort independently, but what about genes located on the same chromosome? Wouldn't they generally be inherited together?

Gene Linkage

The answer to these questions, as Thomas Hunt Morgan first realized in 1910, is yes. Morgan's research on fruit flies led him to the principle of linkage. After identifying more than 50 *Drosophila* genes, Morgan discovered that many of them appeared to be "linked" together in ways that, at first glance, seemed to violate the principle of independent assortment. For example, a fly with reddish-orange eyes and miniature wings, like the one shown in **Figure 11–18**, was used in a series of crosses. The results showed that the genes for those traits were almost always inherited together and only rarely became separated from each other.

Morgan and his associates observed so many genes that were inherited together that before long they could group all of the fly's genes into four linkage groups. The linkage groups assorted independently, but all of the genes in one group were inherited together. *Drosophila* has four linkage groups. It also has four pairs of chromosomes, which led to two remarkable conclusions. First, each chromosome is actually a group of linked genes. Second, Mendel's principle of independent assortment still holds true. **It is the chromosomes, however, that assort independently, not individual genes.**

How did Mendel manage to miss gene linkage? By luck, or by design, six of the seven genes he studied are on different chromosomes. The two genes that are found on the same chromosome are so far apart that they also assort independently.

Gene Maps

If two genes are found on the same chromosome, does this mean that they are linked forever? Not at all. Crossing-over during meiosis sometimes separates genes that had been on the same chromosome onto homologous chromosomes. Crossover events occasionally separate and exchange linked genes and produce new combinations of alleles. This is important because it helps to generate genetic diversity.

Guide for Reading

Key Concept
• What structures actually assort independently?

Vocabulary
gene map

Reading Strategy:
Predicting Before you read, preview **Figure 11–19.** Predict how a diagram like this one can be used to determine how likely genes are to assort independently. As you read, note whether or not your prediction was correct.

▼ **Figure 11–18** The genes for this fruit fly's reddish-orange eyes and miniature wings are almost always inherited together. The reason for this is that the genes are close together on a single chromosome. Chromosomes assort independently, not individual genes.

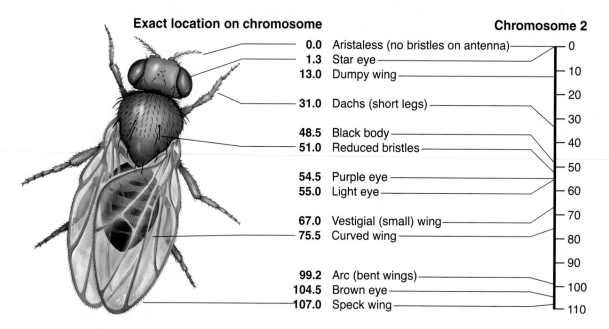

Exact location on chromosome

Chromosome 2

Location	Gene
0.0	Aristaless (no bristles on antenna)
1.3	Star eye
13.0	Dumpy wing
31.0	Dachs (short legs)
48.5	Black body
51.0	Reduced bristles
54.5	Purple eye
55.0	Light eye
67.0	Vestigial (small) wing
75.5	Curved wing
99.2	Arc (bent wings)
104.5	Brown eye
107.0	Speck wing

▲ **Figure 11–19** This gene map shows the location of a variety of genes on chromosome 2 of the fruit fly. The genes are named after the problems abnormal alleles cause, not the normal structure. **Interpreting Graphics** *Where on the chromosome is the "purple eye" gene located?*

In 1911, a Columbia University student was working part time in Morgan's lab. This student, Alfred Sturtevant, hypothesized that the rate at which crossing-over separated linked genes could be the key to an important discovery. Sturtevant reasoned that the farther apart two genes were, the more likely they were to be separated by a crossover in meiosis. The rate at which linked genes were separated and recombined could then be used to produce a "map" of distances between genes. Sturtevant gathered up several notebooks of lab data and took them back to his room. The next morning, he presented Morgan with a **gene map** showing the relative locations of each known gene on one of the *Drosophila* chromosomes, as shown in **Figure 11–19**. Sturtevant's method of using recombination rates, which measure the frequencies of crossing-over between genes, has been used to construct genetic maps, including maps of the human genome, ever since.

11–5 Section Assessment

1. 🔑 **Key Concept** How does the principle of independent assortment apply to chromosomes?

2. What are gene maps, and how are they produced?

3. How does crossing-over make gene mapping possible?

4. **Critical Thinking Inferring** If two genes are on the same chromosome but usually assort independently, what does that tell you about how close together they are?

📱 **TEXT** **Assessment** Use iText to review the important concepts in Section 11–5.

Take It to the NET
For his pioneering research on fruit flies, Thomas Hunt Morgan won a Nobel Prize. Create a time line that shows at least four highlights of Morgan's life as a scientist. Use the links provided in the Biology area at the Prentice Hall Web site for help in completing this activity: **www.phschool.com**

Modeling Meiosis

Meiosis results in 4 new cells, each containing half the number of chromosomes in the original cells. Using the procedures below, you will build a model to demonstrate the process of meiosis and explore how it can lead to genetic changes.

Problem What happens to the chromosomes in cells during meiosis?

Materials

- 4 colors of yarn (2 shades of red and 2 shades of green)
- scissors
- transparent tape
- index cards
- felt-tip marker

Skills Using Models, Communicating Results

Procedure

1. You will use yarn and index cards to model each stage of meiosis. Use 2 shades of red yarn to represent one homologous pair of chromosomes and 2 shades of green yarn to represent another pair. Use an index card to represent a cell.

2. Cut 2 pieces of yarn about 5 cm long from each color of yarn. Each piece of yarn will represent a chromatid.

3. Tape pieces of red and green yarn to an index card to show the appearance of two tetrads in a cell at the beginning of meiosis.

4. Tape pieces of yarn to additional index cards to model the numbers and positions of the chromosomes and cells at each stage of meiosis. Be sure to include an example of crossing-over at the correct stage. Use a felt-tip marker to label each card with the name of the stage it represents.

5. Arrange the finished cards to show the complete process of meiosis. Label the stages at which genetic segregation and crossing-over occur and chromosome number changes.

6. Use your cards to explain the process of meiosis to a classmate. Then, trade roles and have your classmate use his or her models to explain the process of meiosis to you.

Analyze and Conclude

1. **Using Models** What is the result of the first meiotic division (meiosis I)?

2. **Using Models** What is the result of the second meiotic division (meiosis II)?

3. **Drawing Conclusions** How does meiosis lead to increased genetic variation?

4. **Predicting** How would the gametes be affected if a pair of chromatids failed to separate in the second meiotic division?

Go Further

Using Models Make a second set of models that shows the differences between the formation of sperm and the formation of eggs.

Chapter 11 Study Guide

11–1 The Work of Gregor Mendel
 Key Concepts

- The principle of dominance states that some alleles are dominant and others are recessive.

- When each F_1 plant flowers, the two alleles are segregated from each other so that each gamete carries only a single copy of each gene. Therefore, each F_1 plant produces two types of gametes—those with the allele for tallness and those with the allele for shortness.

Vocabulary
- genetics, p. 263 • true-breeding, p. 263
- trait, p. 264 • hybrid, p. 264
- gene, p. 265 • allele, p. 265
- segregation, p. 266 • gamete, p. 266

11–2 Probability and Punnett Squares
Key Concept

- The principles of probability can be used to predict the outcomes of genetic crosses.

Vocabulary
- probability, p. 267 • Punnett square, p. 268
- homozygous, p. 268 • heterozygous, p. 268
- phenotype, p. 268 • genotype, p. 268

11–3 Exploring Mendelian Genetics
Key Concepts

- The principle of independent assortment states that genes for different traits can segregate independently during the formation of gametes.

- Some alleles are neither dominant nor recessive, and many traits are controlled by multiple alleles or multiple genes.

Vocabulary
independent assortment, p. 271
incomplete dominance, p. 272
codominance, p. 272
multiple alleles, p. 273
polygenic traits, p. 273

11–4 Meiosis
Key Concepts

- Meiosis is a process of reduction division in which the number of chromosomes per cell is cut in half through the separation of homologous chromosomes in a diploid cell.

- Mitosis results in the production of two genetically identical diploid cells, whereas meiosis produces four genetically different haploid cells.

Vocabulary
- homologous, p. 275 • diploid, p. 275
- haploid, p. 275 • meiosis, p. 276
- tetrad, p. 276 • crossing-over, p. 277

11–5 Linkage and Gene Maps
Key Concept

- The chromosomes assort independently; individual genes do not.

Vocabulary
gene map, p. 280

Thinking Visually
Using the information in this chapter, complete the following flowchart about meiosis.

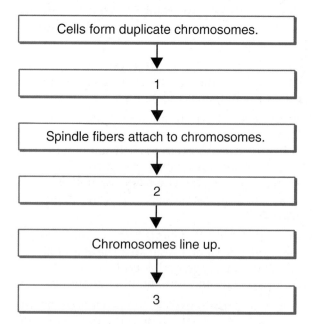

Cells form duplicate chromosomes.
↓
1
↓
Spindle fibers attach to chromosomes.
↓
2
↓
Chromosomes line up.
↓
3

Chapter 11

Part A

Multiple Choice

For each statement or question, select the number of the word or expression that, of those given, best completes the statement or answers the question.

1 Different forms of a gene are called
  (1) hybrids   (3) dominant factors
  (2) alleles   (4) recessive factors

2 If a homozygous tall pea plant and a homozygous short pea plant are crossed,
  (1) the recessive trait seems to disappear
  (2) the offspring are of medium height
  (3) no hybrids are produced
  (4) all the offspring are homozygous

3 Which arrangement of cell-related terms correctly represents the relationships involved?
  (1) A nucleus includes chromosomes that contain several genes.
  (2) Several nuclei make up genes that are located on chromosomes.
  (3) A gene is made up of chromosomes that are located in the cytoplasm.
  (4) Chromosomes are composed of nuclei that include several genes.

4 The physical characteristics of an organism are its
  (1) genetics   (3) alleles
  (2) phenotype   (4) genotype

5 To maintain the chromosome number of an organism, the gametes must
  (1) come with a complete set of genetic instructions
  (2) result in genetically identical cells
  (3) be produced by mitosis
  (4) be produced by meiosis

6 What stage of meiosis is represented in the cell illustrated below?
  (1) prophase I   (3) anaphase II
  (2) telophase I   (4) metaphase I

7 Unlike mitosis, meiosis results in the formation of
  (1) two cells, each containing half the genetic information of the parent cell
  (2) two cells, each containing a complete set of chromosomes
  (3) four cells, each containing a complete set of chromosomes
  (4) four cells, each containing half the genetic information of the parent cell

8 Which statement would be an accurate description of a gene map?
  (1) A gene map shows the number of possible forms of a gene.
  (2) A gene map shows the relative locations of genes on a chromosome.
  (3) A gene map shows where chromosomes are located in a cell.
  (4) A gene map shows how crossing-over occurs.

9 What happens to the chromosome number of a cell during meiosis?
  (1) It doubles.   (3) It stays the same.
  (2) It quadruples.   (4) It halves.

10 Two pink-flowering plants are crossed. The offspring flower as follows: 25% red, 25% white, 50% pink. What pattern of inheritance does flower color in these flowers follow?
  (1) dominance
  (2) multiple alleles
  (3) incomplete dominance
  (4) recessiveness

For question 11, complete the analogy by selecting the correct number. In analogies, A : B :: C : means "A is to B as C is to ___?___."

11 Mitosis : diploid daughter cells :: meiosis :
  (1) egg cells   (3) four daughter cells
  (2) sperm cells   (4) haploid daughter cells

Test-Taking Tip To complete an analogy, write a sentence that uses the two given words of the first pair. Then, rewrite the sentence with the third given word and a blank. Try each of the answer choices in the blank to see which one works best. If more than one answer choice seems to fit, refine the original sentence and repeat the process.

Parts B and C

Multiple Choice and Extended Response

For those questions that ask you to select a response, choose the one that best completes the statement or answers the question. For all others follow the directions given.

12 A genetic disease is one that can be inherited from one or both of an individual's parents. Examine the following description of disease inheritance in a particular family.

Child: has the disease; possesses two disease-causing forms of the gene for the trait

Father: does not have the disease; possesses one disease-causing form of the gene for the trait

Mother: does not have the disease

What is the most likely genetic makeup of the mother for this genetic disease?

(1) She possesses two normal forms of the gene for the trait.

(2) She possesses two disease-causing forms of the gene for the trait.

(3) She possesses one normal and one disease-causing form of the gene for the trait.

(4) She possesses an abnormal number of genes for the trait.

For questions 13 through 15, select the best choice among those listed below. A choice may be used once, more than once, or not at all.

(1) Phenotype
(2) Hybrids
(3) Genotype
(4) Homozygous
(5) Multiple alleles

13 Offspring of crosses between parents with different traits

14 Genetic makeup of an organism

15 Having two identical alleles for a given gene

16 State the four basic principles of genetics that Mendel discovered in his experiments. Briefly describe each of these principles.

17 What is probability? Describe how probability relates to genetics.

18 State two ways that multiple alleles and polygenic traits differ.

Base your answers to questions 19 and 20 on the information below and on your knowledge of biology.

A student calculates the recombination frequency of genes A, B, C, and D on one chromosome. The recombination frequencies are as follows: C-D: 25 map units; A-B: 12 map units; B-D: 20 map units; and A-C: 17 map units.

19 Assuming the student's calculations are correct, how many map units apart are genes A and D?

(1) 5   (3) 10
(2) 8   (4) 12.5

20 Which gene map below best reflects the student's data?

(1) A   (3) C
(2) B   (4) D

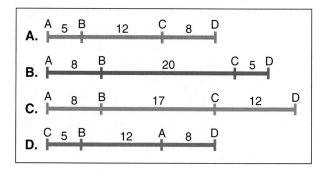

21 In rabbits, *B* is an allele for black coat and *b* is an allele for brown coat.
• Write the genotype for a rabbit that is homozygous for black coat.
• Write the genotype for a rabbit that is heterozygous for black coat.

22 Describe the process of meiosis. In your description, be sure to include
• the number of cells produced
• the number of chromosomes present in each cell at the start and at the conclusion of the process
• the number of cytoplasmic divisions that occur

23 In sheep, the allele for white wool (*A*) is dominant over the allele for black wool (*a*). How would you determine the genotype of a white ram (male sheep)?

24 Explain why horse breeders will pay a lot of money to breed one of their horses with a horse that has won the Kentucky Derby.

Base your answers to questions 25 through 27 on the passage below and on your knowledge of biology.

DNA is a long, threadlike molecule. Basically it contains the instructions for everything our cells do from the moment of conception until death. Most human cells contain 46 chromosomes (23 pairs). Each chromosome contains a DNA molecule with hundreds or thousands of genes along it. Genes typically code for the production of specific proteins. The instructions for making proteins are in the form of a four-letter code. A single misspelling in the DNA sequence can result in an incorrect protein or no protein being made, which, in turn, may result in an upset in homeostasis—in this case a genetic disease.

Connecting a particular defective gene with a disease has been a very slow process. In 1989, geneticists had identified four genes associated with such diseases. They did this by sorting through the hereditary history of families and examining the genetic makeup of individuals with the disease and those not having the disease. As a result of the Human Genome Project (HGP), a huge study to find out more about all of the DNA in human cells and the cells of other organisms, the list of diseases known to be linked to specific genes was up to 100 by 1998.

One of the first diseases linked to a gene was cystic fibrosis. It took teams of scientists nine years to identify the gene. As a result of the technology and information sharing associated the HGP, the gene for Parkinson disease was mapped in nine days and precisely described in just nine months. This means that scientists knew the letter code and the location on a chromosome of the Parkinson in less than a year after they started the search!

As the understanding of diseases at the DNA level becomes clearer, scientists might be able to prevent such diseases, design individualized treatments for them, and in some cases, actually cure the diseases.

(Adapted from: "Genetics: The Future of Medicine" NIH Publication No. 00-4873)

25 According to the reading passage, two diseases linked to genes are
  (1) the common cold and cystic fibrosis
  (2) HGP and Parkinson disease
  (3) Parkinson disease and cystic fibrosis
  (4) the common cold and HGP

26 Which of the following would be the best title for this reading?
  (1) Predicting the Inheritance of Human Genetic Diseases
  (2) The Human Genome Project
  (3) The Gene for Cystic Fibrosis
  (4) Mapping Human Genetic Diseases

27 State one reason it is important to study the inheritance of human genetic diseases.

28 Genes that control hair or feather color in some animals are expressed differently in the winter than in the summer. For example, snowshoe hares are white in winter and brown in summer. How might such a difference in expression be beneficial to the snowshoe hare? Does the genotype of the snowshoe hare change from season to season? In your answer be sure to discuss:
  • environmental conditions
  • inheritance of traits

29 Explain why it is chromosomes, not individual genes, that assort independently.

30 In pea plants, the allele for yellow seeds is dominant to the allele for green seeds.
  • Predict the genotypic ratio of offspring produced by crossing two parents heterozygous for this trait.
  • Draw a Punnett square to illustrate your prediction.

Take It to the NET

Have you ever heard the phrase "a horse of a different color"? Visit the Prentice Hall Web site at **www.phschool.com** to find out what this phrase means in terms of genetics. Then, answer the following questions:
  • How is the color of a horse's coat determined?
  • What does the *W* gene control? The *E* gene?
  • What will a horse that is genotype *wwEE* look like?
  • If a mare with the genotype wwee is crossed with a *wwEE* stallion, what proportion of the foals will have the ability to form black hair?

12 DNA and RNA

These models show the structure of DNA, the molecule that carries genetic information.

Inquiry Activity

How do codes work?

Procedure

1. Obtain 12 pop beads of four different colors.
2. Select a word that contains at least five different letters from the text on the next page. Use your beads to develop a code for your word.
3. Exchange your code and your coded bead chain with a classmate. Use the classmate's code to decipher his or her word.

Think About It

1. **Using Models** How were you able to encode five different letters using only four colors?
2. **Calculating** How many different letters could you encode by using two beads to stand for each letter used in your message?
3. **Analyzing Data** Could you encode the whole alphabet by using three beads for each letter?

12–1 DNA

How do genes work? What are they made of, and how do they determine the characteristics of organisms? Are genes single molecules, or are they longer structures made up of many molecules? In the middle of the 1900s, questions like these were on the minds of biologists everywhere.

To truly understand genetics, biologists first had to discover the chemical nature of the gene. If the structures that carry genetic information could be identified, it might be possible to understand how genes control the inherited characteristics of living things.

Griffith and Transformation

Like many stories in science, the discovery of the molecular nature of the gene began with an investigator who was actually looking for something else. In 1928, British scientist Frederick Griffith was trying to figure out how bacteria make people sick. More specifically, Griffith wanted to learn how certain types of bacteria produce a serious lung disease known as pneumonia.

Griffith had isolated two slightly different strains, or types, of pneumonia bacteria from mice. Both strains grew very well in culture plates in his lab, but only one of the strains caused pneumonia. The disease-causing strain of bacteria grew into smooth colonies on culture plates, whereas the harmless strain produced colonies with rough edges. The differences in appearance made the two strains easy to distinguish.

Guide for Reading

Key Concepts
• What did scientists discover about the relationship between genes and DNA?
• What is the overall structure of the DNA molecule?

Vocabulary
transformation
bacteriophage
nucleotide
base pairing

**Reading Strategy:
Summarizing** As you read, find the key ideas for the text under each blue heading. Write down a few key words from each main idea. Then, use the key words in your summary. Revise your summary, keeping only the most important ideas.

◀ **Figure 12–1** White mice like these are commonly used in scientific experiments.

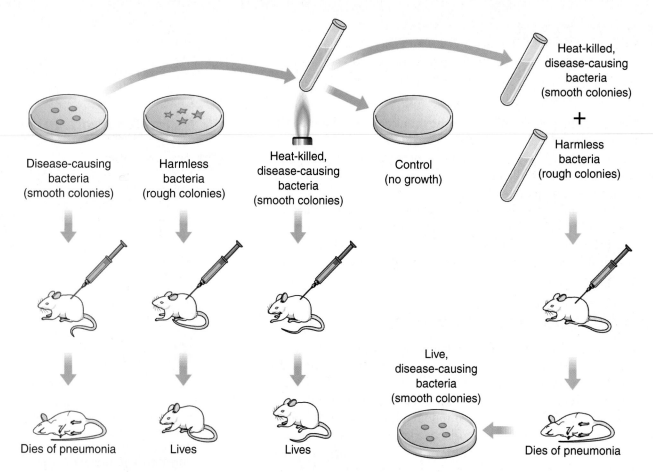

Disease-causing bacteria (smooth colonies)

Harmless bacteria (rough colonies)

Heat-killed, disease-causing bacteria (smooth colonies)

Control (no growth)

Heat-killed, disease-causing bacteria (smooth colonies)

+

Harmless bacteria (rough colonies)

Dies of pneumonia

Lives

Lives

Live, disease-causing bacteria (smooth colonies)

Dies of pneumonia

▲ **Figure 12–2** Griffith injected mice with four different samples of bacteria from the smooth and rough colonies. When injected separately, neither heat-killed, disease-causing bacteria nor live, harmless bacteria killed the mice. The two types injected together, however, caused fatal pneumonia. Some factor from the dead bacteria had "transformed" the harmless bacteria into disease-causing ones. From this experiment, biologists inferred that genetic information could be transformed from one bacterium to another.

Griffith's Experiments When Griffith injected mice with the disease-causing strain of bacteria, the mice developed pneumonia and died. When mice were injected with the harmless strain, they didn't get sick at all. Griffith wondered if the disease-causing bacteria might produce a poison.

To find out, he took a culture of these cells, heated the bacteria to kill them, and injected the heat-killed bacteria into mice. The mice survived, suggesting that the cause of pneumonia was not a chemical poison released by the disease-causing bacteria. The results of Griffith's experiments are shown in **Figure 12–2.**

Transformation Griffith's next experiment produced an amazing result. He mixed his heat-killed, disease-causing bacteria with live, harmless ones and injected the mixture into mice. By themselves, neither should have made the mice sick. But to Griffith's amazement, the mice developed pneumonia and many died. When he examined the lungs of the mice, he found them filled with the disease-causing bacteria.

Somehow the heat-killed bacteria had passed their disease-causing ability to the harmless strain. Griffith called this process **transformation** because one strain of bacteria (the harmless strain) had apparently been changed into another (the disease-causing strain). Griffith hypothesized that when the live, harmless bacteria and the heat-killed bacteria were mixed together, some factor was transferred from the heat-killed cells into the live cells. That factor, he hypothesized, might contain a gene with the information that could change harmless bacteria into disease-causing ones.

Avery and DNA

In 1944, a group of scientists led by Canadian biologist Oswald Avery at the Rockefeller Institute in New York decided to repeat Griffith's work. They did so to determine which molecule in the heat-killed bacteria was most important for transformation. If transformation required just one particular molecule, that might well be the molecule of the gene.

Avery and his colleagues made an extract, or juice, from the heat-killed bacteria. They then carefully treated the extract with enzymes that destroyed proteins, lipids, carbohydrates, and other molecules, including the nucleic acid RNA. Transformation still occurred. Obviously these molecules were not responsible for the transformation. If they had been, transformation would not have occurred, because the molecules would have been destroyed by the enzymes.

Avery and the other scientists repeated the experiment, this time using enzymes that would break down DNA. When they destroyed the nucleic acid DNA in the extract, transformation did not occur. There was just one possible conclusion. DNA was the transforming factor. **Avery and other scientists discovered that DNA is the nucleic acid that stores and transmits the genetic information from one generation of an organism to the next.**

The Hershey-Chase Experiment

Scientists are a skeptical group. It usually takes several experiments to convince them of something as important as the chemical nature of the gene. The most important of these experiments was performed in 1952 by two American scientists, Alfred Hershey and Martha Chase. They studied viruses, nonliving particles smaller than a cell that can infect living organisms.

Bacteriophages One kind of virus that infects and kills bacteria is known as a **bacteriophage** (bak-TEER-ee-uh-fayj), which means "bacteria eater." **Figure 12–3** shows a typical bacteriophage. Bacteriophages are composed of a DNA or RNA core and a protein coat. When a bacteriophage enters a bacterium, the virus attaches to the surface of the cell and injects its DNA into it. The viral genes act to produce many new bacteriophages, and they gradually destroy the bacterium. When the cell splits open, hundreds of new viruses burst out.

CHECKPOINT *What is a bacteriophage?*

KEEP CURRENT WITH . . .

SCIENCE NEWS®

To find out more about the topics in this chapter, go to: www.phschool.com

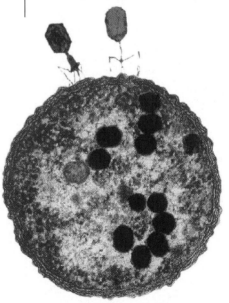

▼ **Figure 12–3** A bacteriophage is a type of virus that infects and kills bacteria. This image shows two T2 bacteriophages (purple) invading an *E. coli* cell (green). **Comparing and Contrasting** *How large are viruses compared with bacteria?*

(magnification: 25,000×)

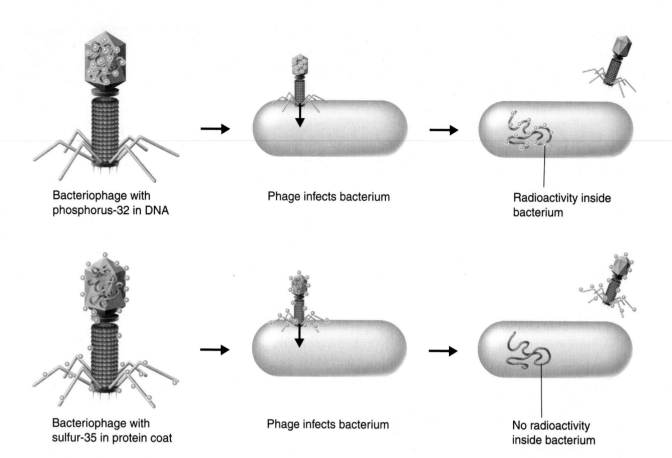

Bacteriophage with
phosphorus-32 in DNA

Phage infects bacterium

Radioactivity inside
bacterium

Bacteriophage with
sulfur-35 in protein coat

Phage infects bacterium

No radioactivity
inside bacterium

▲ **Figure 12–4** Alfred Hershey
and Martha Chase used different
radioactive markers to label the
DNA and proteins of bacteriophages. The bacteriophages
injected only DNA into the bacteria,
not proteins. **From these
results, Hershey and Chase
concluded that the genetic
material of the bacteriophage
was DNA.**

Radioactive Markers Hershey and Chase reasoned that if
they could determine which part of the virus—the protein coat
or the DNA core—entered the infected cell, they would learn
whether genes were made of protein or DNA. To do this, they
grew viruses in cultures containing radioactive isotopes of
phosphorus-32 (^{32}P) and sulfur-35 (^{35}S). This was a clever
strategy because proteins contain almost no phosphorus and
DNA contains no sulfur. The radioactive substances could be
used as markers. If ^{35}S was found in the bacteria, it would mean
that the viruses' protein had been injected into the bacteria. If
^{32}P was found in the bacteria, then it was the DNA that had
been injected.

The Hershey-Chase experiment is shown in **Figure 12–4.**
The two scientists mixed the marked viruses with bacteria.
Then, they waited a few minutes for the viruses to inject their
genetic material. Next, they separated the viruses from the
bacteria and tested the bacteria for radioactivity. Nearly all the
radioactivity in the bacteria was from phosphorus (^{32}P), the
marker found in DNA. **Hershey and Chase concluded
that the genetic material of the bacteriophage was DNA,
not protein.**

CHECKPOINT *What part of the virus did the Hershey-Chase experiment
show had entered the bacteria?*

The Structure of DNA

You might think that knowing genes were made of DNA would have satisfied scientists, but that was not the case at all. Instead, they wondered how DNA, or any molecule for that matter, could do the three critical things that genes were known to do: First, genes had to carry information from one generation to the next; second, they had to put that information to work by determining the heritable characteristics of organisms; and third, genes had to be easily copied, because all of a cell's genetic information is replicated every time a cell divides. For DNA to do all of that, it would have to be a very special molecule indeed.

DNA is a long molecule made up of units called **nucleotides.** As **Figure 12–5** shows, each nucleotide is made up of three basic parts: a 5-carbon sugar called deoxyribose, a phosphate group, and a nitrogenous (nitrogen-containing) base. There are four kinds of nitrogenous bases in DNA. Two of the nitrogenous bases, adenine (AD-uh-neen) and guanine (GWAH-neen), belong to a group of compounds known as purines. The remaining two bases, cytosine (SY-tuh-zeen) and thymine (THY-meen), are known as pyrimidines. Purines have two rings in their structures, whereas pyrimidines have one ring.

The backbone of a DNA chain is formed by sugar and phosphate groups of each nucleotide. The nitrogenous bases stick out sideways from the chain. The nucleotides can be joined together in any order, meaning that any sequence of bases is possible.

If you don't see much in **Figure 12–5** that could explain the remarkable properties of the gene, don't be surprised. In the 1940s and early 1950s, the leading biologists in the world thought of DNA as little more than a string of nucleotides. They were baffled, too. The four different nucleotides, like the 26 letters of the alphabet, could be strung together in many different ways, so it was possible they could carry coded genetic information. However, so could many other molecules, at least in principle. Was there something more to the structure of DNA?

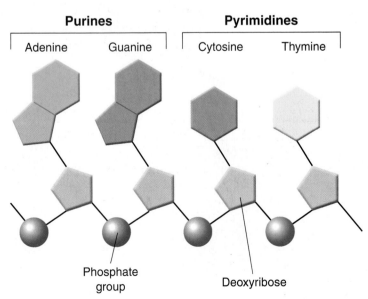

Purines

Adenine   Guanine

Pyrimidines

Cytosine   Thymine

Phosphate group

Deoxyribose

◀ **Figure 12–5** DNA is made up of a series of monomers called nucleotides. Each nucleotide has three parts: a deoxyribose molecule, a phosphate group, and a nitrogenous base. There are four different bases in DNA: adenine, guanine, cytosine, and thymine. **Interpreting Graphics** *How are the nucleotides joined together to form the DNA chain?*

Percentages of Bases in Four Organisms				
Source of DNA	A	T	G	C
Streptococcus	29.8	31.6	20.5	18.0
Yeast	31.3	32.9	18.7	17.1
Herring	27.8	27.5	22.2	22.6
Human	30.9	29.4	19.9	19.8

▲ **Figure 12–6** Erwin Chargaff showed that the percentages of guanine and cytosine in DNA are almost equal. The same is true for adenine and thymine. **Interpreting Graphics** *Which organism has the highest percentage of adenine?*

Chargaff's Rules One of the puzzling facts about DNA was a curious relationship between its nucleotides. Years earlier, Erwin Chargaff, an American biochemist, had discovered that the percentages of guanine [G] and cytosine [C] bases are almost equal in any sample of DNA. The same thing is true for the other two nucleotides, adenine [A] and thymine [T], as shown in **Figure 12–6.** The observation that [A] = [T] and [G] = [C] became known as Chargaff's rules. Despite the fact that DNA samples from organisms as different as bacteria and humans obeyed this rule, neither Chargaff nor anyone else had the faintest idea why.

X-Ray Evidence In the early 1950s, a British scientist named Rosalind Franklin began to study DNA. She used a technique called X-ray diffraction to get information about the structure of the DNA molecule. Aiming a powerful X-ray beam at concentrated DNA samples, she recorded the scattering pattern of the X-rays on film. Franklin worked hard to make better and better patterns from DNA until the patterns became clear.

Biology and History

Discovering the Role of DNA

Genes and the laws of heredity were discovered before scientists identified the molecules that genes are made of. With the discovery of DNA, scientists have been able to explain how genes are replicated and how they function.

Rosalind Franklin
Franklin studies the DNA molecule using a technique called X-ray diffraction.

1952

1900

1950

1913
Henry Ford introduces the first assembly line.

Frederick Griffith
Griffith discovers that a factor in heat-killed, disease-causing bacteria can "transform" harmless bacteria into ones that can cause disease.

1928

1944
Oswald Avery
Avery's team determines that genes are composed of DNA.

1951
Linus Pauling Robert Corey
Pauling and Corey determine that the structure of a class of proteins is a helix.

By itself, Franklin's X-ray pattern does not reveal the structure of DNA, but it does carry some very important clues. The X-shaped pattern in the time-line photograph shows that the strands in DNA are twisted around each other like the coils of a spring, a shape known as a helix. The angle of the *X* suggests that there are two strands in the structure. Other clues suggest that the nitrogenous bases are near the center of the molecule.

✓**CHECKPOINT** *What technique did Franklin use to study DNA?*

The Double Helix At the same time that Franklin was continuing her research, Francis Crick, a British physicist, and James Watson, an American biologist, were trying to understand the structure of DNA by building three-dimensional models of the molecule. Their models were made of cardboard and wire. They twisted and stretched the models in various ways, but their best efforts did nothing to explain DNA's properties.

Then, early in 1953, Watson was shown a copy of Franklin's remarkable X-ray pattern. The effect was immediate. In his book *The Double Helix,* Watson wrote: "The instant I saw the picture my mouth fell open and my pulse began to race." Watson reported the pattern's clues to Crick at once. Within weeks, Watson and Crick had figured out the structure of DNA. They published their results in a historic one-page paper in April of 1953. 🔑 **Watson and Crick's model of DNA was a double helix, in which two strands were wound around each other.**

Writing Activity

Do research in the library or on the Internet to find out what James Watson or Francis Crick has worked on since discovering the structure of DNA. Organize your findings about the scientist's work and write a short essay describing it.

Sydney Brenner
Brenner and other scientists show the existence of messenger RNA.

1960

Human Genome Project
The Human Genome Project—an attempt to sequence all human DNA—is essentially complete.

2000

2000

1953

James Watson
Francis Crick
Watson and Crick develop the double-helix model of the structure of DNA.

1977

Walter Gilbert
Gilbert, Allan Maxam, and Frederick Sanger develop methods to read the DNA sequence.

DNA and RNA **293**

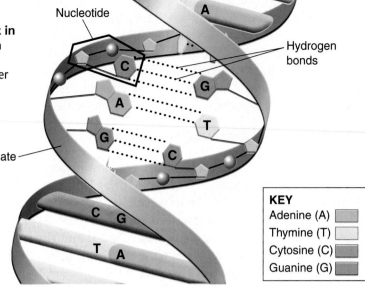

▶ **Figure 12–7** 🔵 DNA is a double helix in which two strands are wound around each other. Each strand is made up of a chain of nucleotides. The two strands are held together by hydrogen bonds between adenine and thymine and between guanine and cytosine.

Nucleotide

Hydrogen bonds

Sugar-phosphate backbone

KEY
Adenine (A)
Thymine (T)
Cytosine (C)
Guanine (G)

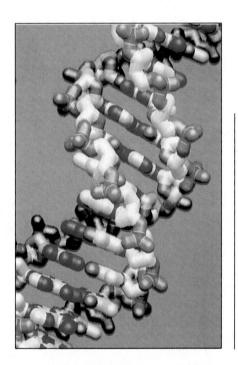

A double helix looks like a twisted ladder or a spiral staircase. The double helix accounted for many of the features in Franklin's X-ray pattern but did not explain what forces held the two strands together. Watson and Crick found the answer. They discovered that hydrogen bonds could form between certain nitrogenous bases and provide just enough force to hold the two strands together. As **Figure 12–7** shows, hydrogen bonds can form only between certain base pairs—adenine and thymine and guanine and cytosine. Once they saw this, they also realized that this principle, called **base pairing,** explained Chargaff's rules. Now there was a reason that [A] = [T] and [G] = [C]. For every adenine in a double-stranded DNA molecule, there had to be exactly one thymine molecule; for each cytosine molecule, there was one guanine molecule.

12–1 Section Assessment

1. 🔑 **Key Concept** List the conclusions Griffith, Avery, Hershey, and Chase drew from their experiments.

2. 🔑 **Key Concept** Describe Watson and Crick's model of the DNA molecule.

3. What are the four kinds of bases found in DNA?

4. How did Watson and Crick's model explain why there are equal amounts of thymine and adenine in DNA?

5. **Critical Thinking Inferring** Why did Hershey and Chase grow viruses in cultures that contained both radioactive phosphorus and radioactive sulfur? What might have happened if they had used only one radioactive substance?

🧍 **TEXT** **Assessment** Use iText to review the important concepts in Section 12–1.

MAKING CONNECTIONS

Scientific Methods
Using either Griffith's, Avery's, or Hershey-Chase's experiment as an example, develop a flowchart that shows the scientific process. Be sure to identify each process. (*Hint:* You may wish to review Chapter 1, which describes the scientific method.)

12–2 Chromosomes and DNA Replication

DNA is present in such large amounts in many tissues that it's easy to extract and analyze. But where is DNA found in the cell? How is it organized? Where are the genes that Mendel first described a century and a half ago?

DNA and Chromosomes

Prokaryotic cells lack nuclei and many of the organelles found in eukaryotes. Their DNA molecules are located in the cytoplasm. Most prokaryotes have a single circular DNA molecule that contains nearly all of the cell's genetic information. This large DNA molecule is usually referred to as the cell's chromosome, as shown in **Figure 12–8.**

Eukaryotic DNA is a bit more complicated. Many eukaryotes have as much as 1000 times the amount of DNA as prokaryotes. This DNA is not found free in the cytoplasm. Eukaryotic DNA is generally located in the cell nucleus in the form of a number of chromosomes. The number of chromosomes varies widely from one species to the next. For example, diploid human cells have 46 chromosomes, *Drosophila* cells have 8, and giant sequoia tree cells have 22.

DNA Length DNA molecules are surprisingly long. The chromosome of the prokaryote *E. coli*, which can live in the human colon, contains 4,639,221 base pairs. The length of such a DNA molecule is roughly 1.6 mm, which doesn't sound like much until you think about the small size of a bacterium. A typical bacterium is less than 1.6 μm in diameter, so the DNA molecule must be folded into a space only one one-thousandth of its length.

Key Concept
• What happens during DNA replication?

Vocabulary
chromatin
histone
replication
DNA polymerase

Reading Strategy:
Asking Questions Before you read, study the diagram in **Figure 12–11.** Make a list of questions about the diagram. As you read, write down the answers to your questions.

▼ **Figure 12–8** Most prokaryotes, such as this *E. coli* bacterium, have only a single circular chromosome. This chromosome holds most of the organism's DNA.

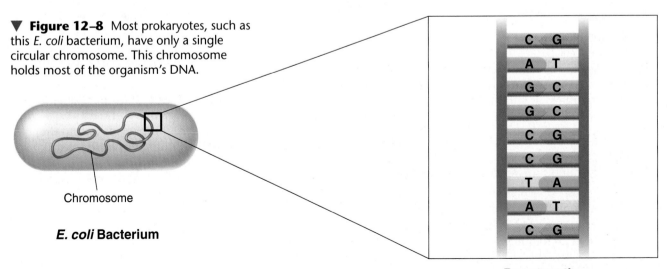

Chromosome

***E. coli* Bacterium**

Bases on the Chromosome

▲ **Figure 12–9** The DNA in a bacterium is about 1000 times as long as the bacterium itself. It must therefore be very tightly folded. **Making Analogies** *Compare DNA in a bacterium to jamming rope into a backpack.*

To get a rough idea of what this means, think of a large school backpack. Then, imagine trying to pack a 300-meter length of rope into the backpack! **Figure 12–9**, which shows DNA spilling out from a ruptured bacterium, indicates how dramatically the DNA must be folded to fit within the cell.

Chromosome Structure The DNA in eukaryotic cells is packed even more tightly. A human cell contains almost 1000 times as many base pairs of DNA as a bacterium. This means that the nucleus of a human cell contains more than 1 meter of DNA. Even the smallest human chromosome contains more than 30 million base pairs of DNA, making its DNA nearly 10 times as long as many bacterial chromosomes. How is so much DNA folded into tiny chromosomes? The answer can be found in the composition of eukaryotic chromosomes.

Eukaryotic chromosomes contain both DNA and protein, tightly packed together to form a substance called **chromatin.** Chromatin consists of DNA that is tightly coiled around proteins called **histones,** as shown in **Figure 12–10.** Together, the DNA and histone molecules form a beadlike structure called a nucleosome. Nucleosomes pack with one another to form a thick fiber, which is shortened by a system of loops and coils.

During most of the cell cycle, these fibers are dispersed in the nucleus so that individual chromosomes are not visible. During mitosis, however, the fibers of each individual chromosome are drawn together, forming the tightly packed chromosomes you can see through a light microscope in dividing cells. The tight packing of nucleosomes may help separate chromosomes during mitosis. There is also some evidence that changes in chromatin structure and histone-DNA binding are associated with changes in gene activity and expression.

Analyzing Data

Genome Replication

Replication of the 4,639,221 base pairs of DNA in the bacterium *E. coli* begins at a single point and continues in both directions until the entire circular chromosome is copied. The bacterium can complete replication of its chromosome in as little as 20 minutes.

1. **Calculating** Two DNA replication complexes move around the *E. coli* chromosome. Approximately how many bases are copied by each complex during the replication process?

2. **Calculating** Calculate the number of bases that must be copied per second by each replication complex in order to replicate the entire *E. coli* genome in 20 minutes.

3. **Calculating** Calculate how long a single replication complex moving at the same speed as an *E. coli* complex would take to copy the DNA of a single human cell. (*Hint:* Refer to your answer to question 2.)

4. **Inferring** The human genome consists of approximately 3 billion base pairs of DNA. Calculate how long a single replication complex moving at the same speed as an *E. coli* complex would take to copy the DNA of a single human cell. Does this length of time seem reasonable to you? (Assume that a human replication complex works at the same speed as an *E. coli* replication complex. Refer to your answer to question 3.)

Chromosome

Nucleosome

Coils

Supercoils

Histones

DNA double helix

▲ **Figure 12–10** Eukaryotic chromosomes contain DNA wrapped around proteins called histones. The strands of nucleosomes are tightly coiled and supercoiled to form chromosomes. **Interpreting Graphics** *What is each DNA-histone complex called?*

What do nucleosomes do? Nucleosomes seem to be able to fold enormous lengths of DNA into the tiny space available in the cell nucleus. This is such an important function that the histone proteins themselves have changed very little during evolution—probably because mistakes in DNA folding could harm a cell's ability to reproduce.

More recently, biologists have discovered that nucleosomes may play a role in regulating how genes are "read" to make proteins. The first step in activating certain genes has turned out to be a rearrangement of their nucleosomes. By opening up regions of DNA that previously were hidden, these chromatin rearrangements can allow different genes to be "read," changing which proteins are produced.

✓ CHECKPOINT **What is chromatin?**

DNA Replication

When Watson and Crick discovered the double helix structure of DNA, there was one more remarkable aspect that they recognized immediately. The structure explained how DNA could be copied, or replicated. Each strand of the DNA double helix has all the information needed to reconstruct the other half by the mechanism of base pairing. Because each strand can be used to make the other strand, the strands are said to be complementary. If you could separate the two strands, the rules of base pairing would allow you to reconstruct the base sequence of the other strand.

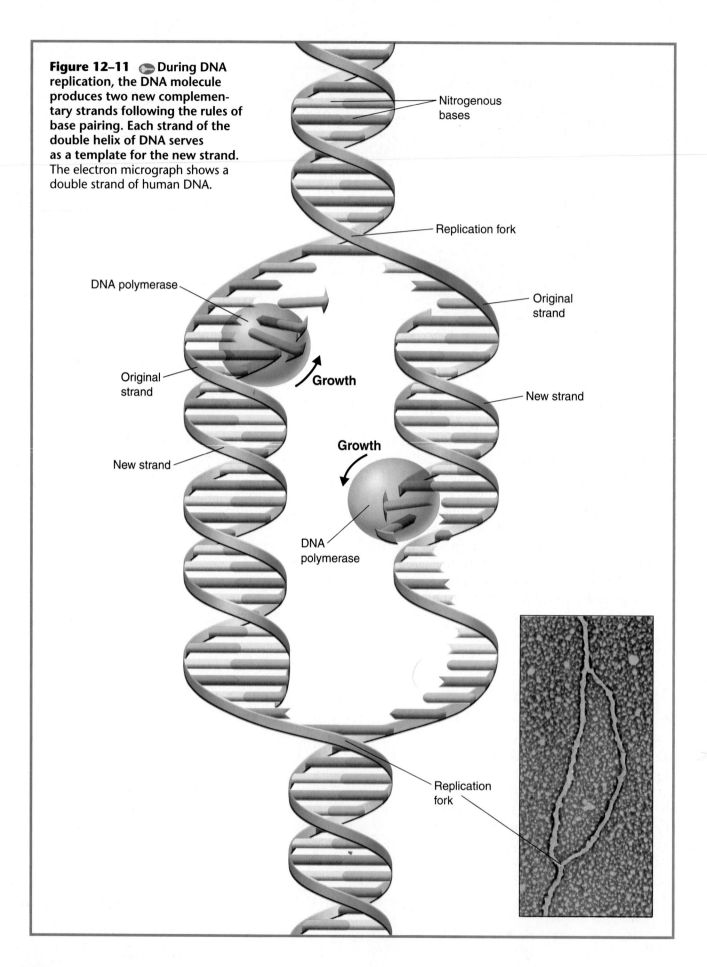

Figure 12–11 During DNA replication, the DNA molecule produces two new complementary strands following the rules of base pairing. Each strand of the double helix of DNA serves as a template for the new strand. The electron micrograph shows a double strand of human DNA.

Nitrogenous bases

Replication fork

DNA polymerase

Original strand

Original strand

Growth

New strand

New strand

Growth

DNA polymerase

Replication fork

Duplicating DNA Before a cell divides, it duplicates its DNA in a copying process called **replication.** This process ensures that each resulting cell will have a complete set of DNA molecules.

🔑 **During DNA replication, the DNA molecule separates into two strands, then produces two new complementary strands following the rules of base pairing. Each strand of the double helix of DNA serves as a template, or model, for the new strand.**

In most prokaryotes, DNA replication begins at a single point in the chromosome and proceeds, often in two directions, until the entire chromosome is replicated. In the larger eukaryotic chromosomes, DNA replication occurs at hundreds of places. Replication proceeds in both directions until each chromosome is completely copied. The sites where separation and replication occur are called replication forks.

How Replication Occurs DNA replication is carried out by a series of enzymes. These enzymes "unzip" a molecule of DNA. The unzipping occurs when the hydrogen bonds between the base pairs are broken and the two strands of the molecule unwind. Each strand serves as a template for the attachment of complementary bases.

For example, a strand that has the bases TACGTT produces a strand with the complementary bases ATGCAA. The result is two DNA molecules identical to each other and to the original molecule. Note that each DNA molecule resulting from replication has one original strand and one new strand.

DNA replication involves a host of enzymes and regulatory molecules. You may recall that enzymes are highly specific. For this reason, they are often named for the reactions they catalyze. The principal enzyme involved in DNA replication is called **DNA polymerase** (PAHL-ih-mur-ayz) because it polymerizes individual nucleotides to produce DNA. DNA polymerase also "proofreads" each new DNA strand, helping to maximize the odds that each molecule is a perfect copy of the original DNA.

12–2 Section Assessment

1. 🔑 **Key Concept** Explain how DNA is replicated.

2. Where and in what form is eukaryotic DNA found?

3. How are the long DNA molecules found in eukaryotes packed into short chromosomes?

4. How are histones related to nucleosomes?

5. What is the role of DNA polymerase in DNA replication?

6. **Critical Thinking Comparing and Contrasting** How is the structure of chromosomes in eukaryotes different from the structure of chromosomes in prokaryotes?

ⓘ**TEXT Assessment** Use iText to review the important concepts in Section 12–2.

ALTERNATIVE ASSESSMENT

Creating a Venn Diagram
Make a Venn diagram that compares the process of DNA replication in prokaryotes and eukaryotes. Compare the location, steps, and end products of the process in each kind of cell.

12-3 RNA and Protein Synthesis

Guide for Reading

Key Concepts
- What are the three main types of RNA?
- What is transcription?
- What is translation?

Vocabulary
messenger RNA
ribosomal RNA
transfer RNA
transcription
RNA polymerase
promoter
intron
exon
codon
translation
anticodon

Reading Strategy:
Using Visuals Before you read, preview **Figure 12–18**. As you read, notice what happens in each step of translation, or protein synthesis.

The double helix structure explains how DNA can be replicated, or copied, but it does not explain how a gene works. As you will see, genes are coded DNA instructions that control the production of proteins within the cell. The first step in decoding these genetic messages is to copy part of the nucleotide sequence from DNA into RNA, or ribonucleic acid. These RNA molecules then carry out the process of making proteins.

The Structure of RNA

RNA, like DNA, consists of a long chain of nucleotides. As you may recall, each nucleotide is made up of a 5-carbon sugar, a phosphate group, and a nitrogenous base. There are three main differences between RNA and DNA: The sugar in RNA is ribose instead of deoxyribose, RNA is generally single-stranded, and RNA contains uracil in place of thymine.

You can think of an RNA molecule as a disposable copy of a segment of DNA. In many cases, an RNA molecule is a working copy of a single gene. The ability to copy a single DNA sequence into RNA makes it possible for a single gene to produce hundreds or even thousands of RNA molecules.

Types of RNA

RNA molecules have many functions, but in the majority of cells most RNA molecules are involved in just one job—protein synthesis. The assembly of amino acids into proteins is controlled by RNA. **There are three main types of RNA: messenger RNA, ribosomal RNA, and transfer RNA.** The structures of these molecules are shown in **Figure 12–12**.

▼ **Figure 12–12** The three main types of RNA are messenger RNA, ribosomal RNA, and transfer RNA. Ribosomal RNA is combined with proteins to form ribosomes.

Ribosome

Amino acid

Uracil

Messenger RNA

Ribosomal RNA

Transfer RNA

Most genes contain instructions for assembling amino acids into proteins. The RNA molecules that carry copies of these instructions are known as **messenger RNA** (mRNA) because they serve as "messengers" from DNA to the rest of the cell.

Proteins are assembled on ribosomes. Ribosomes are made up of several dozen proteins, as well as a form of RNA known as **ribosomal RNA** (rRNA).

During the construction of a protein, a third type of RNA molecule transfers each amino acid to the ribosome as it is specified by coded messages in mRNA. These RNA molecules are known as **transfer RNA** (tRNA).

✓CHECKPOINT *What are ribosomes made of?*

Transcription

RNA molecules are produced by copying part of the nucleotide sequence of DNA into a complementary sequence in RNA, a process called **transcription.** Transcription requires an enzyme known as **RNA polymerase** that is similar to DNA polymerase. 🔑 **During transcription, RNA polymerase binds to DNA and separates the DNA strands. RNA polymerase then uses one strand of DNA as a template from which nucleotides are assembled into a strand of RNA.** The process of transcription is shown in **Figure 12–14.**

How does RNA polymerase "know" where to start and stop making an RNA copy of DNA? The answer to this question begins with the observation that RNA polymerase doesn't bind to DNA just anywhere. The enzyme will bind only to regions of DNA known as **promoters,** which have specific base sequences. In effect, promoters are signals in DNA that indicate to the enzyme where to bind to make RNA. Similar signals in DNA cause transcription to stop when the new RNA molecule is completed.

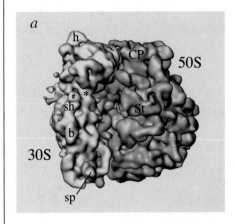

▲ **Figure 12–13** In this detailed model of a ribosome, the two subunits of the ribosome are shown in yellow and blue. The model was produced using cryo-electron microscopy. Data from more than 73,000 electron micrographs, taken at ultracold temperatures to preserve ribosome structure, were analyzed to produce the model.

▼ **Figure 12–14** 🔑 During transcription, RNA polymerase uses one strand of DNA as a template to assemble nucleotides into a strand of RNA.

▢	Adenine (DNA and RNA)
▢	Cytosine (DNA and RNA)
▢	Guanine (DNA and RNA)
▢	Thymine (DNA only)
▢	Uracil (RNA only)

RNA polymerase

RNA

DNA

▲ **Figure 12–15** Many RNA molecules have sections, called introns, edited out of them before they become functional. The remaining pieces, called exons, are spliced together. Then, a cap and tail are added to form the final RNA molecule. **Predicting** *What do you think would happen if the introns were not removed from the pre-mRNA?*

RNA Editing

Like a writer's first draft, many RNA molecules require a bit of editing before they are ready to go into action. A few, including some of the rRNA molecules that make up ribosomes, are produced from larger RNA molecules that are cut and trimmed to their final sizes. Surprisingly, large pieces are removed from the RNA molecules transcribed from many eukaryotic genes before they become functional. These pieces, known as **introns,** or intervening sequences, are cut out of RNA molecules while they are still in the cell nucleus. The remaining portions, called **exons,** or expressed sequences, are then spliced back together to form the final mRNA. This process is shown in **Figure 12–15.**

Why do cells use energy to make a large RNA molecule and then throw parts of it away? That's a good question, and biologists still do not have a complete answer to it. Some RNA molecules may be cut and spliced in different ways in different tissues, making it possible for a single gene to produce several different forms of RNA. Other biologists have suggested that introns and exons may play a role in evolution. This would make it possible for very small changes in DNA sequences to have dramatic effects in gene expression.

✓**CHECKPOINT** *What are introns and exons?*

The Genetic Code

Proteins are made by joining amino acids into long chains called polypeptides. Each polypeptide contains a combination of any or all of the 20 different amino acids. The properties of proteins are determined by the order in which different amino acids are joined together to produce polypeptides. How, you might wonder, can a particular order of nitrogenous bases in DNA and RNA molecules be translated into a particular order of amino acids in a polypeptide?

The "language" of mRNA instructions is called the genetic code. As you know, RNA contains four different bases: A, U, C, and G. In effect, the code is written in a language that has only four "letters." How can a code with just four letters carry instructions for 20 different amino acids? The genetic code is read three letters at a time, so that each "word" of the coded message is three bases long. Each three-letter "word" in mRNA is known as a codon, as shown in **Figure 12–16.** A **codon** consists of three consecutive nucleotides that specify a single amino acid that is to be added to the polypeptide. For example, consider the following RNA sequence:

UCGCACGGU

This sequence would be read three bases at a time as:

UCG-CAC-GGU

The codons represent the different amino acids:

UCG-CAC-GGU

Serine-Histidine-Glycine

▲ **Figure 12–16** A codon is a group of three nucleotides on messenger RNA that specify a particular amino acid. **Observing** *What are the three-letter groups of the two codons shown here?*

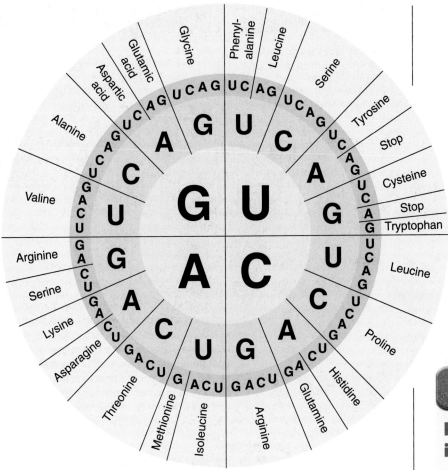

◀ **Figure 12–17** The genetic code shows the amino acid to which each of the 64 possible codons corresponds. To decode a codon, start at the middle of the circle and move outward. **Interpreting Graphics** *For what amino acid does the codon UGC code?*

Because there are four different bases, there are 64 possible three-base codons (4 × 4 × 4 = 64). **Figure 12–17** shows all 64 possible codons of the genetic code. As you can see, some amino acids can be specified by more than one codon. For example, six different codons specify the amino acid leucine, and six others specify arginine.

There is also one codon, AUG, that can either specify methionine or serve as the initiation, or "start," codon for protein synthesis. Notice also that there are three "stop" codons that do not code for any amino acid. Stop codons act like the period at the end of a sentence; they signify the end of a polypeptide.

Translation

The sequence of nucleotide bases in an mRNA molecule serves as instructions for the order in which amino acids should be joined together to produce a polypeptide. However, anyone who has tried to assemble a complex toy knows that instructions generally don't do the job themselves. They need something to read them and put them to use. In the cell, that "something" is a tiny factory called the ribosome.

Quick Lab

How does a cell interpret DNA?

Procedure
1. A certain gene has the following sequence of nucleotides:
    GACAAGTCCACAATC
    Write this sequence on a sheet of paper.
2. From left to right, write the sequence of the mRNA molecule transcribed from this gene.
3. Look at **Figure 12–17.** Reading the mRNA codons from left to right, write the amino acid sequence of the polypeptide translated from the mRNA.
4. Repeat step 3, reading the codons from right to left.

Analyze and Conclude
1. **Appying Concepts** Why did steps 3 and 4 produce different polypeptides?
2. **Drawing Conclusions** Do cells usually decode nucleotides in one direction only or in either direction?

FIGURE 12–18 TRANSLATION

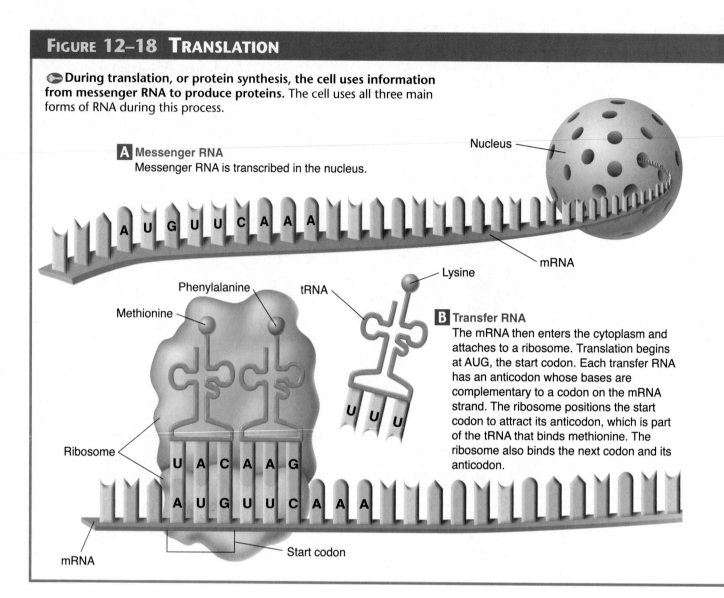

During translation, or protein synthesis, the cell uses information from messenger RNA to produce proteins. The cell uses all three main forms of RNA during this process.

A Messenger RNA
Messenger RNA is transcribed in the nucleus.

Nucleus

mRNA

Phenylalanine

Methionine

tRNA

Lysine

B Transfer RNA
The mRNA then enters the cytoplasm and attaches to a ribosome. Translation begins at AUG, the start codon. Each transfer RNA has an anticodon whose bases are complementary to a codon on the mRNA strand. The ribosome positions the start codon to attract its anticodon, which is part of the tRNA that binds methionine. The ribosome also binds the next codon and its anticodon.

Ribosome

mRNA

Start codon

The decoding of an mRNA message into a polypeptide chain (protein) is known as **translation.** Translation takes place on ribosomes. **During translation, the cell uses information from messenger RNA to produce proteins.** Refer to **Figure 12–18** as you read about translation.

A Before translation can occur, messenger RNA must first be transcribed from DNA in the nucleus and released into the cytoplasm.

B Translation begins when an mRNA molecule in the cytoplasm attaches to a ribosome. As each codon of the mRNA molecule moves through the ribosome, the proper amino acid is brought into the ribosome and attached to the growing polypeptide chain. The ribosome does not "know" which amino acid to match to each codon. That's the job of transfer RNA. Each tRNA molecule has an amino acid attached to one end and a region of three unpaired bases at the other. The three bases on the tRNA molecule, called the **anticodon,** are complementary to one of the mRNA codons.

C The Polypeptide "Assembly Line"
The ribosome joins the two amino acids—methionine and phenylalanine—and breaks the bond between methionine and its tRNA. The tRNA floats away, allowing the ribosome to bind to another tRNA. The ribosome moves along the mRNA, binding new tRNA molecules and amino acids.

Lysine

tRNA

tRNA

U A C

A A G U U U

A U G U U C A A A

mRNA

Ribosome

Translation direction

Growing polypeptide chain

Ribosome

tRNA

G A C

C U G U G A

mRNA

D Completing the Polypeptide
The process continues until the ribosome reaches one of the three stop codons. The result is a growing polypeptide chain.

In the case of the tRNA molecule for methionine, the anti-codon bases are UAC, which pair with the methionine codon, AUG. The ribosome has a second binding site for a tRNA molecule for the next codon. If that next codon is UUC, a tRNA molecule with an AAG anticodon would fit against the mRNA molecule held in the ribosome. That second tRNA molecule would bring the amino acid phenylalanine into the ribosome.

C Like an assembly line worker who attaches one part to another, the ribosome forms a peptide bond between the first and second amino acids, methionine and phenylalanine. At the same time, the ribosome breaks the bond that had held the first tRNA molecule to its amino acid and releases the tRNA molecule. The ribosome then moves to the third codon, where a tRNA molecule brings it the amino acid specified by the third codon.

D The polypeptide chain continues to grow until the ribosome reaches a stop codon on the mRNA molecule. When the ribosome reaches a stop codon, it releases the newly formed polypeptide and the mRNA molecule, completing the process of translation.

The Roles of RNA and DNA

You can compare the different roles played by DNA and RNA molecules in directing protein synthesis to the two types of plans used by builders. A master plan has all the information needed to construct a building. But builders never bring the valuable master plan to the building site, where it might be damaged or lost. Instead, they prepare inexpensive, disposable copies of the master plan called blueprints. The master plan is safely stored in an office, and the blueprints are taken to the job site. Similarly, the cell uses the vital DNA "master plan" to prepare RNA "blueprints." The DNA molecule remains in the safety of the nucleus, while RNA molecules go to the protein-building sites in the cytoplasm—the ribosomes.

Genes and Proteins

Gregor Mendel might have been surprised to learn that most genes contain nothing more than instructions for assembling proteins. He might have asked what proteins could possibly have to do with the color of a flower, the shape of a leaf, a human blood type, or the sex of a newborn baby.

The answer is that proteins have everything to do with these things. Remember that many proteins are enzymes, which catalyze and regulate chemical reactions. A gene that codes for an enzyme to produce pigment can control the color of a flower. Another enzyme-specifying gene helps produce a red blood cell surface antigen. This molecule determines your blood type. Genes for certain proteins can regulate the rate and pattern of growth throughout an organism, controlling its size and shape. In short, proteins are the keys to almost everything that living cells do.

12–3 Section Assessment

1. **Key Concept** List the three main types of RNA.
2. **Key Concept** What happens during transcription?
3. **Key Concept** What happens during translation?
4. Describe the three main differences between RNA and DNA.

5. **Critical Thinking Applying Concepts** Using the genetic code, identify the amino acids that have the following messenger RNA strand codes: UGGCAGUGC.

iTEXT Assessment Use iText to review the important concepts in Section 12–3.

ALTERNATIVE ASSESSMENT

Descriptive Writing
An RNA molecule is looking for a job in a protein synthesis factory, and it asks you to write its résumé. This RNA molecule is not yet specialized and could, with some structural changes, function as either mRNA, tRNA, or rRNA. The résumé you create should reflect the qualifications needed for each type of RNA.

12–4 Mutations

As precise as they are, every now and then cells make mistakes in copying their own DNA, inserting an incorrect base or sometimes even skipping a base as the new strand is put together. These mistakes are called mutations, from the Latin word *mutare,* meaning "to change." **Mutations** are changes in the DNA sequence that affect genetic information. Like the mistakes that people make in their daily lives, mutations come in many shapes and sizes. **Gene mutations result from changes in a single gene. Chromosomal mutations involve changes in whole chromosomes.**

Gene Mutations

Some gene mutations involve several nucleotides, but the majority involve just one. Mutations that affect one nucleotide are called **point mutations** because they occur at a single point in the DNA sequence. Some point mutations simply substitute one nucleotide for another. These substitutions generally, although not always, change one of the amino acids in a protein.

When a point mutation involves the insertion or deletion of a nucleotide, much bigger changes result. Remember that the genetic code is read in groups of three bases known as codons. What happens if a nucleotide is deleted? The base is still read in groups of three, but now the groupings are shifted for every codon that follows. Inserting an extra nucleotide has a similar effect. Changes like these are called **frameshift mutations** because they shift the "reading frame" of the genetic message. By changing the reading frame, frameshift mutations affect every amino acid that follows the point of the insertion or deletion, as shown in **Figure 12–19.** Such mutations can alter a protein so that it is unable to perform its normal functions.

Guide for Reading

Key Concept
• What are gene mutations and chromosomal mutations?

Vocabulary
mutation
point mutation
frameshift mutation

**Reading Strategy:
Using Visuals** Before you read, preview **Figure 12–19** and **Figure 12–20**. As you read, notice the changes that occur in gene and chromosomal mutations.

Figure 12–19 Gene mutations result from changes in a single gene.

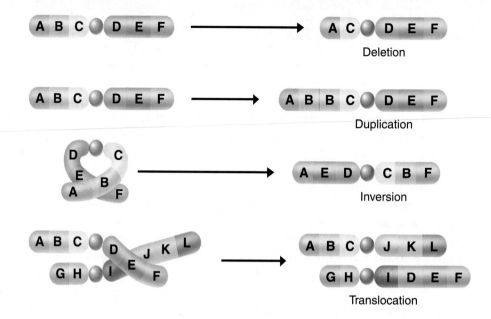

▶ **Figure 12–20**
Chromosomal mutations involve changes in whole chromosomes.

Deletion

Duplication

Inversion

Translocation

Chromosomal Mutations

A chromosomal mutation involves changes in the number or structure of chromosomes. Chromosomal mutations may change the locations of genes on chromosomes and even the number of copies of some genes.

Figure 12–20 shows four types of chromosomal mutations. A deletion involves the loss of all or part of a chromosome. The opposite of a deletion is a duplication, in which a segment of a chromosome is repeated. When part of a chromosome becomes oriented in the reverse of its usual direction, the result is an inversion. A translocation occurs when part of one chromosome breaks off and attaches to another, nonhomologous, chromosome. In most cases, nonhomologous chromosomes exchange segments so that two translocations occur at the same time.

12–4 Section Assessment

1. **Key Concept** What is a gene mutation? What is a chromosomal mutation?

2. What is a point mutation?

3. What are two kinds of frameshift mutations?

4. What are four types of chromosomal mutations?

5. **Critical Thinking Inferring** The effects of a mutation are not always visible. How might a biologist determine whether a mutation has occurred and, if so, what type of mutation it is?

iTEXT **Assessment** Use iText to review the important concepts in Section 12–4.

Take It to the NET
Find out more about the kinds of mutations that can occur in DNA. Then, create a concept map linking each kind of mutation. Use the links provided in the Biology area at the Prentice Hall Web site for help in completing this activity: **www.phschool.com**

12–5 Gene Regulation

Only a fraction of the genes in a cell are expressed at any given time. An expressed gene is a gene that is transcribed into RNA. How does the cell determine which genes will be expressed and which will remain "silent"? A close look at the structure of a gene provides some important clues.

At first glance, the DNA sequence of a gene is nothing more than a confusing jumble of the four letters that represent the bases in DNA. However, if we take the time to analyze those letters, patterns emerge. Molecular biologists have found that certain DNA sequences serve as promoters, binding sites for RNA polymerase. Others serve as start and stop signals for transcription. In fact, cells are filled with DNA-binding proteins that attach to specific DNA sequences and help to regulate gene expression. A typical gene might look something like **Figure 12–21**.

As we've seen, there is a promoter just to one side of the gene. But what are the "regulatory sites" next to the promoter? These are places where other proteins, binding directly to the DNA sequences at those sites, can regulate transcription. The actions of these proteins help to determine whether a gene is turned on or turned off.

Gene Regulation: An Example

How does an organism "know" whether to turn a gene on or off? The common bacterium *E. coli* provides us with a perfect example of how gene expression can be regulated. The 4288 protein-encoding genes in this bacterium include a cluster of three genes that are turned on or off together. A group of genes that operate together is known as an **operon**. Because these genes must be expressed in order for the bacterium to be able to use the sugar lactose as a food, they are called the *lac* operon.

Guide for Reading

Key Concepts
- How are *lac* genes turned off and on?
- How are most eukaryotic genes controlled?

Vocabulary
operon
operator
hox gene

Reading Strategy:
Outlining Before you read, use the headings of the section to make an outline about gene regulation. As you read, fill in subtopics and smaller topics. Then, add phrases or a sentence after each subtopic to provide key information.

Regulatory sites — Promoter (RNA polymerase binding site) — DNA strand — Start transcription — Stop transcription

GAATTCTAATCTCCCTCTCAACCCTACAGTCACCCATTTGGTATATTAAAGATGTGTTG
TCTACTGTCTAGTATCCCTCAAGTAGTGTCAGGAATTAGTCATTTAAATAGTCTGCAAG
CCAGGAGTGGTGGCTCATGTCTGTAATTCCAGCACTGGAGAGGTAGAAGTGGGAG
GACTGCTTGAGCTCAAGAGTTTGATATTATCCTGGACAACATAGCAAGACCTCGTCT
CTACTTAAAAAAAAAAAAAAATTAGCCAGGCATGTGATGTACACCTGTAGTCCCAGCTAC
TCAGGAGGCCGAAATGGGAGGATCCCTTGAGCTCAGGAGGTCAAGGCTGCAGTGA
GACATGATCTTGCCACTGCACTCCAGCCTGGACAGCAGAGTGAAACCTTGCCTCAC
GAAACAGAATACAAAAACAAACAAACAAAAAACTGCTCCGCAATGCGCTTCCTTGAT
GCTCTACCACATAGGTCTGGGTACTTT

◀ **Figure 12–21** A typical gene includes start and stop signals, with the nucleotides to be translated in between. The DNA sequence shown is only a very small part of an actual gene. **Interpreting Graphics** *What is the function of the promoter?*

Gene Expression Repressed

Repressor protein blocks transcription of *lac* genes

Repressor

Promoter

Lac genes

DNA strand

RNA polymerase

Operator

Lactose is added

Gene Expression Activated

Lactose binds, repressor moves away

mRNA

▲ **Figure 12–22** 🔑 **The *lac* genes in *E. coli* are turned off by repressors and turned on by the presence of lactose.** When lactose is not present, the repressor binds to the operator region, preventing RNA polymerase from beginning transcription. Lactose causes the repressor to be released from the operator region.

Why must *E. coli* turn on the *lac* genes in order to use lactose for food? Lactose is a compound made up of two simple sugars, galactose and glucose. To use lactose for food, the bacterium must take lactose across its cell membrane and then break the bond between glucose and galactose. These tasks are performed by proteins coded for by the genes of the *lac* operon. This means, of course, that if the bacterium is grown in a medium where lactose is the only food source, it must transcribe the genes and produce these proteins. On the other hand, if grown on another food source, such as glucose, it would have no need for these proteins.

Remarkably, the bacterium almost seems to "know" when the products of these genes are needed. 🔑 **The *lac* genes are turned off by repressors and turned on by the presence of lactose.** How is the bacterium so smart? The answer tells us a great deal about how genes are regulated.

On one side of the operon's three genes are two regulatory regions. In the promoter (P), RNA polymerase binds and then begins transcription. The other region is the **operator** (O). *E. coli* cells contain several copies of a DNA-binding protein known as the *lac* repressor, which can bind to the O region. As **Figure 12–22** shows, when the *lac* repressor binds to the O region, RNA polymerase is prevented from binding to the promoter. In effect, the binding of the repressor protein turns the operon "off" by preventing the transcription of its genes.

If the repressor protein is always present, then how are the *lac* genes turned on in the presence of lactose? Besides its DNA binding site, the *lac* repressor protein has a binding site for lactose itself. When lactose is added to the medium, a few of the sugar molecules diffuse into the cell and bind to the repressor proteins. The binding of lactose causes the repressor protein to change shape in a way that completely alters its DNA-binding site, causing the repressor to fall off the operator. Now, with the repressor no longer bound to the O site, RNA polymerase can bind to the promoter and transcribe the genes of the operon.

This simple system allows the cell automatically to turn the *lac* genes on and off as needed. The *lac* operon is an example of the ways in which prokaryotic genes are regulated. Many other genes are also regulated by repressor proteins, while others use proteins that enhance the rate of transcription. In some systems, regulation occurs at the level of protein synthesis. Regardless of the actual system involved, the result is the same: Cells are able to turn their genes on and off as needed.

✓ **CHECKPOINT** *What is the function of the operator region?*

Upstream enhancer

TATA box

Introns

Promoter sequences

Exons

Direction of transcription

◀ **Figure 12–23** 🔑 Eukaryotic **genes are more complex than prokaryotic genes.** Many eukaryotic genes include a sequence called the TATA box that may help position RNA polymerase.

Eukaryotic Gene Regulation

The general principles of gene regulation in prokaryotes also apply to eukaryotic cells, although there are some important differences. Operons are generally not found in eukaryotes. 🔑 **Most eukaryotic genes are controlled individually and have regulatory sequences that are much more complex than those of the *lac* operon.**

Figure 12–23 shows some of the features of a typical eukaryotic gene. One of the most interesting is a short region of DNA about 30 base pairs long, with a sequence of TATATA or TATAAA, before the start of transcription. This region is found before so many eukaryotic genes that it even has a name: the "TATA box." The TATA box seems to help position RNA polymerase by marking a point just before the point at which transcription begins. Eukaryotic promoters are usually found just before the TATA box, and they consist of a series of short DNA sequences.

Genes are regulated in a variety of ways by enhancer sequences located before the beginning of transcription. An enormous number of proteins can bind to different enhancer sequences, which is why eukaryotic gene regulation is so complex. Some of these DNA-binding proteins enhance transcription by opening up tightly packed chromatin. Others help to attract RNA polymerase. Still other proteins block access to genes, much like prokaryotic repressor proteins.

Why is gene regulation in eukaryotes more complex than in prokaryotes? Think for a moment about the way in which genes are expressed in a multicellular organism. The genes that code for liver enzymes, for example, are not expressed in nerve cells. Keratin, an important protein in skin cells, is not produced in blood cells. Cell specialization requires genetic specialization, but all of the cells in a multicellular organism carry the complete genetic code in their nucleus. Therefore, for proper overall function, only a tiny fraction of the available genes needs to be expressed in cells of different tissues throughout the body. The complexity of gene regulation in eukaryotes makes this specificity possible.

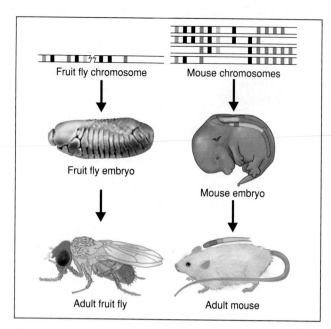

Fruit fly chromosome

Mouse chromosomes

Fruit fly embryo

Mouse embryo

Adult fruit fly

Adult mouse

▲ **Figure 12–24** In fruit flies, a series of hox genes along a chromosome determines the basic structure of the fly's body. Mice have very similar genes on four different chromosomes. **Interpreting Graphics** *What section of the bodies of flies and mice is coded by the genes shown in blue?*

Regulation and Development

Regulation of gene expression is especially important in shaping the way a complex organism develops from a single fertilized cell. In fact, the study of developmental genes has become one of the most exciting areas in all of biology.

Why all the excitement? Molecular studies of embryos have shown that a series of genes, known as the **hox genes,** controls the organs and tissues that develop in various parts of the embryo. These genes determine an animal's basic body plan. How important are these genes? A mutation in one of these "master control genes" can completely change the organs that develop in specific parts of the body. Mutations affecting the hox genes in the fruit fly, *Drosophila,* for example, can replace the fly's antennae with a pair of legs growing right out of its head!

In flies, the hox genes are located side by side in a single cluster, arranged in the exact order in which they are expressed in the body, as shown in **Figure 12–24.** Remarkably, similar clusters exist in the DNA of other animals, including humans. The function of the hox genes in humans seems to be almost the same as it is in flies—to tell the cells of the body which organs and structures they should develop into as the body grows. Careful control of expression in these genes is essential for normal development.

The striking similarity of genes that control development has a simple scientific explanation: Common patterns of genetic control exist because all these genes have descended from the genes of common ancestors. One such gene, called Pax 6, controls eye growth in *Drosophila.* A similar gene was found to guide eye growth in mice and other mammals. When a copy of the mouse gene was inserted into the "knee" of a *Drosophila* embryo, the resulting fruit fly grew an eye on its leg! The fly gene and the mouse gene are similar enough to trade places and still function—even though they come from animals that have not shared a common ancestor in at least 600 million years.

12–5 Section Assessment

1. 🔑 **Key Concept** How is the *lac* operon regulated?

2. 🔑 **Key Concept** Describe how most eukaryotic genes are controlled.

3. What is a promoter?

4. Why are only a limited number of genes expressed in each cell of a multicellular eukaryote?

5. **Critical Thinking Comparing and Contrasting** How is the way hox genes are expressed in mice similar to the way they are expressed in fruit flies? How is it different?

📱 **iTEXT** **Assessment** Use iText to review the important concepts in Section 12–5.

Modeling DNA Replication

Living cells make exact copies of DNA molecules that are passed on to each daughter cell during cell division. In this investigation, you will model DNA replication.

Problem How is DNA replicated?

Materials

- construction paper (tan, gray, green, yellow, red, and purple)
- metric ruler
- scissors
- transparent tape

Skills Using Models

Procedure

1. Cut out rectangles of construction paper in the sizes and colors indicated below:

   Sugars: 36 tan pieces, each 2 cm × 2 cm

   Phosphates: 36 gray pieces, each 1 cm × 2 cm

   Adenines (A): 12 green pieces, each 1 cm × 2 cm

   Thymines (T): 12 yellow pieces, each 1 cm × 2 cm

   Guanines (G): 6 red pieces, each 1 cm × 2 cm

   Cytosines (C): 6 purple pieces, each 1 cm × 2 cm

2. To model a nucleotide, tape together a phosphate group, a sugar, and a guanine molecule (G) (see **Figure 12–5** on page 291).

3. Assemble eight additional nucleotide models with the following nitrogenous bases: 3 thymines (T); 3 adenines (A); 2 cytosines (C).

4. To model a single strand of DNA, tape the sugar of each nucleotide to the phosphate group of the next nucleotide in the following order: G T T A C A A T C.

5. Construct a strand of DNA that is complementary to the first strand. Tape the nucleotides of the second strand together as you did in step 4. Record the positions of the bases in both strands of your model.

6. Place the two strands side by side so that their complementary nucleotides face each other. Do not tape the two strands together. Write "original" on each strand.

7. Separate the two strands. Simulate the action of DNA polymerase by constructing a new complementary strand for each original strand.

8. Tape the bases of each new strand to the complementary bases of its matching strand.

Analyze and Conclude

1. **Comparing and Contrasting** Compare the new double-stranded DNA models with your original DNA model. Are their nucleotide sequences identical?

2. **Using Models** After a cell's DNA is replicated, the cell may divide in two. Each new cell receives one copy of the original cell's DNA. According to your model, how are the new strands and the original strands divided between the two new cells?

3. **Drawing Conclusions** How does the pairing of complementary bases help ensure that the nucleotide sequence is copied accurately during DNA replication?

4. **Drawing Conclusions** What problems would you expect to occur if DNA was not copied accurately as it is replicated?

Go Further

Using Models Before DNA can be replicated, the DNA double helix must be unwound so that the enzymes involved in this process can make contact with the bases. The enzyme DNA polymerase adds the correct complementary nucleotides to the growing new strands. Modify your model or make a new model to show how these processes occur.

12–1 DNA
 Key Concepts

- Avery and other scientists discovered that DNA is the nucleic acid that stores and transmits the genetic information from one generation of an organism to the next.
- Hershey and Chase concluded that the genetic material of the bacteriophage was DNA, not protein.
- Watson and Crick's model of DNA was a double helix, in which two strands were wound around each other.

Vocabulary
- transformation, p. 288 • bacteriophage, p. 289
- nucleotide, p. 291 • base pairing, p. 294

12–2 Chromosomes and DNA Replication
 Key Concept

- During DNA replication, the DNA molecule separates into two strands, then produces two new complementary strands following the rules of base pairing. Each strand of the double helix of DNA serves as a template, or model, for the new strand.

Vocabulary
- chromatin, p. 296 • histone, p. 296
- replication, p. 299 • DNA polymerase, p. 299

12–3 RNA and Protein Synthesis
Key Concepts

- There are three main types of RNA: messenger RNA, ribosomal RNA, and transfer RNA.
- During transcription, RNA polymerase binds to DNA and separates the DNA strands. RNA polymerase then uses one strand of DNA as a template from which nucleotides are assembled into a strand of RNA.
- During translation, the cell uses information from messenger RNA to produce proteins.

Vocabulary
- messenger RNA, p. 301 • ribosomal RNA, p. 301
- transfer RNA, p. 301 • transcription, p. 301
- RNA polymerase, p. 301 • promoter, p. 301
- intron, p. 302 • exon, p. 302 • codon, p. 302
- translation, p. 304 • anticodon, p. 304

12–4 Mutations
Key Concept

- Gene mutations result from changes in a single gene. Chromosomal mutations involve changes in whole chromosomes.

Vocabulary
mutation, p. 307
point mutation, p. 307
frameshift mutation, p. 307

12–5 Gene Regulation
Key Concepts

- The *lac* genes are turned off by repressors and turned on by the presence of lactose.
- Most eukaryotic genes are controlled individually and have regulatory sequences that are much more complex than those of the *lac* operon.

Vocabulary
operon, p. 309
operator, p. 310
hox gene, p. 312

Thinking Visually
Using the information in this chapter, complete the following flowchart about protein synthesis:

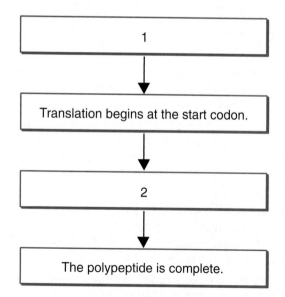

1

↓

Translation begins at the start codon.

↓

2

↓

The polypeptide is complete.

Chapter 12

Part A

Multiple Choice

For each statement or question, select the number of the word or expression that, of those given, best completes the statement or answers the question.

1 Frederick Griffith identified the process by which one strain of bacteria is apparently changed into another strain. This process is called
   (1) transcription   (3) translation
   (2) replication   (4) transformation

2 Bacteriophages are composed of a DNA or RNA core and a protein coat. They are
   (1) tiny bacteria
   (2) ribosome complexes
   (3) enzymes
   (4) viruses

3 A nucleotide does *not* contain
   (1) a 5-carbon sugar
   (2) polymerase
   (3) a nitrogen base
   (4) a phosphate group

4 The diagram below shows the process of DNA
   (1) replication   (3) transcription
   (2) translation   (4) transformation

5 The main enzyme involved in DNA replication that joins individual nucleotides to produce DNA molecules is
   (1) transfer RNA   (3) ribose
   (2) RNA polymerase   (4) DNA polymerase

6 In which way does RNA differ from DNA?
   (1) RNA contains uracil and deoxyribose.
   (2) RNA contains ribose and thymine.
   (3) RNA contains uracil and ribose.
   (4) RNA contains adenine and ribose.

7 The process by which the genetic code of DNA is copied into a complementary sequence of RNA is called
   (1) translation
   (2) replication
   (3) transcription
   (4) transformation

8 In messenger RNA, each codon specifies a particular
   (1) nucleotide   (3) purine
   (2) amino acid   (4) pyrimidine

9 Changes in the DNA sequence that affect genetic information are known as
   (1) replications
   (2) transformations
   (3) mutations
   (4) translations

10 An expressed gene is one that
   (1) functions as a promoter
   (2) is transcribed into RNA
   (3) codes for proteins
   (4) contains an operon

11 In humans, DNA molecules are located in the
   (1) nucleus   (3) ribosome
   (2) cytoplasm   (4) histone

12 The process of decoding mRNA into a polypeptide chain is known as
   (1) translation   (3) transformation
   (2) transpiration   (4) transcription

13 Which of the following does *not* describe the structure of DNA?
   (1) double helix
   (2) nucleotide polymer
   (3) sugar-phosphate backbone
   (4) adenine-uracil pairs

Test-Taking Tip   When asked to find the solution to a problem, such as the complementary sequence of DNA or RNA, first solve the problem on scratch paper. Then, compare your answer with the options provided.

Preparing for the
Living Environment Exam

Parts B and C

Multiple Choice and Extended Response

For those questions that ask you to select a response, choose the one that best completes the statement or answers the question. For all others follow the directions given.

14 Explain why controlling the proteins in an organism controls the organism's characteristics.

15 Compare the appearance of DNA in a typical prokaryotic cell with that of an animal cell.

Base your answers to questions 16 and 17 on the data table below and on your knowledge of biology.

A scientist analyzed several DNA samples to determine the relative proportions of purine and pyrimidine bases. Her data are summarized in the table.

Percentages of Bases in Three Samples				
Sample	G	C	A	T
A	35	35	15	15
B	40	10	40	10
C	25	25	25	25

16 Which sample(s) support(s) the base-pairing rules?
(1) Sample A, only (3) Samples A and B
(2) Sample B, only (4) Samples A and C

17 If the scientist had analyzed mRNA rather than DNA, what percentage of uracil would you expect to find in Sample B?
(1) 10   (3) 35
(2) 25   (4) 15

Base your answers to questions 18 through 20 on the illustration below and on your knowledge of biology.

Transcribed Strand of DNA

T A C C C G A A G T T C A T G

18 List the codons of the mRNA molecule that would be transcribed from this strand of DNA.

19 Using Figure 12–17 on page 303, list the sequence of amino acids that this mRNA molecule specifies.

20 Write a paragraph about the mutations that could occur during DNA replication and transcription. Be sure to explain the difference between point mutations and frameshift mutations.

Base your answers to questions 21 and 22 on the diagram below and on your knowledge of biology.

DNA:	TAC GCA TGG AAT
mRNA:	AUG CGU ACC UUA
Amino acids:	Met – Arg – Thr – Leu

↓ **Substitution**

DNA:	TAC GTA TGG AAT
mRNA:	AUG CAU ACC UUA
Amino acids:	Met – His – Thr – Leu

21 In this mutation, a substitution of a nucleotide results in
(1) no change to the DNA
(2) production of a different amino acid
(3) mRNA dysfunction
(4) an additional chromosome

22 In this example, the codon GCA becomes GTA. This kind of mutation, which affects only one nucleotide, is called a
(1) point mutation
(2) frameshift mutation
(3) chromosomal mutation
(4) translocation mutation

23 A researcher identifies the nucleotide sequence AAC in a long strand of RNA inside a nucleus. In the genetic code, AAC codes for the amino acid asparagine. When that RNA molecule is translated during protein synthesis, will asparagine necessarily appear in the protein? Support your answer with an expanation.

Base your answers to questions 24 through 26 on the passage below and on your knowledge of biology.

Finding Griffith's "Factor"

In 1928, scientist Frederick Griffith tried to determine how certain strains of bacteria caused pneumonia. Figure 12-2 on page 288 shows the procedure that Griffith followed in his experiment. He was surprised to find that when heat-killed, disease-causing bacteria were combined with harmless bacteria and injected into healthy mice, the mice died.

From these results, Griffith hypothesized that some "factor" was transferred from the heat-killed cells to the live cells. Maybe that "factor" contained a gene.

Nearly 20 years later, Oswald Avery repeated Griffith's work. Avery and his colleagues wanted to know which part of the bacteria was most important for transformation. Using enzymes, the scientists destroyed the heat-killed bacteria's proteins, lipids, carbohydrates, and other molecules that might have been responsible for transforming the harmless bacteria. Finally, they identified the "factor" that Griffith had hypothesized about.

24 Griffith learned that some "factor" transformed harmless bacteria into disease-causing bacteria. State a hypothesis about this "factor" that Griffith might have formed.

25 In order for Avery and his colleagues to duplicate and expand on Griffith's experiments, what kinds of information about Griffith's investigations did they need?

26 Why would enzymes be especially useful in carrying out Avery's experiment? How would the action of enzymes be necessary to carry out a controlled experiment?

Base your answers to questions 27 and 28 on the passage below and on your knowledge of biology.

A group of students used the following procedure to extract DNA from a sample of raw wheat germ. They made a solution of wheat germ and water by heating it and mixing until the wheat germ was dissolved. Once dissolved, the students added a small amount of detergent to the solution and stirred gently. After 5 minutes, they added meat tenderizer to the beaker. Then, they used a solution of baking soda to bring the pH of the mixture to about 8. The students poured 6 mL of the wheat germ mixture into a clean test tube, and then gently poured an equal amount of ethanol in a layer on top. After 5 minutes, DNA strands began to appear in the interface between the ethanol and the wheat germ mixture.

27 Detergent and certain enzymes in meat tenderizer work to break down cell parts. Which cell parts must be destroyed in order to release DNA from wheat germ cells?

28 After removing the DNA strands from the mixture and allowing them to dry overnight, the students placed them in a test tube containing 3 mL of a 4% salt solution and added 3 mL of a diphenylamine solution. In a second test tube, they placed 3 mL "standard DNA solution" given to them by their teacher and 3 mL of the diphenylamine solution. Finally, in a third test tube, they placed 3 mL of the 4% salt solution and 3 mL of the diphenylamine solution.

Assuming that the students extracted their DNA successfully and knowing that diphenylamine is an indicator that turns blue in the presence of deoxyribose, which test tubes contain solutions that will turn blue? Support your answer with an explanation.

Take It to the NET

Want to learn more about the genetic code and protein synthesis? Visit the Prentice Hall Web site at **www.phschool.com.** Then, answer the following questions:

• What is the "central dogma" of molecular biology?

• Why is the genetic code said to be degenerate?

• Why is DNA replication considered to be semiconservative?

• List four steps in the control of gene expression. When does each step occur?

13 Genetic Engineering

This animal is part goat and part sheep. It was created by mixing together cells from separate embryos and then implanting the mixed embryo into a surrogate mother.

Inquiry Activity

Can you improve plant breeding?

Procedure

1. Examine 5 apples of different varieties. Record the color, shape, and size of each apple.
2. Record your choices of the varieties that you consider best in color, shape, and size.

Think About It

1. **Formulating Hypotheses** How could you produce an apple that has the best traits of all 5 varieties?

2. **Formulating Hypotheses** Most apple trees do not produce fruit until they are about 15 years old. How could you use your knowledge of DNA to produce a new variety of apple more quickly?

13-1 Changing the Living World

Visit a dog show, and what do you see? Dogs of every breed imaginable, distinguished from one another by an enormous range of characteristics. Striking contrasts are everywhere—the size of a tiny Chihuahua and that of a massive great Dane, the short coat of a Labrador retriever and the curly fur of a poodle, the long muzzle of the wolfhound and the pug nose of a bulldog. The differences among breeds of dogs are so great that someone who had never seen such animals before might think that many of these breeds are different species. They're not, of course, but where did such differences come from? What forces gave rise to the speed of a greyhound, the courage of a German shepherd, and the herding instincts of a border collie?

Selective Breeding

The answer, of course, is that *we* did it. Humans have kept and bred dogs for thousands of years, always looking to produce animals that might be better hunters, better retrievers, or better companions. By **selective breeding,** allowing only those animals with desired characteristics to produce the next generation, humans have produced the many different breeds on display at a dog show.

 Humans use selective breeding to pass desired traits on to the next generation of organisms. Nearly all domestic animals—including horses, cats, and farm animals—and most crop plants have been produced by selective breeding. American botanist Luther Burbank (1849–1926) may have been the greatest selective plant breeder of all time. He developed the disease-resistant Burbank potato, which was later exported to Ireland to help fight potato blight and other diseases. During his lifetime, Burbank developed more than 800 varieties of plants.

Hybridization As one of his tools, Burbank used **hybridization,** crossing dissimilar individuals to bring together the best of both organisms. Hybrids, the individuals produced by such crosses, are often hardier than either of the parents. In many cases, Burbank's hybrid crosses combined the disease resistance of one plant with the food-producing capacity of another. The result was a new line of plants that had the characteristics farmers needed to increase food production. **Figure 13–1** shows hybrid daisies developed using Burbank's techniques.

Guide for Reading

Key Concepts
- What is the purpose of selective breeding?
- Why might breeders try to induce mutations?

Vocabulary
selective breeding
hybridization
inbreeding
polyploid

Reading Strategy:
Outlining Before you read, write down the blue headings of the section. As you read, list the important information under each heading.

▼ **Figure 13–1** Humans use selective breeding to pass desired traits on to the next generation of organisms. Luther Burbank used selective breeding to develop these Shasta daisies, a popular variety.

▶ **Figure 13–2** Inbreeding is required to maintain the characteristics of pedigreed dogs, such as these golden retrievers. However, inbreeding has also increased the breed's susceptibility to diseases and deformities. **Applying Concepts** *What other animals are likely to be inbred?*

▼ **Figure 13–3** 🔑 **Breeders can increase genetic variation by inducing mutations.** This process was used to produce the oil-eating bacteria shown here. This image was made using a scanning electron microsope and has been artificially colored.

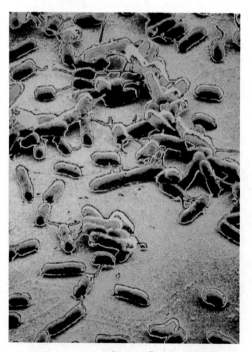

(magnification: 6200×)

Inbreeding To maintain the desired characteristics of a line of organisms, breeders often use a technique known as inbreeding. **Inbreeding** is the continued breeding of individuals with similar characteristics. The many breeds of dogs—from beagles to poodles—are maintained by inbreeding. Inbreeding helps to ensure that the characteristics that make each breed unique will be preserved. The golden retrievers shown in **Figure 13–2** are an example of inbred animals.

Although inbreeding is useful in retaining a certain set of characteristics, it does have its risks. Most of the members of a breed are genetically similar. Because of this, there is always a chance that a cross between two individuals will bring together two recessive alleles for a genetic defect. Serious problems in many breeds of dogs, including blindness and joint deformities in German shepherds and golden retrievers, have resulted from excessive inbreeding.

✓ CHECKPOINT *What is inbreeding?*

Increasing Variation

Selective breeding would be nearly impossible without the wide variation that is found in natural populations. This is one of the reasons biologists are interested in preserving the diversity of plants and animals in the wild. However, sometimes breeders want more variation than exists in nature. 🔑 **Breeders can increase the genetic variation in a population by inducing mutations, which are the ultimate source of genetic variability.**

As you may recall, mutations are inheritable changes in DNA. Mutations occur spontaneously, but breeders can increase the mutation rate by using radiation and chemicals. Many mutations are harmful to the organism. With luck and perseverance, however, breeders can produce a few mutants—individuals with mutations—with desirable characteristics that are not found in the original population.

Producing New Kinds of Bacteria This technique has been particularly useful with bacteria. Their small size enables millions of organisms to be treated with radiation or chemicals at the same time. This increases the chances of producing a useful mutant. Using this technique, scientists have been able to develop hundreds of useful bacterial strains. It has even been possible to produce bacteria that can digest oil, as shown in **Figure 13–3,** and are thus useful in cleaning up oil spills.

Producing New Kinds of Plants Drugs that prevent chromosomal separation during meiosis have been particularly useful in plant breeding. Sometimes these drugs produce cells that have double or triple the normal number of chromosomes. Plants grown from such cells are called **polyploid** because they have many sets of chromosomes. Polyploidy is usually fatal in animals. However, for reasons that are not clear, plants are much better at tolerating extra sets of chromosomes. Polyploidy may instantly produce new species of plants that are often larger and stronger than their diploid relatives. **Figure 13–4** shows some polyploid day lilies. Many important crop plants have been produced in this way, including bananas and many varieties of citrus fruits.

Word Origins

Polyploid comes from the Greek words *polus,* meaning "many," and *-ploos,* meaning "fold." So *polyploid* means "many-fold" or "many times." **How many sets of chromosomes do you think a triploid plant has?**

▶ **Figure 13–4** The day lilies at the right are examples of polyploid plants. New species of plants are produced when the chromosome number is doubled or tripled. **Applying Concepts** *Are any of the fruits and vegetables that you regularly eat polyploid?*

13–1 Section Assessment

1. **Key Concept** Give one example of selective breeding.
2. **Key Concept** Relate genetic variation and mutations to each other.
3. How might a breeder induce mutations?
4. What is polyploidy?

5. **Critical Thinking Problem Solving** Suggest ways that plants could be altered to improve the world's food supply.

iTEXT Assessment Use iText to review the important concepts in Section 13–1.

ALTERNATIVE ASSESSMENT

Interviewing an Expert
Interview a person who breeds plants or animals. Find out what kinds of techniques the person uses. What traits does he or she try to select for? Why?

13–2 Manipulating DNA

Guide for Reading

🔑 **Key Concept**
• How do scientists make changes to DNA?

Vocabulary
genetic engineering
restriction enzyme
gel electrophoresis
recombinant DNA
polymerase chain reaction (PCR)

**Reading Strategy:
Previewing Graphics**
Before you read this section, examine the figures. Read the titles and captions, and identify questions about or predict relationships among the techniques illustrated.

Until very recently, animal and plant breeders could not modify the genetic code of living things. They were limited by the need to work with the variation that already exists in nature. Even when they tried to add to that variation by introducing mutations, the changes they produced in the DNA were random and unpredictable. Imagine, however, that one day biologists were able to go right to the genetic code, rewrite an organism's DNA, and make any changes they wanted. Imagine that biologists could swap genes at will from one organism to another, designing new living things to meet specific needs. That day, as you may know from scientific stories in the news, is already here.

How are changes made to DNA? 🔑 **Scientists use their knowledge of the structure of DNA and its chemical properties to study and change DNA molecules. Different techniques are used to extract DNA from cells, to cut DNA into smaller pieces, to identify the sequence of bases in a DNA molecule, and to make unlimited copies of DNA.** Understanding how these techniques work will help you develop an appreciation for what is involved in genetic engineering.

The Tools of Molecular Biology

Suppose you had a computer game you wanted to change. Knowing that the characteristics of that game are determined by a coded computer program, how would you set about rewriting parts of the program? To make such changes, a software engineer would need a way to get the program out of the computer, read it, make changes in it, and then put the modified code back into the game. **Genetic engineering,** making changes in the DNA code of a living organism, works almost the same way.

▶ **Figure 13–5** 🔑 **Molecular biologists have developed different techniques that allow them to study and change DNA molecules.** This drawing shows how restriction enzymes are used to edit DNA. The restriction enzyme *Eco*RI, for example, finds the sequence CTTAAG on DNA. Then, the enzyme cuts the molecule at each occurrence of CTTAAG. Different restriction enzymes recognize and cut different sequences of nucleotides on DNA molecules.

DNA plus restriction enzyme

Power source

Mixture of DNA fragments

Gel

Longer fragments

Shorter fragments

▲ **Figure 13–6** Gel electrophoresis is used to separate DNA fragments. First, restriction enzymes cut DNA into fragments. The DNA fragments are then poured into wells on a gel, which is similar to a thick piece of gelatin. An electric voltage moves the DNA fragments across the gel. Because longer fragments of DNA move through the gel more slowly, they do not migrate as far across the gel as shorter fragments of DNA. Based on size, the DNA fragments make a pattern of bands on the gel. These bands can then be compared with other samples of DNA. **Inferring** *What kinds of information might the bands from two different DNA sources provide?*

DNA Extraction How do biologists get DNA out of a cell? DNA can be extracted from most cells by a simple chemical procedure: The cells are opened and the DNA is separated from the other cell parts.

Cutting DNA DNA molecules from most organisms are much too large to be analyzed, so biologists cut them precisely into smaller fragments using restriction enzymes. Hundreds of **restriction enzymes** are known, and each one cuts DNA at a specific sequence of nucleotides. As shown in **Figure 13–5,** restriction enzymes are amazingly precise. Like a key that fits only one lock, a restriction enzyme will cut a DNA sequence only if it matches the sequence precisely.

Separating DNA How can DNA fragments be separated and analyzed? One way, a procedure known as gel electrophoresis (ee-lek-troh-fuh-REE-sis), is shown in **Figure 13–6.** In **gel electrophoresis,** a mixture of DNA fragments is placed at one end of a porous gel, and an electric voltage is applied to the gel. When the power is turned on, DNA molecules, which are negatively charged, move toward the positive end of the gel. The smaller the DNA fragment, the faster it moves. Gel electrophoresis can be used to compare the genomes of different organisms or different individuals. It can also be used to locate and identify one particular gene out of the millions of genes in an individual's genome.

Using the DNA Sequence

Once DNA is in a manageable form, its sequence can be read, studied, and even changed. Knowing the sequence of an organism's DNA allows researchers to study specific genes, to compare them with the genes of other organisms, and to try to discover the functions of different genes and gene combinations. The following are some techniques scientists use to read and change the sequence of DNA molecules.

▲ Figure 13-7 ⬤ **Knowing the sequence of an organism's DNA allows researchers to study specific genes.** In DNA sequencing, a complementary DNA strand is made using a small proportion of fluorescently labeled nucleotides. Each time a labeled nucleotide is added, it stops the process of replication, producing a short color-coded DNA fragment. When the mixture of fragments is separated on a gel, the DNA sequence can be read directly from the gel.

Labels in figure:
- Fluorescent dye
- Single strand of DNA
- A C G T G A A G T T C
- C G T G A A G T T C
- G T G A A G T T C
- T G A A G T T C
- Strand broken after A
- Strand broken after C
- Strand broken after G
- Strand broken after T
- Power source
- Gel

Reading the Sequence In many laboratories, "reading" a DNA sequence is now an automated process. **Figure 13-7** shows one technique for reading DNA. Small, single-stranded pieces of DNA are placed in test tubes with an enzyme that can make a complementary DNA strand by using the original DNA strand as a template. A supply of the 4 nucleotide bases found in DNA is then added, along with a small amount of one of the bases that has been labeled with a fluorescent dye. When the enzyme adds one of the labeled bases, the new DNA strand is terminated—producing a short DNA fragment tagged with the colored dye of the last base added.

When this is done for all 4 bases, each labeled with a different color, a series of tiny DNA fragments is generated. These DNA fragments are color-coded according to the fluorescent dye that has been added at the very end. These fragments are then separated according to size, often by gel electrophoresis. The pattern of colored bands tells the exact sequence of bases in the DNA.

Cutting and Pasting DNA sequences can be changed in a number of ways. Short sequences can be assembled using laboratory machines known as DNA synthesizers. "Synthetic" sequences can then be joined to "natural" ones using enzymes that splice DNA together. The same enzymes make it possible to take a gene from one organism and attach it to the DNA of another organism. Such DNA molecules are sometimes called **recombinant DNA** because they are produced by combining DNA from different sources.

Making Copies In order to study genes, biologists often need to make many copies of a particular gene. Like a photocopy machine stuck on "print," a technique known as **polymerase chain reaction (PCR)** allows biologists to do exactly that. **Figure 13–8** shows how PCR works.

The idea behind PCR is surprisingly simple. At one end of a piece of DNA a biologist wants to copy, he or she adds a short piece of DNA that is complementary to a portion of the sequence. At the other end, the biologist adds another short piece of complementary DNA. These short pieces are known as "primers" because they provide a place for the DNA polymerase to start working.

The DNA is heated to separate its two strands, then cooled to allow the primers to bind to single-stranded DNA. DNA polymerase starts making copies of the region between the primers. Because the copies themselves can serve as templates to make still more copies, just a few dozen cycles of replication can produce millions of copies of the DNA between those primers.

Where did Kary Mullis, the American inventor of PCR, find a DNA polymerase enzyme that could stand repeated cycles of heating and cooling? Mullis found it in bacteria living in the hot springs of Yellowstone National Park—a perfect example of the importance of biodiversity to biotechnology.

KEEP CURRENT WITH . . .
SCIENCE NEWS®

To find out more about the topics in this chapter, go to:
www.phschool.com

✓ CHECKPOINT *What is a polymerase chain reaction?*

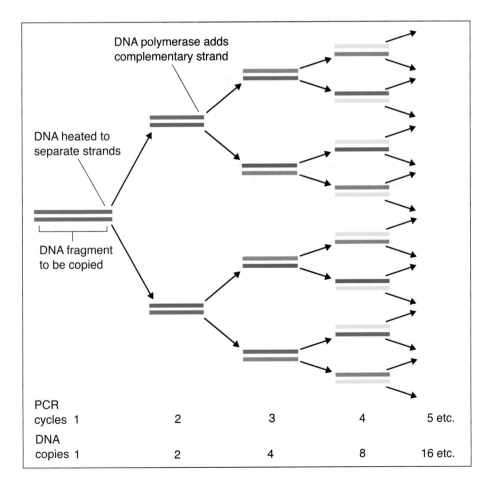

DNA polymerase adds complementary strand

DNA heated to separate strands

DNA fragment to be copied

| PCR cycles | 1 | 2 | 3 | 4 | 5 etc. |
| DNA copies | 1 | 2 | 4 | 8 | 16 etc. |

◀ **Figure 13–8** Polymerase chain reaction (PCR) is used to make multiple copies of genes. **Calculating** *How many copies of the DNA will there be after six cycles?*

Quick Lab

How are restriction enzymes used?

Materials construction paper, scissors, transparent tape

Procedure
1. Write a 50-base double-stranded DNA sequence using the letters A, C, G, and T in random order. Include each of the base sequences shown below at least once in your 50 base-pair sequences.
2. Make 3 copies of your double-stranded sequence on three different-colored strips of paper.
3. Use the drawings below to see how the restriction enzyme *Eco*RI would cut your double-stranded sequence. Use scissors to cut 1 copy of the sequence as *Eco*RI would.

4. Use the procedure in step 3 to cut apart another copy of your sequence as the restriction enzyme

*Bam*I would. Cut apart the third copy as the restriction enzyme *Hae*III would.
5. To model the building of recombinant DNA, tape the single-stranded end of one of your pieces of DNA sequences to a complementary, single-stranded end of one of a classmate's pieces. This will form a single, long DNA molecule.

Analyze and Conclude
1. **Observing** Which restriction enzyme produced the most pieces? The fewest pieces?
2. **Using Models** Were the two pieces you joined cut by the same restriction enzyme? Must both pieces of DNA be cut by the same restriction enzyme before they are joined? Explain your answer.
3. **Inferring** Why are *Eco*RI and *Bam*I better choices than *Hae*III for cutting pieces of DNA to be joined?

13–2 Section Assessment

1. 🔑 **Key Concept** Describe the process scientists use to manipulate DNA.
2. Why might a scientist want to know the sequence of a DNA molecule?
3. How does gel electrophoresis work?
4. Which technique can be used to make multiple copies of a gene? What are the basic steps in this procedure?

5. **Critical Thinking Using Analogies** How is genetic engineering like computer programming?

TEXT Assessment Use iText to review the important concepts in Section 13–2.

Take It to the NET

Design an experiment to carry out PCR in your kitchen at home. Include a list of materials, safety precautions, and a step-by-step procedure that you could follow. Use the links provided in the Biology area at the Prentice Hall Web site for help in completing this activity: **www.phschool.com**

13–3 Cell Transformation

It would do little good to modify a DNA molecule in the test tube if it were not possible to put that DNA back into a living cell and make it work. This sounds tricky, and it is, but you have already seen an example of how this can be done. Remember Griffith's experiments on bacterial transformation? 🔑 **During transformation, a cell takes in DNA from outside the cell. This external DNA becomes a part of the cell's DNA.**

Today, biologists understand that Griffith's extract of heat-killed bacteria must have contained DNA fragments. When he mixed those fragments with live bacteria, a few of them actually took up the DNA molecules. This suggests that bacteria can be transformed simply by placing them in a solution containing DNA molecules—and indeed they can.

Transforming Bacteria

Figure 13–9 shows how bacteria can be transformed using recombinant DNA. The foreign DNA is first joined to a small, circular DNA molecule known as a **plasmid.** Plasmids are found naturally in some bacteria and have been very useful for DNA transfer. Why? The plasmid DNA has two essential features. First, it has a DNA sequence that serves as a bacterial origin of replication. If the plasmid containing the foreign DNA manages to get inside a bacterial cell, this sequence ensures that it will be replicated.

Guide for Reading

🔑 **Key Concepts**
• What happens during cell transformation?
• How can you tell if a transformation experiment has been successful?

Vocabulary
plasmid
genetic marker

Reading Strategy:
Summarizing As you read, take notes on how each kind of cell can be transformed. After you read, go back to your notes and compare the different techniques.

◀ **Figure 13–9** 🔑 **During transformation, a cell incorporates DNA from outside the cell into its own DNA.** One way to make recombinant DNA is to insert a human gene into bacterial DNA. The new combination of genes is then returned to a bacterial cell, and the bacteria can produce the human protein.

Second, the plasmid has a **genetic marker**—a gene that makes it possible to distinguish bacteria that carry the plasmid (and the foreign DNA) from those that don't. Genes for resistance to antibiotics, compounds that can kill bacteria, are commonly used as markers. A marker makes it possible for researchers to mix recombinant plasmids with a culture of bacteria, add enough DNA to transform one cell in a million, and still be able to "find" that cell. After transformation, the culture is treated with an antibiotic. Only those rare cells that have been transformed survive—because only they carry a resistance gene.

✓CHECKPOINT *What is a genetic marker?*

Transforming Plant Cells

Many plant cells can be transformed by using a process that takes advantage of a bacterium. In nature, this bacterium inserts a small DNA plasmid that produces tumors into a plant's cells, as shown in **Figure 13–10**. Researchers have discovered that they can inactivate the tumor-producing gene and insert a piece of foreign DNA into the plasmid. The recombinant plasmid can then be used to infect plant cells.

▼ **Figure 13–10** The bacterium *Agrobacterium tumefaciens* can be used to introduce foreign DNA into plant cells. ⬤ **If the transformation is successful, the DNA will be integrated into one of the cell's chromosomes.**

Gene to be transferred

Recombinant plasmid

Agrobacterium tumefaciens

Cellular DNA

Inside plant cell, *Agrobacterium* inserts part of its DNA into host cell chromosome.

Plant cell colonies

Transformed bacteria introduce plasmids into plant cells.

Complete plant is generated from transformed cell.

When their cell walls are removed, plant cells in culture will sometimes take up DNA on their own. DNA can also be injected directly into some cells. Cells transformed by either procedure can be cultured to produce adult plants. 🔑 **If transformation is successful, the recombinant DNA is integrated into one of the chromosomes of the cell.**

Transforming Animal Cells

Animal cells can be transformed in some of the same ways as plant cells. Many egg cells are large enough that DNA can be directly injected into the nucleus. Once inside the nucleus, enzymes normally responsible for DNA repair and recombination may help to insert the foreign DNA into the chromosomes of the injected cell. Like bacterial plasmids, the DNA molecules used for transformation of animal and plant cells contain marker genes that enable biologists to identify which cells have been transformed.

Recently, it has become possible to "knock out" particular genes by careful design of the DNA molecules used for transformation. As **Figure 13–11** shows, DNA molecules can be constructed with two ends that will sometimes recombine with specific sequences in the host chromosome. Once they do, the host gene between those two sequences may be lost ("knocked out") or specifically replaced with a new gene. This kind of gene replacement has made it possible to pinpoint the specific functions of genes in many organisms, including mice.

▲ **Figure 13–11** Recombinant DNA can replace a gene in an animal's genome. The ends of the recombinant DNA recombine with sequences in the host cell DNA. When the recombinant DNA is inserted into the target location, the host cell's original gene is lost or knocked out of its place. **Applying Concepts** *How might this technique be used to treat disorders caused by a single gene?*

13–3 Section Assessment

1. 🔑 **Key Concept** What is transformation?
2. 🔑 **Key Concept** How can you tell if a transformation experiment has been successful?
3. How are genetic markers related to transformation?
4. What are two features that make plasmids useful for transforming cells?
5. **Critical Thinking Comparing and Contrasting** Compare the transformation of a prokaryotic cell with the transformation of a eukaryotic cell.

ⓘ **TEXT** **Assessment** Use iText to review the important concepts in Section 13–3.

Do Genetically Modified Foods Need Stricter Controls?

Since they were first introduced in 1994, bioengineered, or genetically modified (GM), crops have become common in the American supermarket and diet. Most GM plants are engineered to produce pest-killing chemicals or to resist weed-killing chemicals. For example, in 1998, 20 percent of U.S. corn crops contained a gene for *Bt-toxin*, a natural insecticide that protects corn plants from the European corn borer, a major insect pest. *Bt*-corn, as this GM corn is called, enables farmers to produce more food on fewer acres, increasing food production and profits.

Many consumers, however, are concerned about the long-term impact of these crops. The European Union, for example, has effectively stopped the import of many GM food crops and required that others be prominently labeled as genetically modified. Should GM foods be more tightly controlled?

The Viewpoints

GM Foods Need Tighter Controls

Some people are concerned that GM foods might have unexpected effects on people. For example, GM corn approved only for animal feed has appeared accidentally in tortillas. The corn contains a protein that could cause allergic reactions in people. The contaminated tortillas show that GM crops can get mixed in with non-GM crops.

Genetically modified crops also could pose a hazard to the environment. Plants engineered to produce insecticides can kill beneficial insects as well as pests. Antibiotic-resistance genes used as markers could spread into the environment, resulting in antibiotic-resistant bacteria. Pollen from GM plants might transfer genes to wild plants, resulting in "super weeds" that are impossible to control with weed killers. The spread of natural pesticide genes into wild plants might harm beneficial insects, such as bees and butterflies.

GM Foods Do Not Need More Controls

Recently developed GM food crops contain essential vitamins that are lacking in the diets of many people. For example, golden rice contains genes from daffodils and bacteria that greatly increase its content of beta-carotene, which the body uses to make vitamin A. The high productivity and nutritional benefits of GM crops are especially important in developing countries, where their use may prevent famine and ease human suffering.

Because they increase production and eliminate the need for chemical pesticides, GM crops can be beneficial to the environment. Someday, GM plants could be inexpensive sources of medicines, fuels, and plastics. If GM products are more strictly controlled, companies might give up researching new applications for GM plants.

You Decide

1. **Defining the Issue** In your own words, explain the major issues about GM foods.
2. **Analyzing the Viewpoints** What are the risks and benefits of GM plants?
3. **Forming Your Opinion** Are stricter regulations needed? Give reasons for your opinion.
4. **Role-Playing** Suppose you are a farmer trying to sell your GM crop. The company that usually purchases your crop has decided not to use GM crops. Write a letter to the company explaining your position. Then, take the role of company president and respond to the farmer's letter.

13–4 Applications of Genetic Engineering

As you have just read, the technology of genetic engineering makes it possible to transfer DNA sequences, including whole genes, from one organism to another. Does this mean that genes from organisms as different as animals and plants can be made to work in each other? American researcher Steven Howell and his associates at the University of California at San Diego provided the answer to that question in 1986. They isolated the gene for luciferase, an enzyme that allows fireflies to glow, and inserted it into tobacco cells. When whole plants were grown from the recombinant cells and the gene was activated, the plants glowed in the dark, as you can see in **Figure 13–12.** The fact that the gene for luciferase works perfectly in a plant shows that the basic mechanisms of gene expression are shared by plants and animals.

Transgenic Organisms

The universal nature of genetic mechanisms makes it possible to construct organisms that are **transgenic,** meaning that they contain genes from other organisms. Using the basic techniques of genetic engineering, a gene from one organism can be inserted into cells from another organism. These transformed cells can then be used to grow new organisms. Don't think for a moment that transgenic organisms are of interest only to scientists. **Genetic engineering has spurred the growth of biotechnology, a new industry that is changing the way we interact with the living world.**

Transgenic Microorganisms Because they reproduce rapidly and are easy to grow, transgenic bacteria now produce a host of important substances useful for health and industry. The human forms of proteins such as insulin, growth hormone, and clotting factor were once rare and expensive. Bacteria transformed with the genes for human proteins now produce these important compounds cheaply and in great abundance. People with insulin-dependent diabetes are now treated with pure human insulin produced by human genes inserted into bacteria. In the future, transgenic microorganisms may produce substances designed to fight cancer, as well as the raw materials for plastics and synthetic fibers.

▶ **Figure 13–12** Genetic engineering has changed the way we interact with living things. This transgenic tobacco plant, which glows in the dark, was produced by transferring a gene from a firefly into a tobacco cell.

Guide for Reading

🔑 **Key Concept**
- How are transgenic organisms useful to human beings?

Vocabulary
transgenic
clone

Reading Strategy: Monitoring Your Understanding Make a table with three columns. Before you read, write what you already know about cloning in the first column. Under the next heading, write down what you want to learn about cloning. After you read, write down what you learned about cloning in the last column.

Transgenic Animals Transgenic animals have been used to study genes and to improve the food supply. Strains of mice have been produced with human genes that make their immune systems act similarly to those of humans. This allows scientists to study the effects of diseases on the human immune system. Transgenic livestock have been produced with extra copies of growth hormone genes. Such animals grow faster and produce meat that is less fatty than that from ordinary animals. Efforts are now underway to produce transgenic chickens that will be resistant to the bacterial infections that sometimes cause food poisoning.

In the future, transgenic animals might also provide us with an ample supply of our own proteins. Several labs have engineered transgenic sheep and pigs that produce human proteins in their milk, making it easy to collect and refine the proteins.

Transgenic Plants Transgenic plants are now an important part of our food supply. In the year 2000, 52 percent of the soybeans and 25 percent of the corn grown in the United States were transgenic, or genetically modified (GM). Many of these plants contain genes that produce a natural insecticide, so the crops do not have to be sprayed with synthetic pesticides. Others have genes that enable them to resist weed-killing chemicals, allowing farmers to grow more food by controlling weeds.

▼ **Figure 13–13** In early 1997, Dolly made headlines as the first clone of an adult mammal. **Applying Concepts** *Why did Dolly not look like her foster mother?*

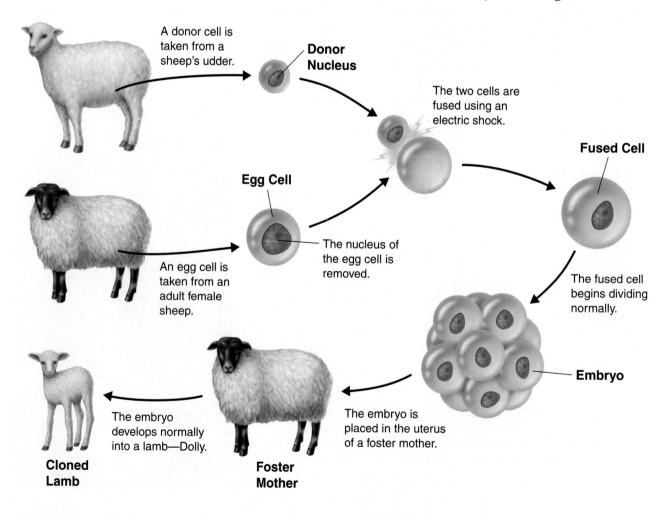

A donor cell is taken from a sheep's udder.

Donor Nucleus

The two cells are fused using an electric shock.

Fused Cell

Egg Cell

An egg cell is taken from an adult female sheep.

The nucleus of the egg cell is removed.

The fused cell begins dividing normally.

Embryo

The embryo develops normally into a lamb—Dolly.

The embryo is placed in the uterus of a foster mother.

Cloned Lamb

Foster Mother

Transgenic plants may soon produce human antibodies that can be used to fight disease; plastics that can now be produced only from petroleum; and foods that are resistant to rot and spoilage. One of the most important new developments in GM foods is a rice plant that adds vitamin A to rice, the major food for billions of the world's people.

Cloning

A **clone** is a member of a population of genetically identical cells produced from a single cell. Cloned colonies of bacteria and other microorganisms are easy to grow, but this is not always true of multicellular organisms, especially animals. For many years, biologists wondered if it might be possible to clone a mammal— to use a single cell from an adult to grow an entirely new individual that is genetically identical to the organism from which the cell was taken. After years of research, many scientists had concluded that this was impossible.

In 1997, Scottish scientist Ian Wilmut stunned biologists by announcing that he had cloned a sheep. How did he do it? **Figure 13–13** shows the basic steps. In Wilmut's technique, the nucleus of an egg cell is removed. The cell is fused with a cell taken from another adult. The fused cell begins to divide and the embryo is then placed in the reproductive system of a foster mother, where it develops normally. The sheep, which Wilmut named Dolly, is shown in **Figure 13–14.** Cloned cows, pigs, mice, and other mammals have been produced by similar techniques. Cloned animals are not necessarily transgenic, but researchers hope that cloning will enable them to make copies of transgenic animals that produce genetically engineered substances that will have medical or scientific value.

Cloning may indeed find wide use in medical and scientific research and even in helping to save endangered species. Cloning, however, also raises serious ethical issues, including the possibility that sooner or later someone may attempt to clone a human being.

▲ **Figure 13–14** The adult sheep is Dolly, the first mammal cloned from an adult cell. The lamb is Dolly's first offspring, called Bonnie. The fact that Dolly was cloned did not affect her ability to produce a live offspring. **Inferring** *Why might it be important for cloned animals to be able to reproduce?*

13–4 Section Assessment

1. 🔑 **Key Concept** List one practical application for each of the following: transgenic bacteria, transgenic animals, transgenic plants.

2. What is a transgenic organism?

3. What basic steps were followed to produce Dolly?

4. **Critical Thinking Making Judgments** List reasons you would or would not be concerned about eating genetically modified food.

 Assessment Use iText to review the important concepts in Section 13–4.

Investigating the Effects of Radiation on Seeds

Mutations occur naturally in all organisms. However, an organism's mutation rate increases when it is exposed to certain chemicals or types of radiation. In this investigation, you will design an experiment to test the effects of X-ray exposure on seeds.

Problem
Do plants grown from irradiated seeds show evidence of increased mutation?

Materials
- irradiated seeds and nonirradiated seeds of the same species
- petri dishes
- paper towels
- plant pots with soil
- glass-marking pencil

Skills
Forming Operational Definitions

Design Your Experiment

Part A: Plan the Experiment

1. **Designing Experiments** Working with two of your classmates, design an experiment to test the hypothesis that radiation increases the rate of mutation in seeds.

2. Discuss your experimental plan with your group. Make certain that you have identified and controlled all important variables and included both irradiated and control seeds in your experimental plan.

3. You will not be able to observe mutations in DNA directly. What observations or measurements can you make that will provide evidence of the number of mutations that have occurred in a seed? With your group, plan what observations you will use to estimate the number of mutations that have occurred in a seed.

4. Design a data table in which to record your observations.

5. Show your experimental plan to your teacher. Once your teacher approves your plan, begin your experiment.

Part B: Carry Out Your Experiment

6. To grow the seeds, follow any instructions that are on the seed packages. If there are no instructions, line a petri dish with a paper towel for each experimental group of seeds. Place the

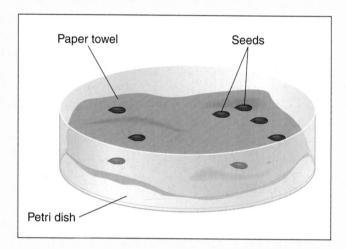

seeds in the petri dishes and cover the seeds with water, as shown in the diagram above. **CAUTION:** *Wash your hands well with warm water and plenty of soap after handling seeds, plants, or soil and before leaving the laboratory.*

7. Place the covers on the petri dishes to protect the seeds from mold and bacteria. Record everything you do to the seeds.

8. Use a glass-marking pencil to label each petri dish. Every petri dish that you use in this experiment should be identified by a different label that includes your name. Store the petri dishes in the location that your teacher designates.

9. Record your observations of each group of seeds every day for 2 weeks. Add water to the petri dishes as necessary to keep the seeds moist.

10. After 2 weeks, carefully transfer the young plants from the petri dishes to pots of soil. Water each pot after you have transferred plants into it. Label each pot with your name and the kind of plants it contains.

11. Place the potted plants in sunlight or under a fluorescent lamp as your teacher directs. Water the plants regularly. Continue to observe the plants daily, according to your experimental plans, for the next 2 weeks. Record your observations each day.

Analyze and Conclude

1. **Comparing and Contrasting** What differences did you observe between the irradiated seeds and the nonirradiated seeds?

2. **Designing Experiments** How could you best determine whether a seed contains mutant DNA?

3. **Forming Operational Definitions** What kinds of observations did you decide to use as evidence of mutations? Explain why you think that these observations are reliable evidence of mutations.

4. **Analyzing Data** What evidence did you see of mutations? Did the irradiated seeds show evidence of more mutations than the nonirradiated seeds?

5. **Formulating Hypotheses** Mutations sometimes cause part of an otherwise healthy-looking leaf or other plant part to appear abnormal. Did you see abnormal-looking areas on any plants? Would you expect this kind of mutation to be inherited? Explain your answer.

6. **Evaluating** What explanations, other than mutation, can you think of for the differences you observed between the irradiated seeds and the nonirradiated seeds?

Go Further

Observing Compare the chromosomes of irradiated and nonirradiated plants to see whether radiation can damage chromosomes. To do this, collect several root tips from plants in each experimental group. Place each root tip on a microscope slide with a drop of methylene blue stain and add a coverslip. Press gently on the coverslip with the handle of a dissecting probe to flatten the root tip. Observe this sample with a microscope to find dividing cells in which the chromosomes are visible.

13–1 Changing the Living World
 Key Concepts

- Humans use selective breeding to pass desired traits on to the next generation of organisms.
- Breeders can increase the genetic variation in a population by inducing mutations, which are the ultimate source of genetic variability.

Vocabulary
selective breeding, p. 319
hybridization, p. 319
inbreeding, p. 320
polyploid, p. 321

13–2 Manipulating DNA
 Key Concepts

- Scientists use their knowledge of the structure of DNA and its chemical properties to study and change DNA molecules. Different techniques are used to extract DNA from cells, to cut DNA into smaller pieces, to identify the sequence of bases in a DNA molecule, and to make unlimited copies of DNA.
- Knowing the sequence of an organism's DNA allows researchers to study specific genes, to compare them with the genes of other organisms, and to try to discover the functions of different genes and gene combinations.

Vocabulary
genetic engineering, p. 322
restriction enzyme, p. 323
gel electrophoresis, p. 323
recombinant DNA, p. 324
polymerase chain reaction (PCR) , p. 325

13–3 Cell Transformation
 Key Concepts

- During transformation, a cell takes in DNA from outside the cell. This external DNA becomes a part of the cell's DNA.
- If transformation is successful, the recombinant DNA is integrated into one of the chromosomes of the cell.

Vocabulary
plasmid, p. 327
genetic marker, p. 328

13–4 Applications of Genetic Engineering
 Key Concepts

- Using the basic techniques of genetic engineering, a gene from one organism can be inserted into cells from another organism. These transformed cells can then be used to grow new organisms.

Vocabulary
transgenic, p. 331
clone, p. 333

Thinking Visually
Using the information in this chapter, complete the following concept map.

Chapter 13

Part A

Multiple Choice
For each statement or question, select the number of the word or expression that, of those given, best completes the statement or answers the question.

1 For thousands of years, humans have been choosing organisms with certain desired characteristics to breed. The result has been the production of many new varieties of cultivated plants. This process is known as
(1) genetic engineering
(2) inbreeding
(3) cloning
(4) selective breeding

2 Selecting and crossing individuals with similar characteristics so that those characteristics will be present in the offspring is called
(1) inbreeding   (3) hybridization
(2) electrophoresis (4) genetic engineering

3 Changing the DNA code of an organism is called
(1) genetic engineering
(2) hybridization
(3) selective breeding
(4) inbreeding

4 DNA can be cut into shorter sequences with the use of
(1) enzymes   (3) chemical mutagens
(2) plasmids   (4) transformed bacteria

5 Which procedure can *not* be used to increase genetic variation?
(1) inbreeding
(2) genetic engineering
(3) inducing mutations
(4) radiation

6 The name of a process that separates DNA fragments by size is
(1) gel electrophoresis
(2) plasmid transfer
(3) genetic engineering
(4) polymerase chain reaction

7 When cell transformation is successful, the recombinant DNA
(1) undergoes mutation
(2) is treated with antibiotics
(3) is integrated into a chromosome
(4) becomes a plasmid

8 What has been produced in the drawing below?
(1) polymerase DNA   (3) a new human gene
(2) recombinant DNA   (4) a new human species

Plasmid

Plasmid isolated from bacterium

Bacterium

Restriction enzyme splits the plasmid open and also removes a section of DNA from donor cell

Section of donor DNA inserted into bacterial plasmid

Strand of DNA from donor cell

Recombinant plasmid inserted back into bacterium

9 Bacteria often contain small circular molecules of DNA known as
(1) clones   (3) plasmids
(2) restrictions   (4) hybrids

10 Organisms that contain genes from other organisms are called
(1) transgenic   (3) donor organisms
(2) mutagenic   (4) cloned organisms

11 A member of a population of genetically identical cells produced from a single cell is a
(1) clone   (3) mutant
(2) plasmid   (4) sequence

Test-Taking Tip For questions containing the words *not* or *except*, begin by eliminating each answer choice that does fit the characteristic in question. After eliminating all but one of the choices, check to see that your answer is correct by confirming that it does not fit the characteristic in question.

Preparing for the
Living Environment Exam

Parts B and C

Multiple Choice and Extended Response

For those questions that ask you to select a response, choose the one that best completes the statement or answers the question. For all others follow the directions given.

12 Compare hybridization and inbreeding. Why are they considered forms of selective breeding?

13 Explain why genetic engineering can be compared to reprogramming a computer game.

Base your answers to questions 14 and 15 on the graph below, which shows data for the polymerase chain reaction, and on your knowledge of biology.

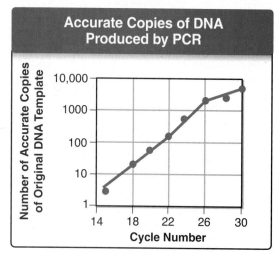

Accurate Copies of DNA Produced by PCR

14 PCR is expected to double the amount of DNA with each cycle. State whether or not this is supported with information from the graph. Use specific data from the graph to explain the basis for your answer.

15 Explain why the amount of DNA produced with PCR is expected to double with each cycle.

16 Describe the process that would allow a scientist to produce many plants containing a gene for resistance to weed killers.

17 Explain the difference between inserting a segment of DNA between two functional genes in a cell and inserting the DNA segment into the middle of a functioning gene in a cell.

18 What did the successful transfer of the luciferase gene from an animal to a plant indicate about the functioning of genes?

19 Explain what genetic markers are, and describe how scientists use them.

20 Describe what a transgenic organism is, and identify three examples of how transgenic bacteria have been used to benefit humans.

21 Describe one or more advantages of producing needed proteins such as insulin through genetic engineering.

22 A plant breeder has three rose bushes with the characteristics shown in the chart below.

Rosebush	Thorniness	Scent	Flower Color
A	thornless	scentless	pink
B	thorny	sweet smell	yellow
C	thorny	scentless	purple

How might the plant breeder develop a purebred variety of thornless sweet-smelling purple roses?

Base your answers to questions 23 through 25 on the diagram below and on your knowledge of biology.

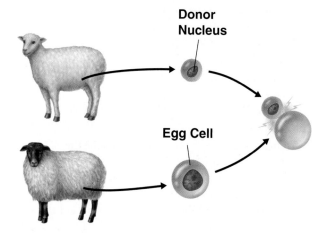

Donor Nucleus

Egg Cell

23 The events shown in the diagram represent part of the process of
(1) selective breeding (3) genetic modification
(2) cloning (4) PCR

24 Compare the amount of genetic information in the nucleus of the donor cell with the amount of genetic information in an intact egg cell.

25 Explain why the nucleus of the egg must be removed before fusing the cells.

26 If a human patient's bone marrow cells were removed, altered genetically, and re-implanted, would the change be passed on to the patient's children? Provide a biological explanation of your answer.

27 Should genetic engineering be performed directly on humans? If so, under what circumstances? Support your answer.

Base your answers to questions 28 and 29 on the diagram below, and on your knowledge of biology.

28 Describe one specific way the enzyme used to produce these fragments differs from other enzymes that cut DNA molecules into fragments.

29 Explain why the same enzyme must be used to cut both the gene from the donor's chromosome and the plasmid into which it is being inserted.

30 Both genetic engineering and selective breeding have been used to make changes in the genetic makeup of certain organisms. Both processes rely on natural variations found in organisms, but use them differently. Compare the way these natural variations are used differently in the two processes. In your answer, be sure to

- explain how breeders use variations to produce offspring with combinations of traits that never existed in any one individual before

- give an example of selective breeding that supports your explanation of how the process works

- explain how genetic engineers use variations to produce organisms with genetic traits that never existed in that species before

- give an example of genetic engineering that supports your explanation of how the process works

31 Hemophilia patients have a condition where their blood lacks factors to clot properly. Normal treatment with frequent blood transfusions can put them at risk of contracting diseases associated with human blood. How could genetic engineering eliminate this risk?

Base your answers to questions 32 through 35 on the passage below and on your knowledge of biology.

The DNA sequence for the Lyme disease pathogen *Borrelia burgdorferi,* comprising over 1.4 million base pairs, has been identified. This achievement, first featured in the scientific journal *Nature,* provides new information that will hopefully lead to better diagnostic tests, second-generation vaccines, discovery of the reasons behind individual susceptibility to chronic symptoms, and other discoveries in the ongoing quest to understand and prevent this multi-faceted disease.

32 A DNA molecule with 1.4 million base pairs is much too large to directly identify its base sequence. What method do scientists use to break DNA into smaller fragments for study?

33 What technique is used to separate a mixture of DNA fragments that vary in size?

34 Why is it important for scientists to publish their research findings in scientific journals, such as *Nature,* that require peer review of all articles they print?

35 How could knowledge of the DNA sequence of a disease-causing organism be used by researchers to help fight the disease?

Take It to the NET

What kinds of foods are the result of selective breeding? Visit the Biology area of the Prentice Hall Web site at **www.phschool.com** to learn about some of the foods that have been produced using selective breeding techniques. Then, answer the following questions:

- Name three fruits that have been developed using selective breeding.

- What is a paradox walnut tree?

- Why did Luther Burbank develop spineless cactuses?

14 The Human Genome

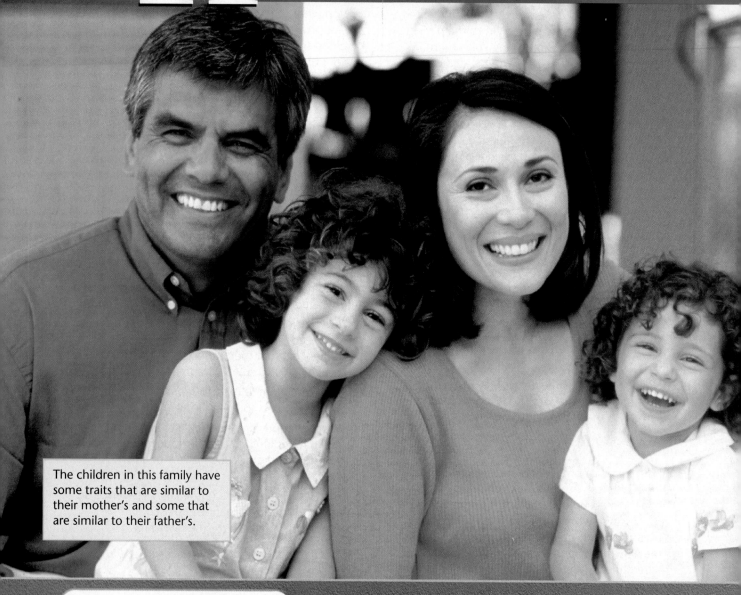

The children in this family have some traits that are similar to their mother's and some that are similar to their father's.

Inquiry Activity

Can you predict chin shape?

Procedure

1. Two parents with cleft chins, both heterozygous for cleft chin *(Cc)*, have three children with cleft chins. The parents are sure that their fourth child will not have a cleft chin. Draw a Punnett square to see if this is possible.

2. Determine the probability that the fourth child will have a cleft chin.

Think About It

1. **Using Models** What information does a Punnett square give? Does the Punnett square support the parents' prediction? Explain your answer.

2. **Predicting** If these parents have a fifth child, what are the chances that the child will have a cleft chin? Explain your answer.

14–1 Human Heredity

"Know thyself" was once a philosopher's first instruction to his students, and it still applies today. Of all the living things that inhabit this remarkable world, there is one in particular that has always drawn our interest, one that has always made us wonder, one that will always fire our imagination. That creature is, of course, ourselves, *Homo sapiens*.

Scientists once knew much less about humans than about other organisms. Until very recently, human genetics lagged far behind the genetics of "model" organisms such as fruit flies and mice. That, however, has changed. Scientists are now on the verge of understanding human genetics at least as well as they understand that of some other organisms. From that understanding will come a new responsibility to use that information wisely.

Human Chromosomes

What makes us human? Biologists can begin to answer that question by taking a look under the microscope to see what is inside a human cell. To analyze chromosomes, cell biologists photograph cells in mitosis, when the chromosomes are fully condensed and easy to see. The biologists then cut out the chromosomes from the photographs and group them together in pairs. A picture of chromosomes arranged in this way is known as a **karyotype** (KAR-ee-uh-typ).

The chromosomes shown in **Figure 14–1** are from a typical human body cell, which contains 46 chromosomes. Each of us began life when a haploid sperm, carrying just 23 chromosomes, fertilized a haploid egg, also with 23 chromosomes. The diploid zygote, or fertilized egg, contained the full complement of 46 chromosomes.

Two of those 46 chromosomes are known as **sex chromosomes,** because they determine an individual's sex. Females have two copies of a large X chromosome. Males have one X and one small Y chromosome. To distinguish them from the sex chromosomes, the remaining 44 chromosomes are known as autosomal chromosomes, or **autosomes.** To quickly summarize the total number of chromosomes present in a human cell, both autosomes and sex chromosomes, biologists write 46XX for females and 46XY for males.

Guide for Reading

 Key Concepts
- How is sex determined?
- How do small changes in DNA cause genetic disorders?

Vocabulary
karyotype
sex chromosome
autosome
pedigree
polygenic

**Reading Strategy:
Using Prior Knowledge**
Before you read, write down what you already know about the inheritance of traits. As you read, compare the information in the text to your notes.

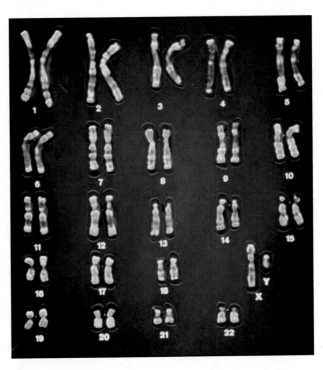

▶ **Figure 14–1** These human chromosomes have been cut out of a photograph and arranged to form a karyotype. **Interpreting Graphics** *How is the X chromosome different from the Y chromosome?*

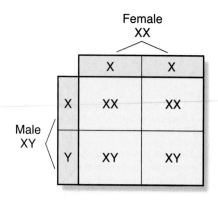

▲ Figure 14–2 ☞Egg cells contain a single X chromosome. Sperm cells contain either one X chromosome or one Y chromosome. Approximately half of the zygotes are XX (female) and half are XY (male).

As you can see in **Figure 14–2,** males and females are born in a roughly 50 : 50 ratio because of the way in which sex chromosomes segregate during meiosis. ☞**All egg cells carry a single X chromosome (23X). However, half of all sperm cells carry an X chromosome (23X) and half carry a Y chromosome (23Y). This ensures that just about half of the zygotes will be 46XX and half will be 46XY.**

Like the chromosomes of other eukaryotes, human chromosomes contain both DNA and protein. Each chromosome contains a single, double-stranded DNA molecule. Human genes are coded directly in the sequences of nucleotides in DNA.

✔CHECKPOINT *What is a karyotype?*

Human Traits

As you read in Chapter 12, human genes are inherited according to the same principles that Gregor Mendel discovered working with garden peas. However, in order to apply Mendelian genetics to humans, biologists must identify an inherited trait controlled by a single gene, which is not always easy. First, they must establish that the trait is actually inherited and not the result of environmental influences. Then, they have to study how the trait is passed from one generation to the next. A **pedigree** chart, which shows the relationships within a family, can be used to help with this task.

The pedigree in **Figure 14–3** shows how a trait is transmitted through three generations of a family. Females who have one allele for the trait are only carriers, while males who have one allele express the trait. In the first row, a female carrier marries a male who does not carry the trait. They have four children: a female carrier, a female who does not carry the trait, a male with the trait, and a male who does not carry the trait. The female carrier child also marries a male who does not carry the

▼ Figure 14–3 This drawing shows what the symbols in a pedigree represent. **Interpreting Graphics** *What is the sex of the last person in the second row? Does that person have the trait?*

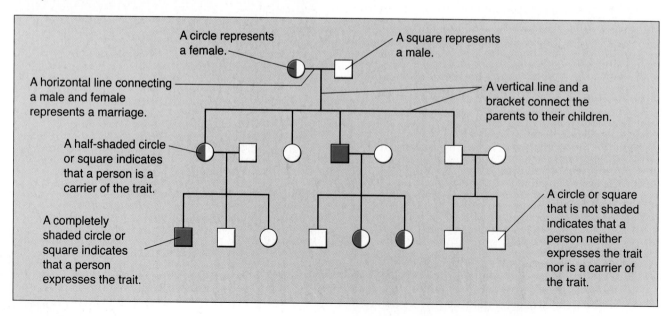

A circle represents a female.

A square represents a male.

A horizontal line connecting a male and female represents a marriage.

A vertical line and a bracket connect the parents to their children.

A half-shaded circle or square indicates that a person is a carrier of the trait.

A circle or square that is not shaded indicates that a person neither expresses the trait nor is a carrier of the trait.

A completely shaded circle or square indicates that a person expresses the trait.

trait, and has children: a male with the trait, a male who does not carry the trait, and a female who does not carry the trait.

Unfortunately for folks who would like to settle burning issues, like which side of the family is responsible for your good looks, some of the most obvious human traits are almost impossible to associate with single genes. There are two reasons for this. First, things you might think of as single traits, such as the shape of your eyes or ears, are actually **polygenic,** meaning they are controlled by many genes. Second, many of your personal traits are only partly governed by genetics. Remember that the phenotype of an organism is only partly determined by its genotype. Many traits are strongly influenced by environmental, or nongenetic, factors, including nutrition and exercise. For example, even though a person's maximum possible height is largely determined by genetic factors, nutritional improvements in the United States and Europe have increased the average height of these populations about 10 centimeters over their average height in the 1800s.

Although it is important to consider the influence of the environment on the expression of some genes, it must be understood that environmental effects on gene expression are not inherited; genes are. Genes that are denied a proper environment in which to reach full expression in one generation can, in a proper environment, achieve full potential in a later generation.

Problem Solving

Using a Pedigree

Imagine that you are a genetic counselor. The pedigree shown illustrates the inheritance of albinism in three generations of a family. A couple from the family have come to you for advice about how the trait is inherited. Your task is to determine whether the allele for albinism is dominant or recessive.

Defining the Problem Define the problem that must be solved to determine whether the allele is dominant or recessive.

Organizing Information Copy the pedigree and the key onto a piece of paper. Label each person on the pedigree with his or her phenotype: normal-pigmented skin or albino.

Creating a Solution Write down how you would analyze the pattern in the inheritance of the albinism trait. Use what you know about patterns of inheritance to determine what information is most important. Describe how you will use your analysis to infer the genotype of as many individuals as possible.

Presenting Your Plan Prepare a step-by-step outline of your plan. Present the plan to your class as if you were explaining the process to the couple involved.

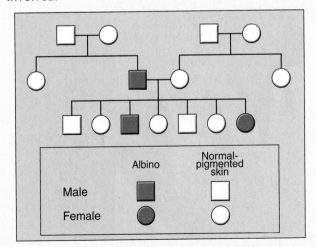

► **Figure 14–4** This table shows the relationship between genotype and phenotype for the ABO blood group. It also shows which blood types can safely be transfused into people with other blood types. **Applying Concepts** *Why are there four different phenotypes, even though there are six different genotypes?*

Blood Groups				
Phenotype (Blood Type)	Genotype	Antigen on Red Blood Cell	Safe Transfusions	
			To	From
A	$I^A I^A$ or $I^A i$	A	A, AB	A, O
B	$I^B I^B$ or $I^B i$	B	B, AB	B, O
AB	$I^A I^B$	A and B	AB	A, B, AB, O
O	ii	none	A, B, AB, O	O

▼ **Figure 14–5** This medical worker is drawing blood from a patient. The blood will be tested to see what types of blood can safely be transfused into the patient. **Applying Concepts** *Why is blood typing so important?*

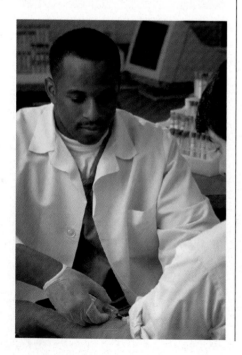

Human Genes

The human genome—our complete set of genetic information—includes tens of thousands of genes. The DNA sequences on these genes determine many characteristics, from the color of your eyes to the detailed structures of proteins within your cells. The exploration of the human genome is now a major scientific undertaking. By 2000, the DNA sequence of the human genome was almost complete.

Until recently, the identification of a human gene took years of scientific work. Studying the genetics of our species is not easy. Humans have long generation times and a complex life cycle, and they produce, at least compared with peas and fruit flies, very few offspring. Still, in a few cases, biologists were able to identify genes that directly control a single human trait. Some of the very first human genes to be identified were those that control blood type.

Blood Group Genes Human blood comes in a variety of genetically determined blood groups. Knowing a person's blood group is critical because using the wrong type of blood for a transfusion during a medical procedure can be fatal. A number of genes are responsible for human blood groups, but the best known are the ABO blood groups and the Rh blood groups.

The Rh blood group is determined by a single gene with two alleles—positive and negative. *Rh* stands for "rhesus monkey," the animal in which this factor was discovered. The positive (Rh+) allele is dominant, so persons who are Rh+/Rh+ or Rh+/Rh- are said to be Rh-positive. Individuals with two Rh- alleles are Rh-negative.

The ABO blood group is more complicated. There are three alleles for this gene, I^A, I^B, and i. Alleles I^A and I^B are codominant. These alleles produce molecules known as antigens that can be recognized by the immune system on the surface of red blood cells. As **Figure 14–4** shows, individuals with alleles I^A and I^B produce both antigens, making them blood type AB. The i allele is recessive. Individuals with alleles $I^A I^A$ or $I^A i$ produce only the A antigen, making them blood type A. Those with $I^B I^B$ or $I^B i$ alleles are type B. Those who are homozygous for the i allele (ii) produce no antigen, and are said to have blood type O.

When a medical worker refers to blood groups, he or she usually mentions both groups at the same time. For example, if a patient has AB-negative blood, it means the individual has I^A and I^B alleles from the ABO gene and the Rh- allele from the Rh gene.

Recessive Alleles Many human genes have become known through the study of genetic disorders. **Figure 14–6** lists some common genetic disorders. In most cases, the presence of a normal, functioning gene is revealed only when an abnormal or nonfunctioning allele affects the phenotype.

One of the first genetic disorders to be understood this way was phenylketonuria (fen-ul-ket-oh-NOOR-ee-uh), or PKU. People with PKU lack the enzyme that is needed to break down phenylalanine. Phenylalanine is an amino acid found in milk and many other foods. If a newborn has PKU, phenylalanine may build up in the tissues during the child's first years of life and cause severe mental retardation. Fortunately, newborns can be tested for PKU and then placed on a low-phenylalanine diet that prevents most of the effects of PKU. PKU is caused by a recessive allele carried on chromosome 12.

Many other disorders are also caused by autosomal recessive alleles. One is Tay-Sachs disease, which is caused by an allele found mostly in Jewish families of central and eastern European ancestry. Tay-Sachs disease results in nervous system breakdown and death in the first few years of life. Although there is no treatment for Tay-Sachs disease, there is a test for the allele. By taking this test, prospective parents can learn whether they are at risk of having a child with the disorder.

▼ **Figure 14–6** This table shows the major symptoms of some well-known genetic disorders. **Interpreting Graphics** *Which disorder causes galactose to accumulate in the tissues?*

	Some Autosomal Disorders in Humans	
Type of Disorder	**Disorder**	**Major Symptoms**
Disorders caused by recessive alleles	Albinism	Lack of pigment in skin, hair, and eyes
	Cystic fibrosis	Excess mucus in lungs, digestive tract, liver; increased susceptibility to infections; death in childhood unless treated
	Galactosemia	Accumulation of galactose (a sugar) in tissues; mental retardation; eye and liver damage
	Phenylketonuria (PKU)	Accumulation of phenylalanine in tissues; lack of normal skin pigment; mental retardation
	Tay-Sachs disease	Lipid accumulation in brain cells; mental deficiency; blindness; death in early childhood
Disorders caused by dominant alleles	Achondroplasia	Dwarfism (one form)
	Huntington's disease	Mental deterioration and uncontrollable movements; appears in middle age
	Hypercholesterolemia	Excess cholesterol in blood; heart disease
Disorders caused by codominant alleles	Sickle cell disease	Sickled red blood cells; damage to many tissues

Dominant Alleles Not all genetic disorders are caused by recessive alleles. You may recall that the effects of a dominant allele are expressed even when the recessive allele is present. Therefore, if you have a dominant allele for a genetic disorder, it will be expressed. Two examples of genetic disorders caused by autosomal dominant alleles are a form of dwarfism known as achondroplasia (ay-kahn-droh-PLAY-zhuh) and a nervous system disorder known as Huntington's disease. Huntington's disease causes a progressive loss of muscle control and mental function until death occurs. People who have this disease generally show no symptoms until they are in their thirties and forties, when the gradual damage to the nervous system begins.

Codominant Alleles Sickle cell disease, a serious disorder found in 1 in 500 African Americans, is caused by a codominant allele. As you will read, the reason for the high incidence of sickle cell in the United States is a story that links genetics, human history, and molecular biology.

✓ CHECKPOINT *What type of allele causes Huntington's disease?*

From Gene to Molecule

How do the actual DNA sequences in genes affect phenotype so profoundly? What is the link between the DNA bases in the allele for a genetic disorder and the disorder itself? For many genetic disorders, scientists are still working to find the answer. But for two disorders, the connection is understood very well indeed. 🔑 **In both cystic fibrosis and sickle cell disease, a small change in the DNA of a single gene affects the structure of a protein, causing a serious genetic disorder.**

Cystic Fibrosis Cystic fibrosis, or CF, is a common fatal genetic disease. Cystic fibrosis is most common among people whose ancestors came from Northern Europe. The disease is caused by a recessive allele on chromosome 7. Children with cystic fibrosis have serious digestive problems. In addition, they produce a thick, heavy mucus that clogs their lungs and breathing passageways. The disease takes a heavy toll. Only about half of the children born with cystic fibrosis survive into their 20s.

Cystic fibrosis involves a very small genetic change. Most cases of cystic fibrosis are caused by the deletion of 3 bases in the middle of a sequence for a protein, as shown in **Figure 14–8.** This protein normally allows chloride ions (Cl^-) to pass across biological membranes. The deletion of these 3 bases removes just one amino acid from this large protein, causing it to fold improperly. Because of this, the cells do not transport the protein to the cell membrane, and the misfolded protein is destroyed. Unable to transport chloride ions, tissues throughout the body malfunction. People with one normal copy of the allele are unaffected, because they can produce enough of the chloride channel protein to allow their tissues to function properly.

▲ **Figure 14–7** This girl is inhaling a fine mist through a nebulizer. The medication in the mist thins the mucus in the lungs, making breathing easier. **Inferring** *Why is it important for people with CF to thin the mucus in their lungs?*

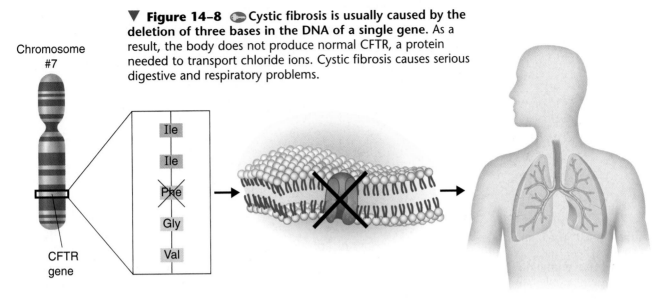

▼ **Figure 14–8** 👁 Cystic fibrosis is usually caused by the deletion of three bases in the DNA of a single gene. As a result, the body does not produce normal CFTR, a protein needed to transport chloride ions. Cystic fibrosis causes serious digestive and respiratory problems.

Chromosome #7

CFTR gene

Ile
Ile
Phe
Gly
Val

A The most common allele that causes cystic fibrosis is missing 3 DNA bases. As a result, the amino acid phenylalanine is missing from the CFTR protein.

B Normal CFTR is a chloride ion channel in cell membranes. Abnormal CFTR cannot be transported to the cell membrane.

C The cells in the person's airways are unable to transport chloride ions. As a result, the airways become clogged with a thick mucus.

Sickle Cell Disease Sickle cell disease is a common genetic disorder found in African Americans. Sickle cell disease is characterized by the bent and twisted shape of the red blood cells, like those shown in **Figure 14–9.** These sickle-shaped red blood cells are more rigid than normal cells and tend to get stuck in the capillaries, the narrowest blood vessels in the body. As a result, blood stops moving through these vessels, damaging cells and tissues beyond the blockage. Sickle cell disease produces physical weakness and damage to the brain, heart, and spleen. In some cases, it may be fatal.

Hemoglobin is the protein that carries oxygen in the blood. The normal allele for this gene differs very little from the sickle cell allele—just one DNA base is changed. This change inserts the amino acid valine in place of glutamic acid. As a result, the abnormal hemoglobin is somewhat less soluble than normal hemoglobin. Any decrease in blood oxygen levels causes many of the hemoglobin molecules to come out of solution and stick together. The stuck-together molecules form long chains and fibers that produce the characteristic shape of sickled cells.

Why do so many African Americans carry the sickle cell allele? Most African Americans can trace their ancestry to west central Africa. Malaria, a serious parasitic disease that infects red blood cells, is common in this region of Africa. People who are heterozygous for the sickle cell allele are generally healthy. In addition, they have the benefit of being resistant to malaria. The relationship between the incidence of malaria and the presence of the sickle cell allele is shown in **Figure 14–10** on the next page.

▼ **Figure 14–9** These red blood cells contain the abnormal hemoglobin characteristic of sickle cell disease. **Observing** *How is this cell different from a normal red blood cell?*

(magnification 1800×)

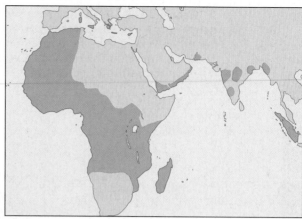

Figure 14–10 The map on the left shows where malaria is common. The map on the right shows regions where people have the sickle cell allele. **Interpreting Graphics** *What is the relationship between malaria and the sickle cell allele?*

Low oxygen levels cause some red blood cells to become sickle shaped. When the body destroys the sickled cells, it gets rid of the parasite at the same time. Because of this, in parts of the world such as west central Africa, where malaria is a major threat to health, the sickle cell allele is actually beneficial in heterozygous persons.

Dominant or Recessive? What makes an allele dominant, recessive, or codominant? CF and sickle cell disease show biologists that it all depends on the nature of a gene's protein product and its role in the cell. In the case of CF, just one copy of the normal allele can supply cells with enough chloride channel proteins to function. Because of this, the normal allele is considered dominant over the recessive CF allele.

The allele for normal hemoglobin was once also considered dominant over the sickle cell allele, but biologists now know that this situation is more complex. An individual with both normal and sickle cell alleles has a different phenotype—resistance to malaria—from someone with only normal alleles. Therefore, the sickle cell alleles are thought to be codominant because both alleles contribute to the phenotype.

14–1 Section Assessment

1. **Key Concept** What are sex chromosomes? What determines whether a person is male or female?

2. **Key Concept** Using an example, explain how a small change in a person's DNA can cause a genetic disorder.

3. How does studying genetic disorders such as PKU help biologists understand normal alleles?

4. What are some problems biologists face in studying human inheritance?

5. **Critical Thinking Predicting** If a woman with type O blood and a man with type AB blood have children, what are the children's possible genotypes?

iTEXT Assessment Use iText to review the important concepts in Section 14–1.

ALTERNATIVE ASSESSMENT

Drawing a Pedigree
Choose a family and a trait that you can trace through three generations. For example, you might choose dimples in a celebrity's family. Find out who in the family has had the trait and who has not. Then, draw a pedigree to represent the family history of the trait.

14–2 Human Chromosomes

A human diploid cell contains more than 6 billion nucleotide pairs of DNA—6 billion individual characters of the genetic code. To get an idea of how long a complete human DNA sequence actually is, consider the following: In this textbook, there are approximately 1500 letters on each page. If a complete human DNA sequence were to be written in the same-size type as this textbook, it would constitute a book more than 4 million pages long.

Despite its size, all of this information is neatly packed into the 46 chromosomes present in every diploid human cell. In its own way, each of these chromosomes is like a library containing hundreds or even thousands of books. Although biologists are many decades away from mastering the contents of those books, biology is now in the early stages of learning just how many books there are and what they deal with.

Human Genes and Chromosomes

Chromosomes 21 and 22 are the smallest human autosomes. Chromosome 22 contains approximately 43 million DNA bases. Chromosome 21 contains roughly 32 million bases. These chromosomes were the first two human chromosomes whose sequences were determined. Their structural features seem to be representative of other human chromosomes.

Chromosome 22 contains as many as 545 different genes, some of which are very important for health. Genetic disorders on chromosome 22 include an allele that causes a form of leukemia and another associated with neurofibromatosis, a tumor-causing disease of the nervous system. However, chromosome 22 also contains long stretches of repetitive DNA that do not code for proteins. These long stretches of repetitive DNA are unstable sites where rearrangements occur.

The structure of chromosome 21 is similar. It contains about 225 genes, including one associated with amyotrophic lateral sclerosis (ALS), also known as Lou Gehrig's disease. Chromosome 21 also has many regions with no genes at all.

As exploration of the larger human chromosomes continues, molecular biologists may gradually learn more about how the arrangements of genes on chromosomes affect gene expression and development.

As you may recall, genes located on the same chromosome are linked, meaning that they tend to be inherited together. This is also true for human genes, so each human chromosome represents a distinct linkage group. You also read earlier that linked genes may be separated by recombination during meiosis; this applies to human chromosomes, as well.

Guide for Reading

 Key Concepts
- Why are sex-linked disorders more common in males than in females?
- What is nondisjunction, and what problems does it cause?

Vocabulary
sex-linked gene
nondisjunction

Reading Strategy:
Outlining Before you read, use the headings of the section to make an outline about human chromosomes. As you read, write a sentence under each head to provide key information.

▲ **Figure 14–11** Lou Gehrig died at age 37 of ALS. ALS causes a progressive loss of muscle control due to the destruction of nerves in the brain and spinal cord.

X Chromosome

Duchenne muscular dystrophy

Melanoma

X-inactivation center

X-linked severe combined immunodeficiency (SCID)

Colorblindness

Hemophilia

Y Chromosome

Testis-determining factor

▲ **Figure 14–12** Genes on X and Y chromosomes are called sex-linked genes. **Interpreting Graphics** *Which chromosome carries more genes?*

Sex-Linked Genes

Is there a special pattern of inheritance for genes located on the X chromosome or the Y chromosome? The answer is yes. Because these chromosomes determine sex, genes located on them are said to be **sex-linked genes.** Many sex-linked genes are found on the X chromosome, as shown in **Figure 14–12.** More than 100 sex-linked genetic disorders have now been mapped to the X chromosome. The human Y chromosome is much smaller than the X chromosome and appears to contain only a few genes.

Colorblindness Three human genes associated with color vision are located on the X chromosome. In males, a defective version of any one of these genes produces colorblindness, an inability to distinguish certain colors. The most common form of this disorder, red-green colorblindness, is found in about 1 in 10 males in the United States. Among females, however, colorblindness is rare—only about 1 female in 100 has colorblindness. Why the difference?

🔑 **Males have just one X chromosome. Thus, all X-linked alleles are expressed in males, even if they are recessive.** In order for a recessive allele, such as the one for colorblindness, to be expressed in females, there must be two copies of the allele, one on each of the two X chromosomes. This means that the recessive phenotype of a sex-linked genetic disorder tends to be much more common among males than among females. In addition, because men pass their X chromosomes along to their daughters, sex-linked genes move from fathers to their daughters and may then show up in the sons of those daughters, as shown in **Figure 14–13.**

Figure 14–13 🔑 X-linked alleles are always expressed in males, because males have only one X chromosome. Males who receive the recessive X^C allele all have colorblindness. Females, however, will have colorblindness only if they receive two X^C alleles.

How is colorblindness transmitted?

Materials 2 plastic cups, 3 white beans, black marker, red bean

Procedure

1. On a sheet of paper, draw a data table with the column headings "Trial," "Colors," "Sex of Individual," and "Number of X-Linked Alleles." Draw 10 rows under the headings and fill in the numbers 1 through 10 under "Trial." Use the marker to label one cup "father" and the other "mother."
2. The white beans represent X chromosomes. Use the marker to mark a dot on 1 white bean to represent the X-linked allele for colorblindness. Place this bean, plus 1 unmarked white bean, into the cup labeled "mother."
3. Mark a black dot on 1 more white bean. Place this bean, plus 1 red bean, into the cup labeled "father." The red bean represents a Y chromosome.
4. Close your eyes and pick one bean from each cup to represent how each parent contributes a sex chromosome to a fertilized egg.
5. In your data table, record the color of each bean and the sex of an individual who would carry this pair of sex chromosomes. Also record how many X-linked alleles the individual has. Put the beans back in the cups they came from.
6. Determine whether the individual would have colorblindness.
7. Repeat steps 4 to 6 for a total of 10 pairs of beans.

Analyze and Conclude

1. **Using Models** Why did you select one bean from each cup?
2. **Drawing Conclusions** How do the sex chromosomes keep the numbers of males and females roughly equal?
3. **Calculating** Share your data with your classmates. Calculate the class totals for each table column. How many females were colorblind? How many males? How would you explain these results?

Hemophilia Hemophilia is another example of a sex-linked disorder. Two important genes carried on the X chromosome help control blood clotting. A recessive allele in either of these two genes may produce a disorder called hemophilia (hee-moh-FIL-ee-uh). In hemophilia, a protein necessary for normal blood clotting is missing. About 1 in 10,000 males is born with a form of hemophilia. People with hemophilia can bleed to death from minor cuts and may suffer internal bleeding from bumps or bruises. Fortunately, hemophilia can be treated by injections of normal clotting proteins.

Duchenne Muscular Dystrophy Duchenne muscular dystrophy (DIS-truh-fee) is a sex-linked disorder that results in the progressive weakening and loss of skeletal muscle. People with Duchenne muscular dystrophy rarely live past early adulthood. In the United States, one out of every 3000 males is born with Duchenne muscular dystrophy. Duchenne muscular dystrophy is caused by a defective version of the gene that codes for a muscle protein. Researchers in many laboratories are trying to find a way to treat or cure this disorder, possibly by inserting a normal allele into the muscle cells of Duchenne muscular dystrophy patients.

✓ **CHECKPOINT** *What causes Duchenne muscular dystrophy?*

▲ **Figure 14–14** This cat's fur color is controlled by a gene on the X chromosome. **Drawing Conclusions** *Is the cat shown a male or a female?*

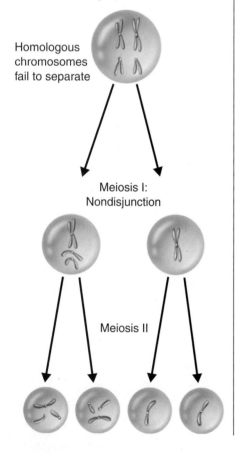

▼ **Figure 14–15** 👁Nondisjunction causes gametes to have abnormal numbers of chromosomes. The result of nondisjunction may be a chromosome disorder such as Down syndrome.

Homologous chromosomes fail to separate

Meiosis I: Nondisjunction

Meiosis II

X-Chromosome Inactivation

Females have two X chromosomes, but males have only one. If just one X chromosome is enough for cells in males, how does the cell "adjust" to the extra X chromosome in female cells? The answer was discovered by the British geneticist Mary Lyon. In female cells, one X chromosome is randomly switched off. That turned-off chromosome forms a dense region in the nucleus known as a Barr body. Barr bodies are generally not found in males because their single X chromosome is still active.

The same process happens in other mammals. In cats, for example, a gene that controls the color of coat spots is located on the X chromosome. One X chromosome may have an allele for orange spots and the other may have an allele for black spots. In cells in some parts of the body, one X chromosome is switched off. In other parts of the body, the other X chromosome is switched off. As a result, the cat's fur will have a mixture of orange and black spots, as shown in **Figure 14–14.** Male cats, which have just one X chromosome, can have spots of only one color. By the way, this is one way to tell the sex of a cat. If the cat's fur has three colors—white with orange and black spots, for example—you can almost be certain that it is female.

Chromosomal Disorders

Most of the time, the mechanisms that separate human chromosomes in meiosis work very well, but every now and then something goes wrong. The most common error in meiosis occurs when homologous chromosomes fail to separate. This is known as **nondisjunction,** which means "not coming apart." Nondisjunction is illustrated in **Figure 14–15.** 👁 **If nondisjunction occurs, abnormal numbers of chromosomes may find their way into gametes, and a disorder of chromosome numbers may result.**

Down Syndrome If two copies of an autosomal chromosome fail to separate during meiosis, an individual may be born with three copies of a chromosome. This is known as a trisomy, meaning "three bodies." The most common form of trisomy involves three copies of chromosome 21 and is called Down syndrome. **Figure 14–16** shows a karyotype of a person with Down syndrome. In the United States, approximately 1 baby in 800 is born with Down syndrome. Down syndrome produces mild to severe mental retardation. It is also characterized by an increased susceptibility to many diseases and a higher frequency of some birth defects.

Why should an extra copy of one chromosome cause so much trouble? That is still not clear, and it is one of the reasons scientists have worked so hard to learn the DNA sequence for chromosome 21. Now that researchers know all of the genes on the chromosome, they can begin experiments to find the exact genes that cause problems when present in three copies.

Figure 14–16 The karyotype on the right is from a person with Down syndrome. Down syndrome causes mental retardation and various physical problems. People with Down syndrome can, however, lead active, happy lives. **Observing** *What is different in this karyotype as compared with the karyotype on page 341?*

Sex Chromosome Disorders Disorders also occur among the sex chromosomes. Two of these abnormalities are Turner's syndrome and Klinefelter's syndrome.

In females, nondisjunction can lead to Turner's syndrome. A female with Turner's syndrome inherits only one X chromosome (genotype XO). Women with Turner's syndrome are sterile because their sex organs do not develop at puberty.

In males, nondisjunction causes Klinefelter's syndrome (genotype XXY). The extra X chromosome interferes with meiosis and usually prevents these individuals from reproducing. Cases of Klinefelter's syndrome have been found in which individuals were XXXY or XXXXY. There have been no reported instances of babies being born without an X chromosome, indicating that the X chromosome contains genes that are vital for normal development.

These sex chromosome abnormalities point out the role of the Y chromosome in sex determination. The Y chromosome contains a sex-determining region that is necessary to produce male sexual development, even in combination with several X chromosomes. However, if this region of the Y chromosome is absent, the embryo develops as a female.

14–2 Section Assessment

1. **Key Concept** Why are sex-linked disorders more common in males than in females?

2. **Key Concept** How does nondisjunction cause chromosome number disorders?

3. List at least two examples of human sex-linked disorders.

4. Describe two sex chromosome disorders.

5. **Critical Thinking Comparing and Contrasting** Distinguish between sex-linked disorders and sex chromosome disorders.

iTEXT Assessment Use iText to review the important concepts in Section 14–2.

Who Controls Your DNA?

April 16. Cpl. John C. Mayfield and Cpl. Joseph Vlacovsky were found guilty of disobeying a lawful order. The U.S. Department of Defense requires DNA samples for a database that could be used to identify soldiers' remains. The two Marines refused.

At their court martial, the two Marines argued that DNA samples could be examined for genes related to disease or even behavior and, therefore, the database was an invasion of privacy. As a result of the concerns raised by this case, the U.S. Department of Defense has changed its policies. It now destroys DNA samples upon request when an individual leaves military service. Do people have a right to control their own DNA samples?

The Viewpoints

DNA Information Is Not Private

As the court recognized, the U.S. Department of Defense had good reasons for requiring that DNA samples be taken and stored. Furthermore, DNA sequences are no more private and personal than fingerprints or photographs, which are taken by private and government agencies all the time. An employer has a right to take and keep such information. Individuals should have no reason to fear the abuse of such databases.

DNA Information Is Private and Personal

The use of DNA for personal identification by the military may be justified. An individual's genetic information, however, is a private matter. A recent study at Harvard and Stanford universities turned up more than 200 cases of discrimination because of genes individuals carried or were suspected of

carrying. Employers with DNA information might use it to discriminate against workers who carry genes they suspect might cause medical or behavioral problems. Individuals must have the right to control their own DNA and to withhold samples from such databases.

You Decide

1. **Defining the Issue** What are the major issues regarding DNA databases?
2. **Analyzing the Viewpoints** Are there any circumstances in which an employer might be justified in demanding DNA samples from its employees? Why might an employee wish to withhold such samples?
3. **Forming Your Opinion** Should the control of DNA databases be a matter of law, or should it be a matter to be negotiated between people, their employers, and insurance companies?
4. **Persuasive Speaking** Suppose you were a doctor working as a consultant to a health insurance company. The insurance company is trying to decide whether to test adults for cystic fibrosis alleles before agreeing to insure their families. What advice would you give to the company about this?

To find out about military uses of DNA, view the videotape "Coming Home: A Nation's Pledge."

14-3 Human Molecular Genetics

Watson and Crick took the first step in making genetics a molecular science when they discovered the double-helical structure of DNA in 1953. Today, the transformation they started is complete. The exploration of human genes is now a major scientific undertaking. Biologists can now read, analyze, and even change the molecular code of genes.

Human DNA Analysis

The roughly 6 billion base pairs you carry in your DNA are a bit like an encyclopedia with thousands of volumes. In principle, biologists would like to know everything the volumes contain, but as a practical matter there isn't enough time to read all of them. Nonetheless, if you've used an encyclopedia you've already learned one of the ways to handle huge amounts of information—you find a way to look up only what you need. In an encyclopedia, you can use an index or an alphabetical list of articles, but in the genome, biologists have to use a different technique. As you might suspect, biologists search the volumes of the human genome using DNA sequences.

Testing for Alleles If two prospective parents suspect they might be carrying recessive alleles for a genetic disorder such as cystic fibrosis (CF) or Tay-Sachs disease, how could they find out for sure? Because the Tay-Sachs and CF alleles have slightly different DNA sequences from their normal counterparts, a variety of genetic tests have been developed that can spot those differences. Sometimes these genetic tests use labeled DNA probes to detect specific sequences found in disease-causing alleles. Some tests use other techniques to detect alleles, including looking at changes in restriction enzyme cutting sites and differences in the lengths of normal and abnormal alleles.

Genetic tests are now available for hundreds of disorders, making it possible to determine whether prospective parents risk passing such alleles to their children. In an increasing number of such cases, DNA testing can pinpoint the exact genetic basis of a disorder, making it possible to develop more effective therapy and treatment for individuals affected by genetic disease.

Guide for Reading

 Key Concepts
- What is the goal of the Human Genome Project?
- What is gene therapy?

Vocabulary
DNA fingerprinting

**Reading Strategy:
Finding Main Ideas** As you read, find evidence to support the following statement: The influence of human molecular genetics on society is growing rapidly.

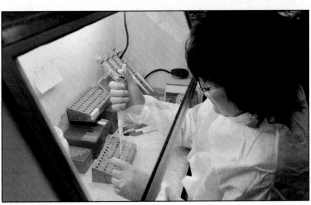

▶ **Figure 14–17** This laboratory worker is preparing a report on DNA evidence. The inset shows vials of DNA lying on a printout of a DNA analysis chart.

Figure 14–18 DNA fingerprinting can be used to determine whether blood, sperm, or other material left at a crime scene matches DNA from a suspect. **Interpreting Graphics** *In the DNA fingerprint below, does the DNA fingerprint from the evidence (E) match suspect 1 (S1) or suspect 2 (S2)?*

A Chromosomes contain large amounts of DNA called repeats that do not code for proteins. This DNA varies from person to person. Here, one sample has 12 repeats between genes A and B, while the second sample has 9 repeats.

B Restriction enzymes are used to cut the DNA into fragments containing genes and repeats. Note that the repeat fragments from these two samples are of different lengths.

C The DNA fragments are separated according to size using gel electrophoresis. The fragments containing repeats are then labeled using radioactive probes. This produces a series of bands—the DNA fingerprint.

DNA fingerprint

Gel electrophoresis

DNA Fingerprinting The great complexity of the human genome ensures that no individual is exactly like any other. Molecular biology has used this biological fact to add a powerful new tool called **DNA fingerprinting** to the identification of individuals. Unlike other forms of testing, DNA fingerprinting does not analyze the cell's most important genes, which are largely identical among most people. Rather, DNA fingerprinting analyzes sections of DNA that have little or no known function but vary widely from one individual to another.

Figure 14–18 shows how DNA fingerprinting works. A small sample of human DNA is cut with a restriction enzyme. The resulting fragments are separated by size using gel electrophoresis. Fragments containing these highly variable regions are then detected with a DNA probe, revealing a series of DNA bands of various sizes. If enough combinations of restriction enzymes and probes are used, a pattern of bands is produced that can be distinguished statistically from the pattern of any other individual in the world, except, of course, for an identical twin. DNA samples can be obtained from blood, sperm, and even hair strands with small pieces of tissue at the base.

DNA fingerprinting has been used in the United States since the late 1980s. The reliability of DNA evidence has helped convict criminals as well as overturn many convictions. The precision that molecular biology brings to the justice system is good news not only for those who are victims of crime but also for those who have been wrongly convicted.

The Human Genome Project

Advances in DNA sequencing technologies at the close of the twentieth century made it possible, for the first time, to sequence entire genomes. At first, biologists worked on relatively small genomes, such as those of viruses and bacteria. The DNA sequence of the common bacterium *Escherichia coli,* which was determined in 1996, contains "only" 4,639,221 base pairs, making it just about as long as this textbook if it were printed on paper in a readable typeface. The genomes of even the simplest eukaryotic organisms are much larger, and the human genome is more than a thousand times as large.

Despite the problem of size, in 1990, scientists in the United States and other countries began the Human Genome Project. ⚷ **The Human Genome Project is an attempt to sequence all human DNA.** Along the way, investigators completed the genomes of several other organisms, including yeast, a single-celled eukaryote, and *Drosophila melanogaster*—the fruit fly. In June 2000, scientists announced that the DNA sequence of the human genome was essentially complete.

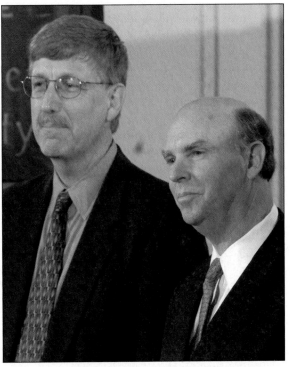

▲ **Figure 14–19** ⚷ The Human Genome Project is an attempt to sequence all human DNA. Dr. Francis Collins and Dr. Craig Venter, who headed the public and private portions of the project, jointly announced the essential completion of the human genome sequence.

Rapid Sequencing How did they do it? First, government scientists laid the groundwork by carefully sequencing widely separated regions of DNA on each chromosome. These "markers" made it possible to find the proper positions of other DNA sequences between them. Scientists at a private company then used a technique known as "shotgun" sequencing in which randomly generated fragments of DNA were automatically sequenced without any thought as to where they might fit into the entire sequence. High-speed computers then found overlapping regions between the fragments and positioned them relative to known markers to assemble the final sequence.

When the Human Genome Project was completed in June 2000, investigators began to count the genes in the sequence. First estimates that it might contain as few as 31,000 genes surprised many scientists. The fruit fly *Drosophila* contains approximately 14,000 genes, and the tiny worm *Caenorhabditis elegans* contains roughly 20,000. Many researchers had expected to find more, and how so few genes manage to produce an organism as complex as a human being now becomes a central question for biologists. In nearly every respect, the interesting part of exploring the human genome is just beginning.

Searching for Genes Molecular biologists continue to hunt for genes as they search through the genome's 24 volumes of information (22 autosomal chromosomes and the 2 sex chromosomes). They can locate genes in several ways. One of these ways is to find a so-called open reading frame. An open reading frame is a series of DNA bases that can produce part of a working mRNA sequence. The mRNA coding regions of most genes are interrupted by introns. Therefore, investigators also have to find the special DNA sequences that mark the boundaries between introns and exons in order to follow the gene through its complete length. When the process is complete, researchers can often pinpoint the gene's promoter, as well as the "start" and "stop" sites for transcription, as shown in **Figure 14–20**.

Research groups around the world are now hard at work analyzing the huge amount of information in the DNA sequence, looking for genes that may provide useful clues to some of the basic properties of life. In addition to its scientific significance, understanding the structure and control of key genes may have commercial value. Biotechnology companies are rushing to find genetic information that may be useful in developing new drugs and treatments for diseases.

A Breakthrough for Everyone One of the most remarkable things about genome research is the open availability of nearly all its data. From its very beginning, data from publicly supported research on the human genome have been posted

▼ **Figure 14–20** Researchers exploring the human genome can use DNA sequences to locate many genes. Promoters are sequences in which RNA polymerase can bind to DNA. On either side of a typical gene are other DNA sequences that may serve as signals for RNA polymerase to start and stop transcription, as shown below.
Interpreting Graphics *In which direction would RNA polymerase move in transcribing the gene shown below?*

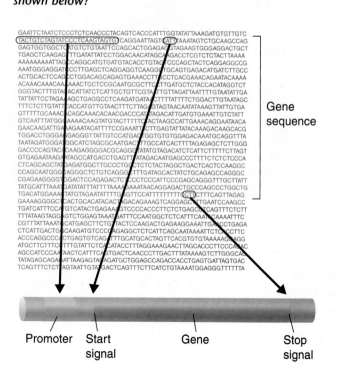

Promoter   Start signal   Gene   Stop signal

Careers in Biology

Geneticist

Job Description: work in the laboratories of universities or large companies doing molecular-level research, or work in a clinic collecting family histories and counseling parents with children who have a genetic disorder or who are at risk for contracting a genetic disorder

Education: a master's or doctor's degree in genetics or related field; some medical research positions require a medical degree, as well

Skills: good verbal and written communication skills, analytical, detail-oriented, self-motivated, organized, curious, and able to meet deadlines

Highlights: You have the opportunity to discover new genes or patterns of heredity that can help treat or cure genetic disorders or to make sure that these types of discoveries are put into practice to improve public health.

Dr. Charmaine Royal focuses on "looking at issues in genetic research related to African Americans." Dr. Royal says her "desire to help people and to relieve suffering in general are what drive me to do what I do. My desire is for all of society to benefit from genetic research."

 Take It to the NET

For more information, visit the Prentice Hall Web site: **www.phschool.com**

on the Internet on a daily basis. Yes, that means that if you have access to the Internet, you can read the latest genome data and, if you wish, analyze it. The Web site for this textbook provides a direct link to the Human Genome Project.

Gene Therapy

One of the most obvious uses of information about the human genome would be to cure genetic disorders by gene therapy. Gene therapy is the process of changing the gene that causes a genetic disorder. **In gene therapy, an absent or faulty gene is replaced by a normal, working gene.** This way, the body can make the correct protein or enzyme it needs, which eliminates the cause of the disorder.

The first authorized attempt to cure a human genetic disorder by gene transfer occurred in 1990. Then, in 1999, a young French girl was apparently cured of an inherited immune disorder when cells from her bone marrow were removed, modified in the laboratory, and then placed back in her body.

Figure 14–21 shows one of the ways in which researchers have attempted to practice gene therapy. Viruses are often used because of their ability to enter a cell's DNA. The virus particles are modified so that they cannot cause disease. Then, a DNA fragment containing a replacement gene is spliced to viral DNA. The patient is then infected with the modified virus particles, which should carry the gene into cells to correct genetic defects.

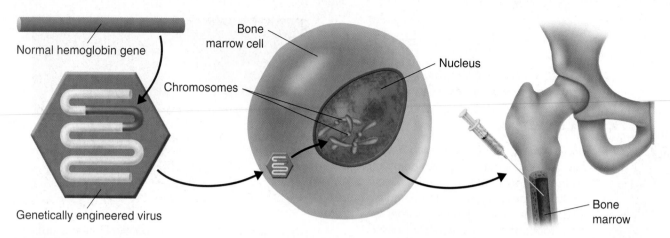

Normal hemoglobin gene

Bone marrow cell

Nucleus

Chromosomes

Genetically engineered virus

Bone marrow

▲ **Figure 14–21** Gene therapy is the process of changing the genes that cause a genetic disorder. This drawing shows how a virus can be used to deliver the gene for normal hemoglobin into a person's bone marrow.

Unfortunately, gene therapy experiments have not always been successful. Attempts to treat cystic fibrosis by spraying genetically engineered viruses into the breathing passages have not produced a lasting cure. For all the promise it holds, in most cases gene therapy remains a high-risk, experimental procedure.

Ethical Issues in Human Genetics

It would be marvelous to be able to cure hemophilia or other genetic diseases. But if human cells can be manipulated to cure disease, should biologists try to engineer taller people or change their eye color, hair texture, sex, blood group, or appearance? What will happen to the human species if we gain the opportunity to design our bodies? What will be the consequences if biologists develop the ability to clone human beings by making identical copies of their cells? These are questions with which science will rapidly force society to come to grips.

The goal of biology is to gain a better understanding of the nature of life. The more biologists understand life, the more they will be able to manipulate it. As biologists' power over nature increases, society will have to learn to use wisely the tools that science has given it. Our society will have to develop a thoughtful and ethical consensus of what should and should not be done with the human genome. Scientists alone should not be expected to assume all of the responsibility for these decisions. Society in its entirety should have to deal with these questions.

14–3 Section Assessment

1. **Key Concept** What is the Human Genome Project?

2. **Key Concept** Describe how gene therapy works.

3. Name two common uses for DNA testing.

4. Describe how molecular biologists identify genes in sequences of DNA.

5. **Critical Thinking Making Judgments** Do you think it should be legal for people to use genetic engineering to affect their children's characteristics? Give reasons for your answer.

iTEXT **Assessment** Use iText to review the important concepts in Section 14–3.

Take It to the NET

Read about genetic counseling. Prepare questions you might ask a genetic counselor if you were seeking advice on getting tested for an inherited disease. Use the links provided in the Biology area at the Prentice Hall Web site for help in completing this activity: **www.phschool.com**

Modeling DNA Probes

A DNA probe is a short, single-stranded DNA molecule bound to a fluorescent dye that makes the probe visible. Because the probe is single stranded, it can bind to other DNA that has a complementary sequence. To find a specific DNA sequence, scientists mix a probe with an unknown DNA sample. The probe will only bind to a DNA sample that has a complementary sequence, showing where the desired sequence is. In this lab, you will model how scientists use DNA probes.

Problem How do DNA probes help to identify individuals?

Materials

- graph paper
- scissors
- colored pencil or marker

Skills Using Models, Classifying

Procedure

Individual 1	ATCTCGAGACTGATAGGCTCTAAGCTCGAG
Individual 2	ATTGGCCACTCGAGACGTTGGCCAAGTCCG
Individual 3	ATGACCATGGCCAGGCTCGAGCTGATGACG
Individual 4	ATATGGCCATTGCTCGAGTGGCCAGATCCG
Individual 5	ACTCGAGGTCCCTCGAGTGTAGGCTCATCG

1. DNA sequences from five individuals are shown. Copy each individual's number and DNA sequence onto graph paper, putting one letter from the DNA sequence into each square. Skip five lines between each sequence and the next one.

2. Copy the following sequence for a six-base DNA probe onto graph paper, as you did the DNA sequences in step 1: T C C G A G

3. Fill in the square that follows the probe sequence with a colored pencil or marker to represent the fluorescent dye bound to the probe.

4. Cut out the strip of graph paper that represents the probe and its attached fluorescent dye.

5. Move the probe along each individual's DNA sequence. As you do so, look for parts of the DNA sequences that are complementary to the probe's sequence.

6. Circle the part of any individual's DNA sequence that is complementary to the sequence of the DNA probe.

7. Record the numbers of the individuals who were identified by the DNA probe.

8. Choose one of the five individuals, and construct a new DNA probe that will identify only that individual. Write out the DNA sequence of this new probe as you did in step 2. Your new probe does not have to be six bases long.

9. Cut out your new probe and exchange it for one written by a classmate.

10. Repeat steps 5 and 6 with the probe you received to identify the individual that your classmate selected.

Analyze and Conclude

1. **Observing** What DNA sequence is complementary to the sequence of the probe shown in step 2?

2. **Classifying** Which individual(s) was (were) identified by the DNA probe given in step 2?

3. **Using Models** Is it possible for the same DNA probe to identify more than one individual? Explain your answer.

4. **Drawing Conclusions** Would DNA probes with longer or shorter sequences be more likely to identify only one individual? Explain your answer.

Go Further

Using Models Restriction enzymes cut DNA at specific base sequences. Make a model of a DNA probe and a restriction enzyme. Use your models to show how DNA probes and restriction enzymes could be used together to create DNA fingerprints for the five individuals shown.

14–1 Human Heredity
🔑 **Key Concepts**

- All egg cells carry a single X chromosome (23X). However, half of all sperm cells carry an X chromosome (23X), and half carry a Y chromosome (23Y). This ensures that just about half of the zygotes will be 46XX (female), and half will be 46XY (male).

- In both cystic fibrosis and sickle cell disease, a small change in the DNA of a single gene affects the structure of a protein, causing a serious genetic disorder.

Vocabulary
karyotype, p. 341
sex chromosome, p. 341
autosome, p. 341
pedigree, p. 342
polygenic, p. 343

14–2 Human Chromosomes
🔑 **Key Concepts**

- Males have just one X chromosome. Thus, all X-linked alleles are expressed in males, even if they are recessive.

- Nondisjunction causes gametes to have abnormal numbers of chromosomes, which in turn causes a chromosome number disorder.

Vocabulary
sex-linked gene, p. 350
nondisjunction, p. 352

14–3 Human Molecular Genetics
🔑 **Key Concepts**

- The Human Genome Project is an attempt to sequence all human DNA.

- In gene therapy, an absent or faulty gene is replaced by a normal, working gene.

Vocabulary
DNA fingerprinting, p. 357

Thinking Visually

Using the information in this chapter, complete the following concept map about chromosome disorders:

Chapter 14

Part A

Multiple Choice

For each statement or question, select the number of the word or expression that, of those given, best completes the statement or answers the question.

1 A normal human zygote contains a full set of
(1) 23 chromosomes, one half from each parent
(2) 46 chromosomes, one half from each parent
(3) chromosomes from the father, only
(4) chromosomes from the mother, only

2 A chart that traces the inheritance of a trait in a family is called a(an)
(1) pedigree (3) karyotype
(2) genome (4) autosome

3 Traits that are caused by the interaction of many genes are said to be
(1) polyploid (3) linked
(2) polygenic (4) autosomal

4 An example of a trait that is determined by multiple alleles is
(1) Huntington's disease
(2) Down syndrome
(3) ABO blood groups
(4) hemophilia

5 Hemophilia is a genetic disorder that is
(1) sex-linked
(2) sex-influenced
(3) fairly common
(4) more common in women than in men

6 Which parental pair could produce females with colorblindness?
(1) homozygous normal-vision mother, father with colorblindness
(2) mother with colorblindness, normal-vision father
(3) heterozygous normal-vision mother, normal-vision father
(4) heterozygous normal-vision mother, father with colorblindness

7 The process of attempting to cure genetic disorders by placing copies of healthy genes into cells that lack them is known as
(1) gene therapy
(2) DNA fingerprinting
(3) rapid sequencing
(4) the Human Genome Project

8 Which can be observed in a person's karyotype?
(1) colorblindness and trisomy 21
(2) Turner's syndrome and cystic fibrosis
(3) colorblindness and cystic fibrosis
(4) Turner's syndrome and trisomy 21

9 A woman is heterozygous for type A blood. A man has AB blood. What is the probability that the couple's child will have type B blood?
(1) 0% (3) 50%
(2) 25% (4) 100%

10 According to the graph below, the frequency of Down syndrome
(1) increases with increase in maternal age
(2) is 15 times more in the 45+ age group than it is in the 30 to 34 age group
(3) is greater in the 25–29 age group than in the 40 to 44 age group
(4) levels off at 2 per 1000 live births in the 15 to 19 age group

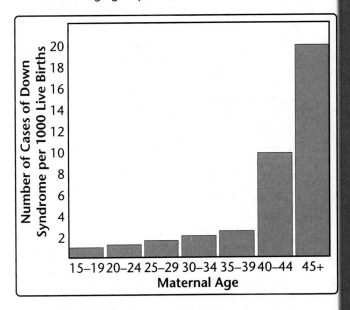

Test-Taking Tip When interpreting a pedigree, first read through all the generations given. Then, go back and assign (either mentally or on scratch paper) a possible genotype to each person represented in the pedigree. Use Punnett squares to test your assigned genotypes to ensure that they could produce each successive generation's phenotypes.

Parts B and C

Multiple Choice and Extended Response

For those questions that ask you to select a response, choose the one that best completes the statement or answers the question. For all others follow the directions given.

11 Describe how a karyotype is prepared.

Base your answers to questions 12 through 14 on the pedigree below and on your knowledge of biology.

A student traced a widow's peak hairline in her family. She drew the following pedigree.

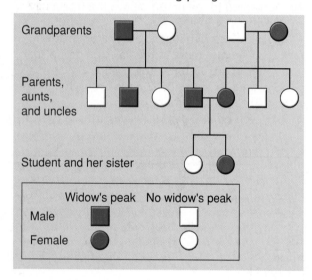

12 Which pattern of inheritance is consistent with the pedigree?
(1) complete dominance
(2) sex-linked
(3) codominance
(4) multiple alleles

13 What are the probable genotypes of the student's parents?
(1) mother is Ww; father is ww
(2) mother is ww; father is Ww
(3) mother is WW; father is WW
(4) mother is Ww; father is Ww

14 The student does not have a widow's peak hairline, but her sister does. What are the girls' possible genotypes?
(1) student is ww; sister is Ww
(2) student is Ww; sister is ww
(3) student is WW; sister is WW
(4) student is ww; sister is ww

Base your answers to questions 15 and 16 on the passage below and on your knowledge of biology.

Knowing the DNA sequence of a gene provides researchers with information about the structure of the protein encoded by that gene. For example, when the cystic fibrosis (CF) gene was identified, the gene's DNA sequence suggested that the CF protein might be a channel protein embedded in the cell membrane. The gene's sequence also hinted to researchers that the protein might be specifically involved with the passage of salt through the cell membrane. This fit with what scientists already knew about cystic fibrosis. It made sense that mucus would accumulate in the lungs and digestive organs of individuals with CF as a result of problems with salt and water transport through a malformed channel protein.

15 How does knowing a gene's sequence allow researchers to determine the protein that might be the problem in a genetic disease such as CF?

16 Individuals with only one defective gene for CF do not have noticeable problems with the passage of salt across their cell membranes. Only individuals with two defective genes have CF. Explain how it is possible that a child who has a parent with CF would not necessarily inherit cystic fibrosis.

17 Describe the process of gel electrophoresis as it is involved in DNA fingerprinting.

18 Two prospective parents learn that they each carry one allele for Tay-Sachs disease.
• Why does neither of them suffer from Tay-Sachs disease?
• If they have children, what are the chances they will have a baby with Tay-Sachs disease?
• What are the chances that one of their healthy children will carry the Tay-Sachs allele?

19 Explain why genetic disorders caused by dominant alleles are less common than genetic disorders caused by recessive alleles.

20 *Plasmodium falciparum,* a protist, causes a fatal form of malaria. Propose a hypothesis to explain why *P. falciparum* can live in red blood cells that contain normal hemoglobin but not in red blood cells that contain the sickle cell allele.

Base your answers to questions 21 through 24 on the reading passage below and on your knowledge of biology.

Gene Therapy Restores Vision in Dogs Which Have Rare Disease

Using gene therapy, scientists have restored vision in dogs with a version of a rare disease that blinds human infants. The dogs had a version of Leber congenital amaurosis, an untreatable condition that causes near-total blindness in infancy. About 10,000 Americans have it, and about 1000 of them have the particular genetic defect that was corrected in the dogs.

An associate professor of ophthalmology at the University of Pennsylvania reports their experiments on three dogs in the May 2001 issue of the journal *Nature Genetics.* The dogs were blind because they lacked a particular gene. Without it, their eyes could not make a pigment necessary to perceive light. Researchers used eye surgery to deliver a copy of the gene, which was carried by a virus that inserted the gene into the DNA of the eye cells. They treated one eye in each animal and used the other eye for comparison.

Four months after treatment, several tests showed that the animals had regained at least some sight in the treated eye. Putting the dogs in a room cluttered with furniture, the dogs were much better at avoiding objects on the same side of their body as the treated eye. The treatment's effects have lasted nine months so far, the researcher reported. If this same gene therapy technique works for human Leber patients, it might pave the way for treating a variety of hereditary vision diseases that strike the retina, known collectively as retinitis pigmentosa, which affects 100,000 to 200,000 Americans.

(Source: *Times Union,* Albany 4/28/01 AP Malcom Ritter)

21 How did scientists actually deliver the missing gene to the eye cells of dogs?

22 How did scientists demonstrate that gene therapy, and not some other factor, improved the dogs' ability to see?

23 Describe three things scientists should do before performing this procedure on people with retinitis pigmentosa to make sure there will be few problems and that the results will last. Support your answer with an explanation.

24 It is hoped that eventually people with retinitis pigmentosa will be able to undergo gene therapy similar to that done with dogs. If the gene is successfully inserted and their vision is corrected, will the new gene be passed along to the children of these individuals? Support your answer with an explanation.

25 Explain how a family pedigree can be helpful in determining the probability of having a child with a genetic disorder.

26 What impact will the Human Genome Project have on society? State one reason the project is valuable. Support your answer with an explanation.

27 What steps can parents take to determine the likelihood of passing certain genes on to their offspring? Cite specific examples.

28 Describe two examples of how an understanding of genetics is making new medical treatments or diagnoses possible.

29 What are the possible genotypes of the parents of a male child with colorblindness?

30 Explain the relationship between meiosis and Down syndrome, Turner's syndrome, and Klinefelter's syndrome. (*Hint:* You might wish to refer to Chapter 11.)

Take It to the NET

What do we know about the human genome? Visit the Prentice Hall Web site at **www.phschool.com** to explore the current results of the Human Genome Project. Then, answer the following questions:

- How many nucleotide bases are in the human genome sequence?

- What proportion of nucleotides are exactly the same in all people?

- How much of the human genome actually codes for proteins?

- What is the ratio of mutations in males and females? What is one explanation for this difference?

- What is "junk DNA"? What important clues does it hold?

Evolution

► Named after the color of their feet, the blue-footed boobies belong to the most common of the three species of boobies found on the Galápagos Islands. Blue-footed boobies are known for their hunting, which involves diving headfirst into the ocean.

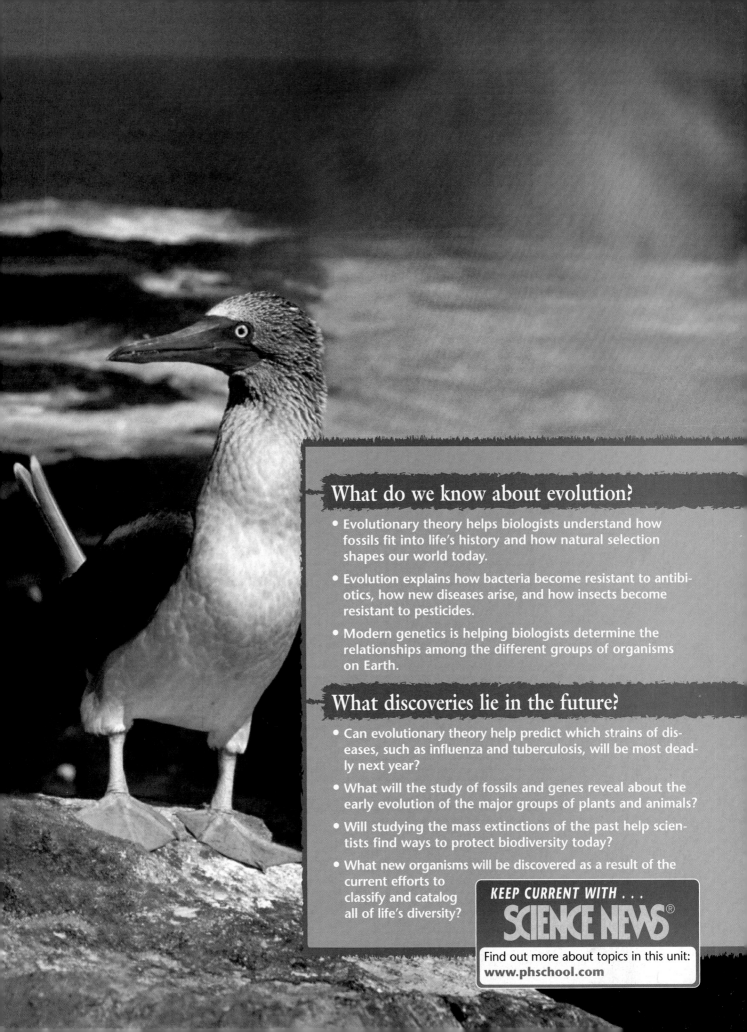

What do we know about evolution?

- Evolutionary theory helps biologists understand how fossils fit into life's history and how natural selection shapes our world today.

- Evolution explains how bacteria become resistant to antibiotics, how new diseases arise, and how insects become resistant to pesticides.

- Modern genetics is helping biologists determine the relationships among the different groups of organisms on Earth.

What discoveries lie in the future?

- Can evolutionary theory help predict which strains of diseases, such as influenza and tuberculosis, will be most deadly next year?

- What will the study of fossils and genes reveal about the early evolution of the major groups of plants and animals?

- Will studying the mass extinctions of the past help scientists find ways to protect biodiversity today?

- What new organisms will be discovered as a result of the current efforts to classify and catalog all of life's diversity?

KEEP CURRENT WITH . . .

SCIENCE NEWS®

Find out more about topics in this unit:
www.phschool.com

15 Darwin's Theory of Evolution

If you look closely at the top of what appears to be a leaf in the center of this photograph, you can see a head. This walking-leaf insect is a superb example of camouflage. Charles Darwin developed an explanation for how such camouflage may have developed.

Inquiry Activity

Do lima beans show variation?

Procedure

1. Count out 10 lima beans and measure the length of each in millimeters. Record your results in a data table.

2. Combine your data with the data of two other classmates. Place all the data on one graph. Plot the length on the *x*-axis and the number of beans of each length on the *y*-axis.

Think About It

1. **Analyzing Data** Calculate the average length of the beans. Are most lima beans close to the average length?

2. **Predicting** How do you think a graph of data from the entire class would be different from your graph of data?

15–1 The Puzzle of Life's Diversity

Nature presents scientists with a puzzle. Humans share the Earth with millions of other kinds of organisms of every imaginable shape, size, and habitat. This variety of living things is called biological diversity. How did all these different organisms arise? How are they related? These questions make up the puzzle of life's diversity.

What scientific explanation can account for the diversity of life? The answer is a collection of scientific facts, observations, and hypotheses known as evolutionary theory. **Evolution,** or change over time, is the process by which modern organisms have descended from ancient organisms. A **theory** is a well-supported testable explanation of phenomena that have occurred in the natural world.

Voyage of the *Beagle*

The individual who contributed more to our understanding of evolution than anyone was Charles Darwin. Darwin was born in England on February 12, 1809—the same day as Abraham Lincoln. Shortly after completing his college studies, Darwin joined the crew of the H.M.S. *Beagle*. In 1831, he set sail from England for a voyage around the world. His route is shown in **Figure 15–1.** Although no one knew it at the time, this was to be one of the most important voyages in the history of science.

 During his travels, Darwin made numerous observations and collected evidence that led him to propose a revolutionary hypothesis about the way life changes over time. That hypothesis, now supported by a huge body of evidence, has become the theory of evolution.

Guide for Reading

Key Concepts
- What was Charles Darwin's contribution to science?
- What pattern did Darwin observe among organisms of the Galápagos Islands?

Vocabulary
evolution • theory
fossil

**Reading Strategy:
Using Visuals** Before you read, examine **Figure 15–1.** Find the British Isles, where Darwin's journey began, then trace his route. Write a statement describing his travels.

▼ **Figure 15–1** On a five-year voyage on the *Beagle,* Charles Darwin visited several continents and many remote islands. Darwin's observations led to a revolutionary theory about the way life changes over time.

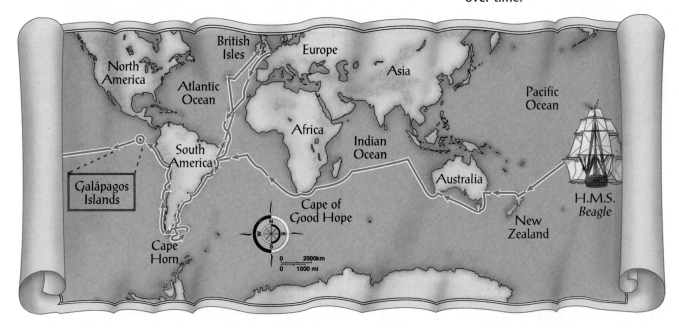

Wherever the ship anchored, Darwin went ashore to collect plant and animal specimens that he added to an ever-growing collection. At sea, between bouts of seasickness, he studied his specimens, read the latest scientific books, and filled many notebooks with his observations and thoughts. Darwin was well educated and had a strong interest in natural history. His curiosity and analytical nature were ultimately the keys to his success as a scientist. During his travels, Darwin came to view every new finding as a piece in an extraordinary puzzle: a scientific explanation for the diversity of life on this planet.

Darwin's Observations

Darwin knew a great deal about the plants and animals of his native country. But he saw far more diversity during his travels. For example, during a single day in a Brazilian forest, Darwin collected 68 different beetle species—despite the fact that he was not even searching for beetles! He began to realize that an enormous number of species inhabit the Earth.

Patterns of Diversity Darwin was intrigued by the fact that so many plants and animals seemed remarkably well suited to whatever environment they inhabited. He was impressed by the many ways in which organisms survived and produced offspring. He wondered if there was some process that led to such a variety of ways of reproducing.

Darwin was also puzzled by where different species lived—and did not live. He visited Argentina and Australia, for example, which had similar grassland ecosystems. Yet, those grasslands were inhabited by very different animals. Also, neither Argentina nor Australia was home to the sorts of animals that lived in European grasslands. For Darwin, these patterns posed challenging questions. Why were there no rabbits in Australia, despite the presence of habitats that seemed perfect for them? Similarly, why were there no kangaroos in England?

Figure 15–2 Many of the fossils that Darwin discovered resembled living organisms but were not identical to them. The glyptodon, an extinct animal known only from fossil remains, is an ancient relative of the armadillo of South America. **Comparing and Contrasting** *What are some similarities and differences between these two types of animals?*

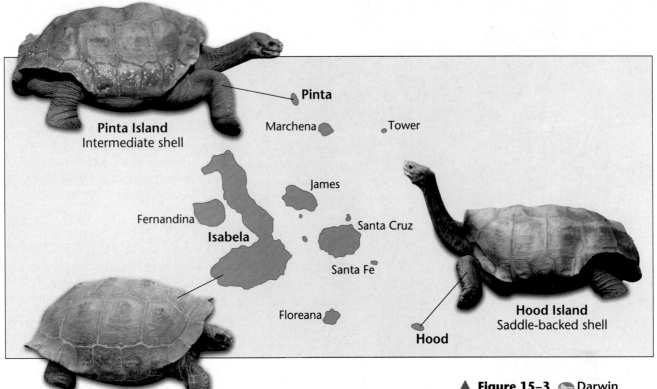

Pinta Island
Intermediate shell

Pinta

Marchena

Tower

James

Fernandina

Isabela

Santa Cruz

Santa Fe

Floreana

Hood

Hood Island
Saddle-backed shell

Isabela Island
Dome-shaped shell

▲ **Figure 15–3** Darwin observed that the characteristics of many animals and plants varied noticeably among the different Galápagos Islands. Among the tortoises, the shape of the shell corresponds to different habitats. The Hood Island tortoise (right) has a long neck and a shell that is curved and open around the neck and legs, allowing the tortoise to reach the sparse vegetation on Hood Island. The tortoise from Isabela Island (lower left) has a dome-shaped shell and a shorter neck. Vegetation on this island is more abundant and closer to the ground. The tortoise from Pinta Island has a shell that is intermediate between these two forms.

Living Organisms and Fossils Darwin soon realized that living animals represented just part of the puzzle posed by the natural world. In many places during his voyage, Darwin collected the preserved remains of ancient organisms, called **fossils.** Some of those fossils resembled organisms that were still alive, as shown in **Figure 15–2.** Others looked completely unlike any creature he had ever seen. As Darwin studied fossils, new questions arose. Why had so many of these species disappeared? How were they related to living species?

The Galápagos Islands Of all the *Beagle*'s ports of call, the one that influenced Darwin the most was a group of small islands located 1000 km west of South America. These are the Galápagos Islands. Darwin noted that although they were close together, the islands had very different climates. The smallest, lowest islands were hot, dry, and nearly barren. Hood Island, for example, had sparse vegetation. The higher islands had greater rainfall and a different assortment of plants and animals. Isabela Island had rich vegetation that tortoises could easily reach.

Darwin was fascinated in particular by the land tortoises and marine iguanas that lived in the Galápagos. He learned from the vice-governor of the islands that the giant tortoises varied in predictable ways from one island to another, as shown in **Figure 15–3.** The shape of a tortoise's shell could be used to identify which island a particular tortoise inhabited. Darwin later admitted in his notes that he "did not for some time pay sufficient attention to this statement."

✓ CHECKPOINT How did the fossils Darwin observed compare with the living organisms he studied?

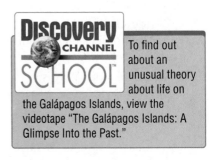

To find out about an unusual theory about life on the Galápagos Islands, view the videotape "The Galápagos Islands: A Glimpse Into the Past."

Darwin's Theory of Evolution **371**

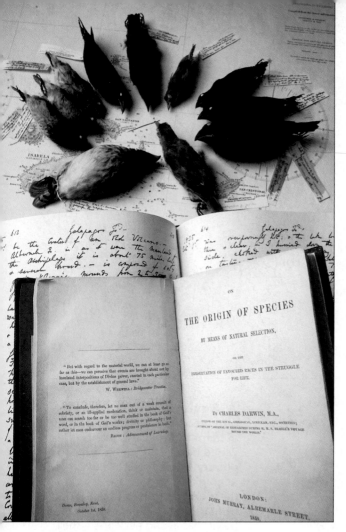

▲ **Figure 15–4** Darwin's notebooks and some of the finch specimens he collected have been preserved for today's scientists to study. *Inferring* *What might modern scientists learn from examining evidence collected by earlier investigators?*

Darwin also saw several types of small, ordinary-looking brown birds hopping around, looking for seeds. As an eager naturalist, he collected several specimens, as shown in **Figure 15–4.** However, he did not find them particularly unusual or important. As Darwin examined the birds, he noted that they had differently shaped beaks. He thought that some of the birds were wrens, some were warblers, and some were blackbirds. But he came to no other conclusions—at first.

The Journey Home

While heading home, Darwin spent a great deal of time thinking about his findings. Examining different mockingbirds from the Galápagos, Darwin noticed that individual birds collected from the island of Floreana looked different from those collected on James Island. They also looked different from individuals collected on other islands. Darwin also remembered what the vice-governor had told him about the tortoises. Although Darwin did not immediately understand the reason for these patterns, he had stumbled across an important finding. 🔑 **Darwin observed that the characteristics of many animals and plants varied noticeably among the different islands of the Galápagos.** After returning to England, Darwin began to wonder if animals living on different islands had once been members of the same species. According to this hypothesis, these separate species would have evolved from an original South American ancestor species after becoming isolated from one another. Was this possible? If so, it would turn people's view of the natural world upside down.

15–1 Section Assessment

1. 🔑 **Key Concept** What did Darwin's travels reveal to him about the number and variety of living species?

2. 🔑 **Key Concept** How did tortoises and birds differ among the islands of the Galápagos?

3. What is evolution? Why is evolution referred to as a theory?

4. What is a fossil?

5. **Critical Thinking Inferring** Darwin found fossils of many organisms that were different from any living species. How would this finding have affected his understanding of life's diversity?

*i***TEXT** **Assessment** Use iText to review the important concepts in Section 15–1.

Take It to the NET

Read the preface to Charles Darwin's book, *The Voyage of the Beagle.* Then, write a letter to Captain Fitz Roy, as Darwin might have written it, expressing the wish to volunteer for the voyage. Use the links provided in the Biology area at the Prentice Hall Web site for help in completing this activity: **www.phschool.com**

15–2 Ideas That Shaped Darwin's Thinking

If Darwin had lived a century earlier, he might have done little more than think about the questions raised during his travels. But Darwin's voyage came during one of the most exciting periods in the history of Western science. Explorers were traversing the globe, and great thinkers were beginning to challenge established views about the natural world. Darwin was powerfully influenced by the work of these scientists, especially those who were studying the history of Earth. In turn, he himself greatly changed the thinking of many scientists and nonscientists. Some people, however, found Darwin's ideas too shocking to accept. To understand how radical Darwin's thoughts appeared, you must understand a few things about the world in which he lived.

Most Europeans in Darwin's day believed that the Earth and all its forms of life had been created only a few thousand years ago. Since that original creation, they concluded, neither the planet nor its living species had changed. A robin, for example, has always looked and behaved as robins had in the past. Rocks and major geological features were thought to have been produced suddenly by catastrophic events that humans rarely, if ever, witnessed.

By the time Darwin set sail, numerous discoveries had turned up important pieces of evidence. A rich fossil record, including the example in **Figure 15–5**, was challenging that traditional view of life. In light of such evidence, some scientists even adjusted their beliefs to include not one but several periods of creation. Each of these periods, they contended, was preceded by a catastrophic event that killed off many forms of life. At first, Darwin accepted these beliefs. But he began to realize that much of what he had observed did not fit neatly into this view of unchanging life. Slowly, after studying many scientific theories of his time, Darwin began to change his thinking dramatically.

Guide for Reading

🔑 **Key Concepts**
- How did Hutton and Lyell describe geological change?
- According to Lamarck, how did species evolve?
- What was Malthus's theory of population growth?

Reading Strategy: Finding Main Ideas
As you read about the individuals who influenced Darwin's thinking, write a sentence briefly describing what Darwin learned from each one.

▶ **Figure 15–5** This engraving, made around 1850, shows the fossil remains of a giant sloth from South America. During the 1800s, explorers were finding the remains of numerous animal types that had no living representatives. **Inferring** *What did such fossil evidence indicate about life in the past?*

An Ancient, Changing Earth

During the eighteenth and nineteenth centuries, scientists examined Earth in great detail. They gathered information suggesting that Earth was very old and had changed slowly over time. Two scientists who formed important theories based on this evidence were James Hutton and Charles Lyell. Hutton and Lyell helped scientists recognize that Earth is many millions of years old, and the processes that changed Earth in the past are the same processes that operate in the present.

▲ **Figure 15–6** These huge rocks, which are composed of sandstone, show distinct layers that were laid down over millions of years. Hutton and Lyell cited geological features such as these rocks as evidence that Earth is many millions of years old. Geological processes acting millions of years ago continue to shape Earth in the present.

Hutton's Theory of Geological Change

In 1795, the geologist James Hutton published a detailed theory about the geological forces that have shaped Earth. He proposed that layers of rock, such as those in **Figure 15–6,** form very slowly. Also, some rocks are moved up by forces beneath Earth's surface. Others are buried, and still others are pushed up from the sea floor to form mountain ranges. The resulting rocks, mountains, and valleys are then shaped by a variety of natural forces—including rain, heat, and cold temperatures. Most of these geological processes operate extremely slowly, often over millions of years. Hutton, therefore, proposed that Earth had to be much more than a few thousand years old.

Biology and History

Origins of Evolutionary Thought

The groundwork for the modern theory of evolution was laid during the 1700s and 1800s. Charles Darwin developed the central idea of evolution by natural selection, but others before and during his time also built essential parts of the theory.

Thomas Malthus
In his *Essay on the Principle of Population,* Malthus predicts that the human population will grow faster than the space and food supplies needed to sustain it.

Boston Tea Party
1773

The United States Constitution is signed.
1787

1798

1750

1800

1785

James Hutton
Hutton proposes that Earth is shaped by geological forces that took place over extremely long periods of time. He estimates Earth to be millions—not thousands—of years old.

1809

Jean-Baptiste Lamarck
Lamarck publishes his theory of the inheritance of acquired traits. The theory is flawed, but he is one of the first to propose a mechanism explaining how organisms change over time.

Lyell's *Principles of Geology* Just before the *Beagle* set sail, Darwin had been given the first volume of geologist Charles Lyell's book, *Principles of Geology*. Lyell stressed that scientists must explain past events in terms of processes that they can actually observe, since processes that shaped the Earth millions of years earlier continue in the present. Volcanoes release hot lava and gases now, just as they did on an ancient Earth. Erosion continues to carve out canyons, just as it did in the past.

Lyell's work explained how awesome geological features could be built up or torn down over long periods of time. Lyell helped Darwin appreciate the significance of geological phenomena that he had observed. Darwin had witnessed a spectacular volcanic eruption. Darwin wrote about an earthquake that had lifted a stretch of rocky shoreline—with mussels and other animals attached to it—more than 3 meters above its previous position. He noted the fossils of marine animals displaced many feet above sea level. Darwin then understood how geological processes could have raised these rocks from the sea floor to a mountaintop.

This understanding of geology influenced Darwin in two ways. First, Darwin asked himself: If the Earth could change over time, might life change as well? Second, he realized that it would have taken many, many years for life to change in the way he suggested. This would have been possible only if the Earth were extremely old.

✓ CHECKPOINT **What are some ways the Earth has changed over time?**

Writing Activity
Use the library or the Internet to find out more about Darwin and Wallace. Write a dialogue between these two men, where the conversation shows the similarities in their careers and theories.

Charles Darwin
Darwin sets sail on the H.M.S. *Beagle,* a voyage that would provide him with vast amounts of evidence that lead to his theory of evolution.

Alfred Wallace
Wallace writes to Darwin, speculating on evolution by natural selection, based on his studies of the distribution of plants and animals. Darwin presents Wallace's essay to the Linnaean Society.

1831

1858

1850

1833

Charles Lyell
In the second and final volume of *Principles of Geology*, Lyell explained that processes occurring now have shaped Earth's geological features over long periods of time.

1849
California Gold Rush

1859
Darwin publishes *On the Origin of Species.*

1861
The United States Civil War begins.

Darwin's Theory of Evolution **375**

Lamarck's Theory of Evolution

One of the best-known scientific theorists to precede Darwin was the French naturalist Jean-Baptiste Lamarck. Lamarck was among the first scientists to recognize that living things have changed over time—and that all species were descended from other species. He also realized that organisms were somehow adapted to their environments. In 1809, the year that Darwin was born, Lamarck published his theory of how organisms changed over time.

🔑 **Lamarck proposed that by selective use or disuse of organs, organisms acquired or lost certain traits during their lifetime. These traits could then be passed on to their offspring. Over time, this process led to change in a species.**

Tendency Toward Perfection Lamarck proposed that all organisms have an innate tendency toward complexity and perfection. As a result, they are continually changing and acquiring features that help them live more successfully in their environments. In Lamarck's view, for instance, the ancestors of birds acquired an urge to fly. Over many generations, birds kept trying to fly, and their wings increased in size and became more suited to flying.

Use and Disuse Because of this tendency toward perfection, Lamarck proposed that organisms could alter the size or shape of particular organs by using their bodies in new ways. For example, by trying to use their front limbs for flying, birds could eventually transform those limbs into wings. Conversely, if a winged animal did not use its wings—an example of disuse—the wings would decrease in size over generations and finally disappear.

Inheritance of Acquired Traits Like many biologists of his time, Lamarck thought that acquired characteristics could be inherited. For example, if during its lifetime an animal somehow altered a body structure, leading to longer legs or fluffier feathers, it would pass that change on to its offspring. By this reasoning, if you spent much of your life lifting weights to build muscles, your children would inherit big muscles, too.

Evaluating Lamarck's Theory Lamarck's theory of evolution, illustrated in **Figure 15–7,** is incorrect in several ways. Lamarck, like Darwin, did not know how traits are inherited. He did not know that an organism's behavior has no effect on its inheritable characteristics. However, Lamarck was one of the first to develop a scientific theory of evolution and realize that organisms are adapted to their environments. In this way, he paved the way for the work of later biologists.

✓ CHECKPOINT *According to Lamarck, how did bird flight evolve?*

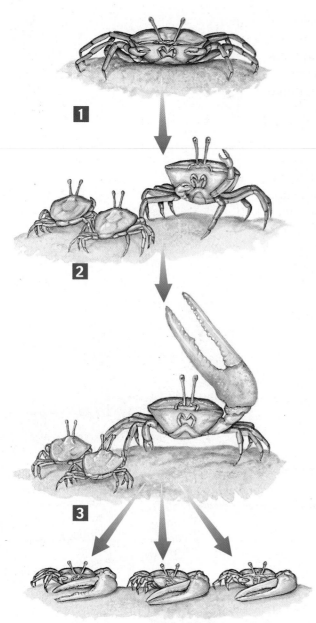

▲ **Figure 15–7** 🔑 One explanation for evolution proposed that the selective use or disuse of an organ led to a change in that organ that was then passed on to offspring. This proposed mechanism is shown here applied to fiddler crabs. (1) The male crab uses its small front claw to attract mates and ward off predators. (2) Because the front claw has been used repeatedly, it becomes larger. (3) The acquired characteristic, a larger claw, is then passed on to the crab's offspring. This explanation, proposed by Lamarck in 1809, was found to be incorrect.

Population Growth

Another important influence on Darwin came from the English economist Thomas Malthus. In 1798, Malthus observed that babies were being born faster than people were dying. **Malthus reasoned that if the human population continued to grow unchecked, sooner or later there would be insufficient living space and food for everyone.** The only forces he observed that worked against this growth were war, famine, and disease. Conditions in nineteenth-century England, illustrated in **Figure 15–8**, reinforced Malthus's somewhat pessimistic view of the human condition.

When Darwin read Malthus's work, he realized that this reasoning applied even more strongly to plants and animals than it did to humans. Why? Because humans produce far fewer offspring than most other species do. A mature maple tree can produce thousands of seeds in a single summer, and one oyster can produce millions of eggs each year. If all the offspring of almost any species survived for several generations, they would overrun the world.

Obviously, this has not happened, because continents are not covered with maple trees, and oceans are not filled with oysters. The overwhelming majority of a species' offspring die. Further, only a few of those offspring that survive succeed in reproducing. What causes the death of so many individuals? What factor or factors determine which ones survive and reproduce, and which do not? Answers to these questions became central to Darwin's explanation of evolutionary change.

▶ **Figure 15–8** 🔑 Malthus proposed that war, famine, and disease limited the growth of human populations. He supported his theory with the evidence he observed in the streets of London.

15–2 Section Assessment

1. 🔑 **Key Concept** What two ideas from geology were important to Darwin's thinking?

2. 🔑 **Key Concept** According to Lamarck, how did organisms acquire traits?

3. 🔑 **Key Concept** According to Malthus, what factors limited population growth?

4. Why has Lamarck's theory of evolution been rejected?

5. **Critical Thinking Inferring** Malthus formed his theory by studying factors that control the population growth of humans. How might factors operating on organisms in nature differ from those of Malthus's theory?

iTEXT Assessment Use iText to review the important concepts in Section 15–2.

ALTERNATIVE ASSESSMENT
Give a Talk Imagine that you are either James Hutton or Charles Lyell addressing an audience of their time. Give a talk explaining your ideas, noting what your listeners will consider new and different.

15–3 Darwin Presents His Case

Guide for Reading

 Key Concepts
- How is natural variation used in artificial selection?
- How is natural selection related to a species' fitness?
- What evidence of evolution did Darwin present?

Vocabulary
natural variation
artificial selection
struggle for existence
fitness
adaptation
survival of the fittest
natural selection
descent with modification
common descent
homologous structure
vestigial organ

**Reading Strategy:
Building Vocabulary** As you read, write a phrase or sentence in your own words to define each boldfaced term.

When Darwin returned to England in 1836, he brought back specimens from around the world. Subsequent findings about these specimens soon had the scientific community abuzz. Darwin learned that his Galápagos mockingbirds actually belonged to three separate species found nowhere else in the world! Even more surprising, the brown birds that Darwin had thought to be wrens, warblers, and blackbirds were all finches. They, too, were found nowhere else. The same was true of the Galápagos tortoises, the marine iguanas, and many plants that Darwin had collected on the islands. Each island species looked a great deal like a similar species on the South American mainland. Yet, the island species were clearly different from the mainland species and from one another.

Publication of *On the Origin of Species*

Darwin began filling notebooks with his ideas about species diversity and the process that would later be called evolution. However, he did not rush out to publish his thoughts. Recall that Darwin's ideas challenged fundamental scientific beliefs of his day. Darwin was not only stunned by his discoveries, he was disturbed by them. Years later, he wrote, "It was evident that such facts as these . . . could be explained on the supposition that species gradually became modified, and the subject haunted me." Although he discussed his work with friends, he shelved his manuscript for years and told his wife to publish it in case he died.

In 1858, Darwin received a short essay from Alfred Russel Wallace, a fellow naturalist who had been doing field work in Malaysia. That essay summarized the thoughts on evolutionary change that Darwin had been mulling over for almost 25 years! Suddenly, Darwin had an incentive to publish his own work. At a scientific meeting later that year, Wallace's essay was presented together with some of Darwin's work.

◀ **Figure 15–9** Each zebra inherits genes that give it a distinctive pattern of stripes. Those visibly different patterns are an example of natural variation in a species. **Formulating Hypotheses** *What might be some inherited variations that are not visible?*

Darwin began writing in earnest. Eighteen months later, in 1859, he published the results of his work: *On the Origin of Species*. In his book, he proposed a mechanism for evolution that he called natural selection. He then presented evidence demonstrating that the process of evolution has been taking place for millions of years—and continues in all living things. Darwin's work caused an immediate sensation. Many people considered his arguments to be brilliant, while others strongly opposed and even ridiculed his message. But what did Darwin actually say?

✓ **CHECKPOINT** *What event motivated Darwin to publish his ideas?*

Natural Variation and Artificial Selection

Darwin began his explanation of evolution by abandoning the idea of a species as perfect and unchanging. He argued that **natural variation,** defined as differences among individuals of a species, is found in all types of organisms. Variation is present in species in nature, as shown in **Figure 15–9,** and in farm crops and livestock. Some cows gave more milk than others, for example, and some plants bore larger fruit than others. Darwin proposed that much of this variation could be inherited, or passed on to the next generation. Today, the fact that variation exists seems obvious. We can easily observe it in so many living things. In Darwin's day, however, it was revolutionary to suggest that variation was a major feature of life.

Despite all his world travels, Darwin actually made some of his greatest progress on evolutionary theory by studying the work of English farmers and breeders. He noted that breeders routinely used variation to improve their crops and livestock. Through a technique called selective breeding, they would determine which individuals to use for breeding based on the natural variation that they found. Only the largest hogs, the fastest horses, or the cows that gave the most milk were selected to produce offspring. Darwin termed this process **artificial selection.** Using artificial selection, breeders were able to produce a wide range of plants and animals that looked very different from their ancestors. ⌐ **In artificial selection, nature provided the variation among different organisms, and humans selected those variations that they found useful.** Artificial selection is still used today to shape a variety of traits, as shown in **Figure 15–10.**

▶ **Figure 15–10** ⌐ In the process of artificial selection, humans select from among the naturally occurring variations in a species. This process can lead to great differences. In some cases, a single ancestral species has given rise to a variety of modern plants.

Quick Lab

New vegetables from old?

Materials various *Brassica* (cabbage family) vegetables

Procedure
Examine each of the vegetables and compare them. Determine which organ of the ancestral plant breeders may have chosen to produce each vegetable.

Analyze and Conclude
Formulating Hypotheses
Choose one of the vegetables. Explain how breeders might have produced that variety from the ancestor plant, shown below.

Brussels sprouts

Cauliflower

Broccoli

Kohlrabi

Ancestral species

Kale

Evolution by Natural Selection

Darwin's next insight was to compare processes in nature to artificial selection. By doing so, he developed a scientific hypothesis to explain how evolution occurs. This is where Darwin made his greatest contribution—and his strongest break with the past.

The Struggle for Existence Darwin was convinced that a process like artificial selection worked in nature. But how? He recalled Malthus's work on population growth. Darwin realized that high birth rates and a shortage of life's basic needs would eventually force organisms into a competition for resources. The **struggle for existence** means that members of each species compete regularly to obtain food, living space, and other necessities of life. In this struggle, the predators that are faster or have a particular way of ensnaring other organisms can catch more prey. Those prey that are faster, better camouflaged, or better protected, such as the porcupine shown in **Figure 15–11**, can avoid being caught. This struggle for existence was central to Darwin's theory of evolution.

Survival of the Fittest A key factor in the struggle for existence, Darwin observed, was how well suited an organism is to its environment. Darwin called the ability of an individual to survive and reproduce in its specific environment **fitness.** Darwin proposed that fitness is the result of adaptations. An **adaptation** is any inherited characteristic that increases an organism's chance of survival. Successful adaptations, Darwin concluded, enable organisms to become better suited to their environment and thus better able to survive and reproduce. Adaptations can be physical characteristics, such as a porcupine's sharp quills, or more complex features, such as behavior in which some animals live and hunt in groups.

▼ **Figure 15–11** Survival of the fittest can take many different forms. For one species, it may be an ability to run fast, whereas for another species, it may be behavioral tactics that it uses to outsmart predators. For the porcupine, sharp quills make a powerful, hungry predator back away from an attack. *Inferring What other types of characteristics might increase chances of survival?*

▸ **Figure 15–12** Each of these baby tanagers has its own set of inherited traits that affect its survival. A stronger bird may take food from a weaker sibling. A faster bird may escape predators more easily. Only those birds that survive and reproduce have the chance to pass their traits to the next generation. ◯ **Over time, natural selection results in changes in the inherited characteristics of a population.**

The concept of fitness, Darwin argued, was central to the process of evolution by natural selection. Generation after generation, individuals compete to survive and produce offspring. The baby birds in **Figure 15–12**, for example, compete for food and space while in the nest. Because each individual differs from other members of its species, each has unique advantages and disadvantages. Individuals with characteristics that are not well suited to their environment—that is, with low levels of fitness—either die or leave few offspring. Individuals that are better suited to their environment—that is, with high levels of fitness—survive and reproduce most successfully. This was a process that Darwin called **survival of the fittest.**

Because of its similarities to artificial selection, Darwin referred to the survival of the fittest as **natural selection.** In both artificial selection and natural selection, only certain individuals of a population produce new individuals. However, in natural selection, the traits being selected—and therefore increasing over time—contribute to an organism's fitness in its environment. Natural selection also takes place without human control or direction. ◯ **Over time, natural selection results in changes in the inherited characteristics of a population. These changes increase a species' fitness in its environment.** Natural selection cannot be seen directly; it can only be observed as changes in a population over many successive generations.

✓ **CHECKPOINT** *What did Darwin mean when he described certain organisms as "more fit" than others?*

Descent With Modification Darwin proposed that over long periods, natural selection produces organisms that have different structures, establish different niches, or occupy different habitats. As a result, species today look different from their ancestors. Each living species has descended, with changes, from other species over time. He referred to this principle as **descent with modification.**

KEEP CURRENT WITH . . .
SCIENCE NEWS®
To find out more about the topics in this chapter, go to:
www.phschool.com

Descent with modification also implies something else: that all living organisms are related to one another. Look back in time, and you will find common ancestors shared by tigers, panthers, and cheetahs. Look farther back, and you will find ancestors that these felines share with horses, dogs, bats, and primates. Farther back still are the common ancestors of mammals, birds, alligators, and fishes. If we look far enough back, the logic concludes, we could find the common ancestors of all living things. This is the principle known as **common descent.** According to this principle, all species—living and extinct—were derived from common ancestors.

Carry the concepts of descent with modification and common descent to their logical conclusion, and what do they produce? A single "tree of life" that links all living things on Earth. Darwin conceived of this idea long before he published his theory of evolution.

Evidence of Evolution

With this unified, dynamic theory of life, Darwin could finally explain many of the observations he had made during his travels aboard the *Beagle*. He presented these observations as evidence of the process of evolution. 🔑 **Darwin argued that living things have been evolving on Earth for millions of years. Evidence for this process could be found in the fossil record, the geographical distribution of living species, homologous structures of living organisms, and similarities in early development.**

The Fossil Record It was well known in Darwin's time that fossils were the remains of ancient life and that different layers of rock had been formed at different times in Earth's history.

▼ **Figure 15–13** 🔑 Darwin argued that the fossil record provided evidence that living things have been evolving for millions of years. Sometimes the fossil record includes similar, intermediate forms of a group of organisms that together suggest gradual modification over time. The four organisms shown here are all cephalopods, a group that includes octopi and squid. Fossil evidence indicates that these organisms gradually evolved a longer, more coiled shell.

However, few people viewed the fossil record as Darwin did, as a detailed record of evolution. Darwin proposed that Earth was hundreds of millions—rather than thousands—of years old. During this time, he stated, countless species of many different forms had appeared on Earth, lived for a time, and then vanished. Fossils that had formed in the different layers of rock were evidence of this gradual change over time. In fact, by examining fossils from sequential layers of rock, one could view how a species had changed and produced different species over time, as shown in **Figure 15–13.**

Geographic Distribution of Living Species

Remember that many parts of the biological puzzle that Darwin saw on his *Beagle* voyage involved living organisms. After Darwin discovered that those little brown birds he collected in the Galápagos were all finches, he began to wonder how they came to be similar, yet distinctly different from one another. Each species was slightly different from every other species. They were also slightly different from the most similar species on the mainland of South America. Could the island birds have changed over time, as populations in different places adapted to different local environments? Darwin struggled with this question for a long time. He finally decided that all these birds could have descended with modification from a common mainland ancestor.

There were other parts to the living puzzle as well. Recall that Darwin found entirely different species of animals on the continents of South America and Australia. Yet, when he looked at similar environments on those continents, he sometimes saw different animals that had similar structures and behaviors. Darwin's theory of descent with modification made scientific sense of this part of the puzzle as well. Species now living on different continents, as shown in **Figure 15–14,** had each descended from different ancestors. However, because some animals on each continent were living under similar ecological conditions, they were exposed to similar pressures of natural selection. Because of these similar selection pressures, different animals ended up evolving certain striking features in common.

CHECKPOINT *How can two species that look very different from each other be more closely related than two other species that look similar to each other?*

▲ **Figure 15–14** The existence of similar but unrelated species was a puzzle to Darwin. Later, he realized that similar animals in different locations were the product of different lines of evolutionary descent. Here, the beaver and the capybara are similar species that inhabit similar environments of North America and South America. The South American coypu also shares many characteristics with the North American muskrat. **Interpreting Graphics** *Which animal has a larger geographical range, the coypu or the muskrat?*

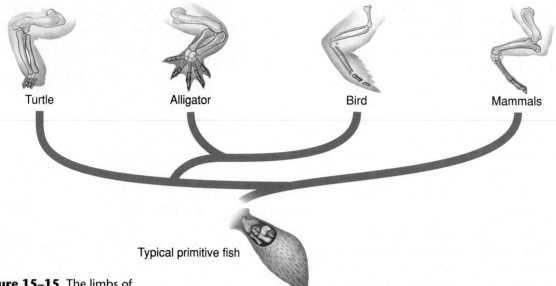

Turtle   Alligator   Bird   Mammals

Typical primitive fish

▲ **Figure 15–15** The limbs of these four modern vertebrates are homologous structures. They provide evidence of a common ancestor whose bones may have resembled those of the ancient fish shown here. Notice that different colors are used to show related structures. ◗ **Homologous structures are one type of evidence for the evolution of living things.**

Word Origins

Homologous, from the Greek words *homos,* meaning "same," and *legein,* meaning "say," describes similar body structures that come from a common ancestor. **If the word** *morphe* **means "shape," what are homomorphic structures?**

Homologous Body Structures Further evidence of evolution can be found in living animals. By Darwin's time, researchers had noticed striking similarities among the body parts of animals with backbones. For example, they described similarities among the bones of different vertebrates, such as reptiles, birds, and mammals. Some of these limbs are arms, whereas others are wings, legs, or even flippers. The limbs differ greatly in form and function, yet they are all constructed from the same basic bones, as shown in **Figure 15–15.**

What is the scientific explanation for these similarities? Each of these limbs has adapted in ways that enable organisms to survive in different environments. Despite these different functions, however, these limb bones all develop from the same clumps of cells in growing embryos. Structures such as these, which have different mature forms but develop from the same embryonic tissues, are called **homologous structures** (hoh-MAH-luh-gus). Homologous structures provide strong evidence that all four-limbed animals with backbones have descended, with modifications, from common ancestors.

There is still more information to be gathered from homologous structures. If we compare the front limbs, we can see that all bird wings are more similar to one another than any of them are to bat wings. Other bones in bird skeletons most closely resemble the homologous bones of certain reptiles—including crocodiles and extinct reptiles such as dinosaurs. The bones that support the wings of bats, by contrast, are more similar to the front limbs of humans, whales, and other mammals than they are to those of birds. These similarities and differences help biologists group animals according to how recently they last shared a common ancestor.

Not all homologous structures serve important functions. The organs of many animals are so reduced in size that they are just vestiges, or traces, of homologous organs in other species.

These **vestigial organs,** shown in **Figure 15–16,** may resemble miniature legs, tails, or other structures. Why would an organism possess organs with little or no function? One possibility is that the presence of a vestigial organ may not affect an organism's ability to survive and reproduce. In that case, natural selection would not cause the elimination of that organ.

Similarities in Early Development The early stages, or embryos, of many animals with backbones are so similar that they can be hard to tell apart. This does not mean that a human embryo is ever identical to a fish or a bird embryo. However, as you can see in **Figure 15–17,** many embryos look especially similar during early stages of development. What do these similarities mean?

There have, in the past, been incorrect explanations for these similarities. Also, the great biologist Ernst Haeckel fudged some of his drawings to make the earliest stages of some embryos seem more similar than they actually are! Errors aside, however, it is clear that the same groups of embryonic cells develop in the same order and in similar patterns to produce the tissues and organs of all vertebrates. These common cells and tissues, growing in similar ways, produce the homologous structures discussed earlier.

✓ CHECKPOINT How can biologists use the idea of homologous structures to determine whether particular species are closely related?

Figure 15–16 These three animals are skinks, a type of lizard. In some species of skinks, legs have become vestigial. They are so reduced that they no longer function in walking. In humans, the appendix is an example of a vestigial organ because it carries out no function in digestion. **Inferring** *How might vestigial organs provide clues to an animal's evolutionary history?*

Chicken   Turtle   Rat

Figure 15–17 In their early stages of development, chickens, turtles, and rats look similar, providing evidence that they shared a common ancestry. **Drawing Conclusions** *How could a study of these embryos help show the relationships among animals with backbones?*

Darwin's Theory of Evolution **385**

Summary of Darwin's Theory

Darwin's theory of evolution presented a new view of life, summarized below. This view, profoundly different from anything known in nineteenth-century England, continues to be upheld by research today. Many would still agree with Darwin, who wrote, "There is grandeur in this view of life, [that] from so simple a beginning, endless forms most beautiful and wonderful have been and are being evolved."

1. Individual organisms in nature differ from one another. Some of this variation is inherited.

2. Organisms in nature produce more offspring than can survive, and many of those that survive do not reproduce.

3. Because more organisms are produced than can survive, members of each species must compete for limited resources.

4. Because each organism is unique, each has different advantages and disadvantages in the struggle for existence.

5. Individuals best suited to their environment survive and reproduce most successfully. The characteristics that make them best suited to their environment are passed on to offspring. Individuals whose characteristics are not as well suited to their environment die or leave fewer offspring.

6. Species change over time. Over long periods, natural selection causes changes in the characteristics of a species, such as in size and form. New species arise, and other species disappear.

7. Species alive today have descended with modifications from species that lived in the past.

8. All organisms on Earth are united into a single tree of life by common descent.

▲ **Figure 15–18** Darwin published *On the Origin of Species* almost 150 years ago. Today, his theory of evolution continues to be upheld in all areas of biology. **Applying Concepts** *New species are continually being discovered. How could you use Darwin's theory to learn more about these new species?*

15–3 Section Assessment

1. 🔑 **Key Concept** How is artificial selection dependent on variation in nature?

2. 🔑 **Key Concept** The theory of evolution by natural selection explains, in scientific terms, how living things evolve over time. What is being selected in this process?

3. 🔑 **Key Concept** What types of evidence did Darwin use to support his theory of change over time?

4. What is the "struggle for existence"? How was this idea based on Malthus's work?

5. **Critical Thinking Comparing and Contrasting** Compare and contrast Darwin's theory of evolution with that of Lamarck. How are they similar? How are they different?

📱**TEXT** **Assessment** Use iText to review the important concepts in Section 15–3.

ALTERNATIVE ASSESSMENT

Writing a Newspaper Article
Write a brief newspaper article reporting on the meeting of the Linnaean Society, where Darwin's and Wallace's hypotheses of evolution were first presented. Explain the theory of evolution by natural selection for an audience who knows nothing about the subject.

Modeling Adaptation

In this game, three families land on an alien planet. At home, the Hunter family survived by hunting in the cold north. The Seeder family farmed the temperate zone. The Fisher family lived on a tropical island. In this investigation, you will model how well each family survives in a new environment.

Problem How do organisms survive in new habitats?

Material

- coin

Skills Using Models, Using Tables and Graphs, Calculating

Procedure

1. Work in groups of three, with each member playing a Hunter, Seeder, or Fisher.

2. Flip a coin. Record the result as 1 for heads, 0 for tails. Toss the coin three more times to produce a series of four 1s and 0s. This 4-digit number is the code for your new habitat.

3. If the first digit in your code is 1, you live in a hot area. If it is 0, the climate is cold. If the second digit is 1, the climate is wet. If it is 0, it's dry. If the third digit is 1, you have a dry cave to live in. If it is 0, you sleep under the stars. If the last digit is 1, there is enough food. If it is 0, food is scarce. Record a description of your habitat.

4. Find your family in the table below. Then, record each number in your row that falls under a heading that describes your habitat (hot or cold and so forth). Record the total of these 4 numbers. This total represents the energy you have accumulated from your food.

5. Subtract 8 from your total to model the energy you must use to survive. If you don't have enough energy to do this, you're out of the game. The player with the most energy wins. Record the score and habitat of each family.

6. **Predicting** Record a prediction of what would happen if you reversed each player's habitat code by changing all the 1s to 0s and the 0s to 1s.

7. Reverse your habitat code as described in step 6. Play a second round with these conditions.

Analyze and Conclude

1. **Comparing and Contrasting** In which habitat were you most successful? Was it similar to your home environment?

2. **Using Models** The numbers in the table are different for each family. How did this fact help you model the survival of different organisms?

3. **Drawing Conclusions** Is one habitat best for all players? Explain in terms of adaptation.

Go Further

Revise the game to reflect the different conditions of summer and winter. Then, demonstrate your game to the class.

Energy Points for Survival							
	Temperature		Water		Shelter		Food	
	Cold	Hot	Dry	Wet	None	Cave	Scarce	Plenty
Hunter	8	-2	0	4	-6	7	-5	8
Seeder	0	3	2	2	-1	2	-2	6
Fisher	-5	8	-2	5	0	1	-1	4

Chapter 15 Study Guide

15–1 The Puzzle of Life's Diversity

 Key Concepts

- During his travels, Charles Darwin made numerous observations and collected evidence that led him to propose a revolutionary hypothesis about the way life changes over time.

- Darwin observed that the characteristics of many animals and plants varied noticeably among the different islands of the Galápagos.

Vocabulary
evolution, p. 369
theory, p. 369
fossil, p. 371

15–2 Ideas That Shaped Darwin's Thinking

Key Concepts

- Hutton and Lyell helped scientists realize that Earth is many millions of years old, and the processses that changed Earth in the past are the same processes that operate in the present.

- Lamarck proposed that by selective use or disuse of organs, organisms acquired or lost certain traits during their lifetime. These traits could then be passed on to their offspring. Over time, this process led to change in a species.

- Malthus reasoned that if the human population continued to grow unchecked, sooner or later there would be insufficient living space and food for everyone.

15–3 Darwin Presents His Case

Key Concepts

- In artificial selection, nature provides the variation among different organisms, and humans select those variations that they find useful.

- Over time, natural selection results in changes in the inherited characteristics of a population. These changes increase a species' fitness in its environment.

- Darwin argued that living things have been evolving on Earth for millions of years. Evidence for this process could be found in the fossil record, the geographical distribution of living species, homologous structures of living organisms, and similarities in early development.

Vocabulary
natural variation, p. 379
artificial selection, p. 379
struggle for existence, p. 380
fitness, p. 380
adaptation, p. 380
survival of the fittest, p. 381
natural selection, p. 381
descent with modification, p. 381
common descent, p. 382
homologous structure, p. 384
vestigial organ, p. 385

Thinking Visually

Use the information in this chapter to complete the table below.

Evidence of Evolution		
Type of Evidence	**Example**	**What Evidence Reveals**
The fossil record	1	2
Geographic distribution of living species	3	4
Homologous body structures	5	6
Similarities in early development	7	8

Chapter 15

Part A

Multiple Choice

For each statement or question, select the number of the word or expression that, of those given, best completes the statement or answers the question.

1 Which scientist observed variations in the characteristics of animals and plants on the Galápagos Islands?
(1) James Hutton
(2) Charles Lyell
(3) Charles Darwin
(4) Thomas Malthus

2 The theory that geological processes had shaped Earth in the past and continued to shape Earth in the present was proposed by
(1) Charles Lyell
(2) Charles Darwin
(3) Jean-Baptiste Lamarck
(4) Thomas Malthus

3 In addition to observing living organisms, Darwin studied the preserved remains of ancient organisms, called
(1) fossils
(2) adaptations
(3) homologous structures
(4) vestigial organs

4 Which idea proposed by Lamarck was later found to be incorrect?
(1) Acquired characteristics can be inherited.
(2) All species are descended from other species.
(3) Living things change over time.
(4) Organisms are adapted to their environments.

5 Differences among individuals of a species
(1) rarely occur
(2) may give some individuals a survival advantage
(3) are found only in some types of organisms
(4) prevent natural selection from occurring

6 Which process would an animal breeder use to produce cows that give more milk?
(1) natural selection
(2) survival of the fittest
(3) descent with modification
(4) artificial selection

7 The concept that each living species has descended, with changes, from other species over time is referred to as
(1) descent with modification
(2) artificial selection
(3) the theory of acquired characteristics
(4) natural selection

8 Structures that have different mature forms but develop from the same embryonic tissue are called
(1) vestigial organs
(2) adaptations
(3) homologous structures
(4) embryonic structures

9 The diagram below best illustrates
(1) Lamarck's theory of evolution
(2) Darwin's theory of evolution
(3) Malthus's principles
(4) Lyell's theory about past changes

10 Which concepts are important in Darwin's theory of evolution by natural selection?
A Struggle for existence
B Survival of the fittest
C Descent with modification
(1) A and B, only
(2) A and C, only
(3) B and C, only
(4) A, B, and C

Test-Taking Tip If you have trouble answering a question, make a mark beside it and go on. (Do not write in this book.) You may find information in later questions that will allow you to eliminate some answer choices in your unanswered question.

Parts B and C

Multiple Choice and Extended Response

For those questions that ask you to select a response, choose the one that best completes the statement or answers the question. For all others follow the directions given.

Base your answers to questions 11 and 12 on the information and drawings below and on your knowledge of biology.

The birds pictured below are two of the 13 species of finches that Darwin found on the Galápagos Islands.

Woodpecker finch   Large ground finch

11 What process produced the two different types of beaks shown?
(1) artificial selection
(2) natural selection
(3) geographical distribution
(4) inheritance of acquired traits

12 The large ground finch obtains food by cracking seeds. Its short, strong beak is an example of
(1) the struggle for existence
(2) the tendency toward perfection
(3) the inheritance of acquired traits
(4) an adaptation

13 A protein similar to the mammalian hormone prolactin, which stimulates the production of milk, is found in amphibians and birds. In amphibians, the protein causes the animals to seek water when they lay their eggs. In birds, it causes the animals to regurgitate material from their crops to feed their young. How might the similarities and differences among these proteins be explained? Support your answer with an explanation.

14 Discuss the accuracy of these statements: Modern giraffes evolved from a short-necked ancestor by stretching their necks to reach leaves on high branches. Over time, adults with longer necks passed the trait to their offspring.

Base your answers to questions 15 through 17 on the information and chart below and on your knowledge of biology.

Plant scientists have produced a new variety of sunflower with seeds used for cooking oil and margarine. The scientists did tests to compare their new variety, C, with two existing varieties, A and B. Their data are shown in the chart.

Variety	Stem Strength (1–9 = weak-strong)	Oil Content per Seed (%)	Time for Seeds to Mature (1–9 = early-late)	Seed Yield (kg/ acre)
A (old)	5	48	8	2050
B (old)	8	41	5	2200
C (new)	7	38	2	2600

15 A good variety of plant should have a strong stem, high yield of oil, and rapid rate of seed maturation. Use the information in the chart to support the use of Variety C.

16 What information would you need to know to determine the accuracy of the results presented in the chart?

17 If the scientists did not directly alter the sunflowers' genetic makeup, how could they have developed Variety C?

Base your answers to questions 18 through 20 on the information below and on your knowledge of biology.

DDT is an insecticide that was first used in the 1940s to kill mosquitoes and stop the spread of malaria. At first, DDT was very effective, but within years, it became less effective as the insects became resistant to the DDT.

18 Explain how resistance to DDT may have evolved.

19 Based on what you know about mosquito resistance to DDT, describe an experiment to test whether bacteria can become resistant to antibiotics.

20 State a hypothesis that would serve as the basis for this experiment.

Base your answers to questions 21 and 22 on the passage below and on your knowledge of biology.

Mule Deer

About 100 years ago, approximately 4000 mule deer roamed the Kaibab Plateau, which is located on the northern rim of the Grand Canyon in Arizona. Their natural enemies, which were wolves and pumas, kept the deer population in check. Then, early in the 1900s, the majority of wolves and pumas were killed by humans, because these predators were also killing cattle and sheep that grazed on the plateau. As a result, the deer population grew unchecked, rising to over 100,000 by the 1920s. The plateau was quickly overgrazed, and the deer population fell rapidly. Observers in the late 1920s discovered that some deer had begun to eat the leaves of trees instead of their usual diet of grasses and the leaves of low shrubs.

21 Compare the adaptations needed by the deer in the early 1900s with those needed in the 1920s.

22 Did the killing of wolves and pumas by humans interfere with the process of natural selection? Support your answer with an explanation.

Base your answers to questions 23 through 27 on the passage below and on your knowledge of biology.

Koalas

About 45 million years ago, Australia separated from Antarctica and gradually drifted northward. Fossil remains of koala-like animals in Australia date back to 25 million years ago. Around that time, the climate changed and Australia grew drier. Plants such as eucalyptus trees evolved, and koalas became dependent on them for food. When Europeans first arrived in Australia in 1788, they cleared forests for farmland, thus reducing the size of koala habitats and food sources. The Europeans also killed millions of koalas for their fur. Many additional koalas died from diseases, such as pneumonia and infections caused by the chlamydia bacteria, because koalas are particularly susceptible to disease when they are stressed by limited food. By 1924, koalas had disappeared from several areas of Australia.

23 Explain why fossils of koala-like animals have not been found in North America.

24 Koalas have strong legs for climbing trees and strong claws for hanging onto tree trunks and branches. Write a paragraph that contrasts how Lamarck might have explained the koala's strong legs and claws with how Darwin might have explained them.

25 Cutting down trees for farmland resulted in smaller patches of forest for koalas. Additional trees died because of soil erosion, loss of soil nutrients, and other related factors. Using Malthus's principles, describe the effect on the koala population of the loss of trees.

26 Scientists think that chlamydia bacteria act as a natural population control in koalas. Explain how natural selection caused by these bacteria might affect future generations of koalas.

27 Since Europeans came to Australia, 80 percent of the eucalyptus trees have been cleared. Although there is government protection for koalas, there is no protection for eucalyptus trees. Assuming koalas do not adapt to the loss of habitat and food sources, describe their fate if the remaining eucalyptus trees are cleared.

Take It to the NET

Dozens of people paved the way for Darwin's theory, and countless others have expanded on it. Visit the Prentice Hall Web site at **www.phschool.com** to learn more about the history of evolutionary thought. Then, answer the following questions:

• Who was the first to hypothesize that fossils were once-living organisms that had been buried at a time before the mountains were raised? When was that person born?

• Who is Carl Linnaeus? What is he most famous for?

• What controversial event occurred between Alfred Russel Wallace and Charles Darwin?

• Why was Thomas Henry Huxley nicknamed "Darwin's Bulldog"?

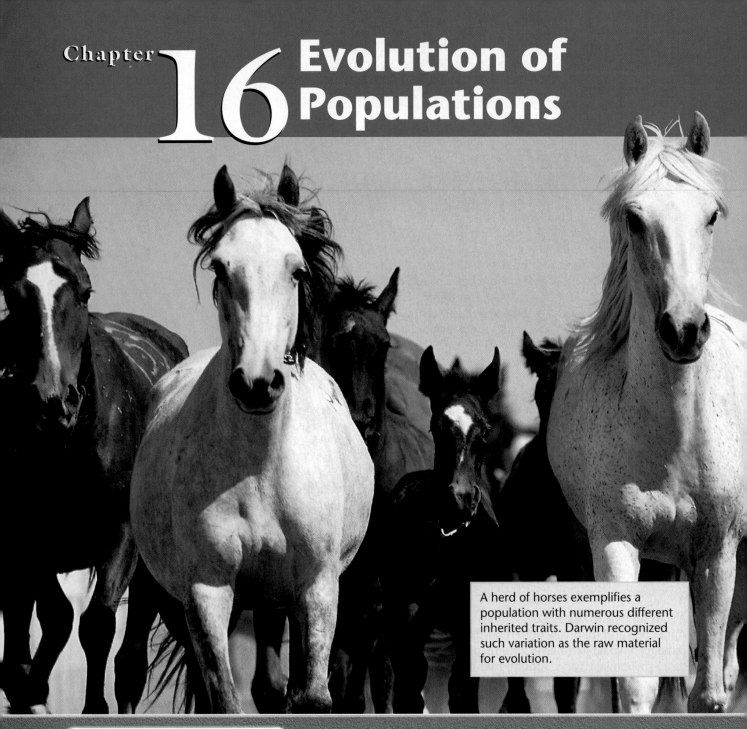

Chapter 16 Evolution of Populations

A herd of horses exemplifies a population with numerous different inherited traits. Darwin recognized such variation as the raw material for evolution.

Inquiry Activity

Does sexual reproduction change genotype ratios?

Procedure

1. Put 33 red and 67 black beads in a 1-L beaker to represent two alleles of a certain gene in a population.

2. To model the genotype of an offspring, remove two beads. Record the genotype. Return the beads.

3. Repeat step 2 for a total of 10 offspring. Add your data to the class total.

Think About It

1. **Calculating** What was the genotype ratio of the offspring?

2. **Comparing and Contrasting** Was the genotype ratio the same as the 1 : 2 : 1 genotype ratio for a cross between two heterozygotes (*Aa* × *Aa*)? Explain.

3. **Predicting** If you repeated this activity over and over, would you expect the genotype ratios to change? Explain.

16–1 Genes and Variation

As you look at the babies in **Figure 16–1,** you will immediately notice many differences among the individuals, such as different size and skin color. The babies also differ in terms of less visible characteristics, such as agility, the ability to fight off disease, and a host of behavioral traits.

Some of those differences are inheritable, which means that they can be passed from one generation to the next. Such differences provide the raw material for natural selection. Over time, those differences that help organisms survive and reproduce in their environment become more common. Meanwhile, differences that are not as beneficial become less common.

Darwin's Ideas Revisited

As Darwin developed his theory of evolution following his return to England in 1836, he worked under a serious disadvantage. He did not know how heredity worked. Although Mendel's work on inheritance was published in the 1860s, which was during Darwin's lifetime, its importance was not recognized until after 1900. Without an understanding of heredity, Darwin was unable to explain two important factors. First, he did not know the source of the variation that was so central to his theory. Second, he could not explain how inheritable traits were passed from one generation to the next.

It was more than fifty years before biologists could begin to determine the details of how evolution takes place. About 1910, biologists began to realize that genes carry the information that determines traits. With this knowledge, they were able to combine Mendel's work on inheritance with Darwin's work on evolutionary theory. Today, genetics, molecular biology, and evolutionary theory work together to explain how inheritable variation appears and how natural selection operates on that variation. This progress in evolutionary theory allows biologists to explain—much more completely than Darwin ever could—how evolution takes place.

 Key Concepts
- What are the main sources of inheritable variation in a population?
- What determines the numbers of phenotypes for a given trait?

Vocabulary
gene pool
relative frequency
single-gene trait
polygenic trait

**Reading Strategy:
Building Vocabulary**
Before you read, make a list of the vocabulary terms above. As you read, take notes about the meaning of each term.

▼ **Figure 16–1** There are two main sources of genetic variation: mutations and the gene shuffling that results from sexual reproduction. Each of these babies has inherited a collection of traits. Some, such as hair color, are visible, while others, such as the ability to resist certain diseases, are not.

Sample Population

48% heterozygous black

16% homozygous black

36% homozygous brown

Frequency of Alleles

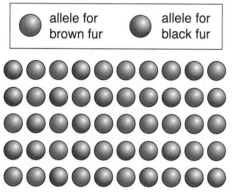

allele for brown fur

allele for black fur

▲ **Figure 16–2** When scientists determine whether a population is evolving, they may look at the sum of the population's alleles, or its gene pool. This diagram shows the gene pool for fur color in a population of mice. **Calculating** *Here, in a total of 50 alleles, 20 alleles are B (black), and 30 are b (brown). How many of each allele would be present in a total of 100 alleles?*

Gene Pools

Today, biologists studying evolution often focus on a particular population. Recall that a population is a collection of individuals of the same species in a given area. Because all members of a population can interbreed, they share a common group of genes, called a gene pool. A **gene pool** is the combined genetic information of all the members of a particular population.

A gene pool typically contains two or more alleles—or forms of a certain gene—for each inheritable trait. For example, a mouse population may have two alleles for fur color, as shown in **Figure 16–2.** The gene pool for that trait is the combination of all the alleles in the population.

The **relative frequency** of an allele is the number of times that allele occurs in a gene pool compared with the number of times other alleles occur. Frequencies are often expressed in percents. Here, for example, 40 percent of the alleles are *B* (black fur).

Sources of Genetic Variation

Biologists can now explain how variation is produced. 🔑 **The two main sources of genetic variation are mutations and the genetic shuffling that results from sexual reproduction.**

Mutations A mutation is any change in a sequence of DNA. Mutations can occur because of mistakes in the replication of DNA or as a result of radiation or chemicals in the environment. Mutations can be limited to one or a few bases of DNA, or they can affect lengthy segments of a chromosome.

Mutations do not always affect an organism's phenotype—its physical, behavioral, and biochemical characteristics. For example, a DNA codon altered by a point mutation from GGA to GGU will still code for the same amino acid, glycine. As a result, that mutation has no effect on the organism's phenotype. Many mutations do produce changes in an organism's phenotype, however. Some of these mutations can affect an organism's fitness, or its ability to survive and reproduce in its environment. Other mutations may have no effect on fitness.

Gene Shuffling Mutations are not the only source of inheritable variation. You do not look exactly like your biological parents, even though they provided you with all your genes. You probably look even less like any brothers or sisters you may have. Yet, no matter how you feel about your relatives, mutant genes are not primarily what makes them so different from you.

Most inheritable differences are due to gene shuffling that occurs during the production of gametes. Recall that each chromosome moves independently during meiosis. As a result, the 23 pairs of chromosomes found in humans can produce 8.4 million different combinations of genes!

Another process, crossing over, can also occur during meiosis. Crossing over further increases the number of different genotypes that can appear in offspring. Recall that a genotype is an organism's genetic makeup. When alleles are recombined during sexual reproduction, they can produce dramatically different phenotypes. Thus, sexual reproduction is a major source of variation within many populations.

Sexual reproduction can thus produce many different phenotypes, but it does not change the relative frequency of alleles in a population. To understand why, compare a population's gene pool to a deck of playing cards. Each card represents an allele found in the population. The exchange of genes during gene shuffling is similar to shuffling a deck of cards. Shuffling leads to different types of hands, but it can never change the relative numbers of aces, kings, or queens in the deck. The probability of drawing an ace off the top of the deck will always be 4 in 52, or one thirteenth (4/52 = 1/13). No matter how many times you shuffle the deck, this probability will remain the same. Similarly, sexual reproduction produces many different combinations of genes, but in itself it does not alter the relative frequencies of each type of allele in a population.

✓**CHECKPOINT** *What are the sources of inheritable variation?*

Single-Gene and Polygenic Traits

Inheritable variation can be expressed in a variety of ways. 🔑 **The number of phenotypes produced for a given trait depends on how many genes control the trait.** Among humans, a widow's peak—a downward dip in the center of the hairline—is a **single-gene trait.** It is controlled by a single gene that has two alleles. As a result, variation in this gene leads to only two distinct phenotypes, as shown in **Figure 16–3.** As you can see, the frequency of phenotypes caused by a single gene is represented on a bar graph. This graph shows that the presence of a widow's peak may be less common in a population than the absence of a widow's peak, even though the allele for a widow's peak is the dominant form. In real populations, allele frequencies may not match Mendelian ratios.

Word Origins

Gene comes from the Greek word *gignesthai,* meaning "to be born," and refers to factors that produce an organism. The prefix *poly-* comes from the Greek word *polys,* meaning "many," so *polygenic* means "having many genes." The prefix *mono-* means "one." **What do you think the term *monogenic* means?**

Figure 16–3 In humans, having a widow's peak (left) or not having a widow's peak (right) is controlled by a single gene with two alleles. As a result, only two phenotypes are possible. 🔑 **The number of phenotypes a given trait has is determined by how many genes control the trait.**

Single-Gene Trait

(Bar graph: x-axis "Phenotype" with categories "Widow's peak" and "No widow's peak"; y-axis "Frequency of Phenotype (%)" from 0 to 100. Widow's peak ≈ 35%, No widow's peak ≈ 65%.)

Figure 16–4 The graph below shows the distribution of phenotypes that would be expected for a trait if many genes contributed to the trait. The photograph shows the actual distribution of heights of a group of young men. **Using Tables and Graphs** *What does the shape of the graph indicate about height in humans?*

Polygenic Trait

Frequency of Phenotype

→ **Phenotype (height)** →

Most traits are controlled by two or more genes and are, therefore, called **polygenic traits.** Each gene of a polygenic trait often has two or more alleles. As a result, one polygenic trait can have many possible genotypes and even more possible phenotypes.

Height in humans is one example of a polygenic trait. You can sample phenotypic variation in this trait by measuring the height of all the students in your class. You can then calculate the average height of this group. Many students will be just a little taller or shorter than average. Some of your classmates, however, will be very tall or very short. If you graph the number of individuals of each height, you may get a graph similar to the one in **Figure 16–4.** The symmetrical bell-like shape of this curve is typical of polygenic traits. A bell-shaped curve is also called a normal distribution.

16–1 Section Assessment

1. 🔑 **Key Concept** What two processes can lead to inherited variation in populations?

2. 🔑 **Key Concept** How does the range of phenotypes differ between single-gene traits and polygenic traits?

3. What is a gene pool? How are allele frequencies related to gene pools?

4. **Critical Thinking Applying Concepts** How could you distinguish between a species in which there is a lot of variation and two separate species?

iTEXT Assessment Use iText to review the important concepts in Section 16–1.

MAKING CONNECTIONS

Genetics How does the process known as independent assortment relate to the genetic variation that results from sexual reproduction? (*Hint:* Refer to Chapter 11.)

16–2 Evolution as Genetic Change

Natural selection does not act directly on genes. Instead, it acts on phenotypes. Natural selection affects which individuals having different phenotypes survive and reproduce and which do not. In this way, natural selection determines which alleles are passed from one generation to the next. Thus, even though natural selection does not operate directly on genes, it can change the relative frequencies of alleles in a population over time.

But exactly what factors change the relative frequencies of alleles in a population? In a deck of cards, it is any situation that causes certain cards to be added to or removed from the deck. In genetic terms, any factor that causes alleles to be added to or removed from a population will change the relative frequencies of alleles. Whenever an individual dies without reproducing, its genes are removed from the population. But if an individual produces many offspring, the proportion of that individual's genes in the gene pool will increase. In genetic terms, evolution is any change in the relative frequencies of alleles in a population's gene pool. Thus, evolution acts on populations, not on individuals.

Natural Selection on Single-Gene Traits

🔑 **Natural selection on single-gene traits can lead to changes in allele frequencies and thus to evolution.** Imagine a population of brown lizards in which mutations produce red and black forms, as shown in **Figure 16–5.** Consider how various conditions might affect lizard survival. If the population lives in an area with dark soil, the red lizards might be easier for predators to see. They would be less likely to survive and reproduce, and over time would pass fewer copies of the allele for red coloring to future generations. That allele could even disappear from the gene pool completely.

Guide for Reading

🔑 **Key Concepts**
- How does natural selection affect single-gene and polygenic traits?
- What is genetic drift?
- What five conditions are needed to maintain genetic equilibrium?

Vocabulary
directional selection
stabilizing selection
disruptive selection
genetic drift
founder effect
Hardy-Weinberg principle
genetic equilibrium

Reading Strategy:
Outlining Before you read, use the headings to make an outline. As you read, add a sentence after each heading to provide key information.

▼ **Figure 16–5** Natural selection on single-gene traits can lead to changes in allele frequencies and thus to evolution. Organisms of one color, for example, may produce fewer offspring than organisms of other colors.

Effect of Color Mutations on Lizard Survival

Initial Population	Generation 10	Generation 20	Generation 30
80%	80%	70%	40%
10%	0%	0%	0%
10%	20%	30%	60%

Suppose that the black lizards in **Figure 16–5** are able to absorb more heat on cold days. If the extra heat allows them to move more quickly on cold days, the lizards may be better able to avoid predators. The new allele for a black body would increase an individual's fitness. Black lizards might then leave behind more offspring than other lizards. The relative frequency of the allele for a black body could, therefore, increase.

It is also possible that a particular color change, such as from brown to gray, would have no effect on the lizard's fitness. In that case, the allele that produces this trait will not be under pressure from natural selection, and its frequency will remain unchanged.

Natural Selection on Polygenic Traits

When traits are controlled by more than one gene, the effects of natural selection are more complex. As you learned earlier, the action of multiple alleles on traits produces a range of phenotypes that often fit a bell curve. The fitness of individuals close to one another on the curve is not very different. But fitness can vary a great deal from one end of a curve to the other. Where fitness varies, natural selection can act. **Natural selection can affect the distributions of phenotypes in any of three ways: directional selection, stabilizing selection, or disruptive selection.**

Directional Selection When individuals at one end of the curve have higher fitness than individuals in the middle or at the other end, **directional selection** takes place. This situation causes the entire curve to move as the character trait changes. In other words, evolution causes an increase in the number of individuals with the trait at one end of the curve.

One observed example of directional selection was an increase in the average size of the beaks in a particular species of Galápagos finches. During a period when food became scarce, the finches had to compete for food. Birds with larger beaks were better able to survive and reproduce. As a result, the average size of the beaks increased, as shown in **Figure 16–6.**

▼ **Figure 16–6** Directional selection occurs when individuals at one end of the curve have higher fitness than individuals in the middle or at the other end. In this example, birds with larger beaks were able to survive more successfully than other birds during a period when food was scarce. In the graph on the right, the dotted line shows the original graph. The solid line shows how the distribution of phenotypes has changed as a result of selection.

Directional Selection

Food becomes scarce.

Number of Birds in Population

Beak Size ⟶

Peak shifts; average beak size increases. ⟶

Number of Birds in Population

Beak Size ⟶

Key

Low mortality, high fitness

High mortality, low fitness

Stabilizing Selection When individuals near the center of the curve have higher fitness than individuals at either end of the curve, **stabilizing selection** takes place. This situation keeps the center of the curve at its current position, but it narrows the overall graph.

As shown in **Figure 16–7,** the weight of human infants at birth is under the influence of stabilizing selection. Human babies born much smaller than average are likely to be less healthy and thus less likely to survive. Babies that are much larger than average are likely to have difficulty being born. The fitness of these larger or smaller individuals is, therefore, lower than that of more average-sized individuals.

Disruptive Selection When individuals at the upper and lower ends of the curve have higher fitness than individuals near the middle, **disruptive selection** takes place. In such situations, selection acts most strongly against individuals of an intermediate type. If the pressure of natural selection is strong enough and lasts long enough, this situation can cause the single curve to split into two. In other words, selection creates two distinct phenotypes.

For example, suppose a population of birds lives in an area where medium-sized seeds become less common and large and small seeds become more common. Birds with unusually small or large beaks would have higher fitness. As shown in **Figure 16–8,** the population might split into two subgroups: one that eats small seeds and one that eats large seeds.

CHECKPOINT *How do stabilizing selection and disruptive selection differ?*

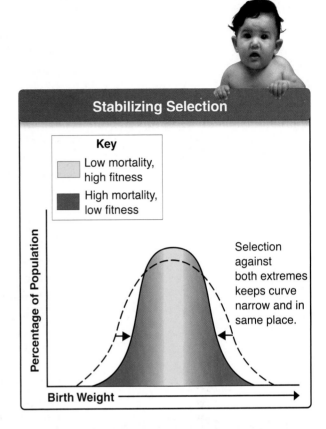

▲ **Figure 16–7** ⬤ Stabilizing selection takes place when individuals near the center of a curve have higher fitness than individuals at either end. This example shows that human babies born at an average weight are more likely to survive than babies born either much smaller or much larger than average.

▼ **Figure 16–8** ⬤ When individuals at the upper and lower ends of the curve have higher fitness than individuals near the middle, disruptive selection takes place. In this example, average-sized seeds become less common, and larger and smaller seeds become more common. As a result, the bird population splits into two subgroups specializing in eating different-sized seeds.

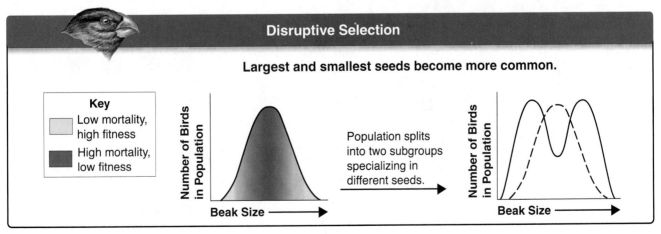

Genetic Drift

Natural selection is not the only source of evolutionary change. In small populations, an allele can become more or less common simply by chance. Recall that genetics is controlled by the laws of probability. These laws can be used to predict the overall results of genetic crosses in large populations. However, the smaller a population is, the farther the results may be from what the laws of probability predict. This kind of random change in allele frequency is called **genetic drift.** How does genetic drift take place? 🔑 **In small populations, individuals that carry a particular allele may leave more descendants than other individuals, just by chance. Over time, a series of chance occurrences of this type can cause an allele to become common in a population.**

Genetic drift may occur when a small group of individuals colonizes a new habitat. These individuals may carry alleles in different relative frequencies than did the larger population from which they came. If so, the population that they found will be genetically different from the parent population. Here, however, the cause is not natural selection but simply chance—specifically, the chance that particular alleles were in one or more of the founding individuals, as shown in **Figure 16–9.** A situation in which allele frequencies change as a result of the migration of a small subgroup of a population is known as the **founder effect.** One example of the founder effect is the evolution of several hundred species of fruit flies found on different Hawaiian Islands. All of those species descended from the same original mainland population. Those species in different habitats on different islands now have allele frequencies that are different from those of the original species.

✔CHECKPOINT *What is genetic drift?*

Figure 16–9 🔘 In small populations, individuals that carry a particular allele may have more descendants than other individuals. Over time, a series of chance occurrences of this type can cause an allele to become more common in a population. This model demonstrates how two small groups from a large, diverse population could produce new populations that differ from the original group.

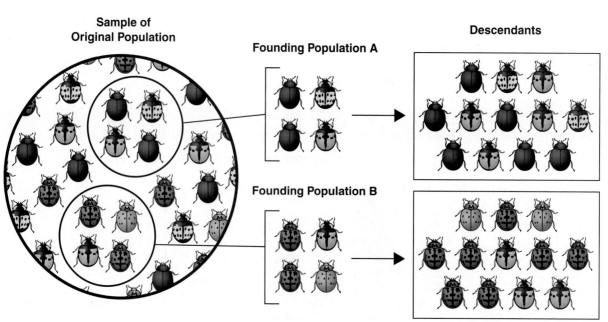

Sample of Original Population

Founding Population A

Founding Population B

Descendants

Can the environment affect survival?

Materials scissors, construction paper (several colors), transparent tape, 15-cm ruler, watch with a second hand

Procedure

1. **Predicting** Predict what would happen to a population of butterflies that includes some individuals that are easy for predators to see and some that blend in with the environment.
2. Choose three different-colored sheets of construction paper. Cut out a butterfly shape from each sheet, 5 × 10 cm in size, as shown. **CAUTION:** *Be careful with scissors.*
3. Tape your butterflies to different-colored surfaces. Then, return to your seat.

4. Record how many shapes of each color you can count from your desk in 5 seconds.
5. Exchange your observations with your classmates to determine the class total for each color.

Analyze and Conclude

1. **Analyzing Data** According to your class data, which colors of butterfly are easiest to see? Which color of butterfly would be most easily caught by a predator?
2. **Inferring** What will happen to the butterfly population after many generations if predators consume most of the easy-to-see butterflies?

Evolution Versus Genetic Equilibrium

You have just seen several of the factors that can cause a population to evolve over time. To clarify how such a set of factors operates, scientists often find it helpful to determine what happens when *no* change takes place. So biologists ask: Are there any conditions under which evolution will not occur? Is there any way to recognize when that is the case? The answers to those questions are provided by the Hardy-Weinberg principle, named after two researchers who independently proposed it in 1908.

The **Hardy-Weinberg principle** states that allele frequencies in a population will remain constant unless one or more factors cause those frequencies to change. The situation in which allele frequencies remain constant is called **genetic equilibrium** (juh-NET-ik ee-kwih-LIB-ree-um). If the allele frequencies do not change, the population will not evolve.

Under what conditions does the Hardy-Weinberg principle hold? **Five conditions are required to maintain genetic equilibrium from generation to generation: There must be random mating; the population must be very large; and there can be no movement into or out of the population, no mutations, and no natural selection.**

In some populations, these conditions may be met or nearly met for long periods of time. If, however, the conditions are not met, the genetic equilibrium will be disrupted, and the population will evolve.

Random Mating All members of the population must have an equal opportunity to produce offspring. Random mating ensures that each individual has an equal chance of passing on its alleles.

In natural populations, however, mating is rarely completely random. Many species, including lions and wolves, select mates based on particular inheritable traits, such as size or strength. Such nonrandom mating means that the genes for those traits are *not* in equilibrium but are under strong selection pressure.

Large Population A large population size is also important in maintaining genetic equilibrium. That is because genetic drift has less effect on large populations, such as the population of birds shown in **Figure 16–10,** than on small ones.

No Movement Into or Out of the Population
Because individuals may bring new alleles into a population, there must be no movement of individuals into or out of a population. In genetic terms, the population's gene pool must be kept together and kept separate from the gene pools of other populations.

No Mutations If genes mutate from one form into another, new alleles may be introduced into the population, and allele frequencies will change.

No Natural Selection All genotypes in the population must have equal probabilities of survival and reproduction. No phenotype can have a selective advantage over another. In other words, there can be no natural selection operating on the population.

▲ **Figure 16–10** One of the five conditions that are needed to maintain genetic equilibrium from one generation to the next is large population size. The allele frequencies of large populations, such as this group of birds, are less likely to be changed through the process of genetic drift.

16–2 Section Assessment

1. **Key Concept** Describe how natural selection can affect traits controlled by single genes.

2. **Key Concept** Describe three patterns of natural selection on polygenic traits. Which one leads to two distinct phenotypes?

3. **Key Concept** How does genetic drift lead to a change in a population's gene pool?

4. **Key Concept** What is the Hardy-Weinberg principle?

5. **Critical Thinking Comparing and Contrasting** How are directional selection and disruptive selection similar? How are they different?

TEXT Assessment Use iText to review the important concepts in Section 16–2.

ALTERNATIVE ASSESSMENT

Using Models Demonstrate natural selection on polygenic traits by cutting a sheet of paper into squares of five different sizes to represent sizes in a population. Use the squares to model directional, stabilizing, and disruptive selection.

Should the Use of Antibiotics Be Restricted?

Natural selection is everywhere. One dramatic example may pose a threat to public health: Disease-causing bacteria are becoming resistant to antibiotics, substances intended to kill them or interfere with their growth.

Antibiotics are one of medicine's greatest weapons against bacterial diseases. When antibiotics were discovered, they were called "magic bullets" and "wonder drugs" because they were so effective. They have made diseases like pneumonia much less of a threat than they were about sixty years ago. However, people may be overusing antibiotics. Doctors sometimes prescribe them for teenagers with acne. Commercial feed for chickens and other farm animals is laced with antibiotics to prevent infection.

As a result of such wide use, many bacteria—including *Mycobacterium tuberculosis,* which causes tuberculosis—are now resistant to antibiotics. The resistance developed because the original treated populations contained a few individuals with the genetic ability to survive the antibiotic. Their descendants thrived and became one of today's dangerous strains. Once-powerful antibiotics are useless against them. Given the risks of this situation, should government agencies such as the Food and Drug Administration restrict the use of antibiotics?

The Viewpoints

Antibiotic Use Should Be Restricted
The danger of an incurable bacterial epidemic is so high that action must be taken on a national level as soon as possible. Doctors overuse antibiotics in humans because patients demand them. The livestock industry likes using antibiotics in animal feeds and will not change their practice unless forced to do so.

Antibiotic Use Should Not Be Restricted
Researchers are coming up with new drugs all the time. These drugs can be reserved for human use only. Doctors need to be able to prescribe antibiotics as they choose, and our food supply depends on the use of antibiotics in agriculture. The medical profession and the livestock industry need the freedom to find solutions that work best for them.

You Decide

1. **Defining the Issues** In your own words, explain the threat caused by overuse of antibiotics.
2. **Analyzing the Viewpoints** List the advantages and disadvantages of restricting the use of antibiotics.
3. **Forming Your Opinion** Should antibiotics be restricted? Are there some situations in which such regulations would be more appropriate than others?
4. **Persuasive Writing** Suppose you are a doctor. You want to use antibiotics to help your patients but are also concerned about the risks of antibiotic-resistant bacteria. Write an article for a newspaper explaining the issue and your position on it.

16–3 The Process of Speciation

Guide for Reading

Key Concepts
- What factors are involved in the formation of new species?
- Describe the process of speciation in the Galápagos finches.

Vocabulary
speciation
reproductive isolation
behavioral isolation
geographic isolation
temporal isolation

Reading Strategy:
Using Visuals Before you read, preview **Figure 16–17.** As you read about speciation of Darwin's finches, notice what happens at each step in the process.

Factors such as natural selection and chance events can change the relative frequencies of alleles in a population. But how do these changes lead to the formation of new species, or **speciation**?

Recall that biologists define a species as a group of organisms that breed with one another and produce fertile offspring. This means that individuals in the same species share a common gene pool. Because a population of individuals has a shared gene pool, a genetic change that occurs in one individual can spread through the population as that individual and its offspring reproduce. If a genetic change increases fitness, that allele will eventually be found in many individuals of that population.

Isolating Mechanisms

You know that the gene pool of a species refers to the sum of its alleles. What happens to a gene pool as one species evolves into one or more species? **As new species evolve, populations become reproductively isolated from each other.** When the members of two populations cannot interbreed and produce fertile offspring, **reproductive isolation** has occurred. At that point, the populations have separate gene pools. They respond to natural selection or genetic drift as separate units. Reproductive isolation can develop in a variety of ways, including behavioral isolation, geographic isolation, and temporal isolation.

Behavioral Isolation One type of isolating mechanism, **behavioral isolation,** occurs when two populations are capable of interbreeding but have differences in courtship rituals or other types of behavior. For example, the eastern and western meadowlarks shown in **Figure 16–11** are very similar birds whose habitats overlap in the center of the United States. Members of the two species will not mate with each other, however, partly because they use different songs to attract mates. Eastern meadowlarks will not respond to western meadowlark songs, and vice versa.

Figure 16–11 The eastern meadowlark (left) and western meadowlark (right) have overlapping ranges. They do not interbreed, however, because they have different mating songs.
Applying Concepts *What type of reproductive isolation does this situation illustrate?*

Abert squirrel

Kaibab squirrel

Geographic Isolation With **geographic isolation,** two populations are separated by geographic barriers such as rivers, mountains, or bodies of water. The Abert squirrel in **Figure 16–12,** for example, lives in the Southwest. About 10,000 years ago, the Colorado River split the species into two separate populations. Two separate gene pools formed. Genetic changes that appeared in one group were not passed to the other. Natural selection worked separately on each group and led to the formation of a distinct subspecies, the Kaibab squirrel.

Geographic barriers do not guarantee the formation of new species, however. Separate lakes may be linked for a time during a flood, or a land bridge may temporarily form between islands, enabling separated populations to mix. If two formerly separated populations can still interbreed, they remain a single species. Also, any potential geographic barrier may separate certain types of organisms but not others. A large river will keep squirrels and other small rodents apart, but it does not necessarily isolate bird populations.

Temporal Isolation A third isolating mechanism is **temporal isolation,** in which two or more species reproduce at different times. For example, three similar species of orchid all live in the same rain forest. Each species releases pollen only on a single day. Because the three species release pollen on different days, they cannot pollinate one another.

✓ CHECKPOINT *How does temporal isolation prevent species from interbreeding?*

Figure 16–12 🔊 When two populations of a species become reproductively isolated, new species can develop. The Kaibab squirrel evolved from the Abert squirrel. The Kaibab squirrels were isolated from the main population by the Colorado River.

Galápagos Islands Finches

Shape of Head and Beak						
Common Name of Finch Species	Vegetarian tree finch	Large insectivorous tree finch	Woodpecker finch	Cactus ground finch	Sharp-beaked ground finch	Large ground finch
Main Food	Fruit	Insects	Insects	Cactus	Seeds	Seeds
Feeding Adaptation	Parrotlike beak	Grasping beak	Uses cactus spines	Large crushing beak	Pointed crushing beak	Large crushing beak
Habitat	Trees	Trees	Trees	Ground	Ground	Ground

▲ **Figure 16–13** Detailed genetic studies have shown that these finches evolved from a species with a more-or-less general-purpose beak. **Formulating Hypotheses** *Suggest how one of these beaks could have resulted from natural selection.*

Testing Natural Selection in Nature

Now that you know the basic mechanisms of evolutionary change, you might wonder if these processes can be observed in nature. The answer is yes! In fact, some of the most important studies showing natural selection in action involve descendants of the finches that Darwin observed in the Galápagos Islands.

Those finch species looked so different from one another that when Darwin first saw them, he did not realize they were all finches. He thought they were blackbirds, warblers, and other kinds of birds! The species he examined differed greatly in the sizes and shapes of their beaks and in their feeding habits, as shown in **Figure 16–13**. Some species fed on small seeds, while others ate large seeds with thick shells. One species used cactus spines to pry insects from dead wood. One species, not shown here, even pecked at the tails of large sea birds and drank their blood!

Once Darwin discovered that these birds were all finches, he hypothesized that they had descended from a common ancestor. Over time, he proposed, natural selection shaped the beaks of different bird populations as they adapted to eat different foods.

That was a reasonable hypothesis. But was there any way to test it? No one thought so, until the work of Peter and Rosemary Grant from Princeton University proved otherwise. For more than twenty years, the Grants, shown in **Figure 16–14,** have been banding and measuring finches on the Galápagos Islands. They realized that Darwin's hypothesis relied on two testable assumptions. First, in order for beak size and shape to evolve, there must be enough inheritable variation in those traits to provide raw material for natural selection. Second, differences in beak size and shape must produce differences in fitness that cause natural selection to occur. The Grants tested these hypotheses on the medium ground finch on Daphne Major, one of the Galápagos islands large enough to support good-sized finch populations, yet small enough to enable the Grants to catch and identify nearly every bird.

Variation The Grants' first task was to identify and measure as many individual birds as possible on a single island. They recorded which birds were still living and which had died, which had succeeded in breeding and which had not. For each individual, they also recorded wing length, leg length, beak length, beak depth, beak color, feather colors, and total bird mass. Many of these characteristics appeared in bell-shaped distributions typical of polygenic traits. From these data, the Grants concluded that there is great variation of inheritable traits among the Galápagos finches.

Natural Selection Other researchers who had visited the Galápagos did not see the different finches competing or eating different foods. During the rainy season, when these researchers visited, there is plenty of food. Under these conditions, finches often eat the most available type of food. During dry-season drought, however, some foods become scarce, and others disappear altogether. At that time, differences in beak size can mean the difference between life and death. To survive, birds become feeding specialists. Each species selects the type of food its beak handles best. Birds with big, heavy beaks, for example, select big, thick seeds that no other species can crack open.

The Grants' most interesting discovery was that individual birds with different-sized beaks had different chances of survival during a drought. When food for the finches was scarce, individuals with the largest beaks were more likely to survive, as shown in **Figure 16–15**. Beak size also plays a role in mating behavior, because big-beaked birds tend to mate with other big-beaked birds. As a result, average beak size in that population increased dramatically. This change in beak size is an example of directional selection.

Rapid Evolution By documenting natural selection in the wild, the Grants provided evidence of the process of evolution: The next generation of finches had larger beaks than did the generation before selection had occurred. An important result of this work was their finding that natural selection takes place frequently—and sometimes very rapidly. Changes in the food supply on the Galápagos caused measurable fluctuations in the finch populations over a period of only decades. This is a markedly different picture from the slow, gradual evolution that Darwin envisioned.

✓**CHECKPOINT** *What type of natural selection did the Grants observe in the Galápagos?*

Figure 16–14
Peter and Rosemary Grant have demonstrated that natural selection is still a force in the evolution of the Galápagos finches.

▼ **Figure 16–15** This graph shows the survival rate of one species of ground-feeding finches, the medium ground finch, or *Geospiza fortis*. **Using Tables and Graphs** *What trend does this graph show?*

Bird Survival Based on Beak Size

Percentage Surviving vs. Beak Size (mm)

Speciation in Darwin's Finches

The Grants' work demonstrates that finch beak size can be changed by natural selection. If we combine this information with other evolutionary concepts you have learned in this chapter, we can devise a hypothetical scenario for the evolution of all Galápagos finches from a single group of founding birds.

🔑 **Speciation in the Galápagos finches occurred by founding of a new population, geographic isolation, changes in the new population's gene pool, reproductive isolation, and ecological competition.** As you read about each step, follow this process in **Figure 16–17** on page 410.

1 Founders Arrive Many years ago, a few finches from the South American mainland—species A—flew or were blown to one of the Galápagos Islands. Finches are small birds that do not usually fly far over open water. These birds may have gotten lost, or they may have been blown off course by a storm. Once they arrived on one of the islands, they managed to survive and reproduce.

2 Separation of Populations Later on, some birds from species A crossed to another island in the Galápagos group. Because these birds do not usually fly over open water, they rarely move from island to island. Thus, finch populations on the two islands were essentially isolated from each other and no longer shared a common gene pool.

Analyzing Data

How Are These Fish Related?

A research team studied two lakes in an area that sometimes experiences flooding. Each lake contained two types of similar fish: a dull brown form and an iridescent gold form. The team wondered how all the fish were related, and they considered the two hypotheses diagrammed on the right.

A = Possible ancestor
B = Contemporary brown form
G = Contemporary gold form
Shows possible line of descent

1. **Interpreting Graphics** Study the two diagrams. What does hypothesis A indicate about the ancestry of the fish in Lake 1 and Lake 2? What does hypothesis B indicate?

2. **Comparing and Contrasting** According to the two hypotheses, what is the key difference in the way the brown and gold fish populations might have formed?

3. **Drawing Conclusions** A DNA analysis showed that the brown and gold fish from Lake 1 are the most closely related. Which hypothesis does this evidence support?

4. **Going Further** What evidence could help determine whether the brown and gold fish are members of separate species?

3 Changes in the Gene Pool Over time, populations on each island became adapted to their local environments. The plants growing on the first island may have produced small thin-shelled seeds, whereas the plants on the second island may have produced larger thick-shelled seeds. On the second island, directional selection would favor individuals with larger, heavier beaks. These birds could crack open and eat the large seeds more easily. Thus, birds with large beaks would be better able to survive on the second island. Over time, natural selection would have caused that population to evolve larger beaks, forming a separate population, B.

4 Reproductive Isolation Now, imagine that a few birds from the second island cross back to the first island. Will the population-A birds breed with the population-B birds? Probably not. These finches choose their mates carefully. As part of the courtship process, they inspect a potential part-ner's beak very closely. Finches prefer to mate with birds that have the same-sized beak as they do. In other words, big-beaked birds prefer to mate with other big-beaked birds, and smaller-beaked birds prefer to mate with other smaller-beaked birds. Because the birds on the two islands have different-sized beaks, it is likely that they would not choose to mate with each other. Thus, differences in beak size, combined with mating behavior, could lead to reproductive isolation. The gene pools of the two bird populations remain isolated from each other—even when individuals live together in the same place. The two populations have now become separate species.

5 Ecological Competition As these two new species live together in the same environment (the first island), they compete with each other for available seeds. During the dry season, individuals that are most different from each other have the highest fitness. The more specialized birds have less compe-tition for certain kinds of seeds and other foods, and the compe-tition among individual finches is also reduced. Over time, species evolve in a way that increases the differences between them. The species-B birds on the first island may evolve into a new species, C.

6 Continued Evolution This process of isolation on different islands, genetic change, and reproductive isolation probably repeated itself time and time again across the entire Galápagos island chain. Over many generations, it produced the 13 different finch species found there today. **Figure 16–17** on page 410 shows how two species with larger and smaller beaks might have formed. Use the steps in this illustration to explain how other Darwin finches, such as the vegetarian tree finch that feeds on fruit, might have evolved.

▲ **Figure 16–16** The Galápagos Islands are actually tips of undersea volcanoes that reach from the ocean floor to just above sea level. **Inferring** *What can you infer about the mechanism of the Galápagos finches' evolution based on the location of these islands?*

Figure 16–17 Speciation in the Galápagos finches occurred by founding of new populations, geographic isolation, gene pool changes, reproductive isolation, and ecological competition. Small groups of finches moved from one island to another, became reproductively isolated, and evolved into new species.

1 Founders Arrive
A few finches travel from South America to one of the islands. There, they survive and reproduce.

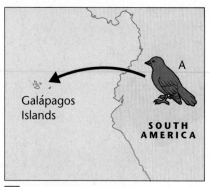

2 Separation of Populations
Some birds from species A cross to a second island. The two populations no longer share a gene pool.

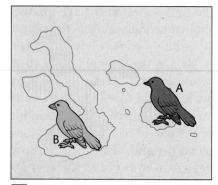

3 Changes in the Gene Pool
Seed sizes on the second island favor birds with larger beaks. The population on the second island evolves into a population, B, with larger beaks.

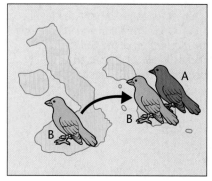

4 Reproductive Isolation
If a few population-B birds cross back to the first island, they will not mate with the birds of population A. The gene pools are now separate. Populations A and B are separate species.

5 Ecological Competition
As species A and B compete for seeds on the first island, they continue to evolve. A new species, C, may evolve. Some members of the original species B may travel to a new island.

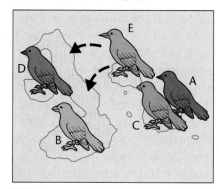

6 Continued Evolution
The process continues, leading to the formation of all 13 finch species on the Galápagos.

16–3 Section Assessment

1. **Key Concept** How is reproductive isolation related to the formation of new species?

2. **Key Concept** What type of isolating mechanism was important in the formation of different Galápagos finch species?

3. Explain how behavior can play a role in the evolution of species.

4. **Critical Thinking Applying Concepts** Leopard frogs and tree frogs share the same habitat. Leopard frogs mate in April; tree frogs mate in June. How are these species isolated from each other?

iTEXT Assessment Use iText to review the important concepts in Section 16–3.

Take It to the NET
Read how DNA data has been used to study Australian birds. Then, write a paragraph comparing the evolution of those Australian birds with that of Darwin's finches. Use the links provided in the Biology area at the Prentice Hall Web site for help in completing this activity: **www.phschool.com**

Investigating Genetic Diversity in Bacteria

Genetic diversity can make a population of organisms more adaptable. Some bacteria are able to survive in the presence of antibiotics that kill other bacteria. In this investigation, you will test a population of bacteria for the presence of antibiotic-resistant bacteria.

Problem How common are antibiotic-resistant bacteria?

Materials

- liquid bacterial culture
- sterile swabs
- sterile agar plate
- glass-marking pencil
- antibiotic paper disks
- forceps
- transparent tape
- 70% alcohol
- metric ruler

Skills Observing, Analyzing Data

Procedure

1. Wash your hands thoroughly with soap and warm water. Without opening the agar plate, use a glass-marking pencil to draw two lines at right angles on the bottom of the plate. This will divide the plate into four equal areas, or quadrants. Label the quadrants 1 to 4, as shown. Write your initials on the plate.

2. Dip a sterile swab in the bacterial culture. Remove the cover of the agar plate and rub the swab gently over the entire surface of the agar. Immediately replace the cover. Follow your teacher's directions for disposing of the swab.

3. Remove the cover of the agar plate again. Use clean forceps to place an antibiotic disk on the agar in the center of each quadrant. Replace the cover; then tape the plate closed.

4. Place the plate upside down in the area designated by your teacher.

5. Return the forceps to your teacher for disinfection. Wipe your work surface with 70% alcohol and a paper towel. Wash your hands well with soap and warm water before leaving the lab.

6. After 24 hours, observe the growth of bacteria around each antibiotic disk. Record your observations. **CAUTION:** *Do not open the plate.*

7. Use the metric ruler to measure the diameter of the zone of reduced bacterial growth, called the zone of inhibition, around each antibiotic disk. Record the diameter of each zone of inhibition.

8. Carefully observe the zones of inhibition. Do you see any evidence of bacterial growth there? Record your observations. Give the used plate to your teacher for safe disposal.

Analyze and Conclude

1. **Observing** How did the antibiotic disks affect the growth of the bacteria?

2. **Inferring** What effect, if any, did the antibiotic disks have on the gene pool of these bacteria?

3. **Classifying** What type of selection (directional, stabilizing, or disruptive) occurred in this experiment? Explain your answer.

4. **Drawing Conclusions** Did your data support the idea that antibiotic-resistant bacteria are common? Explain your answer.

Go Further

Applying Concepts Investigate genetic diversity further by using your school library and the Internet to research the use of wild relatives of food crops to increase genetic variation in plants.

16–1 Genes and Variation
🔑 Key Concepts

- Biologists have discovered that there are two main sources of genetic variation: mutations and the genetic shuffling that results from sexual reproduction.

- The number of phenotypes produced for a given trait depends on how many genes control the trait.

Vocabulary
gene pool, p. 394
relative frequency, p. 394
single-gene trait, p. 395
polygenic trait, p. 396

16–2 Evolution as Genetic Change
🔑 Key Concepts

- Natural selection on single-gene traits can lead to changes in allele frequencies and thus to evolution.

- Natural selection can affect the distributions of phenotypes in any of three ways: directional selection, stabilizing selection, or disruptive selection.

- In small populations, individuals that carry a particular allele may leave more descendants than other individuals, just by chance. Over time, a series of chance occurrences of this type can cause an allele to become common in a population.

- Five conditions are required to maintain genetic equilibrium from generation to generation: There must be random mating; the population must be very large; and there can be no movement into or out of the population, no mutations, and no natural selection.

Vocabulary
directional selection, p. 398
stabilizing selection, p. 399
disruptive selection, p. 399
genetic drift, p. 400
founder effect, p. 400
Hardy-Weinberg principle, p. 401
genetic equilibrium, p. 401

16–3 The Process of Speciation
🔑 Key Concepts

- As new species evolve, populations become reproductively isolated from each other.

- Speciation in the Galápagos finches occurred by founding of a new population, geographic isolation, changes in the new population's gene pool, reproductive isolation, and ecological competition.

Vocabulary
speciation, p. 404
reproductive isolation, p. 404
behavioral isolation, p. 404
geographic isolation, p. 405
temporal isolation, p. 405

Thinking Visually
Using the information in this chapter, complete the following concept map about evolution of populations:

Chapter 16

Part A

Multiple Choice

For each statement or question, select the number of the word or expression that, of those given, best completes the statement or answers the question.

1 The combined genetic information of all the members of a particular population forms a
(1) gene pool   **(3)** phenotype
(2) genotype   **(4)** genetic drift

2 The success of an organism in surviving and reproducing is a measure of its
(1) fitness   **(3)** speciation
(2) founder effect   **(4)** gene pool

3 Traits, such as human height, that are controlled by more than one gene are known as
(1) single-gene traits
(2) polygenic traits
(3) recessive traits
(4) dominant traits

4 The type of selection in which individuals of average size have greater fitness than small or large individuals is called
(1) disruptive selection
(2) stabilizing selection
(3) directional selection
(4) artificial selection

5 The type of selection in which individuals at one end of a curve have the highest fitness is called
(1) artificial selection
(2) disruptive selection
(3) directional selection
(4) stabilizing selection

6 Which term best describes a change in the frequency of an allele in a population that comes about by chance?
(1) a gene pool
(2) genetic drift
(3) genetic variation
(4) natural selection

7 A change in allele frequencies that results when a small subgroup of a population migrates to a new area is called
(1) natural selection
(2) the Hardy-Weinberg principle
(3) the founder effect
(4) genetic equilibrium

8 Similar organisms that can breed with each other and produce fertile offspring in the natural environment make up a
(1) species
(2) gene pool
(3) ecosystem
(4) temporal zone

9 The evolution of Darwin's finches is an example of
(1) genetic equilibrium
(2) speciation
(3) stabilizing selection
(4) artificial selection

10 Which condition may result in speciation?
(1) lack of mutations
(2) sexual selection
(3) absence of genetic variation
(4) small population size

11 In a population of lizards, the smallest and largest lizards are more easily captured by predators than middle-sized lizards. What kind of natural selection is most likely to occur in this situation?
(1) disruptive selection
(2) artificial selection
(3) stabilizing selection
(4) directional selection

12 When two species cannot interbreed because they reproduce at different times, the situation is called
(1) temporal isolation
(2) speciation
(3) genetic drift
(4) geographic isolation

13 Change is to evolution as lack of change is to
(1) genetic equilibrium
(2) polygenic traits
(3) gene pool
(4) genetic variation

> **Test-Taking Tip** If you have trouble answering a question, make a mark beside it and go on. (Do not write in this book.) You may find information in later questions that will allow you to eliminate some answer choices in your unanswered question.

Parts B and C

Multiple Choice and Extended Response

For those questions that ask you to select a response, choose the one that best completes the statement or answers the question. For all others follow the directions given.

14 If coat color in rabbits is a polygenic trait, which process might have produced the situation shown in the graph below?

Darkness of Coat ⟶

(1) stabilizing selection
(2) disruptive selection
(3) directional selection
(4) genetic equilibrium

Base your answers to questions 15 and 16 on the graphs below, which show the changes in a population of crabs living on a particular beach, and on your knowledge of biology.

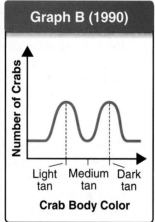

15 Describe how the coloration in the population of crabs changed between 1950 and 1990.

16 Between 1950 and 1990, the color of the sand got lighter and large areas of sand eroded away, leaving areas of darker bedrock exposed. Explain how these changes in the sand could account for the changes in the crab population.

17 Eastern and western meadowlarks do not interbreed because they have different mating songs. This situation is called
(1) geographic isolation
(2) behavioral isolation
(3) temporal isolation
(4) random mating

18 Explain why sexual reproduction is a source of genetic variation.

Base your answers to questions 19 through 21 on Figure 16–5 on page 397 and on your knowledge of biology.

19 How did the frequency of the brown allele change over 30 generations?

20 Some scientists concluded that this lizard population is evolving. Explain how the data in the chart support this conclusion.

21 What role did mutations play in the changes that occurred over 20 generations in this lizard population?

Base your answers to questions 22 through 24 on the graph below, which shows the data on the lengths of beaks of three finch species that live on the ground, and on your knowledge of biology.

22 Which of the three species represented in the graph has the smallest range of beak sizes?

23 Name the species that most likely eats the largest seeds. Explain the basis for your answer.

24 Describe how the graph for Species C would likely change if the seed characteristics changed to make it very difficult for birds with beaks 18 to 21 mm to use the seeds for food.

25 How are speciation and reproductive isolation related?

26 What is genetic drift? In what kinds of situations is it likely to occur?

27 How did the work of Rosemary and Peter Grant reinforce Darwin's hypothesis about finch evolution in the Galápagos Islands?

28 Describe one way that the *lack* of genetic variation could affect the survival of a species.

Base your answers to questions 29 and 30 on the chart below and on your knowledge of biology.

Frequency of Alleles

Year	Frequency of Allele B	Frequency of Allele b
1900	0.99	0.01
1910	0.81	0.19
1920	0.64	0.36
1930	0.49	0.51
1940	0.36	0.64
1950	0.25	0.75
1960	0.16	0.84
1970	0.10	0.90

29 Which statement about the frequencies of alleles between 1900 and 1970 is correct?
(1) Allele B increased in frequency as allele b decreased in frequency.
(2) Allele B decreased in frequency as allele b increased in frequency.
(3) Both alleles decreased in frequency.
(4) Both alleles increased in frequency.

30 The best explanation for the data is that
(1) allele b was needed by the species, and it therefore appeared
(2) organisms carrying allele b had a reduced rate of survival
(3) a change in the environment favored the trait controlled by allele B
(4) a change in the environment favored the trait controlled by allele b

31 Explain what the term *frequency* means as it applies to a trait such as fur color in a species of animal. Provide a specific example with your answer.

32 What is meant by the term *single-gene trait*?

33 Compare the number of phenotypes that are possible for single-gene traits with the number that are possible for polygenic traits.

34 Since antibiotics were discovered in the 1940s, they have become one of the most commonly prescribed types of drugs in the United States. More than 133 million prescriptions for antibiotics are written by doctors each year for nonhospitalized patients, and 190 million doses of antibiotics are administered in United States hospitals each day. However, antibiotics are becoming less effective, because the more they are used, the more resistant bacteria become to them. Explain how natural selection can result in an antibiotic becoming less effective against a particular species of bacteria. In your answer, be sure to describe
• how bacteria originally became resistant to the antibiotic
• how the antibiotic acted as an "agent of natural selection"
• how continued use of the antibiotic can lead to an almost totally resistant population of the bacteria

 Take It to the NET

Can you identify the most genetically valuable animal in a pedigree? Visit the Prentice Hall Web site at **www.phschool.com** to play a game about the science of population management. Then, answer the following questions:
• How do population managers try to maintain variation within a population?
• Which animals in a population are considered the most genetically valuable?
• How do captive breeding programs attempt to compensate for genetic drift?

17 The History of Life

About 25 million years ago, this scorpion was caught in sticky tree resin, which later hardened into amber. Fossils like this one provide evidence that enables scientists to build up a picture of Earth's history.

Inquiry Activity

How can you date a rock?

Procedure

1. Examine a piece of shale with a hand lens. This rock formed from the sediment deposited at the bottom of an ancient lake. As the shale formed, one dark layer and one light layer were deposited each year.

2. Place a transparent metric ruler next to the shale sample. Count and record the number of dark layers in a 5-mm section of the shale.

3. Divide your result in step 2 by 5 to determine the average number of layers per millimeter.

Think About It

1. **Inferring** How many years did it take for your specimen to form?

2. **Calculating** Suppose your specimen came from a deposit of shale that is 600 meters thick. How long did it take for the complete deposit to form?

17–1 The Fossil Record

The history of life on Earth is filled with mystery, life-and-death struggles, and bizarre plants and animals as amazing as any mythological creatures. Studying life's history is one of the most fascinating and challenging parts of biology, and researchers go about it in several ways. One technique is to read the pieces of the story that are "written" in ancient rocks, in the petrified sap of ancient trees, in peat bogs and tar pits, and in polar glaciers. You may recall that these traces and preserved remains of ancient life are called fossils.

Fossils and Ancient Life

Paleontologists (pay-lee-un-TAHL-uh-jists) are scientists who study fossils. They collect fossils such as the one shown in **Figure 17–1.** From these fossils, they infer what past life forms were like—the structure of the organisms, what they ate, what ate them, and the environment in which they lived. Paleontologists also classify fossil organisms. They group similar organisms together and arrange them in the order in which they lived—from oldest to most recent. Together, all this information about past life is called the **fossil record.** **The fossil record provides evidence about the history of life on Earth. It also shows how different groups of organisms have changed over time.**

The fossil record reveals a remarkable fact: Fossils occur in a particular order. Certain fossils appear only in older rocks, and other fossils appear only in more recent rocks. In other words, the fossil record shows that life on Earth has changed over time. In fact, more than 99 percent of all species that have ever lived on Earth have become **extinct,** which means the species died out. Meanwhile, over billions of years, ancient unicellular organisms have given rise to the modern bacteria, protists, fungi, plants, and animals that you will study in later units.

Guide for Reading

Key Concepts
- What is the fossil record?
- What information do relative dating and radioactive dating provide about fossils?
- What are the main divisions of the geologic time scale?

Vocabulary
- paleontologist • fossil record
- extinct • relative dating
- index fossil • half-life
- radioactive dating
- geologic time scale • era
- period

Reading Strategy:
Finding Main Ideas Before you read, write down this idea: Scientists use the fossil record to learn about the history of life on Earth. As you read, make a list of the kinds of evidence that support this main idea.

▶ **Figure 17–1** This remarkably complete dinosaur fossil reveals many characteristics of the original animal. **Inferring** *Based on this dinosaur's teeth, what type of food do you think it ate?*

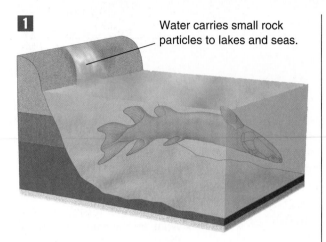

1 Water carries small rock particles to lakes and seas.

2 Dead organisms are buried by layers of sediment, which forms new rock.

3 The preserved remains may later be discovered and studied.

▲ **Figure 17–2** The fossil record provides evidence about the history of life on Earth. Some fossils are formed in sedimentary rock. (1) Water carries small particles from existing rocks to lakes and seas. (2) The rock particles sink to the bottom, sometimes burying dead organisms. The weight of the upper layers compresses the lower layers into new rocks. Minerals replace all or part of the organism's body. (3) The preserved remains may later become exposed. The outline above shows the organism's original shape.

How Fossils Form

A fossil can be as large and complete as an entire, perfectly preserved animal, or as small and incomplete as a tiny fragment of a jawbone or leaf. There are fossil eggs, fossil footprints, and even fossilized animal droppings. For a fossil to form, either the remains of the organism or some trace of its presence must be preserved. The formation of any fossil depends on a precise combination of conditions. Because of this, the fossil record provides incomplete information about the history of life. For every organism that leaves a fossil, many more die without leaving a trace.

Most fossils form in sedimentary rock, as shown in **Figure 17–2.** Sedimentary rock is formed when exposure to rain, heat, wind, and cold breaks down existing rock into small particles of sand, silt, and clay. These particles are carried by streams and rivers into lakes or seas, where they eventually settle to the bottom. As layers of sediment build up over time, dead organisms may also sink to the bottom and become buried. If conditions are right, the remains may be kept intact and free from decay. The weight of layers of sediment gradually compresses the lower layers and, along with chemical activity, turns them into rock.

The quality of fossil preservation varies. In some cases, the small particles of rock surrounding the remains of an organism preserve an imprint of its soft parts. In other cases, the hard parts are preserved when wood, shells, or bones are saturated or replaced with long-lasting mineral compounds. Occasionally, organisms are buried quickly in fine-grained clay or volcanic ash before they begin to decay, so they are perfectly preserved.

✔CHECKPOINT Why is the fossil record described as an incomplete record of life's history?

Interpreting Fossil Evidence

The natural forces that form sedimentary rock can also reveal fossils that have been hidden deep in layers of rock for millions of years. Forces inside Earth lift rocks up into mountain ranges, where wind, rain, and running water erode the rock. Bit by bit, flowing water and wind wear away the upper, younger layers, exposing the older fossil-bearing layers beneath.

When a fossil is exposed, a fortunate (and observant) paleontologist may happen along at just the right time and remove the fossil for study.

Paleontologists occasionally unearth the remains of an entire organism. More often, though, they must reconstruct an extinct species from a few fossil bits—remains of bone, a shell, leaves, or pollen. Fossil reconstruction requires a thorough knowledge of the anatomy of living organisms, as well as great skill. Also, one of the most important pieces of information about a fossil is its age. Paleontologists determine the age of fossils using two techniques: relative dating and radioactive dating.

Relative Dating About two centuries ago, geologists noted that rock layers containing certain fossils consistently appeared in the same vertical order no matter where they were found. Also, a particular species of trilobite—a common fossil and an extinct relative of horseshoe crabs—might be found in one rock layer but be absent from layers above or below it. How might such a pattern be useful?

In **relative dating,** the age of a fossil is determined by comparing its placement with that of fossils in other layers of rock, as shown in **Figure 17–3.** Recall that sedimentary rock is formed from the gradual deposition of layers of sand, rock, and other types of sediment. The rock layers form in order by age— the oldest layers on the bottom, with more recent layers on top, closer to Earth's surface.

Scientists also use **index fossils** to compare the relative ages of fossils. To be used as an index fossil, a species must be easily recognized and must have existed for a short period but have had a wide geographic range. As a result, it will be found in only a few layers of rock, but these specific layers will be found in different geographic locations. ⚷ **Relative dating allows paleontologists to estimate a fossil's age compared with that of other fossils.** However, it provides no information about its absolute age, or age in years.

Word Origins

The word part *paleo-* means "ancient" or "early," and *-zoic* means "life." The word part *meso-* means "middle." The word part *ceno-* means "recent." **Use this information to explain the meaning of *paleozoic, mesozoic,* and *cenozoic.***

▼ **Figure 17–3** In relative dating, a paleontologist estimates a fossil's age in comparison with that of other fossils. Each of these fossils is an index fossil. It enables scientists to date the rock layer in which it is found. Scientists can also use index fossils to date rocks from different locations.

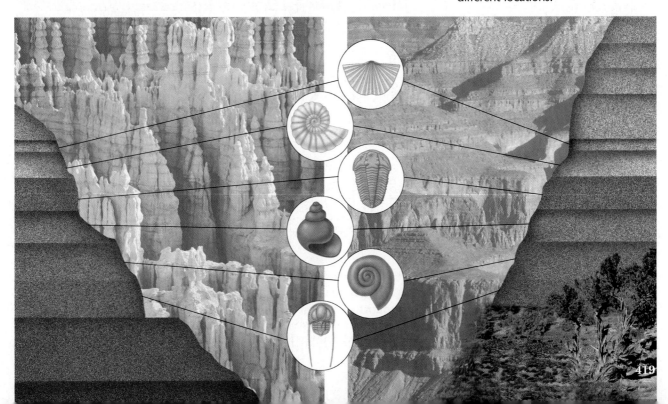

What is a half-life?

Materials 100 1-cm squares of paper, plastic or paper cup

Procedure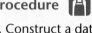

1. Construct a data table with 2 columns and 5 blank rows. Label the columns "Spill number" and "Number of squares returned."
2. Place an *X* on each square of paper, and put all the squares in the cup.
3. Mix up the squares in the cup. Then, spill them out and separate all squares that overlap.
4. Remove the squares that have an *X* showing. Record the number of squares remaining and return them to the cup.
5. Repeat steps 3 and 4 until there are 5 or fewer squares remaining. Make a graph of your results with the number of spills on the *x*-axis and the number of squares remaining on the *y*-axis.

Analyze and Conclude

1. **Analyzing Data** How many spills were required to remove half of the squares? To remove three fourths?
2. **Calculating** If each spill represents one year, what is the half-life of the squares?

Radioactive Dating Scientists use radioactive decay to assign absolute ages to rocks. Some elements found in rocks are radioactive. Radioactive elements decay, or break down, into nonradioactive elements at a steady rate, which is measured in a unit called a half-life. A **half-life** is the length of time required for half of the radioactive atoms in a sample to decay. As shown in **Figure 17–4,** after one half-life, half of the original radioactive atoms in a sample have decayed. Of those remaining atoms, half again are decayed after another half-life.

Radioactive dating is the use of half-lives to determine the age of a sample. 🔑 **In radioactive dating, scientists calculate the age of a sample based on the amount of remaining radioactive isotopes it contains.** Different radioactive elements have different half-lives and therefore provide natural clocks that "tick" at different rates. Carbon-14, for example, has a half-life of about 5730 years. Carbon-14 is taken up by living things while they are alive. After an organism dies, the carbon-14 in its body begins to decay to form nitrogen-14, which escapes into the air. Carbon-12, the most common isotope of carbon, is not radioactive and does not decay. By comparing the amounts of carbon-14 and carbon-12 in a fossil, researchers can determine when the organism lived. The more carbon-12 there is in a sample compared to carbon-14, the older the sample is.

Because carbon-14 has a relatively short half-life, it is useful only for dating fossils younger than about 60,000 years. To date rocks that are billions of years old, researchers use the slower clocks offered by the decay of potassium-40 and other isotopes with longer half-lives.

✓**CHECKPOINT** *What is a half-life?*

▲ **Figure 17–4** 🔑 **Radioactive dating involves measuring the amounts of radioactive isotopes in a sample to determine its actual age.** Such measurements enable scientists to determine the absolute age of rocks and the fossils they contain.

Geologic Time Scale

Paleontologists use divisions of the **geologic time scale** to represent evolutionary time. **Figure 17–5** shows the most recent version of the geologic time scale. Scientists first developed the geologic time scale by studying rock layers and index fossils worldwide. With this information, they placed Earth's rocks in order according to relative age. As geologists studied the fossil record, they found major changes in the fossil animals and plants at specific layers in the rock. These times were used to mark where one segment of geologic time ends and the next begins— long before anyone knew how long these various segments actually were.

Years later, radioactive dating techniques were used to assign specific ages to the various rock layers. Not surprisingly, the divisions of the geologic time scale did not turn out to be of standard lengths, such as 100 million years. Instead, geologic divisions vary in duration by many millions of years. Scientists use several levels of divisions for the geologic time scale. Geologic time begins with Precambrian (pree-KAM-bree-un) Time. Although few multicellular fossils exist from this time, the Precambrian actually covers about 88 percent of Earth's history, as shown in **Figure 17–6** on page 422. After Precambrian Time, the basic divisions of the geologic time scale are eras and periods.

Eras Geologists divide the time between the Precambrian and the present into three **eras.** They are the Paleozoic Era, the Mesozoic Era, and the Cenozoic Era. The Paleozoic (pay-lee-uh-ZOH-ik) began about 544 million years ago and lasted for almost 300 million years. Many vertebrates and invertebrates—animals with and without backbones—lived during the Paleozoic.

The Mesozoic (mez-uh-ZOH-ik) began about 245 million years ago and lasted about 180 million years. Some people call the Mesozoic the Age of Dinosaurs, yet dinosaurs were only one of many kinds of organisms that lived during this era. Mammals began to evolve during the Mesozoic.

Earth's most recent era is the Cenozoic (sen-uh-ZOH-ik). It began about 65 million years ago and continues to the present. The Cenozoic is sometimes called the Age of Mammals because mammals became common during this time.

Geologic Time Scale		
Era	Period	Time (millions of years ago)
Cenozoic	Quaternary	1.8 – present
	Tertiary	65 – 1.8
Mesozoic	Cretaceous	145 – 65
	Jurassic	208 – 145
	Triassic	245 – 208
Paleozoic	Permian	290 – 245
	Carboniferous	363 – 290
	Devonian	410 – 363
	Silurian	440 – 410
	Ordovician	505 – 440
	Cambrian	544 – 505
Precambrian Time	Vendian	650 – 544

▲ **Figure 17–5** The basic units of the geologic time scale after Precambrian Time are eras and periods. Each era is divided into periods.

Cenozoic Era

Mesozoic Era

Paleozoic Era

Precambrian Time

Radiation of mammals

First humans

First land plants

First prokaryotes

First multicellular organisms

First eukaryotes

Accumulation of atmospheric oxygen

▲ **Figure 17–6** Earth's history is often compared to a familiar measurement, such as the twelve hours between noon and midnight. In such a comparison, notice that Precambrian Time lasts from noon until after 10:30 PM. **Interpreting Graphics** *Using this model, about what time did life appear? The first plants? The first humans?*

Periods Eras are subdivided into **periods,** which range in length from tens of millions of years to less than two million years. The Mesozoic Era, for example, includes three periods: the Triassic Period, the Jurassic Period, and the Cretaceous Period. Many periods are named for places around the world where geologists first described the rocks and fossils of that period. The name Cambrian, for example, refers to Cambria, the old Roman name for Wales. Jurassic refers to the Jura Mountains in France. The Carboniferous ("carbon-bearing") Period, on the other hand, is named for the large coal deposits that formed during that period.

17–1 Section Assessment

1. 🔑 **Key Concept** What can be learned from the fossil record?

2. 🔑 **Key Concept** Which type of dating provides an absolute age for a given fossil? Describe how this is done.

3. 🔑 **Key Concept** How are eras and periods related?

4. **Critical Thinking Drawing Conclusions** Many more fossils have been found since Darwin's day, allowing several gaps in the fossil record to be filled. How might this information make relative dating more accurate?

🔲**TEXT** **Assessment** Use iText to review the important concepts in Section 17–1.

17–2 Earth's Early History

In Chapter 1 you read about people's theories and experiments on the origin of life. The theory of spontaneous generation—life from nonlife—was disproved about 140 years ago. But if life comes only from life, then how did life on Earth first begin? This section presents the current scientific view of events on the early Earth. These hypotheses, however, are based on a relatively small amount of evidence. As new evidence is found, scientists' ideas about the early Earth and the origin of life may change.

Formation of Earth

Geologic evidence shows that Earth was not "born" in a single event. Instead, pieces of cosmic debris were probably attracted to one another over the course of about 100 million years. While the planet was young, it was struck by one or more objects, possibly as large as the planet Mars. This collision produced enough heat to melt the entire globe.

Once Earth melted, its elements rearranged themselves according to density. The most dense elements formed the planet's core. There, radioactive decay generated enough heat to convert Earth's interior into molten rock. Moderately dense elements floated to the surface, much as fat floats to the top of hot chicken soup. These elements ultimately cooled to form a solid crust. The least dense elements—including hydrogen and nitrogen—formed the first atmosphere.

This infant planet, shown in **Figure 17–7,** was so different from today's Earth that you would not recognize it. The sky was not blue but pinkish-orange. **Earth's early atmosphere probably contained hydrogen cyanide, carbon dioxide, carbon monoxide, nitrogen, hydrogen sulfide, and water.** Had you been there, a few deep breaths would have killed you!

▼ **Figure 17–7** The early Earth was much hotter than it is now, and there was little or no oxygen in the atmosphere. Earth's early atmosphere was probably made up of hydrogen cyanide, carbon dioxide, carbon monoxide, nitrogen, hydrogen sulfide, and water.

About 4 billion years ago, Earth cooled enough to allow the first solid rocks to form on its surface. For millions of years afterward, violent volcanic activity shook Earth's crust. Comets and asteroids bombarded its surface. Oceans did not exist because the surface was extremely hot.

About 3.8 billion years ago, Earth's surface cooled enough for water to remain a liquid. Thunderstorms drenched the planet, and oceans covered much of the surface. Those primitive oceans were brown because they contained lots of dissolved iron. The earliest sedimentary rocks, which were deposited in water, have been dated to this period. This was the Earth on which life appeared.

✓CHECKPOINT *Why did the early Earth not have oceans?*

The First Organic Molecules

For several reasons, atoms do not assemble themselves into complex organic molecules or living cells on Earth today. For one thing, the oxygen in the atmosphere is very reactive and would destroy any organic molecules that formed. In addition, as soon as organic molecules appeared, something—bacteria or some other life form—would probably eat them! But the early Earth was a very different place. Could organic molecules have evolved under those conditions?

In the 1950s, American chemists Stanley Miller and Harold Urey tried to answer that question by simulating conditions on the early Earth in a laboratory setting. They filled a flask with hydrogen, methane, ammonia, and water to represent the atmosphere. They made certain that no microorganisms could contaminate the results. Then, as shown in **Figure 17–8**, they passed electric sparks through the mixture to simulate lightning.

The results were spectacular. Over a few days, several amino acids—the building blocks of proteins—began to accumulate. **Miller and Urey's experiments suggested how mixtures of the organic compounds necessary for life could have arisen from simpler compounds present on a primitive Earth.** Scientists now know that Miller and Urey's original simulations of Earth's early atmosphere were not accurate. However, similar experiments based on more current knowledge of Earth's early atmosphere have also produced organic compounds. In fact, one of Miller's experiments in 1995 produced cytosine and uracil, two of the bases found in RNA.

▲ **Figure 17–8** Miller and Urey produced amino acids, which are needed to make proteins, by passing sparks through a mixture of hydrogen, methane, ammonia, and water. This and other experiments suggested how simple compounds found on the early Earth could have combined to form the organic compounds needed for life.

Labels on figure: Mixture of gases simulating atmosphere of early Earth; Spark simulating lightning storms; Condensation chamber; Water vapor; Cold water cools chamber, causing droplets to form; Liquid containing amino acids and other organic compounds

How Did Life Begin?

A stew of organic molecules is a long way from a living cell, and the leap from nonlife to life is the greatest gap in scientific theories of Earth's early history. Scientists do know that about 200 to 300 million years after Earth cooled enough to carry liquid water, cells similar to modern bacteria were common. How might these cells have originated?

Formation of Microspheres Under certain conditions, large organic molecules can form tiny bubbles called **proteinoid microspheres,** as shown in **Figure 17–9.** Microspheres are not cells, but they have some characteristics of living systems. Like cells, they have selectively permeable membranes through which water molecules can pass. Microspheres also have a simple means of storing and releasing energy. Several hypotheses suggest that structures similar to proteinoid microspheres might have acquired more and more characteristics of living cells.

Evolution of RNA and DNA Another unanswered question in the evolution of cells is the origin of DNA and RNA. Remember that all cells are controlled by information stored in DNA, which is transcribed into RNA and then translated into proteins. How could this complex biochemical machinery have evolved?

Science cannot yet solve this puzzle, although molecular biologists have made surprising discoveries in this area. Under the right conditions, some RNA sequences can help DNA replicate. Other RNA sequences process messenger RNA after transcription. Still others catalyze chemical reactions. Some RNA molecules can even grow and duplicate themselves—suggesting that RNA might have existed before DNA. A series of experiments that simulated conditions of the early Earth have suggested that small sequences of RNA could have formed and replicated on their own. From this relatively simple RNA-based form of life, several steps could have led to the system of DNA-directed protein synthesis that exists now. This hypothesis is shown in **Figure 17–10.** Future experiments are aimed at refining and retesting this hypothesis.

(magnification: about 10,000×)

▲ **Figure 17–9** Large organic molecules can sometimes form tiny proteinoid microspheres like the ones shown here. **Comparing and Contrasting** *How are proteinoid microspheres similar to cells? How are they different?*

▼ **Figure 17–10** One hypothesis about the origin of life, illustrated here, suggests that RNA could have evolved before DNA. Scientists have not yet demonstrated the later stages of this process in a laboratory setting. **Interpreting Graphics** *How might RNA have stored genetic information?*

Abiotic "stew" of inorganic matter → Simple organic molecules → RNA nucleotides → RNA able to replicate itself, synthesize proteins, and function in informative storage

Proteins build cell structures and catalyze chemical reactions

RNA helps in protein synthesis

DNA functions in informative storage and retrieval

▲ Figure 17–11 Ancient photosynthetic organisms produced a rise in oxygen in Earth's atmosphere. These rocklike formations, called stromatolites, were made by cyanobacteria, which were among the earliest organisms to evolve on Earth. The stromatolites above are growing in the ocean near Australia.

Free Oxygen

Microscopic fossils, or **microfossils,** of single-celled prokaryotic organisms that resemble modern bacteria have been found in rocks more than 3.5 billion years old, as shown in **Figure 17–11.** Those first life forms must have evolved in the absence of oxygen, because Earth's first atmosphere contained little or none of that highly reactive gas.

Over time, as indicated by fossil evidence, photosynthetic bacteria became common in the shallow seas of the Precambrian. By 2.2 billion years ago at the latest, these organisms were steadily churning out oxygen, an end product of photosynthesis. One of the first things oxygen did was to combine with iron in the oceans. In other words, it caused the oceans to rust! When iron oxide was formed, it fell from the sea water to the ocean floor. There, it formed great bands of iron that are the source of most of the iron ore mined today. Without iron, the oceans changed color from brown to blue-green.

Next, oxygen gas started accumulating in the atmosphere. As atmospheric oxygen concentrations rose, concentrations of methane and hydrogen sulfide began to decrease, the ozone layer began to form, and the skies turned their present shade of blue. Over the course of several hundred million years, oxygen concentrations rose until they reached today's levels.

The increase in this highly reactive gas created the first global "pollution" crisis. To the first cells, oxygen was a deadly poison! **The rise of oxygen in the atmosphere drove some life forms to extinction, while other life forms evolved new, more efficient metabolic pathways that used oxygen for respiration.** Organisms that had evolved in an oxygen-free atmosphere were forced into a few airless habitats, where their anaerobic descendants remain today. Some organisms, however, evolved ways of using oxygen for respiration and protecting themselves from oxygen's powerful reactive abilities. The stage was set for the evolution of modern life.

 CHECKPOINT *What process added oxygen to Earth's atmosphere?*

Origin of Eukaryotic Cells

Several important events in the history of life have been revealed through molecular studies of cells and their organelles. One of these events is the origin of eukaryotic cells, which are cells that have nuclei. About 2 billion years ago, prokaryotic cells—cells without nuclei—began evolving internal cell membranes. The result was the ancestor of all eukaryotic cells.

Then, something radical seems to have happened. Other prokaryotic organisms entered this ancestral eukaryote. These organisms did not infect their host, as parasites would have done, and the host did not digest them, as it would have digested prey. Instead, the smaller prokaryotes began living inside the larger cell, as shown in **Figure 17–12.** Over time, a symbiotic, or interdependent, relationship evolved. According to the **endosymbiotic theory,** eukaryotic cells formed from a symbiosis among several different prokaryotic organisms. One group of prokaryotes had the ability to use oxygen to generate energy-rich molecules of ATP. These evolved into the mitochondria that are now in the cells of all multicellular organisms. Other prokaryotes that carried out photosynthesis evolved into the chloroplasts of plants and algae. 🔑 **The endosymbiotic theory proposes that eukaryotic cells arose from living communities formed by prokaryotic organisms.**

This hypothesis was proposed more than a century ago, when microscopists saw that the membranes of mitochondria and chloroplasts resembled the plasma membranes of free-living prokaryotes. Yet, the endosymbiotic theory did not receive much support until the 1960s, when it was championed by Lynn Margulis of Boston University. She and her supporters built their argument on several pieces of evidence: First, mitochondria and chloroplasts contain DNA similar to bacterial DNA.

▼ **Figure 17–12** 🔑 The endosymbiotic theory proposes that eukaryotic cells arose from living communities formed by prokaryotic organisms. Ancient prokaryotes may have entered primitive eukaryotic cells and remained there as organelles.

Aerobic bacteria — **Ancient Prokaryotes**

Photosynthetic bacteria

Nuclear envelope evolving

Mitochondrion

Chloroplast

Plants and plantlike protists

Ancient Anaerobic Prokaryote

Primitive Aerobic Eukaryote

Primitive Photosynthetic Eukaryote

Animals, fungi, and non-plantlike protists

Second, mitochondria and chloroplasts have ribosomes whose size and structure closely resemble those of bacteria. Third, like bacteria, mitochondria and chloroplasts reproduce by binary fission when the cells containing them divide by mitosis. Thus, mitochondria and chloroplasts have many of the features of free-living bacteria. These similarities provide strong evidence of a common ancestry between free-living bacteria and the organelles of living eukaryotic cells.

Sexual Reproduction and Multicellularity

Some time after eukaryotic cells arose, those cells began to reproduce sexually. This development enabled evolution to take place at far greater speeds than ever before. How did sexual reproduction speed up the evolutionary process?

Most prokaryotes reproduce asexually. Often, they simply duplicate their genetic material and divide into two new cells. Although this process is efficient, it yields daughter cells that are exact duplicates of the parent cell. This type of reproduction restricts genetic variation to mutations in DNA. Sexual reproduction, on the other hand, shuffles and reshuffles genes in each generation, much like a person shuffling a deck of cards. The offspring of sexually reproducing organisms, therefore, never resemble their parents exactly. This increase in genetic variation greatly increases the chances of evolutionary change in a species due to natural selection.

A few hundred million years after the evolution of sexual reproduction, evolving life forms crossed another great threshold: the development of multicellular organisms from single-celled organisms. In the blink of an evolutionary eye, these first multicellular organisms, such as the one shown in **Figure 17–13**, experienced a great increase in diversity. The evolution of life was well on its way.

▲ **Figure 17–13** This ancient jellyfish, an early multicellular animal from Precambrian Time, did not have bones or other hard parts, but it left behind a fossil that allowed biologists to infer its overall shape. **Observing** *What evidence shows that this organism had body parts arranged around a central point?*

17–2 Section Assessment

1. 🔑 **Key Concept** What substances probably made up Earth's early atmosphere?

2. 🔑 **Key Concept** What molecules were the end products in Miller and Urey's experiments?

3. 🔑 **Key Concept** How did the addition of oxygen to Earth's atmosphere affect life of that time?

4. 🔑 **Key Concept** According to the endosymbiotic theory, how might chloroplasts and mitochondria have originated?

5. **Critical Thinking**
Formulating Hypotheses
In Chapter 1, you read that the hypothesis of spontaneous generation was disproved. But you just read that life arose from nonlife billions of years ago. Could life arise from nonlife today? Explain.

TEXT Assessment Use iText to review the important concepts in Section 17–2.

Take It to the NET

Read about the supporting evidence for the endosymbiotic theory. Then, draw a cartoon or flowchart that illustrates this evidence. Use the links provided in the Biology area at the Prentice Hall Web site for help in completing this activity: **www.phschool.com**

17–3 Evolution of Multicellular Life

Although the fossil record has missing pieces, paleontologists have assembled good evolutionary histories for many groups of organisms. Further, the fossil record indicates that major changes occurred in Earth's climate, geography, and life forms. In this section, you will get an overview of how multicellular life evolved from its earliest forms to its present-day diversity.

Precambrian Time

Recall that almost 90 percent of Earth's history occurred during the Precambrian. During this time, simple anaerobic forms of life appeared and were followed by photosynthetic forms, which added oxygen to the atmosphere. Aerobic forms of life evolved, and eukaryotes appeared. Some of those organisms gave rise to multicellular forms that continued to increase in complexity. Few fossils exist from this time because the animals were all soft-bodied. Life existed only in the sea.

Paleozoic Era

Early in the Paleozoic Era, the fossil record became rich with evidence of many types of marine life. Scientists once thought that those different forms of life evolved rapidly at the beginning of the Paleozoic, but increasing evidence from Precambrian fossils suggests that life began to diversify much earlier. Regardless of when these forms evolved, fossil evidence shows that life was highly diverse by the first part of the Paleozoic Era, the Cambrian Period. An artist's portrayal of Cambrian life is shown in **Figure 17–14.**

Guide for Reading

Key Concept
• What were the characteristic forms of life in the Paleozoic, Mesozoic, and Cenozoic eras?

Vocabulary
mass extinction

**Reading Strategy:
Using Graphic Organizers**
As you read, make a table of the three geologic eras described in the section. Include information about the typical organisms and main evolutionary events of each era.

▼ **Figure 17–14** Early in the Paleozoic Era, the fossil record became rich with evidence of many types of marine life. These and other unfamiliar organisms dwelt in the sea during the Cambrian Period, a time when animals with hard parts evolved.

Cambrian Period Paleontologists call the diversification of life during the early Cambrian Period the "Cambrian Explosion." For the first time, organisms had hard parts, including shells and outer skeletons, as shown in **Figure 17–14** on page 429. During the Cambrian Period, the first known representatives of most animal phyla evolved. Invertebrates—such as jellyfishes, worms, and sponges—drifted through the water, crawled along the sandy bottom, or attached themselves to the ocean floors. Brachiopods, which were small animals with two shells, were especially common. They resembled—but were unrelated to—modern clams. Trilobites were also common.

✓ CHECKPOINT *What major evolutionary advance occurred during the Cambrian Period?*

Ordovician and Silurian Periods During the Ordovician (awr-duh-VISH-un) and Silurian (sih-LOOR-ee-un) periods, the ancestors of the modern octopi and squid appeared, as did aquatic arthropods like the one in **Figure 17–15.** Some animals of this time grew to a length of almost 13 meters. Among the first vertebrates (animals with backbones) to appear were jawless fishes. These fishes, which had suckerlike mouths, soon became common in the seas. Among the invertebrates, the first insects appeared. The first plants evolved from their aquatic ancestors. These simple plants grew low to the ground in damp areas.

▲ **Figure 17–15** During the Ordovician Period, aquatic arthropods like this eurypterid evolved. Eurypterids had segmented bodies and lived in water. They are now extinct. **Comparing and Contrasting** *Which of today's animals do eurypterids resemble?*

Devonian Period By the Devonian (dih-VOH-nee-un) Period, some plants, such as ferns, had adapted to drier areas, allowing them to invade more habitats. In the seas, both invertebrates and vertebrates thrived. Even though the invertebrates were far more numerous, the Devonian is often called the Age of Fishes because many groups of fishes were present in the oceans. Most fishes of this time had jaws, bony skeletons, and scales on their bodies. Sharks appeared in the late Devonian.

🔑 **During the Devonian, animals began to invade the land.** The first fishes to develop the ability to crawl awkwardly on leglike fins were still fully aquatic animals. Some of these early four-legged vertebrates evolved into the first amphibians. An amphibian (am-FIB-ee-un) is an animal that lives part of its life on land and part of its life in water.

Carboniferous and Permian Periods Throughout the rest of the Paleozoic Era, life expanded over Earth's continents. Other groups of vertebrates, such as reptiles, evolved from certain amphibians. Reptiles are animals that have scaly skin and lay eggs with tough, leathery shells. Winged insects evolved into many forms, including huge dragonflies and cockroaches. Giant ferns and other plants formed vast swampy forests, shown in **Figure 17–16.** The remains of those ancient plants formed thick deposits of sediment that changed into coal over millions of years, giving the Carboniferous its name.

At the end of the Paleozoic, many organisms died out. This was a **mass extinction,** in which many types of living things became extinct at the same time. 🔑 **The mass extinction at the end of the Paleozoic affected both plants and animals on land and in the seas. As much as 95 percent of the complex life in the oceans disappeared.** For example, trilobites, which had existed since early in the Paleozoic, suddenly became extinct. Many amphibians also became extinct. Not all organisms disappeared, however. The mass extinction did not affect many fishes. Numerous reptiles also survived.

Mesozoic Era

The Mesozoic Era lasted approximately 180 million years. 🔑 **Events during the Mesozoic include the increasing dominance of dinosaurs. The Mesozoic is marked by the appearance of flowering plants.**

Triassic Period Those organisms that survived the Permian mass extinction became the main forms of life early in the Triassic (try-AS-ik) Period. Important organisms in this new ecosystem were fishes, insects, reptiles, and cone-bearing plants like the one in **Figure 17–17.** Reptiles were so successful during the Mesozoic Era that this time is often called the Age of Reptiles.

About 225 million years ago, the first dinosaurs appeared. One of the earliest dinosaurs, *Coelophysis,* was a meat-eater that had light, hollow bones and ran swiftly on its hind legs. Mammals also first appeared during the late Triassic Period, probably evolving from mammallike reptiles. Mammals of the Triassic were very small, about the size of a mouse or shrew.

▲ **Figure 17–16** Ancient forests like this one from the Carboniferous Period were characterized by a huge variety of life forms. 🔑 **At the end of the Paleozoic Era, many types of animals and plants became extinct.**

▼ **Figure 17–17** Among the seed plants of the early Mesozoic Era were cone-bearing plants called cycads, which left this modern descendant. **Formulating Hypotheses** *How might the evolution of seeds increase a plant's chances of reproducing successfully?*

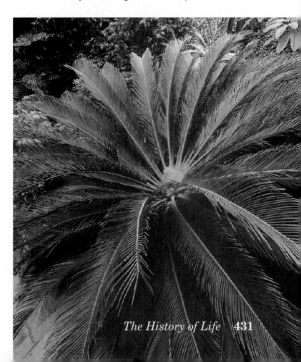

The History of Life **431**

▲ **Figure 17–18** During the Mesozoic Era, dinosaurs were dominant. *Dicraeosaurus* (foreground) was a plant-eater that grew to about 20 meters in length.

Jurassic Period During the Jurassic (joo-RAS-ik) Period, dinosaurs became the dominant animals on land. Dinosaurs "ruled" Earth for about 150 million years, but different types lived at different times. At 20 meters long, *Dicraeosaurus*, shown in **Figure 17–18,** was one of the larger dinosaurs of the Jurassic Period.

One of the first birds, called *Archaeopteryx,* appeared during this time. Many paleontologists now think that birds are close relatives of dinosaurs. Since the 1990s, scientists working in China have found evidence for this hypothesis in other fossils that have the skulls and teeth of dinosaurs but the body structure and feathers of birds.

Cretaceous Period Reptiles were still the dominant vertebrates throughout the Cretaceous (krih-TAY-shus) Period. Dinosaurs such as the meat-eating *Tyrannosaurus rex* dominated land ecosystems, while flying reptiles and birds soared in the sky. Flying reptiles, however, became extinct during the Cretaceous. In the seas, turtles, crocodiles, and extinct reptiles such as plesiosaurs swam among fishes and marine invertebrates.

The Cretaceous also brought new forms of life, including leafy trees, shrubs, and small flowering plants like those you see today. Unlike the conifers, flowering plants produce seeds enclosed in a fruit, which protects the seed and aids in dispersing it to new locations.

At the close of the Cretaceous, another mass extinction occurred. More than half of all plant and animal groups were wiped out, including all of the dinosaurs.

CHECKPOINT *When did flowering plants evolve?*

▶ **Figure 17–19** 🔑 During the Cenozoic Era, mammals evolved adaptations that allowed them to live on land, in water, and even in the air. Two of the traits that contributed to the success of mammals were a covering of hair that provided insulation against the cold and the protection of the young before and after birth.

Cenozoic Era

During the Mesozoic, early mammals competed with dinosaurs for food and places to live. The extinction of dinosaurs at the end of the Mesozoic, however, created a different world. 🔑 **During the Cenozoic, mammals evolved adaptations that allowed them to live in various environments—on land, in water, and even in the air.** One land mammal from the early Cenozoic is shown in **Figure 17–19**. Paleontologists often call the Cenozoic the Age of Mammals.

Tertiary Period During the Tertiary Period, Earth's climates were generally warm and mild. In the oceans, marine mammals such as whales and dolphins evolved. On land, flowering plants and insects flourished. Grasses evolved, providing a food source that encouraged the evolution of grazing mammals, the ancestors of today's cattle, deer, sheep, and other grass-eating mammals. Some mammals became very large, as did some birds.

Careers in Biology

Fossil Preparator

Job description: work for private industries, museums, or universities to expose fossils covered by rock or soil or to construct missing fossil parts

Education: a college degree in biology or geology, knowledge about information concerning the fossils being worked on

Skills: be knowledgeable about many areas of science, ability to use fine tools under a microscope, self-motivated, patient, ability to handle very fragile specimens for long periods

Highlights: work with fossil specimens; work with many types of people—from amateur fossil collectors to professional paleontologists

"When I receive a specimen to prepare, it looks rather drab and more like a rock," says fossil preparator Marc Behrendt. "But when preparation is complete, the fossil stands out in all its glory, and I know I made it this way. It is a great feeling and probably the biggest reason I enjoy my work."

 Take It to the NET

For more career information, visit the Prentice Hall Web site: **www.phschool.com**

► **Figure 17–20** During the Quaternary Period, Earth's climate cooled, producing a series of ice ages. Among the characteristic animals of the time were these huge mammoths. **Inferring** *How might the change to a colder climate have affected different types of organisms?*

Quaternary Period Mammals that had evolved during the Tertiary Period eventually faced a changing environment during the Quaternary Period. During this time, Earth's climate cooled, causing a series of ice ages. Repeatedly, thick continental glaciers advanced and retreated over parts of Europe and North America. So much of Earth's water was frozen in continental glaciers that the level of the oceans fell by more than 100 meters. Then, about 20,000 years ago, Earth's climate began to warm. Over the course of thousands of years, the continental glaciers melted. This caused sea levels to rise again.

In the oceans, algae, coral, mollusks, fish, and mammals thrived. Insects and birds shared the skies. On land, mammals—such as bats, cats, dogs, cattle, and the mammoths shown in **Figure 17–20**—became common. The fossil record suggests that the very earliest ancestors of our species appeared about 4.5 million years ago but that they did not look entirely human. Modern humans, called *Homo sapiens,* may have evolved as early as 100,000 years ago in Africa. From there, they began a series of migrations that ultimately colonized the world.

17–3 Section Assessment

1. **Key Concept** Where did life exist during the early Paleozoic Era?

2. **Key Concept** What evolutionary milestone involving animals occurred during the Devonian Period?

3. **Key Concept** What are two key events from the Mesozoic Era?

4. **Critical Thinking Inferring** If you were a paleontologist investigating fossils from the Cenozoic Era, what fossils might you find?

TEXT **Assessment** Use iText to review the important concepts in Section 17–3.

ALTERNATIVE ASSESSMENT

Creative Writing
Choose one of the periods described in this section. Then, write a story about what life was like during that time. Include information about the terrain, life forms, weather, and other characteristics of the period.

17-4 Patterns of Evolution

The history of life is the story of increasing complexity and diversity, but what does this history reveal about the process of evolution? Does evolution happen at a consistent pace? Do lineages evolve independently of one another, or is evolution an interactive process? Answers to these questions fall under the topic of macroevolution. **Macroevolution** refers to the large-scale evolutionary changes that take place over long periods of time. **Six important patterns of macroevolution are mass extinctions, adaptive radiation, convergent evolution, coevolution, punctuated equilibrium, and changes in developmental genes.**

Mass Extinctions

Extinction occurs all the time. More than 99 percent of all species that ever lived are now extinct. Usually, extinctions happen at a fairly constant rate. Several times, however, huge numbers of species have disappeared in mass extinctions. Recently, paleontologists have begun to reexamine mass extinctions. New fossil studies show that those mass extinctions not only extinguished species but also wiped out whole ecological systems, disrupting energy flow throughout the biosphere and causing food webs to collapse.

What could have caused such widespread destruction? Until recently, most researchers looked for a single major cause. One hypothesis suggests that a huge asteroid caused the Cretaceous extinction. Evidence does suggest that a large asteroid struck Earth at about that time, as depicted in **Figure 17–21.** Such an impact would have thrown huge amounts of dust and water vapor into the atmosphere, altering the global climate. These changes would have affected the plants that dinosaurs ate and thus probably played a role in the demise of the dinosaurs.

However, many paleontologists think that most mass extinctions were caused by multiple factors. At about the time of the Permian and Cretaceous extinctions, many large volcanoes were erupting, continents were changing positions, and sea levels were changing. Thus, it is difficult to pinpoint a single cause for the extinctions. Determining what actually happened will occupy researchers for years to come.

What effects have mass extinctions had on the history of life? As you can imagine, the disappearance of so many species left many habitats open. For the survivors, there was a new world of ecological opportunity. Often, the result was a burst of evolution that produced an abundance of new species.

Guide for Reading

Key Concept
• What are six important patterns of macroevolution?

Vocabulary
macroevolution
adaptive radiation
convergent evolution
coevolution
punctuated equilibrium

Reading Strategy: Summarizing
List the six patterns described in this section. As you read, write a statement describing each pattern.

▼ **Figure 17–21** Mass extinctions are one pattern of macroevolution. A huge asteroid hitting Earth may have caused the extinction of the dinosaurs at the end of the Cretaceous Period. This drawing shows an artist's conception of that event.

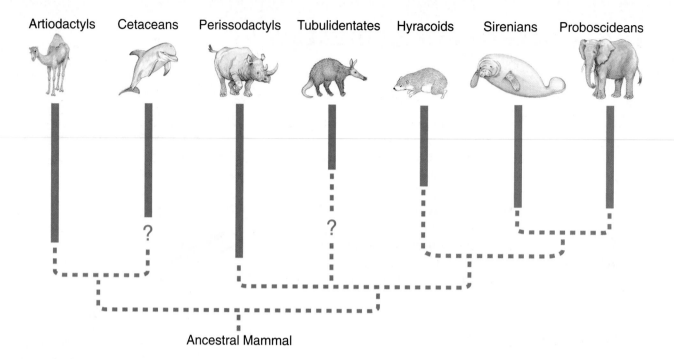

Artiodactyls   Cetaceans   Perissodactyls   Tubulidentates   Hyracoids   Sirenians   Proboscideans

?   ?

Ancestral Mammal

▲ **Figure 17–22** Adaptive radiation occurs when a species or group of species evolves into many new species. This drawing shows how one major group of mammals evolved. **Interpreting Graphics** *According to this diagram, which mammal group is the most closely related to elephants?*

Adaptive Radiation

Often, studies of fossils or of living organisms show that a single species or a small group of species has evolved into several different forms that live in different ways. This process is known as **adaptive radiation.** You have already learned about the adaptive radiation of Darwin's finches. In that case, more than a dozen species evolved from a single species.

Adaptive radiations can also occur on a much larger scale. Dinosaurs, for example, were the products of a spectacular adaptive radiation among ancient reptiles. The first dinosaurs and the earliest mammals evolved at about the same time. Dinosaurs and other ancient reptiles, however, underwent an adaptive radiation first and "ruled" Earth for about 150 million years. During that time, mammals remained small and relatively scarce. But the disappearance of the dinosaurs cleared the way for the great adaptive radiation of mammals. This radiation, part of which is shown in **Figure 17–22,** produced the great diversity of mammals of the Cenozoic.

Convergent Evolution

Adaptive radiations can have an interesting evolutionary "side effect." They can produce unrelated organisms that look remarkably similar to one another. How does that happen? Sometimes, groups of different organisms, such as mammals and dinosaurs, undergo adaptive radiation in different places or at different times but in ecologically similar environments. These organisms start out with different "raw material" for natural selection to work on, but they face similar environmental demands, such as moving through air, moving through water, or eating similar foods.

Shark

Figure 17–23 Each of these animals has a streamlined body and various appendages that enable it to move rapidly through water. Yet, the shark (above) is a fish, the penguin (center) is a bird, and the dolphin (bottom) is a mammal. **Applying Concepts** *How did these different animals come to resemble one another?*

In these situations, natural selection may mold different body structures, such as arms and legs, into modified forms, such as wings or flippers. The wings or flippers function in the same way and look very similar. This process, by which unrelated organisms come to resemble one another, is called **convergent evolution.** Convergent evolution has occurred time and time again in both animals and plants.

Consider swimming animals, for example. An animal can move through the water rapidly with the least amount of energy if its body is streamlined and if it has body parts that can be used like paddles. That is why convergent evolution involving fishes, two different groups of aquatic mammals, and swimming birds has resulted in sharks, dolphins, seals, and penguins whose streamlined bodies and swimming appendages look a lot alike, as shown in **Figure 17–23.** Structures such as a dolphin's flukes and a fish's tail fin, which look and function similarly but are made up of parts that do not share a common evolutionary history, are called analogous structures. There are a surprising number of animals (including one of Darwin's finches) that have evolved adaptations analogous to those of woodpeckers for feeding on insects living beneath the bark of trees and in rotted wood.

Penguins

Dolphin

✓**CHECKPOINT** *How do biologists explain the similar shapes of sharks and dolphins?*

Coevolution

Sometimes organisms that are closely connected to one another by ecological interactions evolve together. Many flowering plants, for example, can reproduce only if the shape, color, and odor of their flowers attract a specific type of pollinator. Not surprisingly, these kinds of relationships can change over time. An evolutionary change in one organism may also be followed by a corresponding change in another organism. The process by which two species evolve in response to changes in each other over time is called **coevolution.**

Figure 17–24 This orchid from Madagascar has an unusually long spur containing a supply of nectar in its tip. The hawk moth of Madagascar has an equally long feeding tube that enables it to feed on the nectar. The flower spur and the feeding tube are an example of coevolution. **Inferring** *How might natural selection bring about the evolution of this orchid and the moth?*

The pattern of coevolution involving flowers and insects is so common that biologists in the field often discover additional examples. When Charles Darwin saw an orchid like the one in **Figure 17–24,** he closely examined the long structure called a spur. At the tip of that 40-centimeter spur is a supply of nectar, which serves as a food source for many insects. Darwin predicted the discovery of a pollinating insect with a 40-centimeter-long structure that could reach the orchid's nectar. About fifty years later, researchers discovered a moth that matched Darwin's prediction.

Consider another example, the relationships between plants and plant-eating insects. Insects have been feeding on flowering plants since both groups emerged during the Mesozoic. Over time, a number of plants have evolved poisonous compounds that prevent insects from feeding on them. In fact, some of the most powerful poisons known in nature are plant compounds that have evolved in response to insect attacks. But once plants began to produce poisons, natural selection in herbivorous insects began to favor any variants that could alter, inactivate, or eliminate those poisons. In a few cases, coevolutionary relationships can be traced back over millions of years.

✓**CHECKPOINT** *What happens during coevolution?*

Analyzing Data

Changing Number of Marine Families

Using fossil evidence, scientists make inferences about the kinds and number of organisms that lived at different times in the past. Further, they classify those organisms in ways that facilitate comparisons between past and present types. The graph on the right gives an estimate of the number of ocean-dwelling families over time. In biology, a family consists of several groups of related species.

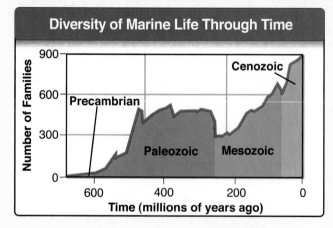

1. **Using Tables and Graphs** What overall trend does this graph show?

2. **Calculating** What was the change in the number of marine families at the end of the Paleozoic Era? At the end of the Mesozoic?

3. **Inferring** What kind of event(s) might explain the changes at the end of the Paleozoic and Mesozoic eras?

4. **Going Further** How do you expect this graph to change in the next 1000 years? The next 10,000,000 years? Explain.

Punctuated Equilibrium

How quickly does evolution operate? Does it always occur at the same speed? These are questions on which some modern biologists would disagree with Darwin. Recall that Darwin was enormously impressed by the way Hutton and Lyell discussed the slow and steady nature of geologic change. Darwin, in turn, felt that biological change also needed to be slow and steady, an idea known as gradualism. In many cases, the fossil record confirms that populations of organisms did, indeed, change gradually over time.

But there is also evidence that this pattern does not always hold. Some species, such as horseshoe crabs, have changed little from the time they first appeared in the fossil record. In other words, much of the time these species are in a state of equilibrium, which means they do not change very much. Every now and then, however, something happens to upset the equilibrium. At several points in the fossil record, changes in animals and plants occurred over relatively short periods of time. Some biologists suggest that most new species are produced by periods of rapid change. (Remember that "short" and "rapid" are relative to the geologic time scale. Short periods of time for geologists can be hundreds of thousands—even millions—of years!)

Rapid evolution after long periods of equilibrium can occur for several reasons. It may occur when a small population becomes isolated from the main part of the population. This small population can then evolve more rapidly than the larger one because genetic changes can spread more quickly among fewer individuals. Or it may occur when a small group of organisms migrates to a new environment. That's what happened with the Galápagos finches, for example. Organisms evolve rapidly to fill available niches. In addition, mass extinctions can open many ecological niches and provide new opportunities to those organisms that survive. Thus, it is not surprising that some groups of organisms have evolved rapidly following mass extinctions.

Scientists use the term **punctuated equilibrium** to describe this pattern of long, stable periods interrupted by brief periods of more rapid change. The concept of punctuated equilibrium, illustrated in **Figure 17–25,** has generated much debate and is still somewhat controversial among biologists today. It is clear, however, that evolution has often proceeded at different rates for different organisms at different times during the long history of life on Earth.

Model of Gradualism

Model of Punctuated Equilibrium

▲ **Figure 17–25** Biologists have considered two different explanations for the rate of evolution, as illustrated in these diagrams. Gradualism involves a slow, steady change in a particular line of descent. Punctuated equilibrium involves stable periods interrupted by rapid changes involving many different lines of descent. **Interpreting Graphics** *How do the diagrams illustrate these explanations?*

Ancient Insects

no wings

pairs of wings
on many segments

Two Types of Modern Insects

two pairs of wings

one pair of wings

▲ **Figure 17–26** Changes in developmental genes are one major pattern of macroevolution. Fossil evidence shows that some ancient insects (top left) had no wings, but others (top right) had winglike structures on many body segments. In modern insects (bottom), genes may turn off wing development in all except one or two body segments.

Developmental Genes and Body Plans

Until recently, biologists could only wonder how animals evolved their diverse body plans, but breakthroughs in molecular biology are changing that. Recall from Chapter 12 that geneticists discovered "master control genes," called hox genes, that control growth as an embryo develops. Some hox genes determine which parts become front, rear, top, and bottom. Others control the growth of body parts such as arms, legs, and wings.

Hox genes can help reveal how evolution occurred. First, molecular studies show that homologous hox genes establish body plans in animals as different as insects and humans—even though these animals have not shared a common ancestor in at least 700 million years!

Second, major evolutionary changes—such as the different numbers of wings, legs, and body segments in insects—may be based on hox genes. For instance, if one gene, called "wingless," is activated in an insect body segment, that segment grows no wings. Thus, ancient insects with winglike structures on every segment, as shown in **Figure 17–26,** could have evolved into the insects of today that have two pairs or one pair of wings.

Finally, geneticists are learning that even small changes in the timing of genetic control during embryonic development can make the difference between long legs and short ones—or long, slender fingers or short, stubby toes—thus contributing to the variation involved in natural selection. This hot field of research is likely to continue revealing major news about the evolution of life.

17–4 Section Assessment

1. **Key Concept** What is macroevolution? Describe two patterns of macroevolution.

2. What role have mass extinctions played in the history of life?

3. Use an example to explain the concept of coevolution.

4. How might hox genes contribute to variation?

5. **Critical Thinking Comparing and Contrasting** Compare and contrast the theories of gradualism and punctuated equilibrium.

iTEXT **Assessment** Use iText to review the important concepts in Section 17–4.

Modeling Coevolution

Flowering plants and the animals that pollinate their flowers include many examples of coevolving species. In this investigation, you will model how these plants and animals evolve in response to one another.

Problem How do flowering plants and their pollinators coevolve?

Materials
- long forceps
- spoon
- dried peas
- 3 25-mL graduated cylinders
- 3 100-mL beakers
- watch or clock with second hand

Skills Using Models, Inferring

Procedure

1. Work in groups of three. Each group member represents a different bird species. To represent the birds' beaks, one group member will use forceps, the second group member will use a spoon, and the third will use two fingertips.

2. On a separate sheet of paper, make a copy of the data table shown. The beakers represent short, open flowers and the graduated cylinders represent long, narrow flowers. The dried peas represent the flowers' nectar, which is the birds' food. Fill the beakers and the graduated cylinders halfway with dried peas.

3. For 1 minute, use the method you chose in step 1 to remove the peas. Remove them one at a time from your beaker. Do not move or tip the beaker as you do this.

4. Record the number of peas you removed in your data table.

5. To produce seeds, a flower must be pollinated by a member of its own species. Assume that 1 flower was pollinated for every 5 peas removed. Record the number of pollinations for each bird.

6. Repeat steps 3 through 5, using the graduated cylinders instead of the beakers.

7. **Calculating** Exchange data with your classmates and record the class averages for each bird species in your data table.

Analyze and Conclude

1. **Analyzing Data** Which bird species obtained the most nectar from the beakers? From the graduated cylinders?

2. **Analyzing Data** From which type of flower was each bird most successful in obtaining food?

3. **Inferring** What is the benefit to a plant of short, open flowers?

4. **Inferring** What is the benefit to a bird of a long, narrow beak?

5. **Drawing Conclusions** Which type of bird is the best pollinator for long, narrow flowers?

6. **Evaluating and Revising** How does this model represent coevolution? How could you improve this model?

Data Table				
Beak Type	Individual Data		Class Average	
	Peas	Pollinations	Peas	Pollinations
Forceps				
Spoon				
Fingers				

Go Further

Using Models Construct a model that demonstrates coevolution between flowers of different colors and pollinating insects attracted to specific colors.

Chapter 17 Study Guide

17–1 The Fossil Record
🔑 Key Concepts

- The fossil record provides evidence about the history of life on Earth. It also shows how different groups of organisms have changed over time.

- Relative dating allows paleontologists to estimate a fossil's age compared with that of other fossils.

- In radioactive dating, scientists calculate the age of a sample based on the amount of remaining radioactive isotopes it contains.

- After Precambrian Time, the basic divisions of the geologic time scale are eras and periods.

Vocabulary
paleontologist, p. 417
fossil record, p. 417
extinct, p. 417
relative dating, p. 419
index fossil, p. 419
half-life, p. 420
radioactive dating, p. 420
geologic time scale, p. 421
era, p. 421
period, p. 422

17–2 Earth's Early History
🔑 Key Concepts

- Earth's early atmosphere probably contained hydrogen cyanide, carbon dioxide, carbon monoxide, nitrogen, hydrogen sulfide, and water.

- Miller and Urey's experiments suggested how mixtures of the organic compounds necessary for life could have arisen from simpler compounds present on a primitive Earth.

- The rise of oxygen in the atmosphere drove some life forms to extinction, while other life forms evolved new, more efficient metabolic pathways that used oxygen for respiration.

- The endosymbiotic theory proposes that eukaryotic cells arose from living communities formed by prokaryotic organisms.

Vocabulary
proteinoid microsphere, p. 425
microfossil, p. 426
endosymbiotic theory, p. 427

17–3 Evolution of Multicellular Life
🔑 Key Concepts

- Early in the Paleozoic Era, the fossil record became rich with evidence of many types of marine life.

- During the Devonian, animals began to invade the land.

- The mass extinction at the end of the Paleozoic affected both plants and animals on land and in the seas. As much as 95 percent of the complex life in the oceans disappeared.

- Events during the Mesozoic include the increasing dominance of dinosaurs. The Mesozoic is marked by the appearance of flowering plants.

- During the Cenozoic, mammals evolved adaptations that allowed them to live in various environments—on land, in water, and even in the air.

Vocabulary
mass extinction, p. 431

17–4 Patterns of Evolution
🔑 Key Concept

- Six important patterns of macroevolution are mass extinctions, adaptive radiation, convergent evolution, coevolution, punctuated equilibrium, and changes in developmental genes.

Vocabulary
macroevolution, p. 435
adaptive radiation, p. 436
convergent evolution, p. 437
coevolution, p. 437
punctuated equilibrium, p. 439

Thinking Visually
Use information from the chapter to create a concept map that shows the four major divisions of geologic time, the periods within those divisions, and an example of a major event from each period.

Chapter 17

Part A

Multiple Choice

For each statement or question, select the number of the word or expression that, of those given, best completes the statement or answers the question.

1 Radioactive dating of rock samples
   (1) is a method of absolute dating
   (2) is a method of relative dating
   (3) provides no information about the age in years of the rock samples
   (4) relies on the use of index fossils

2 Half-life is the length of time required for half the atoms in a radioactive sample to
   (1) decay   (3) double
   (2) expand   (4) be created

3 Earth's first atmosphere contained little or no
   (1) oxygen   (3) hydrogen sulfide
   (2) nitrogen   (4) hydrogen cyanide

4 In Miller and Urey's experiment, electric sparks were passed through a mixture of gases to
   (1) increase temperature
   (2) simulate sunlight
   (3) sterilize the gases
   (4) simulate lightning

5 Evolution is the study of the
   (1) development of fish from mammals
   (2) change from simpler to more complex forms of life
   (3) development of modern transportation
   (4) energy flow in food webs

6 Throughout the history of life on Earth, which factor has probably been the chief cause of the extinction of species?
   (1) human interference with the natural environment
   (2) failure to adapt to environmental change
   (3) competition within species
   (4) volcanic eruptions

7 Outlines of ancient cells that are preserved well enough to identify them as prokaryotes are
   (1) microfossils
   (2) endosymbiotic organisms
   (3) aerobic bacteria
   (4) photosynthethic bacteria

8 Which event occurred at the end of the Paleozoic Era?
   (1) first appearance of flowering plants
   (2) mass extinction of many types of organisms
   (3) evolution of dinosaurs
   (4) extinction of mammals

9 The process that produces a similar appearance among unrelated groups of organisms is
   (1) adaptive radiation
   (2) convergent evolution
   (3) coevolution
   (4) changes in hox genes

10 Evolution is often represented with a tree diagram like the one below.

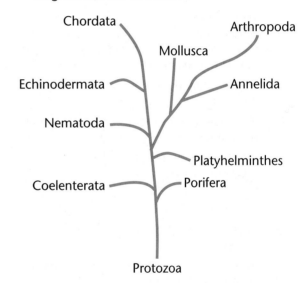

The diagram suggests that different groups of organisms, such as Nematoda and Mollusca, have similar characteristics because they
(1) share a common ancestor
(2) evolved at the same time
(3) share the same environment
(4) evolved at the same rate

Test-Taking Tip If you find particular questions difficult, put a light mark beside them and keep working. (Do not write in this book.) As you answer later questions, you may find information that helps you find the answers you still need.

Parts B and C

Multiple Choice and Extended Response

For those questions that ask you to select a response, choose the one that best completes the statement or answers the question. For all others follow the directions given.

11 The Galápagos Islands in the Pacific Ocean were probably never connected to South America. However, in the various habitats on the islands, there are about 14 species of finches that appear to be related to the finches on the South American mainland. Although the Galápagos finches vary in beak structure, there is a close resemblance among them in plumage, calls, nests, and eggs. These species do not inter-breed or compete for food.

Statement: Isolation from the South American mainland and the different habitats on the Galápagos Islands are important factors in the production of new species.

What is the relationship between the statement and the information given above?

(1) The statement is supported by the information given.

(2) The statement is not supported by the information given.

(3) The statement is contradicted by the information given.

(4) No relevant information is given regarding the statement.

12 How does relative dating enable paleontologists to estimate a fossil's age?

13 Explain how radioactivity is used to date rocks.

14 Explain how proteinoid microspheres are like living cells.

15 Evolutionary biologists say that there is good reason for gaps in the fossil record. Explain why some extinct animals and plants were probably never fossilized.

16 Explain one connection between sexual repro-duction and evolution.

17 Explain the process of adaptive radiation, and give an example of the process.

18 Explain the pattern known as punctuated equilibrium.

Base your answers to questions 19 and 20 on the graph below and on your knowledge of biology.

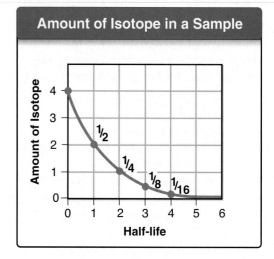

Amount of Isotope in a Sample

19 The half-life of thorium-230 is 75,000 years. How long will it take for $\frac{7}{8}$ of the original amount of thorium-230 in a sample to decay?
(1) 25,000 years   **(3)** 75,000 years
(2) 70,000 years   **(4)** 225,000 years

20 The half-life of potassium-40 is about 1300 million years. The age of a fossil that contains only one half of its original potassium-40 is about
(1) 1300 million years   **(3)** 650 million years
(2) 2600 million years   **(4)** 32.5 million years

Base your answers to questions 21 through 23 on the passage below and on your knowledge of biology.

Biologist Lynn Margulis championed the endosymbi-otic theory, which states that the first eukaryotes formed as the result of symbiosis, or interdepend-ence, among several prokaryotes. According to the theory, some prokaryotes lived inside of bacteria and algae as endosymbionts, using the bacteria and algae as hosts. Eventually, the hosts and the endosymbionts formed such an effective team that the endosymbionts lost the ability to survive on their own. In this way, they evolved into the organelles of eukaryotic cells. In support of the theory, Margulis noted that some of the organelles of eukaryotic cells are similar in structure to prokaryotes. For example, mitochondria closely resemble bacteria, chloroplasts closely resemble blue-green algae, and the flagella of many eukaryotic cells are very similar to a group of bacteria known as spirochetes. In addition, both mitochondria and chloroplasts contain DNA.

21 The endosymbiotic theory includes all of the following *except*

(1) photosynthetic prokaryotes evolved into chloroplasts

(2) eukaryotic cells arose from the merging of different prokaryotic organisms

(3) all organelles evolved from specialized enfoldings of the plasma membrane

(4) eukaryotic cells are the result of an interdependent relationship among different organisms

22 Which statement provides evidence for the endosymbiotic theory?

(1) Mitochondria and chloroplasts contain DNA.

(2) Flagella are used to move chloroplasts from cell to cell.

(3) Endosymbionts can survive outside of host cells when removed.

(4) The cell membrane keeps out flagella, mitochondria, and chloroplasts.

23 The passage states that some prokaryotes lived inside bacteria. How might this have proved valuable to both the bacteria and the prokaryotes?

Base your answers to questions 24 and 25 on the graph below and on your knowledge of biology.

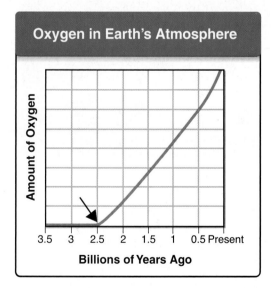

Oxygen in Earth's Atmosphere

Amount of Oxygen

Billions of Years Ago

3.5 3 2.5 2 1.5 1 0.5 Present

24 The graph shows an approximation of the amount of oxygen in the atmosphere since life began. What event occurred at the point indicated by the arrow?

25 How did the addition of oxygen to Earth's atmosphere affect the evolution of life?

26 Describe the sequence of events scientists hypothesize to have occurred in the formation of Earth's early oceans and atmosphere.

27 Use the diagram below to explain the significance of Miller and Urey's experiment.

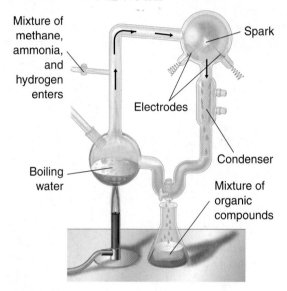

Mixture of methane, ammonia, and hydrogen enters

Spark

Electrodes

Condenser

Boiling water

Mixture of organic compounds

Your answer should include

• the purpose of the mixture of methane, ammonia, and hydrogen

• the reason boiling water was used

• the electrodes and spark and what it simulated

• the source of the organic compounds

Take It to the NET

Do biologists study life only on Earth? Visit the Prentice Hall Web site at **www.phschool.com** to find out about the study of life elsewhere in the universe. Then, answer the following questions:

• What does the term *exobiology* mean?

• Describe the circumstances in which Stanley Miller came to conduct his famous electrical discharge experiment with Harold Urey.

• What advice does Dr. Miller have for a student interested in studying exobiology?

Chapter **18** Classification

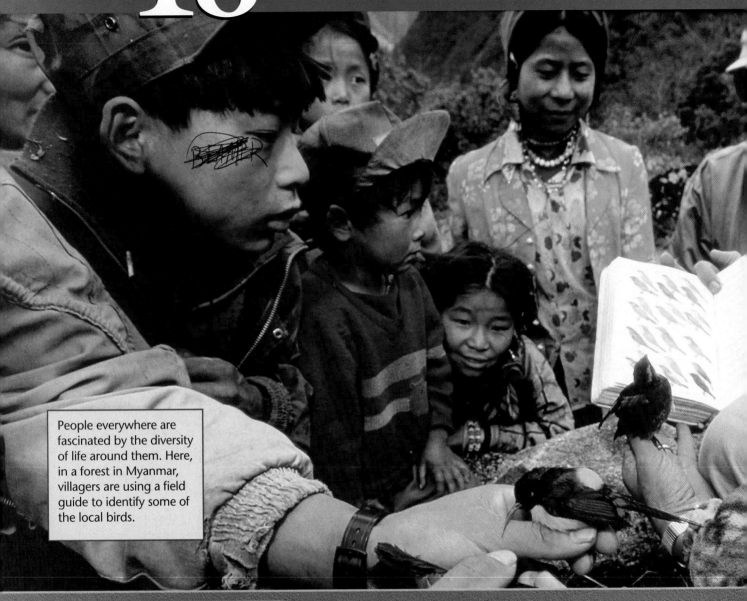

People everywhere are fascinated by the diversity of life around them. Here, in a forest in Myanmar, villagers are using a field guide to identify some of the local birds.

Inquiry Activity

How can you classify fruits?

Procedure

1. Obtain five different fruits. Use a paring knife to cut each fruit open and examine its structure. **CAUTION:** *Use caution with sharp instruments.*

2. Construct a table with five rows and four columns. Label each row with the name of a different fruit.

3. Observe each fruit and choose four characteristics by which you can tell the fruits apart. Label the columns in your table with these four characteristics.

4. Record a description of each fruit in your table.

Think About It

1. **Observing** What characteristics did you use to describe the fruits?

2. **Classifying** Based on your table, which fruits are most closely related? Explain.

18–1 Finding Order in Diversity

For more than 3.5 billion years, life on Earth has been constantly changing. This process has led to a staggering variety of organisms. A tropical rain forest, for example, may support thousands of species per acre. Recall that a species is a population of organisms that share similar characteristics and can breed with one another and produce fertile offspring. Biologists have identified and named about 1.5 million species so far. They estimate that anywhere between 2 and 100 million additional species have yet to be discovered.

Why Classify?

To study this great diversity of organisms, biologists must give each organism a name. Biologists must also attempt to organize living things into groups that have biological meaning. **To study the diversity of life, biologists use a classification system to name organisms and group them in a logical manner.**

In the discipline known as **taxonomy,** scientists classify organisms and assign each organism a universally accepted name. One example appears in **Figure 18–1.** By using a scientific name, biologists can be certain that everyone is discussing the same organism. When taxonomists classify organisms, they organize them into groups that have biological significance. When you hear the word "bird," for example, you immediately form a mental picture of the organism being discussed—a flying animal that has feathers. But science often requires smaller categories as well as larger, more general categories. In a good system of classification, organisms placed into a particular group are more similar to each other than they are to organisms in other groups.

You use classification systems also, for example, when you refer to "teachers" or "mechanics," or more specifically, "biology teachers" or "auto mechanics." Such a process, like scientific classification, uses accepted names and common criteria to group things.

Guide for Reading

Key Concepts
- How are living things organized for study?
- What is binomial nomenclature?
- What is Linnaeus's system of classification?

Vocabulary
taxonomy
binomial nomenclature
genus
taxon
family
order
class
phylum
kingdom

Reading Strategy: Building Vocabulary
As you read about the seven categories established by Linnaeus, list those categories in order, starting with the smallest group. Then, create a memory aid to help you remember them.

▶ **Figure 18–1** Depending on where you live, you might recognize this as a mountain lion, a puma, a cougar, or a panther—all of which are common names for the same animal. The scientific name for this animal is *Felis concolor.* **To avoid the confusion caused by regional names, biologists use a classification system to group organisms in a logical manner and to assign names.**

▲ **Figure 18–2** The problem of naming organisms efficiently continues to challenge biologists as they discover new species. This barking deer was recently discovered near the border of Laos and Vietnam. Its scientific name, which is based on Latin, is *Muntiacus muntjak.* 🔵 **In binomial nomenclature, each animal is assigned a two-part scientific name.**

Word Origins

Binomial and *nomenclature* are built from some familiar roots. *Bi-* is Latin for "two." *Nomen-* is Latin for "name." So *binomial nomenclature* means a two-name system of assigning names. **If *pedis* is Latin for "of the foot," how many feet does a *biped* have?**

Assigning Scientific Names

By the eighteenth century, European scientists recognized that referring to organisms by common names was confusing. Common names vary among languages and even among regions within a single country. The animal you saw in **Figure 18–1,** for example, can be called a cougar, a puma, a panther, or a mountain lion. Furthermore, different species sometimes share a single common name. In the United Kingdom, the word *buzzard* refers to a hawk, whereas in many parts of the United States, *buzzard* refers to a vulture. To eliminate such confusion, scientists agreed to use a single name for each species. Because eighteenth-century scientists understood Latin and Greek, they used those languages for scientific names. This practice is still followed today in naming newly discovered species, such as the barking deer in **Figure 18–2.**

Early Efforts at Naming Organisms The first attempts at standard scientific names often described the physical characteristics of a species in great detail. As a result, these names could be twenty words long! For example, the English translation of the scientific name of a particular tree might be "Oak with deeply divided leaves that have no hairs on their undersides and no teeth around their edges." This system of naming had another major drawback. It was difficult to standardize the names of organisms because different scientists described different characteristics.

Binomial Nomenclature A major step was taken by Carolus Linnaeus, shown in **Figure 18–3,** a Swedish botanist who lived during the eighteenth century. He developed a two-word naming system called **binomial nomenclature** (by-NOH-mee-ul NOH-mun-klay-chur). This system is still in use today. 🔵 **In binomial nomenclature, each species is assigned a two-part scientific name.** The scientific name is always written in italics. The first word is capitalized, and the second word is lowercased.

For example, the grizzly bear shown in **Figure 18–4** is called *Ursus arctos.* The first part of the scientific name—in this case, *Ursus*—is the genus to which the organism belongs. A **genus** (JEE-nus; plural: genera, JEN-ur-uh) is a group of closely related species. The genus *Ursus* contains five other kinds of bears, including *Ursus maritimus,* the polar bear.

The second part of a scientific name—in this case, *arctos* or *maritimus*—is unique to each species within the genus. Often, this part of the name is a Latinized description of some important trait of the organism or an indication of where the organism lives. The Latin word *maritimus,* referring to the sea, comes from the fact that polar bears often live on pack ice that floats in the sea.

✓CHECKPOINT *Do* Ursus arctos *and* Ursus maritimus *belong to the same species? To the same genus?*

Linnaeus's System of Classification

In taxonomy, a group or level of organization is called a taxonomic category, or **taxon** (plural: taxa). 🔑 **Linnaeus's system of classification uses seven taxonomic categories. They are—from smallest to largest—species, genus, family, order, class, phylum, and kingdom.** You can see these seven categories in **Figure 18–5** on the next page. The two smallest categories, genus and species, were discussed in the example of the bears. The giant panda, also shown in **Figure 18–4**, resembles the grizzly bear and the polar bear in important ways. However, it differs enough from these bears and other species in the genus *Ursus* that it is placed in its own genus, *Ailuropoda.*

Genera that share many characteristics, such as *Ursus* and *Ailuropoda,* are grouped in a larger category, the **family**—in this case, Ursidae. These bears, together with six other families of meat-eating animals, such as dogs (Canidae) and cats (Felidae), are grouped together in the order Carnivora. An **order** is a broad taxonomic category composed of similar families. The next larger category, the **class,** is composed of similar orders. For example, carnivores are placed in the class Mammalia, which includes animals that are warm-blooded, have body hair, and produce milk for their young.

Several different classes make up a **phylum** (FY-lum; plural: phyla). A phylum includes many different organisms that nevertheless share important characteristics. The class Mammalia is grouped with birds (class Aves), reptiles (class Reptilia), amphibians (class Amphibia), and all classes of fishes into the phylum Chordata. All these organisms share important features of their body plan and internal functions.

Finally, all animals are placed in the kingdom Animalia. The **kingdom** is the largest and most inclusive of Linnaeus's taxonomic categories. Linnaeus named two kingdoms, Animalia and Plantae.

▲ **Figure 18–3** Carolus Linnaeus (1707–1778) brought order to the process of naming species and classifying them into groups. *Evaluating Why do biologists consider Linnaeus's system an improvement over earlier systems?*

Figure 18–4 The grizzly bear, *Ursus arctos,* and the polar bear, *Ursus maritimus,* are classified as different species in the same genus, *Ursus.* The giant panda is placed in a separate genus. *Inferring What do the names of these organisms tell you about their similarity to each other?*

Grizzly Bear	Polar Bear	Giant Panda
Ursus arctos	*Ursus maritimus*	*Ailuropoda melanoleuca*

Grizzly bear   Black bear   Giant panda   Red fox   Abert squirrel   Coral snake   Sea star

KINGDOM Animalia

PHYLUM Chordata

CLASS Mammalia

ORDER Carnivora

FAMILY Ursidae

▶ **Figure 18–5** Linnaeus's system of classification uses seven taxonomic categories. This illustration shows how a grizzly bear, *Ursus arctos,* is grouped within each taxonomic category. Only some representative species are illustrated for each category above the species level.

GENUS Ursus

SPECIES *Ursus arctos*

18–1 Section Assessment

1. **Key Concept** How are living things organized for study?

2. **Key Concept** Describe the system for naming species that Linnaeus developed.

3. **Key Concept** What are the seven taxonomic categories of Linnaeus's classification system?

4. Why do scientists avoid using common names when discussing organisms?

5. **Critical Thinking Applying Concepts** Which category has more biological meaning—all brown birds or all hawklike birds? Why?

 Assessment Use iText to review the important concepts in Section 18–1.

Take It to the NET

Find out the proper way to use binomial nomenclature in scientific writing. Then, write a paragraph or two about the different species of bears, which illustrates each rule for using this naming system. Use the links provided in the Biology area at the Prentice Hall Web site for help in completing this activity: **www.phschool.com**

18–2 Modern Evolutionary Classification

Linnaeus worked to decide rationally what traits should be considered when classifying organisms. He compared the structures of different organisms as well as many details of anatomy. Based on these features, he grouped organisms into categories—some of which are still in use today.

Problems With Traditional Classification

Suppose you lived during Linnaeus's time. How might you have classified organisms such as dolphins? Would you have classified them as fishes because they live in water and have streamlined bodies with limbs that look like fins? Or would you have classified dolphins as mammals because they are warmblooded and breathe air? How might you have classified the three organisms shown in **Figure 18–6?** The barnacle and the limpet have similarly shaped shells and look quite like each other. The crab, on the other hand, has a very different body form. Based on their anatomy, then, you might classify the barnacle and limpet together, and place the crab in a different group.

Both of these examples point out the problems faced by taxonomists who relied on body structure comparisons. Sometimes, due to convergent evolution, organisms that are quite different from each other evolve similar body structures. These apparent similarities made it difficult for taxonomists to decide how many organisms should be classified.

Key Concepts
- How are evolutionary relationships important in classification?
- How can DNA and RNA help scientists determine evolutionary relationships?

Vocabulary
evolutionary classification
derived character
cladogram
molecular clock

Reading Strategy:
Predicting Before you read, preview **Figure 18-7.** Predict how the field of taxonomy has changed since Linnaeus's time. As you read, note whether or not your prediction was correct.

Figure 18–6 Classifying species based on their anatomy sometimes posed problems for taxonomists. Scientists debated which of these three organisms were more closely related— crabs (top left), barnacles (bottom left), and limpets (right). **Classifying** *Draw two simple diagrams to show two different ways of grouping these three organisms.*

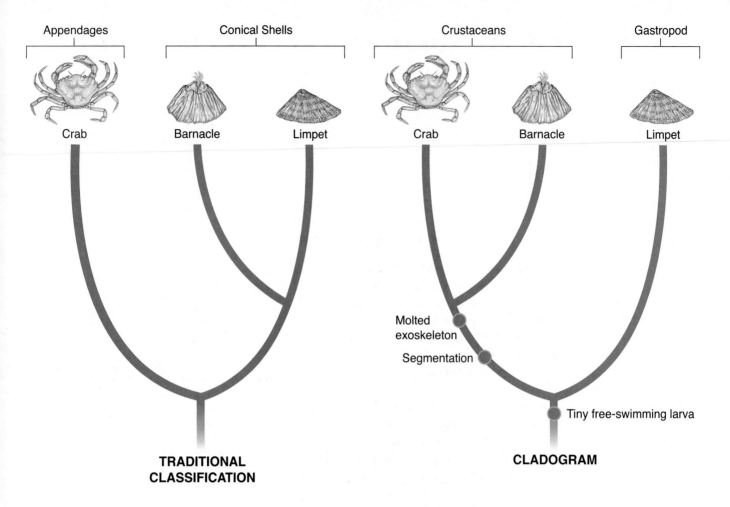

Appendages · Conical Shells · Crustaceans · Gastropod

Crab · Barnacle · Limpet · Crab · Barnacle · Limpet

Molted exoskeleton

Segmentation

Tiny free-swimming larva

TRADITIONAL CLASSIFICATION

CLADOGRAM

Figure 18–7 In traditional classification (left), organisms were grouped according to similarities in appearance. Until about 150 years ago, barnacles and limpets were grouped together because both had conical shells. 🔑 Biologists now group organisms based on evolutionary descent, not just physical similarities. In the cladogram (above), crabs and barnacles are grouped together because they share important evolutionary characteristics, such as a segmented body and an exoskeleton that the organism molts. Limpets do not share these characteristics.

Evolutionary Classification

Darwin's theory of evolution changed the entire way that biologists thought about classification. Scientists began to understand that organisms share certain traits because they share an evolutionary history. This new approach to classification provided answers to many classification questions.

🔑 Biologists now group organisms into categories that represent lines of evolutionary descent, not just physical similarities. In other words, species placed within the same genus should be more closely related to one another than to species of any other genus. Genera placed within a family should be more closely related to one another than to members of any other family. The same is true of all the other taxonomic levels, including kingdoms.

This strategy of grouping organisms together based on their evolutionary history is called **evolutionary classification**. It sounds simple, but it is not easy. Constructing an evolutionary classification scheme requires nothing less than understanding the history of life. It sometimes also requires a radical rethinking of how organisms should be classified. An example of the rethinking that sometimes occurs is shown in **Figure 18–7.** By comparing the two classification schemes, you can see how information about evolutionary history led scientists to change their views of how crabs, barnacles, and limpets should be classified.

Classification Using Cladograms

To refine the process of evolutionary classification, many biologists now prefer a method called cladistic analysis. Cladistic analysis identifies and considers only those characteristics of organisms that are evolutionary innovations—new characteristics that arise as lineages evolve over time. Characteristics that appear in recent parts of a lineage but not in its older members are called **derived characters.**

Derived characters can be used to construct a **cladogram,** a diagram that shows the evolutionary relationships among a group of organisms. You can see an example of a cladogram on the right-hand side of **Figure 18–7.** Notice how derived characters, such as "free-swimming larva" and "segmentation," appear at certain locations along the branches of the cladogram. These locations are the points at which these characteristics first arose. You can see that crabs and barnacles share some derived characters that barnacles and limpets do not. One such shared derived character is a segmented body. Another is a molted exoskeleton. Thus, this cladogram groups crabs and barnacles together as crustaceans and separates them from limpets, which are classified as gastropods.

Cladograms are useful tools that help scientists understand how one lineage branched from another in the course of evolution. Just as a family tree shows the relationships among different lineages within a family, a cladogram represents a type of evolutionary tree, showing evolutionary relationships among a group of organisms.

KEEP CURRENT WITH . . .

SCIENCE NEWS®

To find out more about the topics in this chapter, go to:
www.phschool.com

✓ CHECKPOINT *What is a cladogram?*

Quick Lab

How is a cladogram constructed?

Procedure

1. Identify the organism in the table that is least closely related to the others.
2. Use the information in the table to construct a cladogram of these animals.

Analyze and Conclude

1. **Analyzing Data** What trait separates the least closely related organism from the other animals?
2. **Classifying** List the animals in your cladogram in order of distance from the least closely related organism.

Derived Characters in Organisms			
Organism	**Derived Character**		
	Backbone	**Legs**	**Hair**
Earthworm	Absent	Absent	Absent
Trout	Present	Absent	Absent
Lizard	Present	Present	Absent
Human	Present	Present	Present

3. **Drawing Conclusions** Does your cladogram indicate that lizards and humans share a more recent common ancestor than either does with an earthworm? Explain.
4. **Inferring** Where would you insert a frog if you added it to the cladogram? Explain your answer.

▲ **Figure 18–8** 🔵 Similarities at the molecular level in the genes of organisms can be used to help determine classification. Traditionally, African vultures (top) and American vultures (center) were classified together in the falcon family. But DNA analysis has revealed that American vultures are actually more closely related to storks (bottom).

Similarities in DNA and RNA

All of the classification methods discussed so far are based primarily on anatomical similarities and differences. But suppose you were trying to compare very diverse organisms such as humans and yeasts, which are single-celled organisms. Obviously, it is of little use to compare the anatomical features of such diverse organisms.

But even very different organisms have common traits. For example, all organisms use DNA and RNA to pass on information and to control growth and development. Hidden in the genetic code of all organisms are remarkably similar genes. Because DNA and RNA are so similar across all forms of life, these molecules provide an excellent way of comparing organisms at their most basic level—their genes.

🔑 **The genes of many organisms show important similarities at the molecular level. These similarities can be used as criteria to help determine classification.** Now that scientists can sequence, or "read," the information coded in DNA, they can compare the DNA of different organisms to trace the history of genes over millions of years.

Even the genes of diverse organisms such as humans and yeasts show many surprising similarities. For example, humans have a gene that codes for myosin, a protein found in our muscles. Researchers were surprised to find a gene in yeast that codes for a myosin protein. This was surprising because yeasts don't have muscles! As it turns out, myosin in yeast interacts with other proteins to enable internal cell parts to move. Myosin is just one example of similarities at the molecular level—an indicator that humans and yeasts share a common ancestry.

DNA comparisons have also shed light on classification questions regarding closely related species. For example, you can see that the bird in the top photograph of **Figure 18–8** looks a lot like the bird in the middle photograph. Both birds have traditionally been classified together as "vultures." One group of birds inhabits Africa and Asia, and the other, the Americas. But American vultures have a peculiar habit: When they get overheated, they urinate on their legs so that evaporative cooling removes some body heat. The only other birds known to behave this way are storks, which look quite different from vultures and have always been put in a separate family.

Should American vultures be classified with the other vultures in the falcon family? Or should they be put in a family with the storks? To answer these questions, scientists analyzed the DNA of these three birds. The DNA analysis revealed that American vultures are indeed more closely related to storks than they are to other vultures.

✓CHECKPOINT *What gene indicates that humans and yeast have a common ancestry?*

Molecular Clocks

Comparisons of DNA can also be used to mark the passage of evolutionary time. A model known as a **molecular clock** uses DNA comparisons to estimate the length of time that two species have been evolving independently. To understand molecular clocks, think about a pendulum clock. It marks time with a periodically swinging pendulum. A molecular clock also relies on a repeating process to mark time—mutation.

Simple mutations occur all the time, causing slight changes in the structure of DNA, as shown in **Figure 18–9.** Some mutations have a major positive or negative effect on an organism's phenotype. These mutations are under powerful pressure from natural selection. Other mutations have no effects on phenotype. These neutral mutations accumulate in the DNA of different species at about the same rate. A comparison of such DNA sequences in two species can reveal how dissimilar the genes are. The degree of dissimilarity is, in turn, an indication of how long ago the two species shared a common ancestor.

The use of molecular clocks is not simple, however, because there is not just one molecular clock in a genome. Instead, there are many, each of which "ticks" at a different rate. This is because some genes accumulate mutations faster than others. These different clocks allow researchers to time different kinds of evolutionary events. Think of a conventional clock. If you want to time a brief event, you pay attention to the second hand. To time an event that lasts longer, you use the minute hand or the hour hand. In the same way, researchers would use a different molecular clock to compare modern bird species than they would to estimate the age of the common ancestor of yeasts and humans.

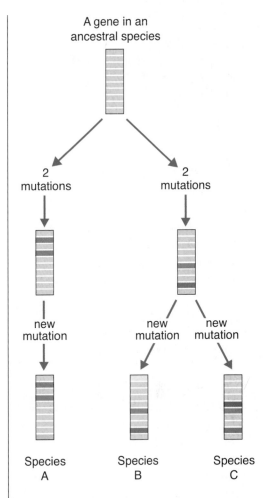

▲ **Figure 18–9** By comparing the DNA sequences of two or more species, biologists estimate how long the species have been separated. **Analyzing Data** *What evidence indicates that species C is more closely related to species B than to species A?*

18–2 Section Assessment

1. 🔑 **Key Concept** How is information about evolutionary relationships useful in classification?

2. 🔑 **Key Concept** How are genes used to help scientists classify organisms?

3. What is the principle behind cladistic analysis?

4. Describe the relationship between evolutionary time and the similarity of genes in two species.

5. **Critical Thinking** **Applying Concepts** How have new discoveries in molecular biology affected the way in which we classify organisms compared with the system used by Linnaeus?

iTEXT Assessment Use iText to review the important concepts in Section 18–2.

Classification **455**

The Search for New Species

How many kinds of living things are there on Earth? So far, scientists have identified about 1.5 million species. Yet, millions more have never been studied. Researchers continue to find new species—not just tiny organisms, but also fish, birds, and mammals.

Because new species are likely to live in remote, hard-to-reach places, scientists call on technology to help in the search, including scuba gear, helicopters, and ultralight airplanes. Remote cameras and e-mail let scientists in one spot follow the work of others continents away.

Exploring the Forest Roof

One place to search for new species is in tropical forests, which are teeming with life. Researchers especially want better ways to study the canopy— the upper layers of the forest. Scientists have used ropes to climb the tall trees, but it is hard to stay up long or collect specimens. Then, French researchers invented an unusual "raft" suspended from a hot-air balloon that floats over the tops of the trees. Scientists on the raft could work together for longer periods of time, collecting many more species.

One canopy explorer, biologist Margaret Lowman, worked with a structural engineer to design and build a canopy walkway as her "green laboratory." The walkway looks like a huge treehouse 75 feet above the forest floor, with platforms on which researchers can work.

Another new and dramatic route into the canopy is a huge construction crane like those used in building skyscrapers. Scientists on the arm of the crane get a close-up look at trees. Today there is a worldwide network of forest crane sites.

New Species or Not?

When researchers spot an unfamiliar organism, they may use simple observation to classify it. How many petals are on the flower? How many toes are on the animal? If the organism does not match known categories, the species may be new. Unusual antlers, for instance, were a major clue in identifying a new deer species in Vietnam.

External appearances can fool you, however. X-rays and electron microscopes may reveal differences that set one species apart from another. The most exciting advances have come with studies of DNA. By analyzing DNA, scientists can demonstrate how two organisms are—or are not—related.

On Your Own

Describe and sketch your own ideas for an invention that would help scientists search for new species in a forest canopy or other location that is hard to reach.

18-3 Kingdoms and Domains

In taxonomy, as in all areas of science, ideas and models change as new information arises. Some explanations have been discarded altogether, whereas others, such as Darwin's theory of evolution by natural selection, have been upheld and refined through years of research. So, it should not be surprising that early attempts at drawing life's universal tree were based on some misguided assumptions. Some of the earliest trees of life were dominated by humans. These models represented vertebrates as the most important and abundant animals. They also implied that "higher" animals evolved from "lower" animals that were identical to modern forms. Biologists now know these notions are incorrect.

The Tree of Life Evolves

The scientific view of life was simpler in Linnaeus's time. The only known differences among living things were the fundamental traits that separated animals from plants. Animals were mobile organisms that used food for energy. Plants were green, photosynthetic organisms that used energy from the sun.

As biologists learned more about the natural world, they realized that Linnaeus's two kingdoms, Animalia and Plantae, did not adequately represent the full diversity of life. First, microorganisms, such as the protist and bacterium in **Figure 18–10**, were recognized as being significantly different from plants and animals. Scientists soon agreed that microorganisms merited their own kingdom, which was named Protista. Then, the mushrooms, yeasts, and molds were separated from the plants and placed in their own kingdom, Fungi. Later still, scientists realized that bacteria lack the nuclei, mitochondria, and chloroplasts found in other forms of life. Therefore, they were placed in another new kingdom, Monera. This process produced five kingdoms—Monera, Protista, Fungi, Plantae, and Animalia.

Guide for Reading

 Key Concepts
• What are the six kingdoms of life as they are now identified?
• What is the three-domain system of classification?

Vocabulary
• domain • Bacteria
• Eubacteria • Archaea
• Archaebacteria • Eukarya
• Protista • Fungi
• Plantae • Animalia

Reading Strategy:
Classifying As you read, write the names of the six kingdoms recognized by biologists. Label each group as either prokaryotes or eukaryotes.

Paramecium caudatum
(magnification: about 1000×)

Streptococcus faecalis
(magnification: 26,000×)

Figure 18–10 The paramecium (left) is a single-celled organism that is eukaryotic, or has a nucleus. *Streptococcus faecalis* (right) is a bacterium that evolved long before eukaryotic cells. Bacteria are prokaryotes—they do not have membrane-bound organelles. The classification of these two organisms has changed greatly over the years. **Classifying** *List reasons that these two organisms should be classified in separate kingdoms.*

Changing Number of Kingdoms						
First Introduced	**Names of Kingdoms**					
1700s	Plantae					Animalia
Late 1800s	Protista			Plantae		Animalia
1950s	Monera		Protista	Fungi	Plantae	Animalia
1990s	Eubacteria	Archaebacteria	Protista	Fungi	Plantae	Animalia

▲ **Figure 18–11** This diagram shows some of the ways organisms have been classified into kingdoms over the years. ⚷ The six-kingdom system includes the following kingdoms: Eubacteria, Archae-bacteria, Protista, Fungi, Plantae, and Animalia.

In recent years, as evidence about microorganisms continued to accumulate, biologists came to recognize that the Monera were composed of two distinct groups. Some biologists consider the differences between these two groups to be as great as those between animals and plants. As a result, the Monera have been separated into two kingdoms, Eubacteria and Archaebacteria, bringing the total number of kingdoms to six.

⚷ **The six-kingdom system of classification includes the kingdoms Eubacteria, Archaebacteria, Protista, Fungi, Plantae, and Animalia.** This system of classification is shown in the bottom row of **Figure 18–11.**

The Three-Domain System

Some of the most recent evolutionary trees have been produced using comparative studies of a small subunit of ribosomal RNA that occurs in all living things. Using a molecular clock model, scientists have grouped modern organisms according to how long they have been evolving independently.

Molecular analyses have given rise to a new taxonomic category that is now recognized by many scientists. The **domain** is a more inclusive category than any other—larger than a kingdom. ⚷ **The three domains are: the domain Bacteria, which corresponds to the kingdom Eubacteria; the domain Archaea, which corresponds to the kingdom Archaebacteria; and the domain Eukarya, which is composed of protists, fungi, plants, and animals.**

Clearly, modern classification is a rapidly changing science, and we must pick a convention to classify life's diversity for the purposes of this book. In this book, we recognize the three domains and also refer frequently to the six kingdoms. The relationship between the three domains and the six kingdoms is shown in **Figure 18–12.** It also summarizes the key characteristics of each kingdom. You can see that some groups share one or more traits with other groups.

Domain Bacteria

The members of the domain **Bacteria** are unicellular and prokaryotic. Their cells have thick, rigid cell walls that surround a cell membrane. The cell walls contain a substance known as peptidoglycan. The domain Bacteria corresponds to the kingdom **Eubacteria.** These bacteria are ecologically diverse, ranging from free-living soil organisms to deadly parasites. Some photosynthesize, while others do not. Some need oxygen to survive, while others are killed by oxygen.

Domain Archaea

Also unicellular and prokaryotic, members of the domain **Archaea** live in some of the most extreme environments you can imagine—volcanic hot springs, brine pools, and black organic mud totally devoid of oxygen. Indeed, many of these bacteria can survive only in the absence of oxygen. Their cell walls lack peptidoglycan, and their cell membranes contain unusual lipids that are not found in any other organism. The domain Archaea corresponds to the kingdom **Archaebacteria.**

✓CHECKPOINT *What characteristics distinguish members of the domain Bacteria from members of the domain Archaea?*

▼ **Figure 18–12** Organisms are grouped in three domains. There is a simple relationship between the three domains and the six kingdoms. This table summarizes key evidence used in classifying organisms into these major taxonomic groups.

Classification of Living Things

DOMAIN	Bacteria	Archaea	Eukarya			
KINGDOM	Eubacteria	Archaebacteria	Protista	Fungi	Plantae	Animalia
CELL TYPE	Prokaryote	Prokaryote	Eukaryote	Eukaryote	Eukaryote	Eukaryote
CELL STRUCTURES	Cell walls with peptidoglycan	Cell walls without peptidoglycan	Cell walls of cellulose in some; some have chloroplasts	Cell walls of chitin	Cell walls of cellulose; chloroplasts	No cell walls or chloroplasts
NUMBER OF CELLS	Unicellular	Unicellular	Most unicellular; some colonial; some multicellular	Most multicellular; some unicellular	Multicellular	Multicellular
MODE OF NUTRITION	Autotroph or heterotroph	Autotroph or heterotroph	Autotroph or heterotroph	Heterotroph	Autotroph	Heterotroph
EXAMPLES	*Streptococcus, Escherichia coli*	Methanogens, halophiles	*Amoeba, Paramecium,* slime molds, giant kelp	Mushrooms, yeasts	Mosses, ferns, flowering plants	Sponges, worms, insects, fishes, mammals

DOMAIN
ARCHAEA

DOMAIN
BACTERIA

?

Kingdoms
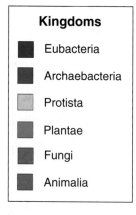 Eubacteria
Archaebacteria
Protista
Plantae
Fungi
Animalia

Domain Eukarya

The domain **Eukarya** consists of all organisms that have a nucleus. It is organized into the four remaining kingdoms of the six-kingdom system: Protista, Fungi, Plantae, and Animalia, as shown in **Figure 18–13.**

Protista The kingdom **Protista** is composed of eukaryotic organisms that cannot be classified as animals, plants, or fungi. Of the six kingdoms, Protista is the least satisfying classification, because its members display the greatest variety. Most protists are single-celled organisms, but some, such as the multicellular algae, are not. Some protists are photosynthetic, while others are heterotrophic. Some share characteristics with plants, others with fungi, and still others with animals.

Fungi Members of the kingdom **Fungi** are heterotrophs. Most feed on dead or decaying organic matter. Unlike other heterotrophs, these fungi secrete digestive enzymes into their food source. They then absorb the smaller food molecules into their bodies.

Most fungi are multicellular. The most recognizable fungi are mushrooms. Some fungi, such as yeasts, are unicellular.

DOMAIN
EUKARYA

▲ **Figure 18–13** The domains Bacteria and Archaea include the same organisms that are in the kingdoms Eubacteria and Archaebacteria. The domain Eukarya includes the protists, fungi, plants, and animals. Biologists continue to investigate how these three large groups originated. **Interpreting Graphics** *Which domain includes organisms from more than one kingdom?*

Plantae Members of the kingdom **Plantae** are multicellular organisms that are photosynthetic autotrophs. In other words, they carry out photosynthesis. Plants are nonmotile—they cannot move from place to place. They also have cell walls that contain cellulose. The plant kingdom includes cone-bearing and flowering plants as well as mosses and ferns. Although older classification systems regard multicellular algae as plants, in this book we group algae with the protists.

Animalia Members of the kingdom **Animalia** are multicellular and heterotrophic. The cells of animals do not have cell walls. Most animals can move about, at least for some part of their life cycle. As you will see in later chapters, there is incredible diversity within the animal kingdom, and many species of animals exist in nearly every part of the planet.

18–3 Section Assessment

1. 🔑**Key Concept** What are the six kingdoms of life as they are now identified?

2. 🔑**Key Concept** What are the three domains of life?

3. Why was the kingdom Monera divided into two separate kingdoms?

4. Why might kingdom Protista be thought of as the "odds and ends" kingdom?

5. **Critical Thinking Classifying** Which kingdoms include only prokaryotes? Which kingdoms include only heterotrophs?

ⓘTEXT **Assessment** Use iText to review the important concepts in Section 18–3.

Using Dichotomous Keys

What tools are available to help people identify unfamiliar organisms? One is a field guide, a book with illustrations that highlight differences between similar-looking organisms. Another tool used to identify organisms is a dichotomous key. A dichotomous key is a series of paired statements that describe physical characteristics of different organisms. In this activity, you will use a dichotomous key to identify tree leaves.

Problem   How are dichotomous keys used and made?

Materials

- 6–8 writing implements or other group of common items

Skills   Observing, Classifying, Forming Operational Definitions

Procedure

Part A: Using a Dichotomous Key

1. To use the dichotomous key for leaves, begin by reading paired statements 1a and 1b. Notice that the statements are opposites.

2. Carefully observe the leaf labeled I on page 463. Decide which statement, 1a or 1b, applies to this leaf. Then, follow the direction at the end of the statement. For example, because the leaf is a simple leaf, go to step 4.

3. Continue reading the paired statements and following the direction at the end of the applicable statement until you determine the identity of leaf I.

4. Repeat steps 2 and 3 for leaves II through VII.

Part B: Constructing a Dichotomous Key

5. Examine the writing implements or other group of items your teacher gives you. List some characteristics you could use to classify these items into groups.

6. Using the dichotomous key from Part A as a model, construct a dichotomous key for your group of items. You may wish to use some of the characteristics you listed in step 5 to construct your key. Make sure that each of the paired statements in your key are opposites.

7. Once your dichotomous key is complete, test it with each item and revise your key, if necessary.

8. Exchange keys and items with a classmate. Use your classmate's key to identify his or her items. Then, suggest ways to improve that key.

Dichotomous Key for Leaves

1. Compound or simple leaf
   - 1a) Compound leaf (leaf divided into leaflets) ....go to step 2
   - 1b) Simple leaf (leaf not divided into leaflets) ....go to step 4

2. Arrangement of leaflets
   - 2a) Palmate arrangement of leaflets (leaflets all attached at one central point) ....*Aesculus* (buckeye)
   - 2b) Pinnate arrangement of leaflets (leaflets attached at several points) ....go to step 3

3. Leaflet shape
   - 3a) Leaflets taper to pointed tips ....*Carya* (pecan)
   - 3b) Oval leaflets with rounded tips ....*Robinia* (locust)

4. Arrangement of leaf veins
   - 4a) Veins branch out from one central point ....go to step 5
   - 4b) Veins branch off main vein in the middle of the leaf ....go to step 6

5. Overall shape of leaf
   - 5a) Leaf is heart shaped ....*Cercis* (redbud)
   - 5b) Leaf is star shaped ....*Liquidambar* (sweet gum)

6. Appearance of leaf edge
   - 6a) Leaf has toothed (jagged) edge ....*Betula* (birch)
   - 6b) Leaf has untoothed (smooth) edge ....*Magnolia* (magnolia)

I

II

III

IV

V

VI

VII

Analyze and Conclude

1. **Classifying** In Part A, identify leaves I through VII.

2. **Applying Concepts** In Part B, how did you choose the characteristics for your key? How did you decide on the key's order?

3. **Evaluating and Revising** Based on your classmate's feedback, does the key you developed in Part B need to be revised? If so, how?

4. **Inferring** Why is it important that the paired statements in a dichotomous key be opposites?

Go Further

Classifying Collect 3 or 4 leaves from different trees in your neighborhood. Then, use a field guide to trees in your area to determine the identity of each tree. Which characteristics of the leaves were useful in determining their identity? In addition to leaves, does the field guide use other characteristics of the trees to help identify them? If so, which ones?

18–1 Finding Order in Diversity
Key Concepts

- To study the diversity of life, biologists use a classification system to name organisms and group them in a logical manner.
- In binomial nomenclature, each species is assigned a two-part scientific name.
- Linnaeus's system of classification uses seven taxonomic categories. They are—from smallest to largest—species, genus, family, order, class, phylum, and kingdom.

Vocabulary
taxonomy, p. 447
binomial nomenclature, p. 448
genus, p. 448
taxon, p. 449
family, p. 449
order, p. 449
class, p. 449
phylum, p. 449
kingdom, p. 449

18–2 Modern Evolutionary Classification
Key Concepts

- Organisms are now grouped into categories that represent lines of evolutionary descent.
- The genes of many organisms show important similarities at the molecular level. These similarities can be used as criteria for classification.

Vocabulary
evolutionary classification, p. 452
derived character, p. 453
cladogram, p. 453
molecular clock, p. 455

18–3 Kingdoms and Domains
Key Concepts

- The six-kingdom system of classification includes the kingdoms, Eubacteria, Archaebacteria, Protista, Fungi, Plantae, and Animalia.
- The three domains are Bacteria, Archaea, and Eukarya.

Vocabulary
- domain, p. 458 • Bacteria, p. 459
- Eubacteria, p. 459 • Archaea, p. 459
- Archaebacteria, p. 459 • Eukarya, p. 460
- Protista, p. 460 • Fungi, p. 460
- Plantae, p. 461 • Animalia, p. 461

Thinking Visually
Use information from the chapter to complete the concept map below.

Chapter 18

Part A

Multiple Choice
For each statement or question, select the number of the word or expression that, of those given, best completes the statement or answers the question.

1 The discipline that specializes in the classification of organisms is
   (1) anatomy   (3) botany
   (2) taxonomy   (4) paleontology

2 Solely from its name, you know that *Rhizopus nigricans* must be
   (1) a plant   (3) in the genus *nigricans*
   (2) an animal   (4) in the genus *Rhizopus*

3 A useful classification system does *not*
   (1) show biological relationships
   (2) reveal evolutionary trends
   (3) use different scientific names for the same organism
   (4) change the taxon of an organism based on new data

4 The largest and most inclusive of Linnaeus's taxonomic categories is the
   (1) kingdom   (3) phylum
   (2) order   (4) species

5 Which is *not* a characteristic of Linnaeus's system for naming organisms?
   (1) a multi-part name describing several traits
   (2) a name that identifies the organism's genus
   (3) a name that includes the organism's species identifier
   (4) a name unique to a single species

6 Which term shows the evolutionary relationships among a group of organisms?
   (1) taxon   (3) binomial nomenclature
   (2) cladogram   (4) molecular clock

7 The three domains are
   (1) Animalia, Plantae, Archaebacteria
   (2) Plantae, Fungi, Eubacteria
   (3) Bacteria, Archaea, Eukarya
   (4) Protista, Bacteria, Animalia

8 A new organism has been discovered that cannot produce its own food. Based on this information, it should *not* be placed into the kingdom
   (1) Protista   (3) Plantae
   (2) Fungi   (4) Eubacteria

9 What is true about using similarities or dissimilarities to classify different species?
   (1) Only similar species, such as two species of rabbits, can be meaningfully compared.
   (2) Genetic similarities are no indication of the relationship between two species.
   (3) Even dissimilar species can be compared at the level of certain genes.
   (4) It is impossible to compare dissimilar species because they have no traits in common.

10 Which organism belongs in the kingdom Animalia?
   (1) tree   (3) mollusk
   (2) protozoan   (4) bacterium

11 If species A and B have very similar genes and proteins, which statement is probably true?
   (1) Species A and B shared a relatively recent common ancestor.
   (2) Species A evolved independently of species B for a long period.
   (3) Species A and B are the same species.
   (4) Species A is older than species B.

12 The length of time that two taxa have been evolving separately can be estimated using a model called a
   (1) phylogenetic tree   (3) molecular clock
   (2) cladogram   (4) six-kingdom system

13 In the six-kingdom system of classifying living things, the kingdom(s) that contain(s) microscopic organisms is (are)
   (1) Eubacteria, only
   (2) Archaebacteria, only
   (3) Eubacteria and Archaebacteria, only
   (4) Eubacteria, Archaebacteria, and Protista

14 *Ursus maritimus* is to scientific name as polar bear is to
   (1) Latin name   (3) genus name
   (2) common name   (4) phylum name

Test-Taking Tip When you open your test booklet, reassure yourself that the question format is similar to the ones that you have seen in these practice tests. Notice that the directions and the number of choices are similar to those with which you have experience.

Parts B and C

Multiple Choice and Extended Response

For those questions that ask you to select a response, choose the one that best completes the statement or answers the question. For all others follow the directions given.

15 The diagram below shows changes over time in the DNA of related species.

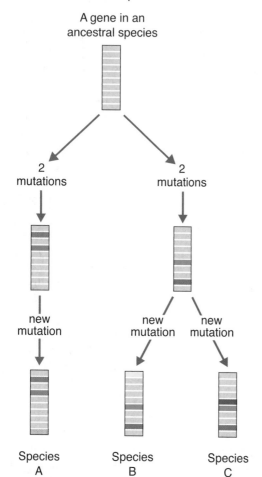

A gene in an
ancestral species

2 mutations

2 mutations

new mutation

new mutation

new mutation

Species A

Species B

Species C

The mutations were most likely
(1) not harmful enough to affect survival
(2) life threatening for species A
(3) life threatening for species B
(4) caused by adaptive radiation

16 State two advantages of using a scientific name to identify organisms.

17 Explain which two of the following three species are most closely related: *Entamoeba histolytica, Escherichia coli,* and *Entamoeba coli.*

18 Species 1 is a multicellular, photosynthetic autotroph with cell walls that contain cellulose. Species 2 has cell walls that lack peptidoglycan and cell membranes that contain lipids not found in other organisms. Many individuals of species 2 live in extreme environments and can survive only in the absence of oxygen. Species 3 is a single-celled eukaryotic organism that has chloroplasts. Place each of these three species in the correct kingdom.

19 Venn diagrams can be used to model classification schemes. In the Venn diagram below, each circular region, labeled A, B, C, or D, represents a collection of organisms at the same taxonomic level. Regions that overlap share common members. Regions that do not overlap do not share common members. Match the following terms to the four regions: All Animals, Animals that Have Backbones, Insects, and Mammals. (Do not write in this book.)

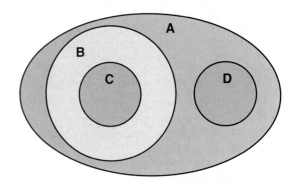

20 Complete the chart below comparing the characteristics of fungi and plants. (Do not write in this book.) Why are mushrooms not placed in the same kingdom as vegetables such as carrots and lettuce?

Kingdom	Plantae	Fungi
Cell Type	Eukaryote	
Cell Structures		Cell walls of chitin
Number of Cells		Most unicellular; some multicellular
Mode of Nutrition	Autotroph	

21 The figure below shows the presumed relationships among three insect taxa.

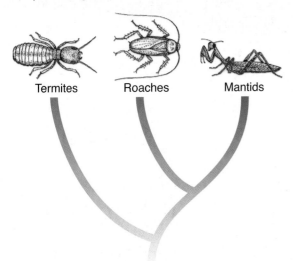

Termites   Roaches   Mantids

Common ancestor

Which statement(s) is (are) true about these three taxa?

A   Roaches and mantids share a more recent common ancestor than do roaches and termites.

B   Roaches and mantids share a more recent common ancestor than do mantids and termites.

C   Termites, roaches, and mantids share a common ancestor.

(1) A, only   (3) A and B, only
(2) B, only   (4) A, B, and C

Base your answers to questions 22 and 23 on the information below and on your knowledge of biology.

The family Felidae is made up of three genera: *Felis,* which includes pumas, ocelots, and the domestic cat; *Panthera,* which includes jaguars, lions, and tigers; *Lynx,* which includes lynx and bobcats. Some cats, such as the puma and house cat, purr. Some cats, such as the tiger and lion, roar. Some cats are adapted for running at great speeds on land, and others for moving quickly through treetops.

22 Bobcats were originally classified in the genus *Felis.* What can be inferred from the fact that the bobcat has been reclassified?

23 Describe how a molecular clock can be used to estimate the length of time that the bobcat and domestic cat have been evolving independently.

Base your answers to questions 24 through 27 on the reading passage below and on your knowledge of biology.

Wealth of the Rain Forests

It has been estimated that there are more unknown species in tropical rain forests than there are known species in the world. Scientists are concerned that the rain forests might be destroyed before the species in them can be discovered and classified.

During his voyage on the *HMS Beagle* in the 1830s, Charles Darwin spent many months collecting different species. Much of that time was spent in and around tropical rain forests. When Darwin returned to England, he classified the organisms he found. Scientists working in tropical rain forests today use some of the same techniques Darwin used to collect and classify organisms. They also use many techniques Darwin would never have thought of.

24 Compare Darwin's methods of gathering organisms with those used by modern scientists.

25 What instruments could Darwin use for observing organisms? Contrast these with the instruments modern scientists can use.

26 How did Darwin compare the similarities and differences among organisms? How do modern scientists make such comparisons?

27 Compare the way Darwin gathered and shared information about organisms with the way modern scientists do these research tasks.

Take It to the NET

How do scientists identify and classify fossils and more recent remains of animals? Visit the Prentice Hall Web site at **www.phschool.com** to find out about how scientists at the Natural History Museum in London identified the remains of what was called the "Beast of Bodmin Moor." Then, answer the following questions:

• What was the first step undertaken in identifying the "beast"?

• What evidence indicated that the skull belonged to a cat?

• What evidence indicated that the "beast" did not die on Bodmin Moor?

Microorganisms and Fungi

▶ These scarlet waxy cap mushrooms, a type of fungus, were photographed growing among the leaves and debris on a forest floor in Tennessee.

What do we know about microorganisms and fungi?

- Bacteria and viruses, too small to be seen without powerful microscopes, are found everywhere and have profound effects on the living world.

- The protists provide us with important sources of food, play key roles in the natural world, and cause some of the most serious of all human diseases.

- The fungi possess extraordinary abilities to decompose and recycle organic material, which makes them essential to other forms of life.

What discoveries lie in the future?

- Viruses are difficult to fight because they use the machinery of the cells they infect to grow and reproduce. Can we discover more effective ways to combat viral infections in order to find cures for viral diseases?

- Can we learn enough about protists to control red tides and blooms of algae, as well as better ways to fight protist diseases such as malaria?

- Can we learn the chemical secrets of fungi that enable them to produce enzymes capable of breaking down just about any molecule found in the living world?

19 Bacteria and Viruses

Bacteria can survive in extreme temperatures. Some bacteria can even survive in this hot spring in Yellowstone National Park.

Inquiry Activity

Where are bacteria found?

Procedure

1. Label 2 sterile agar plates "control" and "exposed."
2. Tape closed the cover of the control plate. Remove the cover of the exposed plate. Leave both plates on the table for 5 minutes. Do not touch or breathe on the agar.
3. After 5 minutes, tape closed the lid of the exposed plate. Store both plates upside down in a warm place.
4. After 2 days, record the number of bacterial colonies on each plate. **CAUTION:** *Do not open the plates. Give them to your teacher for proper disposal.*

Think About It

1. **Observing** Which plate had more bacterial colonies? Explain your answer.
2. **Drawing Conclusions** Where did the bacteria on your plates come from? Explain your answer.

19–1 Prokaryotes

Imagine living all your life as the only family on your street. Then, one morning, you open the front door and discover houses all around you. You see neighbors tending their gardens and children walking to school. Where did all the people come from? What if the answer turned out to be that they had always been there—you just hadn't seen them? In fact, they had lived on your street for years and years before your house was even built. How would your view of the world change? What would it be like to go, almost overnight, from thinking that you were the only folks on the block to just one family in a crowded community? A bit of a shock?

Humans once had just such a shock. Suddenly, the street was very crowded! Thanks to Robert Hooke and Anton van Leeuwenhoek, the invention of the microscope opened our eyes to the world around us.

Microscopic life covers nearly every square centimeter of Earth. There are microorganisms of many different sizes and shapes, even in a drop of pond water. The smallest and most common microorganisms are **prokaryotes**—single-celled organisms that lack a nucleus.

Prokaryotes typically range in size from 1 to 5 micrometers, making them much smaller than most eukaryotic cells, which generally range from 10 to 100 micrometers in diameter. There are exceptions to this, of course. One example is *Epulopiscium fisheloni*, a gigantic prokaryote, shown in **Figure 19–1,** that is about 500 micrometers long.

Classifying Prokaryotes

For many years, most prokaryotes were simply called "bacteria" and placed in a single kingdom—Monera. The word *bacteria* is so familiar that we will continue to use it as a common term to describe prokaryotes. More recently, however, biologists have begun to appreciate that prokaryotes can be divided into two very different groups: the eubacteria (yoo-bak-TEER-ee-uh) and the archaebacteria (ahr-kee-bak-TEER-ee-uh). Each group is now considered to be a separate kingdom. Some biologists think that the split between these two groups is so ancient and so fundamental that they should be called domains, a level of classification even higher than kingdom.

Guide for Reading

Key Concepts
- How do the two groups of prokaryotes differ?
- What factors are used to identify prokaryotes?

Vocabulary
prokaryote
bacillus
coccus
spirillum
flagellum
photoautotroph
chemoautotroph
photoheterotroph
binary fission
conjugation
endospore

Reading Strategy:
Finding Main Ideas Before you read this section, write down the major headings of the section. Then, as you read the section, list the important information under each heading.

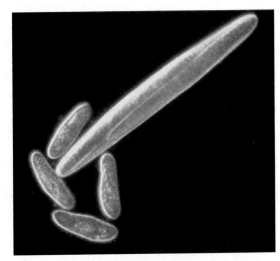

▶ **Figure 19–1** The large cell in this photograph is *Epulopiscium fisheloni,* one of the largest prokaryotes. Notice its size in relation to the neighboring cells, which are eukaryotic paramecia.

(magnification: 100×)

(magnification: 32,300×)

Figure 19–2 A bacterium such as *E. coli* has the basic structure typical of most prokaryotes: cell wall, cell membrane, and cytoplasm. The flagella are used by some prokaryotes for movement. The pili are involved in cell-to-cell contact. **The cell walls of eubacteria contain peptidoglycan, a type of carbohydrate that is not found in archaebacteria.**

Eubacteria The larger of the two kingdoms of prokaryotes is the eubacteria. Eubacteria include a wide range of organisms with different lifestyles. The variety is so great, in fact, that biologists do not agree on exactly how many phyla to divide the kingdom into. Eubacteria live almost everywhere. Some live in the soil, whereas others infect large organisms and cause disease. **Figure 19–2** shows a diagram of *E. coli,* a typical eubacterium that lives in human intestines.

Like other prokaryotes, eubacteria are usually surrounded by a cell wall that protects the cell from injury and determines its shape. The cell walls of eubacteria contain peptidoglycan, a carbohydrate. Within the cell wall is a cell membrane that surrounds the cytoplasm. Some eubacteria have a second, outer, membrane.

Archaebacteria Under a microscope, archaebacteria look very similar to eubacteria. They are equally small, lack nuclei, and have cell walls. **Archaebacteria lack peptidoglycan, a carbohydrate found in the cell walls of eubacteria, and their membrane lipids are quite different. Also, the DNA sequences of key archaebacterial genes are more like those of eukaryotes than those of eubacteria.** Based on this and other data, scientists reason that archaebacteria may be the ancestors of eukaryotes.

Many archaebacteria live in extremely harsh environments. One group of archaebacteria is the methanogens, prokaryotes that produce methane gas. Methanogens live in oxygen-free environments, such as thick mud and the digestive tracts of animals. Other archaebacteria live in extremely salty environments, such as Utah's Great Salt Lake, or in hot springs where temperatures approach the boiling point of water.

✓**CHECKPOINT** *Where do many archaebacteria live?*

Bacilli
(magnification: 7000×)

Cocci
(magnification: 137,000×)

Spirilla
(magnification: about 100,000×)

Figure 19–3 🔑 **Prokaryotes can be identified by their shapes.** Prokaryotes usually have one of three basic shapes: rods (bacilli), spheres (cocci), or spirals (spirilla).

Identifying Prokaryotes

Because prokaryotes are so small, it may seem difficult to identify their characteristics. 🔑 **Prokaryotes are identified by their shapes, the chemical natures of their cell walls, the ways they move, and the ways they obtain energy.**

Shapes Look at the different shapes of prokaryotes shown in **Figure 19–3.** Rod-shaped prokaryotes are called **bacilli** (buh-SIL-eye; singular: bacillus). Spherical prokaryotes are called **cocci** (KAHK-sy; singular: coccus). Spiral and corkscrew-shaped prokaryotes are called **spirilla** (spy-RIL-uh; singular: spirillum).

Prokaryotes can arrange themselves in a number of different ways. Some cocci, including the disease-causing bacteria *Streptococcus* and *Pneumococcus,* form long chains. Others, such as *Staphylococcus,* form large clumps or clusters.

Cell Walls Two different types of cell walls are found in eubacteria. A method called Gram staining is used to tell them apart. The Gram stain consists of two dyes—one violet (the primary stain) and the other red (the counterstain). Bacterial cells with a cell wall containing mainly peptidoglycan absorb only the violet dye, so they appear purple under the microscope, as shown in **Figure 19–4.** These bacteria are called Gram-positive. Other bacteria have a second, outer, layer of lipid and carbohydrate molecules. This extra layer absorbs only the red stain. These bacteria, which appear pink, are said to be Gram-negative.

Movement You can also identify prokaryotes by studying how they move. Some are propelled by **flagella** (singular: flagellum). Flagella are whiplike structures used for movement. Other prokaryotes lash, snake, or spiral forward. Still others glide slowly along a layer of slimelike material they secrete. Many prokaryotes do not move at all.

Figure 19–4 🔑 **Prokaryotes can be identified by the chemical natures of their cell walls.** When treated with Gram stain, Gram-positive bacteria appear purple. Gram-negative bacteria appear pink.

Gram-Positive Bacteria
(magnification: about 3000×)

Gram-Negative Bacteria
(magnification: 150×)

Obtaining Energy

Prokaryotes have diverse adaptations that allow them to live in nearly every environment imaginable. No characteristic of prokaryotes illustrates their diversity better than the ways in which they obtain energy.

Autotrophs Several groups of prokaryotes carry out photosynthesis in a manner similar to green plants, and are called **photoautotrophs** (foh-toh-AW-tuh-trohfs). As you might expect, these organisms are found where light is plentiful, near the surfaces of lakes, streams, and oceans. One group, the cyanobacteria (sy-uh-noh-bak-TEER-ee-uh), contains a bluish pigment and chlorophyll *a*, the key pigment in photosynthesis. Cyanobacteria are found throughout the world—in fresh and salt water and on land. A few species survive in extremely hot water, such as in hot springs. Others survive in the Arctic, where they can even grow on snow. In fact, cyanobacteria are often the very first species to recolonize the site of a natural disaster, such as a volcanic eruption.

Other prokaryotes, called **chemoautotrophs** (keem-oh-AW-tuh-trohfs), obtain energy directly from inorganic molecules. Chemoautotrophs get energy from chemical reactions involving ammonia, hydrogen sulfide, nitrites, sulfur, or iron. Some chemoautotrophs live deep in the darkness of the ocean. They obtain energy from hydrogen sulfide gas that flows from hydrothermal vents on the ocean floor, such as the one shown in **Figure 19–5.**

Heterotrophs Most prokaryotes are heterotrophs like us, obtaining energy by taking in organic molecules and then breaking them down. In many situations, this means that prokaryotes compete directly with us for food. If food is not handled carefully, bacteria like *Staphylococcus aureus* may get to the dinner table before you do! Once there, these bacteria may not only "eat" some of the food ahead of time, but may also release chemicals that cause food poisoning.

A small but very interesting group of prokaryotes combines the autotrophic and heterotrophic styles of life. These organisms are photosynthetic—they capture sunlight for energy. But they also need organic compounds for nutrition. These bacteria are called **photoheterotrophs** (foh-toh-HET-ur-oh-trohfs), and there is nothing quite like them in the rest of the living world.

✓ CHECKPOINT *What are photoheterotrophs?*

◀ **Figure 19–5** Ocean vents, such as this one, are often home to a rich fauna of organisms, including tube worms and other exotic organisms. **Applying Concepts** *Would photoautotrophs survive in this environment? Why or why not?*

Careers in Biology

Epidemiologist

Job Description: work for a university, health department, research or health organization, or medical corporation to identify and track diseases and develop programs that prevent or control the spread of disease

Education: Masters or Doctoral degree in epidemiology, including course work in statistics, demography, research design, and public health

Skills: good communication skills, strong computer skills, knowledge of health and medical conditions

Highlights: You get to ask lots of questions and travel. You can work on infectious diseases such as tuberculosis. Some epidemiologists work on specific issues such as tobacco addiction.

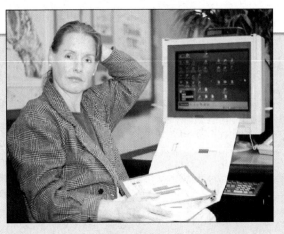

Elizabeth Lawton currently works on the infectious disease tuberculosis. She loves her job. "Because public health works at the population level, I get to help many people at one time," she says.

 Take It to the NET

For more career information, visit the Prentice Hall Web site: **www.phschool.com**

Releasing Energy

Like all organisms, bacteria need a constant supply of energy. This energy is released by the processes of cellular respiration, which requires oxygen, and fermentation, which does not. Organisms that require a constant supply of oxygen in order to live are called obligate aerobes. We, and many species of bacteria, are obligate aerobes. Some bacteria, however, do not require oxygen and, in fact, may be poisoned by it! These bacteria are called obligate anaerobes because they must live in the absence of oxygen. *Clostridium botulinum*—shown in **Figure 19–6**—is an obligate anaerobe found in soil. Because of its ability to grow without oxygen, it can grow in canned food that has not been properly sterilized. The bacteria produce a potentially deadly form of food poisoning known as botulism. Gases produced by the bacteria can cause affected cans of food to bulge.

A third group of bacteria can survive with or without oxygen and are known as facultative anaerobes. Facultative anaerobes do not require oxygen, but neither are they poisoned by its presence. Their ability to switch between cellular respiration and fermentation means that facultative anaerobes are able to grow just about anywhere. These bacteria are found in freshwater lakes and ponds, at the bottom of the ocean, and at the tops of the highest mountains. They are also found in the most thoroughly disinfected hospital rooms, and even in our own digestive systems.

(magnification: 4000×)

▲ **Figure 19–6** Botulism, a kind of food poisoning, is caused by the bacterium *Clostridium botulinum.* This type of bacterium is often found in foods that have not been properly sterilized. **Applying Concepts** *How can you avoid botulism?*

▼ **Figure 19–7** Most prokaryotes reproduce by binary fission (top), producing two identical "daughter" cells. Some prokaryotes take part in conjugation (bottom). Parts of genetic information are transferred from one cell to another by way of a hollow bridge. **Comparing and Contrasting** *Compare the process of conjugation to binary fission.*

(magnification: 26,500×)

(magnification: 7000×)

Growth and Reproduction

When conditions are favorable, prokaryotes can grow and divide at astonishing rates. Some divide as often as every 20 minutes! If unlimited space and food were available to a single prokaryote and if all of its offspring divided every 20 minutes, in just 48 hours (2 days) they would reach a mass approximately 4000 times the mass of Earth! Fortunately, this does not happen. In nature, growth is held in check by the availability of food and the production of waste products.

How do prokaryotes reproduce? When a prokaryote has grown so that it has nearly doubled in size, it replicates its DNA and divides in half, producing two identical "daughter" cells. This type of reproduction is known as **binary fission.** Because binary fission does not involve the exchange or recombination of genetic information, it is an asexual form of reproduction.

Although most prokaryotes reproduce through binary fission, others can transfer genetic material from one cell to another. This exchange of genetic information is called conjugation. During **conjugation,** a hollow bridge forms between two cells, as shown in **Figure 19–7,** and genes move from one cell to the other. This transfer of genetic information increases the genetic diversity in populations of bacteria.

When growth conditions become unfavorable, many bacteria form structures called spores. One type of spore, called an **endospore,** is formed when a bacterium produces a thick internal wall that encloses its DNA and a portion of its cytoplasm. The endospore can remain dormant for months or even centuries, until more favorable growth conditions arise. The ability to form spores makes it possible for some bacteria to survive harsh conditions—such as extreme heat, dryness, or lack of nutrients—that might otherwise kill them.

19–1 Section Assessment

1. **Key Concept** Compare and contrast the two kingdoms of prokaryotes.
2. **Key Concept** What three factors can be used to identify prokaryotes?
3. What are some of the different ways that prokaryotes obtain energy?
4. Describe how prokaryotes reproduce and exchange genetic material.

5. **Critical Thinking Inferring** Why might an infection by Gram-negative bacteria be more difficult to treat than a Gram-positive bacterial infection?

TEXT **Assessment** Use iText to review the important concepts in Section 19–1.

ALTERNATIVE ASSESSMENT

Making a Venn Diagram Create a Venn diagram that illustrates the similarities and differences between eubacteria and archaebacteria.

19–2 Bacteria in Nature

You probably remember the principal actors in the last film you saw. You might even recall some of the supporting actors. Have you ever thought that there would be no film at all without the hundreds of workers who are never seen on screen? Bacteria are just like those unseen workers. **Bacteria are vital to maintaining the living world. Some are producers that capture energy by photosynthesis. Others help to break down the nutrients in dead matter and the atmosphere, allowing other organisms to use the nutrients.**

Decomposers

Every living thing depends on a supply of raw materials. If these materials were lost forever when an organism died, life could not continue. Before long, plants would drain the soil of minerals and die, and the animals that depend on plants for food would starve. As decomposers, bacteria help the ecosystem recycle nutrients. When a tree dies and falls to the forest floor, armies of bacteria attack and digest the dead tissue. The bacteria break down dead matter into simpler substances, which are released into the soil and taken up by the roots of plants. Bacteria, as well as some eukaryotic organisms, such as insects and fungi, play important roles in this process.

As recyclers, bacteria also perform critical steps in sewage treatment. Sewage contains human waste, discarded food, organic garbage, and even chemical waste. Bacteria break down complex compounds in the sewage into simpler ones. This process produces purified water, nitrogen and carbon dioxide gases, and leftover products that can be used as fertilizers.

Guide for Reading

Key Concepts
• What ecological roles do bacteria play in the environment?
• How do bacteria cause disease?

Vocabulary
nitrogen fixation
pathogen
antibiotic
sterilization

Reading Strategy: Using Prior Knowledge
Before you read this section, make a list of five things for which bacteria are known. Then, compare your list to the text as you read.

◀ **Figure 19–8** Bacteria help to break down the nutrients in this tree, allowing other organisms to use the nutrients.

Nitrogen Fixers

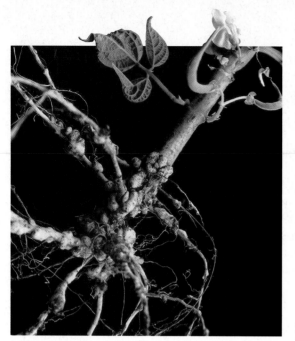

▲ **Figure 19–9** The knoblike structures on the roots of this soybean plant are called nodules. Within these nodules are the rod-shaped, nitrogen-fixing bacteria *Rhizobium.*

Plants and animals depend on bacteria for nitrogen. Plants need nitrogen to make amino acids, which are the building blocks of proteins. Because animals eat plants, plant proteins supply nitrogen for animals. Although Earth's atmosphere is made up of approximately 80 percent nitrogen gas (N_2), plants cannot use that nitrogen directly. Nitrogen must first be "fixed" chemically to ammonia (NH_3) or other nitrogen compounds. Expensive synthetic fertilizers contain these nitrogen compounds, but bacteria produce them naturally. The process of converting nitrogen into a form plants can use is known as **nitrogen fixation.** Certain bacteria are the only organisms that can fix nitrogen in this way.

Many plants have symbiotic relationships with nitrogen-fixing bacteria. For example, soybeans and other legumes host the bacterium *Rhizobium. Rhizobium* grows in nodules, or knobs, that form on the roots of the soybean plant, as shown in **Figure 19–9**. The soybean plant provides a source of nutrients for *Rhizobium,* which converts nitrogen in the air into ammonia, which helps the plant. All plants benefit from nitrogen-fixing bacteria, but soybeans are a step ahead. Soybeans have their own fertilizer factories in their roots!

✓CHECKPOINT **What is nitrogen fixation?**

Biology and History

Eliminating Disease

Early discoveries with vaccination allowed new branches of science and medicine to develop. These new fields, such as bacteriology and immunology, would help in the crusade against diseases caused by bacteria and viruses.

Missouri Compromise temporarily maintains the balance of free and slave states in the United States.

1820

1800

1849

John Snow
Snow proves for the first time that cholera is spread by contaminated drinking water. Cholera is a bacterial infection of the intestines that causes diarrhea.

1856

William Budd
Budd shows that typhoid fever is a contagious disease. Typhoid is a bacterial infection that causes a high fever.

Louis Pasteur
Pasteur develops the first effective vaccine against an infectious bacterial disease, anthrax. Anthrax is one of the oldest recorded diseases of animals.

1881

1900

Bacteria and Disease

Have you ever heard a teacher say that when a few people misbehave, they ruin it for everybody? In a way, that saying could be applied to bacteria. Bacteria are everywhere in nature, but only a few cause disease. However, these **pathogens,** or disease-causing agents, seem to get all the attention, and they give the other bacteria a bad reputation.

🔑 **Bacteria cause disease in one of two general ways. Some damage the tissues of the infected organism directly by breaking them down for food. Other bacteria release toxins (poisons) that harm the body.**

Heterotrophic bacteria can make you sick by damaging cells and tissues. For example, the bacteria that cause tuberculosis break down lung tissue. In contrast, many cases of food poisoning are caused by bacterial toxins. When meat, poultry, and eggs are not cooked properly, these toxins can make you sick. The symptoms of food poisoning range from an upset stomach to serious illness. Bacterial toxins can also travel throughout the body. For example, the *Streptococcus* bacteria that cause strep throat can release toxins into the bloodstream. These toxins can cause a reddish rash over the body called scarlet fever.

Many bacterial diseases can be prevented by stimulating the body's immune system with vaccines. If a bacterial infection does occur, a number of drugs and natural compounds can be used to attack and destroy the invading bacteria. These drugs include antibiotics, such as penicillin and tetracycline.

Word Origins

Pathogen comes from the Greek words *pathos,* meaning "suffering," and *-genes,* meaning "born" or "produced." So a pathogen is something that produces suffering. **The Greek word *karkinos* means "cancer." What do you think a carcinogen is?**

Writing Activity

Use the Internet or a library to find out more about one of the people in this time line. Write a summary of the person's discovery as it might appear in a newspaper story of the time.

Mary Mallon
Mallon is found to be the cause of an epidemic of typhoid fever in New York. She flees authorities, but before her death 51 cases of typhoid and 3 deaths will be attributed to her, giving her the nickname "Typhoid Mary."

1904

Cholera Epidemic
Over 390,000 cases of cholera are reported in 11 countries throughout South and Latin America. The disease appears on the continent after being absent from it for more than 70 years.

1991

2000

1928

Alexander Fleming
Fleming discovers penicillin accidentally when an experiment with bacteria is contaminated by mold. He finds that penicillin is nontoxic but inhibits the growth of many types of disease-causing bacteria.

1980

Smallpox Eradicated
The World Health Organization certifies that smallpox has been eradicated. This was the first major disease to be completely eliminated.

1989

Fall of Berlin Wall; Cold War ends

Common Diseases Caused by Bacteria

Disease	Pathogen	Prevention
Tooth decay	*Streptococcus mutans*	Regular dental hygiene
Lyme disease	*Borrelia burgdorferi*	Protection from tick bites
Tetanus	*Clostridium tetani*	Current tetanus vaccination
Tuberculosis	*Mycobacterium tuberculosis*	Vaccination
Salmonella food poisoning	*Salmonella enteritidis*	Proper food-handling practices
Pneumonia	*Streptococcus pneumoniae*	Maintaining good health
Cholera	*Vibrio cholerae*	Clean water supplies

▲ **Figure 19–10** ◔ **Bacteria cause disease in one of two general ways. Some damage the tissues of an infected organism directly by breaking them down for food. Other bacteria release toxins that hurt the body.** Some of the diseases caused by pathogenic bacteria are listed in the above table.

Antibiotics are compounds that block the growth and reproduction of bacteria. They can be used to cure many bacterial diseases. One of the major reasons for the dramatic increase in life expectancy during the past two centuries is an increased understanding of how to prevent and cure bacterial infections. **Figure 19–10** shows some common bacterial diseases, what pathogens cause them, and how they can be prevented.

Human Uses of Bacteria

Every day, you probably use food products that have been manufactured using bacteria. Bacteria are used in the production of a variety of foods, including cheese, yogurt, buttermilk, and sour cream. The cheeses shown in **Figure 19–11** are examples of such foods. Some bacteria are used to make pickles and sauerkraut, and some make vinegar from wine.

Bacteria are also used in industry. One type of bacterium can digest petroleum, making it very helpful in cleaning up small oil spills. Some bacteria remove waste products and poisons from water. Others can even help to mine minerals from the ground. Still others are used to synthesize drugs and chemicals through the techniques of genetic engineering.

Biotechnology companies have begun to realize that bacteria adapted to extreme environments may be a rich source of heat-stable enzymes. These enzymes can be used in medicine, food production, and industrial chemistry. Recently, a company signed a unique "bioprospecting" agreement with Yellowstone National Park, where more than half of all the hot springs and geysers on Earth are found.

◀ **Figure 19–11** Cheeses are only one kind of food made using bacteria. **Applying Concepts** *What other products are made with the help of bacteria?*

Controlling Bacteria

Most bacteria are harmless, and many are beneficial. However, the risks of bacterial infection are great enough to warrant efforts to control bacterial growth.

Sterilization destroys bacteria by subjecting them either to great heat or to chemical action. Most bacteria cannot survive high temperatures for a long time and can be killed in boiling water. An entire hospital, of course, cannot be dropped into boiling water. But a hospital can be sterilized, one room at a time, by using disinfectants. A disinfectant is a chemical solution that kills bacteria. Disinfectants are also used in the home to clean bathrooms, kitchens, and other rooms where bacteria may cause disease.

Bacteria can cause food to spoil. One method of stopping food from spoiling is refrigeration. Bacteria, like most organisms, usually grow more slowly at low temperatures. Food that is stored at a low temperature will keep longer because the bacteria will take much longer to multiply. In addition, many kinds of food can be sterilized by boiling, frying, or steaming. Each of these cooking techniques raises the temperature of the food to a point where the bacteria are killed.

If food is to be preserved for a long time, a method called canning is sometimes used. The food is heated to a high temperature. It then must be immediately placed into sterile glass jars or metal cans and sealed. Food that has been properly canned will last almost indefinitely. Finally, a number of chemical treatments will inhibit the growth of bacteria in food. These include treating food with everyday chemicals such as salt, vinegar, or sugar. Salted meat, pickled vegetables, and jam are examples of chemically preserved foods.

KEEP CURRENT WITH . . .

SCIENCE NEWS®

To find out more about the topics in this chapter, go to:
www.phschool.com

19–2 Section Assessment

1. 🔑 **Key Concept** What is the importance of bacteria in the environment?

2. 🔑 **Key Concept** How do bacteria cause disease?

3. How are bacterial infections often treated?

4. Describe three methods of preventing bacterial growth in food.

5. **Critical Thinking** **Applying Concepts** You think you might have a bacterial infection. Would it be a good idea to ask for a vaccination against the bacteria? Why or why not?

𝒊 TEXT **Assessment** Use iText to review the important concepts in Section 19–2.

ALTERNATIVE ASSESSMENT

Creative Writing
In *War of the Worlds,* a book written by H. G. Wells, Earth is invaded by aliens. No weapons can kill the invaders, and civilization seems doomed. Earth is saved, however, when the invaders die from diseases they contract. Using a similar premise, write a story about people from Earth voyaging to another planet some time in the future.

19–3 Viruses

Guide for Reading

Key Concepts
- What is the structure of a virus?
- How do viruses cause infection?

Vocabulary
virus
capsid
bacteriophage
lytic infection
lysogenic infection
retrovirus
prion

Reading Strategy:
Using Visuals As you read about viral replication in this section, trace each step in **Figures 19–14** and **19–15.** Then, list the steps, and write a few sentences to describe each step.

Imagine that you have been presented with a great challenge. Farmers in your region have begun to lose a valuable crop to a plant disease. The disease produces large pale spots on the leaves of plants similar to those shown in **Figure 19–12.** The diseased leaves look like mosaics of yellow and green. As the disease progresses, the leaves turn yellow, wither, and fall off, killing the plant.

To determine what is causing the disease, you take leaves from a diseased plant and extract a juice. You place a few drops of the juice on the leaves of healthy plants. A few days later, the mosaic pattern is right where you put the drops. Could the source of disease be in the juice?

You use a microscope to look for a germ that might cause the disease, but none can be seen. Even when the tiniest of cells are filtered out of the juice, it still causes the disease. You infer that the juice must contain pathogens so small that they are not visible under the light microscope. Although you cannot see the disease-causing particles, you're sure they're there. You give them the name *virus,* from the Latin word for "poison."

If you think you could have come to all of these conclusions, congratulations! You're walking in the footsteps of a 28-year-old Russian biologist named Dmitri Ivanovski. In 1892, Ivanovski pinpointed the cause of tobacco mosaic disease to juice extracted from infected plants. In 1897, Dutch scientist Martinus Beijerinck determined that tiny particles in the juice caused the disease, and named these particles viruses.

What Is a Virus?

In 1935, when the American biochemist Wendell Stanley purified the tobacco mosaic virus into a crystal, it became clear that viruses were not living things. **Viruses** are particles of nucleic acid, protein, and in some cases lipids that can reproduce only by infecting living cells. Viruses differ widely in terms of size and structure. You can see examples of the diversity of viruses in **Figure 19–13.** All viruses, however, have one thing in common: They enter living cells and, once inside, use the machinery of the infected cell to produce more viruses.

◄ **Figure 19–12** Tobacco mosaic virus causes the leaves of tobacco plants to develop a pattern of spots called a mosaic.

FIGURE 19–13 VIRUS STRUCTURES

Viruses come in a variety of sizes and shapes. 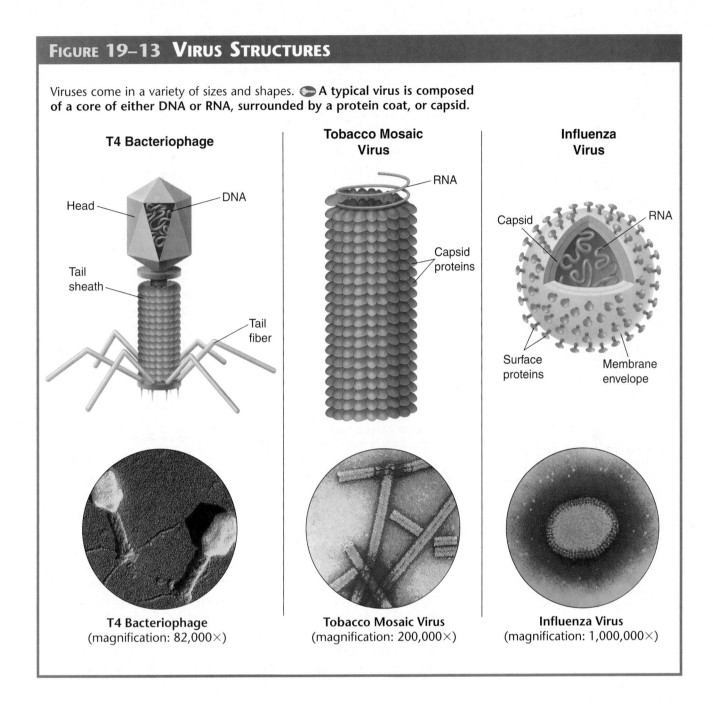 A typical virus is composed of a core of either DNA or RNA, surrounded by a protein coat, or capsid.

T4 Bacteriophage

Head

DNA

Tail sheath

Tail fiber

Tobacco Mosaic Virus

RNA

Capsid proteins

Influenza Virus

Capsid

RNA

Surface proteins

Membrane envelope

T4 Bacteriophage
(magnification: 82,000×)

Tobacco Mosaic Virus
(magnification: 200,000×)

Influenza Virus
(magnification: 1,000,000×)

Most viruses are so small they can be seen only with the aid of a powerful electron microscope. **A typical virus is composed of a core of either DNA or RNA surrounded by a protein coat.** The simplest viruses contain only a few genes, while the most complex may have more than a hundred genes.

A virus's outer protein coat is called its **capsid.** The capsid includes proteins that enable a virus to enter a host cell. The capsid proteins of a typical virus bind to the surface of a cell and "trick" the cell into allowing it inside. Once inside, the viral genes take over. The cell transcribes the viral genes, putting the genetic program of the virus into effect. Sometimes that genetic program may simply cause the cell to make copies of the virus, but often it destroys the host cell.

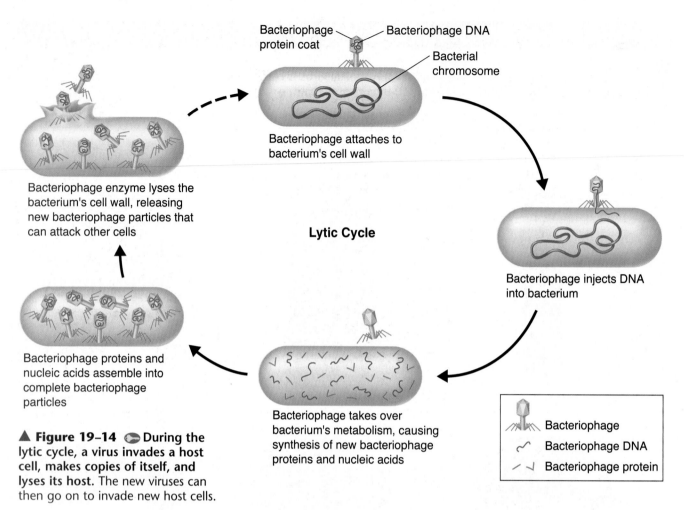

Bacteriophage protein coat — Bacteriophage DNA

Bacterial chromosome

Bacteriophage attaches to bacterium's cell wall

Lytic Cycle

Bacteriophage injects DNA into bacterium

Bacteriophage takes over bacterium's metabolism, causing synthesis of new bacteriophage proteins and nucleic acids

Bacteriophage proteins and nucleic acids assemble into complete bacteriophage particles

Bacteriophage enzyme lyses the bacterium's cell wall, releasing new bacteriophage particles that can attack other cells

Bacteriophage
Bacteriophage DNA
Bacteriophage protein

▲ **Figure 19–14** ⬭ **During the lytic cycle, a virus invades a host cell, makes copies of itself, and lyses its host.** The new viruses can then go on to invade new host cells.

Dɪscovery CHANNEL SCHOOL™ To find out more about the transmission of a virus, view the videotape "Influenza: Tracking a Virus."

Viral Infection

Because viruses must bind precisely to proteins on the cell surface and then use a host's genetic system, most viruses are highly specific to the cells they infect. Plant viruses do not infect animal cells; most animal viruses infect only certain species of animals; and bacterial viruses infect only certain types of bacteria. **Bacteriophages** (bak-TEER-ee-uh-fayj-uz) are viruses that infect bacteria. As examples of how viruses infect cells, we will look at two bacteriophages known as T4 and lambda.

✔CHECKPOINT **What is a bacteriophage?**

Lytic Infection **Figure 19–14** shows the lytic cycle of bacteriophage T4. ⬭ **In a lytic infection, a virus enters a cell, makes copies of itself, and causes the cell to burst.** Bacteriophage T4 has a DNA core inside an intricate capsid that is activated by contact with a host cell. T4 then injects its DNA directly into the cell. In most cases, the host cell cannot tell the difference between its own DNA and the DNA of the virus. Consequently, the cell begins to make messenger RNA from the genes of the virus. This viral mRNA acts like a molecular wrecking crew, shutting down and taking over the infected host cell. Some viral genes turn off the synthesis of molecules that are important to the infected cell.

The virus uses the materials of the host cell to make thousands of copies of itself. Before long, the infected cell lyses, or bursts, and releases hundreds of virus particles that may go on to infect other cells. Because the host cell is lysed and destroyed, this process is called a **lytic infection.**

In its own way, a lytic virus is similar to a desperado in the Old West. First, the outlaw eliminates the town's existing authority (host cell DNA). Then, the desperado demands to be outfitted with new weapons, horses, and riding equipment by terrorizing the local people (using the host cell to make proteins). Finally, the desperado forms a gang that leaves the town to attack new communities (the host cell bursts, releasing hundreds of virus particles).

Lysogenic Infection Other viruses cause a **lysogenic infection,** in which a host cell makes copies of the virus indefinitely. The bacteriophage lambda causes lysogenic infections, as shown in **Figure 19–15.** 🔑 **In a lysogenic infection, a virus embeds its DNA into the DNA of the host cell and is replicated along with the host cell's DNA.** Unlike lytic viruses, lysogenic viruses do not lyse the host cell right away. Instead, a lysogenic virus will insert its DNA into the DNA of the host cell. The viral DNA that is embedded in the host's DNA is called a prophage.

▼ **Figure 19–15** 🔑 In a lysogenic infection, the viral DNA enters a host cell and inserts itself into the host's DNA. Certain conditions can cause a lysogenic virus to enter the lytic cycle.

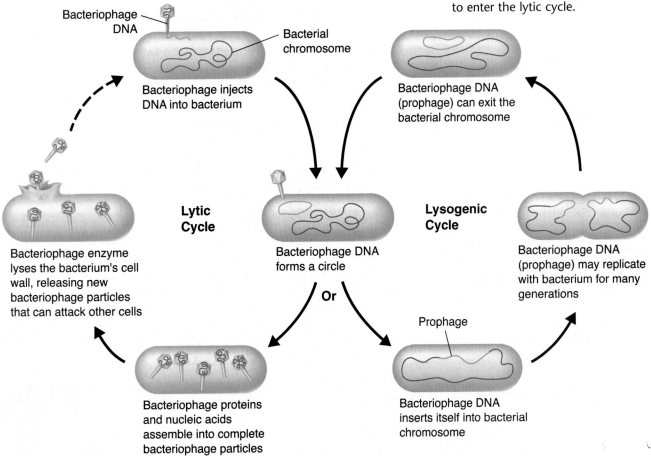

Bacteriophage DNA

Bacterial chromosome

Bacteriophage injects DNA into bacterium

Bacteriophage DNA (prophage) can exit the bacterial chromosome

Lytic Cycle

Bacteriophage DNA forms a circle

Lysogenic Cycle

Bacteriophage DNA (prophage) may replicate with bacterium for many generations

Bacteriophage enzyme lyses the bacterium's cell wall, releasing new bacteriophage particles that can attack other cells

Or

Prophage

Bacteriophage proteins and nucleic acids assemble into complete bacteriophage particles

Bacteriophage DNA inserts itself into bacterial chromosome

To find out more about how scientists study disease, view the videotape "Hantavirus: A Tale of Mice and People."

Viral DNA may not stay in the prophage form indefinitely. Eventually, any one of a number of factors will activate the DNA of the prophage, which will then remove itself from the host cell DNA and direct the synthesis of new virus particles. There are many differences between bacteriophages and the viruses that infect eukaryotic cells. Most viruses, however, show patterns of infection similar to either the lytic or lysogenic cycles of bacteriophages.

Viruses and Disease

Viruses cause human diseases such as polio, measles, AIDS, mumps, influenza, yellow fever, rabies, and the common cold. In most viral infections, viruses attack and destroy certain cells in the body, causing the symptoms of the disease.

The best way to protect against most viral diseases lies in prevention, often by the use of vaccines. A vaccine is a preparation of weakened or killed virus or viral proteins. When injected into the body, a vaccine stimulates the immune system, sometimes producing permanent immunity to the disease.

Most vaccines provide protection only if they are used before an infection begins. Once a viral disease has been contracted, it may be too late to control the infection. However, sometimes the symptoms of the infection can be treated.

Viruses and Cancer Certain viruses called oncogenic viruses cause cancer in animals. Oncogenic viruses generally carry genes that disrupt the normal controls over cell growth and division. By studying such viruses, scientists have identified many of the genes that regulate cell growth in eukaryotes.

Retroviruses Some viruses that contain RNA as their genetic information are called **retroviruses.** When retroviruses infect a cell, they produce a DNA copy of their RNA. This DNA, much like a prophage, is inserted into the DNA of the host cell. Retroviruses get their name from the fact that their genetic information is copied backward—that is, from RNA to DNA instead of from DNA to RNA. Retroviruses are responsible for some types of cancer in animals, including humans. HIV, the virus that causes AIDS, is a retrovirus.

Prions In 1972, American scientist Stanley Prusiner became interested in scrapie, an infectious disease in sheep for which the exact cause was unknown. Although he first suspected a virus, experiments suggested that the disease might actually be caused by tiny particles found in the brain. Unlike viruses, these particles contained no DNA or RNA, only protein. Prusiner called these particles **prions,** short for "protein infectious particles." There is strong evidence that mad cow disease and a similar disease in humans may also be caused by prions.

Are Viruses Alive?

Viruses share the genetic code with living things and affect living things. But most biologists do not consider viruses to be alive because viruses do not have all the characteristics of life, which you learned about in Chapter 1. For example, viruses are not cells and are not able to reproduce independently. However, when viruses do infect living cells, they can make copies of themselves, regulate gene expression, and even evolve.

Although viruses are smaller and simpler than the smallest cells, they could not have been much like the first living things. It seems more likely that viruses developed after living cells. In fact, the first viruses may have evolved from the genetic material of living cells. Viruses have continued to evolve, along with the cells they infect, over billions of years.

▲ **Figure 19–16** Prions may cause several infectious diseases, including mad cow disease. This cow was killed by mad cow disease. **Comparing and Contrasting** How are prions similar to viruses? How are they different?

19–3 Section Assessment

1. 🔑 **Key Concept** What are the parts of a virus?
2. 🔑 **Key Concept** Compare and contrast two ways that viruses cause infection.
3. What is the difference between a bacteriophage and a prophage?
4. What is a retrovirus?

5. **Critical Thinking Making Judgments** Do you think viruses should be considered a form of life? Describe the reasons for your opinion.

*i***TEXT** **Assessment** Use iText to review the important concepts in Section 19–3.

Take It to the NET

Research a virus that is currently in the news. Then, prepare a FAQ (Frequently Asked Questions) sheet about the virus. Use the links provided in the Biology area at the Prentice Hall Web site for help in completing this activity: **www.phschool.com**

Identifying Limits to the Growth of Bacteria

Bacteria can be found nearly everywhere on Earth and are able to reproduce with amazing speed. So, why isn't Earth covered by huge numbers of bacteria? What prevents them from growing and reproducing in nature as quickly as they can in the laboratory? In this investigation, you will determine whether an environmental factor such as temperature can control the growth and reproduction of bacteria.

Problem Does temperature limit the growth and reproduction of bacteria?

Materials

- 3 sterile agar plates
- hand lens
- bacterial culture
- sterile cotton swabs
- glass-marking pencil
- transparent tape
- thermometer

Skills Analyzing Data, Drawing Conclusions

Procedure   ⚠

1. **Predicting** Predict whether temperature will affect the growth rate of bacterial colonies. Record your prediction.

2. Use the hand lens to examine the sterile agar plates. They should appear clean, with no bacterial growth. Return any plates to your teacher that appear to be contaminated by bacteria or mold. **CAUTION:** *Wash your hands with warm water and soap before and after handling the agar plates.*

3. Use a glass-marking pencil to label the agar plates "3°C," "room temperature," and "37°C." Also, mark your name on each plate.

4. Put on your plastic gloves. Dip a sterile swab in the bacterial culture and wipe it back and forth in a zigzag pattern over the entire surface of the agar on one plate. Cover the plate and seal it with transparent tape. **CAUTION:** *Do not open the plates once they have been exposed to the air.*

5. Repeat step 4 with each plate, using a new sterile swab for each plate.

6. On a separate sheet of paper, make a copy of the data table shown. Use a thermometer to measure the room temperature. Record this temperature in the blank row of your copy of the data table.

Salmonella enteritidis **bacteria**
(magnification: 17,000×)

7. Place the plate labeled "3°C" in a refrigerator. Leave the plate labeled "room temperature" at room temperature in a place designated by your teacher. Place the plate labeled "37°C" in an incubator. Be sure to store each plate upside down.

8. After 24 hours, examine each plate with a hand lens. Bacterial colonies look like small white or colored dots on the surface of the agar. In your copy of the data table, record the number of bacterial colonies on each agar plate. Return each of the plates to its location described in step 7.

Data Table		
Temperature	Number of Colonies	
	24 hours	48 hours
3°C		
37°C		

2. Analyzing Data Did the same plate have the most bacteria after 48 hours? The fewest?

3. Analyzing Data Describe the effect of temperature on the growth of bacteria in this experiment. How do you think the results might differ if you included higher temperatures in your experiment?

4. Evaluating Did the results of your experiment confirm your prediction?

5. Inferring What other factors besides temperature would you expect to affect the rate at which bacteria grow and reproduce?

6. Drawing Conclusions How can the results of your experiment help explain why the world is not covered by a thick layer of bacteria?

9. After a second period of 24 hours, record in your data table the number of bacterial colonies on each agar plate. After you have completed your data table, place all your agar plates in the container designated by your teacher for safe disposal.

10. Make a graph of the results in your data table. Plot time on the *x*-axis and number of bacterial colonies on the *y*-axis. Use a different symbol to represent data from each day. After you have plotted all your data on your graph, draw a straight line or smooth curve as close as possible to all the points that represent observations after 24 hours. Draw a second curve or line through the points that represent observations after 48 hours.

Analyze and Conclude

1. **Analyzing Data** According to the graph of your data, at what temperature were the most bacterial colonies visible after 24 hours? At what temperature were the fewest bacterial colonies visible after 24 hours?

> ### Go Further
>
> **Formulating Hypotheses** Temperature is not the only environmental factor that affects the growth of bacteria. Propose a hypothesis about the effects of another variable on the growth of bacteria. Describe an experiment that could test your hypothesis.

19–1 Prokaryotes
Key Concepts

- Archaebacteria lack peptidoglycan, a carbohydrate found in the cell walls of eubacteria, and their membrane lipids are quite different. Also, the DNA sequences of key archaebacterial genes are more like those of eukaryotes than eubacteria.

- Prokaryotes are identified by their shapes, the chemical natures of their cell walls, the ways they move, and the ways they obtain energy.

Vocabulary
prokaryote, p. 471
bacillus, p. 473
coccus, p. 473
spirillum, p. 473
flagellum, p. 473
photoautotroph, p. 474
chemoautotroph, p. 474
photoheterotroph, p. 474
binary fission, p. 476
conjugation, p. 476
endospore, p. 476

19–2 Bacteria in Nature
Key Concepts

- Bacteria are vital to maintaining the living world. Some are producers that capture energy by photosynthesis. Others help to break down the nutrients in dead matter and the atmosphere, allowing other organisms to use the nutrients.

- Bacteria cause disease in one of two general ways. Some damage the tissues of the infected organism directly by breaking them down for food. Other bacteria release toxins (poisons) that harm the body.

Vocabulary
nitrogen fixation, p. 478
pathogen, p. 479
antibiotic, p. 480
sterilization, p. 481

19–3 Viruses
Key Concepts

- A typical virus is composed of a core of either DNA or RNA surrounded by a protein coat.

- In a lytic infection, a virus enters a cell, makes copies of itself, and causes the cell to burst.

- In a lysogenic infection, a virus embeds its genome into the DNA of the host cell and is replicated along with the host cell's DNA.

Vocabulary
virus, p. 482
capsid, p. 483
bacteriophage, p. 484
lytic infection, p. 485
lysogenic infection, p. 485
retrovirus, p. 487
prion, p. 487

Thinking Visually
Complete this concept map, which shows the relationships among the groups of prokaryotes.

Chapter 19

Part A

Multiple Choice

For each statement or question, select the number of the word or expression that, of those given, best completes the statement or answers the question.

1 Prokaryotes are unlike all other organisms in that their cells
 (1) lack nuclei   **(3)** have cell walls
 (2) have organelles   **(4)** lack nucleic acids

2 Which photograph shows bacillus bacteria?

(1)

(3)

(2)

(4)

3 Which group includes the bacteria that contain chlorophyll *a*?
 (1) archaebacteria **(3)** chemoautotrophs
 (2) cyanobacteria   **(4)** pathogens

4 Bacteria reproduce asexually by
 (1) binary fission   **(3)** conjugation
 (2) spores   **(4)** external fertilization

5 The process of converting nitrogen into a form plants can use is known as nitrogen
 (1) conjugation   **(3)** decomposition
 (2) transfer   **(4)** fixation

6 Which term best decribes disease-causing bacteria?
 (1) cocci   **(3)** pathogens
 (2) bacilli **(4)** archaebacteria

7 The outer protein coat of a virus is a
 (1) core of DNA **(3)** capsid
 (2) core of RNA **(4)** membrane envelope

8 Which illness is caused by a virus?
 (1) Lyme disease **(3)** tetanus
 (2) measles   **(4)** food poisoning

9 Which characteristic is *not* used to identify specific prokaryotes?
 (1) cell size   **(3)** cell movement
 (2) cell shape **(4)** cell energy source

10 One group of viruses that contain RNA as their genetic information is
 (1) oncogenic   **(3)** capsids
 (2) retroviruses **(4)** prophages

11 Which method is *not* used to protect food against microorganisms?
 (1) salting   **(3)** vaccination
 (2) freezing **(4)** sterilization

12 Archaebacteria that live in oxygen-free environments include
 (1) protists   **(3)** retroviruses
 (2) methanogens **(4)** bacteriophages

13 Which process is used for the exchange of genetic information between two bacterial cells?
 (1) lytic cycle   **(3)** binary fission
 (2) conjugation **(4)** immunization

14 Spherical prokaryotes are called
 (1) cocci   **(3)** spirilla
 (2) eubacteria **(4)** archaebacteria

15 The process of asexual reproduction in prokaryotes is called
 (1) conjugation   **(3)** lytic cycle
 (2) immunization **(4)** binary fission

For question 16, complete the analogy by selecting the correct number. In analogies, A : B :: C : means "A is to B as C is to ___?___."

16 Cell : cell membrane :: virus :
 (1) cell wall **(3)** bacteriophage
 (2) capsid   **(4)** DNA core

> **Test-Taking Tip** For questions containing the word *not*, begin by jotting down items that do fit the characteristic in question. Then, compare your notes with the answer choices and eliminate those that correspond to your list. Finally, check to see that your answer is correct by confirming that it does not fit the characteristic in question.

Preparing for the
Living Environment Exam

Parts B and C

Multiple Choice and Extended Response

For those questions that ask you to select a response, choose the one that best completes the statement or answers the question. For all others follow the directions given.

Base your answers to questions 17 and 18 on the graph below and on your knowledge of biology.

Bacterial Growth at 37°C

17 At which point in the graph does the number of living bacteria increase at the greatest rate?
(1) between hours 2 and 4
(2) between hours 4 and 6
(3) between hours 6 and 8
(4) between hours 10 and 14

18 Which is the most likely reason for the decrease in population shown?
(1) The temperature of the bacteria culture was too high after 8 hours
(2) The bacteria ceased mating after 8 hours
(3) More nutrients were added to the culture at regular intervals
(4) Waste products from the bacteria accumulated in the nutrient solution

19 State two distinguishing characteristics of prokaryotes.

20 Describe the three main cell shapes of prokaryotes.

21 How do scientists use stains to distinguish between Gram-positive and Gram-negative bacteria?

22 Describe two methods by which prokaryotes move.

23 State one way in which photoautotrophs are similar to chemoautotrophs and one way in which they are different.

24 State one way in which photoheterotrophs are similar to ordinary heterotrophs and one way in which they are different.

25 State one way to distinguish between an obligate aerobe and an obligate anaerobe.

26 Facultative anaerobes can survive with or without oxygen. How is this advantageous to them?

27 What is the role of certain bacteria in changing atmospheric nitrogen into a form usable by plants?

28 State the one thing that all viruses have in common concerning their interactions with living cells.

29 State one way the capsid protein is important to the functioning of a virus.

30 Describe the sequence of events that occurs during the lytic cycle of a T4 bacteriophage.

Base your answers to questions 31 and 32 on the information below and on your knowledge of biology.

An experiment was conducted to determine the effectiveness of different antibiotics against a certain strain of bacteria. Four disks, each soaked in a different antibiotic, were placed in a petri dish where the bacteria were growing. The results are summarized below.

Effects of Antibiotics	
Antibiotic	**Observation After One Week**
A	No growth for 6 mm from disk edge
B	Growth all around disk edge
C	Growth all around disk edge
D	No growth for 2 mm from disk edge

31 State which antibiotics were the least effective at retarding the growth of the bacteria. Support your answer with data from the experiment.

32 State which antibiotic might be most effective for an infection caused by this strain of bacteria. Support your answer with data from the experiment.

33 Describe what happens to a bacterial cell when the bacteriophage DNA exits from the bacterial chromosome.

34 What is the most commonly used method to protect humans against most viral diseases?

35 Explain how other organisms would be affected if bacteria lost the ability to function in the recycling of nitrogen compounds.

36 Bacteria can be grown in the laboratory in a prepared medium. Can all viruses be grown on cultures of bacteria? Support your answer.

37 Explain why foods such as uncooked rice and raisins do not spoil.

38 Bacteria that live on teeth produce an acid that causes decay. Explain why people who do not brush regularly have more cavities than those who do.

39 A scientist finds a new organism but is unsure which kingdom it belongs to. The organism is unicellular, has a cell wall containing peptidoglycan, has a circular DNA molecule, and has ribosomes, but it lacks a nucleus. Based on these characteristics, which kingdom does it belong to?

40 Bacteria and viruses are often considered together because they have some things in common. Yet, they also differ in many significant ways. Compare the features and impact of both bacteria and viruses on humans and the environment. In your answer, be sure to
- compare the overall structure of a bacterial cell with the structure of a virus
- compare the genetic material of bacteria with the genetic material of viruses
- state one specific way each can be harmful to humans
- state one specific way each has been used by humans in a positive way
- state one specific way each has an impact on the environment

41 Explain how the outcome of binary fission differs from that of both endospore formation and conjugation.

42 Describe the design of an experiment to test the hypothesis that contact of an agar plate with a finger results in more bacterial growth than the exposure of the plate to classroom air.

Base your answers to questions 43 and 44 on the information below and on your knowledge of biology.

The data table shows the results of an experiment conducted with one species of bacterium. The bacteria were grown for 24 hours in five dishes with nutrient media at several different pH levels, all at a temperature of 37°C.

pH of the Nutrient Medium	Number of Bacterial Colonies on the Nutrient Medium
5	10
6	50
7	60
8	70
9	5

43 The most appropriate title for this data table is
(1) The Effect of pH of Bacteria on Nutrient Media at 37°C
(2) The Effect of pH on Bacterial Population Growth
(3) The Effect of Bacterial Population Growth on pH
(4) The Effect of Bacteria at 37°C for 24 Hours

44 State an appropriate conclusion that could be drawn from the data reported in the table.

 Take It to the NET

Can bacteria become ill? Visit the Prentice Hall Web site at **www.phschool.com** to learn more about bacteriophages, viruses that infect bacteria. Then, answer the following questions:
- How can you determine whether bacteriophages are present in bacteria?
- Can bacteriophages be used to cure humans of diseases caused by pathogenic bacteria?
- Why are bacteriophages considered to be important tools in bacteriological research?

These colorful diatoms make up a small part of the diverse group of protists.

Inquiry Activity

What are protists?

Procedure

1. Place a drop of water containing a variety of micro-organisms on a microscope slide. Add a drop of methyl cellulose and a coverslip. Observe the slide under the microscope at low and high magnifications.

2. Record your observations. Draw and label each type of organism.

3. Draw a chart listing each type of organism that you observed and its characteristics.

Think About It

1. **Classifying** Are any of these organisms bacteria, animals, or plants? Explain your answer.

2. **Forming Operational Definitions** The organisms you observed are members of a group called protists. Write a definition of *protist*.

20–1 The Kingdom Protista

On a dark, quiet night you sit at the stern of a tiny sailboat as it glides through the calm waters of a coastal inlet. Suddenly, the boat's wake sparkles with its own light. As the stern cuts through the water, glimmering points of light leave a ghostly trail into the darkness. What's responsible for this eerie display? You've just had a close encounter with one group of some of the most remarkable organisms in the world—the protists.

What Is a Protist?

The kingdom Protista is a diverse group that may include more than 200,000 species. Biologists have argued for years over the best way to classify protists, and the issue may never be settled. In fact, protists are defined less by what they are and more by what they are not: A **protist** is any organism that is not a plant, an animal, a fungus, or a prokaryote. **Protists are eukaryotes that are not members of the kingdoms Plantae, Animalia, or Fungi.** Recall that a eukaryote has a nucleus and other membrane-bound organelles. Although most protists are unicellular, quite a few are not, as you can see in **Figure 20–1.** A few protists actually consist of hundreds or even thousands of cells but are still considered protists because they are so similar to others that are truly unicellular.

Evolution of Protists

Protists are members of a kingdom whose formal name, *Protista,* comes from Greek words meaning "the very first." The name is appropriate. The first eukaryotic organisms on Earth, which appeared nearly 1.5 billion years ago, were protists.

Guide for Reading

Key Concept
• What are protists?

Vocabulary
protist

Reading Strategy:
Summarizing As you read, find the main ideas for each blue heading. Write down a few key words from each main idea. Then, use the key words in your summary. Reread and revise your summary, keeping only the most important ideas.

Figure 20–1 Protists are a diverse group of mainly single-celled eukaryotes. Examples of protists include freshwater ciliates, radiolarians, and *Spirogyra*. *Spirogyra* may form slimy floating masses in fresh water. The organism's name refers to the helical arrangement of its ribbonlike chloroplasts.

Euplotes (a freshwater ciliate)
(magnification: about 140×)

Radiolarian
(magnification: 3400×)

Spirogyra
(magnification: 400×)

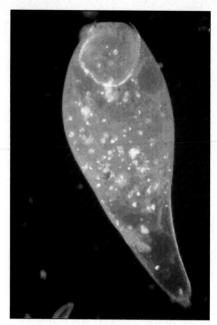

(magnification: 350×)

▲ **Figure 20–2** According to one hypothesis, some organelles in eukaryotic cells were once symbiotic prokaryotes that lived inside other cells. For example, the mitochondria found in this *Stentor* may be descended from early prokaryotes. **Formulating Hypotheses** *What other organelle may originally have been symbiotic cells?*

Where did the first protists come from? American biologist Lynn Margulis has hypothesized that the first eukaryotic cells may have evolved from a symbiosis of several cells. Mitochondria and chloroplasts found in eukaryotic cells may be descended from aerobic and photosynthetic prokaryotes that began to live inside larger cells. **Figure 20–2** shows a typical protist.

Classification of Protists

Protists are so diverse that many biologists have suggested that they should be broken up into several kingdoms. This idea is supported by recent studies of protist DNA indicating that different groups of protists evolved independently from archaebacteria. Unfortunately, at present, biologists simply don't agree on how best to classify the protists. Therefore, in this textbook, we will take the traditional approach of considering the protists as a single kingdom.

One way to classify protists is according to the way they obtain nutrition. Thus, many protists that are heterotrophs are called animallike protists. Those that produce their own food by photosynthesis are called plantlike protists. Finally, those that obtain their food by external digestion—either as decomposers or parasites—are called funguslike protists. This is the way in which we will organize our investigation of the protists.

It is important to understand, however, that these categories are an artificial way to organize a very diverse group of organisms. Categories based on the way protists obtain food do not reflect the evolutionary history of these organisms. For example, all animallike protists did not necessarily share a relatively recent ancestor. The protistan family tree is likely to be redrawn many times as the genes of the many species of protists are analyzed and compared using the powerful tools of molecular biology.

20–1 Section Assessment

1. 🗝 **Key Concept** What is a protist?
2. Describe Margulis's theory about the evolution of protists.
3. Are most protists unicellular or multicellular?
4. What are the three methods that protists use to obtain food?

5. **Critical Thinking Using Analogies** In what way is the kingdom Protista similar to a group of people who do not belong to a political party?

iTEXT Assessment Use iText to review the important concepts in Section 20–1.

20–2 Animallike Protists: Protozoans

At one time, animallike protists were called protozoa, which means "first animals," and were classified separately from more plantlike protists. Like animals, these organisms are heterotrophs. The four phyla of animallike protists are distinguished from one another by their means of movement. As you will read, zooflagellates swim with flagella, sarcodines move by extensions of their cytoplasm, ciliates move by means of cilia, and sporozoans do not move on their own at all.

Zooflagellates

Many protists easily move through their aquatic environments propelled by flagella. Flagella are long, whiplike projections that allow a cell to move. **Animallike protists that swim using flagella are classified in the phylum Zoomastigina and are often referred to as zooflagellates.** Most zooflagellates (zoh-oh-FLAJ-uh-lits) have either one or two flagella, although a few species have many flagella. Two representative zooflagellates are shown in **Figure 20–3**.

Zooflagellates are generally able to absorb food through their cell membranes. Many live in lakes and streams, where they absorb nutrients from decaying organic material. Others live within the bodies of other organisms, taking advantage of the food that the larger organism provides.

Most zooflagellates reproduce asexually by means of binary fission, including mitotic cell division. Binary fission results in two cells that are genetically identical. Some zooflagellates, however, have a sexual life cycle as well. During sexual reproduction, gamete cells are produced by meiosis. When gametes from two organisms fuse, an organism with a new combination of genetic information is formed.

Guide for Reading

Key Concepts
- What are the distinguishing features of the major phyla of animallike protists?
- How do animallike protists harm other living things?

Vocabulary
- pseudopod
- amoeboid movement
- food vacuole • cilium
- trichocyst • macronucleus
- micronucleus • gullet
- anal pore • contractile vacuole
- conjugation

Reading Strategy: Building Vocabulary
Before you read, preview new vocabulary by skimming the section and making a list of the boldfaced terms. Leave space to make notes as you read.

Figure 20–3 Zooflagellates are animallike protists that swim using flagella.

Trichomonas vaginalis
(magnification: 11,500×)

Leishmania donovani
(magnification: 4800×)

▼ **Figure 20–4** Sarcodines use pseudopods for feeding and movement. *Amoeba proteus,* a common sarcodine, moves by first extending a pseudopod away from its body. The organism's cytoplasm then streams into the pseudopod. This shifting of the mass of the cell away from where it originated is a slow but effective way to move from place to place. Amoebas also use pseudopods to surround and ingest prey.

Sarcodines

Members of the phylum Sarcodina, or sarcodines, move by means of temporary projections of cytoplasm known as **pseudopods** (SOO-doh-pahdz). **Sarcodines are animallike protists that use pseudopods for feeding and movement.** The best-known sarcodines are the amoebas, shown in **Figure 20–4.** Amoebas are flexible, active cells with thick pseudopods that extend out of the central mass of the cell. The cytoplasm of the cell streams into the pseudopod, and the rest of the cell follows. This type of locomotion is known as **amoeboid movement.**

Amoebas can capture and digest particles of food and even other cells. They do this by surrounding their meal, then taking it inside themselves to form a food vacuole. A **food vacuole** is a small cavity in the cytoplasm that temporarily stores food. Once inside the cell, the material is digested rapidly and the nutrients are passed along to the rest of the cell. Amoebas reproduce by means of binary fission.

Foraminiferans, another member of Sarcodina, are abundant in the warmer regions of the oceans. Foraminiferans secrete shells of calcium carbonate ($CaCO_3$). As they die, the calcium carbonate from their shells accumulates on the bottom of the ocean. In some regions, thick deposits of foraminiferan shells have formed on the ocean floor. The white chalk cliffs of Dover, England, are huge deposits of foraminiferan skeletons that were raised above sea level by geological processes.

The sarcodines also include a group of organisms known as the heliozoans. The name *Heliozoan* means "sun animal." Heliozoans produce shells of silica (SiO_2). Thin spikes of cytoplasm, supported by microtubules, project from the shells, making heliozoans look like the sun's rays.

(magnification: 330×)

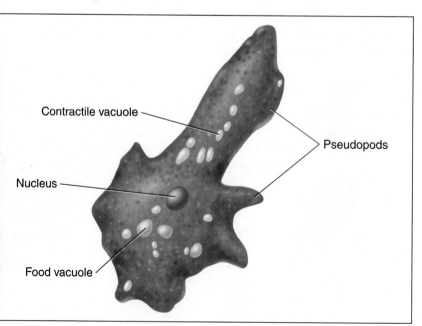

Contractile vacuole

Nucleus

Food vacuole

Pseudopods

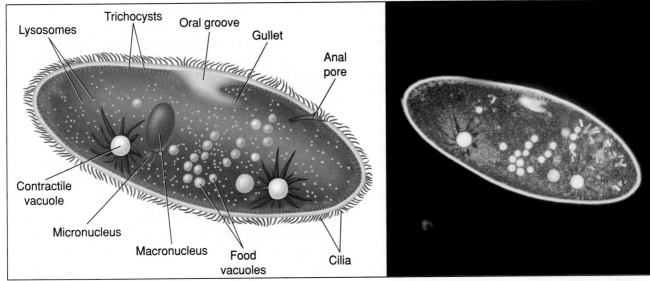

Lysosomes

Trichocysts

Oral groove

Gullet

Anal pore

Contractile vacuole

Micronucleus

Macronucleus

Food vacuoles

Cilia

(magnification: 2500×)

▲ **Figure 20–5** Ciliates use hairlike projections called cilia for feeding and movement. Ciliates, including this paramecium, are covered with short hairlike cilia that propel them through the water. Cilia also line the organism's gullet and move its food—usually bacteria—to the organism's interior. There, the food particles are engulfed, forming food vacuoles. The contractile vacuoles collect and remove excess water.

Ciliates

The phylum Ciliophora is named for **cilia** (singular: cilium), short hairlike projections similar to flagella. **Members of the phylum Ciliophora, known as ciliates, use cilia for feeding and movement.** The internal structure of cilia and flagella are identical. The beating of cilia, like the pull of hundreds of oars in an ancient ship, propels a cell rapidly through water.

Ciliates are found in both fresh and salt water. In fact, a lake or stream near your home might contain many different ciliates. Most ciliates are free living, which means that they do not exist as parasites or symbionts.

CHECKPOINT *What are cilia, and how do ciliates use them?*

Internal Anatomy Some of the best known ciliates belong to the genus *Paramecium.* A paramecium can be as long as 350 micrometers. Its cilia, which are organized into evenly spaced rows and bundles, beat in a regular, efficient pattern. The cell membrane of a paramecium is highly structured and has trichocysts just below its surface. **Trichocysts** (TRY-koh-sists) are very small, bottle-shaped structures used for defense. When a paramecium is confronted by danger, such as a predator, the trichocysts release stiff projections that protect the cell.

A paramecium's internal anatomy is shown in **Figure 20–5.** Like most ciliates, a paramecium possesses two types of nuclei: a macronucleus and one or more smaller micronuclei. Why does a ciliate need two types of nuclei? The **macronucleus** is a "working library" of genetic information—a site for keeping multiple copies of most of the genes that the cell needs in its day-to-day existence. The **micronucleus,** by contrast, contains a "reserve copy" of all of the cell's genes.

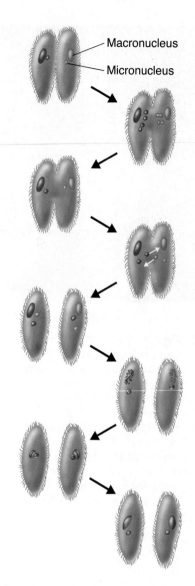

Macronucleus

Micronucleus

▲ **Figure 20–6** During conjugation, two paramecia attach themselves to each other and exchange genetic information. Conjugation increases genetic diversity. **Interpreting Graphics** *What structures do paramecia exchange during conjugation?*

Many ciliates obtain food by using cilia to sweep food particles into the **gullet,** an indentation in one side of the organism. The particles are trapped in the gullet and forced into food vacuoles that form at its base. The food vacuoles pinch off into the cytoplasm and eventually fuse with lysosomes, which contain digestive enzymes. The material in the food vacuoles is digested, and the organism obtains nourishment. Waste materials are emptied into the environment when the food vacuole fuses with a region of the cell membrane called the **anal pore.**

In fresh water, water may move into the paramecium by osmosis. This excess water is collected in vacuoles. These vacuoles empty into canals that are arranged in a star-shaped pattern around contractile vacuoles. **Contractile vacuoles** are cavities in the cytoplasm that are specialized to collect water. When a contractile vacuole is full, it contracts abruptly, pumping water out of the organism.

Conjugation Under most conditions, ciliates reproduce asexually by mitosis and binary fission. When placed under stress, however, paramecia may engage in a process known as **conjugation** that allows them to exchange genetic material with other individuals. The process of conjugation is shown in **Figure 20–6.**

As conjugation begins, two paramecia attach themselves to each other. After meiosis of their diploid micronuclei, each organism is left with four haploid micronuclei. Three of these micronuclei disintegrate. The remaining micronucleus in each organism divides, forming a pair of identical micronuclei. The two organisms then exchange one micronucleus from their pair. The macronuclei disintegrate, and new macronuclei form from micronuclei. The two paramecia that participated in conjugation are both genetically changed from their former state. By the end of the process, they are genetically identical to each other.

Strictly speaking, conjugation is not reproduction because no new individuals are formed. It is, however, a sexual process because new combinations of genetic information are produced. Within a large population, the process of conjugation helps to create and maintain genetic diversity.

Sporozoans

While many animallike protists are free living, some are parasites of animals. 🔑 **Members of the phylum Sporozoa do not move on their own and are parasitic.** Sporozoans are parasites of a wide variety of organisms, including worms, fish, birds, and humans. Many sporozoans have complex life cycles that involve more than one host. Sporozoans reproduce by means of sporozoites. Under the right conditions, a sporozoite can attach itself to a host cell, penetrate it, and then live within it as a parasite.

✓ CHECKPOINT *How do sporozoans reproduce?*

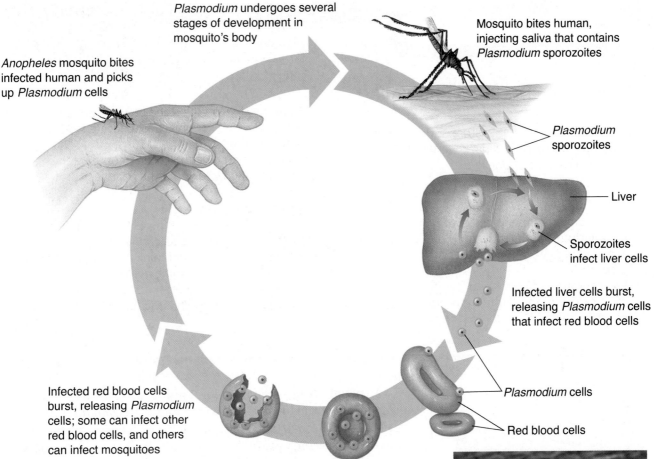

Plasmodium undergoes several stages of development in mosquito's body

Mosquito bites human, injecting saliva that contains *Plasmodium* sporozoites

Anopheles mosquito bites infected human and picks up *Plasmodium* cells

Plasmodium sporozoites

Liver

Sporozoites infect liver cells

Infected liver cells burst, releasing *Plasmodium* cells that infect red blood cells

Plasmodium cells

Red blood cells

Infected red blood cells burst, releasing *Plasmodium* cells; some can infect other red blood cells, and others can infect mosquitoes

Animallike Protists and Disease

Animallike protists are found throughout the world. They are some of the most common organisms in the oceans. They are also abundant in fresh water, on land, and in the bodies of larger organisms. Unfortunately for humans and for other organisms, many protists are disease-causing parasites. ⚷ **Some animal-like protists cause serious diseases, including malaria and African sleeping sickness.**

Malaria Malaria is one of the world's most serious infectious diseases. Between 300 and 500 million people suffer from malaria, and as many as 2 million people die from it every year. The sporozoan *Plasmodium,* which causes malaria, is carried by the female *Anopheles* mosquito.

The cycle of malarial infection is illustrated in **Figure 20–7.** When an infected mosquito bites a human, its saliva, which contains sporozoites of the parasite, enters the bloodstream. Once inside the body, *Plasmodium* infects liver cells and then red blood cells. *Plasmodium* multiplies rapidly within the infected cells. When red blood cells burst, they dump large amounts of toxins, or poisons, into the bloodstream. The toxins produce the chills and fever that are symptoms of malaria.

Figure 20–7 ⚷ **Animallike protists can cause serious diseases, including malaria.** The bite of an *Anopheles* mosquito can transmit *Plasmodium* sporozoites. Once in the human body, *Plasmodium* infects liver cells and red blood cells and multiplies.

Quick Lab

How does a paramecium eat?

Materials paramecium culture, 2 dropper pipettes, microscope, microscope slide, coverslip, *Chlorella* culture, toothpick, carmine dye

Procedure

1. Use separate dropper pipettes to place a drop of paramecium culture and a drop of *Chlorella* (green alga) culture next to each other on a microscope slide.
2. Use a toothpick to transfer a few granules of carmine dye to the drops on the slide. Add a coverslip so that the two drops mix.

3. Place the slide on the stage of a microscope. Use the low-power objective to locate several paramecia.
4. Use the high-power objective to observe the contents and behavior of the paramecia.

Analyze and Conclude

1. **Observing** Where did the *Chlorella* cells and carmine dye granules accumulate?
2. **Inferring** How do you think this happened to the *Chlorella* cells and carmine dye granules?
3. **Formulating Hypotheses** What process in the paramecia do you think resulted in this change?

Although drugs such as chloroquinine are effective against some forms of the disease, many strains of *Plasmodium* are resistant to these drugs. Medical scientists have developed a number of vaccines against malaria, but to date most are only partially effective. Therefore, for the immediate future, the best means of controlling malaria involve controlling the mosquitoes that carry it.

Other Protistan Diseases Zooflagellates of the genus *Trypanosoma* are responsible for African sleeping sickness. The trypanosomes that cause African sleeping sickness are spread by the bite of an insect known as the tsetse fly. Trypanosomes cause chills and rashes, and they can also infect nerve cells. Severe damage to the nervous system causes individuals to lose consciousness, lapsing into the deep and often fatal coma from which the disease gets its name. The control of the tsetse fly and the protist pathogens that it spreads is a major goal of health workers in Africa.

Amebic dysentery, which is characterized by severe diarrhea, is caused by an organism that looks like the harmless amoebas that you may find in a nearby pond. *Entamoeba*, a parasite spread by contaminated drinking water, can attack the wall of the intestine, causing extensive bleeding.

Amebic dysentery is most common in areas with poor sanitation, but even crystal-clear mountain streams may be contaminated with another flagellated pathogen, *Giardia*. *Giardia* produces tough microscopic cysts that can be killed only by boiling water thoroughly or by adding iodine to the water. Infection by *Giardia* can cause severe diarrhea and digestive system problems.

KEEP CURRENT WITH . . .

To find out more about the topics in this chapter, go to:
www.phschool.com

(magnification: 10×)

Figure 20–8 You can see particles of wood inside the body of *Trichonympha*, a wood-digesting protist (below). *Trichonympha* lives in the digestive systems of insects such as termites (left), allowing them to obtain nutrients from the wood they eat. **Predicting** *What would happen if a termite's* Trichonympha *colony died?*

(magnification: about 250×)

Ecology of Animallike Protists

Many animallike protists play essential roles in the living world. Some live symbiotically within other organisms. Others recycle nutrients by breaking down dead organic matter. Many animallike protists live in seas and lakes, where they are eaten by tiny animals, which in turn serve as food for larger animals.

Some animallike protists are beneficial to other organisms. *Trichonympha,* shown in **Figure 20–8,** is a zooflagellate that lives within the digestive systems of termites. This protist makes it possible for the termites to eat wood. Termites do not have enzymes to break down the cellulose in wood. (Incidentally, neither do humans, so it does us little good to nibble on a piece of wood.) How, then, does a termite digest cellulose? In a sense, it doesn't. *Trichonympha* does.

Trichonympha and other organisms in the termites' gut manufacture cellulase. Cellulase is an enzyme that breaks the chemical bonds in cellulose and makes it possible for termites to digest wood. Thus, with the help of their protist partners, termites can munch away, busily digesting all the wood they can eat.

20–2 Section Assessment

1. **Key Concept** What are the four major phyla of animallike protists? How do members of each of these groups move?

2. **Key Concept** What animallike protists cause disease?

3. How does a macronucleus differ in function from a micronucleus?

4. Describe the role of animallike protists in the environment.

5. **Critical Thinking Comparing and Contrasting** Compare animallike protists that have flagella to those that have cilia.

iTEXT Assessment Use iText to review the important concepts in Section 20–2.

ALTERNATIVE ASSESSMENT

Creating a Pamphlet
Write and illustrate a public health pamphlet that features two types of waterborne protists that cause disease in humans. Your pamphlet should list symptoms associated with infection and present information on how to avoid waterborne diseases.

How Should Water Be Protected Against *Cryptosporidium?*

In April of 1993, more than 403,000 people in Milwaukee were infected, and 47 died, in an outbreak of severe intestinal diarrhea spread by public drinking water. The cause was a parasitic protist known as *Cryptosporidium* that attaches itself to the lining of the intestines. The epidemic was brought under control only by requiring the boiling of drinking water.

How did the water become contaminated with *Cryptosporidium?* No one knows for sure, but it's possible that runoff from an animal slaughterhouse had contaminated streams that flow into the city's water supply. Milwaukee's water was purified by filtration and chlorination and met the highest government standards. Unfortunately, *Cryptosporidium* is so small—only 4 to 7 μm in diameter—that it can pass through the high-volume filters used in public water purification systems. *Cryptosporidium* is also resistant to chlorine. What is the best way to protect the public against future outbreaks?

The Viewpoints

Purify at Point of Use
Because public water purification systems cannot control *Cryptosporidium,* public policy should focus on the individual. Consumers everywhere should be advised to purchase and install household filters. The best of these filters can remove 99.9 percent of particles larger than 1 μm, which should effectively eliminate *Cryptosporidium* from the drinking water of most users. In addition, people with weakened immune systems should be advised to boil all of their drinking water.

Purify and Protect the Supply
Point-of-use purification will never provide effective public protection against a Milwaukee-like outbreak. It is unrealistic to expect every houshold to install and maintain high-tech filtering systems.

The best strategy is, therefore, to focus on the water supply itself. Water from streams that feed into public water supplies should be carefully tested for *Cryptosporidium* and vigorously protected against contaminant runoff. Even though absolute removal of all *Cryptosporidium* may not be possible, filters should be installed that reduce contamination to levels low enough to protect the public health.

You Decide

1. **Defining the Issue** What are the major public issues regarding water supply protection from the protist *Cryptosporidium?*
2. **Analyzing the Viewpoints** What are the options for the protection of drinking water? What are the benefits of each option? What are the costs? Who is affected by each option?
3. **Forming Your Opinion** Should public policy focus on the water supply or on point-of-use protection for individuals?
4. **Role-Playing** Suppose you were the head of the water supply board of a major American city that had a small amount of extra money in its annual budget. How would you advise the city council to allocate the money: to public education about *Cryptosporidium* or to research on better ways to lower the level of *Cryptosporidium* in the water supply?

20–3 Plantlike Protists: Unicellular Algae

Many protists contain the green pigment chlorophyll and carry out photosynthesis. Many of these organisms are highly motile, or able to move about. Despite this, the fact that they perform photosynthesis is so important that we group these protists in a separate category, the plantlike protists. Plantlike protists are commonly called "algae."

Some scientists place those algae that are more closely related to plants in the kingdom Plantae. In this textbook, we will consider all forms of algae, including those most closely related to plants, to be protists. There are seven major phyla of algae classified according to a variety of cellular characteristics. The first four phyla, which contain unicellular organisms, are discussed in this section. These four phyla are the euglenophytes, the dinoflagellates, the chrysophytes, and the diatoms. The last three phyla include many multicellular organisms and will be discussed in the next section.

Chlorophyll and Accessory Pigments

One of the key characteristics used to classify algae is the type of photosynthetic pigments they contain. As you will remember, light is necessary for photosynthesis, and it is chlorophyll and the accessory pigments that trap the energy of sunlight.

Life in deep water poses a major difficulty for algae: a shortage of light. As sunlight passes through water, much of the light's energy is absorbed by the water. In particular, sea water absorbs large amounts of the red and violet wavelengths. Therefore, the light becomes dimmer and bluer as the depth of the water increases. Because chlorophyll *a* is most efficient at capturing red and violet light, the dim blue light that penetrates into deep water contains very little light energy that chlorophyll *a* can use.

In adapting to conditions of limited light, various groups of algae have evolved different forms of chlorophyll. Each form of chlorophyll—chlorophyll *a,* chlorophyll *b,* and chlorophyll *c*—absorbs different wavelengths of light. The result of this evolution is that algae can use more of the energy of sunlight than just the red and violet wavelengths.

▶ **Figure 20–9** **Chlorophyll and other pigments allow algae to collect and use energy from sunlight.** These green algae of the species *Acetabularia calyculus* live on the roots of mangrove trees in Florida.

Guide for Reading

🔑 **Key Concepts**
• What is the function of chlorophyll and accessory pigments in algae?
• What are the distinguishing features of the major phyla of unicellular algae?

Vocabulary
accessory pigment
eyespot
pellicle
phytoplankton

Reading Strategy:
Summarizing As you read, make a list of the types of unicellular algae. Write a sentence about each type.

Many algae also have compounds called **accessory pigments** that absorb light at different wavelengths than chlorophyll. Accessory pigments pass the energy they absorb to the algae's photosynthetic machinery. 🔑 **Chlorophyll and accessory pigments allow algae to harvest and use the energy from sunlight.** Because accessory pigments reflect different wavelengths of light than chlorophyll, they give algae a wide range of colors.

Euglenophytes

Members of the phylum Euglenophyta (yoo-glee-nuh-FYT-uh), or euglenophytes, are closely related to the animallike flagellates. 🔑 **Euglenophytes are plantlike protists that have two flagella but no cell wall.** Although euglenophytes possess chloroplasts, in most other respects they are remarkably similar to zooflagellates.

The phylum takes its name from the genus *Euglena*. Euglenas are found in ponds and lakes throughout the world. A typical euglena, such as the one shown in **Figure 20–10,** is about 50 micrometers in length. Euglenas are excellent swimmers. Two flagella emerge from a gullet at one end of the cell, and the longer of these two flagella spins in a pattern that pulls the organism rapidly through the water. Near the gullet end of the cell is a cluster of reddish pigment known as the **eyespot,** which helps the organism find sunlight to power photosynthesis. If sunlight is not available, euglenas can also live as heterotrophs, absorbing the nutrients available in decayed organic material. Euglenas store carbohydrates in small storage bodies.

Euglenas do not have cell walls, but they do have an intricate cell membrane called a **pellicle.** The pellicle is folded into a series of ribbonlike ridges, each ridge supported by microtubules. The pellicle is tough and flexible, allowing euglenas to squirm and crawl through mud when there is not enough water to allow them to swim. Euglenas reproduce asexually by means of binary fission.

✓ CHECKPOINT *What are eyespots, and why are they important to euglenas?*

▼ **Figure 20–10** 🌐 Euglenophytes are plantlike protists that have two flagella but no cell wall. The green structures inside the euglena shown are chloroplasts, which allow the organism to carry on photosynthesis when light is available. Euglenas are covered by a ridged pellicle. A pigmented eyespot helps the organism find the light that powers photosynthesis, while movement is produced by the flagella that protrude from one end of the organism. Like paramecia, euglenas expel excess water through a contractile vacuole.

(magnification: 540×)

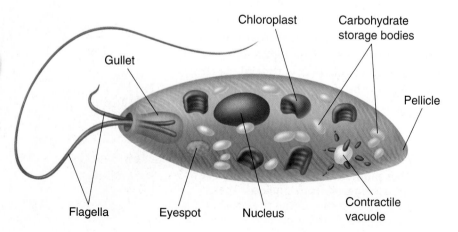

Chloroplast

Carbohydrate storage bodies

Gullet

Pellicle

Flagella   Eyespot   Nucleus

Contractile vacuole

Dinoflagellates

Dinoflagellates are members of the phylum Pyrrophyta (pir-uh-FYT-uh). **About half of dinoflagellates are photosynthetic; the other half live as heterotrophs.** Dinoflagellates generally have two flagella, and these often wrap around the organism in grooves between two thick plates of cellulose that protect the cell, as shown in **Figure 20–11**. Most dinoflagellates reproduce asexually by binary fission.

Many dinoflagellate species are luminescent. When agitated by sudden movement in the water, many dinoflagellates give off light. Some areas of the ocean are so filled with dinoflagellates that the movement of an oar or the hull of a boat will cause the dark water to shimmer with a ghostly blue light. This luminescent property gives the phylum its name, *Pyrrophyta*, which means "fire plants."

Another interesting property of the dinoflagellates has to do with their genetic material. Like other organisms, dinoflagellates store genetic information in the form of DNA. In all other eukaryotic cells, however, that DNA is tightly bound with proteins known as histones. Dinoflagellates do not have histones; in fact, they are the only eukaryotes that do not. The reason for this difference, as well as an explanation of how the functions of histone proteins are carried out when none are present in dinoflagellates, remains a mystery.

(magnification: 1600×)

▲ **Figure 20–11** Some dino-flagellates are photosynthetic, while others are heterotrophs. The paired flagella of a dinoflagellate lie in grooves around its circumference, shown here in red. The flagella propel the organism, spinning, through the water.

Chrysophytes

The phylum Chrysophyta (kris-uh-FYT-uh) includes the yellow-green algae and the golden-brown algae. The chloroplasts of these organisms contain bright yellow pigments that give the phylum its name. *Chrysophyta* means "golden plants." **Members of the phylum Chrysophyta are a diverse group of plantlike protists that have gold-colored chloroplasts.**

The cell walls of some chrysophytes contain the carbohydrate pectin rather than cellulose, while others contain both pectin and cellulose. Chrysophytes generally store food in the form of oil rather than starch. They reproduce both asexually and sexually. Most are solitary, but some form threadlike colonies.

▼ **Figure 20–12** Tiny jewellike diatoms such as this centric diatom have cell walls rich in silicon.

(magnification: 2200×)

Diatoms

Members of the phylum Bacillariophyta (bas-uh-lehr-ee-uh-FYT-uh), or diatoms, are among the most abundant organisms on Earth. They are also some of the most beautiful. **Diatoms produce thin, delicate cell walls rich in silicon (Si)—the main ingredient in glass.** These walls are shaped like the two sides of a petri dish or flat pillbox, with one side fitted snugly into the other. The cell walls have fine lines and patterns that almost seem to be etched, or carved, into their glasslike brilliance, as shown in **Figure 20–12**.

Fertilizers and Algae

The growth of algae in bodies of water is affected by the addition of plant fertilizers—a pollutant. A group of students collected three large, clear containers of pond water. They used a turbidity meter to measure the cloudiness of the water. The cloudiness, or turbidity, is a rough indicator of the amount of algae present.

The students did not add anything to the first container. To the second container, they added 1 mL of undiluted liquid plant fertilizer. To the third container, they added 2 mL of fertilizer. They then left the containers in a window for 1 week and measured the turbidity again on the eighth day. Their data are summarized in the table.

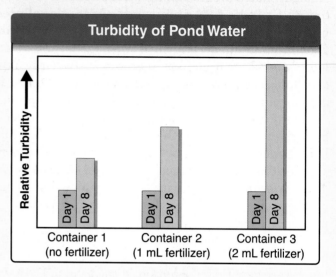

Turbidity of Pond Water

1. **Controlling Variables** What is the responding variable in the students' experiment?

2. **Designing Experiments** What is the role of the first container of water, to which no fertilizer was added?

3. **Using Tables and Graphs** In which container did the algae grow the most?

4. **Drawing Conclusions** What can you conclude about the effect of fertilizers on the growth of algae?

Ecology of Unicellular Algae

Plantlike protists are common in both fresh and salt water, and thus are an important part of freshwater and marine ecosystems. A few species of algae, however, can cause serious problems.

Plantlike protists play a major ecological role on Earth. Plantlike protists are important organisms whose position at the base of the food chain makes much of the diversity of aquatic life possible. They make up a considerable part of the **phytoplankton** (fy-toh-PLANK-tun), the population of small, photosynthetic organisms found near the surface of the ocean. About half of the photosynthesis that occurs on Earth is carried out by phytoplankton. Phytoplankton provide a direct source of nourishment for organisms as diverse as shrimp and whales. Even land animals such as humans obtain nourishment indirectly from the phytoplankton. When you eat a tuna fish sandwich, you are eating fish that fed on smaller fish that fed on still smaller animals that fed on plantlike protists.

Symbiotic Algae Unicellular algae form some spectacular symbiotic relationships with other organisms. For example, many types of coral contain intercellular dinoflagellates. These dinoflagellates allow the tiny coral animals to use the food products of photosynthesis. This food allows coral to grow in areas where nutrients are scarce. In turn, the dinoflagellates can feed on the waste products of the coral animals.

Other dinoflagellates make their homes within other organisms. In the giant clam *Tridacna gigas*, an organ called the mantle contains large numbers of symbiotic photosynthetic protists. These dinoflagellates are positioned so that they gather as much sunlight as possible, thereby increasing the nutrient benefit to the clam.

Algal Blooms Because many protists, including euglenophytes, absorb organic material directly and use it for food, they grow rapidly in regions where sewage is discharged. These protists play a vital role in recycling sewage and other waste materials. When the amount of waste is excessive, however, populations of euglenophytes and other algae may grow into enormous masses known as blooms. While not harmful in themselves, these algal blooms quickly deplete the water of nutrients, and the cells begin to die in great numbers. The decomposition of these dead algae can rob water of its oxygen, choking its resident fish and invertebrate life.

Great blooms of the dinoflagellates *Gonyaulax* and *Gymnodinium* have occurred in recent years on the east coast of the United States, although scientists are not sure of the reason. These blooms, such as the one shown in **Figure 20–13**, are known as "red tides." These species produce a potentially dangerous toxin. Filter-feeding shellfish such as clams can trap *Gonyaulax* and *Gymnodinium* for food and become filled with the toxin. Eating shellfish from water infected with red tide can cause serious illness, paralysis, and even death.

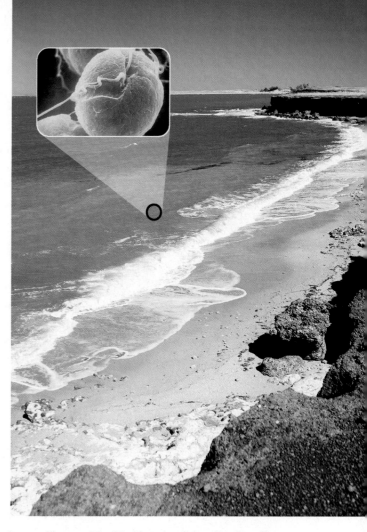

Figure 20–13 Blooms of the dinoflagellate *Gymnodinium* (inset) can produce red tides. *Gymnodinium* contains a toxin that becomes concentrated in the tissue of filter feeders such as clams and oysters. **Inferring** *How can red tides be harmful to humans?*

20–3 Section Assessment

1. **Key Concept** What do chlorophyll and accessory pigments do in algae?

2. **Key Concept** What are the four phyla of unicellular plantlike protists?

3. What is the role of unicellular algae in the environment?

4. How do most unicellular algae get food? How does this differ from the way most animallike protists get food?

5. **Critical Thinking Problem Solving** Identify two ways to reduce the problem of algal blooms in fresh water.

iTEXT Assessment Use iText to review the important concepts in Section 20–3.

Take It to the NET
Read about a group of algae called choanoflagellates. Then, write a brief report on the structure and evolutionary significance of these protists. Use the links provided in the Biology area at the Prentice Hall Web site for help in completing this activity: **www.phschool.com**

20–4 Plantlike Protists: Red, Brown, and Green Algae

Guide for Reading

Key Concepts
- What are the distinguishing features of the major phyla of multicellular algae?
- How do multicellular algae reproduce?

Vocabulary
phycobilin
filament
alternation of generations
gametophyte
spore
sporophyte

Reading Strategy:
Outlining Before you read, use the blue and green headings to make an outline about multicellular algae. As you read, add phrases or a sentence after each heading to provide key information.

Have you ever taken a walk along a rocky beach at low tide? As the water recedes, in many places it reveals a damp forest of green and brown "plants" clinging to the rocks. These seaweeds, as they are generally called, have the size, color, and appearance of plants, but technically they are not plants. They are actually algae. Unlike the algae you studied in the last section, however, most of these algae are multicellular, like plants. They also have reproductive cycles that are sometimes very similar to those of plants. Many of them have cell walls and photosynthetic pigments that are identical to those of plants. Many of these algae also possess highly specialized tissues.

The three phyla of algae that are largely multicellular are commonly known as red algae, brown algae, and green algae. Although there are many differences among these phyla, the most important ones, for which the groups are named, involve their photosynthetic pigments.

Red Algae

Red algae are members of the phylum Rhodophyta (roh-duh-FYT-uh), meaning "red plants." **Red algae are able to live at great depths due to their efficiency in harvesting light energy. Red algae contain chlorophyll *a* and reddish accessory pigments called phycobilins.** Phycobilins (fy-koh-BIL-inz) are especially good at absorbing blue light, enabling red algae to live deeper in the ocean than many other photosynthetic algae. Many red algae are actually green, purple, or reddish black, depending upon the other pigments they contain. Red algae are an important group of marine algae that can be found in waters from the polar regions to the tropics. The highly efficient light-harvesting pigments in these algae enable them to grow anywhere from the ocean's surface to depths of up to 260 meters.

Most species of red algae are multicellular, and all species have complex life cycles. Red algae lack flagella and centrioles.

One common red alga is *Chondrus crispus*, or Irish moss. It grows in tide pools and on rocky coastlines. Other red algae, known as the coralline algae and shown in **Figure 20–14,** play an important role in the formation of coral reefs by helping to stabilize them.

◀ **Figure 20–14** Red algae contain chlorophyll *a* and reddish pigments called phycobilins. Coralline algae, a type of red alga, collect calcium carbonate in their cell walls, giving them a tough, stony texture.

Brown Algae

Brown algae belong to the phylum Phaeophyta (fay-uh-FYT-uh), meaning "dusky plants." 🔑 **Brown algae contain chlorophyll *a* and *c*, as well as a brown accessory pigment, fucoxanthin.** The combination of fucoxanthin (fyoo-koh-ZAN-thin) and chlorophyll *c* gives most of these algae a dark, yellow-brown color. Brown algae are the largest and most complex of the algae. All brown algae are multicellular and most are marine, commonly found in cool, shallow coastal waters of temperate or arctic areas.

The largest known alga is giant kelp, a brown alga that can grow to more than 60 meters in length. Another brown alga called *Sargassum* forms huge floating mats many kilometers long in an area of the Atlantic Ocean near Bermuda known as the Sargasso Sea. Bunches of *Sargassum* often drift on currents to beaches in the Caribbean and southern United States.

One of the most common brown alga is *Fucus*, or rockweed, found along the rocky coast of the eastern United States. Each *Fucus* alga has a holdfast, a structure that attaches the alga to the bottom. The body of the alga consists of flattened stemlike structures called stipes, leaflike structures called blades, and gas-filled swellings called bladders, which float and keep the algae upright in the water. **Figure 20–15** shows the structures of a brown alga.

✔ **CHECKPOINT** *What does a holdfast do?*

Green Algae

Green algae are members of the phylum Chlorophyta (klawr-uh-FYT-uh), which means "green plants" in Greek. 🔑 **Green algae share many characteristics with plants, including their photosynthetic pigments and cell wall composition.** Green algae have cellulose in their cell walls, contain chlorophyll *a* and *b*, and store food in the form of starch, just like land plants. One stage in the life cycle of mosses—small land plants you will learn about in the next unit—looks remarkably like a tangled mass of green algae strands. All these characteristics lead scientists to hypothesize that the ancestors of modern land plants looked a lot like certain species of living green algae. Unfortunately, algae rarely form fossils, so there is no single specific fossil that scientists can call an ancestor of both living algae and mosses. However, scientists think that mosses and green algae shared such a common algaelike ancestor millions of years ago.

Green algae are found in fresh and salt water, and even in moist areas on land. Many species live most of their lives as single cells. Others form colonies, groups of similar cells that are joined together but show few specialized structures. A few green algae are multicellular and have well-developed specialized structures.

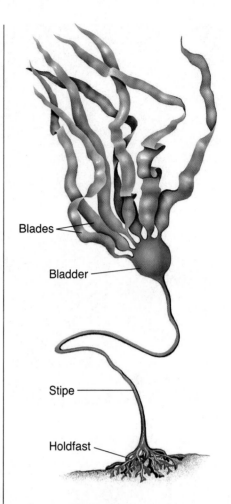

Blades

Bladder

Stipe

Holdfast

▲ **Figure 20–15** 🔑 Brown algae contain chlorophyll *a* and *c*, plus fucoxanthin, a brown pigment.

Chlamydomonas   (magnification: 1000×)

Volvox   (magnification: 450×)

Ulva

Figure 20–16 🔑 Green algae have the same photosynthetic pigments and cell wall compositions as plants. *Chlamydomonas* is a unicellular green alga that lives in ponds. Delicate spherical colonies of the green alga *Volvox* live in fresh water. New colonies can develop within existing colonies and are released when the older colony ruptures. *Ulva* is a multicellular green alga that lives along seacoasts.

Unicellular Green Algae *Chlamydomonas* (kluh-mid-uh-MOHN-uz), a typical single-celled green alga, grows in ponds, ditches, and wet soil. *Chlamydomonas* is a small egg-shaped cell with two flagella and a single large, cup-shaped chloroplast. Within the base of the chloroplast is a region that synthesizes and stores starch. *Chlamydomonas* lacks the large vacuoles found in the cells of land plants. Instead, it has two small contractile vacuoles. *Chlamydomonas* and two other green algae are shown in **Figure 20–16.**

Colonial Green Algae Several species of green algae live in multicellular colonies. The freshwater alga *Spirogyra* forms long threadlike colonies called **filaments,** in which the cells are stacked almost like soda cans placed end to end.

Volvox colonies are more elaborate, consisting of as few as 500 to as many as 50,000 cells arranged to form hollow spheres. The cells in a *Volvox* colony are connected to one another by strands of cytoplasm, enabling them to coordinate movement. When the colony moves, cells on one side of the colony "pull" with their flagella, and the cells on the other side of the colony have to "push." Although most cells in a *Volvox* colony are identical, a few gamete-producing cells are specialized for reproduction. Because it shows some cell specialization, *Volvox* straddles the fence between colonial and multicellular life.

Multicellular Green Algae *Ulva*, or "sea lettuce," is a bright-green marine alga that is commonly found along rocky seacoasts. *Ulva* is a true multicellular organism, containing several specialized cell types. Although the body of *Ulva* is only two cells thick, it is tough enough to survive the pounding of waves on the shores where it lives. A group of cells at its base forms holdfasts that attach *Ulva* to the rocks.

Reproduction in Green Algae

🔑 **The life cycles of many algae include both a diploid and a haploid generation.** Recall from Chapter 11 that diploid cells have two sets of chromosomes, whereas haploid cells have a single set. Many algae switch back and forth between haploid and diploid stages during their life cycles, in a process known as **alternation of generations.** Many species also shift back and forth between sexual and asexual forms of reproduction.

Reproduction in *Chlamydomonas* The single-celled *Chlamydomonas* spends most of its life in the haploid stage. As long as its living conditions are suitable, this haploid cell reproduces asexually, producing cells called zoospores by mitosis. As you learned in Chapter 10, reproduction by mitosis is asexual. The two haploid daughter cells produced by mitosis are genetically identical to the single haploid cell that entered mitosis.

MEIOSIS

Release of haploid cells

Zygote

Pairing of plus and minus gametes

Mature cell

Zoospores

☐ Haploid
☐ Diploid

▲ **Figure 20–17** The green alga *Chlamydomonas* reproduces asexually by producing zoospores and sexually by producing zygotes. **Interpreting Graphics** *Which form of reproduction includes a diploid organism that can survive adverse conditions?*

If conditions become unfavorable, *Chlamydomonas* can also reproduce sexually. The life cycle of *Chlamydomonas* is shown in **Figure 20–17.** The haploid cells continue to undergo mitosis, but instead of releasing zoospores, the cells release gametes. The gametes, which look identical, are of two opposite mating types, + (plus) and − (minus). During sexual reproduction, the gametes gather in large groups. Then + and − gametes form pairs that soon move away from the group. The paired gametes join flagella and spin around in the water. Both members of the pair then shed their cell walls and fuse, forming a diploid zygote.

The zygote sinks to the bottom of the pond and grows a thick protective wall. Within this protective wall, *Chlamydomonas* can survive freezing or drying conditions that would ordinarily kill it. When conditions once again become favorable, the zygote begins to grow. It divides by meiosis to produce four flagellated haploid cells. These haploid cells can swim away, mature, and reproduce asexually. Thus, during its life cycle, *Chlamydomonas* alternates between a haploid stage, in which it spends most of its life, and a brief diploid stage, represented by the zygote cell.

✓ CHECKPOINT **What two types of gametes does Chlamydomonas produce?**

Reproduction in *Ulva* The life cycle of the green alga *Ulva* involves an alternation of generations in which both the diploid and haploid phases are large, multicellular organisms. In fact, the haploid and diploid phases of *Ulva* are so similar that only an expert can tell them apart!

The haploid phase of *Ulva* produces two forms of gametes—male and female. Because they produce gametes, the haploid forms of *Ulva* are known as **gametophytes** (guh-MEET-uh-fyts), or gamete-producing plants.

When male and female gametes fuse, they produce a diploid zygote cell, which then grows into a large, diploid multicellular *Ulva*. The diploid *Ulva* undergoes meiosis to produce haploid reproductive cells called **spores**. Each of these spores is able to grow into a new individual without fusing with another cell. Because the diploid *Ulva* produces spores, it is known as a **sporophyte** (SPOH-ruh-fyt), or spore-producing organism.

Take a close look at the life cycle of *Ulva* in **Figure 20–18**, because the alternation of generations it displays is a pattern you will see repeated over and over again in the plants. *Ulva*'s life cycle includes two separate phases that alternate in a regular pattern: sporophyte, then gametophyte, then sporophyte again. Complex life cycles involving alternation of generations are characteristic of the members of the plant kingdom. This is one of the reasons some biologists favor classifying multicellular algae such as *Ulva* as plants.

▼ **Figure 20–18** 🌐 **The life cycles of most algae include both diploid and haploid generations.** The multicellular green alga *Ulva* exhibits alternation of generations. The haploid generation produces a diploid generation, then the diploid generation produces a haploid generation. The two generations are multicellular and virtually indistinguishable from each other.

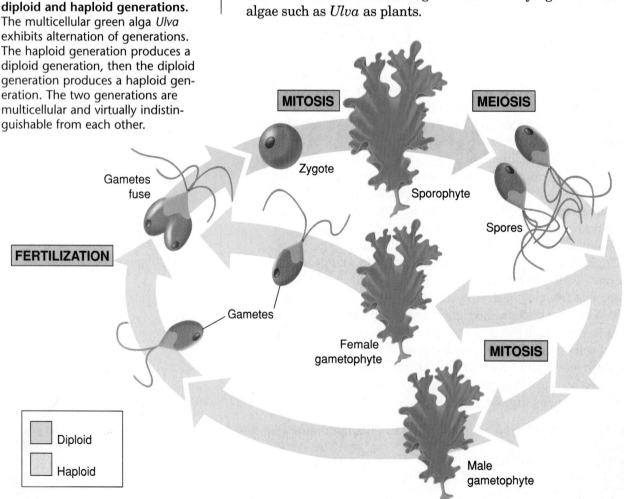

MITOSIS

MEIOSIS

Zygote

Sporophyte

Gametes fuse

Spores

FERTILIZATION

Gametes

Female gametophyte

MITOSIS

Diploid

Haploid

Male gametophyte

Human Uses of Algae

Algae are a major food source for life in the oceans. Algae have even been called the "grasses" of the seas, because they make up much of the base of the food chain upon which sea animals "graze." The enormous brown kelp forests off the coasts of North America are home to many animal species.

Algae produce much of Earth's oxygen through photosynthesis. Scientists calculate that about half of all the photosynthesis that occurs on Earth is performed by algae. This fact alone makes algae one of the most important groups of organisms on the entire planet.

Over the years, people have learned to use algae—and the chemicals produced by algae—in many different ways. Many species of algae are rich in vitamin C and iron. Chemicals in algae are used to treat stomach ulcers, high blood pressure, arthritis, and other health problems.

Have you ever eaten algae? Almost certainly, your answer should be yes. In Japan, the red alga *Porphyra* is grown on special marine farms. Dried *Porphyra*—called *nori* in Japanese—is dark green and paper-thin. Nori is used to wrap portions of rice, fish, and vegetables to make sushi, as shown in **Figure 20–19.** You say you've never had sushi? Well, you've probably eaten ice cream, salad dressing, pudding, or a candy bar. Other products from algae are used in pancake syrups and eggnog.

Industry has even more uses for algae. Chemicals from algae are used to make plastics, waxes, transistors, deodorants, paints, lubricants, and even artificial wood. Algae even have an important use in scientific laboratories. The compound agar, derived from certain seaweeds, thickens the nutrient mixtures scientists use to grow bacteria and other microorganisms.

▲ **Figure 20–19** People have found many different uses for algae. The red alga *Porphyra* is used as a wrapper in Japanese sushi rolls. Ice cream often contains algin, a thickener made from brown algae. **Predicting** *How would your life be different without products made from algae?*

20–4 Section Assessment

1. 🔑 **Key Concept** Describe the main features of the major phyla of multicellular algae.

2. 🔑 **Key Concept** What is alternation of generations?

3. How are multicellular algae important at a global level?

4. Why can red algae live in deeper water than green algae?

5. **Critical Thinking Classifying** Do you think green algae should be classified as plants? Give reasons for your answer.

iTEXT Assessment Use iText to review the important concepts in Section 20–4.

Protists **515**

20–5 Funguslike Protists

Guide for Reading

Key Concepts
- What are the similarities and differences between funguslike protists and fungi?
- What are the defining characteristics of the slime molds and water molds?

Vocabulary
cellular slime mold
acellular slime mold
plasmodium
hypha
zoosporangium
antheridium
oogonium

Reading Strategy:
Predicting Before you read, preview the life cycles in **Figures 20–22** and **20–23.** Predict how these life cycles are similar and how they are different.

I f you look closely at the debris-laden floor of a forest after several days of rain, you may see glistening patches of what looks like brightly colored mold. Funguslike protists grow in damp, nutrient-rich environments and absorb food through their cell membranes, much like fungi. In fact, these organisms have sometimes been classified as fungi, even though their cellular structure more closely resembles that of the protists. **Like fungi, the funguslike protists are heterotrophs that absorb nutrients from dead or decaying organic matter. But unlike most true fungi, funguslike protists have centrioles. They also lack the chitin cell walls of true fungi.** The funguslike protists include the cellular slime molds, the acellular slime molds, and the water molds.

Slime Molds

Slime molds are found in places that are damp and rich in organic matter, such as the floor of a forest or a backyard compost pile. **Slime molds are funguslike protists that play key roles in recycling organic material.** At one stage of their life cycle, slime molds look just like amoebas. At other stages, they form moldlike clumps that produce spores, almost like fungi.

Two broad groups of slime molds are recognized. The individual cells of **cellular slime molds** remain distinct—separated by cell membranes—during every phase of the mold's life cycle. Slime molds that pass through a stage in which their cells fuse to form large cells with many nuclei are called **acellular slime molds.**

Cellular Slime Molds Cellular slime molds belong to the phylum Acrasiomycota (ak-ruh-see-oh-my-KOH-tuh). They spend most of their lives as free-living cells that are not easily distinguishable from soil amoebas. In nutrient-rich soils, these amoeboid cells reproduce rapidly. When their food supply is exhausted, they send out chemical signals that attract other cells of the same species. Within a few days, thousands of cells aggregate into a large sluglike colony that begins to function like a single organism. The colony migrates for several centimeters, then stops and produces a fruiting body, a slender reproductive structure that produces spores. Eventually, the spores are scattered from the fruiting body. Each spore gives rise to a single amoeba-like cell that starts the cycle all over again, as shown in **Figure 20–22.**

▼ **Figure 20–20** Funguslike protists lack chlorophyll and absorb nutrients from dead organic matter. Slime molds like this red raspberry slime mold are often found in the damp, shaded environments preferred by many fungi.

◀ **Figure 20–21** 🔵 Slime molds help recycle organic matter. The two main groups of slime molds are cellular slime molds and acellular slime molds.

In many ways, these remarkable organisms challenge our understanding of what it means to be multicellular. During much of their life cycle, cellular slime molds are unicellular organisms that look and behave like animallike protists. When they aggregate, however, they act very much like multicellular organisms. Slime molds have been especially interesting to biologists who study how cells send signals and regulate development. They have kept biologists busy for decades, but their secrets are still not fully understood.

✔ **CHECKPOINT** *Why is it difficult to classify cellular slime molds as unicellular or multicellular?*

▼ **Figure 20–22** Cellular slime molds reproduce asexually. **Interpreting Graphics** *Is most of the cellular slime mold life cycle haploid or diploid?*

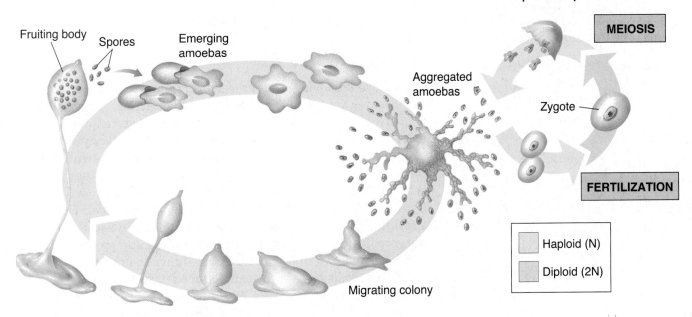

Fruiting body   Spores   Emerging amoebas

Aggregated amoebas

MEIOSIS

Zygote

FERTILIZATION

Migrating colony

Haploid (N)

Diploid (2N)

MEIOSIS

FERTILIZATION

Mature sporangium

Spores

Germinating spore

Young sporangium

Mature plasmodium

Feeding plasmodium

Zygote

Haploid (N)   Diploid (2N)

(magnification: 53×)

Figure 20–23 The plasmodium of an acellular slime mold is the collection of many amoeba-like organisms, but their separateness is not preserved. The plasmodium is a multinucleate structure contained in a single cell membrane. The plasmodium will eventually produce sporangia, which in turn will produce haploid spores. Upon pairing up and fusing, these result in new diploid amoeba-like cells. **Interpreting Graphics** *What stage of the life cycle is shown in the photograph?*

Acellular Slime Molds Acellular slime molds belong to the phylum Myxomycota (myk-suh-my-KOH-tuh). Like cellular slime molds, acellular slime molds begin their life cycles as amoeba-like cells. However, when they aggregate, their cells fuse to produce structures with many nuclei.

These structures are known as **plasmodia** (singular: plasmodium). The large plasmodium of an acellular slime mold, such as the one shown in **Figure 20–23**, is actually a single structure with many nuclei. A plasmodium may grow as large as several meters in diameter!

Eventually, small fruiting bodies, or sporangia, spring up from the plasmodium. The sporangia produce haploid spores by meiosis. These spores scatter to the ground where they germinate into flagellated cells. The flagellated cells then fuse to produce diploid zygotes that repeat the cycle.

Water Molds

If you have seen white fuzz growing on the surface of a dead fish in the water, you have seen a water mold in action. Water molds, or oomycetes, are members of the phylum Oomycota (oh-oh-my-KOH-tuh). **Oomycetes thrive on dead or decaying organic matter in water and are plant parasites on land.** Oomycetes are commonly known as water molds, but they are not true fungi. Water molds produce thin filaments known as **hyphae.** These hyphae do not have walls between their cells; as a result, water mold hyphae are multinucleate. In addition, water molds have cell walls made of cellulose and produce motile spores, two characteristics that fungi do not have.

Water molds have both sexual and asexual phases in their life cycle, as shown in **Figure 20–24.** In asexual reproduction, portions of the hyphae develop into **zoosporangia** (singular: zoosporangium), which are spore cases. Each zoosporangium

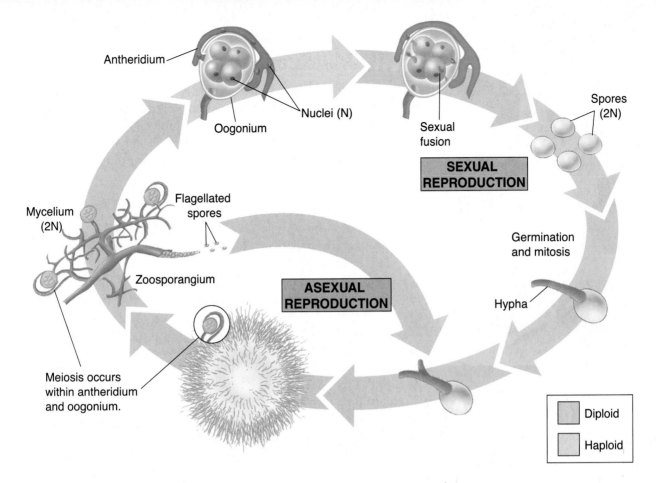

Figure labels:
Antheridium
Oogonium
Nuclei (N)
Sexual fusion
Spores (2N)
SEXUAL REPRODUCTION
Germination and mitosis
Hypha
Flagellated spores
Mycelium (2N)
Zoosporangium
ASEXUAL REPRODUCTION
Meiosis occurs within antheridium and oogonium.
Diploid
Haploid

produces flagellated spores that swim away from the zoosporangium in search of food. When they find food, the spores develop into hyphae, which then grow into new organisms.

Sexual reproduction takes place in specialized structures that are formed by the hyphae. One structure, the **antheridium** (an-thur-ID-ee-um), produces male nuclei. The other structure, the **oogonium** (oh-oh-GOH-nee-um), produces female nuclei. Fertilization, or sexual fusion, occurs within the oogonium, and the spores that form develop into new organisms.

CHECKPOINT *Where does sexual reproduction in water molds take place?*

Ecology of Funguslike Protists

Slime molds and water molds are most important as recyclers of organic material. In plain language, that means that they help things rot. How important is that? A walk through woods or grassland will quickly show that the ground is not littered with the bodies of dead animals and plants. Why not? After these organisms die, their tissues are quickly broken down by slime molds, water molds, mushrooms, and other decomposers. The dark, rich topsoil that provides plants with nutrients is the product of all of this activity.

Some funguslike protists can harm living things. In addition to their beneficial function as decomposers, land-dwelling water molds cause a number of important plant diseases. These diseases include mildews and blights of grapes and tomatoes.

▲ **Figure 20–24** Water molds **live on decaying organic matter in water.** Water molds reproduce both asexually and sexually. During asexual reproduction, flagellated spores are produced by the diploid (2N) mycelium. These spores grow into new mycelia. During sexual reproduction, a male nucleus fuses with a female nucleus.

Protists **519**

Water Molds and the Potato Famine

One water mold helped to permanently change the character of the United States. Roughly 40 million Americans can trace at least some part of their ancestry to Ireland. If you are one of those people, the chances are very good that your life and the lives of your ancestors were changed by the combination of a plant and a protist.

The plant was the potato. Potatoes are native to South America, where they were cultivated by the Incas. Spanish explorers were so impressed with this plant that they introduced it to Europe. By the 1840s, potatoes had become the major food crop of Ireland.

The protist was *Phytophthora infestans*, an oomycete that produces airborne spores that destroy all parts of the potato plant. Potatoes that are infected with *Phytophthora infestans* may appear normal at harvest time. Within a few weeks, however, the protist makes its way into the potato, reducing it to a spongy sac of spores and dust. The summer of 1845 was unusually wet and cool, ideal conditions for the growth of *Phytophthora infestans*. By the end of the growing season, the potato blight caused by this pathogen had destroyed as much as 60 percent of the Irish potato crop. The photographs in **Figure 20–25** show how *Phytophthora infestans* attacks potatoes. The art shows a woman digging for potatoes in a field.

Because the poorest farmers depended upon potatoes for their food, the effects were tragic. The loss of much of the crop in 1845 and an even greater loss in 1846 led to the starvation of more than a million people.

The Great Potato Famine, or the Great Hunger, as the event is also known, led to the immediate migration of about 1.5 million Irish people to the United States. There, they quickly changed the ethnic and political character of many American cities.

Figure 20–25 *Phytophthora infestans* is an oomycete that attacks potatoes (bottom right). In the summer of 1846, *Phytophthora infestans* destroyed nearly the entire potato crop of Ireland in days, leading to the Great Potato Famine. **Applying Concepts** *How did the famine affect the United States?*

20–5 Section Assessment

1. **Key Concept** How are funguslike protists and fungi similar? How are they different?

2. **Key Concept** Compare acellular slime molds, cellular slime molds, and water molds.

3. What is the role of slime molds in the environment?

4. How can water molds affect other living things?

5. **Critical Thinking Comparing and Contrasting** How is the sluglike mass of cellular slime molds similar to the plasmodium of acellular slime molds? How do they differ?

iTEXT **Assessment** Use iText to review the important concepts in Section 20–5.

Investigating Contractile Vacuoles

Most freshwater protists have contractile vacuoles. These organelles regulate the concentration of water in the cytoplasm. In this investigation, you will observe how this structure works under various conditions.

Problem How do the salt concentration and temperature of the environment affect the action of contractile vacuoles?

Materials

- 3 *Paramecium caudatum* cultures at room temperature, 25°C (fresh water, 0.5% salt solution, 1.0% salt solution)
- *Paramecium caudatum* culture at 2°C in fresh water
- dropper pipette
- 4 microscope slides
- coverslips
- microscope
- cotton ball
- forceps
- clock with second hand

Skills Designing Experiments, Observing

Design Your Experiment

1. Use a dropper pipette to put one drop of *Paramecium caudatum* culture in fresh water at 25°C on a microscope slide.

2. Use forceps to pull apart a cotton ball and put a few threads in the drop of water. Cover the drop with a coverslip.

3. Use the low-power objective of the microscope to locate and focus on one paramecium. If necessary, increase the magnification to observe the alternating contractions of the two contractile vacuoles.

4. Record how long a contractile vacuole takes to contract and refill.

5. **Formulating Hypotheses** Record a hypothesis about how salt concentration and temperature will affect the rate at which the contractile vacuole contracts and expands.

6. **Designing Experiments** Design an experiment to test your hypothesis. Construct a data table to record your observations. With your teacher's approval, carry out your experiment.

Analyze and Conclude

1. **Observing** How did an increase in the concentration of salt in its environment affect the paramecium's contractile vacuoles?

2. **Inferring** What can you infer from this result about the rate at which water enters the paramecium in salt solutions? Explain your answer.

3. **Observing** How did temperature affect the contractile vacuoles?

4. **Drawing Conclusions** What can you conclude about the paramecium's use of energy from the effect of temperature on the contractile vacuoles?

Go Further

Designing Experiments Does temperature affect paramecia in other ways? Design an experiment to investigate the effects of temperature on movement or feeding. With your teacher's approval, carry out your experiment.

Chapter 20 Study Guide

20–1 The Kingdom Protista
Key Concept

- Protists are eukaryotes that are not members of the kingdoms Plantae, Animalia, or Fungi.

Vocabulary
protist, p. 495

20–2 Animallike Protists: Protozoans
Key Concepts

- Animallike protists that swim using flagella are classified in the phylum Zoomastigina and are often referred to as zooflagellates.
- Sarcodines are animallike protists that use pseudopods for feeding and movement.
- Members of the phylum Ciliophora, known as ciliates, use cilia for feeding and movement.
- Members of the phylum Sporozoa do not move on their own and are parasitic.
- Some animallike protists cause serious diseases, including malaria and African sleeping sickness.

Vocabulary
- pseudopod, p. 498
- amoeboid movement, p. 498
- food vacuole, p. 498 • cilium, p. 499
- trichocyst, p. 499 • macronucleus, p. 499
- micronucleus, p. 499 • gullet, p. 500
- anal pore, p. 500 • contractile vacuole, p. 500
- conjugation, p. 500

20–3 Plantlike Protists: Unicellular Algae
Key Concepts

- Chlorophyll and accessory pigments allow algae to harvest and use the energy from sunlight.
- Euglenophytes are plantlike protists that have two flagella but no cell wall.
- About half of dinoflagellates are photosynthetic; the other half live as heterotrophs.
- Members of the phylum Chrysophyta are a diverse group of plantlike protists that have gold-colored chloroplasts.
- Diatoms produce thin, delicate cell walls rich in silicon (Si)—the main ingredient in glass.

Vocabulary
- accessory pigment, p. 506 • eyespot, p. 506
- pellicle, p. 506 • phytoplankton, p. 508

20–4 Plantlike Protists: Red, Brown, and Green Algae
Key Concepts

- Red algae are able to live at great depths due to their efficiency in harvesting light energy. Red algae contain chlorophyll *a* and reddish accessory pigments called phycobilins.
- Brown algae contain chlorophyll *a* and *c,* as well as a brown accessory pigment, fucoxanthin.
- Green algae share many characteristics with plants, including their photosynthetic pigments and cell wall composition.
- The life cycles of most algae include both a diploid and a haploid generation.

Vocabulary
phycobilin, p. 510
filament, p. 512
alternation of generations, p. 512
gametophyte, p. 514
spore, p. 514
sporophyte, p. 514

20–5 Funguslike Protists
Key Concepts

- Funguslike protists lack chlorophyll and absorb nutrients from dead or decaying organic matter. But unlike most true fungi, funguslike protists have centrioles. They also lack the chitin cell walls of true fungi.
- Slime molds are funguslike protists that play key roles in recycling organic material.
- Oomycetes thrive on dead or decaying organic matter in water and are plant parasites on land.

Vocabulary
cellular slime mold, p. 516
acellular slime mold, p. 516
plasmodium, p. 518
hypha, p. 518
zoosporangium, p. 518
antheridium, p. 519
oogonium, p. 519

Thinking Visually
Make a table that compares the means of feeding and movement of the four main groups of protists.

Preparing for the
Living Environment Exam

Chapter 20

Part A

Multiple Choice

For each statement or question, select the number of the word or expression that, of those given, best completes the statement or answers the question.

1 Which description applies to most protists?
(1) unicellular prokaryotes
(2) multicellular prokaryotes
(3) unicellular eukaryotes
(4) multicellular eukaryotes

2 For defense, a paramecium uses small, bottle-shaped structures known as
(1) cilia
(2) pseudopodia
(3) trichocysts
(4) micronuclei

3 Which of the diagrams below shows the process of conjugation?

(1)　　(3)

(2)　　(4)

4 The population of small, photosynthetic organisms found near the ocean surface is called
(1) euglenophytes
(2) chrysophytes
(3) phytoplankton
(4) dinoflagellates

5 Which organisms are chiefly involved in the recycling of dead matter?
(1) fungi
(2) algae
(3) carnivores
(4) autotrophs

6 The thin filaments produced by water molds are known as
(1) oogonia
(2) zoosporangia
(3) antheridia
(4) hyphae

7 Slime molds are found primarily in
(1) oceans
(2) rotting wood or compost piles
(3) fast-moving streams
(4) deserts

8 Which structure in a unicellular organism corresponds in function with human lungs?
(1) vacuole
(2) nucleus
(3) cell membrane
(4) mitochondrion

9 Because the relative concentration of water in the pond in which a paramecium lives is greater than the concentration of water in its cytoplasm, water molecules constantly move from the pond into the organism. The best long-term solution to the problem of maintaining a stable internal environment is for the paramecium to
(1) change the water into carbon dioxide and excrete it
(2) store water molecules
(3) incorporate water molecules into its structure
(4) actively transport water molecules out of the cell

10 The cilia of paramecia are tiny hairlike structures that help paramecia to move from one location to another. Which of the following best describes the importance of cilia to paramecia?
(1) Cilia help in maintaining homeostasis.
(2) Cilia are useful in the process of diffusion.
(3) The ability to decompose other organisms is made possible by cilia action.
(4) Asexual reproduction is made possible directly through the activities of cilia.

11 All one-celled organisms are able to continue living because of their ability to
(1) produce food
(2) excrete wastes
(3) produce offspring
(4) produce hormones

Test-Taking Tip As you briefly scan the questions, mark those that may be pure guesswork on your part and save them for last. (Do not write in this book.) Use your time on those questions that you can reason through and for which you can eliminate answers.

Parts B and C

Multiple Choice and Extended Response

For those questions that ask you to select a response, choose the one that best completes the statement or answers the question. For all others follow the directions given.

12 Explain how the terms *animallike, plantlike,* and *funguslike* are useful in classifying protists.

13 Describe the two methods euglenophytes can use to obtain energy.

14 Describe the process of alternation of generations. Explain its significance.

15 Explain the connection between water pollution and the occurrence of a red tide.

16 All freshwater protozoans have contractile vacuoles to get rid of excess water. Describe the process responsible for this excess water.

17 Explain the role of plantlike protists in aquatic food chains.

18 Your teacher asks you to observe and classify into the correct phylum the following protists:

Protist A: Organism has no cell wall, lacks chlorophyll, and moves using pseudopodia

Protist B: Organism has no cell wall, contains chlorophyll, and has two flagella

Protist C: Cells appear amoebalike and seem to fuse to produce structures with nuclei, lack chlorophyll, and have fruiting bodies that produce spores that geminate into flagellated cells

Copy and complete the below chart.

Protist	Traits	Phylum
A		
B		
C		

19 At one time, living things were classified as animals if they moved or ingested food and as plants if they did not move or ingest food. State two difficulties that would arise in trying to classify the protists according to these criteria.

Base your answers to questions 20 through 22 on the graph below and on your knowledge of biology.

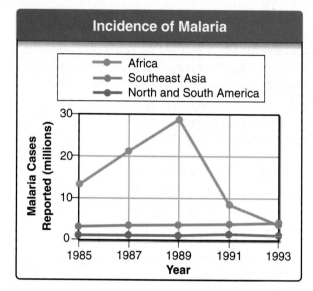

20 Based on the data in the graph, the incidence of malaria is
  (1) decreasing in Southeast Asia and increasing in South America
  (2) increasing in Africa and decreasing in Southeast Asia
  (3) decreasing in Africa and increasing in Southeast Asia
  (4) increasing in Southeast Asia and in North and South America

21 It is estimated that there are at least ten actual cases of malaria for every one reported and shown in the graph. Based on this estimate, how many cases of malaria were there in Africa in 1991?

22 Note the rapid change in malaria cases in Africa after 1989. Many question that the number of actual cases of malaria changed so rapidly. Explain what other factors could have affected the number of cases reported.

Base your answers to questions 23 through 25 on the information and chart below and on your knowledge of biology.

A study was done to determine the effect of different salt concentrations on the number of contractions per minute of contractile vacuoles of paramecia.

Four beakers of water containing different salt concentrations and equal numbers of paramecia were prepared. All other environmental conditions were constant. The paramecia were then observed through a compound light microscope, and the contractions of the contractile vacuoles were counted. Whenever a contractile vacuole contracts, it is pumping water out of a paramecium. The results were recorded in the data table below.

Salt Concentration vs. Contractions

Beaker	Salt Concentration (mg/mL)	Contractions per Minute
A	0.000	5.5
B	0.001	4.0
C	0.010	2.5
D	0.100	1.5

23 Using the information in the data table, construct a line graph on your own sheet of graph paper. Be sure that you
  • label and scale the two axes appropriately
  • plot the data, surround each point with a small circle, and connect the points

24 According to the information in the data table, which statement is true?
  (1) Beaker B has a lower salt concentration than Beaker A.
  (2) Beaker C has a lower salt concentration than Beaker D.
  (3) The paramecia in Beaker A respond the least to the water concentration in the beaker.
  (4) The paramecia in Beaker D have nonfunctioning contractile vacuoles.

25 According to the data, as the salt concentration increases, the number of contractions per minute changes. What most likely accounts for this change?
  (1) a decrease in water concentration outside the paramecium
  (2) a decrease in salt concentration outside the paramecium
  (3) an increased diffusion of salt out of the paramecium
  (4) an increased percentage of water inside the paramecium

For questions 26 through 29, select the structure, chosen from the list below, that is most closely associated with the statement. Then, record the number on your paper. A choice may be used once, more than once, or not at all.

  (1) Contractile vacuole
  (2) Gullet
  (3) Trichocyst
  (4) Food vacuole
  (5) Anal pore

26 Where food particles in a unicellular organism's body are digested

27 Indentation where food particles are trapped

28 Collects and gets rid of excess water

29 Site where waste is released into the environment

Base your answers to questions 30 through 32 on the information below and on your knowledge of biology.

Algae are the foundation of most aquatic food chains in both marine and freshwater ecosystems. Through the process of photosynthesis, algae are able to combine inorganic raw materials into energy-rich organic compounds.

30 Name the reactants and products of photosynthesis. (*Hint:* You may wish to refer back to Chapter 8 for help in answering this question.)

31 Name the organelle that serves as the site of photosynthesis in algal cells.

32 Where might algae get the raw materials they need to carry out photosynthesis?

Take It to the NET

Which protists live in a pond environment? Visit the Prentice Hall Web site at **www.phschool.com** to find out about the residents of a typical pond. Then, answer the following questions:
• What major groups of protists are found in ponds?
• How can you create an image of an algal protist using fluorescence? Which parts will be visible?
• What are mummy-shaped diatoms?
• What is the approximate width of an amoeba?

Chapter 21 Fungi

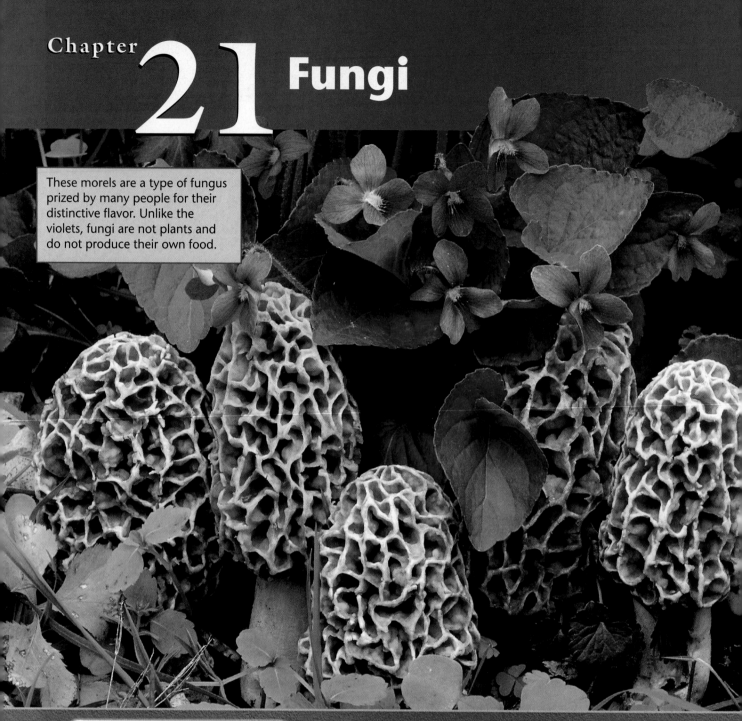

These morels are a type of fungus prized by many people for their distinctive flavor. Unlike the violets, fungi are not plants and do not produce their own food.

Inquiry Activity

What are mushrooms made of?

Procedure

1. Examine a mushroom without damaging it. Record your observations, and include a sketch.

2. Carefully separate the stalk and cap of the mushroom. Try to break the stalk across and lengthwise.

3. Crumble a piece of the stalk. Describe the shape of the parts that make up the stalk.

4. Break the cap in two and examine the thin sheets on the underside of the cap. Record your observations.

Think About It

1. **Observing** Was the stalk made up of parts with specific shapes? If so, what are the shapes of those parts?

2. **Comparing and Contrasting** Compare a mushroom to a plant. How are they similar? Different?

21-1 The Kingdom Fungi

In spring, if you know where to look, you can find one of the most prized of all foods—the common morel—growing wild in woodlands throughout the United States. Its ridged cap is often camouflaged by dead leaves that collect in abandoned orchards or underneath old oaks or tulip poplars. Some morels grow alone, but others grow in groups. They appear suddenly, often overnight, and live for only a few days. What are these mysterious organisms? How do they grow so quickly?

What Are Fungi?

Like mushrooms and molds, morels are fungi. The way in which many fungi grow from the ground once led scientists to classify them as nonphotosynthetic plants. But they aren't plants at all. In fact, fungi are very different from plants.

Fungi are eukaryotic heterotrophs that have cell walls. The cell walls of fungi are made up of **chitin,** a complex carbohydrate that is also found in the external skeletons of insects. Recall that heterotrophs depend on other organisms for food. Unlike animals, fungi do not ingest their food. Instead, they digest food outside of their bodies and then absorb it. Many fungi feed by absorbing nutrients from decaying matter in the soil. Others live as parasites, absorbing nutrients from the bodies of their hosts.

Structure and Function of Fungi

Except for yeasts, all fungi are multicellular. Multicellular fungi are composed of tiny filaments called **hyphae** (HY-fee; singular: hypha). Each hypha is only one cell thick. In some fungi, cross walls divide the hyphae into cells containing one or two nuclei, as shown in **Figure 21–1.** In the cross walls, there are tiny openings through which the cytoplasm and nuclei can move. Other hyphae lack cross walls and contain many nuclei.

Guide for Reading

Key Concepts
- What are the defining characteristics of fungi?
- What is the internal structure of a fungus?
- How do fungi reproduce?

Vocabulary
chitin
hypha
mycelium
fruiting body
sporangium
sporangiophore
gametangium

**Reading Strategy:
Asking Questions**
Before you read, preview **Figures 21–1** and **21–2.** Make a list of questions you have about the structure of fungi. As you read, look for answers to your questions.

Figure 21–1 Fungi are eukaryotes that have cell walls made of chitin. Most fungi are made up of filaments called hyphae. In some fungi, the hyphae are divided by cross walls. These cells may contain one or two nuclei. In other fungi, the hyphae lack cross walls and contain many nuclei.

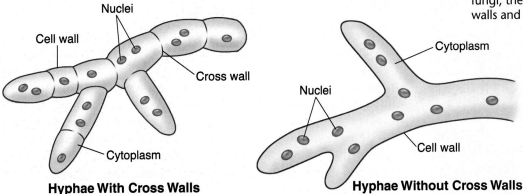

Hyphae With Cross Walls

Hyphae Without Cross Walls

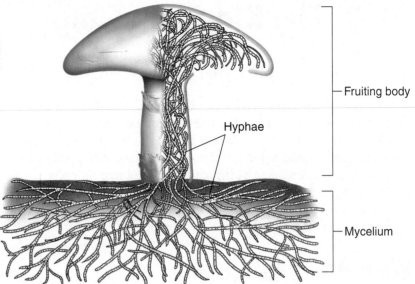

Fruiting body

Hyphae

Mycelium

Figure 21–2 The body of a mushroom is part of a mycelium formed from many tangled hyphae. The major portion of the mycelium grows below ground. The visible portion of the mycelium is the reproductive structure, or fruiting body, of the mushroom.

Figure 21–2 shows the structure of a multicellular fungus. **The bodies of multicellular fungi are composed of many hyphae tangled together into a thick mass called a mycelium.** The **mycelium** (my-SEE-lee-um; plural: mycelia) is well suited to absorb food because it permits a large surface area to come in contact with the food source through which it grows.

What you recognize as a mushroom is actually the fruiting body of a fungus. A **fruiting body** is a reproductive structure that develops from a mycelium that grows below the surface of the ground. Clusters of mushrooms are often part of the same mycelium, which means that they are part of a single organism.

Some mycelia can live for many years. As time goes by, soil nutrients near the center of the mycelium become depleted. As a result, new mushrooms sprout only at the edges of the mycelium, producing a ring like the one in **Figure 21–3.** People once thought fairies dancing in circles during warm nights produced these rings, so they were called "fairy rings." Over many years, fairy rings can become enormous—from 10 to 30 meters in diameter.

✓**CHECKPOINT** What is a fruiting body?

▼ **Figure 21–3** This fairy ring is composed of the fruiting bodies of mushrooms that developed at the outer edges of a single mycelium. **Predicting** *How will the size of the fairy ring change in future years?*

Reproduction in Fungi

Most fungi reproduce both asexually and sexually. Asexual reproduction takes place when cells or hyphae break off from a fungus and begin to grow on their own. Some fungi also produce spores, which can scatter and grow into new organisms. You may recall that a spore is a reproductive cell formed by mitosis that is capable of growing into a new organism. In some fungi, spores are produced in structures called **sporangia** (spoh-RAN-jee-uh; singular: sporangium). Sporangia are found at the tips of specialized hyphae called **sporangiophores** (spoh-RAN-jee-oh-fawrz).

Sexual reproduction in fungi usually involves two different mating types. Because gametes of both mating types are about the same size, they are not called male and female. Rather, one mating type is referred to as "+" (plus), and the other is referred to as "−" (minus). When the hyphae of opposite mating types meet, each hypha forms a **gametangium** (gam-uh-TAN-jee-um; plural: gametangia), or structure that forms gametes. Then, the two gametangia join, and the haploid nuclei contained in them fuse to form a diploid nucleus, or zygote. After the zygote forms, meiosis takes place, producing haploid nuclei that dominate the remainder of the life cycle. In most fungi, the zygote is the only cell in the entire life cycle that is diploid.

How Fungi Spread

Fungal spores are found in almost every environment. This is why molds seem to spring up in any location that has the right combination of moisture and food. Many fungi produce dry, almost weightless spores, as shown in **Figure 21–4**. These spores scatter easily in the wind. On a clear day, a few liters of fresh air may contain hundreds of spores from many species of fungi.

If these spores are to germinate, they must land in a favorable environment. There must be the proper combination of temperature, moisture, and food so that the spores can grow. Even under the best of circumstances, the probability that a spore will produce a mature organism can be less than one in a billion.

Other fungi are specialized to lure animals, which disperse fungal spores over long distances. Stinkhorns smell like rotting meat, which attracts flies. When they land on the stinkhorn, the flies ingest the sticky, smelly fluid on the surface of the fungus. The spore-containing fluid will pass unharmed out of the flies' digestive systems, depositing spores over many kilometers.

▲ **Figure 21–4** Most fungi reproduce both sexually and asexually. One form of asexual reproduction is spore formation. Here, an earthstar puffball (*Geastrum saccatum*) that has been struck by a raindrop expels a cloud of spores.

21–1 Section Assessment

1. **Key Concept** What characteristics do all fungi have in common?

2. **Key Concept** Describe the structure of the body of a typical fungus.

3. **Key Concept** Briefly describe asexual and sexual reproduction in fungi.

4. By what means are fungal spores spread to new locations?

5. **Critical Thinking Applying Concepts** Tissue from several mushrooms gathered near the base of a tree were tested and found to be genetically identical. How might you explain this?

TEXT **Assessment** Use iText to review the important concepts in Section 21–1.

Take It to the NET

Find out more about how fungal spores spread in the environment. Then, choose one fungus and prepare a presentation that explains its mechanism of spore release in detail. Use the links provided in the Biology area at the Prentice Hall Web site for help in completing this activity: **www.phschool.com**

21–2 Classification of Fungi

Guide for Reading

 Key Concept
• What are the characteristics of the four main phyla of fungi?

Vocabulary
zygospore
rhizoid
stolon
conidium
ascus
ascospore
basidium
basidiospore

Reading Strategy:
Finding Main Ideas Before you read, skim the section to identify the four main groups of fungi. Write the name of each group on a note card. As you read, make note of the characteristics of each group.

The kingdom Fungi is a large one, with over 100,000 species. Fungi are classified according to their structure and method of reproduction. As you will read, the methods by which fungi reproduce are unlike those of any other kingdom. The four main groups of fungi are the common molds (Zygomycota), the sac fungi (Ascomycota), the club fungi (Basidiomycota), and the imperfect fungi (Deuteromycota).

The Common Molds

The familiar molds that grow on meat, cheese, and bread are members of the phylum Zygomycota, also called zygomycetes. **Zygomycetes have life cycles that include a zygospore.** A **zygospore** (ZY-goh-spawr) is a resting spore that contains zygotes formed during the sexual phase of the mold's life cycle. The hyphae of zygomycetes generally lack cross walls, although the cells of their reproductive structures do have cross walls.

Structure and Function of Molds One of the best-known zygomycetes is the black bread mold, *Rhizopus stolonifer*. You can grow bread mold by exposing a slice of bread that does not contain preservatives to airborne dust. If you keep the bread warm and moist in a covered container, in a few days a layer of dark fuzz will appear.

Look closely at the moldy bread with a magnifying glass, and you will see tangles of delicate hyphae. Actually, you will be looking at more than one kind of hypha. The rootlike hyphae that penetrate the surface of the bread are called **rhizoids** (RY-zoydz). Rhizoids anchor the fungus to the bread, release digestive enzymes, and absorb digested organic material. The stemlike hyphae that run along the surface of the bread are called **stolons.** The hyphae that push up into the air are the sporangiophores, which form sporangia at their tips. A single sporangium may contain as many as 40,000 spores, each of which can grow into a new fungus.

CHECKPOINT *What is a zygospore?*

Life Cycle of Molds The life cycle of black bread mold is shown in **Figure 21–5.** Sexual reproduction in bread molds and other zygomycetes occurs when two hyphae from different mating types come together, forming gametangia. Haploid (N) gametes produced in the gametangia fuse with gametes of the opposite mating type to form diploid (2N) nuclei, or zygotes, which make up a single zygospore. A thick wall develops around the zygospore, which may remain dormant for months. When conditions become favorable, the zygospore germinates, then undergoes meiosis, and new haploid spores are released.

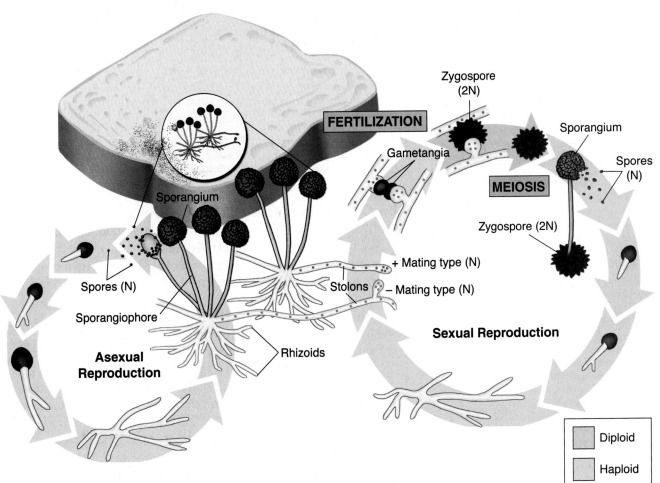

▲ Figure 21–5 ⬤Zygomycetes have life cycles that include a zygospore. During sexual reproduction in the bread mold *Rhizopus stolonifer,* hyphae from two different mating types form gametangia. The gametangia fuse, and zygotes form within a zygospore. The zygospore develops a thick wall and can remain dormant for long periods. The zygospore eventually germinates, and a sporangium emerges. The sporangium reproduces asexually by releasing haploid spores produced by meiosis.

Quick Lab

What is the structure of bread mold?

Materials transparent tape, moldy bread, microscope slide, microscope

Procedure
1. Touch the sticky side of a 2-cm piece of transparent tape to the black "fuzzy" area of a bread mold.
2. Gently stick the tape to a glass slide. Observe the slide under the compound microscope. Make a sketch of your observations.

3. Return all slides to your teacher for proper disposal. Wash your hands before leaving the laboratory.

Analyze and Conclude
1. **Observing** Describe the structures you observed in the bread mold.
2. **Formulating Hypotheses** What do you think the function of the round structures is? Why do you think a single mass of bread mold produces so many of the round structures?
3. **Inferring** How can your observations help explain the ability of molds to appear on foods even in very clean kitchens?

The Sac Fungi

Sac fungi, also known as ascomycetes, belong to the phylum Ascomycota. 🔑 **The phylum Ascomycota is named for the ascus, a reproductive structure that contains spores.** There are more than 30,000 species of ascomycetes, making it the largest phylum of the kingdom Fungi. Some ascomycetes, such as the cup fungi shown in **Figure 21–6,** are large enough to be visible when they grow above the ground. Others, such as yeasts, are microscopic.

Life Cycle of Sac Fungi The life cycle of an ascomycete usually includes both asexual and sexual reproduction. The life cycle of a cup fungus is shown in **Figure 21–7.**

In asexual reproduction, tiny spores called **conidia** (koh-NID-ee-uh; singular: conidium) are formed at the tips of specialized hyphae called conidiophores. These spores get their name from the Greek word *konis,* which means "dust." If conidia land in a suitable environment, they grow into a haploid mycelium.

Sexual reproduction occurs when the haploid hyphae of two different mating types (+ and –) grow close together. The N + N hyphae then produce a fruiting body in which sexual reproduction continues. Gametangia from the two mating types fuse, but the haploid (N) nuclei do not fuse. Instead, this fusion produces hyphae that contain haploid nuclei from each of the mating types (N + N).

The **ascus** (plural: asci) forms within the fruiting body. Within the ascus, two nuclei of different mating types fuse to form a diploid zygote (2N). The zygote soon divides by meiosis, producing four haploid cells. In most ascomycetes, meiosis is followed by a cycle of mitosis, so that eight cells known as **ascospores** are produced. In a favorable environment, an ascospore can germinate and grow into a haploid mycelium.

✓CHECKPOINT **Where are ascospores formed? Are they haploid or diploid?**

▼ **Figure 21–6** These cup fungi are members of the phylum Ascomycota. In cup fungi, asci lie on the interior surface of the cup. At maturity, the spore-filled asci burst, releasing the spores into the air. **Applying Concepts** *What type of spores are formed by the cup fungi?*

Hyphae (N + N)

Fruiting body (N + N)

Ascus (N + N)

Diploid

Haploid

Hyphae (N)

Asci

Zygote (2N)

Gametangia

HYPHAE FUSE

+ Mating type (N)

− Mating type (N)

FERTILIZATION

MEIOSIS

Sexual Reproduction

Conidia (N)

Conidiophore

Hypha (N)

Hypha (N)

Hypha (N)

8 Ascospores (N)

Ascus

Asexual Reproduction

Yeasts Yeasts are unicellular fungi. The yeasts used by humans for baking and brewing are classified as ascomycetes because they form asci with ascospores during the sexual phase of their life cycle.

You might think of yeast as a lifeless, dry powder that is used to make bread. Actually, the dry granules contain ascospores, which become active in a moist environment. To see this for yourself, add a spoonful of dry yeast to half a cup of warm water that contains some sugar. In about 20 minutes, when you examine a drop of this mixture under a microscope, you will be able to see cell division in the rapidly growing yeast cells. The asexual process by which yeasts increase is called budding.

The common yeasts used for baking and brewing are members of the genus *Saccharomyces,* which means "sugar fungi." These yeasts are grown in a rich nutrient mixture containing very little oxygen. Prior to baking, the nutrient mixture is a mound of thick dough. Lacking oxygen, the yeasts within the mixture use the process of alcoholic fermentation to obtain energy. The byproducts of alcoholic fermentation are carbon dioxide and alcohol. The carbon dioxide gas makes beverages bubble and bread rise (by producing bubbles within the dough). The alcohol in bread dough evaporates during baking. In brewing, alcohol remains in the resulting alcoholic beverages.

▲ **Figure 21–7** The life cycle of ascomycetes includes both asexual and sexual reproduction. During asexual reproduction, spores called conidia are formed at the tips of specialized hyphae called conidiophores. During sexual reproduction, hyphae of two mating types fuse to form hyphae with two haploid nuclei (N + N). The N + N hyphae then form a fruiting body, which eventually releases ascospores.
Ascomycetes are named for the ascus, the reproductive structure that contains ascospores.

The Club Fungi

The phylum Basidiomycota, or club fungi, gets its name from a specialized reproductive structure that resembles a club. The spore-bearing structure is called the **basidium** (buh-SID-ee-um; plural: basidia). Basidia are found on the gills that grow on the underside of mushroom caps.

Life Cycle of Club Fungi Basidiomycetes undergo what is probably the most elaborate life cycle of all the fungi. As shown in **Figure 21–8,** a basidiospore germinates to produce a haploid primary mycelium, which begins to grow. Before long, the mycelia of different mating types fuse to produce a secondary mycelium. The cells of the secondary mycelium contain haploid nuclei of each mating type. Secondary mycelia may grow in the soil for years, reaching an enormous size. A few mycelia have been found to be hundreds of meters across, making them perhaps the largest organisms in the world.

When the right combination of moisture and nutrients occurs, spore-producing fruiting bodies push above the ground. You would recognize these fruiting bodies as mushrooms. Each mushroom begins as a mass of growing hyphae that forms a button, or thick bulge, at the soil's surface.

▼ **Figure 21–8** The club fungi are named after the club shape of their reproductive structure, the basidium. The cap of a basidiomycete such as a mushroom is composed of tightly packed hyphae. The lower side of the cap is composed of gills—thin blades of tissue lined with basidia that produce basidiospores.

Fruiting body (N + N)

Gills lined with basidia

Cap

Gills

Stalk

Base

Basidia (N + N)

Button

Secondary mycelium (N + N)

HYPHAE FUSE

FERTILIZATION

Primary mycelium (N)

– Mating type (N)

Zygote (2N)

Haploid

Diploid

+ Mating type (N)

MEIOSIS

Basidiospores (N)

FIGURE 21-9 **DIVERSITY OF CLUB FUNGI**

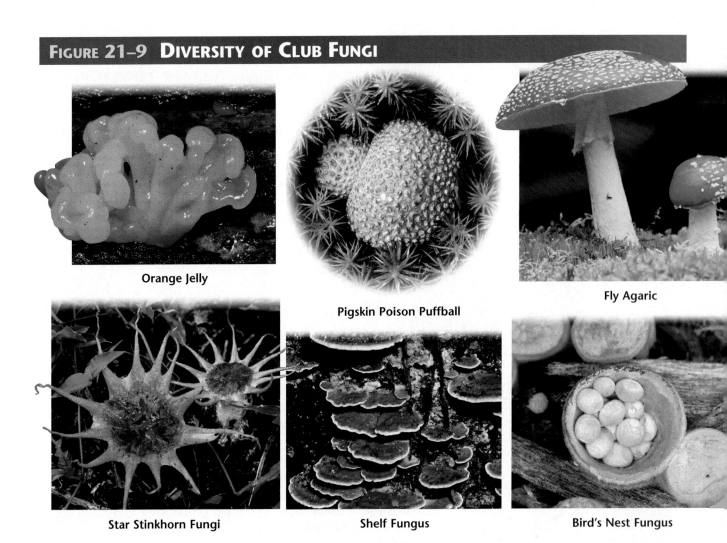

Orange Jelly

Pigskin Poison Puffball

Fly Agaric

Star Stinkhorn Fungi

Shelf Fungus

Bird's Nest Fungus

Fruiting bodies expand with astonishing speed, sometimes producing fully developed mushrooms overnight. This remarkable growth rate is caused by cell enlargement, not cell division. The cells of the hyphae enlarge by rapidly taking in water.

When the mushroom cap opens, it exposes hundreds of tiny gills on its underside. Each gill is lined with basidia. The two nuclei in each basidium fuse to form a diploid (2N) zygote cell, which then undergoes meiosis, forming clusters of haploid **basidiospores.** The basidiospores form at the edge of each basidium and, within a few hours, are ready to be scattered. Mushrooms are truly amazing reproductive structures—a single mushroom can produce billions of spores, and giant puffballs can produce trillions.

Diversity of Club Fungi In addition to mushrooms, basidiomycetes include shelf fungi, which grow near the surfaces of dead or decaying trees. The visible bracketlike structure that forms is a reproductive structure, and it, too, is a prolific producer of spores. Puffballs, earthstars, jelly fungi, and plant parasites known as rusts are other examples of basidiomycetes. **Figure 21-9** shows some examples of basidiomycetes.

CHECKPOINT *On which part of a mushroom would you find basidia?*

Figure 21-9 As you can see, the club fungi are a very diverse group. These fungi are all decomposers, but other kinds of club fungi are parasites of plants and animals. At least two of these fungi, the pigskin poison puffball and the fly agaric, are poisonous. **Inferring** *Can you tell by looking at a fungus whether or not it is poisonous?*

Figure 21–10 🔑 **The phylum Deuteromycota is made up of fungi that cannot be classified in any other phylum.** Under the microscope, the brushlike clusters of many small, spherical conidia characterize *Penicillium notatum*. This organism was the first of the *Penicillium* fungi used to produce the antibiotic penicillin.

(magnification: 930×)

Edible and Inedible Mushrooms Many types of fungi have long been considered delicacies, and several different species of mushrooms are cultivated for food. You may have already tasted sliced mushrooms on pizza, feasted on delicious sautéed portobello mushrooms, or eaten shiitake mushrooms. When properly cooked and prepared, domestic mushrooms are tasty and nutritious.

Wild mushrooms are a different story: Although some are edible, many are poisonous. Because many species of poisonous mushrooms look almost identical to edible mushrooms, you should never pick or eat any mushrooms found in the wild. Instead, mushroom gathering should be left to experts who can positively identify each mushroom they collect. The result of eating a poisonous mushroom can be severe illness, or even death.

The Imperfect Fungi

Deuteromycota is the phylum of imperfect fungi, which are called deuteromycetes. 🔑 **Deuteromycota is an extremely varied phylum. It is composed of those fungi that are not placed in other phyla because researchers have never been able to observe a sexual phase in their life cycles.** A majority of the imperfect fungi closely resemble ascomycetes. Others are similar to basidiomycetes, and a few resemble zygomycetes. The term *imperfect*, by the way, does not mean that the deuteromycetes are defective or less successful than other fungi. The term is just used to refer to fungi that do not appear to have sexual reproduction.

One of the best-known genera of the imperfect fungi is *Penicillium*. The species *Penicillium notatum,* shown in **Figure 21–10,** is a mold that frequently grows on fruit and is the source of the antibiotic penicillin. Like the ascomycetes, *Penicillium* reproduces asexually by means of conidia, leading many biologists to conclude that *Penicillium* evolved from an ascomycete that lost the sexual phase of its life cycle.

21–2 Section Assessment

1. 🔑 **Key Concept** List the four phyla of fungi and the main features that can be used to identify members of each phylum.

2. How do conidia form? What is their function?

3. Which fungal phylum contains the largest number of species?

4. **Critical Thinking Comparing and Contrasting** Compare the structure and function of an ascus and a basidium.

iTEXT Assessment Use iText to review the important concepts in Section 21–2.

ALTERNATIVE ASSESSMENT

In Your Community
Visit a local supermarket to find out how fungi are used in the cuisine of different cultures. Consider fresh and dried mushrooms, blue cheeses, and truffles. Present your findings as a written report or as recipe cards.

21-3 Ecology of Fungi

Fungi have been around since life first moved onto land. In fact, the oldest known fossils of fungi, shown in **Figure 21-11**, were formed about 460 million years ago. At that time, the largest land plants were small organisms similar to mosses. Paleontologists think that fungi helped early plants to obtain nutrients from the ground. Their early appearance suggests that fungi may have been essential to plants' successful colonization of the land, one of the key events in the history of life.

Over time, fungi have become an important part of virtually all ecosystems, adapting to conditions in every corner of Earth. Because most fungi live their lives out of our sight, people often overlook them. But without fungi, the world would be a very different place.

All Fungi Are Heterotrophs

As heterotrophs, fungi cannot manufacture their own food. Instead, they must rely on other organisms for their energy. Unlike animals, fungi cannot move to capture food, but their mycelia can grow very rapidly into the tissues and cells of plants and other organisms. Many fungi are **saprobes,** organisms that obtain food from decaying organic matter. Others are parasites, which harm other organisms while living directly on or within them. Still other fungi are symbionts that live in close and mutually beneficial association with other species.

Although most fungi feed on decaying matter, a few feed by capturing live animals. *Pleurotus ostreatus* is a carnivorous fungus that lives on the sides of trees. As roundworms crawl into the fungus to feed, they are exposed to a fungal chemical that makes them become sluggish. As the worms slow to a stop, fungal hyphae penetrate their bodies, trapping them in place and then digesting them.

Guide for Reading

Key Concepts
- What is the main role of fungi in natural ecosystems?
- What problems do parasitic fungi cause?
- What kinds of symbiotic relationships do fungi form with other organisms?

Vocabulary
saprobe
lichen
mycorrhiza

Reading Strategy: Using Prior Knowledge
Before you read this section, write down all the different ways that you think fungi interact in the environment. As you read, add to or revise your list as necessary.

(magnification: 280×)

(magnification: 560×)

Figure 21-11 These microscopic images show fossils of the earliest known fungi, zygomycetes that lived about 460 million years ago. **A** shows an overview of fossilized hyphae with spores. **B** is a close-up of hyphae growing out of a spore. **Observing** *Can you identify structures similar to those of modern molds?*

Fungi as Decomposers

🔑 **Fungi are found in every ecosystem, where they recycle nutrients by breaking down the bodies and wastes of other organisms.** Like the fungi in **Figure 21–12**, many fungi feed by releasing digestive enzymes that break down leaves, fruit, and other organic material into simple molecules. These molecules then diffuse into the fungus. The mycelia of fungi produce digestive enzymes that speed the breakdown of dead organisms, thereby helping to recycle nutrients and essential chemicals.

Imagine a world without fungi and other decomposers. Without decay, the energy-rich compounds that organisms accumulate during their lifetimes would be lost forever. Many organisms, especially plants, remove important trace elements and nutrients from the soil. If these materials were not eventually returned, the soil would quickly be depleted, and Earth would become lifeless and barren.

Fungi as Parasites

As useful as many fungi are, others cause tremendous losses of food and crops. 🔑 **Parasitic fungi cause serious plant and animal diseases. A few fungi cause diseases in humans.**

Plant Diseases Fungi cause diseases such as corn smut, which destroys the corn kernels, as shown in **Figure 21–13**. Mildews, which infect a wide variety of fruits, are also fungi. Fungal diseases are responsible for the loss of approximately 15 percent of the crops grown in temperate regions of the world. In tropical areas, where high humidity favors fungal growth, the loss of crops is sometimes as high as 50 percent. Fungi are in direct competition with humans for food. Unfortunately for us, sometimes fungi win that competition.

One fungal disease—wheat rust—affects one of the most important crops grown in North America. Rusts are caused by a type of basidiomycete that needs two different plants to complete its life cycle. Spores produced by rust in barberry plants are carried by the wind into wheat fields. There, the spores germinate and infect wheat plants. The patches of rust produce a second type of spore that infects other wheat plants, allowing the disease to spread through the field like wildfire.

Later in the growing season, a new variety of spore is produced by the rust. These tough black spores easily survive through the winter. In spring, they go through a sexual phase and produce spores that infect barberry plants. Once on the barberry leaves, the rust produces the spores that infect wheat plants, and the cycle continues. Fortunately, once agricultural scientists understood the life cycle of the rust, they were able to slow its spread by destroying barberry plants.

✓ CHECKPOINT *What are two examples of plant diseases caused by fungi?*

▲ **Figure 21–12** 🔘 Many fungi are decomposers that recycle nutrients by breaking down the bodies of other organisms. The mycelia of these mushrooms have released enzymes that are breaking down the wood tissues of the decaying tree stump.

Human Diseases

Fungal parasites can also infect humans. One deuteromycete can infect the areas between the toes, causing the infection known as athlete's foot. The fungus forms a mycelium directly within the outer layers of the skin. This produces a red, inflamed sore from which the spores can easily spread from person to person. When the same fungus infects other areas, such as the skin of the scalp, it produces a red scaling sore known as ringworm, which is not a worm at all.

A different type of fungal disease is caused by the yeast *Candida albicans,* which grows in moist regions of the body. Usually its growth is kept in check by competition from bacteria that grow in the body and by the body's immune system. This normal balance can be upset by many factors, including the use of antibiotics, which kill bacteria, or by damage to the immune system. When this happens, *Candida* may produce thrush, a painful mouth infection. Yeast infections of the female reproductive tract usually are due to overgrowth of *Candida.*

Other Animal Diseases

As problematic as human fungal diseases can be, few are as deadly as the infection by one fungus from the genus *Cordyceps.* This fungus infects grasshoppers in rain forests in Costa Rica. Microscopic spores become lodged in the grasshopper, where they germinate and produce enzymes that slowly penetrate the insect's tough external skeleton. The spores multiply in the insect's body, digesting all its cells and tissues until the insect dies. To complete the process of digestion, hyphae develop, cloaking the decaying exoskeleton in a web of fungal material. Reproductive structures, which will produce more spores that will spread the infection, then emerge from the grasshopper's remains, as shown in **Figure 21–14.**

Figure 21–13 Parasitic fungi cause serious diseases in plants and animals. Corn smut (left) grows on the ears, stalks, and leaves of a corn plant, damaging it. The fungus then releases millions of spores that survive in the soil during the winter and begin their life cycle again in the spring. Wheat rust (center) is a basidiomycete that infects both wheat and barberry plants. Athlete's foot (right) infects the outer layers of human skin.

▲ **Figure 21–14** This grasshopper is the victim of a fungus of the genus *Cordyceps.* Once the fungus's tiny spore enters the insect's body, it multiplies rapidly and digests body tissues. Within days, all that is left of the insect is its hard outer shell. The structures growing out of the grasshopper's body are the fungus's fruiting bodies. **Comparing and Contrasting** *Some pathogens rely on their host to spread them to other potential hosts. How does this fungus spread?*

Fungi **539**

▲ **Figure 21–15** Lichens often grow on rocks and in other environments where few organisms can survive. Lichens grow in one of three forms. Crustose lichens (top) are flat, foliose lichens (middle) resemble leaves, and fruticose lichens (bottom) grow upright. **Classifying** *What forms of lichens are visible in these pictures?*

Symbiotic Relationships

Fungi often grow in close association with members of other species in symbiotic relationships. Although fungi are parasites in many of these relationships, that is not always the case. 🔑 **Some fungi form symbiotic relationships in which both partners benefit. Two such mutualistic associations, lichens and mycorrhizae, are essential to many ecosystems.**

Lichens Lichens (LY-kunz) are not single organisms. Rather, they are symbiotic associations between a fungus and a photosynthetic organism. The fungi in lichens are usually ascomycetes, although a few are basidiomycetes. The photosynthetic organism is either a green alga or a cyanobacterium, or both. **Figure 21–16** shows the structure of a lichen.

Lichens are extremely resistant to drought and cold. Therefore, they can grow in places where few other organisms can survive—on dry, bare rock in deserts and on the tops of mountains. Lichens are able to survive in these harsh environments because of the relationship between the two partner organisms. The algae or cyanobacteria carry out photosynthesis, providing the fungus with a source of energy. The fungus, in turn, provides the algae or bacteria with water and minerals that it collects and protects the delicate green cells from intense sunlight.

Lichens are often the first organisms to enter barren environments, gradually breaking down the rocks on which they grow. In this way, lichens help in the early stages of soil formation. Lichens are also remarkably sensitive to air pollution, and they are among the first organisms to be affected when air quality deteriorates.

✓ CHECKPOINT *What two groups of organisms grow together in lichens?*

Densely packed hyphae

Layer of algae/cyanobacteria

Loosely packed hyphae

Densely packed hyphae

▲ **Figure 21–16** 🔑 **Lichens are a mutualistic relationship between a fungus and an alga or a cyanobacterium, or both.** The protective upper surface of a lichen is composed of fungal hyphae. Below this is the layer of cyanobacteria or algae with loosely woven hyphae. The third layer consists of loosely packed hyphae. The bottom layer is a protective surface covered by small projections that attach the lichen to a rock or tree.

Repotting Orchids

You are working in a greenhouse that has just begun to grow orchids. The plants arrive in small pots from a nursery. When they outgrow the pots, your supervisor asks you to place them in larger pots with fresh soil, just as you have done with other plants. However, every time you follow the greenhouse procedure for repotting, which includes carefully washing off the "old" soil and placing the roots into a sterilized soil mix, the plants soon wither and die.

Defining the Problem In your own words, what is the problem the greenhouse faces?

Organizing Information What problems could sterile, microbe-free soil present to a plant? Are there microorganisms in soil that might be essential to orchids? Might the loss of such organisms cause problems for the plants? What kinds of problems?

Creating a Solution Describe an experiment that you could use to find out if the use of sterile soil is causing the problems with repotting. Be sure to devise controls that might determine whether the mechanical stress of repotting is causing the problems, rather than the soil mixture.

Presenting Your Plan Make a poster showing the steps and procedures in your proposed experiment and explain it to the class.

Mycorrhizae Fungi also form mutualistic relationships with plants. Almost half of the tissues of trees are hidden beneath the ground in masses of tangled roots. These roots are woven into a partnership with an even larger web of fungal mycelia. These associations of plant roots and fungi are **mycorrhizae** (my-koh-RY-zee; singular: mycorrhiza).

Scientists have known about this partnership for years, but recent research shows that it is more common and more important than was previously thought. Researchers now estimate that 80 percent of all plant species form mycorrhizae with fungi.

How do plants and fungi benefit from each other? The tiny hyphae of the fungi aid plants in absorbing water and minerals. They do this by producing a network that covers the roots of the plants and increases the effective surface area of the root system. This allows the roots to absorb more water and minerals from the soil. In addition, the fungi release enzymes that free nutrients in the soil. The plants, in turn, provide the fungi with the products of photosynthesis.

The presence of mycorrhizae is essential for the growth of many plants. The seeds of some plants, such as orchids, cannot germinate in the absence of mycorrhizal fungi. Many trees are unable to survive without fungal symbionts. Mycorrhizal associations have even been cited as an adaptation that was critical in the evolution of land plants from more-aquatic ancestors.

Figure 21–17 Plants and fungi often form associations called mycorrhizae (shown in the top photograph). The fungi in the mycorrhizae enable the host plant to absorb more water and nutrients. In the bottom photograph, the lemon seedlings on the left were grown without mycorrhizae. The ones on the right, which are the same age, were grown with mycorrhizae. **Applying Concepts** *What type of symbiotic relationship is illustrated by mycorrhizae?*

Mycorrhizal relationships are often very specialized. For example, the Douglas fir forests of the Pacific Northwest are dependent on the presence of a particular species of white truffle. In Europe, black truffles are found growing with oak and beech trees. The fly agaric grows mostly with birch and pine trees. **Figure 21–17** shows how mycorrhizae affect the growth of young lemon trees.

Why is this networking relationship so important? The partnership between plant and fungus does not end with a single plant. The roots of each plant are plugged into mycorrhizal networks that connect many plants. What's more astounding is that these networks appear to connect plants of different species.

A recent experiment showed that carbon atoms from one tree often end up in another nearby tree. In an experiment using carbon isotopes to track the movement of carbon, ecologist Suzanne Simard found that mycorrhizal fungi transferred carbon from paper birch trees growing in the sun to Douglas fir trees growing in the shade. As a result, the sun-starved fir trees thrived, basically by being "fed" carbon from the birches.

Simard's findings suggest that plants are far from being isolated individuals, as was previously thought. Instead, plants—and their associated fungi—may be evolving as part of an ecological partnership.

21–3 Section Assessment

1. **Key Concept** What is the major role of fungi in an ecosystem?

2. **Key Concept** How can fungi harm humans and other living things?

3. **Key Concept** Describe two mutualistic relationships that fungi form with other organisms.

4. Describe the life cycle of wheat rust.

5. **Critical Thinking Applying Concepts** What might happen to a garden if it were sprayed with a long-acting fungicide?

TEXT Assessment Use iText to review the important concepts in Section 21–3.

MAKING CONNECTIONS

Structure and Function
Both bacteria and fungi are decomposers. What characteristics do these two groups share that allow them to function in this ecological role? Use the information in Chapter 19 to help answer this question.

Examining Seeds for Fungi

The fungi that you are probably most familiar with are mushrooms and the molds that attack stored foods. In this investigation, you will examine how storage conditions affect the growth of fungi on seeds.

Problem What storage conditions best protect seeds from fungi?

Materials

- seeds stored in cold, dry conditions
- seeds stored in warm, moist conditions
- forceps
- microscope slide
- coverslip
- microscope
- aniline blue stain
- scalpel
- dropper pipette
- paper towels

Skills Formulating Hypotheses

Procedure

1. **Formulating Hypotheses** Develop a hypothesis about the effect of temperature and moisture on the growth of a seed-destroying fungus. Predict whether you will find more hyphae in seeds stored in cold, dry conditions or in seeds stored in warm, moist conditions.

2. Use a dropper pipette to place a drop of aniline blue stain on a microscope slide. **CAUTION:** *Avoid getting the stain on your hands or clothing.*

3. Use forceps to carefully remove the outer seed coat from a seed stored in cool, dry conditions. Place the seed in the drop of aniline blue stain.

4. Use the flat side of a scalpel or forceps to gently mash and flatten the seed in the drop of stain. Place a coverslip on top of the mashed seed. Leave the seed in the stain for 1 minute.

5. Use a dropper pipette to place a drop of water on the slide, touching one edge of the coverslip.

6. Touch a paper towel to the edge of the coverslip opposite the drop of water to draw the water under the coverslip. Repeat steps 4 and 5 until you have removed the drop of stain.

7. Use the high-power objective of the microscope to examine the stained seed. Any hyphae that are present will be stained blue. Record your observations as notes and sketches.

8. Repeat steps 1 to 6 with a seed stored in warm, moist conditions.

Analyze and Conclude

1. **Observing** Which seeds had more hyphae?

2. **Analyzing Data** What conditions favor the growth of fungi? What conditions are better for storing seeds?

3. **Drawing Conclusions** Did your observations support your hypothesis? Are the environmental requirements of this fungus typical of most fungi?

4. **Inferring** Aniline blue stains the cell walls of fungi more easily than plant cell walls. What substance in fungi do you think aniline blue binds to? Explain your answer.

Go Further

Designing Experiments Plan an experiment to compare the growth of plants from both healthy and fungus-infected seeds. What are your controlled and manipulated variables? Obtain your teacher's permission before carrying out your experiment.

Chapter 21 Study Guide

21–1 The Kingdom Fungi
🔑 Key Concepts

- Fungi are eukaryotic heterotrophs that have cell walls made of chitin.
- The bodies of multicellular fungi are composed of many hyphae tangled together into a thick mass called a mycelium.
- Most fungi reproduce both asexually and sexually.

Vocabulary
chitin, p. 527 • hypha, p. 527
mycelium, p. 528 • fruiting body, p. 528
sporangium, p. 528 • sporangiophore, p. 528
gametangium, p. 529

21–2 Classification of Fungi
🔑 Key Concepts

- Zygomycetes have life cycles that include a zygospore.
- The phylum Ascomycota is named for the ascus, a reproductive structure that contains spores.
- The phylum Basidiomycota, or club fungi, gets its name from the basidium, a specialized reproductive structure that resembles a club.
- Deuteromycota is an extremely varied phylum. It is composed of those fungi that are not placed in other phyla because researchers have never been able to observe a sexual phase in their life cycles.

Vocabulary
zygospore, p. 530 • rhizoid, p. 530
stolon, p. 530 • conidium, p. 532
ascus, p. 532 • ascospore, p. 532
basidium, p. 534 • basidiospore, p. 535

21–3 Ecology of Fungi
🔑 Key Concepts

- Fungi are found in every ecosystem, where they recycle nutrients by breaking down the bodies of other organisms.
- Parasitic fungi cause serious plant and animal diseases. A few fungi cause diseases in humans.
- Some fungi form symbiotic relationships in which both partners benefit. Two such mutualistic associations, lichens and mycorrhizae, are essential to many ecosystems.

Vocabulary
saprobe, p. 537
lichen, p. 540
mycorrhiza, p. 541

Thinking Visually
Use the information in Section 21–2 to complete the following compare-and-contrast table about the different phyla of Fungi:

Phylum	Examples	Characteristics	Reproduction	
			Asexual	Sexual
Zygomycota (common molds)	*Rhizopus stolonifer* (black bread mold)	1	Spores in sporangiophores	2
Ascomycota (sac fungi)	3	Long stage in which cells have two nuclei; yeasts are unicellular	4	5
Basidiomycota (club fungi)	Mushrooms, puffballs, earthstars, shelf fungi, jelly fungi, rusts	Extremely variable; long stage in which cells have two nuclei	None or conidia on conidiophores	6
Deuteromycota (imperfect fungi)	*Penicillium*, ringworm, and athlete's foot fungus	7	Conidia on conidiophores	8

Chapter 21

Part A

Multiple Choice

For each statement or question, select the number of the word or expression that, of those given, best completes the statement or answers the question.

1 Which is *not* a characteristic of the kingdom Fungi?
(1) All are unicellular.
(2) All have cell walls.
(3) All are eukaryotic.
(4) All are heterotrophs.

2 The body of a typical fungus consists of a tangled mass of filaments called a(an)
(1) basidium   (3) hypha
(2) mycelium   (4) antheridium

3 When hyphae of opposite mating types of fungi meet, each hypha forms a
(1) sporangium   (3) gametangium
(2) zygospore   (4) zoospore

4 In the diagram of bread mold shown below, X is pointing to what structure?
(1) stolon   (3) basidium
(2) rhizoid   (4) ascus

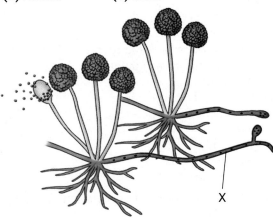

X

5 The asexual spores of ascomycetes are called
(1) zygospores   (3) ascospores
(2) conidia   (4) zoospores

6 In both baking and brewing, yeast cells bud and obtain their energy from the process of
(1) lactic acid fermentation
(2) aerobic respiration
(3) alcoholic fermentation
(4) digestion

7 A mushroom that you see above the ground is actually a
(1) basidiospore (3) fruiting body
(2) gametangium   (4) basidium

8 Sexual reproduction has never been observed in
(1) zygomycetes   (3) basidiomycetes
(2) ascomycetes   (4) deuteromycetes

9 Organisms that obtain food from decaying organic matter are called
(1) mutualists   (3) parasites
(2) autotrophs   (4) saprobes

10 An example of a symbiotic association between a fungus and a photosynthetic organism is a
(1) mycorrhiza   (3) lichen
(2) fruiting body (4) mushroom

11 Which organisms is *not* a fungus?
(1) mushroom   (3) bread mold
(2) water mold   (4) yeast

12 Which is (are) characteristic of some types of fungi?
A Decomposition
B Parasitism
C Mutualism
(1) A, only
(2) B, only
(3) B and C, only
(4) A, B, and C

For questions 13 and 14, complete each analogy by selecting the correct number. In analogies, A : B :: C : means "A is to B as C is to ___?___."

13 Sac fungus : morel :: club fungus :
(1) mushroom   (3) bread mold
(2) yeast   (4) lichen

14 Plant : root :: mold :
(1) gametangium
(2) zygospore
(3) rhizoid
(4) stolon

Test-Taking Tip   Before you begin answering questions, determine the total number of questions on the test and how much time, on average, you have to answer each question. Try to partition your time accordingly.

Parts B and C

Multiple Choice and Extended Response

For those questions that ask you to select a response, choose the one that best completes the statement or answers the question. For all others follow the directions given.

15 What conditions are necessary for fungal spores to germinate?

16 Explain the basis for the classification of fungi.

Base your answers to questions 17 and 18 on the information and graph below and on your knowledge of biology.

The graph below illustrates the growth rates of three species of trees—two individuals of each. One tree of each species grew with mycorrhizae, and one grew without mycorrhizae.

Effect of Mycorrhizae on Tree Height

Mycorrhizae present | Mycorrhizae absent

17 For each species, how does the growth of the two plants compare?

18 Make a generalization about the growth rate of plants with mycorrhizae.

Base your answers to questions 19 through 21 on the information below and on your knowledge of biology.

Ripe grapes are covered with a grayish film called "bloom," which contains yeasts and sometimes other microorganisms. A group of students prepared three test tubes of fresh, mashed grapes. They heated two of the test tubes to the boiling point and then cooled them. They inoculated one of these test tubes with live yeast. They incubated all three test tubes at 30°C for 48 hours and then examined the test tubes for signs of fermentation—the presence of bubbles and alcohol. Their data are summarized in the table below.

Evidence of Fermentation		
Test-Tube Contents	**Alcohol Odor (yes or no)**	**Bubbles (yes or no)**
Unheated grape mash	yes	yes
Boiled grape mash	no	no
Boiled grape mash inoculated with yeast	yes	yes

19 What is the manipulated (independent) variable in the students' investigation?
(1) presence of live yeast
(2) bubbles
(3) odor of alcohol
(4) time

20 What is the responding (dependent) variable in the students' investigation?
A Boiling
B Odor of alcohol
C Presence of bubbles
(1) A, only
(2) B, only
(3) B and C, only
(4) A, B, and C

21 What is an appropriate conclusion, based on the students' results?
A Uninoculated, boiled grape mash does not seem to ferment over a 48-hour period.
B Boiled grape mash that contains live yeast undergoes fermentation.
C Grape mash does not ferment unless live yeast is added.
(1) A and B, only
(2) A and C, only
(3) B and C, only
(4) A, B, and C

22 Complete the following chart by placing the letter of the best choice next to each phrase. A choice may be used once, more than once, or not at all. (Do not write in this book.)

A Lichen   **D** Mycelium
B Mycorrhiza   **E** Chitin
C Penicillium

Description	Choice(s)
Cell wall carbohydrate	
Tangled mass of hyphae	
Plant/fungus symbiont	
Fungal source of antibiotic	

23 Most fungi are heterotrophic, multicellular organisms that produce sexually and asexually. Write an essay that explains reproduction in common molds (zygomycetes). Be sure to include the following terms and their definitions

- hyphae

- spores

- zygospores

- haploid and diploid

24 How are cell walls of fungi similar to the external skeletons of insects?

25 How does a sporangiophore function in the reproduction of fungi?

26 How does the method by which fungi obtain nutrients help in recycling nutrients and essential chemicals?

27 Explain why many biologists think that *Penicillium* evolved from an ascomycete.

28 Distinguish between a saprobe and a parasite.

29 What is the evolutionary significance of mycorrhizae?

30 Why is it dangerous to eat wild mushrooms?

31 Compare the structure and function of rhizoids and stolons.

32 Suppose mushrooms appeared repeatedly in only one small part of your yard. What would this indicate about the soil in that area?

33 Heavily polluted fresh water contains few fungi. How might this affect life in a lake?

Base your answers to questions 34 through 38 on the information below and on your knowledge of biology.

The ABC Drug Company is developing a new, anti-fungal lotion for the treatment of athlete's foot. Tests were conducted to determine how effective the medicine is. The company studied two groups of athlete's foot sufferers. One group consisted of 200 men. The other group consisted of 200 women. Members of each group applied the lotion twice a day for two weeks. After the two week period, 75 percent of the men and 83 percent of the women had no trace of the fungus on their feet.

34 What is the manipulated (independent) variable in this study?

35 Two groups of subjects were used in this study. In order for the results to be valid, what other group(s) should be added? What treatment should that group(s) receive?

36 Fungi that cause athlete's foot belong to the phylum Deuteromycota. What is characteristic about the fungi that belong to this phylum? How might that characteristic affect this study?

37 In order for other scientists to duplicate this study, what additional kinds of information would they need?

38 Consider the conditions necessary for fungal spores to germinate and explain why athlete's foot can be such a problem to cure.

 Take It to the NET

Visit the Prentice Hall Web site at **www.phschool.com** to find out more about fungi gardens that are cultivated by ants. Then, answer the following:

- Describe the nest of a leaf-cutting ant.

- On what material does the fungus grow in the ant nest?

- How do the ants keep unwanted species of fungi out of their garden?

- What part of the fungus do the ants eat?

UNIT 7

Plants

▶ These colorful poppies, found growing on the Kenai Peninsula in Alaska, are only one example of the thousands of species of flowering plants that inhabit the Earth.

548

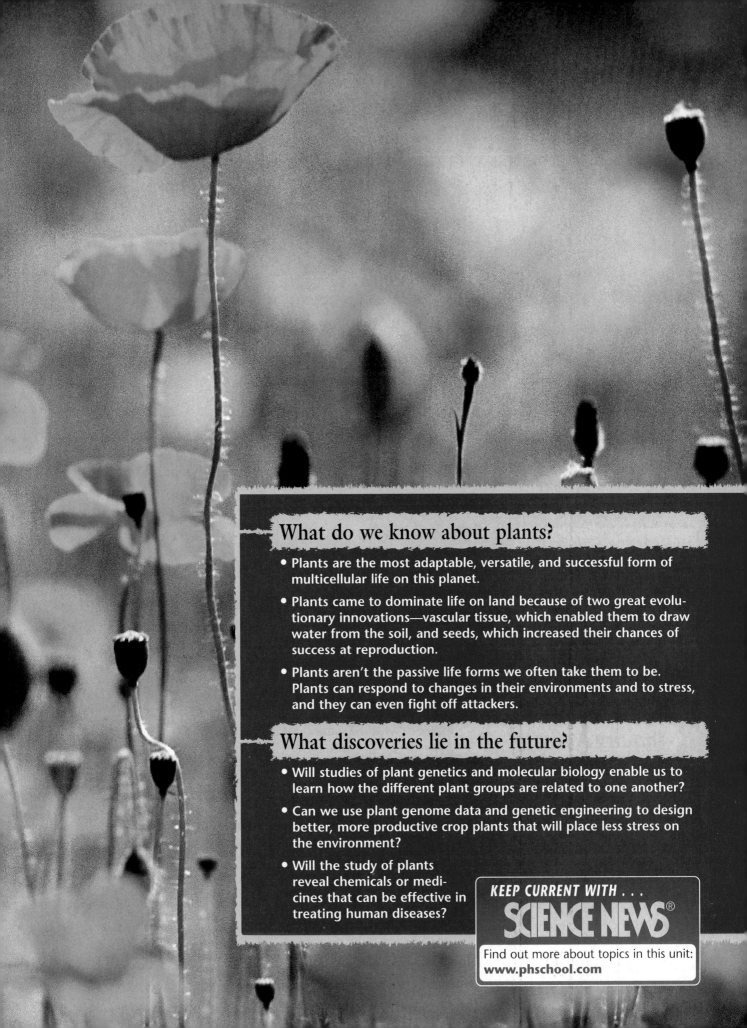

What do we know about plants?

- Plants are the most adaptable, versatile, and successful form of multicellular life on this planet.

- Plants came to dominate life on land because of two great evolutionary innovations—vascular tissue, which enabled them to draw water from the soil, and seeds, which increased their chances of success at reproduction.

- Plants aren't the passive life forms we often take them to be. Plants can respond to changes in their environments and to stress, and they can even fight off attackers.

What discoveries lie in the future?

- Will studies of plant genetics and molecular biology enable us to learn how the different plant groups are related to one another?

- Can we use plant genome data and genetic engineering to design better, more productive crop plants that will place less stress on the environment?

- Will the study of plants reveal chemicals or medicines that can be effective in treating human diseases?

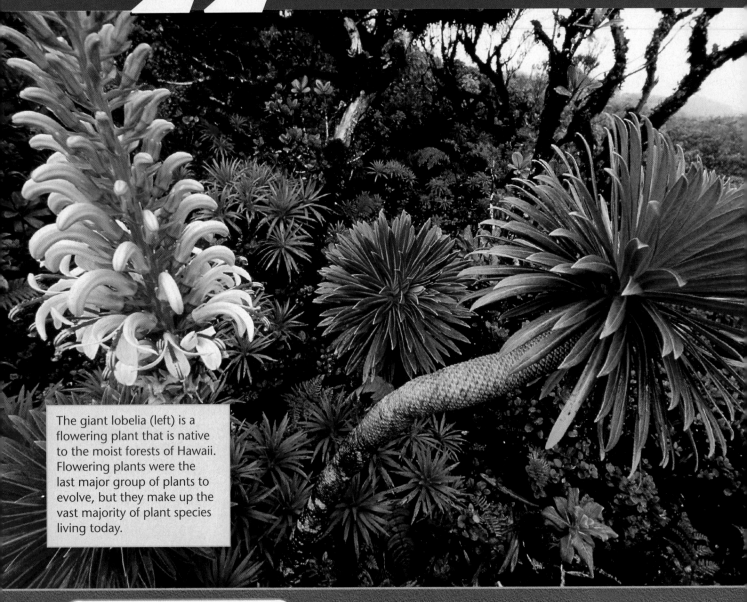

The giant lobelia (left) is a flowering plant that is native to the moist forests of Hawaii. Flowering plants were the last major group of plants to evolve, but they make up the vast majority of plant species living today.

Inquiry Activity

Are all plants the same?

Procedure

1. Obtain three plants, a metric ruler, and a hand lens.

2. Construct a table for recording your data.

3. Identify the major parts of each plant. Measure the heights of the plants and the sizes of their parts.

4. Use the hand lens to examine the plants. Record any other observations you make.

Think About It

1. **Comparing and Contrasting** How are the three plants alike? How do they differ?

2. **Inferring** What are the functions of the major parts of each plant?

3. **Classifying** Use your observations to classify the three plants into two groups. Explain your reasons for classifying them in these groups.

22–1 Introduction to Plants

What color is life? That's a silly question, of course, because living things can be just about any color. But consider it in a different way. Imagine yourself in a place on Earth where the sounds and scents of life are all around you. The place is so abundant with life that when you stand on the ground, living things blot out the sun. Now, what color do you see? If you have imagined a thick forest or a teeming jungle, then one color will fill the landscape of your mind—green—the color of plants.

Plants dominate the landscape. Where plants are plentiful, other organisms, such as animals, fungi, and microorganisms, take hold and thrive. Plants provide the base for food chains on land. They also provide shade, shelter, and oxygen for animals of every size and kind. The oldest fossil evidence of plants dates from about 470 million years ago. Since then, plants have colonized and transformed nearly every corner of Earth.

What Is a Plant?

Plants are members of the kingdom Plantae. **Plants are multicellular eukaryotes that have cell walls made of cellulose. They develop from multicellular embryos and carry out photosynthesis using the green pigments chlorophyll *a* and *b*.** Plants include trees, shrubs, and grasses as well as other organisms such as mosses and ferns. Most plants, including the one in **Figure 22–1,** are autotrophs, although a few are parasites or saprobes that live on decaying materials.

Plants are so different from animals that sometimes there is a tendency to think of them as not being alive. With few exceptions, plants do not gather food, nor do they move about or struggle directly with their predators. Plants can neither run away from danger nor strike blows against an adversary. But as different as they are from animals, plants are everywhere. How have they managed to be so successful?

That question has many answers. In the next few chapters, we will explore some of them. For now, it might help to think of plants as a well-known botanist once described them—as "stationary animals that eat sunlight"!

Guide for Reading

Key Concepts
- What is a plant?
- What do plants need to survive?
- How did the first plants evolve?

Vocabulary
gametophyte
sporophyte

Reading Strategy: Using Prior Knowledge
Before you read the chapter, make a list of the different groups of plants that you know. As you read, revise your list to include new information about plant groups.

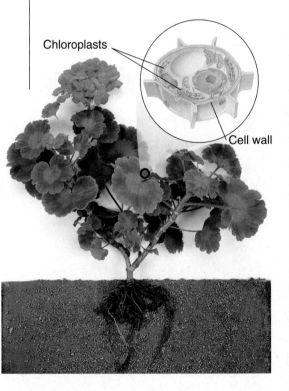

▶ **Figure 22–1** All plants are multicellular eukaryotes that have cell walls made of cellulose. Their leaves appear green because of the photosynthetic pigments chlorophyll *a* and *b*, which are located in chloroplasts.

Chloroplasts

Cell wall

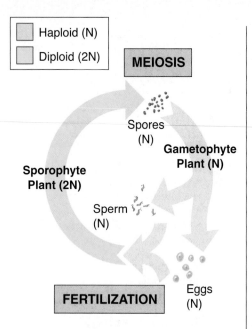

Haploid (N)
Diploid (2N)

MEIOSIS

Spores (N)

Gametophyte Plant (N)

Sporophyte Plant (2N)

Sperm (N)

FERTILIZATION

Eggs (N)

▲ **Figure 22–2** All plants have a life cycle with alternation of generations, in which the haploid gametophyte phase alternates with the diploid sporophyte phase. **Interpreting Graphics** *What stage in the life cycle is produced by fertilization?*

▼ **Figure 22–3** All plants need sunlight, water, minerals, oxygen, carbon dioxide, and a way to move water and nutrients to all their cells. Adaptations allow them to live in even the driest locations, such as this desert.

The Plant Life Cycle

Plants have life cycles that are characterized by alternation of generations, as shown in **Figure 22–2.** As you learned in Chapter 20, the two generations are the haploid (N) **gametophyte,** or gamete-producing plant, and the diploid (2N) **sporophyte,** or spore-producing plant. Recall that gametes—eggs and sperm—are haploid cells that fuse together to produce a new diploid individual. Spores are reproductive cells that produce a new individual by mitosis. Although all plants have a gametophyte stage and a sporophyte stage, their forms differ dramatically from phylum to phylum.

To be fully terrestrial, plants must be able to reproduce in dry environments where there is no water through which gametes can move from plant to plant. Seed plants have evolved reproductive cycles that are carried out independently of water. Many plants also have forms of vegetative, or asexual, reproduction.

What Plants Need to Survive

Surviving as stationary organisms on land is a difficult task, and plants have developed a number of adaptations that make them successful. 🔑 **The lives of plants revolve around the need for sunlight, water and minerals, gas exchange, and the movement of water and nutrients throughout the plant body.**

Sunlight Plants use the energy from sunlight to carry out photosynthesis. As a result, every plant displays adaptations shaped by the need to gather sunlight. Photosynthetic organs such as leaves are typically broad and flat and are arranged on the stem so as to maximize light absorption.

Water and Minerals All cells require a constant supply of water. For this reason, plants must obtain and deliver water to all their cells—even those that grow above ground in the dry air. Water is one of the raw materials of photosynthesis, so it is used up quickly when the sun is shining. Sunny conditions, such as those in the desert shown in **Figure 22–3,** can cause living tissues to dry out. Thus, plants have developed structures that limit water loss.

As they absorb water, plants also absorb minerals. Minerals are nutrients in the soil that are needed for plant growth.

Gas Exchange Plants require oxygen to support respiration as well as carbon dioxide to carry out photosynthesis. They must exchange these gases with the atmosphere without losing excessive amounts of water through evaporation.

Movement of Water and Nutrients Plants take up water and minerals through their roots but make food in their leaves. Most plants have specialized tissues that carry water and nutrients upward from the soil and distribute the products of photosynthesis throughout the plant body. Simpler types of plants carry out these functions by diffusion.

"Plantastic" Voyage

You are part of a team that is planning a space mission that will send astronauts into space for two years. As part of their food, the astronauts will be growing yam plants, *Dioscorea composita*. Your job is to develop a plan to help plants grow on the spacecraft.

Defining the Problem In your own words, state the problem at hand.

Organizing Information Research the types of conditions these plants would need. What requirements would the plants have for moisture? Soil conditions? Light intensity? Day length?

Creating a Solution Make a detailed scale drawing of a container for growing 10 of these plants. (*Dioscorea* plants are vines; assume that each is 10 cm long and 0.5 cm wide.) Determine what material(s) you will use for your container. As you devise your plan, be sure to keep a journal in which you record your team's ideas, drawings, data, and other information.

Presenting Your Plan Prepare a multimedia presentation for your classmates as if they were the managers of the space mission. Describe how your team solved the problem, the sources of information you used, the design itself, and what you learned during the project.

Early Plants

For most of Earth's history, plants did not exist. Life was concentrated in oceans, lakes, and streams. Algae and photosynthetic prokaryotes added the oxygen to our planet's atmosphere and provided food for animals and microorganisms.

When plants appeared, much of the existing life on Earth changed. As these new photosynthetic organisms colonized the land, they changed the environment in ways that made it possible for other organisms to develop. New ecosystems emerged, and organic matter began to form soil. How did plants adapt to the conditions of life on land? How plants evolved structures that acquire, transport, and conserve water is the key to answering this question.

Origins in the Water You may recall from Chapter 20 that green algae, shown in **Figure 22–4,** are photosynthetic, plantlike protists. Many of these algae are multicellular. 🔑 **The first plants evolved from an organism much like the multicellular green algae living today.** Multicellular green algae have the size, color, and appearance of plants. But the resemblance of many green algae to plants is more than superficial. They have reproductive cycles that are similar to those of plants. In addition, green algae have cell walls and photosynthetic pigments that are identical to those of plants.

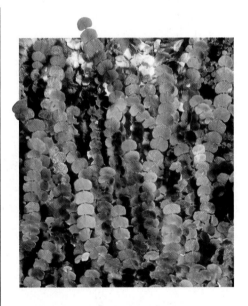

▲ **Figure 22–4** 🔑 **The first plants evolved from an organism much like the modern multicellular green algae.** The alga *Halimeda* is found in Honduras in Central America. It has many cellular features in common with plants.

✓**CHECKPOINT** *What was the greatest "challenge" to plants as they began to live on land?*

▲ **Figure 22–5** One of the earliest fossil plants was *Cooksonia*, which looked similar to mosses living today. *Cooksonia* had simple branched stalks that bore reproductive structures at their tips. **Inferring** *Which structures of this early plant seem to be adapted to carry out photosynthesis? To obtain water and minerals?*

The First Plants The first true plants were still dependent on water to complete their life cycles. But before long, the demands of life on land favored the evolution of plants that were more resistant to the drying rays of the sun, more capable of conserving water, and more capable of reproducing on dry land. Early plants were similar to today's mosses in that they were simple in structure and grew close to the ground. **Figure 22–5** shows how these plants may have looked. Soon these early plants were common in damp and swampy regions, just as most mosses are today.

From these plant pioneers, several major groups of plants evolved. One group developed into mosses and their relatives. Another lineage gave rise to all the other plants on Earth today—ferns, cone-bearing plants, and flowering plants. All of these groups of plants are now successful in living on dry land, but they have evolved very different adaptations for a wide range of terrestrial environments.

✔ **CHECKPOINT** *To what group of living plants were early plants most similar?*

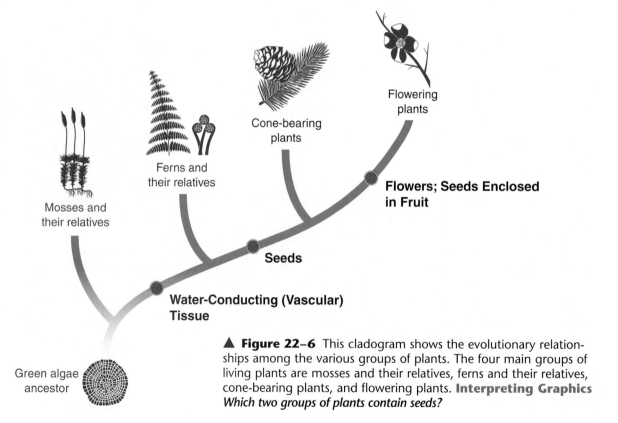

▲ **Figure 22–6** This cladogram shows the evolutionary relationships among the various groups of plants. The four main groups of living plants are mosses and their relatives, ferns and their relatives, cone-bearing plants, and flowering plants. **Interpreting Graphics** *Which two groups of plants contain seeds?*

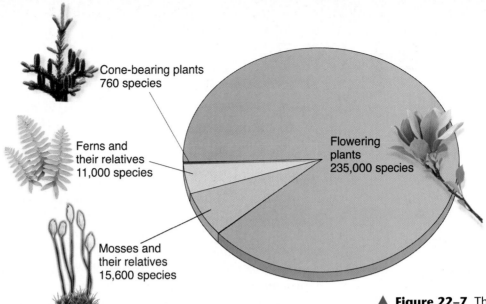

Cone-bearing plants
760 species

Ferns and
their relatives
11,000 species

Mosses and
their relatives
15,600 species

Flowering
plants
235,000 species

▲ **Figure 22–7** The great majority of plants alive today are angiosperms, which are also known as flowering plants. **Interpreting Graphics** *What is the second largest group of plants?*

Overview of the Plant Kingdom

Botanists divide the plant kingdom into four groups based on three important features: water-conducting tissues, seeds, and flowers. The relationship of these groups is shown in **Figure 22–6.** There are, of course, many other features by which plants are classified, including reproductive structures and body plan.

Today, plant scientists can classify plants more precisely by comparing the DNA sequences of various species. Since 1994, a team of biologists from twelve nations has begun to change our view of plant relationships. Their project, known as Deep Green, has provided strong evidence that the first plants evolved from green algae that lived in fresh water, not in the sea as had been thought.

In the rest of this chapter, we will explore how important plant traits evolved over the course of millions of years. In particular, we will examine the success of the flowering plants. As shown in **Figure 22–7,** flowering plants consist of 235,000 species—almost 90 percent of all living species of plants.

KEEP CURRENT WITH . . .

SCIENCE NEWS®

To find out more about the topics in this chapter, go to: **www.phschool.com**

22–1 Section Assessment

1. **Key Concept** What features distinguish plants from other organisms?

2. **Key Concept** To live successfully on land, what substances must plants obtain from their environment?

3. **Key Concept** From which group of protists did the first plants evolve? How are plants similar to these protists?

4. **Critical Thinking Comparing and Contrasting** Compare the gametophyte and sporophyte stages of the plant life cycle. Which is haploid? Which is diploid?

TEXT **Assessment** Use iText to review the important concepts in Section 22–1.

MAKING CONNECTIONS

Cell Structure How do the cells of plants differ from those of animals? How are they different from those of fungi? Refer to Chapters 7 and 21 for help in answering this question.

22–2 Bryophytes

Guide for Reading

Key Concepts
- What adaptations of bryophytes enable them to live on land?
- What are the three groups of bryophytes?
- How do bryophytes reproduce?

Vocabulary
bryophyte
rhizoid
gemma
protonema
antheridium
archegonium

Reading Strategy:
Using Visuals
Before you read, preview **Figure 22–11,** which shows the life cycle of a moss. In your own words, describe the basic process of reproduction shown. As you read the section, add information that you learn about reproduction in bryophytes.

In the cool forests of the northern woods, the moist ground is carpeted with green. When you walk, this soft carpet feels spongy. Look closely and you will see the structure of this carpet—mosses. Mosses and their relatives are generally called **bryophytes** (BRY-oh-fyts), or nonvascular plants. Unlike all other plants, these organisms do not have vascular tissues, or specialized tissues that conduct water and nutrients. **Bryophytes have life cycles that depend on water for reproduction. Lacking vascular tissue, these plants can draw up water by osmosis only a few centimeters above the ground.** This arrangement keeps them relatively small.

During at least one stage of their life cycle, bryophytes produce sperm that must swim through water to reach the eggs of other individuals. Therefore, they must live in places where there is rainfall or dew for at least part of the year.

Groups of Bryophytes

The most recognizable feature of bryophytes is that they are low-growing plants that can be found in moist, shaded areas. Where water is in regular supply—in habitats from the polar regions to the tropics—these plants thrive. **Bryophytes include mosses, liverworts, and hornworts.** Today, most botanists classify these groups of plants in three separate phyla.

Mosses The most common bryophytes are mosses, which are members of the phylum Bryophyta (bry-OH-fy-tuh). Mosses grow most abundantly in areas with water—in swamps and bogs, near streams, and in rain forests. Bryophytes are well adapted to life in wet habitats and nutrient-poor soils. Many mosses can tolerate low temperatures, allowing them to grow in harsh environments where other plants cannot. In fact, mosses are the most abundant plants in the polar regions.

Mosses vary in appearance from miniature evergreen trees to small, filamentous plants that together form a threadlike carpet of green, as shown in **Figure 22–8.** The moss plants that you might have observed on a walk through the woods are actually clumps of gametophytes growing close together. When mosses reproduce, they produce thin stalks, each containing a capsule. This is the sporophyte stage, as shown in **Figure 22–9.** Each moss plant has a thin, upright shoot that looks like a stem with tiny leaves. These are not true stems or leaves, however, because they do not contain vascular tissue.

◀ **Figure 22–8** Mosses grow best in moist environments, such as on the rocks by this waterfall. **Like all bryophytes, mosses have life cycles that depend on water for reproduction.**

Because the "leaves" of mosses are only one cell thick, these plants lose water quickly if the surrounding air is dry. The lack of vascular tissues also means that mosses do not have true roots. Instead, they have **rhizoids,** which are long, thin cells that anchor them in the ground and absorb water and minerals from the surrounding soil. Water moves from cell to cell through the rhizoids and into the rest of the plant.

Liverworts If you have come across odd little plants that look almost like flat leaves attached to the ground, you have probably seen a liverwort, shown in **Figure 22–10.** These plants belong to the phylum Hepaticophyta (hih-pat-ik-OH-fy-tuh) and get their name from the fact that some species resemble the shape of a liver. Liverworts in their gametophyte stage are broad and thin structures that draw up moisture directly from the surface of the soil. When the plants mature, the gameto-phytes produce structures that look like tiny green umbrellas. These "umbrellas" carry the structures that produce eggs and sperm.

Liverworts can also reproduce asexually by means of gem-mae. **Gemmae** (JEM-ee; singular: gemma) are small multicellu-lar spheres that contain many haploid cells. In some species of liverworts, gemmae are produced in cuplike structures called gemma cups. When washed out of the gemma, these cells can divide by mitosis to produce a new individual.

Hornworts Hornworts are members of the phylum Anthocerophyta (an-thoh-sehr-UH-fy-tuh). Like the liverworts, hornworts are generally found only in soil that is damp nearly year-round. Their gametophytes look very much like those of liverworts. The hornwort sporophyte, however, looks like a tiny green horn.

✔CHECKPOINT *How do bryophytes reproduce asexually?*

▲ **Figure 22–9** This illustration shows the structure of a typical moss plant. The green photosyn-thetic portion is the gametophyte. The brown structure on the tip of the gametophyte is the sporo-phyte. **Applying Concepts** *Which stage of the moss plant provides nutrients for the other stage?*

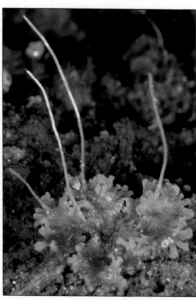

◀ **Figure 22–10** Bryophytes include liverworts and horn-worts. The liverworts (left) pro-duce gametes in structures that look like little green umbrellas. The tiny cuplike structures on the liver-worts are gemma cups. The horn-worts (right) have sporophytes that look like tiny green horns.

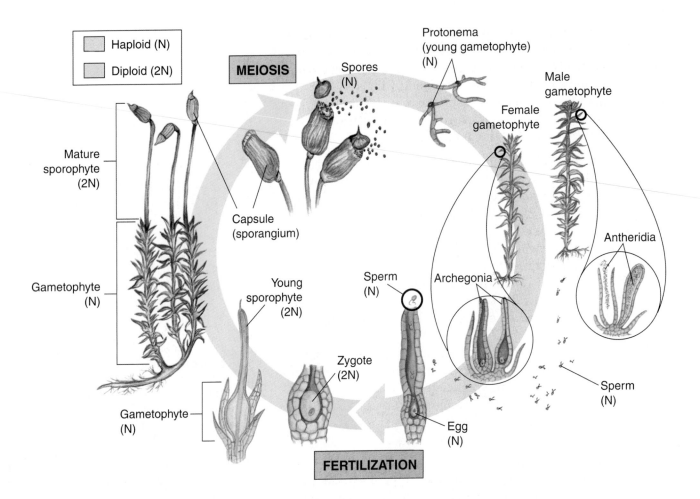

Haploid (N)
Diploid (2N)

MEIOSIS

Spores (N)

Protonema (young gametophyte) (N)

Male gametophyte

Female gametophyte

Mature sporophyte (2N)

Capsule (sporangium)

Antheridia

Gametophyte (N)

Young sporophyte (2N)

Sperm (N)

Archegonia

Zygote (2N)

Sperm (N)

Gametophyte (N)

Egg (N)

FERTILIZATION

▲ **Figure 22–11** 🔑 In bryophytes, the gametophyte is the dominant, recognizable stage of the life cycle and is the form that carries out photosynthesis. Sporophytes, which produce haploid spores, grow at the top of the gametophyte plant. When the spores are ripe, they are shed from the capsule like pepper from a shaker. In some species, gametes (sperm and eggs) are produced on separate male and female gametophyte plants.

Life Cycle of Bryophytes

Like all plants, bryophytes reproduce with alternation of generations. 🔑 **In bryophytes, the gametophyte is the dominant, recognizable stage of the life cycle and is the stage that carries out most of the plant's photosynthesis.** The sporophyte is dependent on the gametophyte for supplying water and nutrients.

Dependence on Water For fertilization to occur, the sperm of a bryophyte must swim to an egg. The sperm may swim through standing water or through a coating of water left by dew. Sometimes raindrops can splash sperm from one plant to another. Because of this limit to reproduction, bryophytes must live in habitats where water is available.

Life Cycle of a Moss The life cycle of a moss, shown in **Figure 22–11,** helps illustrate how bryophytes reproduce. When a moss spore lands in a moist place, it germinates and grows into a mass of tangled green filaments called a **protonema** (proh-toh-NEE-muh). As the protonema grows, it forms rhizoids that grow into the ground and shoots that grow into the air. These shoots grow into the familiar green moss plants, which are the gametophyte stage of its life cycle.

✓ **CHECKPOINT** *What is a protonema?*

Gametes are formed in reproductive structures at the tips of the gametophytes. Sperm with whiplike tails are produced in **antheridia** (an-thur-ID-ee-uh; singular: antheridium), and egg cells are produced in **archegonia** (ahr-kuh-GOH-nee-uh; singular: archegonium). Some species produce both sperm and eggs on the same plant, whereas other species produce sperm and eggs on separate plants. Once sperm are released and reach egg cells, fertilization produces a diploid zygote. This zygote is the beginning of the sporophyte stage of the life cycle. It grows directly out of the body of the gametophyte and actually depends on it for water and nutrients. The mature sporophyte is a long stalk ending in a capsule that looks like a saltshaker. Inside the capsule, haploid spores are produced by meiosis. When the capsule ripens, it opens and haploid spores are scattered to the wind to start the cycle again.

Human Use of Mosses

Sphagnum (SFAG-num) mosses are a group of mosses that thrive in the acidic water of bogs. Dried sphagnum moss absorbs many times its own weight in water and thus acts as a sort of natural sponge. In certain environments the dead remains of sphagnum accumulate to form thick deposits of peat. Peat can be cut from the ground, as shown in **Figure 22–12**, and then burned as a fuel.

Peat moss is also used in gardening. Gardeners add peat moss to the soil because it improves the soil's ability to retain water. Peat moss also has a low pH, so when added to the soil it increases the soil's acidity. Some plants, such as azaleas, grow well only if they are planted in acidic soil.

▼ **Figure 22–12** The compacted remains of sphagnum moss may eventually form thick deposits of peat. When it is cut and dried, it can be burned to produce heat. Peat has been used as a form of fuel in Ireland for many centuries. **Inferring** *What can you infer about the climate of an area where sphagnum moss grows abundantly in peat bogs?*

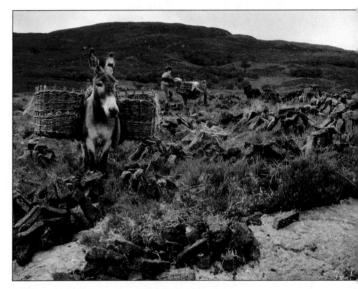

22–2 Section Assessment

1. **Key Concept** How is water essential in the life cycle of a bryophyte?

2. **Key Concept** List the three groups of bryophytes. In what type of habitat do they live?

3. **Key Concept** What is the relationship between the gametophyte and the sporophyte in mosses and other bryophytes?

4. What is an archegonium? An antheridium? How are these structures important in the life cycle of a moss?

5. **Critical Thinking Inferring** What characteristic of bryophytes is responsible for their small size? Explain.

TEXT **Assessment** Use iText to review the important concepts in Section 22–2.

Take It to the NET
Find out more about sphagnum moss. Then, write a paragraph about the growth, harvesting, and use of sphagnum moss. Use the links provided in the Biology area at the Prentice Hall Web site for help in completing this activity: **www.phschool.com**

22-3 Seedless Vascular Plants

Guide for Reading

 Key Concepts
• How is vascular tissue important to ferns and their relatives?
• What are the characteristics of the three phyla of seedless vascular plants?
• What are the stages in the life cycle of ferns?

Vocabulary
• vascular tissue • tracheid
• xylem • phloem • lignin
• root • vein • leaf • stem
• rhizome • frond
• sporangium • sorus

Reading Strategy:
Building Vocabulary
Before you read, preview new vocabulary by skimming the section and making a list of the boldfaced terms. Leave space to make notes about each term as you read.

As you have read, bryophytes have only one way of transporting water—from cell to cell by osmosis. This fact limits them to just a few centimeters in height. About 420 million years ago, something remarkable happened. In just a few million years, plants grew to a whole new scale on the landscape. The small, mosslike plants were still around, of course, just as they are today. But now, they were joined by plants that were more than a meter in height, and others that were as large as small trees. What had happened? Fossil evidence shows that these plants contained **vascular tissue,** a type of tissue that is specialized to conduct water and nutrients through the body of the plant.

Evolution of Vascular Tissue

The first vascular plants had a new type of cell that was specialized to conduct water. **Tracheids** (TRAY-kee-idz), shown in **Figure 22–13,** were one of the great evolutionary innovations of the plant kingdom. They are the key cells in **xylem** (ZY-lum), a form of vascular tissue that carries water upward from the roots to every part of a plant. Tracheids are hollow cells with thick cell walls that resist pressure. Within a plant, they are connected end to end like a series of drinking straws. Tracheids allow water to move through a plant much more efficiently than by diffusion alone.

Vascular plants also possess a second type of vascular tissue called phloem. **Phloem** (FLOH-um) transports solutions of nutrients and carbohydrates produced by photosynthesis. Like xylem, the main cells of phloem are long and specialized to move fluids throughout the plant body. **Both forms of vascular tissue—xylem and phloem—can move fluids throughout the plant body, even against the force of gravity.**

Vascular plants also evolved the ability to produce **lignin,** a substance that makes cell walls rigid. The presence of lignin allows vascular plants to grow upright and to reach great heights.

Vascular tissue

◀ **Figure 22–13** Vascular tissue conducts **water and nutrients throughout the plant body.** It also provides support for the leaves and other organs of the plant. The two types of vascular tissue are xylem, which conducts water, and phloem, which conducts solutions of nutrients. The cross section (top) shows the vascular tissue in a club moss. The bottom photo shows a much-magnified view of tracheids from the xylem of a white pine.

Ferns and Their Relatives

🔑 **Seedless vascular plants include club mosses, horsetails, and ferns.** The most numerous phylum of these is the ferns.

Like other vascular plants, ferns and their relatives have true roots, leaves, and stems. **Roots** are underground organs that absorb water and minerals. Water-conducting tissues are located in the center of the root. **Leaves** are photosynthetic organs that contain one or more bundles of vascular tissue. This vascular tissue is gathered into **veins** made of xylem and phloem. **Stems** are supporting structures that connect roots and leaves, carrying water and nutrients between them.

Club Mosses What was once a large and ancient group of land plants—phylum Lycophyta (ly-KOH-fy-tuh)—exists now as a much smaller group that includes the club mosses. Once, ancient club mosses grew into huge trees—up to 35 meters tall—and some produced Earth's first forests. The fossilized remains of these forests exist today as huge beds of coal.

Today, club mosses are small plants that live in moist woodlands and near streambeds and marshes. *Lycopodium,* the common club moss shown in **Figure 22–14,** looks like a miniature pine tree. For this reason it is also called "ground pine."

Horsetails The only living genus of Arthrophyta (ahr-THROH-fy-tuh) is *Equisetum,* which is a plant that grows about a meter tall. Like the club mosses, *Equisetum* has true leaves, stems, and roots. Its leaves are arranged in distinctive whorls at joints along the stem. *Equisetum* is called horsetail, or scouring rush, because its stems look similar to horses' tails and contain crystals of abrasive silica. During Colonial times, horsetails were commonly used to scour pots and pans.

✓**CHECKPOINT** *What chemical makes the stems of* **Equisetum** *abrasive?*

Club Moss

Horsetail

Figure 22–14 🔑 **Club mosses and horsetails are seedless vascular plants.** The club moss *Lycopodium* (left) looks like a tiny pine tree growing on the forest floor. The only living genus of Arthrophyta is *Equisetum,* or horsetail (above).

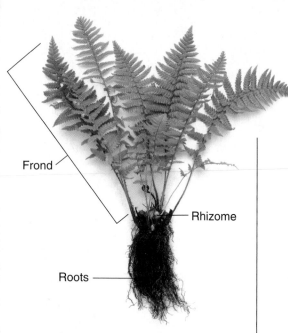

▲ **Figure 22–15** Ferns are easily recognized because of their delicate leaves, which are called fronds. Fronds grow from a rhizome, which grows horizontally through the soil. **Applying Concepts** *Is the plant shown a sporophyte or a gametophyte?*

Ferns Ferns, members of phylum Pterophyta (tehr-OH-fy-tuh), probably evolved about 350 million years ago, when great club moss forests covered the ancient Earth. Ferns have survived during the Earth's long history in numbers greater than any other group of spore-bearing vascular plants. More than 11,000 species of ferns are living today.

Ferns have true vascular tissues, strong roots, creeping or underground stems called **rhizomes,** and large leaves called **fronds,** shown in **Figure 22–15.** Ferns can thrive in areas with little light. They are most abundant in wet, or at least seasonally wet, habitats around the world. They are often found living in the shadows of forest trees, where direct sunlight hardly penetrates the forest's leafy umbrella. Ferns are found in great numbers in the rain forests of the Pacific Northwest. In tropical forests, some species grow as large as small trees.

Life Cycle of Ferns

The large plants we recognize as ferns are actually diploid sporophytes. **Ferns and other vascular plants have a life cycle in which the diploid sporophyte is the dominant stage.** Fern sporophytes produce haploid spores on the underside of their fronds in tiny containers called **sporangia** (spoh-RAN-jee-uh; singular: sporangium). Sporangia are grouped into clusters called **sori** (SOH-ry; singular: sorus), shown in **Figure 22–16.** Spores released from sporangia may be carried by wind and water over long distances.

When the spores germinate, they develop into haploid gametophytes. The small gametophyte first grows a set of rootlike rhizoids. It then flattens into a thin, heart-shaped, green structure that is the mature gametophyte. Although it is tiny, the gametophyte grows independently of the sporophyte.

The antheridia and archegonia are found on the underside of the gametophyte. As in bryophytes, fertilization requires at least a thin film of water, allowing the sperm to swim to the eggs. The diploid zygote produced by fertilization immediately begins to grow into a new sporophyte plant. As the sporophyte grows, the gametophyte withers away. Fern sporophytes often live for many years. In some species, the fronds produced in the spring die in the fall, but the rhizomes live through the winter and sprout again the following spring.

▶ **Figure 22–16** Many clusters of sporangia—each called a sorus—form on the underside of fern leaves. In each sporangium, cells undergo meiosis to produce spores. **Inferring** *Are these spores haploid or diploid?*

Sorus

▲ **Figure 22–17** ◯ **In the life cycle of a fern, the dominant and recognizable stage is the diploid sporophyte.** The tiny, heart-shaped gametophyte grows close to the ground and relies on dampness for the sperm it produces to fertilize an egg. The young sporophyte grows from the gametophyte.

22–3 Section Assessment

1. ◯ **Key Concept** What are the two types of vascular tissue? Describe the function of each.

2. ◯ **Key Concept** What are the three phyla of seedless vascular plants? Give an example of each.

3. ◯ **Key Concept** What is the dominant stage of the fern life cycle? What is the relationship of the fern gametophyte and sporophyte?

4. **Critical Thinking Inferring** The size of plants increased dramatically with the evolution of vascular tissue. How might these two events be related?

ⓘ**TEXT** **Assessment** Use iText to review the important concepts in Section 22–3.

22–4 Seed Plants

Guide for Reading

Key Concepts
- What adaptations allow seed plants to reproduce without standing water?
- What are the four groups of gymnosperms?

Vocabulary
gymnosperm
angiosperm
cone
flower
pollen grain
pollination
seed
embryo
seed coat

Reading Strategy:
Building Vocabulary As you read, make notes about the meaning of each term listed above. After you have read the section, draw a concept map to show the relationship among these terms.

Whether they are acorns, pine nuts, dandelion seeds, or kernels of corn, seeds can be found everywhere. Seeds are so common, in fact, that their importance may be overlooked. Over millions of years, plants with a single trait—the ability to form seeds—became the most dominant group of photosynthetic organisms on land.

Seed plants are divided into two groups: gymnosperms and angiosperms. **Gymnosperms** (JIM-noh-spurmz) bear their seeds directly on the surfaces of cones, whereas **angiosperms** (AN-jee-oh-spurmz), which are also called flowering plants, bear their seeds within a layer of tissue that protects the seed. Gymnosperms include the conifers, such as pines and spruces, as well as palmlike plants called cycads, ancient ginkgoes, and the very weird gnetophytes. Angiosperms include grasses, flowering trees and shrubs, and all wildflowers and cultivated species of flowers. The angiosperms are discussed in Section 22–5. This section begins by exploring some of the reasons that seed plants became so successful.

Reproduction Free From Water

Like all plants, seed plants have a life cycle that alternates between a gametophyte stage and a sporophyte stage. Unlike mosses and ferns, however, seed plants do not require water for fertilization of gametes. As a result, seed plants can live just about anywhere—from moist habitats that are often dominated by seedless plants, to dry and cold habitats where most seedless plants cannot survive. **Adaptations that allow seed plants to reproduce without water include flowers or cones, the transfer of sperm by pollination, and the protection of embryos in seeds.**

Cones and Flowers The gametophytes of seed plants grow and mature within sporophyte structures called **cones,** which are the seed-bearing structures of gymnosperms, and **flowers,** which are the seed-bearing structures of angiosperms. The cones of a common gymnosperm are shown in **Figure 22–18.** The gametophyte generations of seed plants live inside these reproductive structures.

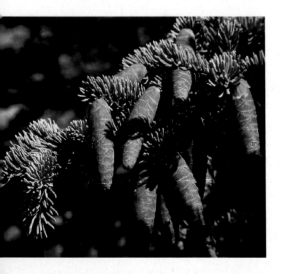

◀ **Figure 22–18** ⚬ Adaptations that allow seed plants to reproduce without water include reproduction in flowers or cones, the transfer of sperm by pollination, and the protection of embryos in a seed. Gymnosperms, such as this spruce tree, bear their seeds on the scales of cones.

Pollen In seed plants, the entire male gametophyte is contained in a tiny structure called a **pollen grain.** Sperm produced by this gametophyte do not swim through water to fertilize the eggs. Instead, the pollen grain is carried to the female gametophyte by wind, insects, birds, small animals, or sometimes even bats. The transfer of pollen from the male gametophyte to the female gametophyte is called **pollination.**

Seeds A **seed** is an embryo of a plant that is encased in a protective covering and surrounded by a food supply. An **embryo** is the early developmental stage of the sporophyte plant. The seed's food supply provides nutrients to the embryo as it grows. The **seed coat** surrounds and protects the embryo and keeps the contents of the seed from drying out. Seeds may also have special tissues or structures that aid in their dispersal to other habitats. Some seed coats are textured so that they stick to the fur or feathers of animals. Other seeds are contained in fleshy tissues that are eaten and dispersed by animals.

After fertilization, the zygote contained within a seed grows into a tiny plant—the embryo. The embryo often stops growing while it is still small and contained within the seed. The embryo can remain in this condition for weeks, months, or even years. When the embryo begins to grow again, it uses nutrients from the stored food supply. As a result of this strategy, seeds can survive long periods of bitter cold, extreme heat, or drought—beginning to grow only when conditions are once again right.

CHECKPOINT *What is a pollen grain?*

A

Seed

B

Wing

▲ **Figure 22–19** This cross section shows the internal structure of the seed of a pine tree. **Predicting** *How might the food stored in the seed affect the reproductive success of the pine tree?*

Quick Lab

How do seeds differ from spores?

Materials Fern frond with sori, microscope, scalpel, microscope slide, coverslip, dropper pipette, peanuts in the shell, brown paper bag, hand lens

Procedure
1. Use a scalpel to scrape sori from the underside of a fern frond onto a microscope slide. Add a drop of water and a coverslip and examine the slide under the low power objective of a microscope. Sketch a few spores. **CAUTION:** *Use care with the scalpel.*
2. **CAUTION:** *Do not perform Steps 2 and 3 if you are allergic to nuts.* Open a peanut shell. Separate the two halves, or cotyledons, of a seed. Examine both halves with a hand lens and sketch the embryo.
3. Rub the nut on brown paper and hold the paper up to the light. A bright spot indicates lipids.

Analyze and Conclude
1. **Observing** What evidence did you observe that nutrients are stored in peanut seeds?
2. **Predicting** A spore and a seed are deposited in an area where the soil is poor in nutrients. Based on your observations in this activity, which is more likely to survive in a nutrient-poor environment—the spore or the seed? Explain.
3. **Formulating Hypotheses** What are the advantages of a plant disseminating millions of tiny spores as it reproduces? What are the advantages of a plant disseminating a relatively few seeds?

▲ **Figure 22–20** Seed ferns are part of the fossil record. They represent a link between ferns that do not form seeds and seed plants. This ancient plant had leaves that resemble the leaves of modern ferns. **Comparing and Contrasting** *If this plant were alive, what structures would distinguish it from a fern?*

Figure 22–21 The *Welwitschia* plant (below), a type of gnetophyte, is an odd desert plant that produces only two leaves during its entire life. Cones are produced at the bases of the two leaves. **Classifying** *In what phylum is this plant classified?*

Evolution of Seed Plants

The ancestors of seed plants evolved a variety of new adaptations that enabled them to survive in many places in which most mosses and ferns could not—from frigid mountains to scorching deserts. The most important of these adaptations was the seed.

Mosses and ferns underwent major adaptive radiations during the Carboniferous and Devonian periods, 300 to 400 million years ago. During these periods, land environments were much wetter than they are today. Tree ferns and other seedless plants grew into lush forests that covered much of Earth. Over a period of millions of years, however, continents became much drier, making it harder for seedless plants to survive and reproduce. For that reason, many moss and fern species became extinct. They were replaced by seed plants with adaptations that equipped them to deal with drier conditions.

Fossils of seed-bearing plants exist from almost 360 million years ago. As shown in **Figure 22–20**, some of these early seed plants outwardly resembled ferns. Seed fern fossils document several evolutionary stages in the development of the seed.

The early seed plants reached every landmass on Earth. Together with now-extinct seed ferns and other seedless vascular plants, seed plants formed dense forests and swamps that spread over much of what is now the eastern United States. Their remains now exist in the form of coal deposits.

Gymnosperms—Cone Bearers

The most ancient surviving seed plants are the gymnosperms. 🔑 **Gymnosperms include gnetophytes, cycads, ginkgoes, and conifers.** These plants all reproduce with seeds that are exposed—gymnosperm means "naked seed."

Gnetophytes About 70 present-day species of the phylum Gnetophyta (nee-TOH-fy-tuh) are known, placed in just three genera. The reproductive scales of these plants are clustered into cones. *Welwitschia,* an inhabitant of the Namibian desert in southwestern Africa, is one of the most remarkable gnetophytes. It has only two huge leathery leaves, shown in **Figure 22–21**, which grow continuously and spread across the ground. The genus *Ephedra* grows in the American southwest and is sometimes known as Mormon tea.

Cycads Cycads, members of the phylum Cycadophyta (si-kad-OH-fy-tuh), are beautiful palmlike plants that reproduce with large cones, as shown in **Figure 22–22.** Cycads first appeared in the fossil record during the Triassic Period, 225 million years ago. Huge forests of cycads thrived when dinosaurs roamed Earth. Today, only nine genera of cycads exist. Cycads can be found growing naturally in tropical and subtropical places such as Mexico, the West Indies, Florida, and parts of Asia, Africa, and Australia.

Ginkgoes Ginkgoes were common when dinosaurs were alive, but today the phylum Ginkgophyta (ging-KOH-fy-tuh) contains only one species, *Ginkgo biloba.* The living ginkgo species looks similar to its fossil ancestors, so it is truly a living fossil. In fact, *Ginkgo biloba,* also shown in **Figure 22–22,** may be one of the oldest seed plant species alive today. Ginkgo trees were carefully cultivated in China, where they were often planted around temples. Ginkgoes are now often planted in urban settings in the United States, where their toughness and resistance to air pollution make them popular shade trees.

CHECKPOINT *How many different species of ginkgoes exist?*

Conifers By far the most common gymnosperms, with more than 500 known species, are the conifers. The phylum Coniferophyta (koh-nif-er-OH-fy-tuh) includes pines, spruces, firs, cedars, sequoias, redwoods, and yews. Some conifers, such as the bristlecone pine tree at right, can live for more than 4000 years. Other species, such as giant redwoods, can grow to more than 100 meters in height.

Figure 22–22 Cycads, ginkgoes, and conifers are gymosperms. Cycads (top left) produce seeds in reproductive structures that look like giant pinecones. The bristlecone pine (top right) is a conifer that can live for thousands of years. The ginkgo tree (bottom) is sometimes called a "living fossil" because it has changed little over millions of years.

Figure 22–23 These longleaf pines in North Carolina grow in an area that receives abundant rainfall. Yet water sinks quickly through the sandy soil, limiting the availability of water to tree roots. In this environment, the pines' water-conserving needles (inset) are an adaptation that contributes to the trees' survival. **Predicting** *What might happen to a tree with large, flat leaves planted in this environment? Explain.*

Ecology of Conifers Today, conifers thrive in a wide variety of habitats: on mountains, in sandy soil, and in cool, moist areas such as the temperate rain forest of the Pacific Northwest. Surprisingly, conifer leaves have specific adaptations to dry conditions. How did these adaptations develop? Scientists have hypothesized that more than 250 million years ago, when conifers evolved, climate conditions were dry and cool. In response to these conditions, most conifers developed leaves that are long and thin, like the pine needles in **Figure 22–23.** This shape reduces the surface area from which water can be lost by evaporation. Another water-conserving adaptation is the thick, waxy layer that covers conifer leaves. In addition, the openings of leaves that allow for gas exchange are located in cavities below the surface of the leaves, also reducing water loss.

Most conifers are "evergreens"—that is, they retain their leaves throughout the year. The needles of most conifer species remain on the plant for 2 to 14 years. Older needles are gradually replaced by new needles, so the trees never become bare. However, not all species are evergreen. Larches and bald cypresses, for example, lose their needles every fall.

22–4 Section Assessment

1. **Key Concept** What are the main characteristics of seed plants?

2. **Key Concept** What are the different groups of gymnosperms?

3. What major change in Earth's climate favored the evolution of seed plants?

4. **Critical Thinking Applying Concepts** Pollination is a process that occurs only in seed plants. What process in seedless plants is analogous to pollination?

TEXT **Assessment** Use iText to review the important concepts in Section 22–4.

ALTERNATIVE ASSESSMENT

Creative Writing
Suppose you could visit Earth as it was about 300 million years ago, when gymnosperms were the dominant plants and angiosperms had not yet developed. Write a story that describes a forest landscape of this period.

22–5 Angiosperms—Flowering Plants

Flowering plants, or angiosperms, are members of the phylum Anthophyta (an-THOH-fy-tuh). Flowering plants first appeared during the Cretaceous Period, about 135 million years ago, making their origin the most recent of all plant phyla. Flowering plants originated on land and quickly came to dominate Earth's plant life. The vast majority of living plant species reproduce with flowers.

Flowers and Fruits

🔑 **Angiosperms have unique reproductive organs known as flowers.** In general, flowers are an evolutionary advantage to plants because they attract animals such as bees, moths, or hummingbirds, which then transport pollen from flower to flower. This means of pollination is much more efficient than the wind pollination of most gymnosperms.

🔑 **Flowers contain ovaries, which surround and protect the seeds.** The presence of an ovary gives angiosperms their name: Angiosperm means "enclosed seed." After pollination, the ovary develops into a fruit, which protects the seed and aids in its dispersal.

The unique angiosperm **fruit**—a thick wall of tissue surrounding the seed—is another reason for the success of these plants. When an animal eats a fruit, seeds from the core of the fruit generally enter the animal's digestive system. By the time these seeds leave the digestive system—ready to sprout—the animal may have traveled many kilometers. By using fruit to attract animals, flowering plants increase the ranges they inhabit, spreading seeds over hundreds of square kilometers.

Guide for Reading

🔑 **Key Concepts**
- What are the characteristics of angiosperms?
- What are monocots and dicots?
- What are the three categories of plant life spans?

Vocabulary
fruit
monocot
dicot
cotyledon
annual
biennial
perennial

Reading Strategy: Finding Main Ideas
Angiosperms are the most diverse group of plants. As you read, make notes of the ways by which their diversity can be organized.

◀ **Figure 22–24** 🔑 Angiosperms have unique reproductive structures known as flowers, which contain ovaries that surround and protect the seeds. Apple flowers (left) produce seeds inside ovaries, which mature into fruits (right).

Diversity of Angiosperms

The angiosperms are an incredibly diverse group. Not surprisingly, there are many different ways of categorizing these plants. These include monocots and dicots; woody and herbaceous plants; and annuals, biennials, and perennials. As you read about each category, keep in mind that the categories can overlap. An iris, for example, is a monocot plant that is also an herbaceous perennial. These categories simply provide a way of appreciating and organizing the diversity of angiosperms.

Monocots and Dicots There are two classes within the angiosperms: the Monocotyledonae, or **monocots,** and the Dicotyledonae, or **dicots.** The general characteristics of both groups are shown in **Figure 22–25.** Monocots and dicots **are named for the number of seed leaves, or cotyledons, in the plant embryo. Monocots have one seed leaf, and dicots have two.** Other differences include the distribution of vascular tissue in stems, roots, and leaves, and the number of petals per flower. Monocots include corn, wheat, lilies, orchids, and palms. Dicots include roses, clover, tomatoes, oaks, and daisies.

✓**CHECKPOINT** *What is a cotyledon?*

Figure 22–25 Monocots and dicots are named for the number of seed leaves, or cotyledons, in the plant embryo. The table compares the characteristics of monocots and dicots.

Characteristics of Monocots and Dicots

	Monocots		Dicots	
Seeds	Single cotyledon		Two cotyledons	
Leaves	Parallel veins		Branched veins	
Flowers	Floral parts often in multiples of 3		Floral parts often in multiples of 4 or 5	
Stems	Vascular bundles scattered throughout stem		Vascular bundles arranged in a ring	
Roots	Fibrous roots		Taproot	

Botanical Illustrator

Job Description: work in a museum, outdoors, in a botanical garden, or at home to illustrate plants and organisms related to the plants

Education: two- or four-year college degree in an art school or other school noted for its art and design department

Skills: ability to observe nature; artistic talent; knowledge of biology; detail oriented; knowledge of the Internet, library, and museum research sources

Highlights: You provide illustrations that help people understand and appreciate biology. You have the pleasure of taking people of all ages on exciting visual adventures into the world of plants.

Linda Seabrooks Campbell is a professional botanical and science illustrator who finds great satisfaction in passing on her knowledge to students. "I take kids on nature hikes," she says, "and show them how to identify and make illustrations of plants."

Take It to the NET

For more career information visit the Prentice Hall Web site: **www.phschool.com**

Woody and Herbaceous Plants The flowering plants can be subdivided into various groups according to the characteristics of their stems. One of the most important and noticeable stem characteristics is woodiness. Woody plants are made primarily of cells with thick cell walls that support the plant body. Woody plants include trees, shrubs, and vines. Shrubs are typically smaller than trees, and vines have stems that are long and flexible. Examples of woody vines are grapes and ivy. Examples of shrubs include blueberries, rhododendrons, and roses.

Plant stems that are smooth and nonwoody are characteristic of herbaceous plants. Herbaceous plants do not produce wood as they grow. Examples of herbaceous plants include dandelions, zinnias, petunias, and sunflowers.

Annuals, Biennials, and Perennials If you've ever planted a garden, you know that many flowering plants grow, flower, and die in a single year. Other types of plants continue to grow from year to year. The lifespan of plants is determined by a combination of genetic and environmental factors. Many long-lived plants continue growing despite yearly environmental fluctuations. However, harsh environmental conditions can shorten the life of other plants. ⚷ **There are three categories of plant life spans: annual, biennial, and perennial.**

Word Origins

Annual comes from the Latin word *annus,* which means "year." The Latin prefix *bi-* means "two." **Based on the characteristics of perennials, what do you think the Latin prefix *per-* means?**

Figure 22–26 Categories of plant life spans include annuals, biennials, and perennials. Zinnias (left) are annual plants, which germinate, grow to maturity, set seed, and die in one growing season. Biennials such as the evening primrose (middle) grow roots, stems, and seeds in their first year, then produce flowers and seeds in their second year. Perennials such as peonies (right) live through many years.

Some plants grow from seed to maturity, flower, produce seeds, and die all in the course of one growing season. Flowering plants that complete a life cycle within one growing season are called **annuals.** Annuals include many garden plants, such as marigolds, petunias, pansies, and the zinnias in **Figure 22–26.** Wheat and cucumbers are also annuals.

Angiosperms that complete their life cycle in two years are called **biennials** (by-EN-ee-ulz). In the first year, biennials germinate and grow roots, very short stems, and sometimes leaves. During their second year, biennials grow new stems and leaves and then produce flowers and seeds. Once the flowers produce seeds, the plant dies. Evening primrose, parsley, celery, and foxglove are biennials.

Flowering plants that live for more than two years are called **perennials.** Perennials usually live through many years. Some perennials, such as peonies, asparagus, and many grasses, have herbaceous stems that die each winter and are replaced in the spring. Most perennials, however, have woody stems. Palm trees, sagebrush, maple trees, and honeysuckle are examples of woody perennials.

22–5 Section Assessment

1. **Key Concept** What reproductive structures are unique to angiosperms? Briefly describe the function of each.

2. **Key Concept** What are monocots and dicots?

3. **Key Concept** How do annuals, biennials, and perennials differ?

4. Compare the growth forms of plants with woody stems and those with herbaceous stems.

5. **Critical Thinking Forming Hypotheses** Which are more likely to be dispersed by animals—the seeds of an angiosperm or the spores of a fern? Explain your reasoning.

TEXT **Assessment** Use iText to review the important concepts in Section 22–5.

ALTERNATIVE ASSESSMENT

Classifying
Prepare a display comparing two specific plants, one monocot and one dicot. On this display, write a brief summary of the basic differences between these two types of angiosperms.

Comparing Mosses and Ferns

As plants evolved from their aquatic ancestors, they adapted to increasingly drier environments. In this investigation, you will compare a moss and a fern to determine which plant is better adapted for life in a dry environment.

Problem Are ferns or mosses better adapted for life in a dry environment?

Materials
- fern plant
- clump of moss plants
- hand lens
- forceps
- microscope slide
- dropper pipette
- coverslip
- compound microscope

Skills Observing, Comparing and Contrasting

Procedure

1. Carefully examine a fern frond. Record whether the surface of the frond is shiny or dull.

2. Gently bend the fern frond back and forth. Record whether the frond bends easily.

3. Remove a few moss plants from the clump of moss. Gently bend one plant back and forth. Record whether the moss bends easily.

4. Use a hand lens to examine a fern leaf. Note whether there are veins in the leaf. Draw and label a diagram of what you observe.

5. Use a forceps to gently transfer a single moss plant from the clump of moss to the center of a clean microscope slide. Use a dropper pipette to place a drop of water on top of the moss plant. Cover the moss with a coverslip.

6. Examine the leafy top of the moss plant under the low-power objective of your microscope. Note whether there are veins in the moss. Draw and label a diagram of what you observe.

Analyze and Conclude

1. **Inferring** Was the surface of the fern frond shiny? What substance on the surface of the fern accounts for this observation? How does this substance help ferns to live on dry land?

2. **Observing** Did you observe veins in the fern? In the moss?

3. **Comparing and Contrasting** Which plant was firmer—the fern or the moss? How can you explain this difference?

4. **Formulating Hypotheses** Why do you think the fern is able to grow larger than the moss?

5. **Drawing Conclusions** Which of the plants shows adaptations that make it better able to survive in a dry environment? Explain your answer.

Go Further

Observing Use a microscope to examine prepared slides of cross sections of mosses and ferns. Draw and label what you see. Where do you see vascular tissue?

Chapter 22 Study Guide

22–1 Introduction to Plants
 Key Concepts

- Plants are multicellular eukaryotes that have cell walls made of cellulose. They develop from multicellular embryos and carry out photosynthesis using the green pigments chlorophyll *a* and *b*.
- The lives of plants revolve around the need for sunlight, water and minerals, gas exchange, and the movement of water and nutrients throughout the plant body.
- The first plants evolved from an organism much like the multicellular green algae living today.

Vocabulary
gametophyte, p. 552
sporophyte, p. 552

22–2 Bryophytes
Key Concepts

- Bryophytes have life cycles that depend on water for reproduction. Lacking vascular tissue, these plants can draw up water by osmosis only a few centimeters above the ground.
- Bryophytes include mosses, liverworts, and hornworts.
- In bryophytes, the gametophyte is the dominant, recognizable stage of the life cycle and is the stage that carries out most of the plant's photosynthesis.

Vocabulary
- bryophyte, p. 556 • rhizoid, p. 557
- gemma, p. 557 • protonema, p. 558
- antheridium, p. 559 • archegonium, p. 559

22–3 Seedless Vascular Plants
Key Concepts

- Both forms of vascular tissue—xylem and phloem—can move fluids throughout the plant body, even against the force of gravity.
- Seedless vascular plants include club mosses, horsetails, and ferns.
- Ferns and other vascular plants have a life cycle in which the diploid sporophyte is the dominant stage.

Vocabulary
- vascular tissue, p. 560 • tracheid, p. 560
- xylem, p. 560 • phloem, p. 560
- lignin, p. 560 • root, p. 561
- leaf, p. 561 • vein, p. 561 • stem, p. 561
- rhizome, p. 562 • frond, p. 562
- sporangium, p. 562 • sorus, p. 562

22–4 Seed Plants
Key Concepts

- Adaptations that allow seed plants to reproduce in areas without water include flowers or cones, the transfer of sperm by pollination, and the protection of embryos in seeds.
- Gymnosperms include gnetophytes, cycads, ginkgoes, and conifers.

Vocabulary
- gymnosperm, p. 564 • angiosperm, p. 564
- cone, p. 564 • flower, p. 564
- pollen grain, p. 565 • pollination, p. 565
- seed, p. 565 • embryo, p. 565
- seed coat, p. 565

22–5 Angiosperms—Flowering Plants
Key Concepts

- Angiosperms have unique reproductive organs known as flowers. Flowers contain ovaries, which surround and protect the seeds.
- Monocots and dicots are named for the number of seed leaves, or cotyledons, in the plant embryo. Monocots have one seed leaf, and dicots have two.
- There are three categories of plant life spans: annual, biennial, and perennial.

Vocabulary
- fruit, p. 569 • monocot, p. 570 • dicot, p. 570
- cotyledon, p 570 • annual, p. 572
- biennial, p. 572 • perennial, p. 572

Thinking Visually

Using the information in this chapter, make a compare-and-contrast table comparing bryophytes, ferns, gymnosperms, and angiosperms. Compare these groups of plants in terms of reproduction (seeds or seedless), tissues (vascular or nonvascular), typical size, and type of habitat.

Chapter 22

Part A

Multiple Choice
For each statement or question, select the number of the word or expression that, of those given, best completes the statement or answers the question.

1 Which is *not* a characteristic of plants?
   (1) eukaryotic
   (2) cell walls contain chitin
   (3) multicellular
   (4) contain chlorophyll

2 The first plants evolved from
   (1) brown algae
   (2) green algae
   (3) red algae
   (4) golden algae

3 The most recognizable stage of a moss is the
   (1) sporophyte   (3) archegonium
   (2) protonema   (4) gametophyte

4 Water is carried upward from the roots to every part of a plant by
   (1) cell walls   (3) cuticle
   (2) phloem   (4) xylem

5 To which group does the plant shown below belong?
   (1) bryophytes   (3) gymnosperms
   (2) ferns   (4) angiosperms

6 In angiosperms, the mature seed is surrounded by a
   (1) cone   (3) fruit
   (2) flower   (4) cotyledon

7 Parsley is an herb that has a life cycle that lasts two years. It is called a
   (1) bryophyte   (3) biennial
   (2) monocot   (4) perennial

8 Plants with seeds produced on the surfaces of cones are
   (1) gymnosperms
   (2) angiosperms
   (3) monocots
   (4) dicots

9 Which is *not* a basic requirement of plants?
   (1) sunlight
   (2) carbon monoxide
   (3) water
   (4) carbon dioxide

10 Cones contain which of these structures?
    A gametophytes
    B spores
    C seeds
    (1) A, only   (3) A and B
    (2) B, only   (4) A and C

11 During the life cycle of a moss, what environmental condition is necessary before fertilization can occur?
    (1) sunlight   (3) high temperature
    (2) water   (4) wind

For questions 12 and 13, complete each analogy by selecting the correct number. In analogies, A : B :: C : means "A is to B as C is to ___?___."

12 Gymnosperms : cones :: angiosperms :
    (1) seeds   (3) leaves
    (2) stems   (4) flowers

13 Monocots : grasses :: dicots :
    (1) day lilies
    (2) two seed leaves
    (3) oak trees
    (4) flowers

Test-Taking Tip If you find particular questions difficult, put a light pencil mark beside them and keep working. (Do not write in this book.) As you answer later questions, you may find information that helps you answer the difficult questions.

Parts B and C

Multiple Choice and Extended Response

For those questions that ask you to select a response, choose the one that best completes the statement or answers the question. For all others follow the directions given.

14 On a separate sheet of paper, copy the chart below. Then, complete the chart by writing the following terms for the correct definitions: gymnosperm, angiosperm, pollen grain, fruit, and cotyledon. (Do not write in this book.)

Definiton	Term
Male gametophyte	
Cone-bearing plant	
Seed leaf	
Flowering Plant	
Plant ovary	

Base your answers to questions 15 and 16 on the information and photograph below and on your knowledge of biology.

The plant below has leaves with parallel veins and flowers with six petals.

15 Is this plant a monocot or dicot? Support your answer with an explanation.

16 What changes would be necessary to make this plant belong to the other class of angiosperm? Include characteristics of leaves, flowers, stems, and roots.

Base your answers to questions 17 through 19 on the information and graph below and on your knowledge of biology.

A group of students placed a sprig of the pondweed, *Elodea*, in a beaker of water. They measured the amount of oxygen given off during a set period of time to determine the rate of photosynthesis. They changed the temperature of the beaker using an ice bucket and a hot plate. Their data are summarized in the graph below.

17 What is the manipulated (independent) variable in the students' investigation?
 (1) light intensity   **(3)** oxygen bubbles
 (2) temperature   **(4)** photosynthesis rate

18 Which variables should the students have held constant?
 A Plant type
 B Temperature
 C Light intensity
 (1) A, only   **(3)** A and C, only
 (2) B, only   **(4)** A, B, and C

19 What is an appropriate conclusion based on the graph?
 (1) The higher the temperature, the more oxygen bubbles are released.
 (2) There is an optimum temperature for photosynthesis in this species of *Elodea*.
 (3) All plants are most efficient at 30°C.
 (4) Temperature has no effect on photosynthesis.

Base your answers to questions 20 through 23 on the information below and on your knowledge of biology.

Recently taxonomists have added several kingdoms to the classification system of living things. Mostly these additions have come about as scientists try to organize different types of unicellular organisms. Overall, there have not been many changes in the classification system for the plant kingdom.

20 Write an essay explaining the classification system for the plant kingdom. Be sure to include

   • four groups of plants

   • the important features used to organize these groups

   • the role of DNA in classification

21 Taxonomists often use fossil evidence to help them classify organisms. What does this evidence show about the origin of the earliest plants?

22 A cladogram is a graphic representation of evolutionary relationships. Draw a cladogram to show how the four groups of plants are related.

23 Use the cladogram and what you know about natural selection to explain how the first nonvascular land plants might have evolved into vascular plants. How would this evolution help the plant?

---

24 Moss plants are small. Ferns can grow as tall as a small tree. Explain why this is so.

25 A friend of yours lives in a desert area of New Mexico. She wants to grow a garden of mosses and liverworts. What environmental conditions would she need to maintain in her garden for it to be successful?

26 One botanist described a seed as "a ship that carries a plant on a voyage to colonize a new land." Describe the role of each part of the seed in this voyage.

27 What adaptations allow conifers to live in dry habitats?

28 How do fruits aid in the dispersal of angiosperms?

29 How was the ability to produce lignin significant to the evolution of plants?

30 The plant below is called *Cooksonia*. At one time, scientists thought that it was the ancestor of all land plants. Suggest how this plant may have been similar to, yet different from, a modern flowering plant such as a geranium.

31 Propose a hypothesis to explain why angiosperms have become the dominant type of plant on Earth.

32 During World War I, the British army used sterilized sphagnum moss to bandage millions of wounds. What properties of sphagnum moss make it suitable for use in bandages?

Take It to the NET

How many kinds of bryophytes are there? Visit the Prentice Hall Web site at **www.phschool.com** to find out about bryophytes in North America. Then, answer the following questions:

• Describe the project undertaken by the New York Botanical Garden.

• How many bryophyte specimens does the New York Botanical Garden have from the United States and Canada?

• How many species of bryophytes have been identified so far?

• What organizations are working on this project with the New York Botanical Garden? List at least five organizations.

23 Roots, Stems, and Leaves

Throughout this cross section of a spruce bud are the different cells and tissues that make up a plant.

Inquiry Activity

What parts of plants do we eat?

Procedure

1. Examine an onion, a potato, and an artichoke. Record your observations as notes and labeled sketches.
2. Use your observations to classify each vegetable as a root, stem, leaf, or other plant part.

Think About It

1. **Classifying** How did you classify the onion? Explain what characteristics you used to make this decision.
2. **Inferring** How did you classify the potato? How is its structure related to its function?
3. **Inferring** How did you classify the artichoke? What does its inner structure tell you about its function?

23–1 Specialized Tissues in Plants

Have you ever wondered if plants were really alive? Day after day, they just seem to sit there, quiet and unmoving. Compared to animals, plants don't seem to do much. Yet, in one sense, plants have been more successful than animals. Individual plants outnumber animals and also make up far more of Earth's biomass. So, it's only fair to admit that plants must be doing something right. And so they are.

If you look deep inside a living plant, that first impression of inactivity vanishes. Instead, you will find a busy and complex organism packed with specialized cells and tissues. Materials are moving throughout the plant, and growth and repair are taking place continually. Plants may act at a pace that you consider slow, but the ways in which their cells act together are remarkably effective in ensuring the survival of plants.

Structure of Seed Plants

The cells of a seed plant are organized into different tissues and organs, as shown in **Figure 23–1** on page 580. **The three principal organs of seed plants are roots, stems, and leaves.**

Roots Roots perform several important functions. They absorb water and dissolved nutrients from moist soil. They anchor plants in the ground. Roots also hold plants upright and prevent them from being knocked over by wind and rain. Roots are able to do all these jobs because as they grow, they develop complex branching networks that penetrate the soil and grow between soil particles.

Stems The stem is the part of the plant that supports the plant body and transports nutrients among different parts of the plant. To compete with other plants for sunlight, many plants have very tall stems that hold a plant's leaves up to the sun. The leaves of a tree can be as high as 100 meters above the ground. To support this weight, the stems of tall plants are sturdy and contain great amounts of vascular tissue that supplies the plant with water and nutrients. The vascular tissue of stems lifts water from roots up to the leaves and sends the products of photosynthesis from the leaves down to the roots.

Leaves Leaves are the principal organs in which plants carry out photosynthesis. The broad, flat surfaces of leaves help increase the amount of sunlight absorbed by plants. Leaves also expose a great deal of tissue to the dryness of the air and must, therefore, be protected against water loss. Adjustable pores in leaves help conserve water while allowing oxygen and carbon dioxide to enter and leave the leaf.

Guide for Reading

Key Concepts
• What are the principal organs and tissues of vascular plants?
• How is meristematic tissue different from other plant tissues?
• What specialized cells make up vascular tissue?

Vocabulary
meristematic tissue
apical meristem
epidermal cell
cuticle
trichome
vessel element
sieve tube element
companion cell
parenchyma
collenchyma
sclerenchyma

Reading Strategy:
Building Vocabulary
Before you read, preview new vocabulary by skimming the section and making a list of the boldfaced terms. Leave space to make notes of definitions as you read.

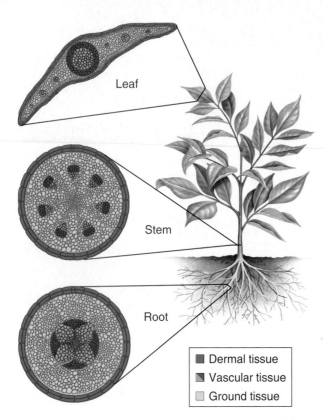

Leaf

Stem

Root

■ Dermal tissue
◣ Vascular tissue
□ Ground tissue

◀ **Figure 23–1** Vascular plants consist of roots, stems, and leaves. Each of these organs contains dermal tissue, vascular tissue, and ground tissue, as shown by the cross sections of the leaf, stem, and root. **Interpreting Visuals** *Which tissue is found in the center of a plant stem?*

Tissue Systems

Within the roots, stems, and leaves of plants are specialized tissue systems. **Plants consist of three tissue systems: dermal tissue, vascular tissue, and ground tissue.** In a sense, dermal tissue forms the "skin" of a plant in that it is the outermost layer of cells. Vascular tissue is like the plant's "bloodstream," transporting water and nutrients throughout the plant, and ground tissue is everything else. A fourth type of tissue, **meristematic tissue** (mehr-uh-stuh-MAT-ik), is found only in the tips of shoots and roots. **Figure 23–2** shows two examples of meristematic tissue, which is responsible for the growth that takes place throughout the life of a plant. It is described first because it is the source of all other tissues in a plant.

Meristematic Tissue

A distinguishing feature of plants is that they have an open, or indeterminate, type of growth. They grow and produce new, undifferentiated cells at their tips for as long as they live. Even a tree that is many years old and that has mature tissues throughout most of its body continually increases in height above ground and in length below ground.

Most mature plant cells do not divide to form new cells. New growth is instead produced in cells that make up meristematic tissue. **Meristematic tissue is the only plant tissue that produces new cells by mitosis.** All the cells of a plant originate in meristems and at first look alike: They divide rapidly and have thin cell walls. As meristematic cells mature, they differentiate into one of the three main tissues of a plant.

Meristematic tissue is found in several places in a plant. At the end, or tip, of each growing stem and root is an apical meristem. An **apical meristem** is a group of undifferentiated cells that divide to produce increased length of stems and roots. **Figure 23–2** shows the location and structure of a shoot apical meristem and a root apical meristem.

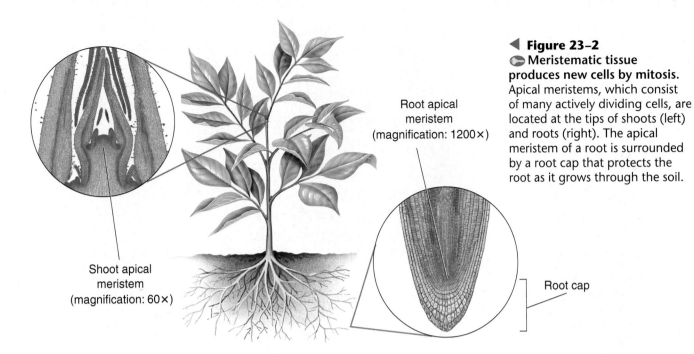

Root apical
meristem
(magnification: 1200×)

Shoot apical
meristem
(magnification: 60×)

Root cap

◀ Figure 23–2
Meristematic tissue produces new cells by mitosis. Apical meristems, which consist of many actively dividing cells, are located at the tips of shoots (left) and roots (right). The apical meristem of a root is surrounded by a root cap that protects the root as it grows through the soil.

Immediately behind each apical meristem, cells increase in size and length. Farther from the meristem, cells take on the structures and functions of mature cells. This ongoing process of cell division, maturation, elongation, and development causes the youngest, least mature cells in any plant to be closest to the meristems.

Many plants also grow in width as a result of meristematic tissue that lines the stems and roots of a plant. Later in the chapter, you will learn how this type of growth takes place.

Dermal Tissue

The outer covering of a plant consists of dermal tissue. Dermal tissue typically consists of a single layer of **epidermal cells,** shown in **Figure 23–3.** The exposed outer surfaces of these cells are often covered with a thick, waxy layer, or **cuticle,** that protects against water loss and injury. The surfaces of some leaves also have tiny cellular projections known as **trichomes** (TRY-kohmz), which help protect the leaf and also give it a fuzzy appearance. In roots, dermal tissue includes root hair cells that provide a large amount of surface area and aid in water absorption. On the underside of leaves, dermal tissue contains guard cells, which regulate water loss and gas exchange.

CHECKPOINT *What is the cuticle?*

▼ Figure 23–3 The photo shows the epidermis of the outer covering of a rosebud. The epidermis is covered with thin, unicellular trichomes as well as large, bulbous trichomes that secrete chemicals that protect the plant against insect attack (magnification: 150×). **Formulating Hypotheses** *Develop a hypothesis to explain how natural selection might have led to the development of plants with large trichomes.*

Cross Section of a Stem

Tracheid

Vessel element

Xylem

Companion cell

Sieve tube element

Phloem

▲ **Figure 23–4** 🔊Vascular tissue is made up of several different types of cells. Xylem consists of tracheids and vessel elements. Phloem consists of sieve tube elements and companion cells. Xylem tissue (left) conducts water from the roots to the rest of the plant. Phloem tissue (right) conducts a variety of materials, mostly carbohydrates, throughout a plant.

Vascular Tissue

Recall from the last chapter that vascular tissue transports water and nutrients throughout the plant. The principal types of vascular tissue are xylem, a water-conducting tissue, and phloem, a food-conducting tissue. 🔊**Vascular tissue contains several different cell types. Xylem consists of tracheids and vessel elements. Phloem consists of sieve tube elements and companion cells.** As you can see in **Figure 23–4**, xylem and phloem are made up of networks of hollow connected cells.

Xylem All seed plants have a type of xylem cell called a tracheid. Tracheids are long, narrow cells with walls that are impermeable to water. These walls, however, are pierced by openings that connect neighboring cells to one another. When tracheids mature, they die, and their cytoplasm disintegrates.

Angiosperms have another kind of xylem cell that is called a **vessel element.** Vessel elements are much wider than tracheids. Like tracheids, they mature and die before they conduct water. Vessel elements are arranged end to end on top of one another like a stack of tin cans. The cell walls at both ends are lost when the cells die, transforming the stack of vessel elements into a continuous tube through which water can move freely.

Phloem The main phloem cells are **sieve tube elements.** These cells are arranged end to end, like vessel elements, to form sieve tubes. The end walls of sieve tube elements have many small holes in them. Materials can move through these holes from one adjacent cell to another. As sieve tube elements mature, they lose their nuclei and most of the other organelles in their cytoplasm. The remaining organelles hug the inside of the cell wall. The rest of the space is a pipeline through which sugars and other foods are carried in a watery stream.

Companion cells are phloem cells that surround sieve tube elements. Companion cells keep their nuclei and other organelles throughout their lifetime. Companion cells support the phloem cells and aid in the movement of substances in and out of the phloem stream.

Ground Tissue

The cells that lie between dermal and vascular tissues make up the ground tissues shown in **Figure 23–5.** In most plants, ground tissue consists mainly of parenchyma. **Parenchyma** (puh-RENG-kih-muh) cells have thin cell walls and large central vacuoles surrounded by a thin layer of cytoplasm. In leaves, these cells are packed with chloroplasts and are the site of most of a plant's photosynthesis. Ground tissue may also contain two types of cells with thicker cell walls. **Collenchyma** (kuh-LENG-kih-muh) cells have strong, flexible cell walls that help support larger plants. Collenchyma cells make up the familiar "strings" of a stalk of celery. **Sclerenchyma** (sklih-RENG-kih-muh) cells have extremely thick, rigid cell walls that make ground tissue tough and strong.

Figure 23–5 Ground tissue is made of cells whose cell walls have different thicknesses. Parenchyma cells have thin walls and function mainly in storage and photosynthesis. The root cells shown are filled with purple-staining starch grains. Collenchyma and sclerenchyma cells both function in support. Collenchyma cells have irregularly shaped walls, but the walls of sclerenchyma cells are much thicker and harder. **Predicting** *Where would you expect to find more sclerenchyma—in the leaves or the stem of a plant?*

Parenchyma
(magnification: about 50×)

Collenchyma
(magnification: about 150×)

Sclerenchyma
(magnification: about 200×)

23–1 Section Assessment

1. 🔑 **Key Concept** List the three tissue systems of plants. Describe how each tissue is distributed in stems, tissues, and leaves.

2. 🔑 **Key Concept** What is the function of meristematic tissue in a plant?

3. 🔑 **Key Concept** What two cell types make up xylem? Phloem?

4. In a stem that needs to support heavy leaves, what type of ground tissue might you expect to find?

5. **Critical Thinking Comparing and Contrasting** The vascular system of a plant has been compared to the circulatory system of a human. How are these two systems similar? How are they different?

🧍 **TEXT** **Assessment** Use iText to review the important concepts in Section 23–1.

Take It to the NET

Choose one of the tissue systems in plants and make a concept map to show the different structures and types of cells formed by that system. Use the links provided in the Biology area of the Prentice Hall Web site for help in completing this activity: **www.phschool.com**

23–2 Roots

Guide for Reading

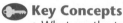

Key Concepts
- What are the two main types of roots?
- What are the main tissues in a mature root?
- What are the different functions of roots?

Vocabulary
taproot
fibrous root
root hair
cortex
endodermis
vascular cylinder
root cap
Casparian strip

Reading Strategy:
Outlining Before you read, use the headings of the section to make an outline about plant roots. As you read, fill in phrases or a sentence after each heading to provide key information.

As soon as a seed begins to grow, it puts out its first root to draw water and nutrients from the soil. Other roots soon branch out from this first root, adding length and surface area to the root system. With continued growth, the overall size of a plant's root system can be astonishing: The total surface area of the root system of a rye plant was measured at more than 600 square meters—130 times greater than the combined surface areas of stems and leaves.

Types of Roots

The two main types of roots are taproots, which are found mainly in dicots, and fibrous roots, which are found mainly in monocots. In some plants, the primary root grows long and thick while the secondary roots remain small. This type of primary root is called a **taproot,** shown in **Figure 23–6.** Taproots of oak and hickory trees grow so long that they can reach water far below the Earth's surface. Carrots, dandelions, beets, and radishes have short, thick taproots that store sugars or starches.

In other plants, such as grasses, **fibrous roots** branch to such an extent that no single root grows larger than the rest. The extensive fibrous root systems produced by many plants help prevent topsoil from being washed away by heavy rain.

✓ **CHECKPOINT** *How do roots help prevent erosion?*

▼ **Figure 23–6** Plants have taproots, fibrous roots, or both. Taproots have a central primary root and generally grow deep into the soil. Fibrous roots are usually shallow and consist of many thin roots.

Taproot   Fibrous Roots

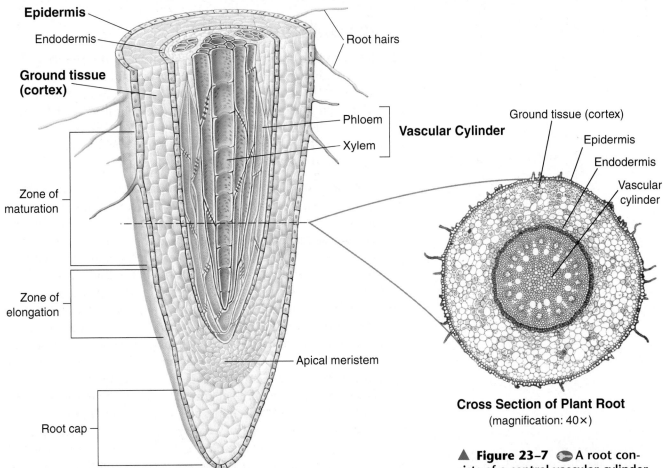

Epidermis

Endodermis

Ground tissue (cortex)

Root hairs

Phloem

Xylem

Vascular Cylinder

Zone of maturation

Zone of elongation

Apical meristem

Root cap

Ground tissue (cortex)

Epidermis

Endodermis

Vascular cylinder

Cross Section of Plant Root
(magnification: 40×)

Root Structure and Growth

You have already learned that roots contain cells from the three tissue systems. 🔑 **A mature root has an outside layer, the epidermis, and a central cylinder of vascular tissue. Between these two tissues lies a large area of ground tissue.** Refer to **Figure 23–7** as you read about the structure of a root. The epidermis of a root is covered with tiny projections called **root hairs.** These hairs penetrate the spaces between soil particles and produce a large surface area through which water can enter the plant. Just inside the epidermis is a spongy layer of ground tissue known as the **cortex.** This layer extends to another layer of cells called the **endodermis.** The endodermis completely encloses vascular tissue in a central region called the **vascular cylinder.**

Roots grow in length as their apical meristem produces new cells near the root tip. These fragile new cells are covered by a tough **root cap** that protects the root as it forces its way through the soil. As the root grows, the root cap secretes a slippery substance that lubricates the progress of the root through the soil. Cells at the very tip of the root cap are constantly being scraped away, and new root cap cells are continually added by the meristem. Most of the increase in root length occurs immediately behind the meristem, where cells are growing longer. At a later stage, these cells mature and take on specialized functions.

▲ **Figure 23–7** 🔑 A root consists of a central vascular cylinder surrounded by ground tissue and the epidermis. Root hairs along the surface of the root aid in water absorption. Only the cells in the root tip divide. In the area just behind the root tip, the newly divided cells increase in length, pushing the root tip farther into the soil. The root cap, located just ahead of the root tip, protects the dividing cells as they are pushed forward. Dicot roots, such as the one shown in the cross section, have a central column of xylem cells arranged in a radiating pattern.

Root Functions

🔑 **Roots anchor a plant in the ground and absorb water and dissolved nutrients from the soil.** How does a root go about the job of absorbing water and minerals from the soil? Although it might seem to, water does not just "soak" into the root from soil. It takes energy on the part of the plant to absorb water. Our explanation of this process begins with a description of soil and plant nutrients.

Uptake of Plant Nutrients An understanding of soil helps explain how plants function. Soil is a complex mixture of sand, silt, clay, air, and bits of decaying animal and plant tissue. Soil in different places and at different depths contains varying amounts of these ingredients. Sandy soil, for example, is made of large particles that retain few nutrients, whereas the finely textured silt and clay soils of the Midwest and southeastern United States are high in nutrients. The ingredients define the soil and determine, to a large extent, the kinds of plants that can grow in it.

To grow, flower, and produce seeds, plants require a variety of inorganic nutrients in addition to carbon dioxide and water. The most important of these nutrients are nitrogen, phosphorus, potassium, magnesium, and calcium. The functions of these essential nutrients within a plant are described in **Figure 23–8.** These nutrients are located in varying amounts in the soil and are drawn up by the roots of a plant. In addition to these essential nutrients, trace elements are required in small quantities to maintain proper plant growth. Trace elements include sulfur, iron, zinc, molybdenum, boron, copper, manganese, and chlorine. Large amounts of trace elements in the soil can be poisonous.

✓CHECKPOINT *What are essential nutrients and trace nutrients?*

▼ **Figure 23–8** Soil contains several nutrients that are essential for plant growth. Each nutrient plays a different role in plant functioning and development, and produces distinct effects when deficient in the soil. **Interpreting Graphics** *If you notice that a plant is becoming paler and more yellow, what nutrient might need to be added?*

Essential Plant Nutrients		
Nutrient	**Role in Plant**	**Result of Deficiency**
Nitrogen	Proper leaf growth and color; synthesis of amino acids, proteins, nucleic acids, and chlorophyll	Stunted plant growth; pale yellow leaves
Phosphorus	Synthesis of DNA; development of roots, stems, flowers, and seeds	Poor flowering; stunted growth
Potassium	Synthesis of proteins and carbohydrates; development of roots, stems, and flowers; resistance to cold and disease	Weak stems and stunted roots; edges of leaves turn brown
Magnesium	Synthesis of chlorophyll	Thin stems; mottled, pale leaves
Calcium	Cell growth and division; cell wall structure; cellular transport; enzyme action	Stunted growth; curled leaves

Epidermis

Cortex

Root hairs

Cortex

Phloem

Xylem

Vascular Cylinder

→ Active transport of minerals

→ Movement of water by osmosis

Endodermis

Casparian strip

Cell wall

Cell membrane

▲ **Figure 23–9** Roots absorb water and dissolved nutrients from the soil. Most water and minerals enter a plant through the tiny hairs on plant roots. Water moves from the outside of the roots into the cortex, then passes through the cells of the endodermis into the vascular cylinder. Finally, water reaches the xylem, where it is transported throughout the plant. Cells in the endodermis are made waterproof by the Casparian strip, which prevents water molecules from seeping back between the cells.

Active Transport of Minerals

The cell membranes of root hairs and other cells in the root epidermis contain active transport proteins. These proteins use ATP (an energy source) to pump mineral ions from the soil into the plant. The high concentration of mineral ions in the plant cells causes water molecules to move into the plant by osmosis, as shown in **Figure 23–9.**

You may recall that osmosis is the movement of water across a membrane toward an area where the concentration of dissolved material is higher. By using active transport to accumulate ions from the soil, cells of the root epidermis create conditions under which osmosis causes water to "follow" those ions and flow into the root. Note that the root does not actually pump water. But by pumping dissolved minerals into its own cells, it does almost the same thing.

Movement Into the Vascular Cylinder

Active transport in the cells of the root epidermis causes water and minerals to move into the cortex. From there, the water and dissolved minerals pass the inner boundary of the cortex and enter the endodermis. This process is shown in **Figure 23–9.**

The endodermis encloses the vascular cylinder and stretches up and down the entire length of the root, like a cylinder. It is composed of many individual cells, each shaped a bit like a brick. Each of these cells is surrounded on four sides by a waterproof strip called a **Casparian strip.** To imagine what the Casparian strip looks like, think of a brick with a thick, sticky rubber band stretched around four sides. The rubber bands stick together like mortar between the bricks. Now imagine many of these bricks placed edge to edge to build a cylinder. When a root is viewed in cross section, the endodermis looks like a circle.

Recall that water moves into the vascular cylinder by osmosis. Because water and minerals cannot pass through the waxy Casparian strip, once they pass through the endodermis, they are trapped in the vascular cylinder. As a result, there is a one-way passage of materials into the vascular cylinder in plant roots.

Root Pressure Why do plants "need" a system that ensures the one-way movement of water and minerals? That system is how the plant generates enough pressure to move water out of the soil and up into the body of the plant. As minerals are pumped into the vascular cylinder, more and more water follows by osmosis, producing a strong pressure. If the pressure were not contained, roots would expand as they filled with water.

Instead, contained within the Casparian strip, the water has just one place to go—up. Root pressure, produced within the cylinder by active transport, forces water through the vascular cylinder and into the xylem. As more water moves from the cortex into the vascular cylinder, more water in the xylem is forced upward through the root into the stem. In **Figure 23–10,** you can see a demonstration of root pressure in a carrot root. Root pressure is the starting point for the movement of water through the vascular system of the entire plant. But it is just the beginning. Once you have learned about stems and leaves, you will see how water and other materials are transported within an entire plant.

Glass tube

Water

Carrot root

◄ **Figure 23–10** As a carrot root absorbs water, root pressure forces water upward into the glass tube, which takes the place of the carrot plant in this demonstration. **Applying Concepts** *Would you expect root pressure to increase or decrease as you go up a plant? Explain your answer.*

23–2 Section Assessment

1. 🔑 **Key Concept** Compare a taproot and a fibrous root.

2. 🔑 **Key Concept** How are tissues distributed in a plant root?

3. 🔑 **Key Concept** Describe the two main functions of roots.

4. How is osmosis involved in the absorption of water and nutrients?

5. **Critical Thinking Inferring** Why is it important that the root endodermis permit only a one-way passage of materials?

🧍 **TEXT** Assessment Use iText to review the important concepts in Section 23–2.

ALTERNATIVE ASSESSMENT

Making a Diagram
Make two diagrams, one showing a root's structure and growth, the other showing how roots absorb water and nutrients. Label the diagrams and write brief descriptions of the processes shown in each.

23–3 Stems

What do a barrel cactus, a tree trunk, a dandelion stem, and a potato have in common? They are all types of stems. Stems vary greatly in size and shape. Some grow entirely underground; others reach far into the air. Stems also vary in their structure and internal arrangement of cells.

Stem Structure and Function

In general, stems have three important functions: They produce leaves, branches and flowers; they hold leaves up in the sunlight; and they transport substances between roots and leaves. The vascular tissue in stems conducts water, nutrients, and other compounds up and down the plant. Xylem and phloem tissues form continuous tubes from the roots through the stems to the leaves. These vascular tissues link all parts of the plant, allowing water and nutrients to be carried throughout the plant. Stems can also function in storage and photosynthesis.

Like the rest of the plant, the stem is composed of three tissue systems: dermal, vascular, and ground tissue. Stems are surrounded by a layer of epidermal cells that have thick cell walls and a waxy protective coating.

In most plants, stems contain distinct **nodes,** where leaves are attached, and **internode** regions between the nodes, as shown in **Figure 23–11.** Small buds are found where leaves attach to the nodes. **Buds** contain undeveloped tissue that can produce new stems and leaves. In larger plants, stems develop woody tissue that helps support leaves and flowers.

Guide for Reading

Key Concepts
- What are the three main functions of stems?
- How do monocot and dicot stems differ?
- How do primary growth and secondary growth occur in stems?

Vocabulary
- node • internode • bud
- vascular bundle • pith
- primary growth
- secondary growth
- vascular cambium
- cork cambium • heartwood
- sapwood • bark

Reading Strategy:
Using Visuals Before you read, preview the art in **Figure 23–15.** As you read the section, refer to this art to learn about the structure of mature woody stems.

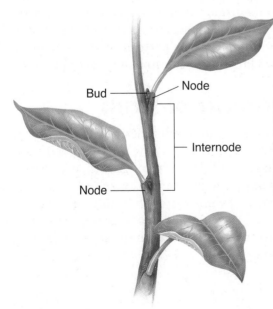

◀ **Figure 23–11** ⟳ Stems produce leaves and branches and hold leaves up to the sunlight, where they carry out photosynthesis. Leaves are attached to a stem at structures called nodes. These nodes are separated by regions of the stem called internodes.

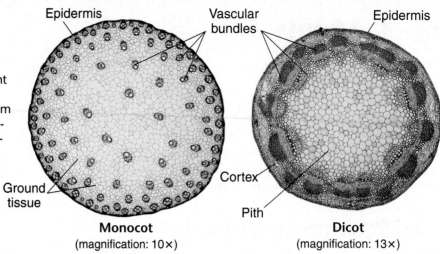

Epidermis

Vascular bundles

Epidermis

Ground tissue

Cortex

Pith

Monocot
(magnification: 10×)

Dicot
(magnification: 13×)

▶ **Figure 23–12** The arrangement of vascular bundles in the stem of a monocot differs from that in the stem of a dicot. ◉ In a monocot, vascular bundles are scattered throughout the stem. In a dicot, vascular bundles are arranged in a ring.

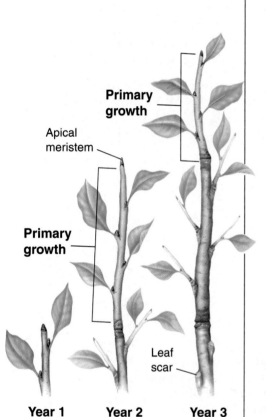

Primary growth

Apical meristem

Primary growth

Leaf scar

Year 1   **Year 2**   **Year 3**

▲ **Figure 23–13** ◉ All seed plants undergo primary growth, which is an increase in length. Every year, apical meristems, shown in red, divide to produce new growth. The primary growth for one season consists of a stem and several leaves.

Monocot and Dicot Stems

The arrangement of tissues in a stem differs among seed plants. ◉ **In monocots, vascular bundles are scattered throughout the stem. In dicots and most gymnosperms, vascular bundles are arranged in a cylinder.** Recall that monocots and dicots are two types of flowering plants, or angiosperms. For a comparison of monocot and dicot stems, look at **Figure 23–12.**

Monocot Stems The cross section of a young monocot stem shows all three tissue systems clearly. The stem has a distinct epidermis, which encloses a series of **vascular bundles,** each of which contains xylem and phloem tissue. Phloem faces the outside of the stem, and xylem faces the center. In monocots, these bundles are scattered throughout the ground tissue. The ground tissue is fairly uniform, consisting mainly of parenchyma cells.

Dicot Stems Young dicot stems have vascular bundles, but they are generally arranged in an organized, ringlike pattern. The parenchyma cells inside the ring of vascular tissue are known as **pith,** while those outside form the cortex of the stem. In dicots these relatively simple tissue patterns become more complex as the plant grows larger and the stem increases in diameter.

Primary Growth of Stems

Plants grow in ways that are distinctly different from other organisms. For their entire life, new cells are produced at the tips of roots and shoots. This type of growth, occurring only at the ends of a plant, is called **primary growth.** The increase in length produced by primary growth from year to year is shown in **Figure 23–13.** ◉ **Primary growth of stems is produced by cell divisions in the apical meristem. It takes place in all seed plants.**

Secondary Growth of Stems

If a plant is to grow larger year after year, its stems must increase in thickness as well as in length. They have more weight to support and more fluid to move through their vascular tissues. Yet, only meristematic tissue can produce new cells for growth. Some monocots, such as palm trees, produce thick stems from a meristem that becomes wider as the plant grows. However, most monocots, such as grasses, produce only fleshy growth and do not grow very tall. Many dicots grow extremely tall and also grow in width to support this extra weight. This growth occurs as a result of meristems other than the apical meristem.

The pattern of growth in which stems increase in width is called **secondary growth**. In **Figure 23–14** you can see the pattern of secondary growth in a dicot stem. 🗝 **In conifers and dicots, secondary growth takes place in lateral meristematic tissues called the vascular cambium and cork cambium.** The type of lateral meristematic tissue called **vascular cambium** produces vascular tissues and increases the thickness of stems over time. **Cork cambium** produces the outer covering of stems. Another kind of cambium enables roots to grow thicker and branch. The addition of new tissue in these cambium layers increases the thickness of the stem.

Formation of the Vascular Cambium In a young dicot stem produced by primary growth, bundles of xylem and phloem are arranged in a ring. Once secondary growth begins, the vascular cambium appears as a thin layer situated between clusters of vascular tissue. This new meristematic tissue forms between the xylem and phloem of each vascular bundle. Divisions in the vascular cambium give rise to new layers of xylem and phloem. As a result, the stem becomes wider. The cambium continues to produce new layers of vascular tissue, causing the stem to become thicker and thicker.

✔CHECKPOINT) *What tissue divides to produce secondary growth in dicots?*

▼ **Figure 23–14** 🗝 Dicots **produce secondary growth from meristematic tissue called vascular cambium.** This tissue forms between the xylem and phloem of the individual vascular bundles, as shown in A. Once the tissue forms, as shown in B, it divides to produce xylem cells toward the center of the stem and phloem cells toward the outside. These different tissues form the bark and wood of a mature stem, shown in C.

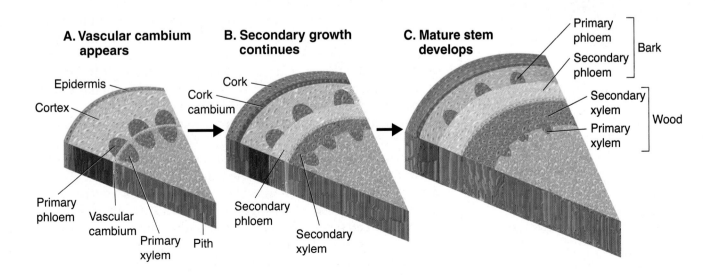

A. Vascular cambium appears
- Epidermis
- Cortex
- Primary phloem
- Vascular cambium
- Primary xylem
- Pith

B. Secondary growth continues
- Cork
- Cork cambium
- Secondary phloem
- Secondary xylem

C. Mature stem develops
- Primary phloem
- Secondary phloem
- Bark
- Secondary xylem
- Primary xylem
- Wood

Reading a Tree's History

The field of dendrochronology (*dendron* means "tree;" *chronos* means "time") analyzes tree rings to determine information about a tree and the environment in which it grew. A tree's age, for example, can be measured by counting its growth rings—each produced by a year of growth. The specific environmental conditions can be inferred for each year of its growth by examining the relative width and color of each ring. Use the photograph below to answer each question.

1. **Interpreting Graphics** Approximately how old was this tree when it was cut down?

2. **Inferring** Areas A and B were both produced by four years of growth, yet they are different widths. What climatic conditions might account for this difference?

3. **Interpreting Graphics** The area at C is blackened from a fire that apparently affected only one side of the tree. Describe how the tree grew after this fire.

4. **Comparing and Contrasting** Areas D and E are two types of wood. Give their names, and explain how they differ.

5. **Applying Concepts** On a separate sheet of paper, draw a simple sketch of the tree, indicating where the xylem and phloem are located. Where are the youngest xylem cells located? The youngest phloem cells? What tissue produces both of these cells?

Formation of Wood Most of what we call "wood" is actually layers of xylem. These cells build up year after year, layer on layer. As woody stems grow thicker, the older xylem near the center of the stem no longer conducts water and instead becomes what is known as **heartwood.** Heartwood usually darkens with age because it accumulates impurities that cannot be removed. Heartwood is surrounded by **sapwood,** which is active in fluid transport and therefore usually lighter in color. Both heartwood and sapwood are shown in **Figure 23–15.**

In most of the temperate zone, tree growth is seasonal. When growth begins in the spring, the vascular cambium begins to grow rapidly, producing large, light-colored xylem cells with thin cell walls. The result is a light-colored layer of wood called early wood. As the growing season continues, the cells become smaller and have thicker cell walls, forming a layer of dark wood. This darker wood is called late wood.

This alternation of dark and light wood produces what we commonly call tree rings. Each ring is composed of a band of light wood and a band of dark wood. Thus, a ring corresponds to a year of growth. By counting the rings in a cross section of a tree, you can estimate its age. The size of the rings may even provide information about weather conditions, such as wet or dry years. Thick rings indicate that weather conditions were favorable for tree growth, whereas thin rings indicate less favorable conditions.

Formation of Bark On most trees, **bark** includes all of the tissues outside the vascular cambium, as shown in **Figure 23–15.** These tissues include phloem, the cork cambium, and cork. How does bark form? Picture a tree as new xylem is being laid down. It is expanding in width, or girth. Recall that the phloem tissue lies to the outside of this xylem. Phloem must grow to accommodate the larger size of the tree. As the vascular cambium increases in diameter, it forces the phloem tissue outward. This expansion causes the oldest tissues to split and fragment as they are stretched by the expanding stem. Were this expansion left unchecked, the outer covering of the stem might eventually split and break.

Another layer of growing tissue, the cork cambium, solves this potential problem. The cork cambium surrounds the cortex and produces a thick protective layer of cork. Cork consists of cells that have thick walls and usually contain fats, oils, or waxes. These waterproof substances help prevent the loss of water from the stem. The outermost cork cells are usually dead. As the stem increases in size, this dead bark often cracks and flakes off in strips or patches.

✓ CHECKPOINT *What is heartwood?*

KEEP CURRENT WITH . . .
SCIENCE NEWS®

To find out more about the topics in this chapter, go to:
www.phschool.com

▼ **Figure 23–15** In a mature tree that has undergone several years of secondary growth, the vascular cambium lies between layers of xylem to the inside, and layers of phloem to the outside. The youngest xylem, called sapwood, transports water and minerals. **Classifying** *Which layer contains meristematic cells?*

Wood

Bark

Cork
Contains old, nonfunctioning phloem that protects the tree

Cork Cambium
Produces protective layer of cork

Phloem
Transports sugars produced by photosynthesis

Vascular Cambium
Produces new xylem and phloem, which increase the width of the stem

Xylem: Heartwood
Contains old, nonfunctioning xylem that helps support the tree

Xylem: Sapwood
Contains active xylem that transports water and minerals

FIGURE 23–16 STEMS ADAPTED FOR STORAGE AND DORMANCY

Many kinds of plants have modified stems that store food. Tubers, rhizomes, bulbs, and corms can remain dormant during cold or dry periods until favorable conditions for growth return.

Bulb

A bulb is made up of a central stem surrounded by short, thick leaves. As in the amaryllis bulb shown here, the leaves wrap around and protect the stem and also store food. A bulb may remain dormant for a long time, yet still grow into a plant.

Amaryllis

Tuber

A tuber is a stem, usually growing underground, that stores food. In potato plants grown from cuttings (shown here), the tubers form at the end of underground stems. In potato plants grown from seed, tubers form at the tips of stems that grow along the ground surface.

Potato

Corm

A corm looks similar to a bulb, but is a thickened stem that stores food. A corm has an outer covering that consists of layers of thin leaves. Plants such as the gladiolus (shown here) and the crocus form corms.

Ginger

Rhizome

The stem of a ginger is a rhizome, which is a horizontal, underground stem. As shown in the ginger, new shoots can form from a rhizome, allowing plants to undergo periods of dormancy.

Gladiolus

23–3 Section Assessment

1. **Key Concept** How do the functions of a stem relate to the roots and leaves of a plant?

2. **Key Concept** Describe how the arrangement of vascular bundles differs between monocot and dicot stems.

3. **Key Concept** Define primary and secondary growth. Which involves divisions of the apical meristem?

4. How do heartwood and sapwood differ?

5. **Critical Thinking Formulating Hypotheses** When European settlers were struggling to clear heavily wooded land in North America, they often "girdled" large trees by removing a strip of bark all the way around the base of the tree. Why would this cause the tree to die?

iTEXT Assessment Use iText to review the important concepts in Section 23–3.

ALTERNATIVE ASSESSMENT

Creative Writing
Pretend that you are small enough to enter a plant through its root system. Describe what you would see as you traveled into a plant and through one of its stems. Include illustrations.

23–4 Leaves

The leaves of a plant are its main organs of photosynthesis. In a sense, plant leaves are the world's most important manufacturers of food. Sugars, starches, and oils manufactured by plants in their leaves are sources of food for virtually all land animals.

Recall from Chapter 8 that photosynthesis uses carbon dioxide and water to produce sugars and oxygen. Leaves, therefore, must have a way of obtaining the materials needed for photosynthesis as well as distributing its end products. Much of the internal structure of leaves can be understood in terms of their functions in carrying out photosynthesis.

Leaf Structure

 The structure of a leaf is optimized for absorbing light and carrying out photosynthesis. As you can see in **Figure 23–17**, leaves may differ greatly in shape, yet share certain structural features. To collect sunlight, most leaves have thin, flattened sections called **blades.** The blade is attached to the stem by a thin stalk called a **petiole.** Like roots and stems, leaves have an outer covering of dermal tissue and inner regions of ground and vascular tissues. As shown in **Figure 23–18**, leaves are covered on the top and bottom by epidermis made of a layer of tough, irregularly shaped cells. The epidermis of many leaves is also covered by the cuticle. Together, the cuticle and epidermal cells form a waterproof barrier that protects tissues and limits the loss of water through evaporation.

The vascular tissues of leaves are connected directly to the vascular tissues of stems. In leaves, xylem and phloem tissues are gathered together into bundles that run from the stem into the petiole. Once they are in the leaf blade, the vascular bundles are surrounded by parenchyma and sclerenchyma cells.

Guide for Reading

Key Concepts
• How does the structure of a leaf enable it to carry out photosynthesis?
• How does gas exchange take place in a leaf?

Vocabulary
blade
petiole
mesophyll
palisade mesophyll
spongy mesophyll
stoma
guard cell
transpiration

Reading Strategy:
Monitoring Your Understanding Make a table with three columns, labeled K, W, and L. Before you read, write what you already know about leaves in the first column (K). Under the next heading, write down what you want to learn about leaves (W). After you read, write down what you learned about leaves in the last column (L).

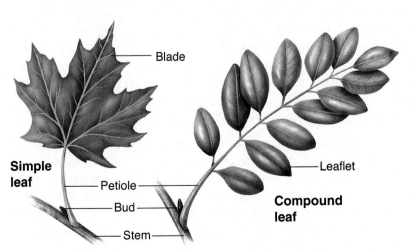

Simple leaf — Blade, Petiole, Bud, Stem

Compound leaf — Leaflet

◀ **Figure 23–17** Most of a leaf consists of a blade attached to the stem by a petiole. The blade of a simple leaf (left) can be different shapes. In a compound leaf (right), the blade is divided into many separate leaflets.

Veins

Cuticle

Epidermis

Palisade mesophyll

Xylem ⎤
        } Vein
Phloem ⎦

Spongy mesophyll

Epidermis

Stoma

Guard cells

▲ **Figure 23–18** 🔊 Leaves absorb light and carry out most of the photosynthesis in a plant. Some of the most important manufacturing sites on Earth are found in the leaves of plants. The cells in plant leaves are able to use light energy to make carbohydrates.

Word Origins

Mesophyll comes from two Greek words: *meso,* meaning "middle," and *phyllon,* meaning "leaf." If the Greek word *chloro* means "green," what does the term *chlorophyll* mean?

Leaf Functions

Plants must take in all the materials needed for photosynthesis. Specialized cells on the underside of the leaf regulate this process.

Photosynthesis The bulk of most leaves is composed of a specialized ground tissue known as **mesophyll,** shown in **Figure 23–18.** Mesophyll cells are packed with chloroplasts and carry out nearly all the photosynthetic activity of most plants. Carbohydrates produced in photosynthesis move from mesophyll cells into phloem vessels, which carry them to the rest of the plant.

Just under the upper epidermis is a layer of tall, column-shaped mesophyll cells called the **palisade mesophyll.** These closely packed cells absorb much of the light that enters the leaf. Beneath the palisade layer is the **spongy mesophyll,** a loose tissue with many air spaces between its cells. These air spaces connect with the exterior through **stomata** (singular: stoma), which are pore-like openings in the underside of the leaf that allow carbon dioxide and oxygen to diffuse in and out of the leaf. Each stoma consists of two **guard cells,** which are specialized cells in the epidermis that control the opening and closing of stomata by responding to changes in water pressure.

Transpiration The surfaces of spongy mesophyll cells are kept moist so that gases can enter and leave the cells easily. This also means that water evaporates from these surfaces and is lost to the atmosphere. Water is lost from leaves in a process called transpiration. **Transpiration** is the loss of water from a plant through its leaves. It is replaced by water drawn into the leaf through xylem vessels in the vascular tissue.

Gas Exchange No leaf could survive completely sealed off from the atmosphere that surrounds it. Leaves take in carbon dioxide and give off oxygen during photosynthesis. When plant cells use the food they make, the cells respire, taking in oxygen and giving off carbon dioxide (just as animals do). Plant leaves allow gas exchange between air spaces in the spongy mesophyll and the exterior by opening their stomata.

You might think that plants would keep their stomata open all the time, allowing gas exchange to take place as quickly as possible—especially when the sun is shining brightly and photosynthesis is running at top speed. However, when stomata are wide open, water evaporates from the damp surfaces of mesophyll cells and is lost through the stomata to the atmosphere. If stomata were kept open all the time, water loss due to transpiration would be so great that few plants would be able to take in enough water to survive. Therefore, plants maintain a kind of balance. **Plants keep their stomata open just enough to allow photosynthesis to take place, but not so much that they lose an excessive amount of water.**

Guard cells control the stomata and thus regulate the movement of gases, especially water vapor, into and out of leaf tissues. The stomata open and close in response to changes in water pressure within the guard cells, as shown in **Figure 23–19.** When water pressure within the guard cells is high, the thin outer walls of the cells are forced into a curved shape. This pulls the thick inner walls of the guard cells away from each other, opening the stoma. When water pressure within the guard cells decreases, the inner walls pull together and the stoma closes.

In general, stomata are open during the daytime when photosynthesis is active, and then closed at night, when open stomata would only lead to water loss. However, stomata may be closed even in bright sunlight under hot, dry conditions in which water conservation is a matter of life and death.

✓ CHECKPOINT *What factor regulates the opening and closing of stomata?*

Figure 23–19 Plants regulate opening and closing of their stomata to balance water loss with rates of photosynthesis. A stoma opens or closes in response to the changes in pressure within the guard cells that surround the opening. When the guard cells are swollen with water (bottom, left), the stoma is open. When the guard cells lose water, the opening closes, limiting further water loss from the leaf.

(magnification: 420×)

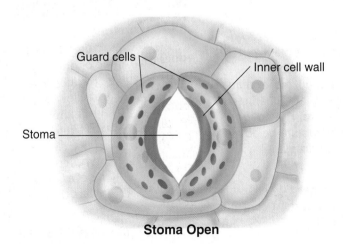

Stoma Open

Guard cells — Inner cell wall

Stoma

Stoma Closed

Guard cells — Inner cell wall

FIGURE 23–20 ADAPTATIONS OF LEAVES

The leaves of many plant species show specific adaptations to dry or low nutrient conditions.

Pitcher plant
The leaf of a pitcher plant is modified to attract and then digest insects and other small prey. Carnivorous plants typically live in nutrient-poor soils and rely on insects as their source of nitrogen.

Cactus
Cactus leaves are actually nonphotosynthetic thorns that protect against herbivores. Most of the plant's photosynthesis is carried out in its stem.

Pine
The narrow leaves of a pine tree contain a waxy epidermis as well as stomata that are sunken below the surface of the leaf. This arrangement reduces water loss from the leaf.

Rock plant
The leaves of a rock plant are adapted for hot, dry conditions. They are round, with few stomata, and often have clear tissue that allows light to penetrate into the leaf.

23–4 Section Assessment

1. 🔑 **Key Concept** Describe how the structure of a leaf is optimized for light absorption.

2. 🔑 **Key Concept** What factors regulate the opening and closing of guard cells?

3. Are stomata more likely to be open or closed on a hot day? Explain your answer.

4. Describe the cell types found within a typical leaf.

5. **Critical Thinking Inferring** The leaves of desert plants often have two or more layers of palisade mesophyll, rather than the single layer that is characteristic of most leaves. How might this modified structure be advantageous to a desert plant?

TEXT **Assessment** Use iText to review the important concepts in Section 23–4.

MAKING CONNECTIONS

Leaf Structure Where within the structure of a leaf does each stage of photosynthesis occur? How does the structure of a leaf allow it to obtain energy and materials for photosynthesis? Refer to Chapter 8, pp. 208–213, for details on photosynthesis. Then draw and label a diagram that answers these questions.

23–5 Transport in Plants

The pressure created by water entering the tissues of a root can push water upward in a plant stem. This creates more than enough pressure to force water into the vascular system and out of the root. However, root pressure does not exert enough pressure to lift water up into trees, such as the topmost needles of a redwood tree 90 meters above the ground. To draw water to such great heights, plants take advantage of some of water's most interesting physical properties.

Water Transport

Recall that xylem tissue forms a continuous set of tubes that stretch from roots through stems and out into the spongy mesophyll of leaves. Active transport and root pressure cause water to move from soil into plant roots. Root pressure alone, however, cannot account for the movement of water and dissolved materials throughout an entire plant. Obviously, other forces are at work. These include capillary action and transpiration. **The combination of root pressure, capillary action, and transpiration provides enough force to move water through the xylem tissue of even the largest plant.** As you will learn, transpiration is the most powerful of these forces.

Capillary Action Water molecules are attracted to one another by a force called cohesion. Recall from Chapter 2 that cohesion is the attraction of molecules of the same substance to each other. Because of cohesion, water molecules have a tendency to form hydrogen bonds with each other. Water molecules can also form hydrogen bonds with other substances. This results from a force called **adhesion,** which is attraction between unlike molecules. Place empty glass tubes of various widths into a dish of water, as shown in **Figure 23–21,** and you will see both forces at work. The tendency of water to rise in a thin tube is called **capillary action.** Water is attracted to the walls of the tube, and water molecules are attracted to each other. The thinner the tube, the higher the water will rise inside it.

Guide for Reading

Key Concepts
- How is water transported throughout a plant?
- How are the products of photosynthesis transported throughout a plant?

Vocabulary
adhesion
capillary action
pressure-flow hypothesis

Reading Strategy:
Making Comparisons This section describes how xylem and phloem function in transport. As you read, write down statements about similarities and differences between the functions of these two tissues.

▶ **Figure 23–21** Capillary action—the result of water molecules' ability to stick to one another and to the walls of a tube—contributes to the movement of water up the cells of xylem tissue. As shown here, capillary action causes water to move much higher in a narrow tube than in a wide tube. **Applying Concepts** *Which force—adhesion or cohesion—causes the water to stick to the walls of the glass tube?*

► **Figure 23–22** Root pressure, capillary action, and transpiration contribute to the movement of water within a plant. Transpiration is the movement of water molecules out of leaves. The faster water evaporates from a plant, shown in A, the stronger the pull of water upward from the roots, shown in B.

A   **B**

▼ **Figure 23–23** In hot, dry conditions, transpiration can lead to water loss that is severe enough to cause wilting, shown here in a coleus plant. High transpiration rates can cause a loss of osmotic pressure in a plant's cells. In leaves, this loss of pressure causes guard cells to close, thereby slowing down the rate of transpiration. *Inferring* *Why do hot, dry conditions cause transpiration rates to increase?*

What does capillary action have to do with water movement through xylem? Recall that there are two main types of xylem tissue in flowering plants: tracheids and vessel elements. Recall that both tracheids and vessel elements form hollow connected tubes similar to a thin, glass capillary tube. Capillary action in the tubelike structures formed by both types of cells causes water to rise well above the level of the ground.

Transpiration For trees and other large plants, the combination of root pressure and capillary action does not provide enough force to lift water to the topmost branches and leaves. The major force in water transport is provided by the evaporation of water from leaves during transpiration. When water is lost through transpiration, osmotic pressure moves water out of the vascular tissue of the leaf, as shown in **Figure 23–22.** Then, like a locomotive pulling a train with hundreds of cars, the movement of water out of the leaf "pulls" water upward through the vascular system all the way from the roots. This process is known as transpiration pull.

How important is transpiration pull? On a hot day, even a small tree may lose as much as 100 liters of water to transpiration. The hotter and drier the air, and the windier the day, the greater the amount of water lost. As a result of this water loss, the plant draws up even more water from the roots.

Controlling Transpiration To understand what regulates the rate of transpiration, it helps to follow the path water takes through a leaf. Water enters the leaf through the xylem and moves into the spongy mesophyll. This movement of water into the leaf raises the water pressure in the guard cells, opening the stomata. The rate of transpiration increases as water vapor escapes through the open stomata. Falling water pressure in the leaf also affects the guard cells, which then close the stomata. This limits further water loss from the leaf and helps the plant to maintain homeostasis.

What is the role of leaves in transpiration?

Materials 3 stalks of celery with leaves, 250-mL beaker, food coloring, petroleum jelly, cotton swab, scalpel, metric ruler

Procedure
1. Cut 1 cm off the bottoms of the celery stalks.
   CAUTION: *Use the scalpel with care.*
2. Remove the leaves from one stalk. Use a cotton swab to apply petroleum jelly to both sides of all the leaves on another stalk. Place all three stalks into a beaker containing 5 cm of water and food coloring.
3. Place the beaker in a sunny location. Observe the celery at the end of the class and the next day. Record your observations each day.

Analyze and Conclude
1. **Observing** In which stalk did the colored water rise the most? The least?
2. **Inferring** What effect did the petroleum jelly have on transpiration? What part of the leaf did the petroleum jelly affect?
3. **Drawing Conclusions** How are leaves involved in transpiration?

Transpiration and Wilting Osmotic pressure keeps a plant's leaves and stems rigid, or stiff. High transpiration rates can lead to wilting, shown in **Figure 23–23.** Wilting results from the loss of water—and therefore of the pressure in a plant's cells. Without this internal pressure to support them, the plant's cell walls bend inward, and the plant's leaves and stems wilt. When a leaf wilts, its stomata close. As a result, transpiration slows down significantly. Thus, wilting helps a plant to conserve water.

✓ CHECKPOINT) *What happens when a plant wilts?*

Nutrient Transport

You have learned how transpiration *pulls* water upward through a plant. But most plant nutrients, including sugars, minerals, and complex organic compounds, are *pushed* through phloem.

Functions of Phloem Many plants pump sugars into their fruits. This action often requires moving sugars out of leaves or roots into stems, and then through stems to the fruits. All of this movement takes place in the phloem. In cold climates, many plants pump food down into their roots for winter storage. This stored food must be moved back into the trunk and branches of the plant before growth begins again in the spring. Phloem carries out this seasonal movement of sugars within a plant.

Movement of water

Movement of sugar

Sugar molecules

Source cell

Sink cell   Phloem   Xylem

Movement From Source to Sink A process of phloem transport moves sugars through a plant from a source to a sink. The source can be any cell in which sugars are produced by photosynthesis. The sink is a cell where the sugars are used or stored. How does phloem transport take place?

One idea put forward by many plant scientists is called the **pressure-flow hypothesis.** As you can see in **Figure 23–24**, sugars are pumped into the phloem at one point, called the source. For example, sugars produced by photosynthesis may move from a leaf. As concentrations of sugar increase in the phloem, water from the xylem moves in by osmosis. This movement causes an increase in pressure at that point, forcing nutrient-rich fluid to move through the phloem away from nutrient-producing regions and toward a region that uses these nutrients, called the sink.

Conversely, if part of a plant actively absorbs nutrients from the phloem, osmosis causes water to follow. This movement of water decreases pressure and causes a movement of fluid in the phloem toward the sink. **When nutrients are pumped into or removed from the phloem system, the change in concentration causes a movement of fluid in that same direction. As a result, phloem is able to move nutrients in either direction to meet the nutritional needs of the plant.**

◀ **Figure 23–24** The diagram shows the movement of sugars and water throughout the phloem and xylem as explained by the pressure-flow hypothesis. Materials move from a source cell, where photosynthesis produces a high concentration of sugars, to a sink cell, where sugars are lower in concentration. **Interpreting Diagrams** *What is the source of the water that forces nutrients through phloem tissue?*

23–5 Section Assessment

1. **Key Concept** What three processes work together to cause water to flow upward through a plant?

2. **Key Concept** How does the pressure-flow hypothesis explain the function of phloem?

3. Why is capillary action insufficient to move water through a plant?

4. **Critical Thinking Predicting** If a plant's stomata close on a hot, dry day, how could this affect the plant's rate of photosynthesis?

TEXT **Assessment** Use iText to review the important concepts in Section 23–5.

Identifying the Growth Zones in a Plant

Do roots grow at the tips or do existing root tissues grow longer? In this investigation, you will answer this question by examining root growth.

Problem
In which part of a root does most growth occur?

Materials
- 150-mL beaker
- metric ruler
- paper towels
- India ink
- 4 large seeds
- toothpick
- petri dish

Skills
Measuring, Analyzing Data

Procedure

1. Fill a 150-mL beaker loosely with crumpled paper towels. Wet the towels with water.

2. Place 4 seeds between the towels and the sides of the beaker. Cover the beaker with a petri dish. Keep the paper towels damp. On a separate sheet of paper, make a copy of the data table shown.

3. When the roots appear, gently place one seedling on a wet paper towel. Use a ruler to measure the length of the root. Record this length in your copy of the data table. Use another sprout if this one becomes damaged.

4. Pick up a very small drop of India ink on the tip of a toothpick. Use the toothpick to mark the root with small dots of ink 3, 10, 15, and 20 mm from the root tip. **CAUTION:** *India ink stains skin and clothing.*

5. Allow the ink dots to dry. Return the sprout to the beaker and replace the cover. Keep the paper towels in the beaker moist.

6. **Predicting** Record your prediction of which part of the root will grow the most over the next 3 days.

7. **Measuring** Record the length of the root and the positions of the dots in your data table each day for 3 days.

Data Table					
Days	Position of Mark (mm from root tip)				Root Length (mm)
	3	10	15	20	
1					
2					
3					

Analyze and Conclude

1. **Observing** Did most of the growth occur at the tip of the root (0–3 mm) or farther up?

2. **Analyzing Data** Which part of the root grew the most?

3. **Drawing Conclusions** Do your data support the idea that roots grow mostly at their tips or that growth farther up the root pushes the root tip through the soil?

Go Further

Designing Experiments Design a similar experiment to determine where most stem growth occurs. With your teacher's permission, perform your experiment.

Take It to the NET Log on to the the Prentice Hall Web site at **www.phschool.com** to enter your data for this lab. Compare your results to the data entered by other students around the country.

23–1 Specialized Tissues in Plants
 Key Concepts

- The three principal organs in seed plants are roots, stems, and leaves.
- Plants consist of three tissue systems: dermal tissue, vascular tissue, and ground tissue.
- Meristematic tissue is the only plant tissue that produces new cells by mitosis.
- Vascular tissue contains several different cell types. Xylem consists of tracheids and vessel elements, and phloem consists of sieve tube elements and companion cells.

Vocabulary
- meristematic tissue, p. 580
- apical meristem, p. 580 • epidermal cell, p. 581
- cuticle, p. 581 • trichome, p. 581
- vessel element, p. 582
- sieve tube element, p. 582
- companion cell, p. 583 • parenchyma, p. 583
- collenchyma, p. 583 • sclerenchyma, p. 583

23–2 Roots
 Key Concepts

- The two main types of roots are taproots, found mainly in dicots, and fibrous roots, found mainly in monocots.
- A mature root has an outside layer of epidermal cells and a central cylinder of vascular tissue separated by a large area of ground tissue called the cortex.
- Roots anchor a plant in the ground and absorb water and dissolved nutrients from the soil.

Vocabulary
- taproot, p. 584 • fibrous root, p. 584
- root hair, p. 585 • cortex, p. 585
- endodermis, p. 585 • vascular cylinder, p. 585
- root cap, p. 585 • Casparian strip, p. 587

23–3 Stems
 Key Concepts

- Stems have three important functions: They produce leaves, branches, and flowers; they hold leaves up in the sunlight; and they transport various substances between roots and leaves.
- In monocots, vascular bundles are scattered throughout the stem. In dicots and most gymnosperms, vascular bundles are arranged in a cylinder.

- In all seed plants, primary growth of stems is produced by cell divisions in the apical meristem.
- In conifers and dicots, secondary growth takes place in lateral meristematic tissues called the vascular cambium and cork cambium.

Vocabulary
- node, p. 589 • internode, p. 589
- bud, p. 589 • vascular bundle, p. 590
- pith, p. 590 • primary growth, p. 590
- secondary growth, p. 591
- vascular cambium, p. 591 • cork cambium, p. 591
- heartwood, p. 592 • sapwood, p. 592
- bark, p. 593

23–4 Leaves
Key Concepts

- The structure of a leaf is optimized for absorbing light and carrying out photosynthesis.
- Plants keep their stomata open just enough to allow photosynthesis to take place, but not so much that they lose an excessive amount of water.

Vocabulary
- blade, p. 595 • petiole, p. 595
- mesophyll, p. 596 • palisade mesophyll, p. 596
- spongy mesophyll, p. 596 • stoma, p. 596
- guard cell, p. 596 • transpiration, p. 596

23–5 Transport in Plants
Key Concepts

- Root pressure, capillary action, and transpiration work together to move water through the xylem tissue of even the largest plant.
- When nutrients are pumped into or removed from the phloem system, the change in concentration causes a movement of water in that same direction. As a result, phloem is able to move nutrients in either direction to meet the nutritional needs of the plant.

Vocabulary
- adhesion, p. 599 • capillary action, p. 599
- pressure-flow hypothesis, p. 602

Thinking Visually
Make a flowchart of the tissues through which water passes, from when it enters a plant at the root until it escapes from the plant through the leaves. Use the following terms in your flowchart: *spongy mesophyll, root epidermis, stomata, cortex, endodermis, xylem.*

Chapter 23

Part A

Multiple Choice

For each statement or question, select the number of the word or expression that, of those given, best completes the statement or answers the question.

1 The plant structure that is responsible for support of the plant and for carrying nutrients between different parts of the plant is the
(1) root   **(3)** stem
(2) leaf   **(4)** flower

2 Which type of plant tissue would be found only in the circled areas of the plant shown below?
(1) meristematic tissue
(2) vascular tissue
(3) dermal tissue
(4) ground tissue

3 The dissolved sugars produced in the leaves of a maple tree move to the tree's roots through the
(1) xylem   **(3)** phloem
(2) guard cells   **(4)** epidermal cells

4 Tracheids and vessel elements make up
(1) phloem   **(3)** trichomes
(2) xylem   **(4)** meristem

5 Within a leaf, there are many air spaces between the cells of the
(1) palisade layer   **(3)** spongy mesophyll
(2) meristem   **(4)** cuticle

6 Increases in the thickness of stems over time result from the production of vascular tissue by the
(1) vascular cambium
(2) cork cambium
(3) apical meristem
(4) ground tissue

7 Guard cells open and close pores in leaves to regulate
(1) water loss and gas exchange
(2) growth of the apical meristem
(3) the uptake of plant nutrients from the soil
(4) the number of chloroplasts present in the leaf

8 The rise of water in a tall plant depends on root pressure and
(1) osmosis
(2) evaporation
(3) capillary action
(4) transpiration pull

9 Tree bark is made of which tissues?
(1) xylem and phloem, only
(2) cork and vascular cambium, only
(3) heartwood and sapwood
(4) phloem, cork, and cork cambium

10 Where does most of the photosynthesis occur in a plant?
(1) stomata
(2) guard cells
(3) vascular cambium
(4) mesophyll tissue

For questions 11 and 12, complete each analogy by selecting the correct letter. In analogies, A : B :: C : means "A is to B as C is to __?__."

11 Ground tissue : sclerenchyma :: vascular tissue :
(1) cuticle   **(3)** apical meristem
(2) xylem   **(4)** collenchyma

12 Taproot : carrot :: fibrous root :
(1) dandelion   **(3)** beet
(2) grass   **(4)** radish

Test-Taking Tip When presented with questions that are related to data in a table, study each column and row of the table for the information you need to answer the questions.

Parts B and C

Multiple Choice and Extended Response

For those questions that ask you to select a response, choose the one that best completes the statement or answers the question. For all others follow the directions given.

13 Name two different kinds of vascular tissue in plants. Describe one function of each.

Base your answers to questions 14 through 16 on the information below and on your knowledge of biology.

A student compared the average number of stomata (pores regulated by guard cells) on the top side and the underside of leaves obtained from different plant species growing in the same area. His data are summarized in the table below.

Average Number of Stomata (per square mm)		
Plant	**Top Surfaces of Leaves**	**Bottom Surfaces of Leaves**
Pumpkin	29	275
Tomato	12	122
Bean	40	288

14 What generalization can be made based on the data?
   (1) All plants have more stomata on the top side of their leaves than on the bottom side.
   (2) Plants have fewer stomata on the top side of their leaves than on the bottom side.
   (3) Some plants have more stomata on the top side of their leaves than on the bottom side.
   (4) The number of stomata varies greatly from plant to plant.

15 Pumpkins, tomatoes, and beans grow in direct sunlight. Assuming the plants receive plenty of water, stomata on the lower surface of their leaves would be regulated by guard cells to
   (1) be always closed
   (2) close only during daylight hours
   (3) never close at night
   (4) stay open during daylight hours

16 Describe three steps the student should follow when preparing a wet mount slide of the leaf tissue being examined.

Base your answers to questions 17 through 20 on the graph below and on your knowledge of biology.

During transpiration, water evaporates from the leaves of plants into the air.

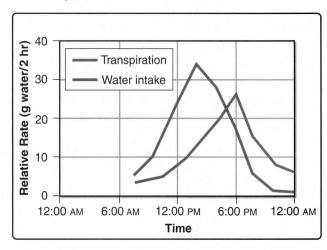

17 What does the graph illustrate?

18 During which span of time is the greatest amount of water lost through transpiration?

19 About how many grams of water are lost every two hours when the transpiration curve is at its highest peak?

20 Describe the relationship between transpiration and water intake.

21 If your classmate gave you a cross section of a dicot, describe how you would know whether the section was from a root or a stem.

22 Describe two ways root hairs are important to plants.

23 Describe the function of the vascular cambium in the secondary growth of stems.

24 What are the three main functions of leaves?

25 What properties of water are important in its movement up a plant?

26 What is the difference between bark and wood in terms of their functions and the tissues that give rise to these layers?

27 Cork is a lightweight, spongy material made from the outer bark of a type of oak tree. How must cork be removed to avoid killing the tree?

28 Explain why maple trees are tapped for their sugar in the early spring rather than in the summer or autumn.

Base your answers to questions 29 through 31 on the information and data table below and on your knowledge of biology.

For nine days, two genetically identical plants of the same stem length were grown in identical environments that differed only in temperature. The stem length of the two plants was measured and recorded as indicated in the data table below.

Time (days)	Length of Stem (mm)	
	Plant A (grown at 15°C)	Plant B (grown at 25°C)
1	15	21
3	30	50
5	44	78
7	53	96
9	54	99

29 Use the information in the data table to construct a line graph on your own graph paper. Label each axis, including units, placing time on the horizontal axis and length on the vertical axis. Mark an appropriate scale on each axis. Next, plot the data for plant A, grown at 15°C, on the graph. Surround each point with a small circle, and connect the points. Finally, plot the data for plant B, grown at 25°C, on the graph. Surround each of the points with a small triangle, and connect the points.

30 Which conclusion can be made from your graph and the information given in the data table?
 (1) The growth rate of plant A was greater than the growth rate of plant B.
 (2) The growth rate of plant B was greater than the growth rate of plant A.
 (3) The growth rate of plant A was equal to the growth rate of plant B.
 (4) Not enough information was obtained to make inferences about comparable growth rates.

31 Which plant would most likely survive if the environmental temperature decreased over time to 15°C? Explain your answer using data from the table.

32 In Japan, the art of growing miniature trees is highly valued. By cutting the roots and tips of the branches, gardeners can keep a tree small. The trunk of the tree, however, continues to increase in diameter. How do you explain the ever-increasing growth of the diameter of the trunk? In your answer be sure to
 • describe what tissue is removed when the tips of the shoots and roots are removed
 • explain why removing that tissue keeps the plants small
 • name the tissue that must be left undamaged in order to allow the stems to grow in thickness

33 The two main types of root systems found in plants are taproots and fibrous. Both are designed to anchor a plant in the ground and absorb water and dissolved nutrients. Compare taproots with fibrous roots. In your answer be sure to
 • describe the advantages and disadvantages provided by each type of root
 • name a plant that has a taproot
 • name a plant that has a fibrous root system

34 During the nineteenth century, people often raised ferns and delicate plants in enclosed glass containers called Wardian cases. Although these types of plants normally required a great deal of water, plants grown in Wardian cases did not have to be watered for years. What is the most logical explanation for this? Be sure to
 • explain how water in the Wardian cases could be recycled by the plants
 • describe how evaporation and condensation would be involved

 Take It to the NET

Can you tell how old a tree is? Visit the Prentice Hall Web site at **www.phschool.com** to find out how to count tree rings. Then, answer the following questions:
• What is dendrochronology?
• How can you use tree rings from different trees to date events that are older than one tree?
• What factors affect the ring growth patterns in bristlecone pines?

24 Reproduction of Seed Plants

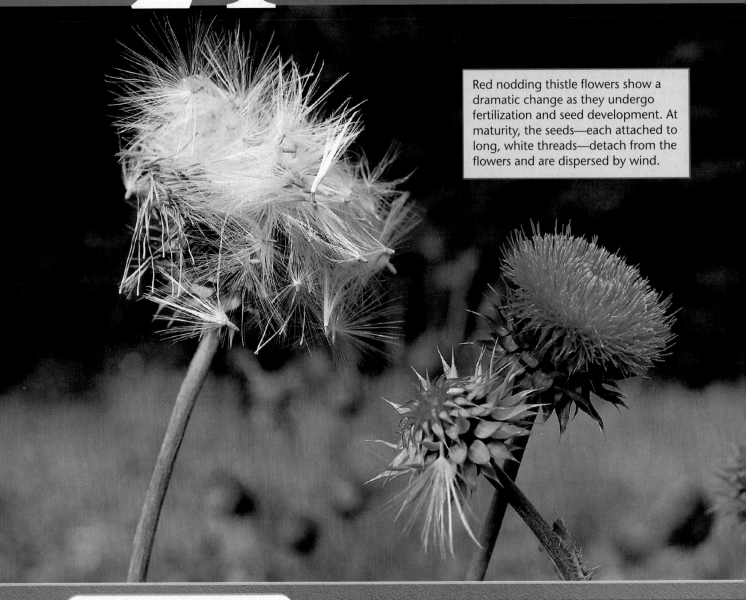

Red nodding thistle flowers show a dramatic change as they undergo fertilization and seed development. At maturity, the seeds—each attached to long, white threads—detach from the flowers and are dispersed by wind.

Inquiry Activity

How do seeds and fruits vary?

Procedure

1. Use a hand lens to examine a variety of seeds and fruits. (*Hint:* Review the material on seeds in Chapter 22, page 565). Record your observations.

2. Place each seed in a petri dish and use a scalpel to cut the seed lengthwise. **CAUTION:** *Use care with sharp instruments.* Use a hand lens to examine the inside of each seed. Draw and label the structures you observe. Label the embryo of each seed.

Think About It

1. **Observing** What types of structures did you observe in all the seeds?

2. **Formulating Hypotheses** A seed contains stored nutrients that nourish the new plant until it becomes autotrophic. Which part of the seed might contain these nutrients?

3. **Predicting** What structures did you observe that could help spread the offspring of a plant over a larger area? Explain your answer.

24–1 Reproduction With Cones and Flowers

Seed plants are well adapted to the demands of life on land, especially in the way that they reproduce. As you may recall, the gametes of seedless plants, such as ferns and mosses, need water for fertilization to be successful. Water allows gametes to move from plant to plant. The gametes of seed plants, however, can achieve fertilization even when the plants are not wet from rain or dew. As a result, they can reproduce just about anywhere. The way in which seed plants reproduce has allowed them to survive the dry conditions of life on land.

Alternation of Generations

All plants have a life cycle in which a diploid sporophyte generation alternates with a haploid gametophyte generation. Gametophyte plants produce male and female gametes—sperm and eggs. When the gametes join, they form a zygote that begins the next sporophyte generation. In some plants, the two stages of the life cycle are distinct, independent plants. In most ferns, for instance, the gametophyte is a small, heart-shaped plant that grows close to the ground. The sporophyte is the familiar fern plant itself made up of graceful fronds.

Where are these two generations in seed plants? Recall from Mendel's work on peas that seed-bearing plants are diploid. Therefore, the recognizable part of seed-bearing plants must be the diploid sporophyte.

If the sporophyte is what we recognize as the plant, then where is the gametophyte? The answer may surprise you. As shown in **Figure 24–1,** the gametophytes of seed plants are actually hidden deep within tissues of the sporophyte plant. In gymnosperms they are found inside cones, and in angiosperms they are found inside flowers.

Guide for Reading

🔑 **Key Concepts**
- What are the reproductive structures of gymnosperms and angiosperms?
- How does pollination differ between angiosperms and gymnosperms?

Vocabulary
- pollen cone • seed cone
- ovule • pollen tube
- sepal • petal • stamen
- filament • anther • carpel
- ovary • style • stigma
- embryo sac • endosperm
- double fertilization

Reading Strategy: Making Comparisons
Before you read, preview **Figure 24–4** and **Figure 24–7.** As you read, compare the life cycles of gymnosperms and angiosperms.

Gametophyte (N)
Sporophyte (2N)

Bryophytes   Ferns   Seed plants

◀ **Figure 24–1** An important trend in plant evolution is the reduction of the gametophyte and the increasing size of the sporophyte. Bryophytes consist of a relatively large gametophyte and smaller sporophytes that are located on stalks. Seedless vascular plants, such as ferns, have a small gametophyte and a larger sporophyte. Seed plants have an even smaller gametophyte that is contained within sporophyte tissues. **Interpreting Graphics** *How does the relative size of the haploid and diploid stages of plants differ between bryophytes and seed plants?*

Life Cycle of Gymnosperms

Pine trees and other gymnosperms are diploid sporophytes. As you will see, this sporophyte develops from a zygote that is contained within a seed. How and where is this seed produced? 🔑 **Reproduction in gymnosperms takes place in cones, which are produced by a mature sporophyte plant.** Gymnosperms produce two types of cones: pollen cones and seed cones.

Pollen Cones and Seed Cones **Pollen cones,** shown in **Figure 24–2,** are also called male cones. Pollen cones produce the male gametophytes, which are called pollen grains. As tiny as it is, the pollen grain makes up the entire male gametophyte stage of the gymnosperm life cycle. One of the haploid nuclei in the pollen grain will divide later to produce two sperm nuclei.

The more familiar **seed cones,** which produce female gametophytes, are generally much larger than pollen cones. Near the base of each scale are two **ovules** in which the female gametophytes develop. Within the ovules, meiosis produces haploid cells that grow and divide to produce female gametophytes. These gametophytes may contain hundreds or thousands of cells. When mature, each gametophyte contains a few large egg cells, each ready for fertilization by sperm nuclei.

Pollination The gymnosperm life cycle typically takes two years to complete. The cycle begins in the spring as male cones release enormous numbers of pollen grains. This pollen is carried by the wind, as shown in **Figure 24–3.** Some of these pollen grains reach female cones. There, some pollen grains are caught in a sticky secretion on one of the scales of the female cone. This sticky material, known as a pollination drop, ensures that pollen grains stay on the female cone.

CHECKPOINT *What are pollen cones and seed cones?*

▲ **Figure 24–2** 🔑 **Reproduction in gymnosperms takes place in structures called cones.** Pollen cones, shown on the top in this pine tree, produce male gametophytes, which are pollen grains. Seed cones, shown on the bottom, produce female gametophytes that develop into a new embryo following fertilization.

Figure 24–3 Pollen grains are male gametophytes. Pollen is carried by the wind until it reaches a female cone. **Inferring** *Male and female cones are distributed on a plant such that pollen usually lands on a different plant from where it started. Why might this strategy have evolved?*

Pollen Grains
(magnification: 750×)

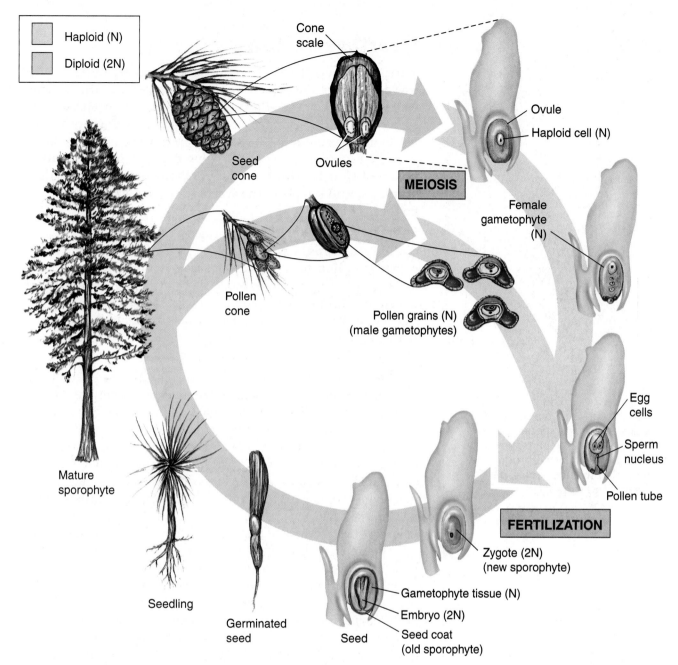

Haploid (N)

Diploid (2N)

Cone scale

Seed cone

Ovules

MEIOSIS

Ovule

Haploid cell (N)

Female gametophyte (N)

Pollen cone

Pollen grains (N) (male gametophytes)

Egg cells

Sperm nucleus

Pollen tube

Mature sporophyte

FERTILIZATION

Zygote (2N) (new sporophyte)

Gametophyte tissue (N)

Embryo (2N)

Seed coat (old sporophyte)

Seedling

Germinated seed

Seed

Fertilization and Development If a pollen grain lands near an ovule, the grain splits open and begins to grow a structure called a **pollen tube,** which contains two haploid sperm nuclei. Once the pollen tube reaches the female gametophyte, one sperm nucleus disintegrates, and the other fertilizes the egg contained within the female gametophyte. If sperm from another pollen tube reaches the female gametophyte, both egg cells may be fertilized, but just one embryo grows. As shown in **Figure 24–4,** fertilization produces a diploid zygote—the new sporophyte plant. This zygote grows into a small embryo. During this time, it is encased within what will soon develop into a seed. The seed consists of three generations of the life cycle. The outer seed coat is part of the old sporophyte generation, the haploid cells surrounding the embryo are part of the female gametophyte, and the embryo is the new sporophyte plant.

▲ **Figure 24–4** This illustration shows the life cycle of a typical gymnosperm. A pine tree—the mature sporophyte—produces male and female cones. Male cones produce pollen, and female cones produce ovules located on cone scales. If an egg is fertilized by the sperm, it becomes a zygote that is nourished by the female cone. In time, the zygote develops into a new sporophyte plant. **Classifying** *Classify each of the following terms as to whether they belong to the haploid or diploid stage of the pine tree's life cycle: pollen tube, seed cone, embryo, ovule, seedling.*

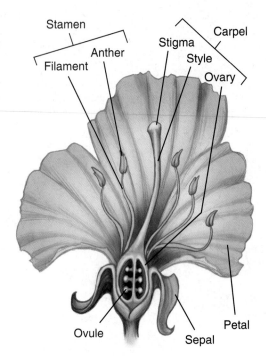

Stamen
Anther
Filament
Carpel
Stigma
Style
Ovary
Ovule
Petal
Sepal

▲ **Figure 24–5** This cross section shows the parts of a typical flower. The flowers of some species, however, may not have all the parts shown here. ◖— **Flowers are reproductive organs that include sepals, petals, stamens, and carpels.**

Figure 24–6 Flowers vary enormously in structure. The tulip (left) has only a single carpel, whereas the rose flower (right) has many carpels, each of which develops into the fleshy part of a rose fruit. Some flowerlike structures are actually clusters of many individual flowers. In the sunflower (facing page), disk flowers toward the inside of the cluster are reproductive, whereas ray flowers toward the outside are nonreproductive and form what look like petals. **Formulating Hypotheses** *How might it be an advantage for a plant to have many flowers together in a single structure?*

Structure of Flowers

You may think of flowers as decorative objects that brighten the world. However, the presence of so many flowers in the world is visible evidence of something else—the stunning evolutionary success of the angiosperms, or flowering plants. Flowers are the key to understanding why angiosperms have been so successful.

◖— **Flowers are reproductive organs that are composed of four kinds of specialized leaves: sepals, petals, stamens, and carpels.** These structures are shown in the flower in **Figure 24–5.**

Sepals and Petals The outermost circle of floral parts contains the **sepals,** which in many plants are green and closely resemble ordinary leaves. Sepals enclose the bud before it opens, and they protect the flower while it is developing. **Petals,** which are often brightly colored, are found just inside the sepals. The petals attract insects and other pollinators to the flower. Because they do not produce reproductive cells, the sepals and petals of a flower are sometimes called sterile leaves.

Stamens and Carpels Within the ring of petals are the structures that produce male and female gametophytes. The male parts consist of an anther and a filament, which together make up the **stamen.** The **filament** is a long, thin stalk that supports an anther. At the tip of each filament is an **anther,** an oval sac where meiosis takes place, producing haploid male gametophytes—pollen grains. In most angiosperms, each flower has several stamens. If you rub your hand on the anthers of a flower, a yellow-orange dust may stick to your skin. This is pollen, which consists of thousands of individual pollen grains.

The innermost floral parts are **carpels,** also called pistils, which produce the female gametophytes. Each carpel has a broad base forming an **ovary,** which contains one or more ovules where female gametophytes are produced. The diameter of the carpel narrows into a stalk called the **style.** At the top of the style is a sticky portion known as the **stigma,** where pollen grains frequently land. Some flowers have several carpels fused together to form a single reproductive structure called a compound carpel.

Carpel
Anthers
Tulip

Anthers
Carpel
Wild Rose

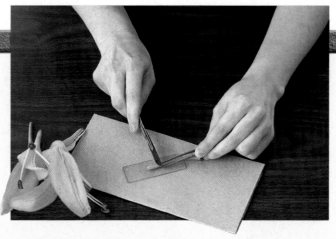

What is the structure of a flower?

Materials flower, forceps, scalpel, microscope slide, dropper pipette, coverslips, microscope

Procedure
1. Examine a flower carefully. Make a detailed drawing of the flower and label as many parts as you can. Note whether the anthers are above or below the stigma.
2. Remove an anther and place it on a slide. While holding the anther with forceps, use the scalpel to cut one or more thin slices across the anther. **CAUTION:** *Be careful with sharp tools.*
3. Lay the slices flat on the microscope slide and add a drop of water and a coverslip. Observe the slices with the microscope at low power. Make a labeled drawing of your observations.
4. Repeat steps 2 and 3 with the ovary.

Analyze and Conclude
1. **Observing** Are the anthers in this flower located above or below the stigma? How could this affect what happens to the pollen produced by the anthers? Explain your answer.
2. **Applying Concepts** What structures did you identify in the anther? What is the function of these structures?
3. **Applying Concepts** What structures did you identify in the ovary? What is the function of these structures?
4. **Drawing Conclusions** Which parts of the flower will become the seeds? The fruit?

Flowers vary greatly in shape, color, and size, as shown in **Figure 24–6.** A typical flower produces both male and female gametophytes. In some plants, however, male and female gametophytes are produced in separate flowers on the same individual. Corn, for example, has separate male and female flowers on the same plant. The tassel is a flower that produces male gametophytes, and the silk is the style of a flower that contains the female gametophyte. In other cases, many flowers grow together to form a composite structure that looks like a single flower, as shown in the sunflower.

✓CHECKPOINT *What are the male structures in a typical flower? The female structures?*

Ray flowers   Disk flowers

Sunflower

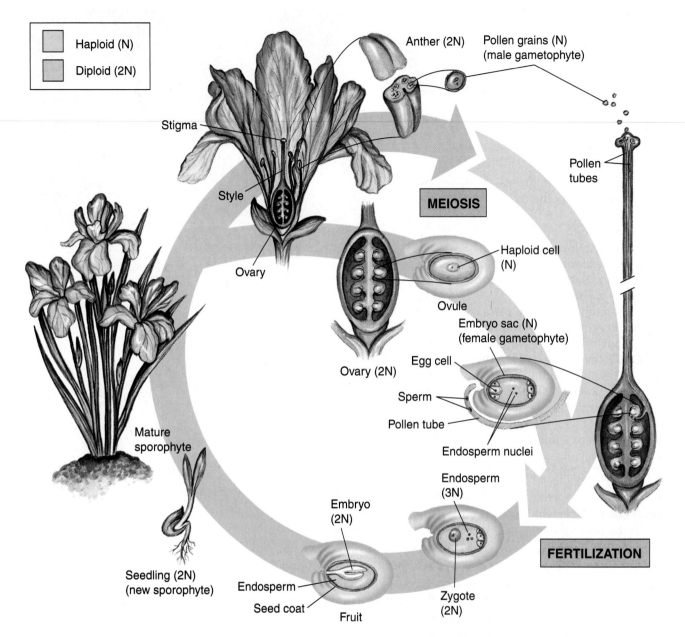

Haploid (N)

Diploid (2N)

Stigma

Anther (2N)

Pollen grains (N)
(male gametophyte)

Style

Pollen
tubes

MEIOSIS

Ovary

Haploid cell
(N)

Ovule

Embryo sac (N)
(female gametophyte)

Egg cell

Ovary (2N)

Sperm

Pollen tube

Mature
sporophyte

Endosperm nuclei

Endosperm
(3N)

Embryo
(2N)

FERTILIZATION

Seedling (2N)
(new sporophyte)

Endosperm

Seed coat

Fruit

Zygote
(2N)

▲ **Figure 24–7** This illustration
shows the life cycle of a typical
angiosperm—an iris. The developing seeds of a flowering plant are
protected and nourished inside the
ovary, which is located at the base
of the flower. 🔑Reproduction in
angiosperms takes place within
the flower. After pollination, the
seeds of angiosperms develop
inside protective structures.

Life Cycle of Angiosperms

🔑 **Reproduction in angiosperms takes place within the
flower. Following pollination and fertilization, the seeds
develop inside protective structures.** The life cycle of
angiosperms is shown in **Figure 24–7.** You can think of the
angiosperm life cycle as beginning when the mature sporophyte
produces flowers. Each flower contains anthers and an ovary.
Inside the anthers—the male part of the flower—each cell undergoes meiosis and produces four haploid spore cells. Each of these
cells becomes a single pollen grain. The wall of each pollen grain
thickens, protecting the contents of the pollen grain from dryness
and physical damage when it is released from the anther.

The nucleus of each pollen grain undergoes one mitotic
division to produce two haploid nuclei. The pollen grain, which
is the entire male gametophyte, usually stops growing until it
is released from the anther and deposited on a stigma.

The ovary of the flower contains the ovules, in which the female gametophyte develops. A single diploid cell goes through meiosis to produce four haploid cells, three of which disintegrate. The remaining cell undergoes mitosis to produce eight nuclei. These eight nuclei and the surrounding membrane are called the **embryo sac**. The embryo sac, contained within the ovule, is the female gametophyte of a flowering plant. One of the eight nuclei, near the base of the gametophyte, is the egg nucleus—the female gamete. If fertilization takes place, this cell will become the zygote that grows into a new sporophyte plant.

✓CHECKPOINT **Where does the female gametophyte develop?**

Pollination

Once the gametophytes have developed inside the flower, pollination takes place. 🔑 **Most gymnosperms and some angiosperms are wind pollinated, whereas most angiosperms are pollinated by animals.** These animals, mainly insects, birds, and bats, carry pollen from one flower to another. Because wind pollination is less efficient than animal pollination, wind-pollinated plants, such as the oak tree in **Figure 24–8,** rely on favorable weather and sheer numbers to get pollen from one plant to another. Animal-pollinated plants have a variety of adaptations, such as bright colors and sweet nectar, to attract animals. Animals have developed behaviors to help them find flowers. They have also evolved body shapes that enable them to reach nectar deep within certain flowers.

Insect pollination is adaptive because it increases the fitness of both organisms. It is beneficial to insects and other animals because it provides a dependable source of food. The food may take the form of pollen itself or the sugar-rich liquid called nectar. Plants also benefit because the insects take their pollen directly from flower to flower. Insect pollination is much more efficient than wind pollination, giving insect-pollinated plants a higher probability of reproductive success. In fact, many plant biologists suggest that the angiosperms displaced the gymnosperms so thoroughly during the past 100 million years in part because of insect pollination.

Figure 24–8 🔑 Most angiosperms are pollinated by animals, although some are pollinated by wind. The shape of a flower often indicates how it is pollinated. The flowers of an oak tree (A) are typical of wind-pollinated flowers in that they are small, are not brightly colored, and produce vast amounts of pollen. To attract insects and other animals, many animal-pollinated flowers are large and brightly colored. The rose flower (B) is pollinated by a variety of insects, whereas the trumpet creeper flower (C) has a tube shape that is adapted specifically to the long beak of a hummingbird.

A

B

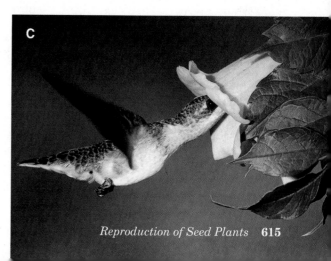
C

Fertilization in Angiosperms

If a pollen grain lands on the stigma of an appropriate flower, it begins to grow a pollen tube. The generative nucleus within the pollen grain divides and forms two sperm nuclei. The pollen tube now contains a tube nucleus and two sperm nuclei. The pollen tube grows into the style. There, it eventually reaches the ovary and enters the ovule.

Inside the embryo sac, two distinct fertilizations take place. First, one of the sperm nuclei fuses with the egg nucleus to produce a diploid zygote. The zygote will grow into the new plant embryo. Second, the other sperm nucleus does something truly remarkable—it fuses with two endosperm nuclei in the embryo sac to form a triploid (3N) cell. This cell will grow into a food-rich tissue known as **endosperm,** which nourishes the seedling as it grows.

As shown in **Figure 24–9,** a seed of corn, a monocot, contains a rich supply of endosperm. In many dicots, including garden beans, the cotyledons absorb the endosperm as the seed develops. The cotyledons then serve as the stored food supply for the embryo when it begins to grow.

Because two fertilization events take place between the male and female gametophytes, this process is known as **double fertilization.** Double fertilization may be one of the reasons why the angiosperms have been so successful. Recall that in gymnosperms, the food reserve built up in seeds is produced before fertilization takes place. As a result, if an ovule is not fertilized, those resources are wasted. In angiosperms, if an ovule is not fertilized, the endosperm does not form, and food is not wasted by preparing for a nonexistent zygote.

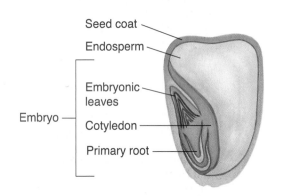

Seed coat

Endosperm

Embryonic leaves

Embryo —

Cotyledon

Primary root

▲ **Figure 24–9** The endosperm of a corn seed develops through the process of double fertilization. After one sperm nucleus fertilizes the egg cell, the zygote forms. Then, the other sperm nucleus fuses with the two endosperm nuclei to form a triploid cell, which develops into the endosperm. **Predicting** *What will happen to the endosperm when the seed begins to grow?*

24–1 Section Assessment

1. 🔑 **Key Concept** What are the reproductive structures of gymnosperms?

2. 🔑 **Key Concept** Describe the flower and how it is involved in reproduction.

3. 🔑 **Key Concept** Are angiosperms typically wind pollinated or animal pollinated? How does this process take place?

4. What is endosperm? Where does it form in a flowering plant?

5. **Critical Thinking Inferring** Many flowers have bright patterns of coloration that directly surround the reproductive structures. How might this type of coloration be advantageous to the plant?

🧍**iTEXT** **Assessment** Use iText to review the important concepts in Section 24–1.

MAKING CONNECTIONS

Alternation of Generations Review the life cycle of the green alga *Chlamydomonas* in Chapter 20, p. 513. Make a compare-and-contrast table comparing alternation of generations in seed plants and *Chlamydomonas*. Include in the table which stage of each organism's life cycle is dominant (haploid or diploid), the process by which zygotes form, and when meiosis occurs.

Flowers by Design

What's your favorite flower? Like many people, you might have said "the rose." Roses are the world's most popular ornamental flowers, prized for their beauty and fragrance. They come in many colors. Chances are you've seen red, white, pink, or even yellow roses. But have you ever seen a blue rose? Probably not! Roses do not have the enzymes to produce blue pigments, so even the best efforts of plant breeders have not produced a blue rose.

What Makes a Flower?

Plant biologists have discovered that flower development is controlled by a series of genes. By manipulating these genes, scientists have produced plants that will flower earlier and much more quickly than normal. Even young seedlings have been induced to flower.

Changing the color of a flower, however, has proved a little more difficult. Knowing that petunias often produce blue flowers, in 1991 Australian researchers isolated the gene for the enzyme that produces blue pigment. Then, they transferred this "blue gene" to a rose. To their disappointment, however, the new roses were just as red as ever. Apparently, flower color is a tricky and unpredictable business—particularly in roses—that involves complex interactions with other genes and pigments.

A White Sportcoat and a Violet Carnation?

When the Australian scientists turned from roses to carnations, they succeeded in producing a carnation with unique violet flowers. Again, they

inserted the gene from the blue petunias into a carnation plant. The result, shown in the photos, was a deep violet carnation unlike any ever seen in nature. In 1999, these genetically modified carnation plants were introduced for sale in Europe and the United States. A number of biotech companies are now rushing to master the intricacies of color genetics in flowers. Before long, one of these companies may have what they've all been seeking—a blue rose.

On Your Own

1. In addition to new varieties of flowers, plant breeders have developed genetically modified fruits, vegetables, and grains. Pick a common food crop and research how plant breeders have modified it to give it specific characteristics.

2. Suppose you are a plant geneticist and you want to create a new color of lily. Select the flower color you would like to produce. Then, write down the scientific steps that you would take to produce the new flower color.

24–2 Seed Development and Germination

Guide for Reading

 Key Concepts
- How do fruits form?
- How are seeds dispersed?
- What factors influence the dormancy and germination of seeds?

Vocabulary
dormancy
germination

Reading Strategy:
Summarizing As you read, take notes on the development, dispersal, dormancy, and germination of seeds. Write a few sentences summarizing each of these processes.

The development of the seed was a major factor in the success of plants on land. Seeds provide nourishment and protection for delicate embryos. As you will see, the angiosperm seed, enclosed within a fruit formed by the ovary wall, offers something else. In many cases, it helps get the seed into the best possible location to start its new life.

Seed and Fruit Development

Once fertilization is complete, nutrients flow into the flower tissue and support the development of the growing embryo within the seed. **As angiosperm seeds mature, the ovary walls thicken to form a fruit that encloses the developing seeds.** A fruit is a ripened ovary that contains angiosperm seeds. Examples of fruits are shown in **Figure 24–10**. Parts of the ovule toughen to form a seed coat, which is the outer layer that protects the delicate embryo and its tiny food supply. The ovary wall then thickens and joins with other parts of the flower stem. These structures together form a fruit that encloses the seeds.

The term *fruit,* biologically speaking, applies to any seed that is enclosed within its embryo wall. The term applies to the things we usually think of as fruits, such as apples, grapes, and strawberries. However, foods such as peas, corn, beans, rice, cucumbers, and tomatoes, which we commonly call vegetables, are also fruits. Whether it tastes sweet or not, if it contains a seed enclosed inside the ovary wall, it is a fruit.

The ovary wall surrounding a simple fruit may be fleshy, as it is in grapes and tomatoes, or tough, like the pod of a bean. In some fruits, such as peaches and cherries, the inner wall of the ovary is attached rigidly to the surface of the seed. In others, such as the maple, the dry fruit forms an aerodynamic shape that helps the seed whirl gracefully down when it is released from the parent plant.

✓ CHECKPOINT *What is a fruit?*

Figure 24–10 As seeds mature, the ovary walls thicken to form a fruit that encloses the developing seeds. Like the flowers from which they develop, fruits vary in structure. They can contain one seed, as in the lychee nut, or several, as in the apple. Fruits also have different amounts of tissue, which often relates to the mode of seed dispersal.

Maple

Seed

Seeds

Apple

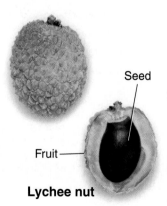

Seed

Fruit

Lychee nut

Seed Dispersal

What are fruits for? They are certainly not there to nourish the seedling—the endosperm does that. Why should an entire phylum of plants have seeds that are wrapped in an additional layer of tissue—tissue that is often packed with nutrients and is later discarded when the fruit is released from the plant? It seems to make no sense.

Think of the blackberries that grow wild in the forests of North America. Each seed is enclosed in a sweet, juicy fruit, making it a tasty treat for all kinds of birds and mammals. What good does all that sweetness do the fruit? All it does is get the seed eaten! Well, believe it or not, that's exactly the point.

Dispersal by Animals The seeds of many plants, especially those with sweet, fleshy fruits, are eaten by animals, as shown in **Figure 24–11.** The seeds are covered with tough coatings that protect them from digestive chemicals, enabling them to pass through an animal's digestive system unharmed. The seeds then sprout in the feces eliminated from the animal. **Seeds dispersed by animals are typically contained in fleshy, nutritious fruits.** These fruits provide nutrition for the animal and also help the plant disperse its seeds—often to areas where there is less competition with the parent plants.

Dispersal by Wind and Water Animals are not the only means by which plants can scatter their seeds. Seeds are also adapted for dispersal by wind and water. **Seeds dispersed by wind or water are typically lightweight, allowing them to be carried in the air or to float on the surface of the water.** The seeds of ash and maple trees are encased in winglike structures that spin and twirl as they are released, helping them glide considerable distances from their parent plants. Westerners are familiar with tumbleweed plants, shown in **Figure 24–12.** These plants break off at their roots and tumble along the dry plains, scattering their seeds as they are blown by the wind. An example of a seed that is dispersed by water is the coconut. This seed contains a liquid endosperm layer (the "milk" of the coconut). A coconut is buoyant enough to float in sea water within its protective coating for many weeks. Water dispersal is one reason for the success of this species in reaching remote islands.

▲ **Figure 24–11** Seeds that are dispersed by animals typically contain fleshy, sweet tissue. A cedar waxwing feasts on mountain ash berries. Berries are enclosed in sugary tissue that is eaten by birds or other animals. Berries contain seeds that pass through the animal and are dispersed away from the parent plant.

▶ **Figure 24–12** Wind-dispersed seeds are typically lightweight. Tumbleweed plants release small seeds as the plants are blown along open stretches of land.

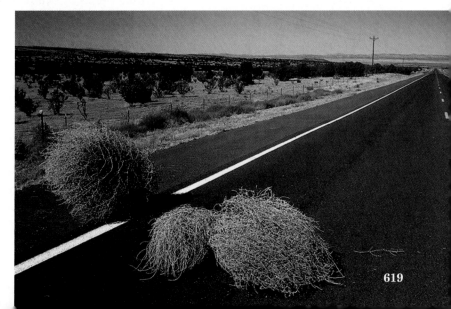

Temperature and Seed Germination

Arisaema dracontium—"green dragon"—is a plant that grows from the southern United States to Canada. The graph shows germination properties of *Arisaema* seeds gathered from Clinton, Ontario, and from Baton Rouge, Louisiana. Seeds from both locations were stored at two different temperatures: 3°C and 24°C. The graph indicates the rate of seed germination following storage at these different temperatures.

1. **Interpreting Graphics** What effect does chilling have on germination of seeds from Ontario? How does chilling affect the seeds from Louisiana?

2. **Forming Hypotheses** Keeping in mind that annual temperatures are much lower in Ontario than in Louisiana, describe how the different rates of seed germination might be explained in terms of adaptation to the local climate.

Effect of Temperature on Seed Germination

Seed Dormancy

Some seeds sprout so rapidly that they are practically instant plants. Bean seeds are a good example. With proper amounts of water and warmth, a newly planted mature bean seed rapidly develops into a bean plant. But many seeds will not grow when they first mature. Instead, these seeds enter a period of **dormancy,** during which the embryo is alive but not growing. The length of dormancy varies in different plant species. 🔑 **Environmental factors such as temperature and moisture can cause a seed to end dormancy and germinate.**

Seed dormancy can be adaptive in several ways. It can allow for long-distance dispersal, as in a coconut that floats across the sea for weeks or even months until it washes ashore. It may also allow seeds to germinate under ideal growth conditions. The seeds of many temperate plants do not germinate during the summer or winter, since the extremes of temperature would make it impossible for seedlings to survive. Instead, most seeds germinate in the spring, when conditions are best for growth. The long period of cold temperatures during which the seeds are dormant is required before growth can begin.

Other environmental conditions can end seed dormancy. Some pine trees, for example, produce seeds in sealed cones. These seeds remain dormant until the high temperatures generated by forest fires cause the cones to open, as shown in **Figure 24–13.** This process activates the seeds, allowing the plants to reclaim the forest floor quickly after a fire.

▼ **Figure 24–13** 🔑 Environmental factors such as temperature and moisture can end dormancy. The cones of this bishop pine open and release seeds only after being exposed to the heat of a forest fire.

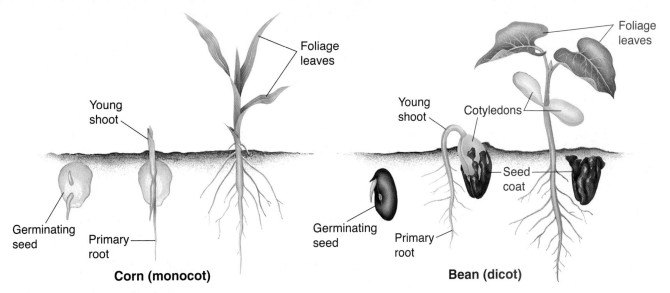

Corn (monocot)

Bean (dicot)

Seed Germination

Seed **germination** is the early growth stage of the plant embryo. **Figure 24–14** shows germination in monocots and dicots. When seeds germinate, they absorb water. The absorbed water causes the endosperm to swell, cracking open the seed coat. Through the cracked seed coat, the young root emerges and begins to grow.

Recall that monocots have a single cotyledon, or seed leaf. In most monocots, the single cotyledon remains underground. The growing shoot emerges while protected by a sheath. In dicots, which have two cotyledons, germination takes place in one of two ways. In some species, the cotyledons emerge above ground and protect the first foliage leaves. They then wither and drop off the plant. In other species, such as the bean plant in **Figure 24–14**, the cotyledons remain below the soil and provide a food source for the growing seedling. In this case, the young shoot grows longer and forms an arch that protects the delicate shoot tip. As the arch lengthens, it pulls the cotyledons and the shoot tip above the surface.

▲ **Figure 24–14** The corn seedling (left) is a monocot in which the shoot grows directly upward, protected by its sheath. The garden bean (right) is a dicot in which the cotyledons emerge above ground. **Applying Concepts** *How does germination differ between monocots and dicots?*

24–2 Section Assessment

1. 🔑 **Key Concept** Describe what happens as fertilized angiosperm seeds mature.

2. 🔑 **Key Concept** Compare the typical structure of seeds that are dispersed by animals to those dispersed by wind and water.

3. 🔑 **Key Concept** Why is it adaptive for some seeds to remain dormant before they germinate?

4. **Critical Thinking Applying Concepts** Many environmentalists state that controlling fires in the western United States will change the structure of the ecosystem. How might the example of seed dormancy in certain types of pines support their case?

📱 **Assessment** Use iText to review the important concepts in Section 24–2.

Take It to the NET

Read about different ways that seeds can travel. Then, make a concept map to summarize the different ways in which seeds are dispersed. Use the links provided in the Biology area at the Prentice Hall Web site for help in completing this activity:
www.phschool.com

24–3 Plant Propagation and Agriculture

Guide for Reading

 Key Concepts
- What forms of vegetative reproduction occur in plants?
- What is plant propagation?
- Which crops are the major food supply for humans?

Vocabulary
vegetative reproduction
stolon
grafting
budding

Reading Strategy: Using Prior Knowledge
Before you read the section, make a list of methods that humans use to grow food plants such as fruit trees and grains. As you read, add new information to your list.

S eed plants have been essential to human life from the beginnings of our existence on this planet. The earliest humans gathered plants for food, shelter, and medicine. Over time, humans learned to collect and plant edible seeds, thus domesticating wild plants. The technology of growing crops and propagating desirable plant species is the basis of modern society.

Vegetative Reproduction

Although we have concentrated on patterns of sexual reproduction, many kinds of flowering plants also reproduce asexually by **vegetative reproduction.** Vegetative reproduction enables a single plant that is well adapted to a particular environment to produce many offspring genetically identical to itself. This process takes place naturally in many plants, and it is also used as a technique by horticulturalists who want to produce many copies of an individual plant.

 Vegetative reproduction includes the production of new plants from horizontal stems, from plantlets, and from underground roots.

Because vegetative reproduction does not involve pollination or seed formation, it can enable plants to reproduce very quickly. Several species of angiosperms, such as the spider plant shown in **Figure 24–15,** produce tiny plants, or plantlets, along their leaves or stems. If the parent plant is knocked over or if plantlets fall to the soil, they can take root and grow into new plants. New plants can also grow from the leaves of a parent plant if the leaves fall to the ground under conditions that allow them to root.

Another way in which plants reproduce vegetatively is by growing horizontal stems. Strawberry plants, shown in **Figure 24–16,** send out long trailing stems called **stolons** that produce roots when they touch the ground. Once the roots are well established, each stolon may be broken, forming a new plant that is truly independent of its parent. Bamboo plants grow long underground stems that can send up new shoots in several places. In fact, bamboo forests that cover huge areas are often the descendants of a single bamboo plant that reproduced asexually.

◀ **Figure 24–15** The production of plantlets is a form of asexual reproduction. The spider plant produces plantlets at the tips of its leaves. When a plantlet reaches the soil, it can develop roots and grow into a new spider plant.

◄ **Figure 24–16** The strawberry plant reproduces vegetatively by producing thin, horizontal stems called stolons. Each node along the stolon produces roots that anchor the plant into the ground.
Applying Concepts *Describe how asexual reproduction might allow a plant to become established rapidly in a new area.*

Plant Propagation

Sometimes the characteristics of a particular plant are so attractive or beneficial that horticulturists want to make many exact copies of the plant. But the growers also want to avoid the variation that would result if the plant reproduced sexually by seeds. In addition, new varieties of some plants, such as grapefruits and navel oranges, do not produce seeds. **In plant propagation, horticulturists use cuttings, grafting, or budding to make many identical copies of a plant or to produce offspring from seedless plants.**

Cuttings One of the simplest ways to reproduce plants vegetatively is by cuttings. A grower "cuts" from the plant a length of stem that includes a number of buds containing meristematic tissue. That stem is then partially buried in soil or in a special rooting mixture. Some common plants, such as coleus, root so easily that no other treatment is necessary. The cuttings of many woody plants, however, do not develop roots easily. To help cuttings of these plants form roots, growers use mixtures of plant hormones called rooting powders.

Grafting and Budding Grafting and budding are used to reproduce seedless plants and varieties of woody plants that do not produce strong root systems. In both of these techniques, new plants are grown on plants that have strong root systems. To do this, a piece of stem or a lateral bud is cut from the parent plant and attached to another plant. The cut piece is called the scion, and the plant to which it is attached is called the stock. When stems are used as scions, the process is called **grafting,** shown in **Figure 24–17.** When buds are used as scions, the process is called **budding.**

Grafting usually works best when plants are dormant because the wounds created can heal before new growth starts. In all cases, grafts are successful only if the vascular cambiums of scion and stock are firmly connected to each other.

✓CHECKPOINT *What are the different techniques used to propagate woody plants?*

▼ **Figure 24–17** Plant propagation uses a variety of techniques to make identical copies of a single plant. Here, a scion of a commercial orange tree is being grafted to a larger, established tree.

▲ **Figure 24–18** 🔵 Most of the world's food supply comes from a few crop plants. Rice, here being planted by hand, is a staple crop in China and many nations of Southeast Asia.

Agriculture

The importance of agriculture—the systematic cultivation of plants—should be obvious, even to those of us who live in urban areas and seldom visit a farm. Modern farming is the foundation on which human society is built. North America has some of the richest, most productive cropland in the world. As a result, farmers in the United States and Canada produce so much food that they are able to feed millions of people around the world as well as their own citizens.

Worldwide Patterns of Agriculture Many scholars now trace the beginnings of human civilization to the cultivation of crop plants. Evidence suggests that agriculture developed separately in many parts of the world about 10,000 to 12,000 years ago. Once people discovered how to grow plants for food, the planting and harvesting of crops tended to keep them in one place for much of the year, leading directly to the establishment of social institutions. Even today, agriculture, shown in **Figure 24–18**, is the principal occupation of more human beings than any other activity.

Thousands of different plants—nearly all of which are angiosperms—are raised for food in various parts of the world. 🔑 **Most of the people of the world depend on a few crop plants, such as wheat, rice, and corn, for the bulk of their food supply.** The same crops are also used to feed livestock.

Biology and History

The Evolution of Agriculture

More than 10,000 years ago, humans began a gradual transition from hunter-gatherer societies to civilizations that were reliant on cultivated crops—many of which are still cultivated today. Because of regional differences in climate, soil type, and naturally occurring plant life, the crops planted today arose in different parts of the world.

Chilies and avocados are cultivated as important additions to the diets of Mesoamerican people. Chilies are used for flavoring foods, and avocados provide vitamins and oils.

7000 BC

8000 BC

Inhabitants of the Middle East begin to cultivate wheat. The change from gathering a crop in the wild to farming it eventually contributes to the rise of one of the earliest Middle Eastern civilizations.

5500 BC

Barley is cultivated in the Nile Valley of Egypt. About 2000 years later, farming settlements are united throughout the Nile Valley, and Egyptian culture flourishes.

You may not have thought of it this way, but the food we take from crop plants is stored in their seeds. Recall that the food stored within the seeds of all angiosperms is a tissue known as endosperm. Worldwide, then, most of humanity depends for food on the endosperm of only a few carefully cultivated species of grass. The pattern in the United States is similar. Roughly 80 percent of all U.S. cropland is used to grow just four crops: wheat, corn, soybeans, and hay. Of these crops, three—wheat, corn, and hay—are derived from grasses.

✓ **CHECKPOINT** *How is endosperm related to the world's food supply?*

Changes in Agriculture The discovery and introduction of new plants has changed human history. Before they were discovered in the Americas, many important crops—including corn, peanuts, beans, and potatoes—were unknown in Europe. The introduction of these plants changed European agriculture rapidly. Within a century, many of these foods had become important parts of the European diet. We think of boiled potatoes, for example, as traditional staples of German and Irish cooking, but 400 years ago they were new items in the diets of Europeans.

The efficiency of agriculture has been improved through the selective breeding of crop plants and improvements in farming techniques. The corn grown by Native Americans, for example, was developed more than 8000 years ago from teosinte, a wild grass found in Mexico.

KEEP CURRENT WITH . . .

SCIENCE NEWS®

To find out more about the topics in this chapter, go to:
www.phschool.com

Writing Activity

The domestication of all major crops had a major impact on the growth of civilizations. Choose one of the crops discussed below and research how that crop contributed to the rise of civilization and culture in that region.

Rice cultivation becomes well established in southern China, southeast Asia, and northern India. Rice farming spreads widely from these regions, and rice later becomes a major Chinese export.

4500 BC

5000 BC

People in central Mexico domesticate corn, also called maize. Early corncobs are only about an inch long and have a few dozen kernels. The ancestor of corn was probably a wild grass called *teosinte*.

3500 BC

The potato is domesticated in the Andes Mountains of South America. Early Andean farmers eventually produce 700 varieties of potatoes by cultivating them on irrigated terraces built on mountain slopes.

Annual Corn Yield in the United States

▲ **Figure 24–19** Between 1970 and 2000, the amount of corn grown per acre in the United States increased more than 60 percent. A field of corn, also called *Zea mays,* is shown in the photograph. **Interpreting Graphics** *Describe the trend shown in the graph for the years 1983 and 1988.*

In more recent times, other familiar crops have been the product of selective breeding. Sugar beets, the source of most refined sugar from the United States, were produced from the ordinary garden beet using selective breeding. Plants as different as cabbage, broccoli, and Brussels sprouts have been developed from a single species of wild mustard.

Improvements in farming techniques have contributed to dramatic improvements in crop yields, as shown in **Figure 24–19.** Some of the most important techniques have been the use of pesticides and fertilizers. These improvements have lowered the price of food and enabled farmers to feed many more people without any expansion of the amount of land under cultivation.

24–3 Section Assessment

1. **Key Concept** Define vegetative reproduction. How do the offspring produced compare to the parent plant?

2. **Key Concept** What is the purpose of plant propagation?

3. **Key Concept** What are the main food crops? What techniques have improved crop yields during the past several decades?

4. Compare grafting and budding. Why are these techniques preferable to sexual propagation of woody plants?

5. **Critical Thinking Inferring** Dandelions employ an unusual form of reproduction that produces seeds but does not involve meiosis and the production of haploid gametes. The pollen produced within flowers is sterile and produces seeds without fertilization. What advantages might this system have over sexual reproduction of viable seeds?

TEXT **Assessment** Use iText to review the important concepts in Section 24–3.

ALTERNATIVE ASSESSMENT

Creative Writing
Write a short story describing how a new plant could form by vegetative reproduction or plant propagation. Your story should include the part played by tissues in stems in the process. (*Hint:* Review the blue heading on stem structure and function on page 589 in Chapter 23.)

Investigating Pollination

In this investigation, you will design an experiment to test a hypothesis about the chemical signals that steer the growth of pollen tubes toward the ovary.

Problem What controls the direction of pollen tube growth?

Materials

- flowering plants, such as beans or *Brassicas*
- hand lens
- small paintbrush
- forceps
- pollen nutrient solution
- pollen nutrient solution without calcium
- concentrated calcium chloride solution
- dissecting probe
- microscope slides
- coverslips
- dropper pipette

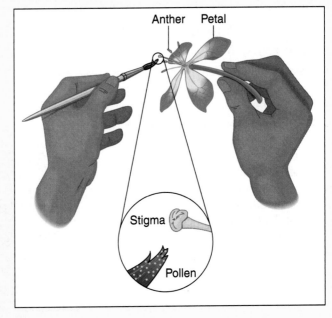

Anther Petal

Stigma

Pollen

Skills Designing Experiments, Controlling Variables

Design Your Experiment

1. Use a hand lens to observe the flowers of a flowering plant. Identify the anthers and stigma of a flower.

2. Use a small paintbrush to transfer pollen from several flowers to the stigmas of other flowers.

3. Use forceps to transfer several anthers to a microscope slide. Add a drop of pollen nutrient solution. Gently tap the anthers with the tip of a dissecting probe to release pollen.

4. Discard the anthers and add a coverslip. Observe the pollen with the microscope at low power. Make a labeled drawing of your observations.

5. Your teacher will provide slides containing pollen that has been in pollen nutrient solution for several hours. Observe these slides with the microscope. Record your observations.

6. Pollen tubes have been found to grow toward calcium or pieces of ovaries. Design an experiment to test the hypothesis that calcium is the chemical signal that guides the growing pollen tube toward the ovary.

7. As you plan your experiment, be sure to control all important variables. If observing pollen tube growth in a flower directly is too difficult, you will need to choose some other method to test the hypothesis. Have your teacher check your plan before you begin your experiment.

Analyze and Conclude

1. **Applying Concepts** The pollen of most plants will not germinate in pure water. What function of the stigma and style did the pollen nutrient solution replace?

2. **Observing** Did the pollen tubes grow toward a source of calcium? Toward ovary tissue?

3. **Drawing Conclusions** In many experiments, pollen tubes grow toward either calcium or ovary tissue. From these results, could you conclude that calcium directs pollen tube growth toward the ovary in flowers? Explain.

Go Further

Designing Experiments Plan an experiment to test the effect of light on the rate and direction of pollen tube growth.

24–1 Reproduction With Cones and Flowers

Key Concepts

- Reproduction in gymnosperms takes place in cones, which are produced by a mature sporophyte plant.

- Flowers are reproductive organs that are composed of four kinds of specialized leaves: sepals, petals, stamens, and carpels.

- Reproduction in angiosperms takes place within the flower. Following pollination and fertilization, the seeds develop inside protective structures called fruits.

- Most gymnosperms are wind pollinated, whereas most flowering plants are pollinated by animals.

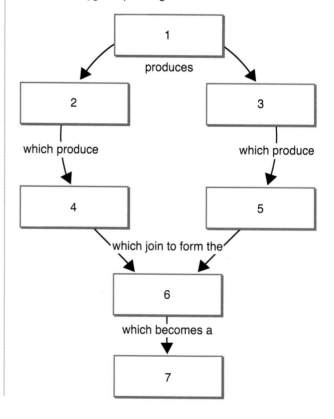

Vocabulary

- pollen cone, p. 610 • seed cone, p. 610
- ovule, p. 610 • pollen tube, p. 611
- sepal, p. 612 • petal, p. 612 • stamen, p. 612
- filament, p. 612 • anther, p. 612 • carpel, p. 612
- ovary, p. 612 • style, p. 612 • stigma, p. 612
- embryo sac, p. 615 • endosperm, p. 616
- double fertilization, p. 616

24–2 Seed Development and Germination

Key Concepts

- As angiosperm seeds mature, the ovary walls thicken to form a fruit that encloses the developing seeds.

- Seeds dispersed by animals are typically contained in fleshy, nutritious fruits.

- Seeds dispersed by wind or water are typically lightweight, allowing them to be carried in the air or to float on the surface of the water.

- Environmental factors such as temperature and moisture can cause a seed to end dormancy and germinate.

Vocabulary

dormancy, p. 620
germination, p. 621

24–3 Plant Propagation and Agriculture

Key Concepts

- Vegetative reproduction includes the production of new plants from horizontal stems, cuttings, leaves, plantlets, and underground roots.

- Horticulturists use plant propagation to make many identical copies of a plant or to produce offspring from seedless plants.

- Most of the people of the world depend on a few crop plants, such as wheat, rice, and corn, for the bulk of their food supply.

Vocabulary

- vegetative reproduction, p. 622
- stolon, p. 622 • grafting, p. 623
- budding, p. 623

Thinking Visually

Use the following terms to complete the flowchart about reproduction in gymnosperms: *female gametophyte, seed, pollen cone, mature sporophyte, seed cone, zygote, pollen grains.*

```
              ┌──────────┐
              │    1     │
              └──────────┘
                produces
           ↙              ↘
    ┌──────────┐      ┌──────────┐
    │    2     │      │    3     │
    └──────────┘      └──────────┘
  which produce       which produce
        ↓                   ↓
    ┌──────────┐      ┌──────────┐
    │    4     │      │    5     │
    └──────────┘      └──────────┘
         ↘  which join to form the  ↙
              ┌──────────┐
              │    6     │
              └──────────┘
             which becomes a
                   ↓
              ┌──────────┐
              │    7     │
              └──────────┘
```

Chapter 24

Part A

Multiple Choice

For each statement or question, select the number of the word or expression that, of those given, best completes the statement or answers the question.

1 Two structures specialized for reproduction in seed plants are
 (1) cones and flowers
 (2) cones and lateral buds
 (3) lateral and terminal buds
 (4) meristems and flowers

2 Which statement is *not* true of reproduction in a pine tree?
 (1) The pollen tube contains two diploid sperm.
 (2) One sperm fertilizes the egg.
 (3) One sperm disintegrates.
 (4) The zygote grows into an embryo.

3 In angiosperms, the structures that produce the male gametophyte are called the
 (1) anthers   (3) pollen tubes
 (2) sepals   (4) stigmas

4 Pollination occurs when pollen lands on the
 (1) style   (3) filament
 (2) stigma   (4) anther

5 The thickened ovary wall of a plant joins with other parts of the flower stem to become the
 (1) fruit   (3) endosperm
 (2) seed   (4) cotyledon

6 The food-rich tissue that nourishes seedlings as they grow is known as
 (1) endosperm   (3) radicles
 (2) carpels   (4) cotyledons

7 In seed plants, the structure that encloses the male gametophyte and transports it to another plant is called a
 (1) pollen grain (3) flower
 (2) seed   (4) pollinator

8 The period during which the embryo is alive but not growing is called
 (1) fertilization (3) dormancy
 (2) germination (4) vegetative growth

9 A scientist wants to artificially pollinate a flower. Where would he find the pollen grains?
 (1) sepal   (3) anther
 (2) carpel   (4) ovary

10 The process in which a single plant produces many offspring genetically identical to itself is called
 (1) sexual reproduction
 (2) agriculture
 (3) dormancy
 (4) vegetative reproduction

11 The illustration above shows the germination of a pea plant. The feature labeled A is a(an)
 (1) anther   (3) cotyledon
 (2) seed coat   (4) root

12 Which part of a flower develops into a fruit?
 (1) pollen tube (3) anther
 (2) carpel   (4) ovary

13 Which flower structure below includes all of the others listed?
 (1) style   (3) ovary
 (2) stigma   (4) carpel

14 All of the following are fruits *except*
 (1) tomatoes   (3) beets
 (2) corn   (4) cucumbers

> **Test-Taking Tip** When answering questions pertaining to experimental situations, read all of the questions first. Then, read the passage carefully and examine any accompanying data, looking for the specific information required to answer the questions.

Preparing for the
Living Environment Exam

Parts B and C

Multiple Choice and Extended Response

For those questions that ask you to select a response, choose the one that best completes the statement or answers the question. For all others follow the directions given.

15 Complete the following chart that identifies types of vegetative reproduction. (Do not write in this book.) Explain the process of reproduction, and name a plant that exemplifies each type.

Type	Process	Example
Stolon		
Cutting		
Grafting		

16 Is vegetative reproduction sexual or asexual? How do the traits of the new plant compare to those of the parent?

17 Draw and label a diagram showing the stages in the life cycle of a typical gymnosperm.

18 Describe at least two ways in which pollen is transferred from one plant to another.

19 Some plants form flowers that produce stamens but no carpels. Could fruit form on one of these flowers? Support your answer with an explanation.

20 The seeds of lupines, an arctic plant, can remain dormant for thousands of years. Why might this trait be important to a plant in an arctic environment?

21 Explain how seed germination is similar in monocots and dicots. How is it different?

22 What does a plant need that makes it necessary for seed germination to start with the emergence of a root rather than a shoot?

Base your answers to questions 23 through 25 on the information and data table below and on your knowledge of biology.

A scientist measured the average time it took different fruits to fall 1 meter from the parent tree. Assume that for every second a fruit falls, it is carried 1.5 meters away from the parent tree.

Relationship Between Fruit Type and Dispersal Time

Type of Tree	Average Time (sec) for Seed to Fall 1 m
Norway maple	0.98
Silver maple	0.64
White ash	0.30
Shagbark hickory	0.16
Red oak	0.16

Norway maple   Silver maple

White ash   Shagbark hickory   Red oak

23 Which fruit was carried the farthest from the parent tree?
(1) Norway maple   (3) white ash
(2) silver maple   (4) shagbark hickory

24 According to these data, what benefit does a winged fruit have over an acorn?
A It is lighter.
B It is heavier.
C It will travel farther.
(1) A, only   (3) C, only
(2) B, only   (4) A and C

25 What other means of seed dispersal is used by the shagbark hickory and the red oak?

26 Female cones secrete a sticky material.
• Explain how this trait is advantageous to gymnosperms.
• How might this trait have evolved?

27 A child runs through a field of daisies. She sees bees buzzing above the flowers and Japanese beetles crawling across the petals. When she returns home, she admires the long neck of a trumpet flower in the garden. It was planted to attract hummingbirds to the yard. In evolutionary terms, which flower is more fit? Support your answer with an explanation.

28 A friend suggests that seeds do not need cotyledons to grow. You argue that cotyledons are important to seeds. Design an experiment that shows the effect that removing cotyledons has on seed growth. Be sure to identify

- the importance of cotyledons
- your hypothesis
- the procedures you will follow
- the type of data you will collect
- how you will present the data

29 The graph below shows the increase in the annual yield of corn in the U.S. over a 30-year period. The yield of corn has nearly doubled in that time span. Much of this increase is due to the use of improved fertilizers and pesticides. In addition, farmers have used selective breeding methods to improve production.

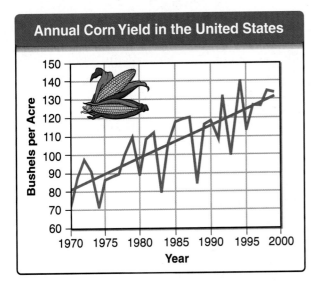

Annual Corn Yield in the United States

Write an essay discussing these issues. Be sure to address

- the environmental consequences of fertilizers
- the effect of pesticides on the food chain
- the traits of corn that farmers would choose in a selective breeding program

30 Explain what purposes are served by seed dormancy.

31 It is important to store seeds in a dry, dark place. Predict what might happen if water from a leaky ceiling were to drip onto packages of seeds on a store shelf. Support your prediction with an explanation.

Base your answers to questions 32 and 33 on the diagram below and on your knowledge of biology.

The diagram below shows the parts of a typical flower.

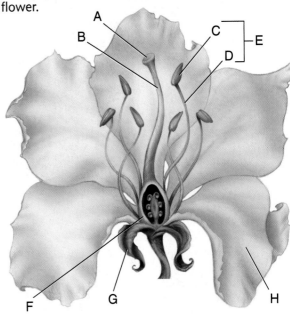

32 Write a short description of Structure A. Be sure to include its name, function, the results of its function, and any organisms or environmental conditions necessary to perform that function.

33 Identify Structure H, and write a short description about its role in pollination.

34 Briefly describe each stage in the life cycle of an angiosperm, starting with germination of the seed.

Take It to the NET

Do all flowers smell sweet? Visit the Prentice Hall Weg site at **www.phschool.com** to find out about flowers that smell unpleasant. Then, answer the following questions:

- What is a carrion flower? Why do some smell like rotting flesh?
- What happens to the maggots that are laid in a carrion flower?
- Describe five other flowers that have unusual or unpleasant odors. How are they pollinated?

25 Plant Responses and Adaptations

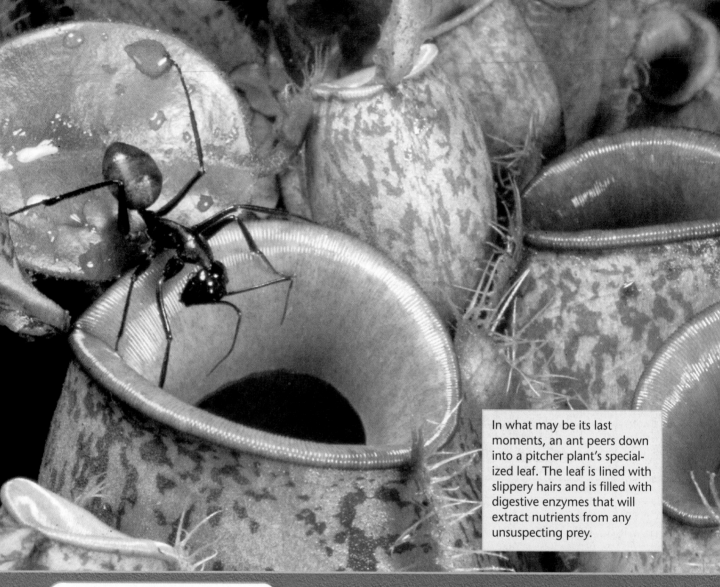

In what may be its last moments, an ant peers down into a pitcher plant's specialized leaf. The leaf is lined with slippery hairs and is filled with digestive enzymes that will extract nutrients from any unsuspecting prey.

Inquiry Activity

How are plants adapted to their environments?

Procedure

1. Examine several desert plants and several rain forest plants. Note any differences between these two groups of plants. Record your observations.

2. List the characteristics that distinguish desert plants and rain forest plants. List any characteristics that you observed in both types of plants.

Think About It

1. **Classifying** What characteristics did you identify that distinguish desert plants and rain forest plants?

2. **Formulating Hypotheses** How could these characteristics help desert and rain forest plants survive in their environments?

3. **Predicting** Draw a real or an imaginary plant that is adapted for warm, dry summers and rainy, cold winters. Write a paragraph describing the adaptations of your plant.

25–1 Hormones and Plant Growth

Unlike most animals, plants do not have a rigidly set organization to their bodies. Cows have four legs, ants have six, and spiders have eight; but tomato plants do not have a predetermined number of leaves or branches. However, plants such as the baobab tree in **Figure 25–1** show distinct patterns of growth. As a result, you can easily tell the difference between a tomato plant and a corn plant, between an oak tree and a pine tree.

Patterns of Plant Growth

Although plant growth is not determined precisely, it still follows general patterns that differ among species. What controls these patterns of development? Biologists have discovered that plant cells send signals to one another that indicate when to divide and when not to divide, and when to develop into a new kind of cell.

There is another difference between growth in plants and animals. Once most animals reach adulthood, they stop growing. In contrast, even plants that are thousands of years old continue to grow new needles, add new wood, and produce cones or new flowers, almost as if parts of their bodies remained "forever young." As you have learned, the secrets of plant growth are found in meristems, regions of tissue that can produce cells that later develop into specialized tissues. Meristems are found at places where plants grow rapidly—the tips of growing stems and roots, and along the outer edges of woody tissues that produce new growth every year.

If meristems are the source of plant growth, how is that growth controlled and regulated? Plants grow in response to environmental factors such as light, moisture, temperature, and gravity. But how do roots "know" to grow down, and how do stems "know" to grow up toward light? How do the tissues of a plant determine the right time of year to produce flowers? How do plants ensure that their growth is evenly balanced—that the trunk of a tree grows large enough to support the weight of its leaves and branches? The answers to these questions involve the actions of chemicals that direct, control, and regulate plant growth.

Guide for Reading

 Key Concepts
- What are plant hormones?
- How do auxins, cytokinins, gibberellins, and ethylene affect plant growth?

Vocabulary
hormone
target cell
phototropism
auxin
gravitropism
lateral bud
apical dominance
herbicide
cytokinin
gibberellin
ethylene

**Reading Strategy:
Finding Main Ideas**
Before you read, skim the section to identify the key ideas about plant hormones. Then, read the section carefully, making a list of supporting details for each main idea.

▶ **Figure 25–1** All plants follow a highly regulated pattern of growth that continues throughout the life of the plant. This pattern of growth leads to distinct shapes, such as the thick trunk and widely spaced branches of this baobab tree. **Applying Concepts** *In which plant tissue does growth occur?*

633

Hormone-producing cells

Movement of hormone

Target cells

▲ **Figure 25–2** Plant hormones are chemical substances that control patterns of development as well as plant responses to the environment. Hormones are produced in apical meristems, in young leaves, in roots, and in growing flowers and fruits. From their place of origin, hormones move to other parts of the plant, where target cells respond in a way that is specific to the hormone.

Plant Hormones

In plants, the division, growth, maturation, and development of cells are controlled by a group of chemicals called hormones. A **hormone** is a substance that is produced in one part of an organism and affects another part of the same individual. ⬤ **Plant hormones are chemical substances that control a plant's patterns of growth and development, and the plant's responses to environmental conditions.**

The general mechanism of hormone action in plants is shown in **Figure 25–2.** As you can see, the hormone moves through the plant from the place where it is produced to the place where it triggers its response. The portion of an organism affected by a particular hormone is known as its **target cell** or target tissue. To respond to a hormone, the target cell must contain a hormone receptor—usually a protein—to which the hormone binds. If the appropriate receptor is present, the hormone can exert an influence on the target cell by changing its metabolism, affecting its growth rate, or activating the transcription of certain genes. Cells that do not contain receptors are generally unaffected by hormones.

Different kinds of cells may have different receptors for the same hormone. As a result, a single hormone may affect two different tissues in different ways. For example, a particular hormone may stimulate growth in stem tissues but inhibit growth in root tissues.

✓**CHECKPOINT** *In which cells do hormones carry out their functions?*

Auxins

The experiment that led to the discovery of the first plant hormone was carried out by Charles Darwin. In 1880, Darwin and his son Francis published a book called *The Power of Movement in Plants.* In this book, they described an experiment in which oat seedlings demonstrated a response known as phototropism. **Phototropism** is the tendency of a plant to grow toward a source of light.

Figure 25–3 shows an experiment similar to the one carried out by the Darwins. Notice that the tip of one of the oat seedlings was covered with an opaque cap. This plant did not bend toward the light, even though the rest of the plant was uncovered. However, if an opaque shield was placed a few centimeters below the tip, the plant would bend toward the light as if the shield were not there. Clearly, something was taking place at the tip of the seedling.

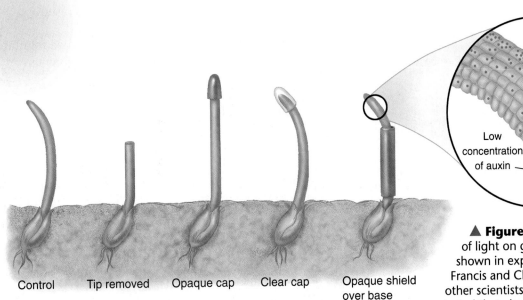

Control   Tip removed   Opaque cap   Clear cap   Opaque shield over base

High concentration of auxin

Low concentration of auxin

▲ **Figure 25–3** The effect of light on growing plants was shown in experiments by Francis and Charles Darwin and other scientists. They demonstrated that chemical substances (later called auxins) are produced in the growing tip of a plant. Auxins move from their source into the rest of the plant, where they stimulate cell elongation. A higher concentration of auxins accumulate in the shaded part of a stem, and cause the plant to bend toward a light source.

Auxins and Phototropism The Darwins suspected that the tip of each seedling produced substances that regulated cell growth. Forty years later, these substances were identified and named **auxins.** Auxins are produced in the apical meristem and are transported downward into the rest of the plant. They stimulate cell elongation. When light hits one side of the stem, a higher concentration of auxins develops in the shaded part of the stem. This change in concentration stimulates cells on the dark side to elongate. As a result, the stem bends away from the shaded side and toward the light. Recent experiments have shown that auxins migrate toward the shaded side of the stem, possibly due to changes in membrane permeability in response to light.

Auxins and Gravitropism Auxins are also responsible for **gravitropism,** which is the tendency of a plant to grow in a direction in response to the force of gravity. By mechanisms that are still not understood, auxins build up on the lower sides of roots and stems. In stems, auxins stimulate cell elongation, helping turn the plant upright, as shown in **Figure 25–4.** In roots, however, the effects of auxins are exactly the opposite. There, auxins inhibit cell growth and elongation, causing the roots to grow downward.

Auxins are also involved in the way roots grow around objects in the soil. If a growing root is forced sideways by an obstacle such as a rock, auxins accumulate on the lower side of the root. Once again, high concentrations of auxins inhibit the elongation of root cells. The uninhibited cells on the top elongate more than the auxin-inhibited cells on the bottom of the root. As a result, the root grows downward.

▶ **Figure 25–4** Auxins are responsible for the plant response called gravitropism. Auxins caused the tip of this tree stem to grow upright. **Comparing and Contrasting** *Compare how auxins affect the growth of stems and roots.*

Plant Responses and Adaptations **635**

A Auxins produced in the apical meristem inhibit the growth of lateral buds.

B Without the inhibiting effect of auxins from the apical meristem, lateral buds produce many branches.

▲ **Figure 25–5** Apical dominance, shown here, is controlled by the relative amounts of auxins and cytokinins. During normal growth (A), lateral buds are kept dormant because of the production of auxins in the apical meristem. If the apical meristem is removed (B), the concentration of auxins drops. 🔑 Cytokinins then stimulate cell division and the growth of lateral buds.

Auxins and Branching Auxins also regulate cell division in meristems. As a stem grows in length, it produces lateral buds, as shown in **Figure 25–5.** A **lateral bud** is a meristematic area on the side of a stem that gives rise to side branches. Most lateral buds do not start growing right away. The reason for this delay is that growth at the lateral buds is inhibited by auxins. Because auxins move out from the apical meristem, the closer a bud is to the stem's tip, the more it is inhibited. This phenomenon is called **apical dominance.**

Although not all gardeners have heard of auxins, most of them know how to overcome apical dominance. If you snip off the tip of a plant, the side branches begin to grow more quickly, resulting in a rounder, fuller plant. Why does this happen? When the tip is removed, the apical meristem—the source of the growth-inhibiting auxins—goes with it. Without the influence of auxins, meristems in the side branches grow more rapidly, changing the overall shape of the plant.

Auxinlike Weed Killers Chemists have produced many compounds that mimic the effects of auxins. Because high concentrations of auxins inhibit growth, many of these compounds are used as **herbicides,** which are compounds that are toxic to plants. Herbicides include a chemical known as 2,4-D (2,4-dichlorophenoxyacetic acid), which is used to kill weeds. A mixture containing 2,4-D was used as Agent Orange, a chemical defoliant sprayed during the Vietnam War.

✓ **CHECKPOINT** *What role do auxins play in apical dominance?*

Cytokinins

Cytokinins are plant hormones that are produced in growing roots and in developing fruits and seeds. 🔑 **In plants, cytokinins stimulate cell division and the growth of lateral buds, and cause dormant seeds to sprout.** Cytokinins also delay the aging of leaves and play important roles in the early stages of plant growth.

Cytokinins often produce effects opposite to those of auxins. For example, auxins stimulate cell elongation, whereas cytokinins inhibit elongation and cause cells to grow thicker. Auxins inhibit the growth of lateral buds, whereas cytokinins stimulate lateral bud growth. Recent experiments show that the rate of cell growth in most plants is determined by the ratio of the concentration of auxins to cytokinins. In growing plants, therefore, the relative concentrations of auxins, cytokinins, and other hormones determine how the plant grows.

Auxins and Plant Growth

Auxins affect plant growth in a variety of ways. This graph shows the results of experiments in which carrot cells were grown in the presence of varying concentrations of auxins. The orange line on the graph shows the growth pattern of the carrot plants' roots. The green line shows the growth pattern of the carrot plants' stems.

1. **Analyzing Data** At what auxin concentration are the stems stimulated to grow the most?

2. **Analyzing Data** How is the growth of the roots affected by the auxin concentration at which stems grow the most?

3. **Drawing Conclusions** Use the data in the graph to describe the relationship between the concentration of auxins and the growth of carrot plant stems.

4. **Inferring** If you were a carrot farmer, what concentration of auxin should you apply to your fields to produce the largest-sized carrots?

Effects of Hormone Concentration on Plant Growth

Gibberellins

For years, farmers in Japan knew of a disease that weakened rice plants by causing them to grow unusually tall. They called the disease the "foolish seedling" disease. In 1926, Japanese biologist Eiichi Kurosawa discovered that this extraordinary growth was caused by a fungus: *Gibberella fujikuroi.* His experiments showed that the fungus produced a growth-promoting substance that was named **gibberellin.**

Before long, other researchers had learned that plants themselves produce more than 60 similar compounds, all of which are now known as gibberellins. 🔑 **Gibberellins produce dramatic increases in size, particularly in stems and fruit.** Their effects on a flower are shown in **Figure 25–6.** Gibberellins are also produced by seed tissue and are responsible for the rapid early growth of many plants.

✓ CHECKPOINT *How were gibberellins discovered?*

▼ **Figure 25–6** 🔵 **Gibberellins cause an increase in the overall size of plants and individual plant structures.** Their effect can be seen in the difference between an untreated geranium flower (left) and a geranium flower treated with gibberellin (right).

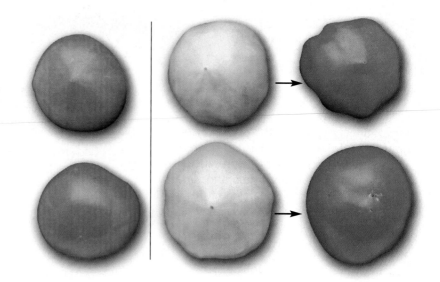

▶ **Figure 25–7** 🔑 Ethylene is a plant hormone that causes fruits to ripen. The tomatoes on the left were allowed to ripen naturally, whereas those in the middle were genetically altered to prevent transcription of the gene that produces ethylene. Only when ethylene gas was added did the tomatoes ripen, as you can see on the right.

Ethylene

When natural gas was used in city street lamps in the nineteenth century, people noticed that trees along the street suffered leaf loss and stunted growth. This effect was eventually traced to **ethylene,** one of the minor components of natural gas.

Today, scientists know that plants produce their own ethylene, and that it affects plants in a number of ways. 🔑 **In response to auxins, fruit tissues release small amounts of the hormone ethylene. Ethylene then stimulates fruits to ripen.**

Commercial producers of fruit sometimes use this hormone to control the ripening process. Many crops, including lemons and tomatoes, shown in **Figure 25–7,** are picked before they ripen so that they can be handled without damage to the fruit. Just before they are delivered to market, the fruits are treated with synthetic ethylene to produce a ripe color quickly. This trick does not always produce a ripe flavor, which is one reason why naturally ripened fruits often taste much better.

25–1 Section Assessment

1. 🔑 **Key Concept** What effects do hormones have within a growing plant?
2. 🔑 **Key Concept** List the four main types of hormones. What parts of the plant does each hormone affect?
3. Compare the effects of auxins and cytokinins on plant growth.

4. **Critical Thinking Inferring** A person who trims trees for a living must know the effect of apical dominance on the shape of trees. Explain.

i **TEXT** Assessment Use iText to review the important concepts in Section 25–1.

ALTERNATIVE ASSESSMENT
Crossword Puzzle
Create a crossword puzzle that reviews some of the information you learned in this section. Then, exchange puzzles with a classmate to complete.

25–2 Plant Responses

Like all living things, plants respond to changes in their environments. Some biologists call these responses "plant behavior," which is a useful way of thinking about them. Plants generally do not respond as quickly as animals do, but that does not make their responses any less effective. Some plant responses are so fast that even animals cannot keep up with them!

Tropisms

Plants change their patterns and directions of growth in response to a multitude of cues. The responses of plants to environmental stimuli are called **tropisms,** from a Greek word that means "turning." **Plant tropisms include gravitropism, phototropism, and thigmotropism. Each of these responses demonstrates the ability of plants to respond effectively to conditions in which they live.**

Gravitropism and Phototropism

You have already read about gravitropism, the response of a plant to gravity, and phototropism, the response of a plant to light. Both of these responses are controlled by the hormone auxin. Gravitropism causes the shoot of a germinating seed to grow out of the soil—against the force of gravity. It also causes the roots of a plant to grow with the force of gravity and into the soil.

Phototropism causes a plant to grow toward a light source. This response can be so quick that young seedlings reorient themselves in a matter of hours.

Thigmotropism

The response of plants to touch is called **thigmotropism** (thig-MAH-troh-piz-um). A plant that is touched regularly, for example, may be stunted in its growth—sometimes quite dramatically. Another example of thigmotropism is the growth of vines and climbing plants. The stems of these plants do not grow straight up. Rather, the growing tip of each stem points sideways and twists in circles as the shoot grows. When the tip encounters an object, it quickly wraps around it. Some climbing plants have long, twisting leaf tips or petioles that wrap tightly around small objects. Other plants, such as the grapes in **Figure 25–8,** have extra growths called tendrils that emerge near the base of the leaf and wrap tightly around any object they encounter.

Guide for Reading

🔑 **Key Concepts**
• What are plant tropisms?
• What is photoperiodism?
• How do deciduous plants prepare for winter?

Vocabulary
tropism
thigmotropism
short-day plant
long-day plant
photoperiodism
phytochrome
dormancy
abscission layer

**Reading Strategy:
Using Visuals** Before you read, preview **Figure 25–10.** From this figure, what can you conclude about the topic of photoperiodism?

▶ **Figure 25–8** 🔑 **Plant tropisms include gravitropism, phototropism, and thigmotropism.** One effect of thigmotropism—growth in response to touch—is that plants curl and twist around objects, as shown by the stems of this grapevine.

Figure 25–9 The mimosa plant responds to touch by folding in its leaves quickly. This response is produced by decreased osmotic pressure in cells near the base of each leaflet. **Inferring** *What adaptive value might rapid responses have for a plant?*

Rapid Responses

Some plant responses do not involve growth. In fact, they are so rapid that it would be a mistake to call them tropisms.

Figure 25–9 shows what happens if you touch a leaf of *Mimosa pudica,* appropriately called the "sensitive plant." Within only two or three seconds, its two leaflets fold together completely. The secret to this movement is changes in osmotic pressure. Recall that osmotic pressure is caused by the diffusion of water into cells. The leaves are held apart due to osmotic pressure where the two leaflets join. When the leaf is touched, cells near the center of the leaflet pump out ions and lose water due to osmosis. Pressure from cells on the underside of the leaf, which do not lose water, force the leaflets together.

The carnivorous Venus' flytrap also demonstrates rapid responses. When a fly triggers sensory cells on the inside of the flytrap's leaf, electrical signals are sent from cell to cell. A combination of changes in osmotic pressure and cell wall expansion causes the leaf to snap shut, trapping the insect inside.

Quick Lab

Can a plant find its way through a maze?

Materials scissors, masking tape, cardboard box, cardboard dividers, 4 bean seeds, small flower pot containing soil

Procedure

1. Make a maze by taping cardboard dividers upright inside a cardboard box as shown. Cut a hole in the side of the box at the end of the maze.
   CAUTION: *Use care when handling scissors.*
2. Plant 4 bean seeds in a small flowerpot of soil. Water the flowerpot.
3. Place the flowerpot in the box at the beginning of the maze. Close the box so that the only light in the box comes from the hole that you cut.
   CAUTION: *Wash your hands with soap and warm water after handling soil or plants.*

4. Over the next 2 weeks, open the box every 2 to 3 days to water the seeds and observe the seedlings. Record your observations each day.

Analyze and Conclude
1. **Observing** Summarize what happened to the seedlings.
2. **Inferring** What caused the plants to grow the way they did?

Photoperiodism

"To everything there is a season." Nowhere is this more evident than in the regular cycles of plant growth. Year after year, some plants flower in the spring, others in summer, and still others in the fall. Plants such as chrysanthemums and poinsettias flower when days are short and are therefore called **short-day plants.** Plants such as spinach and irises flower when days are long and are therefore known as **long-day plants.**

How do all these plants manage to time their flowering so precisely? In the early 1920s, scientists discovered that tobacco plants flower according to the number of hours of light and darkness they receive. Additional research showed that many other plants also respond to periods of light and darkness, a response called **photoperiodism.** This type of response is summarized in **Figure 25–10.**

🔑 **Photoperiodism in plants is responsible for the timing of seasonal activities such as flowering and growth.**

It was later discovered that a plant pigment called **phytochrome** (FYT-uh-krohm) is responsible for photoperiodism. Phytochrome absorbs red light and activates a number of signaling pathways within plant cells. By mechanisms that are still not understood completely, plants respond to regular changes in these pathways. These changes determine the patterns of a variety of plant responses.

Winter Dormancy

Phytochrome also regulates the changes in activity that prepare many plants for dormancy as winter approaches. **Dormancy** is the period during which an organism's growth and activity decrease or stop.

The changes that prepare a plant for dormancy are important adaptations that protect plants over the cold winter months. 🔑 **As cold weather approaches, deciduous plants turn off photosynthetic pathways, transport materials from leaves to roots, and seal leaves off from the rest of the plant.** In early autumn, the shorter days and lower temperatures gradually reduce the efficiency of photosynthesis. With these changing conditions, the plant gains very little by keeping its leaves alive. In fact, the thin, delicate leaves produced by most flowering plants would have little chance of surviving a tough winter, and their continued presence would be costly in terms of water loss.

CHECKPOINT *What is dormancy? What changes do plants undergo as colder weather approaches?*

Effect of Photoperiod on Flowering

Short-Day Plant   Long-Day Plant

Midnight / Noon
Long Day

Midnight / Noon
Short Day

Midnight / Noon
Interrupted Night

▲ **Figure 25–10** 🔑 Photoperiodism controls the timing of flowering and seasonal growth. The response of flowering, shown here, is controlled by the amount of darkness plants receive. Short-day plants, such as chrysanthemums, flower only when exposed to an extended period of darkness every night—and thus a short period of light during the day. Long-day plants, such as irises, flower when exposed to a short period of darkness or to a long period of darkness interrupted by a brief period of light.

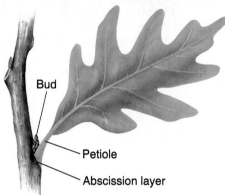

Bud

Petiole

Abscission layer

Figure 25–11 Deciduous plants undergo changes in preparation for winter dormancy. Photosynthetic pathways in leaves shut down (top). An abscission layer of cells forms at the petiole to seal the leaf off from the rest of the plant (bottom). Eventually, the leaf falls off.

Leaf Abscission In temperate regions, most flowering plants lose their leaves during the colder months. During the warm growing season, auxins are produced in leaves. At summer's end, the phytochrome in leaves absorbs less light as days shorten and nights become longer. Auxin production drops, but the production of ethylene increases. The change in the relative amounts of these two hormones starts a series of events that gradually shut down the leaf.

The chemical pathways for chlorophyll synthesis stop first. When light destroys the remaining green pigment, other pigments that have been present all along—including yellow and orange carotenoids—become visible for the first time. Production of new plant pigments—the reddish anthocyanins—begins in the autumn. The brilliant colors of autumn leaves are a direct result of these processes.

Behind the scenes, enzymes extract nutrients from the broken-down chlorophyll. These nutrients are then transported to other parts of the plant, where they are stored until spring. Every available carbohydrate is transported out of the leaf, and much of the leaf's water is extracted. Finally, an **abscission layer** of cells at the petiole seals the leaf off from the plant's vascular system. The location of the abscission layer is shown in **Figure 25–11.** Before long, the leaf falls to the ground, a sign that the tree is fully prepared for winter.

Overwintering of Meristems Hormones also produce important changes in apical meristems. Instead of continuing to produce leaves, meristems produce thick, waxy scales that form a protective layer around new leaf buds. Enclosed in its coat of scales, a terminal bud can survive the coldest winter days. At the onset of winter, xylem and phloem tissues pump themselves full of ions and organic compounds. These molecules act like antifreeze in a car, preventing the tree's sap from freezing, thus making it possible to survive the bitter cold.

25–2 Section Assessment

1. **Key Concept** Describe three types of plant tropisms.

2. **Key Concept** Compare short-day and long-day plants. Which type of plant is likely to bloom in the summer?

3. **Key Concept** What changes occur in plants before winter? How do these changes help the plant to survive?

4. Describe the process of leaf abscission.

5. **Critical Thinking Designing Experiments** How could a garden store owner determine what light conditions are needed for a particular flowering plant to bloom? Design a controlled experiment to find out.

TEXT Assessment Use iText to review the important concepts in Section 25–2.

MAKING CONNECTIONS

Evolution Review what you learned about evolution by natural selection in Chapter 15. Then, using what you know about natural selection, describe how plant adaptations for dormancy may have developed over time.

25–3 Plant Adaptations

Flowering plants grow in a variety of places—in deserts, in ponds, on mountaintops, in salt water, in polar regions, and in the tropics. Angiosperms can survive in these areas because they have evolved features through natural selection that allow them to live in each location. In this section, we explore how plants have become adapted to various environments through evolutionary change.

Aquatic Plants

Aquatic plants typically grow in mud that is saturated with water and nearly devoid of oxygen. **To take in sufficient oxygen, many aquatic plants have tissues with large air-filled spaces through which oxygen can diffuse.** In water-lilies, shown in **Figure 25–12**, there are large open spaces in the long petioles that reach from the leaves down to the roots at the bottom. Oxygen diffuses from these open spaces into the roots.

Many other plants show similar adaptations. Several species of mangrove trees grow in shallow water along tropical seacoasts. Mangroves survive because they have specialized air roots with air spaces in them, just like waterlily stems. These spaces conduct air down to the buried roots, allowing the root tissues to respire normally. Stately bald cypress trees thrive in freshwater swamps in the southern United States. These trees grow structures called knees, which protrude above the water. The knees bring oxygen-rich air down to the roots.

The reproductive adaptations of aquatic plants include seeds that can float in water and delay germination until after long periods of flooding. Many aquatic plants grow quickly after germination, thereby extending the growing shoot above the surface of the water.

Guide for Reading

Key Concepts
- How are plants adapted to different environments?
- How do plants obtain nutrients from sources other than photosynthesis?
- How do plants defend themselves from insects?

Vocabulary
xerophyte
epiphyte

Reading Strategy:
Using Prior Knowledge
Before you read, list the different environments in which plants grow. Next to each environment listed, describe adaptations you might expect to find in plants. As you read, compare your predictions with information about different plant adaptations.

▼ **Figure 25–12** Aquatic plants have air-filled spaces in their tissues that allow for the uptake and diffusion of oxygen. These waterlilies transport oxygen from the air to their roots through large spaces in their petioles.

Xerophyte comes from the Greek words *xeros,* meaning "dry," and *phyton,* meaning "plant." **Where do you think hydrophytes live?**

Salt-Tolerant Plants

When plant roots take in dissolved minerals, a difference in the concentration of water molecules is created between the root cells and the surrounding soil. This concentration difference causes water to enter the root cells by osmosis. For plants that grow in salt water, such as mangroves, this means taking in much more salt than the plant can use. The roots of salt-tolerant plants are adapted to salt concentrations that would quickly destroy the root hairs on most plants. The leaves of these plants have specialized cells that pump salt out of the plant tissues and onto the leaf surfaces, where it is washed off by rain.

Desert Plants

Desert plants, also called **xerophytes,** must survive where strong sun and daytime heat combine with sandy soil and infrequent rainfall. Instead of staying near the surface, rainwater sinks rapidly through desert soils. The hot, dry air quickly removes moisture from any wet surface, making life difficult for plants. **Plant adaptations to a desert climate include extensive roots, reduced leaves, and thick stems that can store water.**

One familiar group of desert plants is the cactuses (family Cactaceae), shown in **Figure 25–13.** Cactuses have root systems that either spread out for long distances just beneath the soil surface or that reach deep down into the soil. In addition, the roots have many hairs that quickly absorb water after a rainstorm, before the water sinks too deeply into the soil.

To reduce water loss due to transpiration, cactus leaves have been reduced to thin, sharp spines. Cactuses also have thick green stems that carry out photosynthesis and are adapted to store water. The stems of cactuses swell during rainy periods and shrivel during dry spells, when the plants are forced to use up their water reserves.

▼ **Figure 25–13** Desert plants typically have deep roots; reduced leaves; and thick, photosynthetic stems. Spines, which are visible on many of these plants, are actually reduced leaves that carry out little or no photosynthesis and, as a result, lose little water. Most of the plant's photosynthesis is carried out in its fleshy stem.

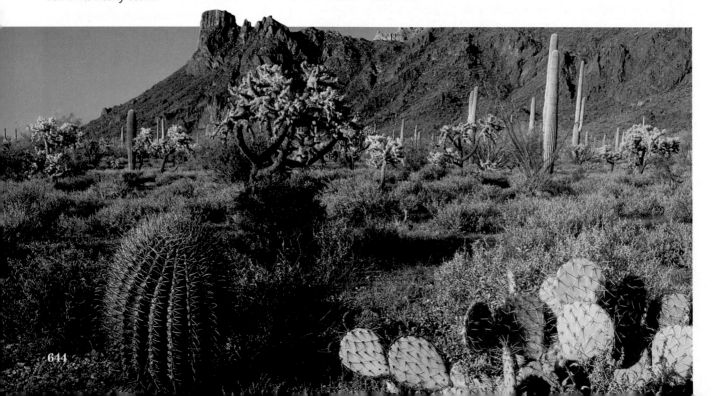

Seeds of many desert plants can remain dormant for years, germinating only when sufficient moisture guarantees them a chance for survival. Other desert plants have bulbs, tubers, or other specialized stems that can remain dormant for years. When rain does come, the plants mature, flower, and set seed in a matter of weeks or even days, before the water disappears.

✓ CHECKPOINT **How are the roots and leaves of desert plants specialized for the environment in which they live?**

Nutritional Specialists

Some plants grow in environments that have low concentrations of nutrients in the soil. ⚷ **Plants that have specialized features for obtaining nutrients include carnivorous plants and parasites.**

Carnivorous Plants Some plants live in bogs, wet and acidic environments where there is very little or no nitrogen present. Because conditions are too wet and too acidic, bacteria that cause decay cannot survive. Without these bacteria, neither plant nor animal material is broken down into the nutrients plants can use.

A number of plants that live in these habitats obtain nutrients using specialized leaves that trap and digest insects. Pitcher plants drown their prey in pitcher-shaped leaves that hold rainwater and digestive enzymes. Sundews trap insects on leaf hairs tipped with sticky secretions. The best known of the carnivorous plants is the Venus' flytrap, shown in **Figure 25–14.** This plant has leaf blades that are hinged at the middle. If an insect touches the trigger hairs on the leaf, the leaf folds up suddenly, trapping the animal inside. Over a period of several days, the leaf secretes enzymes that digest the insect and release nitrogen for the plant to use.

Parasites Some plants extract water and nutrients directly from a host plant. Like all parasites, these plants harm their host organisms and sometimes even pose a serious threat to other species. The dodder plant *Cuscuta* is a parasitic plant that has no chlorophyll and thus does not produce its own food. The plant grows directly into the vascular tissue of its host. There, it extracts nutrients and water. Mistletoe grows as a parasite on many plants, including conifers in the western United States.

Epiphytes

Plants that grow directly on the bodies of other plants are known as **epiphytes.** Epiphytes are attached to the plants they grow on, but, unlike parasites, they gather their own moisture, generally from rainfall, and produce their own food. One of the most common epiphytes found in warm, moist regions is Spanish moss. This plant is actually not a moss at all but a member of the bromeliad family. Many orchids are epiphytes as well, growing on the surfaces of other plants.

Carnivorous Plant: Venus' flytrap

Parasite: Mistletoe

Figure 25–14 ⊝ Plants that have specialized features for obtaining nutrients include carnivorous plants and parasites. Carnivorous plants, such as the Venus' flytrap, digest insects—and occasionally frogs—as a source of nutrients. Parasites grow into the tissues of their host plant and extract water and nutrients, causing harm to the host.

Figure 25–15 Many plants produce chemical compounds that ward off potential predators. *Digitalis* (left), which is also called foxglove, is poisonous when eaten. The monarch caterpillar (right) is able to eat milkweed—which is toxic to most animals—because it can store the toxic compounds in its body.

Chemical Defenses

Seed plants and insects have had such a long relationship that each has had plenty of time to adapt to the other. The beginnings of the relationship are obvious—plants represent an important source of food for insects, as shown in **Figure 25–15.** Plants, therefore, fall prey to a host of plant-eating insects. Because plants cannot run away, you might think that they are defenseless against insects that are armed with biting and sucking structures. But plants have their own defenses.

Many plants defend themselves against insect attack by manufacturing compounds that have powerful effects on animals. Some of these chemicals are poisons that can be lethal when eaten. Other chemicals act as insect hormones, disrupting normal growth and development and preventing insects from reproducing. These chemicals include those used in aspirin, codeine, and scores of other drugs that humans use as medicines.

As you may know, nicotine is a chemical that is found in tobacco plants. When a person smokes tobacco in the form of cigarettes, the nicotine in the tobacco affects the human nervous system. Biologists hypothesize that nicotine is a natural insecticide that disrupts the nervous system of many insects, protecting tobacco plants from potential predators.

25–3 Section Assessment

1. **Key Concept** Compare the adaptations of aquatic plants and desert plants. Which plants have adaptations for obtaining sufficient oxygen?

2. **Key Concept** Describe how carnivorous plants and parasites obtain their nutrients.

3. **Key Concept** How do some plants defend themselves from insect predators?

4. How are salt-tolerant plants adapted to their environment?

5. **Critical Thinking Drawing Conclusions** Why might the production of poisonous compounds be higher in plants that live in areas with dense insect populations?

iTEXT Assessment Use iText to review the important concepts in Section 25–3.

ALTERNATIVE ASSESSMENT

Creating Artwork
Choose one of the plants discussed in this section. Then, create a piece of artwork that shows how the plant is adapted to live in its natural environment.

Are Herbal Drugs Safe?

A Chinese herb that damaged the kidneys of dozens of dieters in the 1990s appears to pack a second punch—cancer and pre-cancerous lesions, according to a report in the *New England Journal of Medicine*. These findings draw one of the strongest links yet between the use of an herbal product and cancer.

Natural herbal medicines and dietary supplements can be found in the medicine cabinets of millions of Americans. Last year, Americans spent more than $6 billion on dietary supplements—a third of which was spent on herbal remedies. These remedies include products such as St. John's wort, for treatment of depression; *Echinacea* for cold and flu; and *Ephedra* for weight loss.

Because these preparations are made from plants and plant extracts, they are considered to be foods and food supplements, not drugs. As a result, the Food and Drug Administration (FDA) cannot require studies to determine the safety and effectiveness of herbal substances. Advocates for herbal products say that additional regulations are not needed. Critics worry that many of these products are as powerful and as dangerous as drugs.

The Viewpoints

Herbal Remedies Are Safe

Natural herbal products have been used for thousands of years by people of every culture. *Ephedra,* for example, comes from the Chinese herb *ma huang* and has been used to treat asthma and nasal congestion for centuries. Remedies using *Echinacea* were developed long ago by Native Americans. Such substances should continue to be exempt from new FDA regulations and available without a prescription. Herbal substances present consumers with increased health benefits combined with low risks.

Herbal Remedies Are Potentially Dangerous Drugs

Just because a product is "natural" does not mean it is safe. Plants produce many substances more powerful and dangerous than synthetic drugs. In 1992, more than 50 people in Belgium suffered kidney problems due to a diet remedy containing the herb *Aristolochia*. *Ephedra* itself is a powerful stimulant that can cause hypertension and stroke. St. John's wort interferes with the functions of many drugs, including medications for AIDS, epilepsy, and heart disease. As with other drugs, the FDA should regulate and test herbal substances for safety and effectiveness.

You Decide

1. **Defining the Issue** Explain the major issue being debated about herbal substances.
2. **Analyzing the Viewpoints** Why do some people prefer herbal remedies to drugs? Why do others feel that herbal remedies should be better regulated?
3. **Forming Your Opinion** If an extract of an herb such as *Echinacea,* shown below, produces effects as powerful as those of synthetic drugs, should it be regulated in the same way? What principles should shape government policies regarding these substances?
4. **Role-Playing** You are the owner of a natural foods store for which herbal products make up a growing percentage of annual sales. How would you react to a proposal requiring that new herbal products be tested for several years before they could be sold in your store?

Using Hormones to Control Plant Development

Plant hormones have many practical uses. Growers spray gibberellins on sugar cane and fruits to promote their growth. Orchid growers use cytokinins when they clone orchids. Auxins are used to keep potatoes from sprouting and apples from falling from trees before they are ripe. Auxins are also used to stimulate pineapples to flower and develop fruits. Some synthetic auxins are used as weed killers. In this investigation, you will use auxins to identify the locations of meristems that can be forced to form roots on leaf and stem cuttings.

Problem How do auxins affect plant development?

Materials

- large coleus plants (total of at least 4 branches)
- scalpel
- metric ruler
- rooting compound (auxin powder)
- potting soil
- 12 paper cups
- flat, wooden toothpick

Skills Observing, Formulating Hypotheses, Comparing and Contrasting

Procedure

Part A: Observing the Effects of Auxins on Root and Leaf Development

1. Use a scalpel to cut a piece containing a stem tip from a coleus plant as shown. The stem-tip cutting should include a stem tip and 2 nodes that are at least 1 cm from the tip of the stem. Cut the stem tip 3 mm below these 2 nodes. Cut 3 more stem-tip cuttings. **CAUTION:** *Be careful with sharp instruments.*

2. Cut off the petioles growing from the bottom node of each stem-tip cutting. Make sure the cut is 3 mm from the stem. See the illustration.

3. Cut the top from each stem-tip cutting, 3 mm above the top node. Using a toothpick, apply only enough rooting compound to coat the cut surfaces on the tops of 2 stem-tip cuttings.

4. Cut 8 pieces from the lower stems of each plant as shown. As in step 1, each stem cutting should contain at least 2 nodes and be cut 3 mm below the lower node.

5. Dip the stem-tip cuttings and 6 of the lower stem cuttings into powdered rooting hormone (an auxin) so that the bottom node is covered with powder. Leave 2 stem cuttings untreated.

6. Use a scalpel to punch several small drainage holes in the bottoms of the paper cups. Fill each paper cup with potting soil. Push the bottom of each cutting into the potting soil in a paper cup so that the bottom nodes are buried. Keep the soil moist but not wet. Label the paper cups to indicate what type of cutting each cup contains.

7. After 1 week, carefully pull 1 treated and 1 untreated stem cutting from the potting soil. Gently wash the soil off the roots and observe the differences. Record your observations and discard the cuttings you removed. Repeat this procedure after 2 weeks.

8. Allow the stem-tip cuttings to grow for 3 weeks. Observe and record any differences in leaf growth between the treated and untreated plants.

Stem-Tip Cutting

At least 1 cm

Nodes

Petioles

3 mm

Cut here

Step 1

Cut here

Cut here

3 mm

Step 2

Cut here — 3 mm

Step 3

Stem Cutting

Cut here

3 mm
Cut here

Step 4

Part B: Using the Effects of Auxins

9. **Formulating Hypotheses** Because auxins stimulate meristems to produce new roots and other plant parts, auxins can be used to locate meristems. Record a hypothesis about whether there are meristems in stems between nodes and in the veins on the bottoms of leaves.

10. **Designing Experiments** Design an experiment to test your hypothesis. You may need to nick the leaf veins slightly with a scalpel to expose any meristems in the veins to the rooting compound and moist soil. With your teacher's approval, carry out your experiment.

Analyze and Conclude

1. **Comparing and Contrasting** What differences did you see between the roots of the auxin-treated and untreated cuttings after 1 week? How can you explain these differences?

2. **Comparing and Contrasting** Was there more difference between roots of treated cuttings and untreated cuttings after 1 week or 2 weeks? How can you explain this result?

3. **Inferring** In step 8, what differences did you observe between the leaves of the treated and untreated stem-tip cuttings? Explain your observations.

4. **Drawing Conclusions** Did the results of your experiment in step 10 show that there are meristem cells in the stem between nodes? Explain your conclusion.

5. **Drawing Conclusions** Did the results of your experiment in step 10 show that there are meristem cells in the veins on the underside of the leaves? Explain your conclusion.

Go Further

Designing Experiments Grow your coleus plants until they develop small blue flowers. Design an experiment to determine how ethylene gas affects the development of flowers and leaves. You can use an apple that has been bruised and left to sit for 4 days as a source of ethylene gas.

25–1 Hormones and Plant Growth
Key Concepts

- Plant hormones are chemical substances that control a plant's patterns of growth and development, and the plant's responses to environmental conditions.
- Auxins are produced in the apical meristem and are transported downward into the rest of the plant. They stimulate cell elongation.
- Cytokinins are produced in growing roots and in developing fruits and seeds. They stimulate cell division and the growth of lateral buds, and cause dormant seeds to sprout.
- Gibberellins produce dramatic increases in size, particularly in stems and fruit.
- In response to auxins, fruit tissues release small amounts of the hormone ethylene. Ethylene then stimulates fruits to ripen.

Vocabulary
hormone, p. 634 • target cell, p. 634
phototropism, p. 634 • auxin, p. 635
gravitropism, p. 635 • lateral bud, p. 636
apical dominance, p. 636 • herbicide, p. 636
cytokinin, p. 636 • gibberellin, p. 637
ethylene, p. 638

25–2 Plant Responses
Key Concepts

- Plant tropisms include gravitropism, phototropism, and thigmotropism. Each of these responses demonstrates the ability of plants to respond effectively to conditions in which they live.
- Photoperiodism in plants is responsible for the timing of seasonal activities such as flowering and growth.
- As cold weather approaches, deciduous plants turn off photosynthetic pathways, transport materials from leaves to roots, and seal leaves off from the rest of the plant.

Vocabulary
tropism, p. 639 • thigmotropism, p. 639
short-day plant, p. 641 • long-day plant, p. 641
photoperiodism, p. 641 • phytochrome, p. 641
dormancy, p. 641 • abscission layer, p. 642

25–3 Plant Adaptations
Key Concepts

- To take in sufficient oxygen, many aquatic plants have tissues with large air-filled spaces through which oxygen can diffuse.
- Plant adaptations to a desert climate include extensive roots, reduced leaves, and thick stems that can store water.
- Plants that have specialized features for obtaining nutrients include carnivorous plants and parasites.
- Many plants defend themselves against insect attack by manufacturing compounds that have powerful effects on animals.

Vocabulary
xerophyte, p. 644
epiphyte, p. 645

Thinking Visually
Using the information in this chapter, complete the following flowchart about leaf abscission.

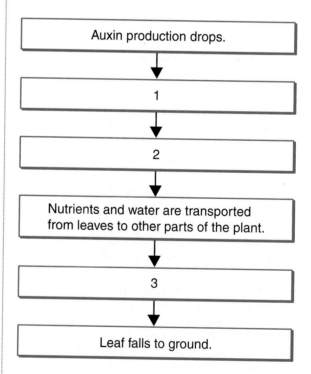

Auxin production drops.

↓

1

↓

2

↓

Nutrients and water are transported from leaves to other parts of the plant.

↓

3

↓

Leaf falls to ground.

Chapter 25

Part A

Multiple Choice

For each statement or question, select the number of the word or expression that, of those given, best completes the statement or answers the question.

1 What is the name for a substance produced in one part of a plant that affects target cells in another part of the plant?
(1) an enzyme   (3) a hormone
(2) a herbicide   (4) a phytochrome

2 Substances that stimulate cell division and cause dormant seeds to sprout are
(1) gibberellins   (3) cytokinins
(2) auxins   (4) xerophytes

3 In the illustration below, what phenomenon is responsible for the shape of the plant on the left?
(1) gravitropism   (3) phytochromes
(2) dormancy   (4) apical dominance

4 A high concentration of auxins can inhibit plant growth. Compounds containing such high concentrations are commercially produced and sold as
(1) fruit ripeners   (3) pesticides
(2) growth stimulants   (4) herbicides

5 Japanese scientists found that a fungus causes a disease that resultes in the extraordinary growth of certain rice plants. This led to the discovery of a growth-promoting chemical called
(1) auxin   (3) cytokinin
(2) gibberellin   (4) ethylene

6 The period during which an organism's growth and activity decreases or stops is called
(1) abscission   (3) thigmotropism
(2) dormancy   (4) gravitropism

7 Plants that have air-filled spaces in their tissues are likely to be
(1) desert plants   (3) epiphytes
(2) aquatic plants   (4) parasites

8 Plants that grow directly on the bodies of other plants but manufacture their own food are
(1) epiphytes   (3) carnivorous plants
(2) aquatic plants   (4) parasites

9 The ripening of fruit is most closely associated with
(1) auxins   (3) ethylene
(2) cytokinins   (4) gibberellins

10 Which choice best illustrates a thigmotropism?
(1) leaf abscission
(2) climbing vines
(3) branching stems
(4) blooming period

11 Which statement best describes a short-day plant?
(1) It will bloom if the dark period is long enough.
(2) It will bloom if the light period is long enough.
(3) It will not bloom when days are short.
(4) It will not bloom when nights are long.

12 Scientists have learned that growth patterns in plants result from hormone signals sent through plant tissues. This suggests that
(1) homeostasis in plants is disrupted when target cells receive hormone signals
(2) homeostatic mechanisms involving hormones have evolved in many plants
(3) plants use the same hormones as animals to maintain homeostasis
(4) plants do not need to maintain homeostasis when their hormones are functioning correctly

Test-Taking Tip Take the time to read each question completely, including all the answer choices. Consider each possible choice before determining which answer is correct.

Parts B and C

Multiple Choice and Extended Response

For those questions that ask you to select a response, choose the one that best completes the statement or answers the question. For all others follow the directions given.

Base your answers to questions 13 through 15 on the information below, which summarizes an experiment with oat seedlings, and on your knowledge of biology.

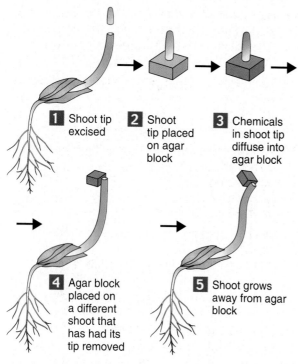

1 Shoot tip excised

2 Shoot tip placed on agar block

3 Chemicals in shoot tip diffuse into agar block

4 Agar block placed on a different shoot that has had its tip removed

5 Shoot grows away from agar block

13 Which is the best conclusion that can be made from the results of this experiment?
- **(1)** Hormones are produced in the growing tips of plants.
- **(2)** Oat plants grow toward the sun because of compounds produced in their stems.
- **(3)** Chemicals produced in plant stems stimulate plant growth.
- **(4)** Compounds produced in shoot tips can cause oat seedlings to bend.

14 If the cells of the stem near the agar block were examined with a compound light microscope, they would not all look the same. Make a sketch to illustrate the difference between the cells nearest the block and those on the other side of the stem.

15 To make these experimental results more valid, the experimenter should have
- **(1)** used a smaller agar block to soak up the chemicals
- **(2)** tested a second seedling with its tip removed and used an untreated agar block
- **(3)** left the shoot tip on the agar block when it was placed on the seedling
- **(4)** used a seedling from a different plant species

Base your answers to questions 16 through 18 on the information below and on your knowledge of biology.

A scientist used the following experimental setup to study the effects of gibberellic acid on plant growth. He measured and recorded the change in height of each plant at the same time every day for one week.

Effects of Gibberellic Acid on Plant Growth			
Container	**Type of Plant**	**Volume of Solution in Flask**	**Percent Gibberellic Acid**
Flask 1	Bean seedling	200 mL	0.0
Flask 2	Bean seeding	200 mL	0.1
Flask 3	Bean seedling	200 mL	1.0
Flask 4	Bean seedling	200 mL	10.0

16 Identify the manipulated (independent) variable in this investigation.

17 State one possible hypothesis that could be tested with this experimental setup.

18 Which column headings would be most appropriate in a table that summarizes the data obtained from this experiment?
- **(1)** Percent Gibberellic Acid and Total Growth After 7 Days
- **(2)** Container Number and Percent Gibberellic Acid
- **(3)** Day Number and Total Growth After 7 Days
- **(4)** Container Number and Daily Growth for 7 Days

19 Explain why plants with apical meristem tissue show a different growth pattern than plants from which the apical meristem tissue has been removed.

20 Tropisms are important adaptations common to many species of plants. Explain how some plants rely on tropisms for survival. Be sure to:
- explain what a tropism is
- identify one tropism that affects plant stems
- identify one tropism that affects plant roots
- explain why each tropism you identify is important for plant survival

21 Describe what happens to the leaves and buds of deciduous trees and shrubs as they prepare for winter dormancy.

Base your answers to questions 22 and 23 on the information and illustration below and on your knowledge of biology.

The experiment shown below was intended to test the effect of gravitropism on plant growth. The conclusion drawn from the experiment was that plant stems grow upward because they are growing away from the force of gravity.

22 State the probable hypothesis for this experiment.

23 Explain why this experiment may *not* have successfully tested the effect of gravity on plant growth.

24 The Venus' flytrap is a green photosynthetic plant, yet it must feed on insects to survive in its native habitat. Why is it essential for this plant to have insects for food?

25 A student wanted to investigate the effect of gibberellin on the average diameter of flowers produced by a particular plant species. Seven groups were tested, each consisting of 10 plants. All groups were treated in the same manner, except for the concentration of gibberellin solution applied to the developing flower buds. The results of the experiment are shown in the table below.

Micrograms of Gibberellin in a Constant Volume of Water	Average Diameter of Flowers (in mm)
0.00	110
0.05	230
0.10	305
0.25	365
0.50	395
1.00	410
2.00	410

How do the flowers of this plant species respond to varying concentrations of gibberellin? In your answer be sure to
- state the effect of low concentrations of gibberellin on flower diameter
- state the effect that higher concentrations of gibberellin have on flower diameter
- predict how flowers of this species would respond to a treatment of 4 mg of gibberellin in the same volume of water

Take It to the NET

Do plants grow differently in the absence of gravity? Visit the Prentice Hall Web site at **www.phschool.com** to find out about plant responses in space. Then, answer the following questions:
- What happens when plants are grown in space?
- What is graviperception?
- What is graviresponse?
- Describe the work being done on gravitropism in two different scientific labs.

UNIT 8

Invertebrates

▶ Thorn bugs got their name from the fact that they look like thorns, thus scaring away any predators. The close resemblance of an organism such as these thorn bugs to an object in its environment—in this case thorns—is known as mimicry.

What do we know about invertebrates?

- The earliest members of many modern land invertebrate groups, such as the fossil dragonfly, first appeared during the beginning of the Carboniferous Period, more than 360 million years ago.

- Some of the most devastating and gruesome human diseases are caused by invertebrates such as nematodes and flatworms.

- There are more different species of insects than of all other multi-cellular organisms combined.

- Coral reefs are the most diverse and productive aquatic ecosystems on Earth today.

What discoveries lie in the future?

- What will research from the fossil record and DNA tell us about how the major groups of invertebrates are related to one another?

- Can a better understanding of insects help protect farms from insect pests and protect humans from insect-borne diseases?

- What will research reveal about the best ways to save the coral reefs?

KEEP CURRENT WITH . . .

SCIENCE NEWS®

Find out more about topics in this unit:
www.phschool.com

26 Sponges and Cnidarians

A worker washes soft sponges recently harvested along the coast of Florida. Sponges are simple animals that live in either marine or freshwater habitats.

Inquiry Activity

What makes an animal an animal?

Procedure

1. Observe the specimens or photographs of organisms provided by your teacher. Some of the organisms are animals, whereas others are not. Examine each organism carefully.

2. Make a list of each organism's characteristics.

Think About It

1. **Classifying** Classify the organisms into two groups: animals and nonanimals. Give your reasons for putting each organism into a particular group.

2. **Forming Operational Definitions** List at least three characteristics shared by each of the organisms you classified as animals. Describe how these characteristics separate them from the nonanimals.

26–1 Introduction to the Animal Kingdom

Of all the kingdoms of organisms, the animal kingdom is the most diverse in appearance. Some animals look familiar to us, whereas others resemble creatures from a nightmare or a horror movie. Some animals are so small that they live on or inside the bodies of other animals. Others are many meters long and live in the depths of the sea. Animals can be black, white, brightly colored, or transparent. They may walk, swim, crawl, burrow, or fly—or not move at all. As you will see, each major group, or phylum, has its own typical body plan.

What Is an Animal?

As different as they are, all animals share certain characteristics. Animals, including those in **Figure 26–1**, are all heterotrophs, meaning that they obtain nutrients and energy by feeding on organic compounds from other organisms. Animals are multicellular, or composed of many cells. The cells that make up animal bodies share certain characteristics as well. All animal cells are eukaryotic, meaning that they contain a nucleus and membrane-bound organelles. Unlike the cells of algae, fungi, and plants, animal cells do not have cell walls. **Animals, members of the kingdom Animalia, are multicellular, eukaryotic heterotrophs whose cells lack cell walls.**

Over 95 percent of all animal species are often grouped in a single, informal category: invertebrates. This group is defined in an odd way—by describing a characteristic that its members do *not* have. **Invertebrates** are animals that have no backbone, or vertebral column. They range in size from microscopic dust mites to the giant squid, which is more than 20 meters in length. They include groups as diverse as sea stars, worms, jellyfish, and insects. The other 5 percent of animals, including fishes, amphibians, reptiles, birds, and mammals, are called **vertebrates,** because they have a backbone.

Guide for Reading

Key Concepts
- What characteristics do all animals share?
- What essential functions do animals carry out?
- What are the important trends in animal evolution?

Vocabulary
- invertebrate • vertebrate
- parasite • host
- blastula • protostome
- deuterostome • anus
- endoderm • mesoderm
- ectoderm • radial symmetry
- bilateral symmetry
- cephalization

Reading Strategy: Monitoring Your Understanding Before you read, write down what you already know about animals. After you have read this section, write down what you learned about animals.

▶ **Figure 26–1** The animal kingdom includes an incredible diversity of forms and lifestyles. **Despite their differences in appearance, both the collared lizard and the grasshopper are eukaryotic heterotrophs whose cells lack cell walls.**

What Animals Do to Survive

All animals survive and respond to the environment in different ways. 🔑 **Animals carry out the following essential functions: feeding, respiration, circulation, excretion, response, movement, and reproduction.** Over millions of years, animals with different body plans have evolved an extraordinary variety of ways to carry out these functions. Some of these are shown in **Figure 26–2**. For each animal group you read about in the next several chapters, you will examine these functions and learn about the cells, tissues, organs, and organ systems that perform them.

Feeding Animals have evolved a variety of ways to feed. Herbivores are animals that eat plants, including roots, stems, leaves, flowers, and fruits. Carnivores feed on other animals. Filter feeders are aquatic animals that strain tiny floating plants and animals from the water around them. Detritivores (dee-TRYT-uh-vawrz) are animals that feed on pieces of decaying plant and animal material called detritus (dee-TRYT-us).

Animals can also form symbiotic relationships, in which two species live in close association with each other. A **parasite,** for example, is a type of symbiont that lives within or on another organism, the **host.** The parasite feeds on the host, harming it.

Respiration Whether they live in water or on land, all animals respire, which means that they take in oxygen and give off carbon dioxide. Because of their very simple, thin-walled bodies, some animals can rely on the diffusion of these substances through their skin. Most other animals, however, have evolved complex tissues and organ systems for respiration.

Circulation Many small aquatic animals, such as some aquatic worms, rely solely on diffusion to transport oxygen, nutrients, and waste products among all their cells. Diffusion is sufficient because these animals are only a few cell layers thick. Larger animals, however, have some kind of circulatory system to move materials around within their bodies.

Feeding

Respiration

Circulation

Excretion

Excretion A primary waste product of cellular metabolism is ammonia, a poisonous substance that contains nitrogen. A buildup of ammonia and other waste products would kill an animal. Therefore, excretion is critical to life. Most animals have an excretory system that either eliminates ammonia quickly or converts it into a less toxic substance that is removed from the body. Excretory systems vary from groups of cells that pump water out of the body to complex organs such as kidneys.

Response Animals respond to events in their environment using specialized cells called nerve cells. In most animals, nerve cells hook up together to form a nervous system. Some cells, called receptors, respond to sound, light, and other stimuli. Other nerve cells process information and determine how the animal responds. The arrangement of nerve cells in the body changes dramatically from phylum to phylum.

Movement Some animals live their entire adult lives attached to a single spot. Most animals, however, are motile, meaning they can move. But both stick-in-the-muds and jet-setters usually have either muscles or musclelike tissues that generate force by becoming shorter when stimulated. Muscle contraction enables motile animals to move around, usually by working in combination with a support structure called a skeleton. Muscles also help even sedentary animals feed and pump water and fluids through their bodies.

Reproduction Most animals reproduce sexually by producing haploid gametes. Sexual reproduction helps create and maintain genetic diversity in populations. It therefore helps improve species' abilities to evolve when the environment changes. Many animals, especially invertebrates, can also reproduce asexually. Asexual reproduction produces offspring that are genetically identical to the parent. It allows animals to increase their numbers rapidly.

✓ **CHECKPOINT** *How do sexual and asexual reproduction differ?*

Figure 26–2 🔄 **Animals carry out seven essential functions: feeding, respiration, circulation, excretion, response, movement, and reproduction.** Snakes feed by constricting, or squeezing, their prey. Humans respire by breathing oxygenated air into lungs. A rabbit's circulatory system pumps blood through closed vessels, which are visible in its ears. Crabs rid their bodies of metabolic wastes by excreting fluid. Like many insects, moths respond to stimuli that they detect from the environment using specialized sense organs such as antennae. Herons move using a system of muscles attached to a low-density skeleton. Animals reproduce either sexually or asexually; lions reproduce sexually and have only a few offspring per litter.

Reproduction

Response

Movement

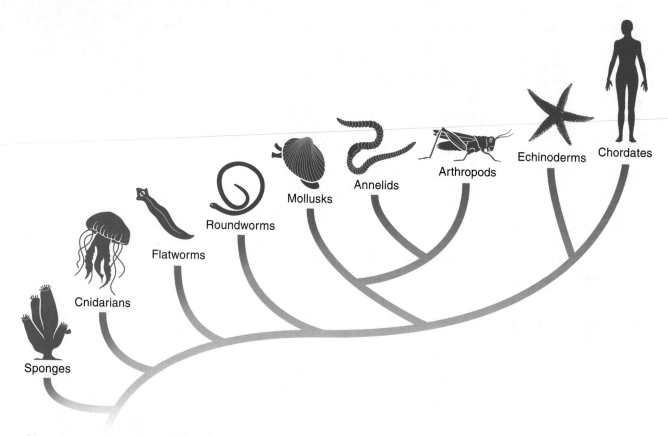

Sponges

Cnidarians

Flatworms

Roundworms

Mollusks

Annelids

Arthropods

Echinoderms

Chordates

Single-celled ancestors

▲ **Figure 26–3** This cladogram indicates evolutionary relationships among major groups of animals. Groups shown close together, such as echinoderms and chordates, are more closely related than groups that are shown farther apart, such as echinoderms and cnidarians. During the course of evolution that produced these different groups, important traits evolved. ⬤ Animals that are more complex typically have specialized cells, bilateral body symmetry, cephalization, and a body cavity.

Trends in Animal Evolution

Your survey of the animal kingdom will begin with simple forms and move through more complicated ones. These different phyla are related to one another by a common evolutionary heritage. The cladogram in **Figure 26–3** shows our most current understanding of evolutionary relationships among groups of living animals. A comparison of the groups in the cladogram shows important trends in animal evolution. ⬤ **Complex animals tend to have high levels of cell specialization and internal body organization, bilateral body symmetry, a front end or head with sense organs, and a body cavity.** In addition, the embryos of complex animals develop in layers.

Cell Specialization and Levels of Organization

As animals have evolved, their cells have become specialized to carry out different functions, such as movement and response. Large animals need greater efficiency in body processes than do very small animals. Single-celled organisms, such as amoebas, move nutrients and waste products directly across their cell membranes. In multicellular organisms such as animals, however, each cell type has a structure and chemical composition that enable it to perform a specialized function. Groups of specialized cells form tissues. Tissues join together to form organs and organ systems—all of which work together to carry out a variety of complex functions.

Early Development Animals that reproduce sexually begin life as a zygote, or fertilized egg. **Figure 26–4** shows development after fertilization. The zygote undergoes a series of divisions to form a **blastula** (BLAS-tyoo-luh), which is a hollow ball of cells. The blastula becomes flattened on one side and folds in on itself, forming a single opening called a blastopore. The process of blastopore formation changes a simple ball of cells—similar to an inflated balloon—into an elongated structure with a tube inside, as if you were holding the balloon and pushing your thumbs toward the center.

The blastopore leads into a central tube that runs the length of the developing embryo. This tube becomes the digestive tract and is formed in one of two ways. A **protostome** (PROH-tuh-stohm) is an animal whose mouth is formed from the blastopore. Most invertebrate animals are protostomes. A **deuterostome** (DOO-tur-uh-stohm) is an animal whose anus is formed from the blastopore. The **anus** is the opening through which wastes leave the digestive tract. The mouth is formed second, after the anus (*deuterostome* means "second mouth"). Echinoderms and all vertebrates are deuterostomes.

During early development, the cells of most animal embryos differentiate into three layers called germ layers. The **endoderm,** or innermost germ layer, develops into the linings of the digestive tract and much of the respiratory system. The **mesoderm,** or middle layer, gives rise to muscles and much of the circulatory, reproductive, and excretory organ systems. The **ectoderm,** or outermost layer, gives rise to sense organs, nerves, and the outer layer of the skin.

✓ CHECKPOINT **Which layer develops into the muscles and the circulatory, reproductive, and excretory systems?**

▶ **Figure 26–4** During the early development of animal embryos, cells divide to produce a hollow ball of cells called a blastula. A tube called a blastopore forms in the center of this ball. In protostomes, the blastopore develops into the mouth. In deuterostomes, the blastopore forms an anus, and the mouth forms later. **Interpreting Diagrams** *Which cell layer lines the digestive tract in both protostomes and deuterostomes?*

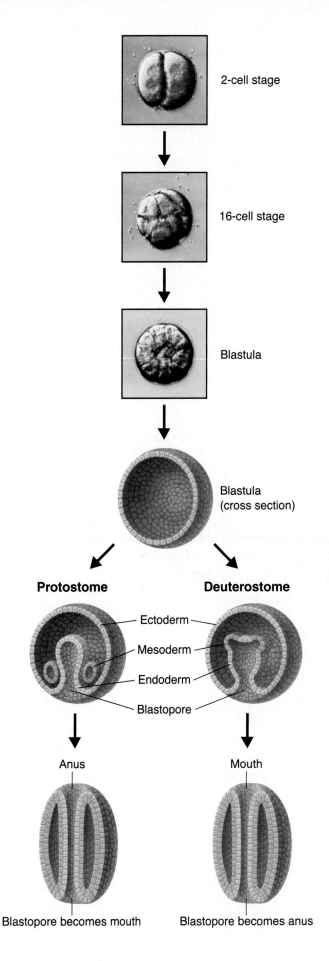

2-cell stage

16-cell stage

Blastula

Blastula (cross section)

Protostome   **Deuterostome**

Ectoderm
Mesoderm
Endoderm
Blastopore

Anus   Mouth

Blastopore becomes mouth   Blastopore becomes anus

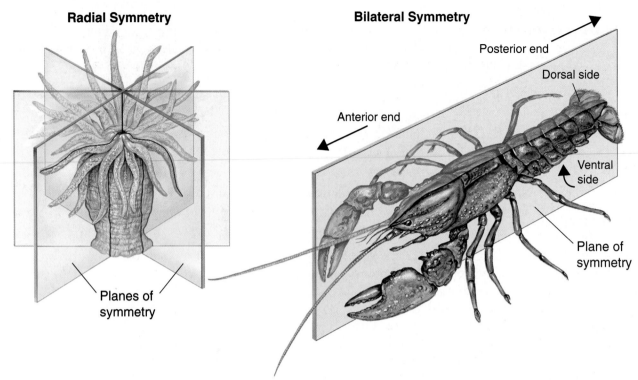

Radial Symmetry

Planes of symmetry

Bilateral Symmetry

Posterior end

Dorsal side

Anterior end

Ventral side

Plane of symmetry

▲ **Figure 26–5** Animals with radial symmetry, such as the sea anemone, have body parts that extend from a central point. Animals with bilateral symmetry, such as the crayfish, have distinct anterior and posterior ends and right and left sides. **Interpreting Graphics** *How many planes of symmetry does the crayfish have?*

Quick Lab

How can body symmetry affect movement?

Material modeling clay

Procedure

1. Use modeling clay to make models of two animals. Make one model radially symmetrical and the other long, narrow, and bilaterally symmetrical.
2. Make grooves to divide each model into similar segments.
3. Add legs to some segments of your models.

Analyze and Conclude

1. **Inferring** Which type of body symmetry is more suited to walking forward?
2. **Using Models** Are most walking animals bilaterally symmetrical? Why do you think this is?

Body Symmetry With the exception of sponges, all animals exhibit some type of body symmetry. Many simple animals, such as the sea anemone shown on the left in **Figure 26–5,** have body parts that repeat around the center of the body. These animals exhibit **radial symmetry,** similar to that of a bicycle wheel, in which any number of imaginary planes can be drawn through the center, each dividing the body into equal halves.

In animals with **bilateral symmetry,** such as the crayfish in **Figure 26–5,** only a single imaginary plane can divide the body into two equal halves. Animals with bilateral symmetry have left and right sides. They also usually have front and back ends and upper and lower sides. The anterior is the front end, and the posterior is the back end. The dorsal is the upper side, and the ventral is the lower side.

A body plan with bilateral symmetry allows for segmentation, in which the body is constructed of many repeated and similar parts, or segments. Animals with bilateral symmetry, such as worms, insects, and vertebrates, typically have external body parts that repeat on either side of the body. The combination of bilateral symmetry and segmentation is found in two of the most successful animal groups—arthropods and vertebrates. Geneticists are now beginning to learn how gene interactions during development control the growth and form of segments and appendages. Amazingly, the same controls are found in humans and insects!

✔ CHECKPOINT *How do radial symmetry and bilateral symmetry differ?*

◀ **Figure 26–6** Animals with cephalization, such as this dragonfly, have the brain and other sense organs toward the front of the body. This end of the body comes into contact with the environment first, allowing animals to respond effectively to stimuli. **Inferring** *How might cephalization help animals to move quickly?*

Cephalization Animals with bilateral symmetry usually exhibit what is called cephalization (sef-uh-lih-ZAY-shun). **Cephalization** is the concentration of sense organs and nerve cells at the anterior, or front, end of the body. Animals with cephalization, such as the dragonfly in **Figure 26–6,** respond to the environment more quickly and in more sophisticated ways than simpler animals can. Animals with bilateral symmetry usually move with the anterior end forward, so this end comes in contact with new parts of the environment first. As sense organs such as eyes and ears have evolved, they have tended to gather at the anterior end, as have nerve cells that process information and "decide" what the animal should do. In general, the more complex animals become, the more pronounced their degree of cephalization. The anterior end is often different enough from the rest of the body that it is called a head.

Body Cavity Formation Most animals have a body cavity, which is a fluid-filled space that lies between the digestive tract and the body wall. A body cavity is important because it provides a space in which internal organs can be suspended so that they are not pressed on by muscles or twisted out of shape by body movements. Body cavities also allow for specialized regions to develop, and they provide room for internal organs to grow and expand. In some animals, body cavities contain fluids that are involved in circulation, feeding, and excretion.

26–1 Section Assessment

1. 🔑 **Key Concept** What is an animal?

2. 🔑 **Key Concept** Describe the seven essential functions performed by all animals.

3. 🔑 **Key Concept** In what ways are complex animals different from simple animals?

4. How are body symmetry and cephalization related?

5. **Critical Thinking Applying Concepts** How might having specialized cells increase efficiency in multicellular animals?

🧍**TEXT** **Assessment** Use iText to review the important concepts in Section 26–1.

ALTERNATIVE ASSESSMENT

Constructing a Chart
Make a two-column chart of the different functions that enable animals to survive and respond to the environment. In the first column, list each function. In the second column, include a drawing, photograph, or magazine clipping that illustrates an example of that function.

26–2 Sponges

Guide for Reading

Key Concepts
- Why are sponges classified as animals?
- How do sponges carry out essential functions?

Vocabulary
choanocyte
osculum
spicule
archaeocyte
internal fertilization
larva
gemmule

Reading Strategy:
Using Visuals Before you read, preview **Figure 26–8** and **Figure 26–9**. For each figure, write a brief statement that summarizes the content of the illustration. Once you have read the section, explain how each illustration reinforces or enhances the content of the section.

S ponges are the simplest and probably the most unusual animals. Living on Earth for at least 540 million years, sponges are also the most ancient animals. Today, most sponges live in the ocean, from the Arctic and Antarctic regions to the tropics, and from shallow water to depths of several hundred meters. To humans, however, they are probably best known in their dried form—the natural sponges used for bathing.

What Is a Sponge?

Sponges are placed in the phylum Porifera (poh-RIF-ur-uh), which means "pore-bearers." This name is appropriate because sponges have tiny openings, or pores, all over their bodies, as shown in **Figure 26–7**. Sponges are sessile, meaning that they live their entire adult life attached to a single spot.

Given these unusual features, why are sponges considered animals? **Sponges are classified as animals because they are multicellular, heterotrophic, have no cell walls, and contain a few specialized cells.** Because sponges are so different from other animals, some scientists think that they evolved independently from all other animals. Other evidence suggests that sponges share a common ancestor with other animals, but that they separated from this ancestor long before the other groups did.

✓ **CHECKPOINT** *Why is the phylum name Porifera appropriate for sponges?*

Form and Function in Sponges

Sponges have nothing resembling a mouth or gut, and they have no tissues or organ systems. Simple functions are carried out by a few specialized cells.

▼ **Figure 26–7** Sponges are animals because they are heterotrophic and have specialized cells. Sponges are probably the least typical of what we think of as animals. They grow in irregular shapes and live attached to the floor of oceans and freshwater bodies. Water enters the body of a sponge through small holes called pores (inset photo).

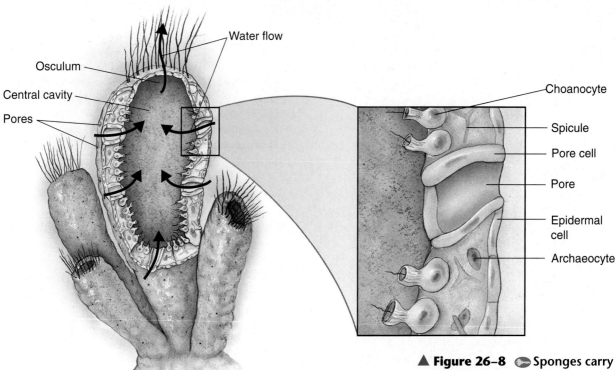

Water flow
Osculum
Central cavity
Pores

Choanocyte
Spicule
Pore cell
Pore
Epidermal cell
Archaeocyte

▲ **Figure 26–8** Sponges carry out basic functions, such as feeding and circulation, by moving water through their bodies. Choanocytes use flagella to move water through pores in the wall of the sponge and out through the osculum. As water moves through the sponge, food particles are filtered from the water, and wastes are removed from the sponge.

Body Plan Sponges are asymmetrical; they have no front or back ends, and no left or right sides. A sponge can be thought of as a large, cylindrical water pump. The body of a sponge, shown in **Figure 26–8,** forms a wall around a large central cavity through which water is circulated continually. **Choanocytes** (koh-AN-uh-sytz) are specialized cells that use flagella to move a steady current of water through the sponge. This water—in some cases, several thousand liters per day—enters through pores located in the body wall. Water then leaves through the **osculum** (AHS-kyoo-lum), a large hole at the top of the sponge. 🔑 **The movement of water through the sponge provides a simple mechanism for feeding, respiration, circulation, and excretion.**

Sponges have a simple skeleton. In harder sponges, the skeleton is made of spiny spicules. A **spicule** is a spike-shaped structure made of chalklike calcium carbonate or glasslike silica. Spicules are made by **archaeocytes** (ARK-ee-uh-sytz), which are specialized cells that move around within the walls of the sponge. Softer sponges have an internal skeleton made of spongin, a network of flexible protein fibers. These are the sponges that are harvested and used as natural bath sponges.

Feeding Sponges are filter feeders that sift microscopic food particles from the water. Digestion is intracellular, meaning that it takes place inside cells. As water moves through the sponge, food particles are trapped and engulfed by choanocytes that line the body cavity. These particles are then digested or passed on to archaeocytes. The archaeocytes complete the digestive process and transport digested food throughout the sponge.

MEIOSIS

Haploid (N)
Diploid (2N)

1 Sperm from a sponge are released into the surrounding water. Water currents carry the sperm to other sponges.

Sperm (N)

New sponge

Mature sponge (2N)

Egg (N)

Swimming larva

3 The zygote develops into a free-swimming larva. Water currents carry the larva until it attaches to a surface and grows into a new sponge.

Larva (2N)

2 Sperm enter another sponge through pores. The sperm are carried to eggs inside the body wall. Sperm fertilize eggs.

FERTILIZATION

▲ **Figure 26–9** Most sponges reproduce sexually, and many have internal fertilization. **Interpreting Graphics** *Is an adult sponge haploid or diploid?*

Respiration, Circulation, and Excretion Sponges rely on the movement of water through their bodies to carry out body functions. As water moves through the body cavity, oxygen dissolved in the water diffuses into the surrounding cells. At the same time, carbon dioxide and other wastes, such as ammonia, diffuse into the water and are carried away.

Response Sponges do not have nervous systems that would allow them to respond to changes in their environment. However, many sponges protect themselves by producing toxins that make them unpalatable or poisonous to potential predators.

Reproduction Sponges can reproduce either sexually or asexually. The steps in sexual reproduction are diagrammed in **Figure 26–9.** In most sponge species, a single sponge forms both eggs and sperm. A sponge usually produces its eggs and sperm at different times. In sponges, eggs are fertilized inside the sponge's body, a process called **internal fertilization.** Sperm are released from one sponge and are carried by water currents until they enter the pores of another sponge. Archaeocytes carry the sperm to an egg, which is located in the wall of the sponge. After fertilization, the zygote develops into a larva. A **larva** is an immature stage of an organism that looks different from the adult form. The larvae of sponges are motile and are usually carried by currents before they settle to the sea floor.

Sponges can reproduce asexually by budding or by producing gemmules. In budding, part of a sponge breaks off of the parent sponge, settles to the sea floor, and grows into a new sponge. When faced with difficult environmental conditions, some sponges produce **gemmules** (JEM-yoolz), which are groups of archaeocytes surrounded by a tough layer of spicules. Gemmules can survive freezing temperatures and drought conditions that would kill adult sponges. When conditions become favorable, a gemmule grows into a new sponge.

Ecology of Sponges

Sponges play an important part in the ecology and survival of numerous aquatic organisms. Sponges have an irregular shape and many are large. These characteristics make sponges ideal habitats for marine animals such as snails, sea stars, sea cucumbers, and shrimp, such as the shrimp in **Figure 26–10.** More important to the sponges are their mutually beneficial relationships with bacteria, algae, and plantlike protists. In fact, many sponges are colored green because these organisms are living in their tissues. These photosynthetic organisms provide food and oxygen to the sponge, while the sponge provides a protected area where these organisms can thrive. Because of this relationship, sponges containing photosynthetic organisms play an important role in the ecology and primary productivity of coral reefs.

Sponges usually live attached to the sea floor, where they are often many meters from the water surface and receive only low levels of filtered sunlight. Recently, scientists have found clues to the mystery of how organisms within the sponge get enough light to carry out photosynthesis. The spicules of some sponges look like cross-shaped antennae. Like a lens or magnifying glass, they focus and direct incoming sunlight to cells lying below the surface of the sponge—where symbiotic organisms carry out photosynthesis. This adaptation may allow sponges to survive in a wider range of habitats.

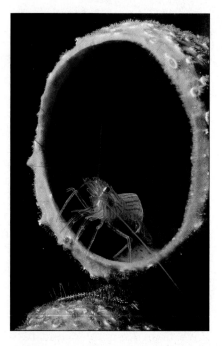

▲ **Figure 26–10** Sponges often provide habitats for other organisms. Observe how the sponge provides shelter for this snapping shrimp. **Inferring** *How might the sponge protect the shrimp from predators?*

26-2 Section Assessment

1. 🔑 **Key Concept** What features do sponges share with all other animals?

2. 🔑 **Key Concept** How do sponges use water to carry out essential functions?

3. Describe the different types of sponge skeletons.

4. Why are symbiotic relationships critical to the ecology of sponges?

5. **Critical Thinking Drawing Conclusions** Why would sponges be unable to live on land?

🔲**TEXT** **Assessment** Use iText to review the important concepts in Section 26–2.

Sunscreen From the Sea

When it comes to inventing new gadgets, high technology cannot be beat. But when it comes to searching for new compounds that affect living organisms, sometimes the best approach is "low tech." One way of generating new medicines and drugs, for example, is to look for them in nature. Organisms of all kinds have been battling each other and their physical environment since life began. So, researchers can take 100-million-year shortcuts by searching for molecules that have been assembled and tested by the oldest process for generating new compounds on Earth—natural selection.

Natural UV Protection in Corals

One of these "new" molecules may be the world's first naturally produced sunscreen. Known as Sunscreen 855, this compound was discovered by researchers at the Australian Institute of Marine Science. These researchers were studying corals that live in shallow waters along Australia's Great Barrier Reef. During the low tide, these corals are exposed to the air and full sunlight. Investigators reasoned that these corals might have evolved some sort of protection against the damaging ultraviolet (UV) radiation of intense sunlight. Sure enough, their search turned up a UV-blocking compound in the tissues of these corals.

From Natural to Synthetic

After isolating and analyzing the compound in Sunscreen 855, the researchers learned that it was structurally different from the compounds used in synthetic sunscreens. They devised a way to produce it in the laboratory so that corals would not need to be harvested to make the sunscreen. Preliminary tests have shown that the sunscreen is highly efficient in absorbing radiation in the damaging UV-B region of the spectrum.

But Sunscreen 855 is not sold in any drugstore—nor will it be for several years. Researchers are working with investors, lawyers, and businesspeople to test the new product for effectiveness and safety. If it passes final tests, Sunscreen 855 could be the best—and most natural—protection yet against the harmful effects of the sun.

On Your Own

Suppose that Sunscreen 855 were made into a product that people could buy. Make a list of things that the product should do. Make another list of things it should not do (such as harmful side effects it might cause). Describe how you would test these different claims.

26–3 Cnidarians

Imagine that you are swimming in warm, tropical waters. Far away, delicate jellyfishes float in the ocean currents. Within arm's reach, sea fans sway in the shallow currents. Brightly colored sea anemones cling to rocks, looking more like underwater flowers than animals. All these creatures are animals in the phylum Cnidaria (ny-DAYR-ee-uh), a group that includes hydras, jellyfishes, sea anemones, and corals. These fascinating animals are found in waters all over the world. Some cnidarians live as individuals. Others live in colonies composed of dozens or even thousands of connected individuals.

What Is a Cnidarian?

A few important features unite the cnidarians as a group. **Cnidarians are soft-bodied, carnivorous animals that have stinging tentacles arranged in circles around their mouths. They are the simplest animals to have body symmetry and specialized tissues.** Cnidarians get their name from the **cnidocytes** (NY-duh-syts), or stinging cells, that are located along their tentacles. **Figure 26–11** shows the structure of cnidocytes. Cnidarians use these cells for defense and to capture prey. Within each cnidocyte is a nematocyst (NEM-uh-toh-sist). A **nematocyst** is a poison-filled, stinging structure that contains a tightly coiled dart. When an unsuspecting shrimp or small fish brushes up against the tentacles, thousands of nematocysts explode into the animal, releasing enough poison to paralyze or kill the prey.

✓ **CHECKPOINT** *What is the function of cnidocytes?*

Guide for Reading

🔑 **Key Concepts**
- What is a cnidarian?
- What two body plans exist in the cnidarian life cycle?
- What are the three groups of cnidarians?

Vocabulary
cnidocyte
nematocyst
polyp
medusa
gastrovascular cavity
nerve net
hydrostatic skeleton
external fertilization

**Reading Strategy:
Finding Main Ideas** Before you read, skim the section to identify the key concepts. Read the section carefully, then write down the information that supports each key concept.

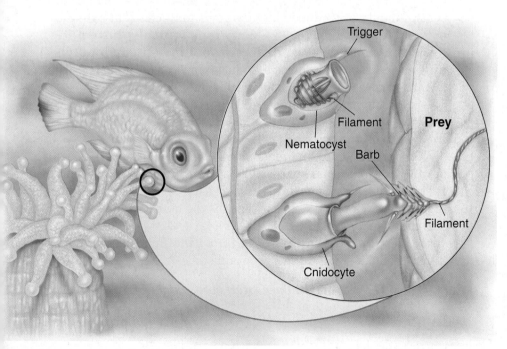

Trigger
Filament
Nematocyst
Prey
Barb
Filament
Cnidocyte

◀ **Figure 26–11**
🔑 Cnidarians are carnivorous animals that have stinging tentacles arranged around their mouths. Stinging cells called cnidocytes are used to capture and paralyze prey. Within each cnidocyte is a stinging structure called a nematocyst. Here, a sea anemone captures a fish that has brushed the trigger of the nematocyst. When an animal touches the trigger of a nematocyst, the filament inside uncoils and shoots a barb into the animal.

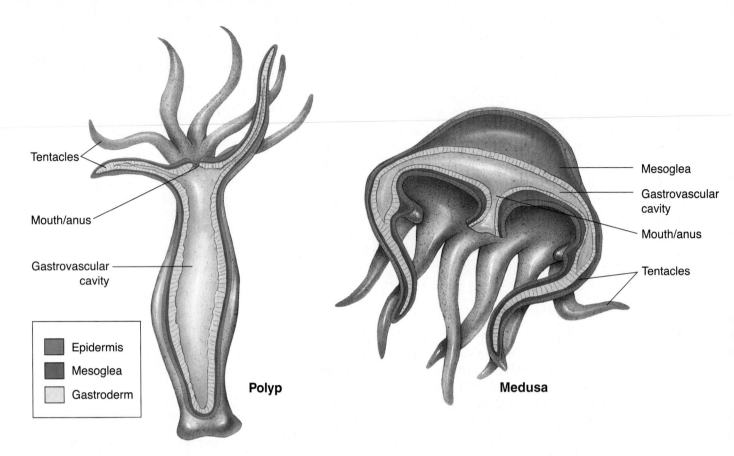

Tentacles

Mouth/anus

Gastrovascular cavity

Epidermis

Mesoglea

Gastroderm

Polyp

Mesoglea

Gastrovascular cavity

Mouth/anus

Tentacles

Medusa

▲ **Figure 26–12** 🔑 Many cnidarians have both a polyp stage (left) and a medusa stage (right). Both stages have an outer epidermal tissue; a gastroderm tissue, which lines the gastrovascular cavity; and a mesoglea layer, which lies between the two tissues. (Note that a medusa's tentacles are much narrower than in the illustration.)

Word Origins

Medusa is the name of a monster in Greek mythology. In the myth, Medusa was once a beautiful woman, but she bragged about her beauty, and so a jealous goddess changed her into a hideous monster. Medusa had long, twisting snakes for hair. **In what way are cnidarian medusas similar to the monster named Medusa?**

Form and Function in Cnidarians

Cnidarians are only a few cells thick and have simple body systems. Most of their responses to the environment are carried out by specialized cells and tissues. These tissues function in processes such as feeding and movement.

Body Plan Cnidarians are radially symmetrical. They have a central mouth surrounded by numerous tentacles that extend outward from the body. 🔑 **Cnidarians typically have a life cycle that includes two different-looking stages: a polyp and a medusa.** Both forms are shown in **Figure 26–12.** A **polyp** (PAHL-ip) is a cylindrical body with armlike tentacles. In a polyp, the mouth points upward. Polyps are usually sessile. A **medusa** (muh-DOO-suh) has a motile, bell-shaped body with the mouth on the bottom.

Cnidarian polyps and medusas each have a body wall that surrounds an internal space called a gastrovascular cavity. The gastroderm is the inner lining of the gastrovascular cavity, where digestion takes place. The epidermis is the outer layer of cells. The mesoglea (mez-uh-GLEE-uh) is a layer that lies between these two tissues. It varies from a thin, noncellular membrane to a thick, jellylike material that contains cells.

✔CHECKPOINT *What are the three layers in cnidarians?*

Before   **After**

Figure 26–13 Cnidarians have nerve nets that consist of many individual nerve cells, as shown in the hydra below. Many cnidarians respond to touch by pulling their tentacles inside their bodies. This response, shown at left in cup corals, is cued by nerve cells located in the tentacles. **Formulating Hypotheses** *How might a nerve net differ between motile and sessile cnidarians?*

Feeding After paralyzing its prey, a cnidarian pulls the prey through its mouth and into its **gastrovascular cavity,** a digestive chamber with one opening. Food enters and wastes leave the body through that opening. Digestion—the breakdown of food—begins in the gastrovascular cavity. The digestion that occurs in the gastrovascular cavity is extracellular, meaning that it takes place outside of cells. Partially digested food is absorbed by the gastroderm. Digestion is completed intracellularly, within cells in the gastroderm. Any materials that cannot be digested are passed out of the body through the mouth.

Respiration, Circulation, and Excretion Following digestion, nutrients are usually transported throughout the body by diffusion. Cnidarians respire and eliminate the wastes of cellular metabolism by diffusion through their body walls.

Response Cnidarians gather information from their environment using specialized sensory cells. Both polyps and medusas have a nerve net, shown in **Figure 26–13.** A **nerve net** is a loosely organized network of nerve cells that together allow cnidarians to detect stimuli such as the touch of a foreign object. The nerve net is usually distributed uniformly throughout the body, although in some species it is concentrated around the mouth or in rings around the body. Cnidarians also have statocysts, which are groups of sensory cells that help determine the direction of gravity. Ocelli (oh-SEL-eye; singular: ocellus) are eyespots made of cells that detect light.

Movement Different cnidarians move in different ways. Some cnidarians, such as sea anemones, have a hydrostatic skeleton. The **hydrostatic skeleton** consists of a layer of circular muscles and a layer of longitudinal muscles that, together with the water in the gastrovascular cavity, enable the cnidarian to move. For example, if the anemone's circular muscles contract when the anemone's mouth is closed, the water inside the cavity can't escape. The pressure of the water makes the body become taller. In contrast, medusas move by jet propulsion. Muscle contractions cause the bell-shaped body to close like a folding umbrella. This action pushes water out of the bell, moving the medusa forward, as shown in **Figure 26–14.**

Nerve cells

▲ **Figure 26–14** Jellyfishes move by means of jet propulsion. The body contracts to force water out, moving the jellyfish in the opposite direction. **Applying Concepts** *Is the body plan of this jellyfish a medusa or a polyp?*

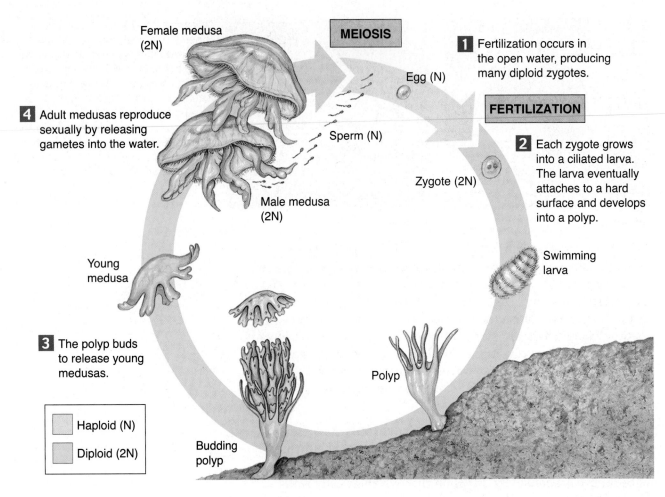

MEIOSIS

1 Fertilization occurs in the open water, producing many diploid zygotes.

Female medusa (2N)

Egg (N)

FERTILIZATION

4 Adult medusas reproduce sexually by releasing gametes into the water.

Sperm (N)

Zygote (2N)

2 Each zygote grows into a ciliated larva. The larva eventually attaches to a hard surface and develops into a polyp.

Male medusa (2N)

Swimming larva

Young medusa

3 The polyp buds to release young medusas.

Polyp

Haploid (N)

Diploid (2N)

Budding polyp

▲ **Figure 26–15** Jellyfishes reproduce sexually by producing eggs and sperm. Depending on the species, fertilization is either internal or external. In *Aurelia,* shown here, fertilization is external, occurring after eggs and sperm are released into the water. **Interpreting Graphics** *What cells are formed by the process of meiosis?*

Reproduction Most cnidarians reproduce both sexually and asexually. Polyps can reproduce asexually by budding. The new animal is genetically identical to the parent animal. One type of budding begins with a swelling on the side of an existing polyp. This swelling grows into a new polyp. In another type of budding, polyps produce tiny medusas that separate and become new individuals.

In most cnidarians, sexual reproduction takes place with external fertilization in water. **External fertilization** takes place outside the female's body. The sexes are usually separate—each individual is either male or female. The female releases eggs into the water, and the male releases sperm. The life cycle of *Aurelia,* a common jellyfish, is shown in **Figure 26–15.** Observe that the zygote grows into a free-swimming larva. The larva eventually attaches to a hard surface and develops into a polyp. Then, the polyp buds and releases a medusa that begins the cycle again.

Groups of Cnidarians

All cnidarians live under water, and nearly all live in the ocean. 🔑 **Cnidarians include jellyfishes, hydras and their relatives, and sea anemones and corals.** Some of the most familiar cnidarians are the jellyfishes.

Figure 26–16 Like many marine organisms, jellyfishes use bioluminescence, or the production of light by an organism, to ward off predators. The entire body of this jellyfish becomes bioluminescent when it is threatened (inset). **Hypothesizing** *How might bioluminescence discourage potential predators?*

Jellyfishes The class Scyphozoa (sy-fuh-ZOH-uh) contains the jellyfishes, such as the jellyfish shown in **Figure 26–16.** Scyphozoans, which means "cup animals," live their lives primarily as medusas. The polyp form of jellyfishes is restricted to a small larval stage, and no elaborate colonies ever form. Jellyfishes can be quite large—the largest jellyfish ever found was almost 4 meters in diameter and had tentacles more than 30 meters long. Jellyfishes reproduce sexually.

Hydras and Their Relatives The class Hydrozoa (hy-druh-ZOH-uh) contains hydras and other related animals. The polyps of most hydrozoans grow in branching colonies that sometimes extend more than a meter. Within the colony, polyps are specialized to perform different functions. In the Portuguese man-of-war, shown in **Figure 26–17,** one polyp forms a balloonlike float that keeps the entire colony afloat. Other polyps in the colony produce long tentacles that hang several meters under water and sting prey (and humans!) using nematocysts. Some polyps digest food held by the tentacles, while others make eggs and sperm.

The most common freshwater hydrozoans are hydras. Hydras differ from other cnidarians in this class because they lack a medusa stage. Instead, they live only as solitary polyps. Hydras reproduce asexually, by budding, or sexually, by producing eggs and sperm in the body wall. Many hydras get their nutrition from capturing, stinging, and digesting small prey. Some hydras, however, get their nutrition from symbiotic photosynthetic protists that live in their tissues.

✓**CHECKPOINT** *How do hydras reproduce?*

▶ **Figure 26–17** Jellyfishes, hydrozoans, sea anemones, and corals are all cnidarians. The Portuguese man-of-war, shown here, is a colonial hydrozoan that is composed of many specialized polyps. A single polyp that is enlarged and full of air helps keep the animal afloat, while other specialized polyps below water function in feeding and reproduction.

673

Coral Vanishing Act

The World Resources Institute, an organization that examines global environmental problems, recently announced that 58 percent of the world's coral reefs are in danger of dying. Threats to coral reefs fall into four broad categories shown in the graph. The graph indicates the percentage of reefs that are threatened by each of these categories. It also rates the threat as medium or high, based on the distance between the coral reef and the source of the threat.

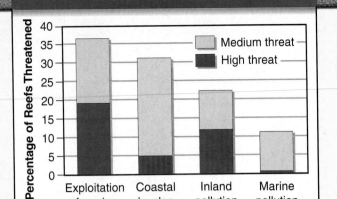

Threats to Coral Reefs

1. **Classifying** Place the four categories of risk in order from greatest high threat to least high threat.

2. **Using Tables and Graphs** Approximately how much greater is the high threat of overexploitation than the high threat of coastal development?

3. **Inferring** Based on the graph, write a generalization about the effect of human activities on the destruction of coral reefs.

4. **Going Further** Assume that you are a legislator drafting a law to protect coral reefs. Choose one of the threats shown in the graph, and outline a law that you would propose to counter the threat.

▼ **Figure 26–18** Coral reefs are home to many types of organisms and are rivaled only by rain forests in their biological diversity. Each flowerlike form shown in this photograph is an entire colony made of thousands of individual coral polyps. **Drawing Conclusions** *How would you describe the symmetry of individual coral polyps?*

Sea Anemones and Corals The class Anthozoa (an-thuh-ZOH-uh) contains sea anemones and corals, animals that have only the polyp stage in their life cycle. Anthozoans all have a central body surrounded by tentacles—a form that gave them their name, *anthozoa,* which means "flower animal." Many species are colonial, or composed of many individual polyps. The appearance of an entire reef can include varied forms, as shown in **Figure 26–18.**

Sea anemones are solitary polyps that live at all depths of the ocean. Using nematocysts, they catch a variety of marine organisms. Many shallow-water species also depend on nutrition from photosynthetic symbionts.

Individual coral polyps look like miniature sea anemones. But most corals are colonial, and their polyps grow together in large numbers. Hard coral colonies are usually founded when a motile larva settles onto a hard surface and develops into a single polyp. New polyps are produced by budding, and as the colonies grow, they secrete an underlying skeleton of calcium carbonate, or limestone. These colonies grow slowly and may live for hundreds or even thousands of years. Many coral colonies growing near one another produce the magnificent structures known as coral reefs.

Anthozoans reproduce sexually by producing eggs and sperm that are released into the water. The zygote grows into a ciliated larva that becomes a new polyp. Some species can also reproduce asexually by budding or splitting into two halves.

Ecology of Corals

The worldwide distribution of corals is determined by a few variables: temperature, water depth, and light intensity. The "stony" or "hard" corals that build coral reefs require high levels of light. Why should light be a requirement for an animal? Light is necessary because these corals rely on symbioses with algae that capture solar energy, recycle nutrients, and help corals lay down their calcium carbonate skeletons. Symbionts provide as much as 60 percent of the energy that corals need. This arrangement allows coral reefs to live in water that carries few nutrients.

Many coral reefs are now suffering from human activity. For example, recreational divers sometimes damage coral reefs. Silt and other sediments from logging, farming, mining, and construction can wash onto reefs and smother corals. Chemical fertilizers, insecticides, and industrial pollutants can poison the corals. Overfishing can upset the ecological balance of coral reefs. Even when human-caused problems do not kill corals, they can cause stress that makes reefs susceptible to other threats.

Meanwhile, a problem called coral bleaching has become common. High temperatures can kill the algae that usually live in the tissues of corals, leaving behind only transparent cells atop ghostly white skeletons. The results of coral bleaching are shown in **Figure 26–19**. In the past, bleaching was a rare and short-term event from which many corals recovered. Over the last 20 years, however, bleaching has become more common and more severe, causing many corals to die. Researchers fear that rising ocean temperatures, produced by global warming, may be contributing to this problem. If this is the case, many reefs around the world could soon be in serious danger.

▲ **Figure 26–19** Under normal conditions, algae live within coral tissues, carrying out photosynthesis and giving the coral its green appearance. However, when stressed by pollutants or increasing temperatures, these algae can die, so only the clear cells of the coral remain. **Inferring** *What effect might the loss of symbiotic algae have on the coral?*

KEEP CURRENT WITH . . .

SCIENCE NEWS®

To find out more about the topics in this chapter, go to: **www.phschool.com**

26–3 Section Assessment

1. 🔑 **Key Concept** Describe three characteristics that all cnidarians share.

2. 🔑 **Key Concept** How do the two body plans of cnidarians differ?

3. 🔑 **Key Concept** Describe the three groups of cnidarians and give an example from each.

4. Describe how the digestion and absorption of food take place in cnidarians.

5. **Critical Thinking Inferring** A medusa typically has more specialized organs for movement and response than a polyp does. Why might this be the case? (*Hint:* How does the lifestyle of a medusa differ from that of most polyps?)

iTEXT Assessment Use iText to review the important concepts in Section 26–3.

Take It to the NET

View photographs of animals from one of the three groups of cnidarians. Then, prepare a 3-minute presentation on the diversity of that group. Use the links provided in the Biology area at the Prentice Hall Web site for help in completing this activity: **www.phschool.com**

Examining the Responses of Hydras

Hydras, a type of cnidarian, are some of the simplest known animals to have a nervous system. What kinds of behavior can their simple nerve nets produce? Can they detect food and move toward it? Can they detect predators and move away from them? How do they respond to light, temperature, and other physical factors? How do these responses help them to survive? In this investigation, you will observe and try to explain the behavior of hydras.

Problem   How do hydras respond to light?

Materials
- 6 test tubes with screw caps
- test-tube rack
- green hydras
- brown hydras
- aluminum foil
- pond or spring water
- glass-marking pencil
- dropper pipette
- transparent tape

Skills   Inferring, Drawing Conclusions

Procedure

1. Make a copy of the data table shown. Number 6 test tubes 1 through 6 near the top of each tube. Fill the test tubes with pond water or spring water to within 2 cm of the top. **CAUTION:** *Do not drink the water.*

2. Use a dropper pipette to gently place 3 brown hydras in the bottoms of the test tubes labeled 1 through 3, and place 3 green hydras in the bottoms of the test tubes labeled 4 through 6.

3. Wrap the bottom half of each test tube in aluminum foil.

4. Tightly cap all 6 test tubes. Place test tubes 1 and 4 right side up in the test-tube rack and test tubes 2 and 5 upside down.

5. Label the test-tube rack with your name and place it in a brightly lit place.

6. Lay test tubes 3 and 6 on their sides next to the test-tube rack so that all 6 test tubes are equally well lit. Tape test tubes 3 and 6 in place. Place the tape over the foil and caps so that it does not block the light.

7. **Predicting** Record the time that you completed step 6. Make a prediction of where the hydras will move—either away from or toward the light. Record your prediction of any other behavior that you expect to see, along with the reasons for your predictions.

8. Observe the test tubes. Record a description of any hydra behavior you observe. Include such information as when the behavior occurred, how many hydras you saw, what they did, and any other observations you made. Leave the test tubes overnight. Be sure to wash your hands before leaving the lab.

9. The next day, observe the test tubes and again record any hydra behavior you observe. Count the number of hydras in the light and in the dark in each test tube. Record these observations in your data table.

10. Share your observations with the class to complete the Class Total columns of your data table.

Data Table

Tube	Hydras	Source of Light	Number of Hydras		Class Total	
			In light	In dark	In light	In dark
1	brown	above				
2	brown	below				
3	brown	side				
4	green	above				
5	green	below				
6	green	side				

Analyze and Conclude

1. **Observing** Which type of hydra moved toward the light? Which type avoided light?

2. **Observing** How did the hydras move? Were their movements random or in a specific direction?

3. **Observing** What differences between the behavior of green and brown hydras did you observe?

4. **Inferring** Green hydras are green because of the presence of green algae in their bodies. What seems to be the relationship between the presence of algae and the behavior of green hydras?

5. **Drawing Conclusions** How might their response to light help green hydras survive?

6. **Comparing and Contrasting** The nervous system directs animal behavior. Compare the behavior of hydras to the behavior of animals with more complex nervous systems that you have observed, such as dogs and insects.

Go Further

Design an Experiment What are some other behaviors that hydras exhibit? Do they react to changes in temperature, differences in prey behavior, or the presence of predators? Do they wander at random, or do they benefit from moving in specific ways and directions? Can they learn? Design an experiment to investigate a specific question about hydra behavior. Have your teacher approve your plan before you perform your experiment.

Take It to the NET Visit the Prentice Hall Web site at **www.phschool.com** and enter your results from this investigation. Compare your results with those that other students have posted on this Web site. Hydras do not always behave in predictable ways. Did some students observe behaviors that you did not? Does this larger set of data support your conclusions from your own experiment?

Chapter 26 Study Guide

26–1 Introduction to the Animal Kingdom
Key Concepts

- An animal is a multicellular, eukaryotic heterotroph whose cells lack cell walls.
- Animals are specialized to carry out the following essential functions: feeding, respiration, circulation, excretion, response, movement, and reproduction.
- In general, complex animals tend to have high levels of cell specialization and internal organization, bilateral body symmetry, cephalization, and a body cavity.

Vocabulary
invertebrate, p. 657
vertebrate, p. 657
parasite, p. 658
host, p. 658
blastula, p. 661
protostome, p. 661
deuterostome, p. 661
anus, p. 661
endoderm, p. 661
mesoderm, p. 661
ectoderm, p. 661
radial symmetry, p. 662
bilateral symmetry, p. 662
cephalization, p. 663

26–2 Sponges
Key Concepts

- Sponges are classified as animals because they are multicellular, heterotrophic, have no cell walls, and contain a few specialized cells.
- The movement of water through a sponge provides a simple mechanism for feeding, respiration, circulation, and excretion.

Vocabulary
choanocyte, p. 665
osculum, p. 665
spicule, p. 665
archaeocyte, p. 665
internal fertilization, p. 666
larva, p. 666
gemmule, p. 667

26–3 Cnidarians
Key Concepts

- Cnidarians are soft-bodied, carnivorous animals that have stinging tentacles arranged in circles around their mouth. They are the simplest animals to have body symmetry and specialized tissues.
- Cnidarians typically have a life cycle that includes two different-looking stages, a polyp and a medusa.
- Cnidarians include jellyfishes, hydras and their relatives, sea anemones, and corals.

Vocabulary
cnidocyte, p. 669
nematocyst, p. 669
polyp, p. 670
medusa, p. 670
gastrovascular cavity, p. 671
nerve net, p. 671
hydrostatic skeleton, p. 671
external fertilization, p. 672

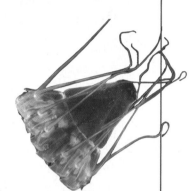

Thinking Visually
Complete the following concept map using information from the chapter:

Chapter 26

Part A

Multiple Choice

For each statement or question, select the number of the word or expression that, of those given, best completes the statement or answers the question.

1 The process by which animals take in oxygen and give off carbon dioxide is known as
   (1) circulation   (3) reproduction
   (2) respiration   (4) response

2 Animals that have a backbone, also called a vertebral column, are known as
   (1) vertebrates   (3) deuterostomes
   (2) prokaryotes   (4) invertebrates

3 Symmetry with distinct front and back ends is called
   (1) radial   (3) circular
   (2) bilateral   (4) dorsal

4 Which pairing of terms most closely applies to the developing embryo shown below?

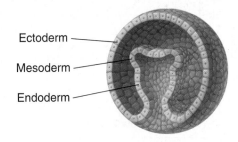

   Ectoderm
   Mesoderm
   Endoderm

   (1) protostome; simple invertebrates
   (2) protostome; vertebrates
   (3) deuterostome; echinoderms and chordates
   (4) deuterostome; invertebrates

5 An animal whose mouth is formed from the blastopore is a
   (1) deuterostome   (3) protostome
   (2) detritivore   (4) carnivore

6 Animals in the phylum Porifera include
   (1) chordates   (3) sponges
   (2) sea stars   (4) sea anemones

7 A concentration of sense organs and nerve cells at the anterior end of the body is known as
   (1) fertilization   (3) symmetry
   (2) cephalization   (4) anteriorization

8 The sessile body form of a cnidarian is a
   (1) polyp   (3) planula
   (2) medusa   (4) nematocyst

9 A soft-bodied animal with stinging tentacles arranged around its mouth is a
   (1) spicule   (3) vertebrate
   (2) cnidarian   (4) choanocyte

10 Which are the three germ layers that arise in the early development of most animal embryos?
   (1) endoderm, gastrula, and blastula
   (2) ectoderm, mesoderm, and blastula
   (3) mesoderm, gastrula, and ectoderm
   (4) endoderm, mesoderm, and ectoderm

11 In hydra and other cnidarians, gas exchange occurs by diffusion across membranes of
   (1) the cells of the tentacles, only
   (2) the outer layer of cells, only
   (3) the inner layer of cells, only
   (4) all the cells of the organism

12 Respiratory gases are exchanged between a hydra and its environment primarily by the process of
   (1) mitosis
   (2) diffusion
   (3) active transport
   (4) hormone signals

13 An adult sponge has all the characteristics below *except*
   (1) body symmetry
   (2) the inability to move from place to place
   (3) cells without cell walls
   (4) a central cavity

For questions 14 and 15, complete each analogy by selecting the correct number. In analogies, A : B :: C : means "A is to B as C is to ___?___."

14 Radial symmetry : jellyfish :: asymmetry :
   (1) medusa   (3) polyp
   (2) coral   (4) sponge

15 Hard sponge : spicule :: soft sponge :
   (1) nematocyst   (3) hydrostatic skeleton
   (2) spongin   (4) calcium carbonate

Test-Taking Tip   When evaluating multiple-choice answers, read all the answer choices, even if the first choice seems to be the correct one. By doing so, you can make sure that the answer you choose is the best one.

Parts B and C

Multiple Choice and Extended Response

For those questions that ask you to select a response, choose the one that best completes the statement or answers the question. For all others follow the directions given.

16 Explain the characteristics that all animals share.

17 What are archaeocytes?

18 Most cnidarians do not swim toward their prey. Instead, they capture prey carried by water currents. Describe how this behavior is related to their body plan.

19 The comb jelly below has a body made of two layers separated by mesoglea. Its digestive system includes an anal opening through which wastes can pass. Radiating around its body are eight "combs" of cilia, which produce movement. A pair of tentacles enable it to capture food. Should this animal be classified as a cnidarian? Support your answer.

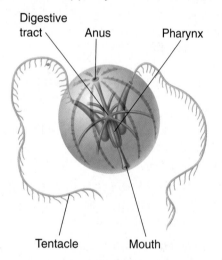

20 If you were asked to draw a jellyfish and a sponge and to label the drawings, which of the following terms would be appropriate to each: anterior, posterior, bilateral symmetry, radial symmetry, dorsal, ventral, lateral, sessile, and motile?

21 Explain how sponges are similar to most other animals. How are they different?

22 Describe the process of feeding in cnidarians.

23 Describe the life cycle of *Aurelia,* a common jellyfish. Be sure to include how the polyp form alternates with the medusa form.

24 What is the function of statocysts?

25 Explain the advantages that cephalization confers on an animal.

26 Distinguish between a protostome and a deuterostome.

27 Describe the mutually beneficial relationships that exist between many sponges and certain photosynthetic organisms.

28 Describe two ways in which budding occurs in polyps.

Base your answers to questions 29 through 31 on the graph below, which shows the growth rate of a hypothetical coral species under different conditions, and on your knowledge of biology.

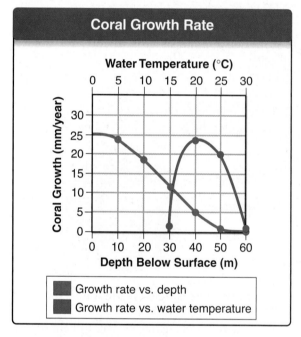

29 According to the graph, at what depth and temperature does the coral grow best?
(1) 0–10 m; 20°C
(2) less than 10 m; 15°C
(3) less than 10 m; 28°C
(4) more than 10 m; 21°C

30 Which statement best explains the trend shown in the graph?
(1) The growth rate of the coral increases as the depth below the water surface increases.
(2) At temperatures of 15°C or above, the growth rate depends only on temperature.
(3) Corals cannot grow below 30 m.
(4) This coral grows best from 18° to 21°C.

31 What is the responding (dependent) variable shown on this graph?

Base your answers to questions 32 and 33 on the information below and on your knowledge of biology.

You place harmless tiny particles in water surrounding a vase-shaped sponge. After a while, you notice these particles coming out of the top of the sponge.

32 Describe the path the particles took through the sponge.

33 What was responsible for the movement of the particles?

Base your answers to questions 34 through 36 on the reading passage below and on your knowledge of biology.

Coral Reefs in Peril

Coral reefs are the "rain forests" of the ocean. Life is abundant and varied. Coral reefs are in trouble for many reasons. Some reefs are being damaged as a result of exploitation by humans for resources. Coastal development damages other reefs.

Inland pollution is an issue in reef destruction. As chemicals and sediment wash downstream to the ocean, these materials wash out into the ocean and damage coral reefs. Pollution of the ocean by tankers, the oil industry, and the dumping of wastes is also a huge problem.

Global warming poses a large threat in the form of coral bleaching. High temperatures kill the algae that live in the tissues of corals.

34 Explain why killing the algae living in coral tissues is harmful to coral.

35 Choose one human activity that can harm coral reefs. Then, describe one measure people can take to reduce the damage.

36 Evaluate the impact that the measure you described in your answer to question 35 might have on human society.

---

37 Some claim that the life cycle of most cnidarians is more complex than the life cycle of sponges. Others claim exactly the opposite. State whether or not you think the cnidarian life cycle is more complex. Support your answer with details from cnidarian and sponge life cycles.

38 Describe how the nerve net of a cnidarian might be related to the functioning of the cnidarian's cnidocytes.

39 Animals that reproduce sexually begin life as a zygote. The zygote undergoes a series of divisions to form a hollow ball of cells. During the early development of most animal embryos, the cells differentiate into three germ layers. These layers give rise to various tissues. Discuss these layers and their significance. In your answer be sure to
- identify the three germ layers
- name one or more body structures that develop from each layer

40 Sponges are classified as animals because they are multicellular, heterotrophic, and eukaryotic. They are, however, so different from other animals that many scientists think sponges evolved independently. No matter what the differences, though, sponges must carry out essential life functions. Briefly describe how sponges carry out several of these life functions. In your answer discuss how sponges carry out these functions
- feeding
- respiration
- excretion

41 The gemmules of some sponges can survive periods of severe drought or freezing. If you were given the opportunity to study gemmules, what are three questions related to this ability to survive harsh conditions that you could investigate in a scientific experiment?

Take It to the NET

Coral reefs are an important part of the Earth's marine ecosystems. Visit the Prentice Hall Web site at **www.phschool.com** to find out more about coral reefs. Then, answer the following questions:
- What are the four main types of coral reefs?
- How are mangrove forests, sandy beaches, and sea grass beds important for coral reefs' health?
- In what parts of the world can coral reefs be found? Where is it impossible for corals to grow?

27 Worms and Mollusks

The tips of the beautiful, tentacle-like structures of this nudibranch, *Flavella affinis,* release venom for defense against predators. A nudibranch is a kind of mollusk.

Inquiry Activity

Does a planarian have a head?

Procedure

1. Using black construction paper, cover half of the outside of a petri dish. Place a white sheet of paper under the other half. Place a planarian in the center of the dish, and add spring water to keep it moist. Observe the planarian for 2 minutes. Record how long it stays on each side of the petri dish.

2. Where did the planarian spend more time? Hypothesize why the planarian preferred this side.

3. Tape a 4-cm piece of rubber band to a pencil so that 1 cm of the rubber band hangs freely. Use the tip of the rubber band to gently prod each end of the planarian. Observe its behavior.

Think About It

1. **Observing** When the planarian moved, did one end always go first?

2. **Drawing Conclusions** How might the behaviors that you observed help the planarian survive?

27–1 Flatworms

When most people think of worms, they think of long, squiggly earthworms. But there are many other kinds of worms. Some are the length of your body or as thick as your arm. Others look like glowing, furry blobs. Worms can flutter and glide, or climb around with paddlelike bristles. Still others are very small and live in tubes cemented to rocks.

How is their body shape beneficial to worms? A long, slender body allows an animal to move about more rapidly than a radially symmetrical body, like that of a cnidarian. Worms can move forward in a single direction rather than remaining stationary or drifting in currents. In addition, the mouth, sense organs, and brain (if there is one) are usually located at the anterior end, or head, of the body. This arrangement allows worms to locate food and respond to stimuli as they move. Many groups of organisms have worm-shaped bodies. The familiar earthworm is a segmented worm, which you will read about later in this chapter. The unsegmented worms include flatworms and roundworms. The simplest of these are the flatworms.

What Is a Flatworm?

The phylum Platyhelminthes (plat-ih-hel-MIN-theez) consists of the flatworms. Most flatworms are no more than a few millimeters thick. **Flatworms are soft, flattened worms that have tissues and internal organ systems. They are the simplest animals to have three embryonic germ layers, bilateral symmetry, and cephalization.**

Flatworms are known as **acoelomates** (ay-SEE-luh-mayts), meaning "without coelom." A **coelom** (SEE-lum) is a fluid-filled body cavity that is lined with mesoderm. No coelom forms between the tissues of flatworms. **Figure 27–1** shows that the digestive cavity, which is lined with endoderm, is the only body cavity. Flatworms also have bilateral symmetry. Bilateral symmetry means that the animal has two well-formed sides that can be identified as left and right. Most flatworms exhibit enough cephalization to have what is called a head.

Guide for Reading

🔑 **Key Concepts**
• What are the defining features of flatworms?
• What are the characteristics of the three groups of flatworms?

Vocabulary
• acoelomate • coelom
• pharynx • flame cell
• ganglion • eyespot
• hermaphrodite
• fission • scolex
• proglottid • testis

Reading Strategy:
Outlining Before you read, use the headings of the section to make an outline about the characteristics of flatworms. As you read, fill in subtopics where they apply in the outline. Add phrases after each subtopic to provide key information.

Digestive cavity

| ▢ Ectoderm | ▢ Mesoderm | ▢ Endoderm |

Figure 27–1 🔑 **Flatworms are the simplest animals to have three embryonic germ layers—ectoderm, endoderm, and mesoderm.** Shown here is the tropical, free-living flatworm *Pseudobiceros gloriosus*.

Form and Function in Flatworms

Because flatworms are thin and most of their cells are close to the external environment, materials can pass easily into and out of their bodies. All flatworms rely on diffusion for some essential body functions, such as respiration and circulation. Other processes are carried out in different ways in different species. Free-living flatworms have organ systems for digestion, excretion, response, and reproduction.

Parasitic species of flatworms, such as the fluke in **Figure 27–2,** probably evolved from free-living ancestors. As the worms evolved into parasites, internal organs and other structures were modified or even lost. As a result, parasitic species are typically simpler in structure than their free-living relatives.

▲ **Figure 27–2** Blood flukes are parasitic flatworms that mature in the blood vessels of humans. Unlike free-living flatworms, parasitic worms take in nutrients from another organism. **Comparing and Contrasting** *How do the internal structures of parasitic flatworms compare to those of free-living flatworms?*

Feeding Free-living flatworms can be carnivores that feed on tiny aquatic animals, or they can be scavengers that feed on recently dead animals. **Figure 27–3** shows the internal structures of a planarian, a typical flatworm. Like cnidarians, flatworms have a gastrovascular cavity with a single opening, or mouth, through which food and wastes pass. Near the mouth is a muscular tube called a **pharynx** (FAR-inks). Flatworms extend the pharynx out of the mouth. The pharynx then pumps food into the cavity. Once inside, food is digested by cells of the gut, or digestive cavity, where digestion and nutrient absorption take place. Digested food diffuses from the gastrovascular cavity into all other body tissues.

Parasitic worms feed on blood, tissue fluids, or pieces of cells within the host's body. Many parasitic worms obtain nutrients from foods that have already been digested by their host. Therefore, most parasitic worms do not need a complex digestive system. Many parasitic species have a digestive tract that is simpler than that of free-living forms. Some species have a pharynx that pumps food into a pair of dead-end intestinal sacs for digestion. Tapeworms, on the other hand, have no digestive tract at all. They live within the intestine of their host, such as a cow or a human, and simply absorb digested nutrients that are in their host's intestine.

Respiration, Circulation, and Excretion Because their bodies are so flat and thin, many flatworms do not need a circulatory system to transport materials. Instead, flatworms rely on diffusion to transport oxygen and nutrients to their internal tissues, and to remove carbon dioxide and other wastes from their bodies. Flatworms have no gills or other respiratory organs, and no heart, blood vessels, or blood.

Some flatworms have flame cells that function in excretion. **Flame cells** are specialized cells that filter and remove excess water from the body. They also remove metabolic wastes such as ammonia and urea. Many flame cells are joined together to form a network of tubes that empties into the outside environment through tiny pores in the animal's skin.

✓ **CHECKPOINT** *What is the function of flame cells?*

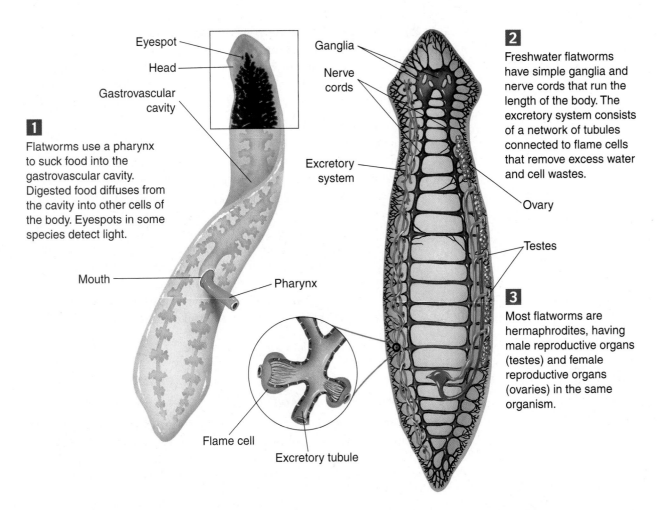

Eyespot

Head

Gastrovascular cavity

1

Flatworms use a pharynx to suck food into the gastrovascular cavity. Digested food diffuses from the cavity into other cells of the body. Eyespots in some species detect light.

Mouth

Pharynx

Flame cell

Excretory tubule

Ganglia

Nerve cords

Excretory system

2

Freshwater flatworms have simple ganglia and nerve cords that run the length of the body. The excretory system consists of a network of tubules connected to flame cells that remove excess water and cell wastes.

Ovary

Testes

3

Most flatworms are hermaphrodites, having male reproductive organs (testes) and female reproductive organs (ovaries) in the same organism.

▲ **Figure 27–3** All flatworms, including this planarian, have organ systems that perform essential life functions. The gastrovascular cavity (left) is branched throughout the body and opens to the outside through the pharynx. The diagram on the right shows the excretory system, nervous system, and reproductive system. The excretory system (in purple) consists of many flame cells (in red) that remove waste. The nervous system (in dark gray) consists of ganglia and two nerve cords that run the length of the body. The reproductive system (in green) has testes and ovaries, or male and female reproductive organs, along both sides of the body. **Inferring** *How is a branched gastrovascular cavity advantageous to a flatworm?*

Response Most flatworms have more complex structures for detecting and responding to their enviroment than those of cnidarians or sponges. In free-living flatworms, a head encloses several **ganglia** (singular: ganglion), or groups of nerve cells, that control the nervous system. These ganglia are not complex enough to be called a brain. Two long nerve cords run from the ganglia along both sides of the body. Locate these nerve cords in **Figure 27–3.** Observe that shorter nerve cords run across the body, like the rungs of a ladder. Parasitic flatworms interact little with their external environment and typically have a less complex nervous system.

Many free-living flatworms have what look like eyes near the anterior end of their body. Each "eye" is actually an **eyespot,** or group of cells that can detect changes in the amount of light in their environment. In addition to having eyespots, most flatworms have specialized cells that detect stimuli, such as chemicals found in food or the direction in which water is flowing. These cells are usually scattered throughout the body.

The nervous systems of free-living flatworms allow them to gather information from their environment. They use this information to locate food and to find dark hiding places beneath stones and logs during the day.

Movement Free-living flatworms typically move in two ways. Cilia on their epidermal cells help them glide through the water and over the bottom of a stream or pond. Muscle cells controlled by the nervous system allow them to twist and turn so that they are able to react rapidly to environmental stimuli.

Reproduction Most free-living flatworms are hermaphrodites that reproduce sexually. A **hermaphrodite** (hur-MAF-roh-dyt) is an individual that has both male and female reproductive organs. During sexual reproduction, two worms join in a pair. The worms in the pair deliver sperm to each other. The eggs are laid in clusters and hatch within a few weeks.

Asexual reproduction is common in free-living flatworms. It takes place by **fission,** in which an organism splits in two, and each half grows new parts to become a complete organism. In some species, a worm simply "falls to pieces," and each piece grows into a new worm. Parasitic flatworms often have complex life cycles that involve both sexual and asexual reproduction.

✓ CHECKPOINT *What does an eyespot detect?*

Groups of Flatworms

Flatworms are an enormously diverse group with many different forms. The three main groups of flatworms are turbellarians, flukes, and tapeworms. Most turbellarians are free-living. Most other flatworm species are parasites that depend on hosts such as snails, dogs, cattle, and humans.

Turbellarians Free-living flatworms belong to the class Turbellaria (tur-buh-LAYR-ee-uh). 🔑 **Turbellarians are free-living flatworms. Most live in marine or fresh water.** Most species are bottom dwellers, living in the sand or mud under stones and shells. In fact, if you put a piece of liver in a freshwater stream, it will probably soon attract many turbellarians. The most familiar flatworms of this group are the planarians, the "cross-eyed" freshwater worms. Turbellarians can vary greatly in color, form, and size, as shown in **Figure 27–4.**

Figure 27–4 🌀 Free-living flatworms are called turbellarians. Turbellarians vary immensely in size, shape, coloration, and habitat. The species at left is feeding on a coral reef, and the species at right lives in the leaf litter in a tropical forest.

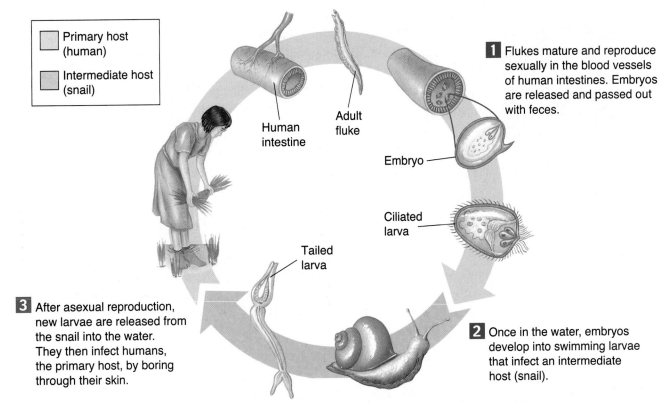

Legend:
- Primary host (human)
- Intermediate host (snail)

Human intestine

Adult fluke

1 Flukes mature and reproduce sexually in the blood vessels of human intestines. Embryos are released and passed out with feces.

Embryo

Ciliated larva

Tailed larva

3 After asexual reproduction, new larvae are released from the snail into the water. They then infect humans, the primary host, by boring through their skin.

2 Once in the water, embryos develop into swimming larvae that infect an intermediate host (snail).

▲ **Figure 27–5** Flukes usually infect the internal organs of their host. The life cycle of the blood fluke *Schistosoma mansoni* involves two hosts: humans and snails. In humans, it matures in blood vessels. After *Schistosoma* eggs are fertilized, embryos pass out of the body in feces. If the embryos reach water, they develop into larvae that can infect freshwater snails. The larvae multiply asexually and then exit the snail, searching for a human host.

Flukes Members of the class Trematoda (trem-uh-TOH-duh) are known as flukes. 🔑 **Flukes are parasitic flatworms. Most flukes infect the internal organs of their host.** They can infect the blood or virtually any internal organ of the host. Some flukes are external parasites that live on the skin, mouth, gills, or other outside parts of a host.

The blood fluke *Schistosoma mansoni* has a life cycle that is typical of parasitic flukes and of many parasites in general. As shown in **Figure 27–5**, the fluke lives in multiple hosts. Its primary host, the organism in which it reproduces sexually, is a human. Blood flukes infect humans by burrowing through exposed skin. Once inside, they are carried to the tiny blood vessels of the intestine. There, the flukes mature into adults, reproduce sexually, and release embryos into the intestine. The embryos are passed out of the body in feces.

If the embryos reach water, they develop into swimming larvae and infect freshwater snails, the intermediate host. An intermediate host is an organism in which a parasite reproduces asexually. Larvae that result from asexual reproduction are eventually released to begin the cycle again.

The *Schistosoma* fluke causes schistosomiasis (shis-tuh-soh-MY-uh-sis) in humans. Schistosomiasis is a serious disease in which the *Schistosoma* eggs clog blood vessels, causing swelling and tissue decay in the lungs, liver, spleen, or intestines. Schistosomiasis affects millions of people worldwide. It is particularly widespread in tropical areas that lack proper sewage systems, where human wastes are tossed into streams or used as fertilizer. There, the parasites are transmitted to intermediate hosts and back to humans with deadly efficiency.

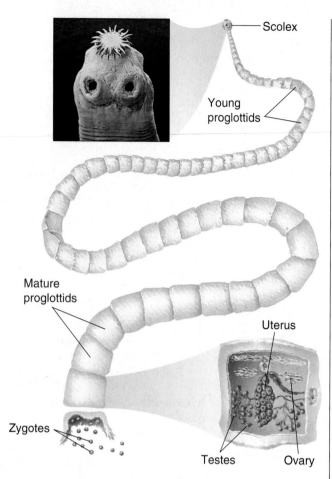

Scolex

Young proglottids

Mature proglottids

Uterus

Zygotes

Testes   Ovary

▲ **Figure 27–6** 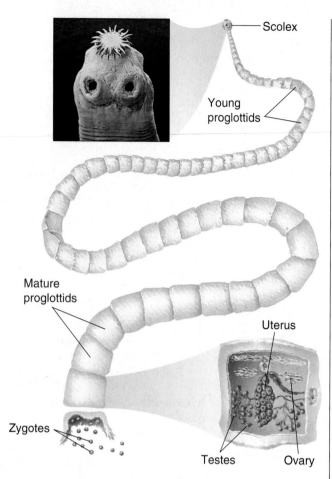Tapeworms are parasitic flatworms that live in the intestine of their host. A tapeworm attaches to the host using hooks or suckers on its scolex. A single tapeworm is made of many proglottids. The youngest proglottids are at the anterior (head) end, and the largest and most mature proglottids are at the posterior (tail) end. When mature, proglottids break off and release eggs that are then fertilized and passed out of the host in feces.

Tapeworms Members of the class Cestoda (ses-TOHD-uh) are called tapeworms. **Tapeworms are long, flat, parasitic worms that are adapted to life inside the intestines of their hosts.** There, they are surrounded by food that has already been digested, so it can be absorbed directly through their body walls. They have no digestive tract.

Figure 27–6 shows the structure of a tapeworm. The head of an adult tapeworm is called a **scolex** (SKOH-leks), a structure that can contain suckers or hooks. The tapeworm uses its scolex to attach to the intestinal wall of its host, where it absorbs nutrients from the host's intestine. Behind the scolex is a narrow neck region that divides to produce many **proglottids** (proh-GLAHT-idz), which are the segments that make up most of the worm's body. Mature proglottids contain both male and female reproductive organs. Sperm produced by the **testes,** or male reproductive organs, can fertilize eggs of other tapeworms or of the same individual. Mature proglottids break off and burst to release embryos. These embryos are passed out of the host in feces.

If food or water contaminated with tapeworm zygotes is consumed by cows, fishes, or other intermediate hosts, the eggs enter the host and hatch into larvae. These larvae grow and then burrow into the muscle tissue of the intermediate host. There they form a dormant protective stage called a cyst. If a human eats incompletely cooked meat containing these cysts, the larvae become active and grow into adult worms within the human's intestines, beginning the cycle again.

27–1 Section Assessment

1. **Key Concept** What is a flatworm?

2. **Key Concept** List the three groups of flatworms and give an example of each.

3. How do the feeding methods of parasitic and free-living flatworms relate to their specific environments?

4. Describe the life cycle of the blood fluke, *Schistosoma mansoni.*

5. **Critical Thinking Applying Concepts** Explain why you should cook meat and fish thoroughly, especially in areas that have parasitic worms.

iTEXT Assessment Use iText to review the important concepts in Section 27–1.

ALTERNATIVE ASSESSMENT

Organizing Information Create an exhibit that compares free-living and parasitic flatworms. You may want to include photographs, drawings, or models in your exhibit.

27–2 Roundworms

Members of the phylum Nematoda (nee-muh-TOHD-uh), also known as roundworms, are among the most numerous of all animals. It is difficult to imagine how many live around us. A single rotting apple can contain as many as 90,000 roundworms. A cubic meter of garden soil can be home to more than a million!

What Is a Roundworm?

Roundworms are slender, unsegmented worms with tapering ends. They range in size from microscopic to a meter in length. Most species of roundworms are free-living, inhabiting soil, salt flats, aquatic sediments, and water, from polar regions to the tropics. Many others are parasitic and live in hosts that include almost every kind of plant and animal.

Like the flatworms, all roundworms develop from three germ layers. However, roundworms have a body cavity between the endoderm and mesoderm tissues. Because this cavity is lined only partially with mesoderm tissue, it is called a **pseudocoelom** (soo-doh-SEE-lum), which means "false coelom." Observe the pseudocoelom in **Figure 27–7.**

Also, unlike the flatworms, roundworms have a digestive tract with two openings. This body plan is often called a tube-within-a-tube. The inner tube is the digestive tract, and the outer tube is the body wall. This arrangement makes digestion in roundworms very different from that in flatworms because food moves in one direction through the digestive tract. Any material in the food that cannot be digested leaves through the anus. The **anus** is the posterior opening of the digestive tract. Roundworms are unsegmented worms that have pseudocoeloms and digestive systems with two openings—a mouth and an anus.

Guide for Reading

Key Concepts
• What are the defining features of roundworms?
• What roundworms are important in human disease?

Vocabulary
pseudocoelom
anus

**Reading Strategy:
Using Visuals** As you read, write a statement explaining how each illustration or photograph reinforces or enhances the content of the section.

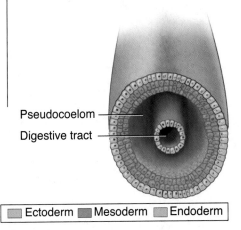

Pseudocoelom
Digestive tract

☐ Ectoderm ☐ Mesoderm ☐ Endoderm

Figure 27–7 Roundworms such as the hookworms are unsegmented worms that have a pseudocoelom and a digestive system with a mouth and an anus. Roundworms develop from three germ layers, and a pseudocoelom forms between the endoderm and mesoderm layers. The pseudocoelom allows for greater specialization and movement of internal organs.

Figure 27–8 🔑 Parasitic round-worms include trichinosis-causing *Trichinella* worms (top) and hook-worms (inset). *Trichinella* worms reproduce in the intestines of their host—including pigs and other ver-tebrates—and then form cysts in the muscle tissue. Hookworms affect as many as one quarter of the world's population. They suck the host's blood from inside the intestines, weakening the host.

Form and Function in Roundworms

Roundworms have specialized tissues and organ systems that carry out essential body functions. In general, the body systems of free-living roundworms tend to be more complex than those of parasitic forms, shown in **Figure 27–8.**

Feeding Many free-living roundworms are carnivores that use grasping mouthparts and spines to catch and eat other small animals. Some soil-dwelling and aquatic forms eat algae, fungi, or pieces of decaying organic matter. Others digest the bacteria and fungi that break down dead animals and plants.

Respiration, Circulation, and Excretion Like flatworms, roundworms exchange gases and excrete metabolic waste through their body walls. They have no internal transport system. Therefore, they depend on diffusion to carry nutrients and waste through their bodies.

Response Roundworms have simple nervous systems, con-sisting of several ganglia. Several nerves extend from ganglia in the head and run the length of the body. These nerves transmit sensory information and control movement. Roundworms have several types of sense organs, simple structures that detect chemicals given off by prey or hosts.

Movement The muscles of roundworms extend the length of their bodies. Together with the fluid in the pseudocoelom, these muscles function as a hydrostatic skeleton. Aquatic roundworms contract these muscles to move like snakes through the water. Soil-dwelling roundworms simply push their way through the soil by thrashing around.

Reproduction Roundworms reproduce sexually, and most species of roundworms have separate males and females. Roundworms reproduce using internal fertilization. Usually, the male deposits sperm inside the female's reproductive tract. Parasitic roundworms, such as hookworms or ascarid worms, often have complex life cycles that involve two or three different hosts or several organs within a single host.

✓**CHECKPOINT** *How do free-living roundworms that are carnivores obtain their food?*

Roundworms and Human Disease

Although most roundworms are free-living, the phylum is better known for species that parasitize their hosts, including humans. Parasitic roundworms, such as those in **Figure 27–8,** have been evolving relationships with other organisms for hundreds of millions of years. Unfortunately, this process has produced worms that cause a great deal of pain and suffering in humans. 🔑 **Parasitic roundworms include trichinosis-causing worms, filarial worms, ascarid worms, and hookworms.**

Meat Inspector

Job description: work with farms and meat-processing plants to ensure that all meat and poultry products use healthy animals, are processed in a sanitary manner, and are labeled truthfully with no harmful ingredients added; enforce government regulations to ensure that proper safety, sanitation, preservation, disposal, and packaging procedures are followed

Education: college courses in sanitation and public health; USDA certification

Skills: knowledge of food-borne illnesses, proper sanitation practices, and regulations; public relations skills for dealing with different people in the industry; patience and communication skills for educating the public; ability to work independently and with a team

Highlights: You help protect the safety of the public by working to eliminate food-borne illnesses. You inspect farms to make sure that sanitary procedures are followed.

"We are basically 'silent guardians' of the public's health. When you buy meat or order it at a restaurant, you can rest assured that the food is safe because meat inspectors have done their job."

Take It to the NET
For more information about this career, visit the Prentice Hall Web site: **www.phschool.com**

Trichinosis-Causing Worms Trichinosis (trik-ih-NOH-sis) is a terrible disease caused by the roundworm *Trichinella*. Adult worms live and mate in the intestines of their hosts, which include humans, pigs, and other mammals. Females carrying fertilized eggs burrow into the intestinal wall and then release larvae. These larvae travel through the bloodstream and burrow into organs and tissues, causing terrible pain for the host. The larvae form cysts and become inactive in the host's muscle tissue. *Trichinella* completes its life cycle only when another animal eats muscle tissue containing these cysts.

Filarial Worms Filarial worms, which are found primarily in tropical regions of Asia, are threadlike worms that live in the blood and lymph vessels of birds and mammals, including humans. They are transmitted from one primary host to another through biting insects, especially mosquitoes. In severe infections, large numbers of filarial worms may block the passage of fluids within the lymph vessels. This causes elephantiasis, shown in **Figure 27–9**, a condition in which the affected part of the body swells enormously.

▲ **Figure 27–9** Filarial worms are one kind of parasitic roundworm. Elephantiasis, shown here in an advanced stage, is a disease caused by filarial worms.

CHECKPOINT *Describe the cause of elephantiasis.*

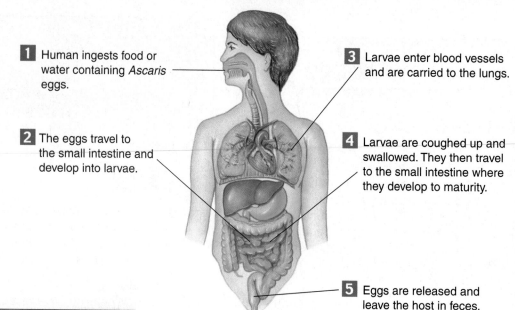

1 Human ingests food or water containing *Ascaris* eggs.

2 The eggs travel to the small intestine and develop into larvae.

3 Larvae enter blood vessels and are carried to the lungs.

4 Larvae are coughed up and swallowed. They then travel to the small intestine where they develop to maturity.

5 Eggs are released and leave the host in feces.

Figure 27–10 *Ascaris lumbricoides* fill the host's intestine. These worms absorb the host's digested food and can cause severe malnutrition. Blockage of the intestine can be severe enough, as shown in a pig intestine in the photograph, that it causes death. **Interpreting Graphics** *What is the sequence of organs that* Ascaris *travels through in humans?*

Ascarid Worms *Ascaris lumbricoides* is a serious parasite of humans and many other vertebrate animals. It causes malnutrition in more than 1 billion people worldwide, including many people living in the southeastern United States. It is commonly spread by eating vegetables or other foods that are not washed properly.

The life cycle of *Ascaris* is summarized in **Figure 27–10** above. *Ascaris* matures in the intestines of its host, such as a human, and can reach a length of almost 50 cm. In the intestine, the ascarid worms produce a large number of fertilized eggs, which leave the body in the feces. If food or water contaminated with these feces is eaten by another host, then the eggs hatch in the small intestine of the new host. The young worms burrow into the walls of the intestines and enter the surrounding blood vessels. The worms are carried in the blood until they reach the lungs. There, they spread into air passages and into the throat, where they are swallowed. Carried back into the intestines, they mature, and the cycle repeats itself.

Species that are closely related to *Ascaris* affect horses, cattle, pigs, chickens, dogs, cats, and many other animals. *Ascaris* and its relatives, which are collectively known as ascarids, have life cycles that are similar to one another. One of the reasons puppies are wormed while they are young is to rid them of the ascarid worms that affect dogs.

✓ CHECKPOINT *How are* Ascaris *eggs spread?*

Hookworms Today, as many as one quarter of the people in the world are infected with hookworms. Hookworm eggs hatch outside the body of the host and develop in the soil. If they find an unprotected foot, they use sharp toothlike plates and hooks to burrow into the skin and enter the bloodstream. Hookworms travel through the blood of their host to the lungs and down to the intestines. There, they suck the host's blood, causing weakness and poor growth.

Figure 27–11 The DNA of *C. elegans,* a free-living roundworm, was the first genome of any multicellular animal to be sequenced completely. Biologists used techniques such as gel electrophoresis, shown at right, to determine the exact sequence of base pairs in each chromosome. **Predicting** *How might these results be important to our understanding of human development?*

Research on C. *elegans*

Roundworms have recently been making headlines in scientific research. The free-living roundworm *Caenorhabditis elegans*, or *C. elegans*, is shown in **Figure 27–11**, above left. This worm lives a modest existence feeding on rotting vegetation. However, this species is extraordinary because its DNA was the first of any multicellular animal's to be sequenced completely.

Scientists now have the sequence of all 97 million base pairs of *C. elegans* DNA. This is roughly one thirtieth the number of base pairs in human DNA. They have also traced the development of each body cell of *C. elegans*, starting from a single fertilized egg. Researchers are still learning how this development is controlled by the animal's DNA. This research will lead to a better understanding of how eukaryotes became multicellular. Information from *C. elegans* may also shed light on how genes make multicellular organisms both similar to and different from one another.

KEEP CURRENT WITH . . .

SCIENCE NEWS®

To find out more about the topics in this chapter, go to: **www.phschool.com**

27–2 Section Assessment

1. **Key Concept** What is a roundworm?

2. **Key Concept** What are the parasitic roundworms?

3. Describe how humans become infected with the parasitic roundworm *Ascaris*.

4. How do hookworms enter the human body?

5. **Critical Thinking Problem Solving** How might the spread of elephantiasis be reduced?

TEXT **Assessment** Use iText to review the important concepts in Section 27–2.

ALTERNATIVE ASSESSMENT

Creating a Poster
Choose a type of roundworm that can cause disease in humans. Design an educational poster that promotes prevention of the disease. Be sure to include information about how the roundworm infects humans.

27-3 Annelids

Guide for Reading

Key Concepts
- What are the defining features of annelids?
- What are the characteristics of the three classes of annelids?

Vocabulary
- septum • seta
- crop • gizzard
- closed circulatory system
- gill • nephridium
- clitellum

Reading Strategy:
Using Visuals Before you read, preview **Figure 27-16.** How does this animal seem to differ from the other worms you have already studied? Briefly summarize any differences you notice.

If you have ever dug in a garden in the spring, you have probably seen earthworms wriggling through the soil. Earthworms are annelids, members of the phylum Annelida. Other annelids include exotic seafloor worms and parasitic, blood-sucking leeches. Because their bodies are long and narrow, some annelids look a bit like flatworms or roundworms. However, the annelids are a distinct group that is probably more closely related to clams and octopi. One piece of evidence for this relationship is the fact that annelids, clams, and octopi all share a similar larval stage.

What Is an Annelid?

The name Annelida (uh-NEL-ih-duh) is derived from the Latin word *annellus*, which means "little ring." The name refers to the ringlike appearance of annelids' body segments. The body of an annelid is divided into segments that are separated by **septa** (singular: septum), which are internal walls between each segment. Most segments are similar to one another, although they may be modified to perform special functions. Some body segments may carry one or more pairs of eyes, several pairs of antennae, and other sense organs. Other segments may be specialized for functions such as respiration. In many annelids, bristles called **setae** (SEE tee; singular: seta) are attached to each segment.

Annelids are worms with segmented bodies. They have a true coelom that is lined with mesoderm. These structures are shown in **Figure 27-12.** Recall that flatworms have no coelom, whereas roundworms have a pseudocoelom that forms between the endoderm and the mesoderm. Like the roundworms, annelids have a tube-within-a-tube digestive tract that food passes through from the mouth to the anus.

✓ CHECKPOINT *What are some functions performed by specialized segments?*

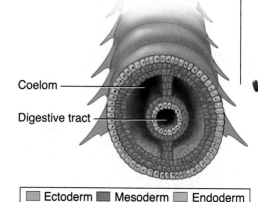

Coelom

Digestive tract

☐ Ectoderm ■ Mesoderm ☐ Endoderm

Figure 27-12 🔑 Annelids are among the simplest animals to have a true coelom that is lined with mesoderm. Annelids are also called segmented worms because the body is divided into many similar segments. The photo shows a marine annelid.

Does an earthworm have a heartbeat?

Materials earthworm; dropper pipette; nonchlorinated water; large, clear plastic soda straw; dissecting microscope

Procedure
1. Carefully insert an earthworm into a clear plastic straw. Do not force the worm into the straw. **CAUTION:** *Handle the earthworm carefully to avoid harming it. Wash your hands after handling the worm.*
2. Use a dropper pipette to add a drop or two of nonchlorinated water into the straw.

3. Examine the straw using a microscope. Direct light through the straw from below. Look near the front of the worm for the large ring blood vessels. Count how often these organs beat. Observe the rest of the circulatory system.

Analyze and Conclude
1. **Inferring** Did you see the worm breathing? Explain your answer. Why must the earthworm's skin be kept moist? How do your answers relate to how earthworms live in their environment?
2. **Observing** Is an earthworm's circulatory system open or closed? Explain your answer.

Form and Function in Annelids

Annelids have complex organ systems. Many of these systems are unique because of the segmented body plan of this group.

Feeding and Digestion Annelids range from filter feeders to predators that are fearsome—at least for their size. Many annelids get their food using a pharynx. In carnivorous species, such as the *Nereis* in **Figure 27–13**, the pharynx usually holds two or more sharp jaws that are used to attack prey. In annelids that feed on decaying vegetation, the pharynx is covered with sticky mucus. The worm collects food particles by extending its pharynx and pressing it against the surrounding sediments. Other annelids obtain nutrients by filter feeding. They fan water through tubelike burrows and catch food particles in a mucus bag.

In earthworms, the pharynx pumps food and soil into a tube called the esophagus. The food then moves through the **crop,** where it can be stored, and through the **gizzard,** where it is ground into smaller pieces. The food is absorbed farther along in the digestive tract, in an organ called the intestine.

Circulation Annelids typically have a **closed circulatory system,** in which blood is contained within a network of blood vessels. An earthworm's blood circulates through two major blood vessels that run from head to tail. Blood in the dorsal (top) vessel moves toward the head of the worm. Blood in the ventral (bottom) vessel runs from head to tail. In each body segment, a pair of smaller blood vessels called ring vessels connect the dorsal and ventral blood vessels and supply blood to the internal organs. The dorsal blood vessel functions like a heart because it contracts rhythmically and helps pump blood.

▲ **Figure 27–13** The annelid *Nereis* uses jaws to capture prey. When prey approaches, the worm lunges forward, rapidly extends its pharynx, and grabs the prey using its jaws. **Inferring** *How is the structure of a Nereis's jaws related to their function?*

▲ **Figure 27–14** These feather-duster worms exchange gases underwater using feathery gills. **Applying Concepts** *How do land-dwelling annelids exchange gases?*

Respiration Aquatic annelids often breathe through gills. A **gill** is a filamentous organ specialized for the exchange of gases underwater. In feather-duster worms, shown in **Figure 27–14**, feathery gills protrude from the opening of the worm's burrow or tube. Land-dwelling annelids, such as earthworms, take in oxygen and give off carbon dioxide through their moist skin. These annelids secrete a thin protective coating of mucus, which keeps their skins moist.

Excretion Like other animals, annelids produce two kinds of waste. Digestive waste passes out through the anus at the end of the digestive tract. Cellular waste containing nitrogen is eliminated by **nephridia** (nee-FRID-ee-uh; singular: nephridium), which are excretory organs that filter fluid in the coelom.

Response Most annelids have a well-developed nervous system consisting of a brain and several nerve cords. However, the sense organs are best developed in free-living marine annelids. Many of these species have a variety of adaptations for detecting stimuli: sensory tentacles, chemical receptors, statocysts that help detect gravity, and two or more pairs of eyes.

Movement Annelids have two major groups of body muscles that function as part of a hydrostatic skeleton. Longitudinal muscles run from the front of the worm to the rear and can contract to make the worm shorter and fatter. Circular muscles wrap around each body segment and can contract to make the worm longer and thinner. The earthworm moves by alternately contracting these two sets of muscles. Burrowing annelids use their muscles to force their way through heavy sediment. Marine annelids also have paddlelike appendages, or parapodia (singular: parapodium), on each segment, which they use for swimming and crawling.

Reproduction Most annelids reproduce sexually. Some species use external fertilization and have separate sexes—each individual is either male or female. Other annelids, such as earthworms and leeches, are hermaphrodites: each worm produces both sperm and eggs. Individuals rarely fertilize their own eggs. Instead, two worms attach to each other, as shown in **Figure 27–15**, exchange sperm, and then store the sperm in special sacs. When eggs are ready for fertilization, a **clitellum** (kly-TEL-um), or band of thickened, specialized segments, secretes a mucus ring into which eggs and sperm are released. Fertilization takes place within this ring. The ring then slips off the worm's body and forms a protective cocoon. Young worms hatch weeks later.

▶ **Figure 27–15** Some annelids, including these earthworms, are hermaphrodites. Each worm produces both eggs and sperm. During mating, the worms exchange sperm, which will eventually be used to fertilize egg cells. **Applying Concepts** *When are the eggs fertilized?*

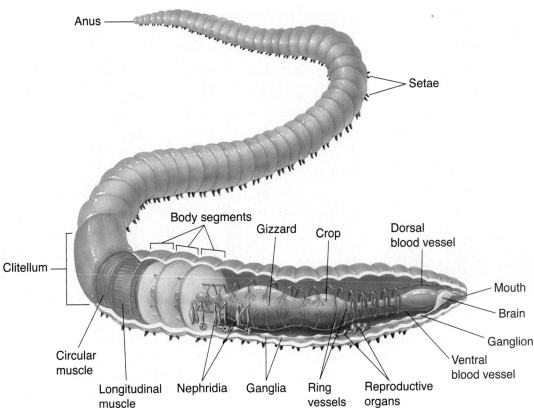

Anus

Setae

Body segments

Gizzard

Crop

Dorsal blood vessel

Clitellum

Mouth

Brain

Ganglion

Ventral blood vessel

Circular muscle

Longitudinal muscle

Nephridia

Ganglia

Ring vessels

Reproductive organs

▲ **Figure 27–16** 🔑 **Earthworms are oligochaetes that live in soil.** Earthworms carry out essential functions using digestive, circulatory, excretory, nervous, and reproductive systems. Many organs, including nephridia and blood vessels, repeat in nearly every body segment.

Groups of Annelids

Because of their visible segmentation, all annelids show a basic similarity. Annelids are divided into three classes—oligochaetes, leeches, and polychaetes.

Oligochaetes The class Oligochaeta, or oligochaetes (AHL-ih-goh-keets), contains earthworms and their relatives. 🔑 **Oligochaetes are annelids that typically have streamlined bodies and relatively few setae compared to polychaetes. Most oligochaetes live in soil or fresh water.** Earthworms, such as the one diagrammed in **Figure 27–16,** are long, pinkish-brown worms that are common in woods, fields, and gardens. Tubifex worms—another common oligochaete—are red, threadlike aquatic worms that are sold in pet stores as food for tropical fish.

Although earthworms spend most of their lives hidden underground, you may find evidence of their presence above ground in the form of squiggles of mud known as castings. Recall that an earthworm—which swallows just about anything it can get into its mouth—uses its pharynx to suck a mixture of detritus and soil particles into its mouth. As the mixture of food and soil passes through the intestine, part of it is digested and absorbed. Sand grains, clay particles, and indigestible organic matter pass out through the anus in large quantities, producing castings. Some tropical earthworms produce enormous castings—as large as 18 centimeters long and 2 centimeters in diameter!

✓ **CHECKPOINT** *What are earthworm castings?*

Word Origins

Oligochaete comes from the Greek words *oligos*, meaning "few" or "small," and *chaite*, meaning "hair." If *poly-* means "many," **what is a characteristic of the group of annelids known as polychaetes?**

Figure 27–17 Most leeches are external parasites. Medicinal leeches, such as the one below, were once used routinely to attempt to treat conditions ranging from headaches to mental illness to obesity. Doctors believed that diseases were caused by an excess of blood, so they applied leeches to the patient's skin to remove blood from the body. Here, a man who lived in the Middle Ages has become so fat that he has been confined to a room and covered with leeches.

▼ **Figure 27–18** Polychaetes are marine annelids. The bearded fireworm is a polychaete that lives in coral reefs. It is best known for its method of defense—its setae, or bristles, break off when touched and cause irritation and burning.

Leeches The class Hirudinea (hir-yoo-DIN-ee-uh) contains the leeches, most of which live in moist habitats in tropical countries. **Leeches are typically external parasites that suck the blood and body fluids of their host.** Roughly one fourth of all leeches are carnivores that feed on soft-bodied invertebrates such as snails, worms, and insect larvae.

Leeches have powerful suckers at both ends of their bodies that help them cling to their hosts. The posterior sucker can also anchor a leech to rocks or leaves as it waits for a host to pass. Some leeches force a muscular extension called a proboscis (proh-BAHS-is) into the tissue of their host. Others slice into the skin with a razor-sharp pair of jaws. Once a wound has been made, the leech uses its pharynx to suck blood from the area. Some leeches also release a substance that anesthetizes the wound—keeping the host from knowing it has been bitten!

Leeches were once commonly used to treat medical conditions, as shown in **Figure 27–17.** Today the use of medicinal leeches is undergoing a revival of sorts. Doctors are finding that leeches can reduce swelling after surgery. After surgeries in which a body part is reattached, hungry leeches are applied to the area. These leeches can suck several milliliters of blood at a time—up to five times their own weight! They also secrete a fluid that prevents blood from clotting. This anti-clotting mechanism helps relieve pressure and congestion in the healing tissues.

Polychaetes The class Polychaeta, or polychaetes (PAHL-ih-keets), contains sandworms, bloodworms, and their relatives. **Polychaetes are marine annelids that have paired, paddlelike appendages tipped with setae.** The setae are the brushlike structures on the worm shown in **Figure 27–18.** Polychaetes live in cracks and crevices in coral reefs; in sand, mud, and piles of rocks; or even out in the open water. Some burrow through or crawl over sediment.

Ecology of Annelids

The importance of earthworms in nature was noted as far back as ancient Greece, when Aristotle called them "the intestines of the earth." Charles Darwin was impressed enough with earthworms that he devoted years—and an entire book—to their study. Earthworms, like the one shown in **Figure 27–19**, and many other annelids spend their lives burrowing through soil, aerating it, and mixing it to depths of 2 meters or more. Their tunnels provide passageways for plant roots and water and allow the growth of beneficial, oxygen-requiring soil bacteria. Earthworms pull plant matter down into the soil and pass it through the gut. There, they grind it, partially digest it, and mix it with bacteria that help the plant matter decompose. Worms also "mine" minerals from deeper soil layers, bringing them up to the surface. Earthworm feces (castings) are rich in nitrogen, phosphorus, potassium, micronutrients, and beneficial bacteria.

You've probably seen a bird struggling to pull an earthworm out of the ground. Earthworms are an important part of the diet of many birds, such as robins. Moles, skunks, toads, and snakes also feed on earthworms.

In the sea, annelids participate in a wide range of food chains. Many marine annelids have free-swimming larvae that are part of the animal plankton that is consumed by fishes and other plankton feeders. As adults, some marine annelids are mud-dwelling filter feeders that are common in areas where sediment is disturbed or large amounts of organic material are present. These worms are especially numerous where pollution from sewage promotes the growth of bacteria and algae. As any fisher knows, many bottom-dwelling polychaetes are important in the diets of fishes as well as crustaceans, such as crabs and lobsters.

▲ **Figure 27–19** Some annelids, including this earthworm, burrow through soil, mixing it as they go. **Applying Concepts** *What is the role of an annelid in the ecology of the sea?*

27–3 Section Assessment

1. 🔑 **Key Concept** What features distinguish annelids from roundworms?

2. 🔑 **Key Concept** List the defining characteristics for each class of annelid.

3. Describe the feeding strategies of earthworms and leeches.

4. **Critical Thinking Inferring** An earthworm has more light-sensitive cells in its anterior and posterior segments than in other parts of its body. Explain how this is advantageous for the worm.

📱 **iTEXT Assessment** Use iText to review the important concepts in Section 27–3.

What Can Be Done About the Zebra Mussel?

Zebra mussels (*Dreissena polymorpha*) were introduced into the United States from Eastern Europe and Asia when ships from the areas emptied their ballast tanks. They were first spotted in the Great Lakes in the mid-1980s. Zebra mussels have few natural enemies here and reproduce very rapidly. Carried mainly by the normal flow of water and boat traffic, zebra mussels have already colonized the entire Great Lakes region and have spread to rivers in more than ten states, including Mississippi and Arkansas. The map shows the distribution of zebra mussels in the United States.

Zebra mussels live attached to almost any surface—from metal pipes to fiberglass boats—and can form layers up to 20 centimeters thick. As a result, they have caused serious structural damage and have clogged water supply lines to power plants and water treatment facilities. One paper company along Lake Michigan, for example, spent over a million dollars to remove zebra mussels that were clogging its cooling pipes.

Zebra mussels also threaten the ecology of aquatic communities. They can tolerate a wide range of temperatures and light intensities. In some habitats, they have displaced native mollusks, almost making them extinct. Because they feed largely on phytoplankton, zebra mussels have also depleted a critical food source for many fish species.

What can be done to control zebra mussels and other exotic (non-native) species and prevent new ones from arriving?

The Viewpoints

Control and Prevention
Many scientists believe that there is no way to remove zebra mussels and many other established exotic species. Instead, these scientists attempt to control the growth of populations and prevent the transfer of exotic species to new areas. One regulation, for example, could require boaters to filter and chemically clean all ballast water.

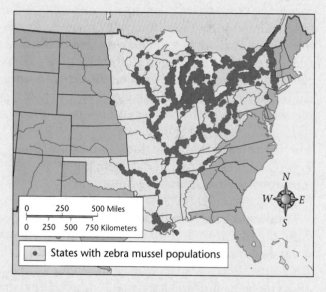

0	250	500 Miles
0	250	500	750 Kilometers

● States with zebra mussel populations

Another approach would be to find beneficial uses for zebra mussels. Scientists are already exploring the ability of zebra mussels to filter large volumes of waste water.

Eradication
Other groups contend that zebra mussels should be eradicated. Engineers, for example, are developing robotic submarines that can remove mussels from pipelines. Chemists are testing chemicals for the potential to destroy or disrupt the life cycle of zebra mussels. Other scientists are adding chemicals to paints and plastics to prevent mussels from attaching to new surfaces.

You Decide

1. **Defining the Issue** In your own words, explain the major issues surrounding the problem of dealing with zebra mussels.
2. **Analyzing the Viewpoints** What are the advantages and disadvantages of each proposed solution to the problems caused by zebra mussels?
3. **Forming Your Opinion** What measures do you think would be most effective in dealing with exotic species?

27–4 Mollusks

They climb trees in tropical rain forests and float over coral reefs. They crawl into garbage cans, eat their way through farm crops, and speed through the deep ocean. Some are so small that you can hardly see them with the unaided eye, while others are 20 meters long! They are the mollusks—one of the oldest and most diverse phyla. Mollusks come in so many sizes, shapes, and forms that you might wonder why they are classified in the same phylum. To learn the answer, read on.

What Is a Mollusk?

Members of the phylum Mollusca, known as mollusks, are named from the Latin word *molluscus*, which means "soft." **Mollusks are soft-bodied animals that usually have an internal or external shell.** Mollusks include snails, slugs, clams, squids, and octopi. But a snail looks very different from a squid, which looks very different from a clam. So why are they all placed in the same phylum? One reason is that many mollusks share similar developmental stages. Many aquatic mollusks have a free-swimming larval stage called a **trochophore** (TRAHK-oh-fawr). The trochophore larva, shown in **Figure 27–20**, is also characteristic of annelids, indicating that these two groups are probably closely related. Molecular studies suggest that a common ancestor of annelids and mollusks lived more than 550 million years ago.

Guide for Reading

Key Concepts
- What are the defining features of mollusks?
- What is the basic body plan of mollusks?
- What are the characteristics of the three main classes of mollusks?

Vocabulary
- trochophore • foot
- mantle • shell • visceral mass
- radula • siphon
- open circulatory system

Reading Strategy: Building Vocabulary
As you read, make notes about the meaning of each term in the list above. After you read the section, make a table listing the different types of mollusks on the left and the vocabulary words that apply on the right.

Trochophore larva

Mouth

Cilia

Stomach

Anus

Figure 27–20 Mollusks are an incredibly diverse group, including clams, octopi, and snails, as well as the lesser known cuttlefish, shown here. Many mollusks have a larval stage called a trochophore (right), which has at least one band of cilia encircling its body. **All mollusks have a soft body, and most mollusks have an internal or external shell.**

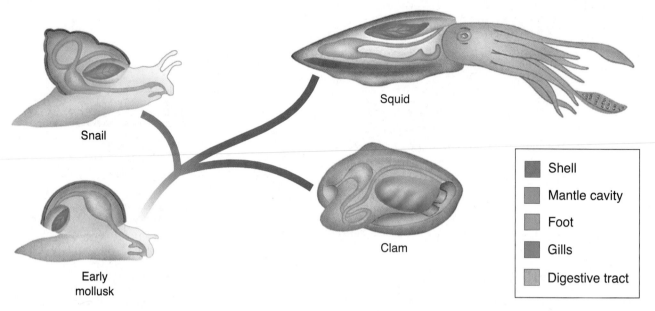

Snail

Squid

Early mollusk

Clam

Shell
Mantle cavity
Foot
Gills
Digestive tract

▲ **Figure 27–21** 🔑 The body plan of most mollusks includes a foot, mantle, shell, and visceral mass. Early mollusks may have looked like the animal shown at the bottom. As they evolved, their body parts became adapted for different functions.

Form and Function in Mollusks

Like the annelids, mollusks have true coeloms surrounded by mesoderm tissue. They also have complex organ systems that carry out processes such as respiration and excretion.

Body Plan The different body shapes of mollusks are variations on a single body plan, shown in **Figure 27–21**. 🔑 **The body plan of most mollusks has four parts: foot, mantle, shell, and visceral mass.** The muscular **foot** takes many forms, including flat structures for crawling, spade-shaped structures for burrowing, and tentacles for capturing prey. The **mantle** is a thin layer of tissue that covers most of the mollusk's body, much like a cloak. The **shell** is made by glands in the mantle that secrete calcium carbonate. The shell has been reduced or lost in slugs and some other mollusk groups. Just beneath the mantle is the **visceral mass,** which consists of the internal organs.

Feeding Mollusks can be herbivores, carnivores, filter feeders, detritivores, or parasites. Snails and slugs feed using a flexible, tongue-shaped structure known as a **radula** (RAJ-oo-luh; plural: radulae), shown in **Figure 27–22**, to which hundreds of tiny teeth are attached. Herbivorous mollusks use their radula to scrape algae off rocks or to eat the soft tissues of plants. Carnivorous mollusks use their radula to drill through shells of other animals and to tear up and swallow the prey's soft tissue.

✓CHECKPOINT How is a mollusk's shell made?

Figure 27–22 Snails use a radula for feeding. The teeth of a radula give it the look and feel of sandpaper. Beneath the radula is a stiff supporting rod of cartilage. When the mollusk feeds, it places the tip of the radula on its food and pulls the sandpapery layer back and forth. **Formulating Hypotheses** *How might radulae with different structures allow snails to inhabit different environments?*

Teeth   Radula

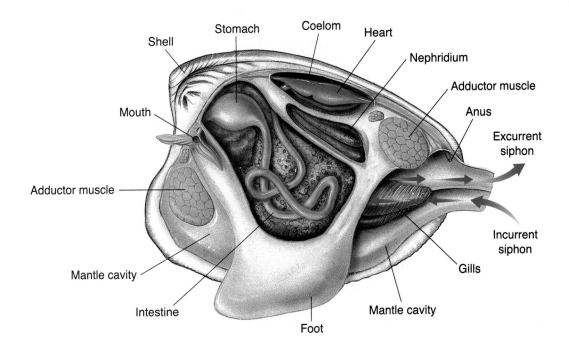

Shell · Stomach · Coelom · Heart · Nephridium · Adductor muscle · Anus

Mouth

Excurrent siphon

Adductor muscle

Incurrent siphon

Mantle cavity

Gills

Intestine

Mantle cavity

Foot

Octopi and certain sea slugs use their sharp jaws to eat their prey. To subdue their prey, some octopi also produce poisons. Some of these poisons are strong enough to harm humans! Clams, oysters, and scallops lead a quieter existence by filter feeding using feathery gills. Food is carried by water, which enters through the incurrent siphon, shown on the right in **Figure 27–23**. A **siphon** is a tubelike structure through which water enters and leaves the body. The water flows over the gills and then leaves by the excurrent siphon. As water passes over the gills, plankton become trapped in sticky mucus. Cilia on the gills move the mixture of mucus and food into the mouth.

Respiration Aquatic mollusks such as snails, clams, and octopi typically breathe using gills inside their mantle cavity. As water passes through the mantle cavity, oxygen and carbon dioxide diffuse over the surface of the animal's gills. Land snails and slugs do not have gills. Instead, they respire using a mantle cavity that has a large surface area lined with blood vessels. Because this lining must be kept moist so that oxygen can diffuse across its surface, land snails and slugs typically live only in moist places.

Circulation Oxygen and nutrients are carried to all parts of a mollusk's body by a circulatory system. The circulatory system of mollusks is either open or closed. "Open" does not mean that blood can spill to the outside of the animal! In an **open circulatory system,** blood is pumped through vessels by a simple heart. Blood eventually leaves the vessels and works its way through different sinuses. A sinus is a large saclike space. The blood passes from the sinuses to the gills, where oxygen and carbon dioxide are exchanged, and then back to the heart.

▲ **Figure 27–23** The anatomy of a clam, shown here, is typical of bivalves, or two-shelled mollusks. The mantle and part of the foot have been cut away to show internal organs. The adductor muscles are used to open and shut the two exterior shells. The gills exchange oxygen and carbon dioxide between the body and the surrounding water. The arrows show the path of water over the gills. **Predicting** *What might happen if a clam's incurrent siphon became blocked?*

Open circulatory systems work well for slow-moving mollusks such as snails and clams, in which the demand for oxygen is relatively low. Faster-moving mollusks such as octopi and squid have a closed circulatory system. A closed circulatory system can transport blood through an animal's body much more quickly than an open circulatory system.

Excretion Cells of the body release nitrogen-containing waste into the blood in the form of ammonia. Tube-shaped nephridia remove ammonia from the blood and release it outside the body.

Response The complexity of the nervous system and the ability to respond to environmental conditions vary greatly among mollusks. Clams and other two-shelled mollusks typically lead inactive lives, burrowing in the mud or sand. They have a simple nervous system consisting of small ganglia near the mouth, a few nerve cords, and simple sense organs, such as chemical receptors and eyespots.

In contrast, octopi and their relatives, such as the octopus in **Figure 27–24,** are active and intelligent predators that have the most highly developed nervous system of all invertebrates. Because of their well-developed brains, these animals can remember things for long periods and may be more intelligent than some vertebrates. Octopi are capable of complex behavior, such as opening a jar to get food inside, and they have been trained to perform different tasks for a reward or to avoid punishment.

Movement Mollusks move in many different ways. Snails—which are legendary for their lack of speed—secrete mucus along the base of the foot, and then move over surfaces using a rippling motion of the foot. The fast-moving octopus uses a form of jet propulsion. It draws water into the mantle cavity and then forces the water out through a siphon. Water leaving the body propels the octopus in the opposite direction.

Reproduction Mollusks reproduce in a variety of ways. Many snails and two-shelled mollusks reproduce sexually by external fertilization. They release enormous numbers of eggs and sperm into the open water. The eggs are fertilized in the water and then develop into free-swimming larvae. In tentacled mollusks and certain snails, fertilization takes place inside the body of the female. Some mollusks are hermaphrodites, having both male and female reproductive organs. Individuals of these species usually fertilize eggs from another individual.

Figure 27–24 Mollusks have evolved a variety of ways of responding to potential danger. Snails (above) protect themselves by withdrawing into their shells in a matter of seconds. A hard plate blocks the entrance to the shell, protecting the snail inside. Once the danger has passed, the snail re-emerges and moves forward on its muscular foot. Octopi (right) and squids squirt ink from inside their digestive tracts. The ink startles predators and may also cause temporary numbness. **Predicting** *How might the hard plate protect snails during a period of drought?*

Groups of Mollusks

Mollusks are divided into several classes according to characteristics of the foot and the shell. The three major classes of mollusks are gastropods, bivalves, and cephalopods.

Gastropods Members of the class Gastropoda, or gastropods (GAS-truh-pahdz), include pond snails, land slugs, sea butterflies, sea hares, limpets, and nudibranchs (NOO-duh-branks). 🔑 **Gastropods are shell-less or single-shelled mollusks that move by using a muscular foot located on the ventral side.**

Many gastropods, such as the snails shown on the top right in **Figure 27–25**, have a single shell that protects their bodies. When threatened, they can pull completely into their shells. Some snails are also protected by a hard disk on the foot that forms a solid "door" when they withdraw.

Land slugs and nudibranchs have no shell but protect themselves in other ways. Most land slugs spend daylight hours hiding under rocks and logs, hidden from birds and other potential predators. Some sea hares, when threatened, can squirt ink into the surrounding water, producing a "smoke screen" that confuses predators.

Some nudibranchs have chemicals in their bodies that taste bad or are poisonous. Many nudibranchs are able to recycle the nematocysts from cnidarians they eat, using them to sting predators. These "booby-trapped" nudibranchs are usually brightly colored. The bright coloring serves as a warning to potential predators.

✓ CHECKPOINT *How do shell-less gastropods protect themselves?*

Figure 27–25 🔑 Gastropods move by using a large, muscular foot located on the ventral side. They can be shell-less, such as the nudibranch or sea slug (top left), or have a single shell, such as the tree snail (top right). Many sea hares (bottom) have a reduced shell covered by the mantle. The sea hare defends itself by "inking"—squirting ink at potential predators.

▲ **Figure 27–26** 🔑 Bivalves are two-shelled mollusks that include clams, mussels, oysters, and scallops like the one above. Observe the tiny blue eyespots along the open edges of the shell.

Word Origins

Cephalopod comes from the Greek *kephale*, meaning "head," and *podos*, meaning "foot."
Pseudopods are structures found in some single-celled organisms. If *pseudo-* means "false," what does *pseudopod* mean?

Bivalves 🔑 **Members of the class Bivalvia have two shells that are held together by one or two powerful muscles.** Common bivalves include clams, oysters, mussels, and scallops. Most bivalves stay in one place for much of the time. Clams, shown in **Figure 27–26**, burrow in mud or sand, whereas mussels use sticky threads to attach themselves to rocks. Scallops are the least sedentary bivalves and can move around rapidly by flapping their shells when threatened.

Currents created by cilia on the gills circulate water through the body cavities of bivalves. Once water is inside the body, filter-feeding bivalves use mucus and cilia on their gills to trap food particles in the water. Some bivalves feed on material deposited in sand or mud. They use long, muscular extensions of tissue that surround the mouth to collect food particles from the surrounding sediments. The indigestible sand or mud particles are expelled from the mantle cavity.

Cephalopods Cephalopods (SEF-uh-luh-pahdz)—members of the class Cephalopoda—are the most active of the mollusks. This class includes octopi, squids, cuttlefishes, and nautiluses. 🔑 **Cephalopods are typically soft-bodied mollusks in which the head is attached to a single foot. The foot is divided into tentacles or arms.** Cephalopods have eight or more tentacles equipped with sucking disks that grab and hold prey. Nautiluses have many more tentacles than other cephalopods—in some cases up to 90! Their tentacles lack suckers but have a sticky, mucuslike covering.

As with some of the gastropods, most modern cephalopods have only small internal shells or no shells at all. The only present-day cephalopods with external shells are nautiluses, such as the one shown in **Figure 27–27**. These animals can control their depth in the water by regulating the amount of gas in their shells. Nautiluses look much like ammonites, an extinct group of cephalopods that dominated the seas more than 500 million years ago.

✓ CHECKPOINT *Where is a cephalopod's foot located?*

Figure 27–27 Nautiluses like the one shown here are the most primitive group of cephalopods. **Comparing and Contrasting** *How does this nautilus differ from most cephalopods?*

Raising Clams

Aquaculture is the growth of aquatic animals and plants for use by humans. In one example of aquaculture, hard clams are first grown in commercial hatcheries under very favorable conditions. The young clams are then removed from the hatcheries and placed into the mud beds of creeks, where they develop into adults. At that time, the size of the young clams is around 40 millimeters.

Because Georgian clams grow so quickly, they are ideal for aquaculture. Unlike the hard clams in the northeastern United States that grow only during the warm months, Georgian hard clams grow year-round. As a result, the Georgian clams grow to market size in less than half the time that the northeastern clams need to grow. The graph shows how clam shells grow over a period of 10 years.

1. **Interpreting Graphics** Approximately how many years does it take clams to reach a size at which they can be removed from hatcheries and put in creeks?

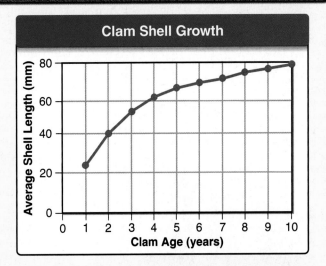

Clam Shell Growth

2. **Applying Concepts** How does climate affect the growth of most clams?

3. **Interpreting Graphics** How much did the clams grow during the first 5 years? The next 5 years?

4. **Formulating Hypotheses** Formulate a hypothesis to explain the slower growth rate from years 5–10.

5. **Drawing Conclusions** What general trends do you observe about growth from the graph?

Cuttlefishes have small shells inside their bodies. These are the cuttlebones given to pet birds to condition their beaks. A squid's internal shell has evolved into a thin supporting rod known as a pen. Octopi have lost their shells completely.

Cephalopods also have numerous complex sense organs that help them distinguish shapes by sight and texture by touch. The eyes of many cephalopods, such as the squid shown in **Figure 27–28,** are as complex as those of some vertebrates, such as fishes and humans. Cephalopod eyes can be large—the size of a dinner plate in some species—and can distinguish objects as small as 0.5 centimeters from a meter away, allowing squids to locate a wide variety of prey. Though cephalopod eyes may look something like vertebrate eyes from the outside, their internal structures are quite different.

◀ **Figure 27–28** Most **cephalopods are mollusks in which the head is attached to a single foot that is divided into tentacles or arms.** They have the most complex nervous system of all the mollusks, with a highly developed brain and sense organs, such as the eye of this common squid.

Ecology of Mollusks

Mollusks play many different roles in living systems. For example, they feed on plants, prey on animals, and "clean up" their surroundings by filtering algae out of the water or by eating detritus. Some of them are hosts to symbiotic algae or to parasites; others are themselves parasites. In addition, mollusks are an important source of food for many organisms, including humans.

Biologists' understanding of molluskan diversity and ecology is growing all the time. Recent explorations around deep-sea volcanic vents called "black smokers" have revealed a fascinating community that includes several bivalves. Researchers have discovered symbiotic bacteria within the foot-long bivalves clustered around these vents. These bacteria extract chemical energy from simple compounds released in the superheated water. From this energy, the bacteria produce food molecules that the mollusks can use. Without such a relationship, these mollusks would be unable to inhabit this extreme environment. Other research has discovered a similar symbiosis between related bacteria and bivalves that live in the mud of salt marshes and mangrove swamps.

Scientists have found some new uses for mollusks. Because filter-feeding bivalves concentrate dangerous pollutants and microorganisms in their tissues, they can be used to monitor water quality. Careful checks of bivalves can warn biologists and public health officials of health problems long before scientists can detect these dangers in the open water. Besides acting as environmental monitors, mollusks also serve as subjects in biological research. Some current investigations are based on the observation that snails and other mollusks never seem to develop any form of cancer. If scientists can determine what protects the cells of these animals from cancer, they will gain valuable insights into how to fight cancer in humans.

▲ **Figure 27–29** These clams will find their way to many people's dinner tables. **Applying Concepts** *Besides providing food for humans and other animals, what are some other roles that mollusks play in ecosystems?*

27–4 Section Assessment

1. 🔑 **Key Concept** What is a mollusk?
2. 🔑 **Key Concept** List and describe the four parts of the mollusk body plan.
3. 🔑 **Key Concept** Describe the main characteristics of the three major classes of mollusks.
4. Why are land snails restricted to moist environments?

5. **Critical Thinking Comparing and Contrasting** Compare open and closed circulatory systems. Why are open circulatory systems found mostly in small animals that move slowly?

iTEXT **Assessment** Use iText to review the important concepts in Section 27–4.

Take It to the NET

Choose one species of mollusk and create a collage about it. Include a detailed diagram of the mollusk. Use the links provided in the Biology area at the Prentice Hall Web site for help in completing this activity: **www.phschool.com**

Investigating Land Snails

Although most mollusks are aquatic, some snails live on land. In this investigation, you will explore how land snails are adapted to survive in this environment.

Problem How do land snails move and react to various stimuli?

Materials

- land snail
- glass slides
- dropper pipette
- dissecting tray
- black construction paper
- paper towels
- 40-watt desk lamp
- metric ruler
- dissecting microscope
- petri dish
- clock with second hand

Skills Observing, Calculating, Using Tables and Graphs

Procedure 🔲 🔳 ⚡ 🐭

1. Using a clean pipette, put a drop of water in the center of a glass slide. Gently place the snail in the water drop. Look for the mucus trail as the snail begins to move.

2. Gently turn the slide over and place it on top of a petri dish. Place the petri dish under the dissecting microscope and observe the movement of the muscular foot under low power. Look for the radula as it scrapes the slide.

3. Copy the data table onto a separate sheet of paper. Line each half of a dissecting tray with a separate piece of paper towel. Place a sheet of black construction paper above one half of the tray. Shine the desk lamp on the other half of the tray from a distance of 30 cm. **CAUTION:** *Do not touch the lamp, because it may be hot.*

4. Place the snail in the center of the tray and observe its behavior. Record the number of seconds in each minute that the snail spends in the dark.

5. Exchange data with the class and determine class averages.

6. Return the snail to its habitat, clean up your materials, and wash your hands.

Data Table

Time (minutes)	Time in Dark (seconds)	
	Group	Class Average
0-1		
1-2		
2-3		
3-4		
4-5		

Analyze and Conclude

1. **Drawing Conclusions** Describe the movement of the snail across the glass slide. Name one advantage and one limitation of this type of movement.

2. **Using Tables and Graphs** Make a bar graph of the class average data that shows the time the snails spent in the dark for each of the five minutes. What trend do you see in your graph? How can you explain this result?

3. **Drawing Conclusions** Do snails prefer dark places or bright places? How does this behavior help snails survive?

Go Further

Take It to the NET
Visit the Prentice Hall Web site at **www.phschool.com** and follow the links to this lab. Add your data to the combined data of students across the country. Compare your class averages to those of other classes. Why might they be different?

27–1 Flatworms

🔑 Key Concepts

- Flatworms are soft, flattened worms that have tissues and internal organ systems. They are the simplest animals to have three embryonic germ layers, bilateral symmetry, and cephalization.

- Turbellarians are free-living marine or freshwater flatworms.

- Flukes are parasitic flatworms that usually infect the internal organs of their hosts.

- Tapeworms are long, flat, parasitic worms that are adapted to life inside the intestines of their hosts.

Vocabulary

- acoelomate, p. 683 • coelom, p. 683
- pharynx, p. 684 • flame cell, p. 684
- ganglion, p. 685 • eyespot, p. 685
- hermaphrodite, p. 686 • fission, p. 686
- scolex, p. 688 • proglottid, p. 688
- testis, p. 688

27–2 Roundworms

🔑 Key Concepts

- Roundworms are unsegmented worms that have pseudocoeloms and digestive systems with two openings—a mouth and an anus.

- Parasitic roundworms include trichinosis-causing worms, filarial worms, ascarid worms, and hookworms.

Vocabulary

- pseudocoelom, p. 689 • anus, p. 689

27–3 Annelids

🔑 Key Concepts

- Annelids are worms with segmented bodies. They have a true coelom that is completely lined with mesoderm.

- Oligochaetes are annelids that typically have streamlined bodies and relatively few setae compared to polychaetes. Most oligochaetes live in soil or fresh water.

- Leeches are typically external parasites that suck the blood and body fluids of their host.

- Polychaetes are marine annelids that have paired, paddlelike appendages tipped with setae.

Vocabulary

- septum, p. 694 • seta, p. 694 • crop, p. 695
- gizzard, p. 695 • closed circulatory system, p. 695
- gill, p. 696 • nephridium, p. 696
- clitellum, p. 696

27–4 Mollusks

🔑 Key Concepts

- Mollusks are soft-bodied animals that usually have an internal or external shell.

- The typical mollusk body plan has four parts: foot, mantle, shell, and visceral mass.

- Gastropods are shell-less or single-shelled mollusks that move by using a muscular foot located on the ventral side.

- Bivalves have two shells that are held together by one or two powerful muscles.

- Cephalopods are typically soft-bodied mollusks in which the head is attached to a single foot. The foot is divided into tentacles or arms.

Vocabulary

- trochophore, p. 701 • foot, p. 702
- mantle, p. 702 • shell, p. 702
- visceral mass, p. 702 • radula, p. 702
- siphon, p. 703 • open circulatory system, p. 703

Thinking Visually

Create a concept map that shows the classes and main characteristics of mollusks. Include at least two examples of types of mollusks within each class.

Chapter 27

Part A

Multiple Choice

For each statement or question, select the number of the word or expression that, of those given, best completes the statement or answers the question.

1 The muscular tube found near the mouth of the gastrovascular cavity in flatworms is called a(an)
(1) proglottid
(3) anus
(2) scolex
(4) pharynx

2 The head of an adult tapeworm is called a
(1) flame cell
(3) cuticle
(2) scolex
(4) mantle

3 Waste products are excreted from the body of a planarian by
(1) nephridia
(3) proglottids
(2) flame cells
(4) cilia

4 The body cavity of a roundworm is called a
(1) coelom
(3) gizzard
(2) pseudocoelom
(4) crop

5 What are the clusters of nerve cells in roundworms called?
(1) flame cells
(3) proglottids
(2) ganglia
(4) radulae

6 In the earthworm, waste created by cellular metabolism is eliminated by the
(1) crop
(3) gizzard
(2) nephridia
(4) flame cell

7 Which invertebrates have segmented bodies?
(1) flatworms
(3) roundworms
(2) annelids
(4) flukes

8 The digestive organ in which an earthworm stores food is indicated by the letter
(1) a
(3) c
(2) b
(4) d

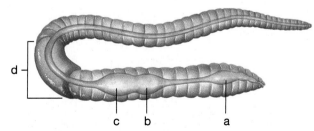

9 In earthworms, the clitellum is used in
(1) digestion
(3) reproduction
(2) excretion
(4) respiration

10 The tongue-shaped structure that some mollusks use for feeding is the
(1) sinus
(3) mantle
(2) radula
(4) proglottid

11 Mollusks eliminate nitrogen-containing wastes through simple tube-shaped organs called
(1) gills
(3) radulae
(2) nephridia
(4) nephrons

12 A mollusk with a shell consisting of two parts is a member of the class
(1) Cephalopoda
(3) Bivalvia
(2) Annelida
(4) Gastropoda

13 All of the following are mollusks *except*
(1) leeches
(3) octopi
(2) squids
(4) snails

14 Which are *not* parasitic roundworms?
(1) hookworms
(3) ascarid worms
(2) filarial worms
(4) tapeworms

15 The body cavity in annelids is called a(an)
(1) coelom
(3) pseudocoelom
(2) trochophore
(4) acoelom

16 The figure below shows an animal with three germ layers.

The simplest animal to develop from three germ layers belongs in the phylum
(1) Mollusca
(3) Annelida
(2) Nematoda
(4) Platyhelminthes

Test-Taking Tip For questions containing the words *not*, *except*, and so on, begin by eliminating each answer choice that does fit the characteristic in question. After eliminating three choices, check to see that your answer is correct by confirming that it does not fit the characteristic in question.

Parts B and C

Multiple Choice and Extended Response

For those questions that ask you to select a response, choose the one that best completes the statement or answers the question. For all others follow the directions given.

Base your answers to questions 17 and 18 on the information and photo below and on your knowledge of biology.

This nudibranch is a hermaphrodite.

17 What are the characteristics of a hermaphrodite?

18 Hermaphrodites rarely fertilize their own eggs. Explain why fertilization of another individual is more advantageous than self-fertilization. (Hint: See Section 1 in Chapter 26.)

Base your answers to questions 19 through 21 on the information and illustration below and on your knowledge of biology.

This two-headed planarian was created by cutting a planarian's head in half lengthwise. Use your knowledge about flatworms to answer the questions that follow.

19 The process illustrated in the diagram is known as
(1) fission   (3) sexual reproduction
(2) regeneration   (4) hermaphroditism

20 Two spots on the head of the planarian are sensitive to
(1) heat   (3) sound
(2) light   (4) chemicals

21 Which characteristics apply to flatworms?
  A Cephalization
  B Bilateral symmetry
  C Segmented bodies
(1) A, only   (3) A and B, only
(2) B, only   (4) A, B, and C

Use the lettered choices below to answer questions 22 through 26. Select the best lettered choice. A choice may be used once, more than once, or not at all.
  A Flatworms   **D** Snails
  B Roundworms   **E** Mollusks
  C Annelids

22 Include gastropods, bivalves, and cephalopods

23 Have internal walls, or septa, between body segments

24 Usually have an internal or external shell

25 Have a pseudocoelom

26 Include turbellarians, flukes, and tapeworms

Base your answers to questions 27 through 30 on the information below and on your knowledge of biology.

A student conducts an experiment to test the hypothesis that earthworms aid in the growth of plant roots. She grows two identical plants in Pots A and B but adds earthworms only to Pot B. Over a three-week period, she waters and fertilizes both pots the same. Every fourth day, she measures the height of each plant, collecting the following data.

Day	Pot A	Pot B
1	5 cm	5 cm
3	5 cm	5 cm
6	6.5 cm	8 cm
9	8 cm	8 cm
12	9.5 cm	10.5 cm
15	12 cm	11 cm
18	14 cm	12 cm
21	15.5 cm	13 cm

27 What are the manipulated (independent) variable and the responding (dependent) variable in the student's experiment?

28 The data showed that the plant in Pot A grew taller. The student determined that earthworms do not aid in the growth of plant roots. She shared her data and conclusions with another student. Her friend found a serious flaw in the experimental design. Explain what that flaw is.

29 Redesign this experiment to test the original hypothesis. Be sure to include the following
   • hypothesis

   • identification of the manipulated (independent) and responding (dependent) variable

   • procedure

   • data-collection methods

30 From your knowledge of the ecology of annelids, is the student's hypothesis supported in nature? Give examples.

---

31 Explain how feeding and digestion occur in planarians.

32 Explain the process by which earthworms move.

Base your answers to questions 33 through 36 on the reading passage and data table below and on your knowledge of biology.

Heartworms

Dirofilaria immitis, the dog heartworm, is a large, whitish roundworm found circulating around the heart in dogs. After reproduction, the females produce tiny embryos called microfilariae, which are found circulating throughout the dog's body. The microfilariae are spread by mosquitoes. A mosquito picks up blood when it bites an infected dog. The heartworm embryo grows inside the mosquito and is deposited into the next dog when the mosquito has its next meal. The microfilariae move through the dog's blood vessels until they get to the right side of the dog's heart. They settle there and in the pulmonary arteries, where they can reproduce and remain for many years.

   Some scientists wanted to determine if the development of the microfilariae in the mosquito is dependent on temperature. To do this, they kept 100 microfilariae at various temperatures for a two-week period and then counted the surviving organisms. Their data are shown in the following table.

Survival Rate of *Dirofilaria sp.*

Temperature in °C	Number of Microfilariae/100
0	0
5	0
10	0
15	19
40	48
41	65
30	86
40	82
41	85
45	74

33 On a separate sheet of paper, construct a graph from the data table that shows the distribution of organisms by temperature.

34 Based on the data, what observations can you make about microfilariae development?

35 What conclusions can be drawn from this data about seasonal and geographical transmission of heartworm disease in North America?

36 Dogs are often infected with the roundworms *Ascaris.* How does the parasite/host relationship of *Ascaris* differ from that of *Dirofilaria?*

Take It to the NET

Trichinosis infection occurs worldwide. Visit the Prentice Hall Web site at **www.phschool.com** to find out more about the disease. Then, answer the following questions:

• How can people get trichinosis?

• What are the first symptoms of trichinosis? How soon after infection will those symptoms appear?

• What are five ways to prevent trichinosis?

28 Arthropods and Echinoderms

Papilio maacki, a butterfly native to Japan and China, is one of more than 750,000 species of arthropods—the largest phylum of animals.

Inquiry Activity

What is an arthropod?

Procedure

1. Examine a variety of specimens or photographs of arthropods. Make a list of features that all of these organisms have in common.

2. Look at some organisms that are not arthropods. Make a list of features that all of these organisms have in common.

3. Compare the two lists.

Think About It

1. **Formulating Operational Definitions** Write a definition of the term *arthropod.* Include in your definition at least two characteristics that all arthropods share but most other organisms do not.

2. **Classifying** Classify the arthropods you observed into two or more groups. Which characteristics did you use to distinguish the groups?

28–1 Introduction to the Arthropods

If you have ever admired a spider's web, watched the flight of a butterfly, or eaten shrimp, you have had close encounters with members of the phylum Arthropoda (ahr-THRAHP-oh-duh). In terms of evolutionary success, which is measured as the number of living species, arthropods are the most successful animals of all time. At least three quarters of a million species have been identified—more than three times the number of all other animal species combined!

What Is an Arthropod?

Arthropods include animals such as insects, crabs, centipedes, and spiders. **Arthropods have a segmented body, a tough exoskeleton, and jointed appendages. Figure 28–1** shows these features in a millipede. Like annelids, arthropods have bodies that are divided into segments. The number of these segments varies among groups of arthropods.

Arthropods are also surrounded by a tough external covering, or **exoskeleton.** The exoskeleton is like a suit of armor that protects and supports the body. It is made from protein and a carbohydrate called **chitin** (KY-tun). Exoskeletons vary greatly in size, shape, and toughness. The exoskeletons of caterpillars are firm and leathery, whereas those of crabs and lobsters are so tough and hard that they are almost impossible to crush by hand. The exoskeletons of many terrestrial, or land-dwelling, species have a waxy covering that helps prevent the loss of body water. Terrestrial arthropods, like all animals that live entirely on land, need adaptations that hold water inside their bodies.

All arthropods have jointed appendages. **Appendages** are structures such as legs and antennae that extend from the body wall. Jointed appendages are so distinctive of arthropods that the phylum is named for them: *arthron* means "joint" in Greek, and *podos* means "foot."

Guide for Reading

Key Concepts
• What are the main features of arthropods?
• What are the important trends in arthropod evolution?
• What happens when an arthropod outgrows its exoskeleton?

Vocabulary
exoskeleton
chitin
appendage
tracheal tube
spiracle
book lung
Malpighian tubule
molting

Reading Strategy:
Finding Main Ideas Before you read, skim the section to find the three boldfaced sentences. Copy each sentence onto a note card. As you read, make notes of supporting details.

◀ **Figure 28–1** Arthropods such as the cave millipede have a body usually composed of segments, a tough exoskeleton, and jointed appendages. Observe the millipede's legs, which are adapted for walking.

Evolution of Arthropods

The first arthropods appeared in the sea more than 600 million years ago. Since then, arthropods have moved into all parts of the sea, most freshwater habitats, the land, and the air. ⚷ **The evolution of arthropods has led to fewer body segments and highly specialized appendages for feeding, movement, and other functions.**

A typical primitive arthropod was composed of many identical segments, each carrying a pair of appendages. Its body probably closely resembled that of a trilobite (TRY-loh-byt), shown in **Figure 28–2.** This early body plan was modified gradually. Body segments were lost or fused over time. Most living arthropods, such as spiders and insects, have only two or three body segments. Arthropod appendages also evolved into different forms that have different functions. These appendages include antennae, claws, walking legs, wings, flippers, mouthparts, tails, and other specialized structures.

These gradual changes in arthropods are similar to the changes in modern cars since the Model T, the first mass-produced automobile. The Model T had all the basic components, such as an internal combustion engine, wheels, and a frame. Over time, the design and style of each component changed, producing cars as different as off-road vehicles, sedans, and sports cars. Similarly, modifications to the arthropod body plan have produced creatures as different as a tick and a lobster.

▲ **Figure 28–2** Trilobites, such as the fossilized one shown above, were marine arthropods that were abundant more than 500 million years ago. They were divided into many body segments, each with a walking leg. Trilobites became extinct some 200 million years ago. ⚷**Living arthropods generally have fewer body segments and more specialized appendages than ancestral arthropods.**

✓**CHECKPOINT** *What are the differences between modern arthropods and primitive arthropods?*

Form and Function in Arthropods

Arthropods use complex organ systems to carry out different essential functions. Some of these organs are found only in this phylum. Most arthropods use tracheal tubes or other specialized organs for respiration, have an open circulatory system, and excrete wastes through saclike tubules.

Feeding Arthropods include herbivores, carnivores, and omnivores. There are arthropod bloodsuckers, filter feeders, detritivores, and parasites. Arthropod mouthparts have evolved in ways that enable different species to eat almost any food you can imagine. Their mouthparts range from pincers or fangs to sickle-shaped jaws that can cut through the tissues of captured prey. The mouthparts of a nut weevil are shown in **Figure 28–3.**

◀ **Figure 28–3** This nut weevil uses its mouthparts to bore into and eat nuts. **Applying Concepts** *Do you think a nut weevil would be able to capture and eat other arthropods? Explain your answer.*

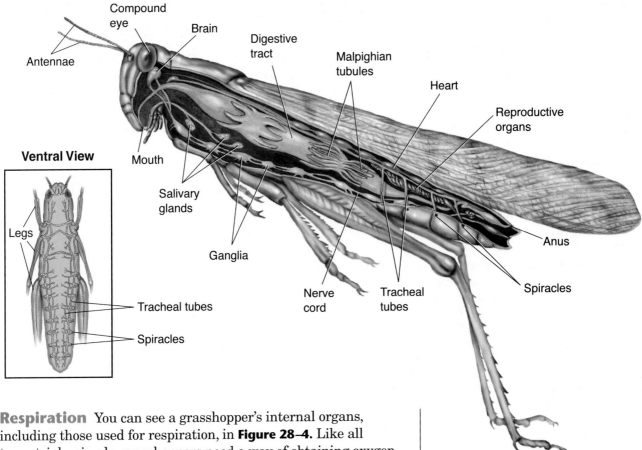

Ventral View

Compound eye
Brain
Antennae
Digestive tract
Malpighian tubules
Heart
Reproductive organs
Mouth
Salivary glands
Ganglia
Legs
Tracheal tubes
Spiracles
Nerve cord
Tracheal tubes
Anus
Spiracles

Respiration You can see a grasshopper's internal organs, including those used for respiration, in **Figure 28–4.** Like all terrestrial animals, grasshoppers need a way of obtaining oxygen from air rather than from water. Most terrestrial arthropods breathe through a network of branching **tracheal** (TRAY-kee-ul) **tubes** that extend throughout the body. Air enters and leaves the tracheal tubes through **spiracles** (SPEER-uh-kulz), which are small openings located along the side of the body. Other terrestrial arthropods, such as spiders, respire using book lungs. **Book lungs** are organs that have layers of respiratory tissue stacked like the pages of a book. Most aquatic arthropods, such as lobsters and crabs, respire through featherlike gills. The horseshoe crabs, however, respire through organs called book gills.

Circulation Arthropods have an open circulatory system. A well-developed heart pumps blood through arteries that branch and enter the tissues. Blood leaves the blood vessels and moves through sinuses, or cavities. The blood then collects in a large sinus surrounding the heart. From there, it re-enters the heart and is again pumped through the body.

Excretion Most terrestrial arthropods, such as insects and spiders, dispose of nitrogenous wastes using Malpighian (mal-PIG-ee-un) tubules. **Malpighian tubules** are saclike organs that extract wastes from the blood and then add them to feces, or digestive wastes, that move through the gut. In aquatic arthropods, diffusion moves cellular wastes from the arthropod's body into the surrounding water.

▲ **Figure 28–4** The grasshopper has organ systems typical of most arthropods. These organ systems carry out functions such as circulation, excretion, response, and movement. Arthropods have several different types of respiratory organs. In insects, tracheal tubes (inset) move air throughout the tissues of the body. **Interpreting Graphics** *Where is the grasshopper's nerve cord located?*

✔**CHECKPOINT** *What is the function of Malpighian tubules?*

Quick Lab

Do crickets respond to odors?

Materials live crickets in terrarium, wooden blocks

Procedure 🔒

1. **Predicting** Crickets are common in grassy areas. They eat leaves and are eaten by mice, some birds, and other animals. Record a prediction of how they will respond to the odors of grass, soil, and hair.
2. On a separate sheet of paper, copy the data table shown. Your teacher will provide a set of blocks labeled with the odors they carry. Place the blocks in the container with the crickets so that the blocks do not touch each other. **CAUTION:** *Place the blocks in the container gently to avoid injuring the crickets.*

3. In your data table, record the number of crickets on each block every minute for 10 minutes.

Analyze and Conclude
1. **Observing** Did the crickets tend to climb on some blocks more than others? If so, which blocks did they prefer?
2. **Inferring** What can you infer from these results about the ability of crickets to respond to odors?
3. **Drawing Conclusions** How could the behavior you observed help crickets survive? Explain your answer.

Data Table

Time (min)	Number of crickets			
	Grass	Soil	Hair	Control
1				
2				

Response Most arthropods have a well-developed nervous system. All arthropods have a brain. The brain serves as a central switchboard that receives incoming information and then sends outgoing instructions to muscles. Two nerves that encircle the esophagus connect the brain to a ventral nerve cord. Along this nerve cord are several ganglia, or groups of nerve cells. These ganglia coordinate the movements of individual legs and wings. Most arthropods have sophisticated sense organs, such as eyes and taste receptors, for gathering information from the environment.

Movement Arthropods move using well-developed groups of muscles that are coordinated and controlled by the nervous system. These muscles generate force by contracting and then pulling on the exoskeleton. At each body joint, different muscles either flex (bend) or extend (straighten) the joint. This process is diagrammed in **Figure 28–5**. The pull of muscles against the exoskeleton allows arthropods to beat their wings against the air to fly, push their legs against the ground to walk, or beat their flippers against the water to swim.

✓**CHECKPOINT** *How do arthropods move?*

■ Exoskeleton
■ Muscle that flexes the joint
■ Muscle that extends the joint

Flexed

Extended

◀ **Figure 28–5** This diagrammatic representation shows how muscles attached to the exoskeleton bend and straighten the joints. (Actual muscles are much larger than those shown here.) **Applying Concepts** *How are muscles controlled and coordinated?*

Reproduction Terrestrial arthropods have internal fertilization. In some species, males have a reproductive organ that places sperm inside females. In other species, the males deposit a sperm packet that is picked up by the females. Aquatic arthropods may have internal or external fertilization. External fertilization takes place outside the female's body. It occurs when females release eggs into the external environment and males shed sperm around the eggs.

Growth and Development in Arthropods

An exoskeleton does not grow as the animal grows. Imagine that you are wearing a suit of armor fitted exactly to your measurements. Think of it not only as skintight but as part of your skin. What would happen when you grew taller and wider? Arthropods have this same difficulty. **When they outgrow their exoskeletons, arthropods undergo periods of molting.** During **molting,** an arthropod sheds its entire exoskeleton and manufactures a larger one to take its place.

As the time for molting approaches, skin glands digest the inner part of the exoskeleton, and other glands secrete a new skeleton. When the new exoskeleton is ready, the animal pulls itself out of what remains of the original skeleton, as shown in **Figure 28–6.** This process can take several hours. While the new exoskeleton is still soft, the animal fills with air or fluids to allow room for growth before the next molting. Most arthropods molt several times between hatching and adulthood. This process is dangerous because the animal is vulnerable to predators while its shell is soft. To protect themselves, arthropods typically hide during the molting period.

▲ **Figure 28–6** When they become too large for their exoskeletons, arthropods **undergo periods of molting.** This cicada has just molted and is climbing out of its old exoskeleton.

28–1 Section Assessment

1. **Key Concept** What are the main features of arthropods?
2. **Key Concept** What is the evolutionary trend for segmentation in arthropods?
3. **Key Concept** How is the process of molting related to growth in arthropods?
4. What organs are used in arthropod respiration? Which are found in terrestrial arthropods? Aquatic arthropods?

5. **Critical Thinking** Inferring Terrestrial arthropods often have valves that can open and close their spiracles. How are these valves an adaptation to life on land?

iTEXT Assessment Use iText to review the important concepts in Section 28–1.

ALTERNATIVE ASSESSMENT

Creative Writing
Use information from the section to write a one-page short story about a day in the life of an arthropod. Write the story from the point of view of the arthropod.

28-2 Groups of Arthropods

Guide for Reading

Key Concepts
- How are arthropods classified?
- What are the distinguishing features of the three major groups of arthropods?

Vocabulary
cephalothorax
thorax
abdomen
carapace
mandible
cheliped
swimmeret
chelicera
pedipalp
spinneret

Reading Strategy:
Building Vocabulary
Before you read, preview new vocabulary by skimming the section and making a list of the boldfaced terms. Leave space to make notes as you read.

You are a naturalist sent to the rain forests of Brazil to bring back a representative sample of arthropods from the region. You have nets, collection jars, and a good knowledge of arthropods. As you search the forest, your collection grows to include an astonishing array of arthropods—butterflies several centimeters across, armored wormlike animals that move about using dozens of legs, and beetles that defend themselves by shooting out a stream of poisonous liquid. You must organize your collection before you return home, but you know that there are hundreds of thousands of arthropod species. Where to begin?

This is the challenge that has faced biologists for many decades—how to catalogue all the world's arthropods. The diversity of arthropods is daunting to any biologist interested in classification. As you will see, however, arthropod classification is based on a few characteristics. **Arthropods are classified based on the number and structure of their body segments and appendages—particularly their mouthparts.** The three major groups of arthropods are crustaceans, spiders and their relatives, and insects and their relatives.

Crustaceans

The crustaceans (krus-TAY-shunz) are primarily aquatic and include organisms such as crabs, shrimps, lobsters, crayfishes, and barnacles. Crustaceans range in size from small terrestrial pill bugs to spider crabs that have masses around 20 kilograms. **Crustaceans typically have two pairs of branched antennae, two or three body sections, and chewing mouthparts called mandibles.** An example of a crustacean is shown in **Figure 28–7.**

▶ **Figure 28–7** Arthropods are classified based on the number and structure of their body segments and appendages. The fiddler crab shown here is an example of a crustacean.

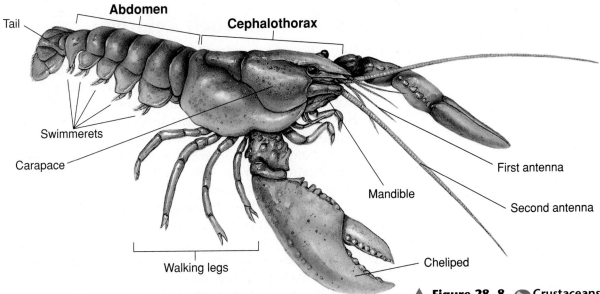

Tail

Abdomen

Cephalothorax

Swimmerets

Carapace

First antenna

Mandible

Second antenna

Walking legs

Cheliped

The crayfish has a body plan, shown in **Figure 28-8,** that is typical of many crustaceans. Its body is divided into a cephalothorax (sef-uh-loh-THAWR-aks) and an abdomen. The anterior **cephalothorax** is formed by fusion of the head with the **thorax,** which lies just behind the head and houses most of the internal organs. The **abdomen** is the posterior part of the body. The **carapace** is the part of the exoskeleton that covers the cephalothorax.

Crustacean appendages vary in form and function. The first two pairs of appendages are antennae, which bear many sensory hairs. In crayfish, antennae are primarily sense organs. In other crustaceans, they are used for filter feeding or swimming. The third pair of appendages are the mandibles. A **mandible** is a mouthpart adapted for biting and grinding food. Gills are attached to the appendages associated with the cephalothorax.

Crayfishes, lobsters, and crabs are members of the largest group of crustaceans: the decapods. The decapods have five pairs of legs. In crayfishes, the first pair of legs, called **chelipeds,** bear large claws that are modified to catch, pick up, crush, and cut food. Behind these legs are four pairs of walking legs. Along the abdomen are several pairs of **swimmerets,** which are flipperlike appendages used for swimming. The final abdominal segment is fused with a pair of paddlelike appendages to form a large, flat tail. When the abdominal muscles contract, the crayfish's tail snaps beneath its body. This pushes the animal backward.

The barnacles are another group of crustaceans. Unlike the decapods, barnacles are sessile, or attached to a single spot. Barnacles are crustaceans that have lost their abdominal segments and no longer use mandibles. Because of their outer shell-like coverings, barnacles were once classified as mollusks. Barnacles attach themselves to rocks along the shore and in tide pools. They even attach to the surface of marine animals such as whales. Barnacles use their appendages to capture and draw food particles into their mouths.

✓ CHECKPOINT *What are the body sections of a crustacean?*

▲ **Figure 28–8** Crustaceans typically have two pairs of antennae, two or three body sections, and chewing mouthparts called mandibles. Notice these structures in this illustration of a crayfish, an aquatic crustacean.

Word Origins

Decapod comes from the Greek word *deka* meaning "ten" and the Greek word *podos* meaning "foot." So, *decapod* means "ten-footed." If *cephalo* means "head," what do you think the term *cephalopod* means?

Spiders and Their Relatives

Horseshoe crabs, spiders, ticks, and scorpions are chelicerates. 🔑 **Chelicerates have mouthparts called chelicerae and two body sections, and nearly all have four pairs of walking legs.** Locate these structures in the spider in **Figure 28–9.** Note that chelicerates lack the antennae found on most other arthropods. As in crustaceans, the bodies of chelicerates are divided into a cephalothorax and an abdomen. The cephalothorax contains the brain, eyes, mouth, and walking legs. The abdomen contains most of the internal organs.

Chelicerates have two pairs of appendages attached near the mouth that are adapted as mouthparts. One pair, called **chelicerae** (kuh-LIS-ur-ee; singular: chelicera), contain fangs and are used to stab and paralyze prey. The other pair, called **pedipalps** (PED-ih-palps), are longer than the chelicerae and are usually modified to grab prey. Chelicerates respire using either book gills or book lungs. Horseshoe crabs, which are aquatic, move water across the membranes of book gills. In spiders, which are terrestrial, air enters through spiracles and then circulates across the surfaces of the book lung.

Chelicerates are divided into two main groups: horseshoe crabs and arachnids. The arachnids include spiders, mites, ticks, and scorpions.

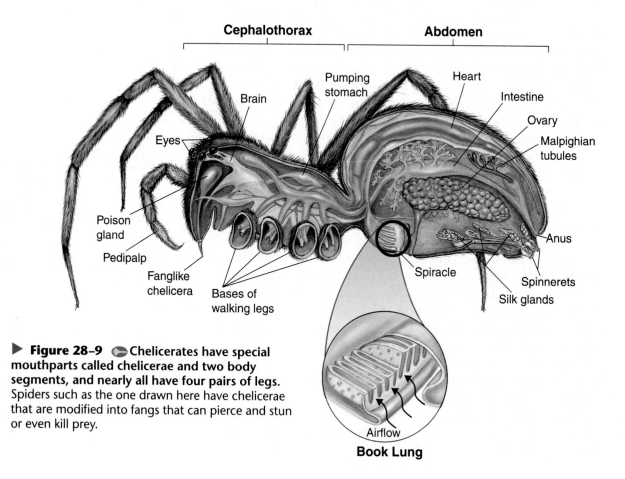

Cephalothorax   **Abdomen**

Brain — Pumping stomach — Heart — Intestine — Eyes — Ovary — Malpighian tubules — Poison gland — Anus — Pedipalp — Spiracle — Fanglike chelicera — Spinnerets — Bases of walking legs — Silk glands

Airflow

Book Lung

▶ **Figure 28–9** 🔑 Chelicerates have special mouthparts called chelicerae and two body segments, and nearly all have four pairs of legs. Spiders such as the one drawn here have chelicerae that are modified into fangs that can pierce and stun or even kill prey.

Horseshoe Crabs Horseshoe crabs, shown in **Figure 28–10,** are among the oldest living arthropods. They first appeared more than 500 million years ago and have changed little since that time. Despite their name, horseshoe crabs are not true crabs at all. They are heavily armor-plated, like crabs, but have an anatomy closer to that of spiders. They have chelicerae, five pairs of walking legs, and a long spikelike tail that is used for movement. Horseshoe crabs grow to about the size—and shape—of a large frying pan. They are common along the marshes and shallow bays of the eastern United States seacoast.

Spiders Spiders, the largest group of arachnids, capture and feed on animals ranging from other arthropods to small birds. They catch their prey in a variety of ways. Some spin webs of a strong, flexible protein called silk, which they use to catch flying prey. Others, including the tarantula shown in **Figure 28–11,** stalk and then pounce on their prey. Others lie in wait beneath a camouflaged burrow, leaping out to grab insects that venture too near.

Because spiders do not have jaws for chewing, they must liquefy their food to swallow it. Once a spider captures its prey, it uses fanglike chelicerae to inject paralyzing venom into it. When the prey is paralyzed, the spider injects digestive enzymes into the wounds. These enzymes break down the prey's tissues, enabling the spider to suck the tissues into a specialized pumping stomach. The stomach forces the liquefied food through the rest of the spider's digestive system.

Whether or not they spin webs, all spiders produce silk. Spider silk is much stronger than steel! Spiders spin silk into webs, cocoons for eggs, and wrappings for prey. They do this by forcing liquid silk through **spinnerets,** which are organs that contain silk glands. As the silk is pulled out of the spinnerets, it hardens into a single strand. Web-spinning spiders use that strand to make a web. Spiders can spin webs almost as soon as they hatch; the complicated procedure of spinning webs seems to be preprogrammed behavior.

✓ **CHECKPOINT** *How do chelicerates respire?*

▲ **Figure 28–10** Horseshoe crabs look a bit like true crabs, but their bodies more closely resemble those of spiders and other chelicerates. The abdomen and cephalothorax of these animals are encased in a hard shell. *Inferring From this photograph, what can you infer about the habitat of horseshoe crabs?*

▲ **Figure 28–11** The tarantula shown here is an example of a chelicerate. The chelicerae, or specialized mouthparts, can inject poison by way of a painful bite. **Applying Concepts** *How might this action be useful to tarantulas?*

Ticks and Lyme Disease

Lyme disease is caused by a bacterium found in two species of small ticks, the deer tick (*Ixodes scapularis*) and the western black-legged tick (*Ixodes pacificus*). Both species are most common in humid, wooded areas. They feed by sucking blood from deer, mice, birds, or humans. In warmer climates where reptiles such as lizards and snakes are most common, deer ticks prefer to feed on reptiles. The disease-causing bacteria are transmitted to the host by the bite of an infected tick. In humans the bacteria can cause a rash, fever, fatigue, joint and muscle pain, and damage to the nervous system. The bacteria do not survive well in reptiles.

The map shows the distribution of the two tick species and reported cases of Lyme disease. Use the map to help you answer the following questions:

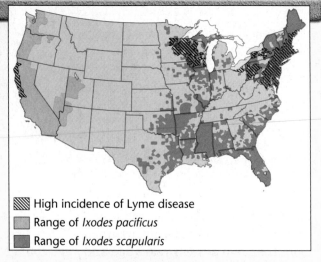

▨ High incidence of Lyme disease
▨ Range of *Ixodes pacificus*
▨ Range of *Ixodes scapularis*

1. **Interpreting Graphics** How can you explain the differences in the incidence of Lyme disease within the range of deer ticks?

2. **Formulating Hypotheses** What are two possible reasons that Lyme disease is not common in the parts of the dry southwest where western black-legged ticks are found?

▼ **Figure 28–12** Scorpions are easily recognized by their clawlike pedipalps and curved abdomen that bears a stinger at its tip. Although scorpions inflict stings on humans—usually causing as much pain as a wasp sting—they typically prey on other invertebrates, such as insects. **Comparing and Contrasting** *How do scorpions and spiders capture their prey?*

Mites and Ticks Mites and ticks are small arachnids that are usually parasitic. Their chelicerae and pedipalps are specialized for digging into a host's tissues and sucking out blood or plant fluids. In many species, the chelicerae are needlelike structures that are used to pierce the skin of the host. The pedipalps are often equipped with claws for attaching to the host. These mouthparts are so strong that if a tick begins to feed on you and you try to pull it off, its cephalothorax may separate from its abdomen and remain in your skin!

Mites and ticks parasitize a variety of organisms. Spider mites damage houseplants and are major agricultural pests on crops such as cotton. Others—including chiggers, mange, and scabies mites—cause itching or painful rashes in humans and other mammals. Ticks can transmit bacteria that cause serious diseases, such as Rocky Mountain spotted fever and Lyme disease.

Scorpions Scorpions are widespread in warm areas around the world, including the southern United States. Scorpions have pedipalps that are enlarged into claws, as shown in **Figure 28–12.** The long, segmented abdomen of a scorpion carries a venomous stinger that can kill or paralyze prey. Unlike spiders, scorpions chew their prey, using their chelicerae.

✓ **CHECKPOINT** *Where are scorpions usually found?*

Insects and Their Relatives

Centipedes, millipedes, and insects are all uniramians (yoo-nuh-RAY-mee-unz), a group that contains more species than all other groups of animals alive today. Uniramians have jaws, one pair of antennae, and unbranched appendages. Although they all have unbranched appendages, uniramians have widely varying forms and lifestyles. Centipedes and millipedes have long, wormlike bodies composed of many leg-bearing segments, as shown in **Figure 28–13**. Insects have compact, three-part bodies, and most are adapted for flight. The insects are so diverse and important as a group that they are discussed separately, in the next section.

Centipedes Centipedes have from a few to more than 100 pairs of legs, depending on the species. Most body segments bear one pair of legs each. Centipedes are carnivores whose mouthparts include a pair of venomous claws. They use these claws to catch and stun or kill their prey—including other arthropods, earthworms, toads, small snakes, and even mice. Centipedes usually live beneath rocks or in the soil. Their spiracles cannot close, and they lack a waterproof coating on their exoskeleton. As a result, their bodies lose water easily. This characteristic restricts centipedes to moist or humid areas.

Millipedes Like the centipedes, millipedes have a highly segmented body. However, each millipede segment bears two, not one, pairs of legs. These two pairs of legs per segment develop from the fusion of two segments in the millipede embryo. Millipedes live under rocks and in decaying logs. They feed on dead and decaying plant material. Unlike centipedes, they are timid creatures. When disturbed, many millipedes roll up into a ball to protect their softer undersides. They may also defend themselves by secreting unpleasant or toxic chemicals.

Figure 28–13 Uniramians such as centipedes and millipedes have jaws, one pair of antennae, and unbranched appendages. A centipede (top) is a carnivore that feeds on earthworms and other small animals. A millipede (bottom) is a herbivore that feeds on rotting vegetation.

28–2 Section Assessment

1. **Key Concept** What characteristics are used to classify arthropods?
2. **Key Concept** How do the three largest groups of arthropods differ?
3. Describe the process of digestion in spiders.
4. Compare and contrast the body plans and feeding habits of millipedes and centipedes.

5. **Critical Thinking Applying Concepts** Suppose you want to catch a crayfish with a net. Should you try to scoop it up head first or tail first? Explain.

iTEXT Assessment Use iText to review the important concepts in Section 28–2.

ALTERNATIVE ASSESSMENT

Designing an Arthropod Use information from this section to design a new type of arthropod. Make sure that the arthropod has all the characteristics described in this section. Draw the arthropod and give it a name. Include a brief description of what it eats and where it lives.

28–3 Insects

Guide for Reading

Key Concepts
- What are the distinguishing features of insects?
- What two types of development can insects undergo?
- What types of insects form societies?

Vocabulary
incomplete metamorphosis
nymph
complete metamorphosis
pupa
pheromone
society
caste

Reading Strategy:
Summarizing As you read, find the most important concepts in each paragraph. Then, use the important concepts to write a summary of what you have read.

What animals other than humans have the greatest impact on the activities of this planet? If you said "insects," you would be correct. From bees that flit from flower to flower to weevils that feed on crops, insects seem to be everywhere. As **Figure 28–14** shows, this single class of animals contains more species than any other group of animals. Ants and termites alone account for nearly one third of all the animal biomass in the Amazon basin.

Many characteristics of insects have contributed to their evolutionary success. These include different ways of responding to stimuli; the evolution of flight, which allowed insects to disperse long distances and colonize new habitats; and a life cycle in which the young differ from adults in appearance and feeding methods. These features have allowed insects to thrive in almost every terrestrial habitat on Earth, as well as in many freshwater and some marine environments.

The insects cover an incredible variety of life forms—from stunning, iridescent beetles and butterflies to the less attractive fleas, weevils, cockroaches, and termites. Biologists sometimes disagree on how to classify insects, and the number of living orders ranges from 26 to more than 30.

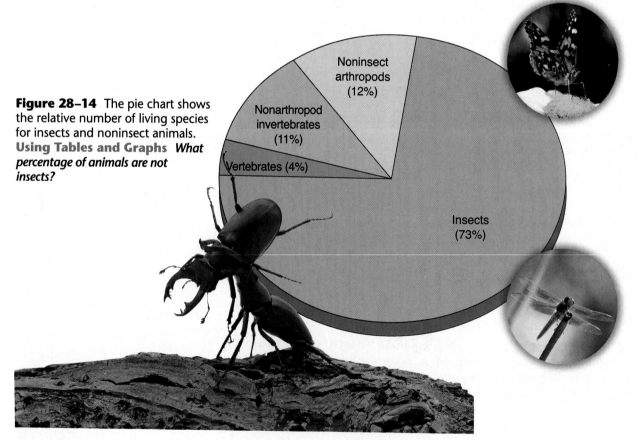

Figure 28–14 The pie chart shows the relative number of living species for insects and noninsect animals. **Using Tables and Graphs** *What percentage of animals are not insects?*

Noninsect arthropods (12%)

Nonarthropod invertebrates (11%)

Vertebrates (4%)

Insects (73%)

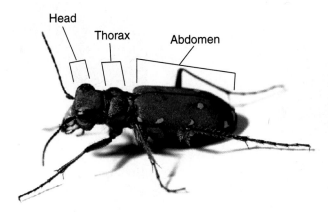

Head

Thorax

Abdomen

◀ **Figure 28–15** 🔑 Insects have a body divided into three parts—head, thorax, and abdomen. Three pairs of legs are attached to the thorax. In addition to these features, this green tiger beetle has other characteristics of a typical insect—wings, antennae, compound eyes, and tracheal tubes for respiration.

What Is an Insect?

Like all arthropods, insects have a segmented body, an exoskeleton, and jointed appendages. They also have several features that are specific to insects. 🔑 **Insects have a body divided into three parts—head, thorax, and abdomen. Three pairs of legs are attached to the thorax.** The beetle in **Figure 28–15** exhibits these characteristics. In many insects such as ants, the body parts are clearly separated from each other by narrow connections. In other insects, such as grasshoppers, the divisions between the three body parts are not as sharply defined. A typical insect also has a pair of antennae and a pair of compound eyes on the head, two pairs of wings on the thorax, and tracheal tubes that are used for respiration.

The essential life functions in insects are carried out in basically the same ways as they are in other arthropods. However, insects have a variety of interesting adaptations that deserve a closer look.

✓ CHECKPOINT *What are the names of the three parts of an insect's body?*

Responses to Stimuli Insects use a multitude of sense organs to respond to stimuli. Compound eyes are made of many lenses that detect minute changes in color and movement. The brain assembles this information into a single, detailed image. Compound eyes produce an image that is less detailed than what we see. However, eyes with multiple lenses are far better at detecting movement—one reason it is so hard to swat a fly!

Insects have chemical receptors for taste and smell on their mouthparts, as might be expected, and also on their antennae and legs. When a fly steps in a drop of water, it knows immediately whether the water contains salt or sugar. Insects also have sensory hairs that detect slight movements in the surrounding air or water. As objects move toward insects, the insects can feel the movement of the displaced air or water and respond appropriately. Many insects also have well-developed ears that hear sounds far above the human range. These organs are located in what we would consider odd places—behind the legs in grasshoppers, for example.

Mandibles used to
saw and grind food
Ant

Tubelike mouthpart
used to suck nectar
Moth

Spongelike mouthpart
used to lap up food
Fly

▲ **Figure 28–16** Insect mouthparts are specialized for a variety of functions. An ant's mouthparts can saw through and then grind food into a fine pulp. The mouthpart of a moth consists of a long tube that can be uncoiled to sip nectar from a flower. Flies have a spongy mouthpart that is used to stir saliva into food and then lap up the food. **Applying Concepts** *What is the function of saliva?*

Adaptations for Feeding Insects have three pairs of appendages that are used as mouthparts, including a pair of mandibles. These mouthparts can take on a variety of shapes, as shown in **Figure 28–16.**

Insect adaptations for feeding are not restricted to their mouthparts. Many insects produce saliva containing digestive enzymes that help break down food. The chemicals in bee saliva, for example, help change nectar into a more digestible form— honey. Glands on the abdomen of bees secrete wax, which is used to build storage chambers for food and other structures within a beehive.

Movement and Flight Insects have three pairs of legs, which in different species are used for walking, jumping, or capturing and holding prey. In many insects, the legs have spines and hooks that are used for grasping and defense.

Many insects can fly, as shown in **Figure 28–17.** Flying insects typically have two pairs of wings made of chitin—the same substance that makes up an insect's exoskeleton.

The evolution of flight has allowed insects to disperse long distances and to colonize a wide variety of habitats. Flying abilities and styles vary greatly among the insects. Butterflies usually fly slowly. Flies, bees, and moths, however, can hover, change direction rapidly, and dart off at great speed. Dragonflies can reach speeds of 50 kilometers per hour.

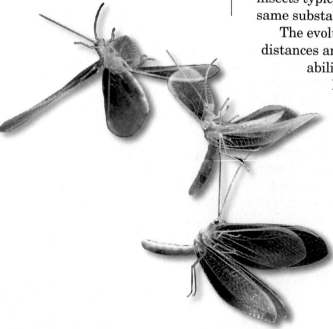

◀ **Figure 28–17** Flying insects, such as this lacewing, move their wings using two sets of muscles. The muscles contract to change the shape of the thorax, alternately pushing the wings down and lifting them up and back. In some small insects, these muscles can produce wing speeds of up to 1000 beats per second! **Drawing Conclusions** *How might the evolution of flight change an animal's habitat?*

Metamorphosis The growth and development of insects usually involve metamorphosis, which is a process of changing shape and form. Insects undergo either incomplete metamorphosis or complete metamorphosis. Both complete and incomplete metamorphosis are shown in **Figure 28–18**. The immature forms of insects that undergo gradual or **incomplete metamorphosis,** such as the chinch bug, look very much like the adults. These immature forms are called **nymphs** (NIMFS). Nymphs lack functional sexual organs and other adult structures, such as wings. As they molt several times and grow, the nymphs gradually acquire adult structures. This type of development is characterized by a similar appearance throughout all stages of the life cycle.

Many insects, such as bees, moths, and beetles, undergo a more dramatic change in body form during a process called **complete metamorphosis.** These animals hatch into larvae that look and act nothing like their parents. They also feed in completely different ways from adult insects. The larvae typically feed voraciously and grow rapidly. They molt a few times and grow larger but change little in appearance. Then they undergo a final molt and change into a **pupa** (PYOO-puh; plural: pupae)—the stage in which an insect changes from larva to adult. During the pupal stage, the body is completely remodeled inside and out. The adult that emerges seems like a completely different animal. Unlike the larva, the adult typically can fly and is specialized for reproduction. **Figure 28–18** shows the complete metamorphosis of a ladybug beetle.

Discovery CHANNEL SCHOOL

To find out how insect metamorphosis plays a part in forensic science, view the videotape "Insect Clues: The Smallest Witnesses."

Figure 28–18 The growth and development of insects usually involve metamorphosis, which is a process of changing shape and form. Insects undergo incomplete metamorphosis or complete metamorphosis. The chinch bug (left) undergoes incomplete metamorphosis, and the developing nymphs look similar to the adult. The ladybug (right) undergoes complete metamorphosis, and during the early stages the developing larva and pupa look completely different from the adult.

✓ **CHECKPOINT** *What is a pupa?*

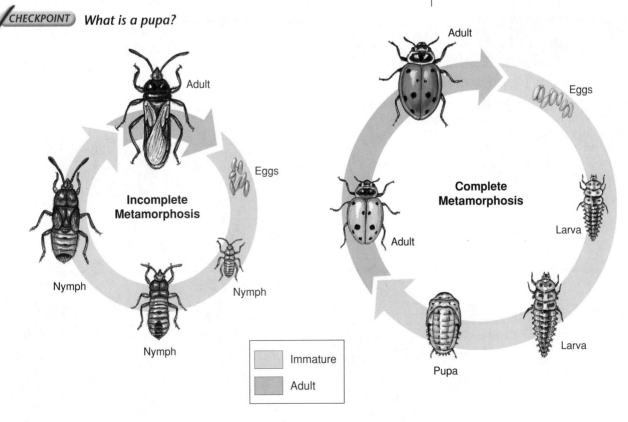

Incomplete Metamorphosis

Adult
Eggs
Nymph
Nymph
Nymph

Complete Metamorphosis

Adult
Eggs
Larva
Larva
Pupa
Adult

| | Immature |
| | Adult |

Insects and Humans

Many insects are known for their negative effects. Termites destroy wood structures, moths eat their way through wool clothing and carpets, and bees and wasps produce painful stings. Insects such as desert locusts cause billions of dollars in damage each year to livestock and crops. Boll weevils are notorious for the trouble they cause cotton farmers in the South. Mosquitoes are annoying and have been known to spoil many a leisurely outdoor activity. Only female mosquitoes bite humans and other animals to get a blood meal for their developing eggs. Male mosquitoes, on the other hand, do not bite; they feed on nectar. Many insects, including mosquitoes, cause far more serious damage than itchy bites. Their bites can infect humans with microorganisms that cause devastating diseases such as malaria, yellow fever, and bubonic plague.

Despite their association with destruction and disease, insects also contribute enormously to the richness of human life. Agriculture would be very different without the bees, butterflies, wasps, moths, and flies that pollinate many crops. One third of the food you eat depends on plants pollinated by animals, including insects. Insects also produce commercially valuable products such as silk, wax, and honey. They are even considered a food delicacy in certain countries of Africa and Asia.

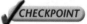 **CHECKPOINT** *How do insects affect humans negatively? Positively?*

Biology and History

Insect-Borne Diseases

For as long as humans and insects have shared planet Earth, humans have been victims of diseases carried by insects. Researchers have discovered which insects transmit specific diseases. Such discoveries have often shed light on how the diseases can be controlled.

African sleeping sickness is discovered in inhabitants of central Africa. The disease is caused by a protist transmitted by tsetse flies that live in forests and areas near water.

1924

1900

1906

Robert Koch discovers that fleas transmit the bubonic-plague bacterium. The plague killed 25% of Europe's population between 1347 and 1351.

1909

Charles Nicolle discovers that one form of typhus, which is caused by a bacterium, is transmitted by the body louse.

1920

Nineteenth amendment to U.S. Constitution gives women the right to vote.

1943

DDT, a powerful insecticide, is used for the first time during World War II to control the spread of typhus. It is also used to control outbreaks of malaria.

Insect Communication

Insects communicate using sound, visual, chemical, and other types of signals. Much of their communication involves finding a mate. To attract females, male crickets chirp by rubbing their forewings together, and male cicadas buzz by vibrating special membranes on the abdomen. Some insects use sound waves to locate prey.

Male fireflies use visual cues to communicate with potential mates. As shown in **Figure 28–19**, a light-producing organ in the abdomen is used to produce a distinct series of flashes. When female fireflies see the signal, they flash back a signal of their own, inducing the males to fly to them. This interaction is sometimes more complicated, however, because the carnivorous females of one genus of fireflies can mimic the signal of another genus—and then lure unsuspecting males to their death!

Many insects communicate using chemical signals. Female moths, for example, attract distant males to them by releasing chemicals. These chemicals are called **pheromones** (FER-uh-mohnz), which are specific chemical messengers that affect the behavior or development of other individuals of the same species. Some pheromones function to signal alarm or alert other insects to the death of a member of the colony. Other pheromones enable males and females to communicate during courtship and mating.

▲ **Figure 28–19** Fireflies use light to communicate with other individuals of their species. They are programmed to respond to specific patterns of light. **Applying Concepts** *What are some other ways in which insects communicate?*

Writing Activity

Some insect-borne diseases have an intermediate host in which the parasite reproduces asexually. Conduct research on the bubonic plague to identify its intermediate host. Write a report on how this host was discovered and how the discovery affected control of the disease.

The World Health Organization begins to get rid of the black fly population of West Africa. Black flies transmit river blindness, which is caused by a roundworm.

First satellite launched into orbit

1957

1974

2000

1972

Use of DDT is severely restricted in the United States because it is found to be toxic to fishes, birds, and possibly humans.

1999

An outbreak of West Nile virus occurs in New York City and its suburbs—the first sighting of this disease in the Western Hemisphere. The disease is carried by mosquitoes and can affect humans as well as birds and livestock. Officials order spraying of insecticides near bodies of water in which mosquitoes might breed.

Major Workers
A colony of leaf-cutter ants grows fungus for food. The fungus needs leaf tissue to grow. Major workers use large, sawlike mandibles to cut through leaf tissue. Smaller worker ants ride atop the leaf, keeping alert for potential threats.

Soldiers
Soldier ants are the largest of the worker ants. They guard the nest from potential attackers and respond quickly to pheromone signals that indicate danger.

Queen
The queen's sole purpose is to lay eggs. Most of these eggs become worker ants, which are nonreproducing females. The males exist only to reproduce. The females that will become queens leave the nest, mate with males, and lay eggs to start a new colony.

Dump Chambers
Dump chambers are filled with wastes, exhausted plant materials, and dead fungus and ants. Openings directly to the outside provide ventilation.

Minor Workers
A variety of different worker castes tend to the fungus gardens. These ants chop the leaves into a fine paste, clean and tend to the gardens, infect new gardens with fungus, and harvest fungus for other members of the colony.

▲ **Figure 28–20** Some insects, such as these tropical leaf-cutter ants, form societies. In a tropical leaf-cutter society, only a single queen reproduces. The queen can produce thousands of eggs in a single day. Several different castes of leaf-cutter ants perform all other tasks within the colony. They care for the queen and her eggs and young; they grow fungus for food; and they build, maintain, and defend the colony's home. One group of workers even cultivates bacteria that produce antibiotics! These antibiotics prevent the growth of parasitic molds on the fungus that the ants use for food.

Insect Societies

Just as people form teams that work together toward a common goal, some insects live and work together in groups. Unlike people, however, insects act instinctively rather than voluntarily. **Ants, bees, termites, and some of their relatives form complex associations called societies.** A **society** is a group of closely related animals of the same species that work together for the benefit of the whole group. Insect societies may consist of more than 7 million individuals. A tropical leaf-cutter ant colony is shown in **Figure 28–20.**

Castes Within a society, individuals may be specialized to perform particular tasks, or roles. These are performed by groups of individuals called **castes.** Each caste has a body form specialized for its role. The basic castes are reproductive females called queens (which lay eggs), reproductive males, and workers. Most insect societies have only one queen, which is typically the largest individual in the colony.

Communication in Societies A sophisticated system of communication is necessary for the functioning of a society. Each species of social insect has its own "language" of visual, touch, sound, and chemical signals that convey information among members of the colony. When a worker ant finds food, for example, she leaves behind a trail of a special pheromone as she heads back to the nest. Her nest mates can then detect her trail to the food by using sensory hairs on their antennae.

Honeybees communicate with complex movements as well as with pheromones. Worker bees are able to convey information about the type, quality, direction, and distance of a food source by "dancing." As shown in **Figure 28–21,** bees have two basic dances: a round dance and a waggle dance. In the round dance, the bee that has found food circles first one way and then the other, over and over again. This dance tells the other bees that there is food within a relatively short distance from the hive. The frequency with which the dancing bee changes direction indicates the quality of the food source: The more frequent the changes in direction, the greater the energy value of the food.

In the waggle dance, the bee that has found food runs forward in a straight line while waggling her abdomen. She circles around one way, runs in a straight line again, and circles around the other way. The waggle dance tells the other bees that the food is a longer distance away. The longer the bee takes to perform the straight run and the more she waggles, the farther away the food. The direction of the straight run indicates in which direction the food is to be found. The angle of the bee indicates the direction of the food in relation to the sun. For example, if the dancer runs straight up the vertical part of the honeycomb, the food is in the same direction as the sun.

Round Dance

Waggle Dance

▲ **Figure 28–21** Bees use dances to communicate information about food sources. The round dance indicates that food is fairly close to the hive. The waggle dance indicates that food is farther away. **Interpreting Graphics** *In what direction does the food lie, according to this bee's waggle dance?*

28–3 Section Assessment

1. 🔑 **Key Concept** Describe the basic body plan of an insect.

2. 🔑 **Key Concept** Compare the processes of incomplete and complete metamorphosis. Which involves a dramatic change in form?

3. 🔑 **Key Concept** Describe the organization of a leaf-cutter ant society. What are the roles of the different castes?

4. What information is passed on by the dances of honeybees? Compare the messages of both types of dances.

5. **Critical Thinking Drawing Conclusions** The compound eyes of insects are better at detecting movement than the fine details of an image. Why might the ability to detect movement be more important in insects than in some other animals, such as humans?

🧍 **TEXT Assessment** Use iText to review the important concepts in Section 28–3.

MAKING CONNECTIONS

Cells and Societies
Recall from Chapter 7 that the cells in multicellular organisms are specialized to perform specific functions. Compare the individual cells in an organism with the individual members of an insect society.

28–4 Echinoderms

Guide for Reading

 Key Concepts
- What are the distinguishing features of echinoderms?
- What functions are carried out by the water vascular system of echinoderms?
- What are the different classes of echinoderms?

Vocabulary
endoskeleton
water vascular system
madreporite
tube foot

Reading Strategy:
Using Visuals Before you read, preview **Figure 28–23.** As you read, notice where in the sea star each function occurs.

One of the most unusual sights along the seashore might be the sea stars, sea urchins, and sand dollars that have washed up on the beach. These animals look like stars, pincushions, and coins. They are all echinoderms (ee-KY-noh-durmz), members of the phylum Echinodermata. *Echino-* means "spiny," and *dermis* means "skin." If you have ever touched a sea star, you will know why this name is appropriate. The skin of echinoderms is stretched over an internal skeleton, or **endoskeleton,** that is formed of hardened plates of calcium carbonate. These plates give the animal a bumpy and irregular texture. Echinoderms live only in the sea. Some are delicate, brightly colored, feathery-armed creatures. Others look like mud-brown half-rotten cucumbers!

What Is an Echinoderm?

The body plan of echinoderms is like no other in the animal kingdom. Adult echinoderms typically have no anterior or posterior end and lack cephalization. However, the bodies of most echinoderms are two-sided. The side in which the mouth is located is called the oral surface, and the opposite side is called the aboral surface.

     Echinoderms are characterized by spiny skin, an internal skeleton, a water vascular system, and suction-cuplike structures called tube feet. Most adult echinoderms exhibit five-part radial symmetry. The body parts, which usually occur in multiples of five, are arranged around the central body like the spokes of a wheel. The brittle star in **Figure 28–22** exhibits this kind of symmetry. Although radial symmetry is characteristic of simpler animals such as cnidarians, echinoderms are actually more closely related to humans and other vertebrates. The larvae of echinoderms are bilaterally symmetrical, indicating that body symmetry evolved differently in this group than in simpler animals. Also, echinoderms are deuterostomes, animals in which the blastopore develops into an anus. This type of development is found in echinoderms and vertebrates, indicating that these groups are closely related.

◀ **Figure 28–22** Echinoderms such as this brittle star have spiny skin, five-part radial symmetry, an internal skeleton, a water vascular system, and suction-cuplike structures called tube feet. Observe that the brittle star has five arms. The bodies of most echinoderms are divided into parts that are multiples of five.

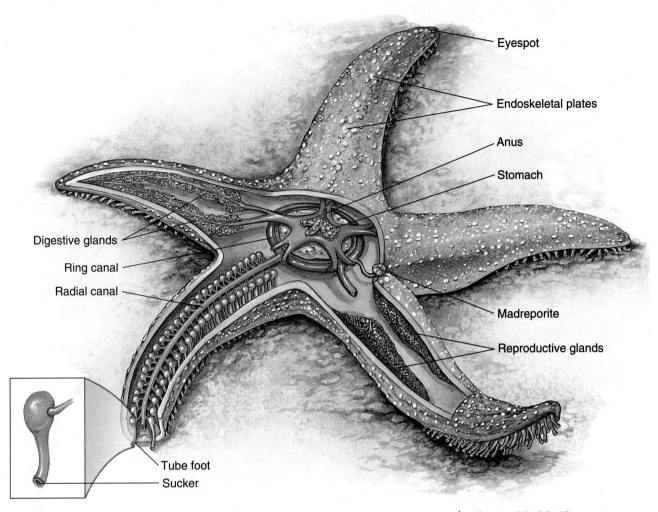

Eyespot

Endoskeletal plates

Anus

Stomach

Digestive glands

Ring canal

Radial canal

Madreporite

Reproductive glands

Tube foot

Sucker

▲ **Figure 28–23** The most distinctive system of echinoderms is the water vascular system, shown here in a sea star. 🔑 **The water vascular system, which extends throughout the body, functions in respiration, circulation, and movement.**

Form and Function in Echinoderms

A unique feature of echinoderms is a system of internal tubes called a **water vascular system,** which is shown in **Figure 28–23**. 🔑 **The water vascular system, which is filled with fluid, carries out many essential body functions in echinoderms, including respiration, circulation, and movement.** It opens to the outside through a sievelike structure called a **madreporite** (MAD-ruh-pawr-yt). In sea stars, the madreporite connects to a ring canal that forms a circle around the animal's mouth. From the ring canal, five radial canals extend along body segments.

Attached to each radial canal are hundreds of tube feet. A **tube foot** is a structure that operates much like a suction cup. Each tube foot has a sucker on the end. Muscles pull the center of the sucker upwards, forming a cup shape. This action creates suction on the surface to which the foot is attached, so the tube foot pulls on the surface. Hundreds of tube feet acting together create enormous force, allowing echinoderms to "walk" and even to pull open shelled prey such as clams.

✔ **CHECKPOINT** *What is the system of internal tubes in echinoderms?*

▲ **Figure 28–24** Echinoderms use all types of feeding methods. Sea stars, like the one shown above, are carnivores that typically feed on mussels and other bivalves. **Comparing and Contrasting** *How do other groups of echinoderms feed?*

Feeding Echinoderms have several methods of feeding. Sea urchins use five-part jawlike structures to scrape algae from rocks. Sea lilies use tube feet along their arms to capture floating plankton. Sea cucumbers move like bulldozers across the ocean floor, taking in sand and detritus. Sea stars usually feed on mollusks such as clams and mussels, as shown in **Figure 28–24**. Once the prey's shell is open, the sea star pushes its stomach out through its mouth, pours out enzymes, and digests the mollusk in its own shell. Then the sea star pulls its stomach and the partially digested prey into its mouth.

Respiration and Circulation Other than the water vascular system, echinoderms have few adaptations to carry out respiration or circulation. In most species, the thin-walled tissue of the tube feet provides the main surface for respiration. In some species, small outgrowths called skin gills also function in gas exchange.

Circulation of needed materials and wastes takes place throughout the water vascular system. Oxygen, food, and wastes are carried by the water vascular system.

Excretion In most echinoderms, solid wastes are released as feces through the anus. Nitrogen-containing cellular wastes are excreted primarily in the form of ammonia. This waste product is passed into surrounding water through the thin-walled tissues of tube feet and skin gills.

Response As you might expect in animals that have no head, echinoderms do not have a highly developed nervous system. Most have a nerve ring that surrounds the mouth, and radial nerves that connect the ring with the body sections. Most echinoderms also have scattered sensory cells that detect light, gravity, and chemicals released by potential prey.

Movement Most echinoderms move using tube feet and thin layers of muscle fibers attached to their endoskeleton. An echinoderm's mobility is determined in part by the structure of its endoskeleton. Sand dollars and sea urchins have movable spines attached to the endoskeleton. Sea stars and brittle stars have flexible joints that enable them to use their arms for locomotion. In sea cucumbers, the plates of the endoskeleton are reduced and contained inside a soft, muscular body wall. These echinoderms crawl along the ocean floor by the combined action of tube feet and the muscles of the body wall.

Reproduction Echinoderms reproduce by external fertilization. In most sea star species, the sexes are separate. Sperm are produced in testes, and eggs are produced in ovaries. Both types of gametes are shed into open water, where fertilization takes place. The larvae, which have bilateral symmetry, swim around for some time and then swim to the ocean bottom, where they develop into adults that have radial symmetry.

✓ **CHECKPOINT** *How do echinoderms move?*

Groups of Echinoderms

There are roughly 7000 species of echinoderms—all of which live in the world's oceans. ⬤ **Classes of echinoderms include sea urchins and sand dollars; brittle stars; sea cucumbers; sea stars; sea lilies and feather stars.** Some of these echinoderms are shown in **Figure 28–25.**

Sea Urchins and Sand Dollars This class includes sea urchins and disk-shaped sand dollars. These echinoderms are unique in having large, solid plates that form a box around their internal organs. Many are detritivores or grazers that eat large quantities of algae. They defend themselves in different ways. Sand dollars often burrow under layers of sand or mud. Some sea urchins wedge themselves in rock crevices during the day, whereas others defend themselves using long, sharp spines.

Brittle Stars Brittle stars are common in many parts of the sea, especially on coral reefs. They have slender, flexible arms and can scuttle around quite rapidly to escape predators. In addition to using speed for protection, brittle stars shed one or more arms when attacked. The detached arm keeps moving, distracting the predator while the brittle star escapes. Brittle stars are filter feeders and detritivores that hide by day and wander around under cover of darkness.

Sea Cucumbers Sea cucumbers look like warty, moving pickles. Most sea cucumbers are detritus feeders that move along the sea floor while sucking up organic matter and the remains of other animals and plants. Herds containing hundreds of thousands of sea cucumbers roam across the deep-sea floor.

Sea Stars Sea stars are probably the best-known group of echinoderms. They move by creeping slowly along the ocean floor. Most are carnivorous, preying on bivalves that they encounter. Many sea stars have incredible abilities to repair themselves when damaged. If a sea star is pulled into pieces, each piece will grow into a new animal, as long as it contains a portion of the central part of the body.

Figure 28–25 ⬤ Sea urchins, brittle stars, sea cucumbers, and sea stars represent different classes of echinoderms. Observe the characteristics of these representatives of each class.

Long-Spined Sea Urchin

Brittle Star

Red-Lined Sea Cucumber

Sun Star

Figure 28–26 Sea lilies belong to the most ancient class of echinoderms, known as crinoids. The red crinoid (top) is one of the few species of this class that are alive today. This stalked crinoid fossil (bottom) is an example of the types of crinoids that dominated Earth during the Paleozoic Era. **Comparing and Contrasting** *How are sea lilies different from other echinoderms?*

Sea Lilies and Feather Stars These filter feeders, which have long, feathery arms, make up the oldest class of echinoderms. Sea lilies and feather stars are common in tropical oceans today, and a rich fossil record shows that they were distributed widely throughout ancient seas. Like modern sea lilies, their fossilized ancestors lived attached to the ocean bottom by a long, stemlike stalk, as seen in **Figure 28–26.** Many modern feather stars live on coral reefs, where they perch on top of rocks and use their tube feet to catch floating plankton.

Ecology of Echinoderms

Echinoderms are common in a variety of marine habitats. In many areas, a sudden rise or fall in the number of echinoderms can cause major changes to populations of other marine organisms. Sea urchins help control the distribution of algae and other forms of marine life. Sea stars are important carnivores that help control the numbers of other organisms such as clams and corals.

A major threat to coral reefs is the sea star called the crown-of-thorns. This echinoderm is named for the rows of poisonous spines located along its arms. It feeds almost exclusively on coral. In the Great Barrier Reef of Australia—one of the largest reef systems in the world—this organism has destroyed extensive areas of coral.

28–4 Section Assessment

1. **Key Concept** What is an echinoderm?
2. **Key Concept** What is the water vascular system? How is it important to echinoderms?
3. **Key Concept** List the major classes of echinoderms and describe their characteristics.
4. Echinoderms are deuterostomes. What does this indicate about their relationship to other animals?

5. **Critical Thinking Inferring** Why is tearing a sea star apart and throwing it back into the water an ineffective way of trying to reduce sea star populations?

iTEXT **Assessment** Use iText to review the important concepts in Section 28–4.

Take It to the NET
Describe how sea stars, sea cucumbers, and sea urchins eat and reproduce. Share this information with your class in the form of a report. Be sure to include drawings or photographs. Use the links provided in the Biology area at the Prentice Hall Web site for help in completing this activity:
www.phschool.com

Observing Ant Behavior

Unlike most insects, many ant species live in large, social groups. The ants within each group work together to support the group. In this investigation, you will design an experiment to determine how ants respond to members of other colonies and other species.

Problem
How do ants respond to members of other colonies and other species?

Materials
- covered petri dish containing 10 ants of species A from the same colony (**CAUTION:** *Do not use fire ants.*)
- hand lens or dissecting microscope
- field guide
- watch or clock with a second hand
- 3 covered petri dishes, each containing 5 ants of species A from different colonies
- covered petri dish containing 5 ants from species B (**CAUTION:** *Do not use fire ants.*)

Skills
Predicting, Drawing Conclusions

Design Your Experiment

Part A: Observing Ants That Are Related

1. Obtain a petri dish containing 10 ants from the same colony. Look at the ants under a hand lens or dissecting microscope. Use a field guide to identify the species to which they belong.

2. For 30 seconds, count the number of ants that are fighting with one another. Record this number on a sheet of paper. If the ants are not fighting, write "0."

3. **Predicting** Record your prediction of whether ants from separate colonies of the same species will fight, and whether ants of two different species will fight.

Part B: Observing Ants That Are Not Related

4. **Designing Experiments** Design experiments to test your predictions. Write a hypothesis for each experiment and control all variables except the one you are testing. **CAUTION:** *Ants are delicate, and some have stinging bites. Do not try to pick them up with your hands.* Have your teacher check your plan before you begin to perform your experiment.

Analyze and Conclude

1. **Observing** Did most of the ants fight in step 2? How would you explain the behavior you observed?

2. **Observing** What happened when you put ants from two different colonies of the same species together? When you put ants from two different species together? Were your predictions correct?

3. **Drawing Conclusions** How do you think the behavior you observed helps the ants survive?

Go Further

Posing Questions Think of some other aspects of ants and their behavior that you would like to learn about. For example, you might be curious about how different environmental conditions affect an ant colony, or which foods individual ants prefer. Write your ideas as a series of questions. Choose one of your questions and find an answer to it, either by finding information in reference materials or designing an experiment. Before performing any experiments, obtain your teacher's approval.

28–1 Introduction to the Arthropods
 Key Concepts

- Arthropods have a segmented body, a tough exoskeleton, and jointed appendages.
- In many groups of arthropods, continuing evolution has led to fewer body segments and highly specialized appendages for feeding, movement, and other functions.
- When they outgrow their exoskeletons, arthropods undergo periods of molting.

Vocabulary
exoskeleton, p. 715
chitin, p. 715
appendage, p. 715
tracheal tube, p. 717
spiracle, p. 717
book lung, p. 717
Malpighian tubule, p. 717
molting, p. 719

28–2 Groups of Arthropods
Key Concepts

- Arthropods are classified based on the number and structure of their body segments and appendages, particularly their mouthparts.
- Crustaceans typically have two pairs of branched antennae, two or three body sections, and chewing mouthparts called mandibles.
- Chelicerates have mouthparts called chelicerae and two body sections, and most have four pairs of walking legs.
- Uniramians have jaws, one pair of antennae, and unbranched appendages.

Vocabulary
cephalothorax, p. 721
thorax, p. 721
abdomen, p. 721
carapace, p. 721
mandible, p. 721
cheliped, p. 721
swimmeret, p. 721
chelicera, p. 722
pedipalp, p. 722
spinneret, p. 723

28–3 Insects
 Key Concepts

- Insects have a body divided into three parts—head, thorax, and abdomen. Three pairs of legs are attached to the thorax.
- The growth and development of insects usually involve metamorphosis, which is a process of changing shape and form. Insects undergo either incomplete metamorphosis or complete metamorphosis.
- Ants, bees, termites, and some of their relatives form complex associations called societies.

Vocabulary
incomplete metamorphosis, p. 729
nymph, p. 729
complete metamorphosis, p. 729
pupa, p. 729
pheromone, p. 731
society, p. 732
caste, p. 732

28–4 Echinoderms
Key Concepts

- Echinoderms are characterized by spiny skin, five-part radial symmetry, an internal skeleton, a water vascular system, and suction-cuplike structures called tube feet.
- The water vascular system carries out many essential body functions in echinoderms, including respiration, circulation, and movement.
- Classes of echinoderms include sea lilies and feather stars, sea stars, brittle stars, sea urchins and sand dollars, and sea cucumbers.

Vocabulary
endoskeleton, p. 734
water vascular system, p. 735
madreporite, p. 735
tube foot, p. 735

Thinking Visually
Construct two concept maps—one for arthropods and the other for echinoderms. Each concept map should show how the members of each phylum are classified. Include specific examples for each group.

Chapter 28

Part A

Multiple Choice

For each statement or question, select the number of the word or expression that, of those given, best completes the statement or answers the question.

1 One body feature that all arthropods have in common is
 (1) gills   (3) jointed appendages
 (2) antennae   (4) chelicerae

2 Most terrestrial arthropods breath using branched, air-filled structures called
 (1) gills   (3) tracheal tubes
 (2) book gills   (4) book lungs

3 Transport of materials in most arthropods is by way of
 (1) no circulatory system
 (2) an open circulatory system
 (3) a closed circulatory system
 (4) a four-chambered circulatory system

4 Crustaceans are the only arthropods that have
 (1) three pairs of legs
 (2) two pairs of antennae
 (3) chitin in their exoskeleton
 (4) chelicerae

5 Which of the organisms below belongs in the subphylum Chelicerata?

(1)

(3)

(2)

(4)

6 All insects have
 (1) two pairs of legs
 (2) three antennae
 (3) three pairs of wings
 (4) three body sections

7 The type of symmetry exhibited by most adult echinoderms is
 (1) bilateral   (3) top and bottom
 (2) radial   (4) no symmetry

8 Oxygen is transported throughout the body of a sea star in its
 (1) madreporite stalk
 (2) Malpighian tubules
 (3) water vascular system
 (4) open circulatory system

9 Mites and ticks are example of
 (1) crustaceans
 (2) uniramians
 (3) arachnids
 (4) chelicerae

10 Which combination correctly pairs the structure with its function?
 (1) spiracle—digestion of food
 (2) madreporite—muscle coordination
 (3) spinnerets—molting
 (4) mandible—feeding

11 Which is *not* a characteristic of an echinoderm?
 (1) an internal skeleton
 (2) a pair of antennae
 (3) tube feet
 (4) a water vascular system

12 Which animals have four pairs of walking legs?
 (1) centipedes   (3) ants
 (2) insects   (4) arachnids

13 Chemical messengers that affect the behavior or development of other individuals of the same species are called
 (1) trilobites   (3) chitins
 (2) pheromones   (4) chelicerae

14 An extinct group of marine arthropods that were abundant more than 500 million years ago were the
 (1) arachnids   (3) pheromones
 (2) trilobites   (4) brittle stars

Test-Taking Tip If you are taking a long time to answer a question, consider coming back to it later. As you answer the other questions, you may remember the information you need to answer the skipped question.

Preparing for the
Living Environment Exam

Parts B and C

Multiple Choice and Extended Response

For those questions that ask you to select a response, choose the one that best completes the statement or answers the question. For all others follow the directions given.

15 In many insect species, insect adults and larvae feed on different substances. How might this characteristic help members of those species survive?

Base your answers to questions 16 through 19 on the information below and on your knowledge of biology.

A biology student is investigating the relationship between cricket chirps and temperature. He catches a cricket and places it in a jar. He leaves the jar outside, and each day he measures the number of chirps during a 15-second period. At the same time, he records the outside temperature near the cricket. His data are shown in the data table below.

Relationship Between Temperature and Cricket Chirping

Day	Number of Chirps in 15 Seconds	Outside Temperature (°C)
Monday	31	23
Tuesday	20	16
Wednesday	12	11
Thursday	29	21
Friday	25	19

16 Make a copy of the following data table on your answer paper and complete it according to these directions.
  - Arrange the number of chirps in order from least to most, then fill in the appropriate temperatures in degrees Celsius.
  - Calculate the temperature in degrees Fahrenheit by multiplying the Celsius temperature by 1.8 and then adding 32. Round off to the nearest degree.
  - Fill in the Fahrenheit temperatures you calculate in the appropriate places in the table.

Relationship Between Temperature and Cricket Chirping

Chirps in 15 Seconds	Outside Temperature (°C)	Outside Temperature (°F) (°C x 1.8) + 32 = °F

17 The student obtained 20 more crickets and repeated his procedure with each of them. Nearly identical results were obtained each time. What is the most valid conclusion that can be drawn from this experiment?
  - **(1)** Crickets cannot chirp more than 31 times in 15 seconds.
  - **(2)** The number of chirps decreases when the temperature decreases.
  - **(3)** Crickets cannot chirp less than 12 times every 11 seconds.
  - **(4)** The number of chirps increases when the temperature decreases.

18 At which temperature would a cricket be most likely to chirp 9 times in 15 seconds?
  - **(1)** 2°C
  - **(2)** 10°C
  - **(3)** 18°C
  - **(4)** 25°C

19 The student concluded that the number of chirps could be used to estimate the cricket's environmental temperature in degrees Fahrenheit. Compare the number of chirps with the temperature in degrees Fahrenheit. Then, state how you could use the number of chirps in 15 seconds to arrive at an estimate of the environmental temperature in degrees Fahrenheit.

20 Many adult insects are capable of flying. Explain how this characteristic can lead to more reproductive success for a species.

21 Explain how the structural variations among the insects that make up an anthill are of value to the insect society to which they are a part. Support your explanation with an example.

22 The legs and bodies of honeybees are covered with hairs that collect pollen and other materials. How is this adaptation helpful to both flowering plants and honeybees?

23 Blue crabs usually have hard shells. During certain times of the year some of the blue crabs have thin, papery shells. State why these blue crabs would have soft shells.

24 An animal is discovered that has an exoskeleton, sucking mouthparts, head fused with thorax, no wings, and four pairs of walking legs. It is decided that this animal is not an insect. State the two features of this animal that would lead to the decision that it could not be an insect, and explain how insects would differ in these two features.

Base your answers to questions 25 and 26 on the information and graph below and on your knowledge of biology.

The graph below shows the effect of water temperature on the time it takes for brine shrimp eggs to hatch. Brine shrimp are small crustaceans found in salty lakes and ponds.

Effect of Temperature on Egg Development

Temperature (°C) vs Time for Eggs to Hatch (hours)

25 Based on the graph, state a valid conclusion about the relationship between water temperature and hatching time.

26 Predict how many hours it would take for eggs to hatch at 10°C, 18°C, and 25°C.

27 How does the term *society* relate to ants, bees, and termites?

28 What is the function of a crustacean's carapace?

29 Compare incomplete metamorphosis with complete metamorphosis. In your answer be sure to
• describe the stages of each process

  • state one way a nymph differs from a pupa

  • give an example of an organism that undergoes each process

30 In a stagnant pool of water, a crayfish may spend much of its time lying with one side of its carapace near the surface of the water. In this position, it will move the walking legs on that side in a back-and-forth motion. State one life activity that this behavior is likely to aid and explain how it may be of value to the animal's survival.

31 Female insects release certain pheromones into the air to attract males for mating. Some companies have produced devices that use pheromones to attract specific insects and trap them. Compare the usefulness of pheromones and insect poisons, which are often used in the control of pest insects. In your answer be sure to state
• one environmental benefit of using pheromones instead of the usual insect poisons

  • one way that using a pheromone for controlling these insects may not be as effective as expected in controlling a pest insect population

Take It to the NET

What insects do we find in art? What insects affect us psychologically? Visit the Prentice Hall Web site at **www.phschool.com** to learn about a subject called cultural entomology. Then, answer the following questions:
• Which insects are frequently found in Native American myths, and why?

• How did the ancient Chinese regard cicadas?

• What is entomophobia?

• What was the most important use of insects to Australian Aborigines? Give three examples.

The spotted cleaner shrimp lives among, and cleans, the tentacles of this anemone. The anemone protects the shrimp from predators.

Inquiry Activity

Which protective covering is best?

Procedure

1. Examine some arthropod exoskeletons and mollusk shells. Observe as many differences as you can between these two types of protective coverings.

2. List the differences you observed. Next to each item, note how that difference in protective covering is adaptive to the organism in its own particular niche and habitat.

Think About It

1. **Drawing Conclusions** Which covering is more difficult for a predator to penetrate? Explain.

2. **Predicting** Animals must use energy to move. Which type of covering is more useful to an active, motile animal? Explain your answer.

3. **Drawing Conclusions** How can your observations help explain the fact that most mollusks are slow-moving animals, whereas many arthropods are more active?

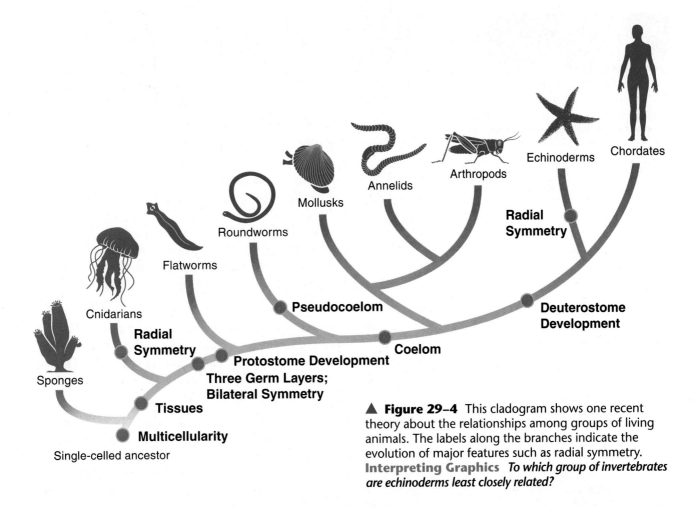

Figure 29–4 This cladogram shows one recent theory about the relationships among groups of living animals. The labels along the branches indicate the evolution of major features such as radial symmetry. **Interpreting Graphics** *To which group of invertebrates are echinoderms least closely related?*

What features of the Cambrian animals made them so successful? One way of determining this is to find their common features—especially those that are present in animals today. Burgess Shale animals typically had body symmetry, segmentation, some type of skeleton, a front and a back end, and appendages adapted for a multitude of functions. These features are characteristic of most invertebrates living today.

Modern Evolutionary Relationships

The cladogram in **Figure 29–4** shows the evolutionary relationships among major groups of living invertebrates. It also indicates the sequence in which some important features evolved. These features include tissues and organs, patterns of early development, body symmetry, cephalization, segmentation, and the formation of three germ layers and a coelom. Many of these features, which have persisted up to modern times, evolved in animals of the Cambrian Period. As you review the major trends in invertebrate evolution, consider how each feature might have contributed to the evolutionary success of animals.

CHECKPOINT *What groups of animals are deuterostomes?*

Word Origins

The word *germ* in the term *germ layers* comes from the Latin word *germen*, which means "embryo" or "sprout." **If the suffix *-ate* means "to become," what happens to a seed when it germinates?**

KEEP CURRENT WITH . . .
SCIENCE NEWS®

To find out more about the topics in this chapter, go to:
www.phschool.com

Evolutionary Trends

The appearance of each phylum in the fossil record represents the evolution of a successful and unique body plan. Features of this body plan typically change over time, leading to the formation of many new traits. The major trends of invertebrate evolution are summarized in **Figure 29–5.**

Specialized Cells, Tissues, and Organs Modern sponges and cnidarians have little internal specialization. They carry out essential functions using individual cells or simple tissues. As larger and more complex animals evolved, specialized cells joined together to form tissues, organs, and organ systems that work together to carry out complex functions. Flatworms have simple organs for digestion, excretion, response, and reproduction. More complex animals, such as mollusks and arthropods, have organ systems.

Body Symmetry Sponges lack body symmetry. **All invertebrates except sponges exhibit some type of body symmetry.** Cnidarians and echinoderms exhibit **radial symmetry**—body parts extend from the center of the body. Worms, mollusks, and arthropods exhibit **bilateral symmetry,** or have mirror-image left and right sides.

Cephalization Most invertebrates with bilateral symmetry rely on movement for feeding, defense, and other important functions. The evolution of this body plan and lifestyle was accompanied by the trend toward **cephalization,** which is the concentration of sense organs and nerve cells in the front of the body. **Invertebrates with cephalization can respond to the environment in more sophisticated ways than can simpler invertebrates.** In most worms and arthropods, nerve cells are arranged in structures called ganglia. In more complex invertebrates, such as certain mollusks, nerve cells form an organ called a brain.

✓ **CHECKPOINT** How does cephalization benefit an animal?

▶ **Figure 29–5** This table shows the major characteristics of the main groups of invertebrates. **Germ layers, body symmetry, cephalization, and development of a coelom are more common in complex invertebrates than in simple ones.** Mollusks, for example, have all of these features, but sponges have none of them.

Comparing Invertebrates

	Sponges	Cnidarians	Flatworms
Germ Layers	Absent	Two	Three
Body Symmetry	Absent	Radial	Bilateral
Cephalization	Absent	Absent	Present
Coelom	Absent	Absent	Absent
Early Development	——	——	Protostome

Ectoderm | Mesoderm | Endoderm

Acoelomate
Digestive cavity

Pseudocoelomate
Pseudocoelom
Digestive tract

Coelomate
Coelom
Digestive tract

Segmentation Most invertebrates with bilateral symmetry also have segmented bodies. Over the course of evolution, different segments have often become specialized for specific functions. Because the same structures are repeated in each body segment, segmentation also allows an animal to increase in body size with a minimum of new genetic material.

Coelom Formation Jellyfishes have a simple construction in which a jellylike layer lies between ectoderm and endoderm tissues. Other invertebrates develop from three germ layers, the endoderm, mesoderm, and ectoderm, as shown in **Figure 29–6.** Invertebrate phyla differ in the arrangement of these layers. Flatworms are acoelomates, meaning that no **coelom,** or body cavity, forms between the germ layers. Pseudocoelomates, such as roundworms, have a body cavity lined partially with mesoderm. 🔑**Most complex animal phyla have a true coelom that is lined completely with mesoderm.**

Early Development In most invertebrates, the zygote divides repeatedly to form a blastula—a hollow ball of cells. In protostomes, the blastopore, or the opening of the blastula, develops into a mouth. In deuterostomes, the blastopore forms an anus. Worms, arthropods, and mollusks are protostomes, and echinoderms are deuterostomes.

▲ **Figure 29–6** Acoelomates do not have a coelom, or body cavity, between their germ layers. Pseudocoelomates have body cavities that are partially lined with mesoderm. 🔑**Most complex animal phyla are coelomates, meaning that they have a true coelom that is lined completely with mesoderm.**

Roundworms	Annelids	Mollusks	Arthropods	Echinoderms
Three	Three	Three	Three	Three
Bilateral	Bilateral	Bilateral	Bilateral	Radial (adults)
Present	Present	Present	Present	Absent (adults)
Pseudocoelom	True coelom	True coelom	True coelom	True coelom
Protostome	Protostome	Protostome	Protostome	Deuterostome

Creating an Imaginary Invertebrate

The moth in the photo is a real animal, but you may think that it looks like a science-fiction monster. Several of the most frightening "monsters" dreamed up for the science-fiction films of the past 20 years have actually been based on bits and pieces of anatomy and behavior of real invertebrates. Now that you have studied all the invertebrate phyla, you can take a turn at devising the "perfect invertebrate" for a habitat of your choice.

Defining the Problem First, choose a habitat: a temperate zone desert, a tropical coral reef, or inside the body of a mammal. Depending on which habitat you chose, define the environmental challenges (such as heat, cold, or lack of water) and the biological needs (such as food and oxygen) that your organism must meet.

Organizing Information Once you have defined the problem, look back over the characteristics of all the invertebrate groups you have studied, and pick the kind of body systems that you think would work best in your chosen habitat.

Creating a Solution Assemble the body systems you have chosen into an imaginary animal. Make sure that the systems you use can work in harmony. You could not, for example, expect an animal to breathe through its skin if it had an impermeable exoskeleton covering its entire body! Make sure that you have

considered all the organism's needs. Give your animal an appropriate name.

Presenting Your Plan Create external and cutaway diagrams of your animal, including any larval stages. Label the diagrams, including the name of the real-life invertebrate system that fulfills each essential function. Conclude by describing the complete life cycle of your organism.

29–1 Section Assessment

1. 🔑 **Key Concept** Describe three major trends in the evolution of invertebrates.

2. Compare the first multicellular animals with those of the Burgess Shale.

3. How was the evolution of internal specialization important to invertebrate form and function?

4. Compare the body structures and other characteristics of cnidarians and arthropods.

5. **Critical Thinking**
   Inferring Evolutionary relationships are inferred from both molecular and body-structure data. Why might this approach be more accurate than only studying body structure?

   📱 **TEXT** Assessment Use iText to review the important concepts in Section 29–1.

29–2 Form and Function in Invertebrates

To survive, all animals perform the same essential tasks: feeding and digestion, respiration, circulation, excretion, response, movement, and reproduction. In many ways, each animal phylum represents an "experiment" in the adaptation of body structures to carry out these tasks. The appearance of each phylum in the fossil record, therefore, represents the evolutionary development of a unique body plan. The continued history of each phylum is the story of further evolutionary changes to that plan.

Biologists can learn a great deal about the nature of life by comparing body systems among groups of living invertebrates. Body systems that perform the essential tasks of life have taken many different forms in different phyla. Each phylum has a particular type of breathing device, a certain type of body support system, and numerous variations on other body functions. More complicated systems are not necessarily better than simpler systems. The fact that any system is found in living animals testifies to its success in performing functions adequately. This section reviews the basic evolutionary trends in each body system, using examples from a variety of invertebrate groups.

Feeding and Digestion

Invertebrates have evolved many different ways of obtaining food. The spider in **Figure 29–7**, for example, is feeding on a caterpillar after killing it with venom. Before food can be used for energy, the food must be broken down, or digested. The digested food must then be absorbed into the animal's body. Complex animals accomplish these processes in different ways than simpler ones.

Intracellular and Extracellular Digestion Invertebrates have evolved different ways of digesting food. **The simplest animals break down food primarily through intracellular digestion, but more complex animals use extracellular digestion.** Sponges digest their food inside archaeocytes, which pass nutrients to other cells by diffusion. Because food is digested inside cells, this process is known as **intracellular digestion.** In contrast, mollusks, annelids, arthropods, and echinoderms rely almost entirely on extracellular digestion. In **extracellular digestion,** food is broken down outside the cells in a digestive cavity or tract and then absorbed into the body. Flatworms and cnidarians use both intracellular and extracellular digestion.

Guide for Reading

Key Concept
• How do different invertebrate phyla carry out their essential life functions?

Vocabulary
intracellular digestion
extracellular digestion
open circulatory system
closed circulatory system
hydrostatic skeleton
exoskeleton
endoskeleton
external fertilization
internal fertilization

Reading Strategy:
Finding Main Ideas Before you read, skim the section to identify the key ideas. Then, carefully read the section, making a list of supporting details for each main idea.

▶ **Figure 29–7** Complex animals break down food using extracellular digestion. The spider's venom is breaking down the tissues of the caterpillar. Later, the broken-down food molecules will be absorbed into the spider's digestive tract.

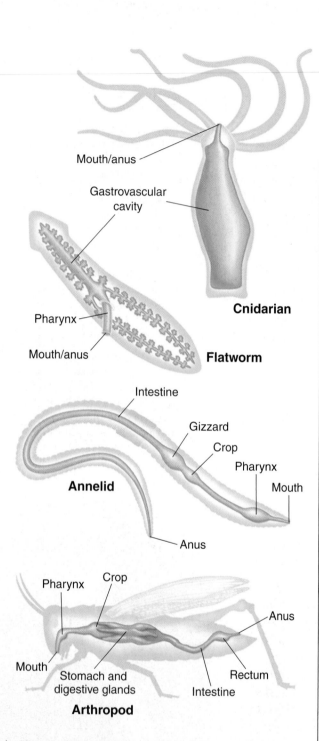

Mouth/anus

Gastrovascular
cavity

Cnidarian

Pharynx

Mouth/anus

Flatworm

Intestine

Gizzard

Crop

Pharynx

Mouth

Annelid

Anus

Crop

Pharynx

Anus

Mouth

Stomach and
digestive glands

Rectum

Intestine

Arthropod

▲ **Figure 29–8** Cnidarians and flatworms have a digestive system with only one opening. In more complex animals, the digestive system has two openings. In addition, the digestive organs have become more specialized. **Interpreting Graphics** *Which of these animals has the least specialized digestive system?*

Patterns of Extracellular Digestion

Invertebrates have a variety of digestive systems, as shown in **Figure 29–8.** Simple animals such as cnidarians and flatworms ingest food and expel wastes through a single opening. Food is digested in the gastrovascular cavity through both extracellular and intracellular means. Some cells of the gastrovascular cavity secrete enzymes and absorb the digested food. Other cells surround food particles and digest them in vacuoles. Digested food then diffuses throughout the body.

More-complex animals digest food in a tube called the digestive tract. Food enters the body through the mouth, and wastes leave through the anus. A one-way digestive tract (which is characteristic of roundworms, annelids, mollusks, arthropods, and echinoderms) often has specialized regions, such as a stomach and intestines. Specialization of the digestive tract allows food to be processed more efficiently, because each step in the process takes place in order, at a specific place along the digestive tract.

Respiration

All animals must exchange oxygen and carbon dioxide with the environment. The more surface area that is exposed to the environment, the greater the amount of gas exchange that can occur. In addition, gases diffuse most efficiently across a thin, moist membrane. Given these principles, all respiratory systems share two basic features. 🔑 **Respiratory organs have large surface areas that are in contact with the air or water. Also, for diffusion to occur the respiratory surfaces must be moist.**

Aquatic Invertebrates Aquatic animals, such as cnidarians and some flatworms, naturally have moist respiratory surfaces. Many animals even respire through their skins. However, for most active animals larger than worms, skin respiration alone is not sufficient. Aquatic mollusks, arthropods, and many annelids exchange gases through gills. Gills are feathery structures that expose a large surface area to the water. Gills are rich in blood vessels that bring blood close to the surface for gas exchange.

How do clams and crayfishes breathe?

Materials live clam, food coloring, crayfish, small container of water

Procedure 🐁

1. Put a drop of food coloring in the water near a clam's siphons. Observe what happens to the coloring.
2. Put a drop of food coloring in the water near the middle of a crayfish's carapace. **CAUTION:** *Keep your fingers away from the crayfish's pincers.* Observe what happens to the coloring.

Analyze and Conclude

1. **Observing** Describe what happened to the coloring in step 1. How does water move past a clam's gills?
2. **Inferring** What is the clam's main defense? How is the location of the clam's siphons related to this defense?
3. **Comparing and Contrasting** What happened in step 2? Compare the flow of water past the gills of clams and crayfish.
4. **Inferring** Why do you think the crayfish has gills rather than spiracles, as some other arthropods do?

Terrestrial Invertebrates In terrestrial animals, respiratory surfaces are covered with water or mucus, thereby minimizing water loss. In addition, air is moistened as it travels through the body to the respiratory surface.

Terrestrial invertebrates have several types of respiratory surfaces. The mantle cavity of a land snail is a moist tissue that has an extensive surface area lined with blood vessels. Spiders respire using organs called book lungs, such as the one shown in **Figure 29–9.** Book lungs are made of parallel, sheetlike layers of thin tissues that contain blood vessels. In insects, air enters the body through openings called spiracles. It then enters a network of tracheal tubes, where gases diffuse in and out of surrounding body fluids.

✓**CHECKPOINT** *How does respiration in aquatic invertebrates differ from respiration in terrestrial invertebrates?*

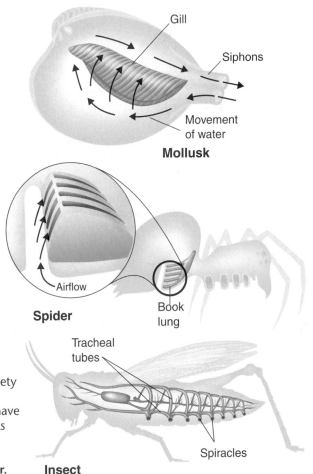

Mollusk

Spider

Insect

▶ **Figure 29–9** Invertebrates have a variety of respiratory structures. Clams and other aquatic mollusks have gills. Many spiders have book lungs. Grasshoppers and other insects have spiracles and tracheal tubes. 🔵**All respiratory organs have large, moist surface areas in contact with air or water.**

**Insect: Open
Circulatory System**

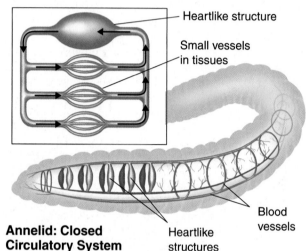

**Annelid: Closed
Circulatory System**

▲ **Figure 29–10** Most complex animals have one or more hearts to move fluid through their bodies in either an open or closed circulatory system. An insect has an open circulatory system in which blood leaves blood vessels and then moves through sinuses, or body cavities. An annelid has a closed circulatory system in which blood stays in blood vessels as it moves through the body.

Circulation

All cells require a constant supply of oxygen and nutrients, and the cells must also remove metabolic wastes. The smallest and thinnest animals meet this requirement by simple diffusion between their body surface and the environment. But this system is usually insufficient for larger animals. **Most complex animals move blood through their bodies using one or more hearts and either an open or closed circulatory system.** Both types of circulatory systems are shown in **Figure 29–10.**

Open Circulatory Systems
In an **open circulatory system,** blood is only partially contained within a system of blood vessels. Instead, one or more hearts or heartlike organs pump blood through blood vessels into a system of sinuses, or spongy cavities. The blood comes in direct contact with the tissues and eventually makes its way back to the heart. Open circulatory systems are characteristic of arthropods and most mollusks.

Closed Circulatory Systems
In a **closed circulatory system,** a heart or heartlike organ forces blood through vessels that extend throughout the body. The blood stays within these blood vessels. Materials reach body tissues by diffusing across the walls of the blood vessels. Closed circulatory systems are characteristic of larger, more active animals. Because blood trapped within the blood vessels is kept at high pressure, it can be circulated more efficiently than in an open circulatory system. Among the invertebrates, closed circulatory systems are found in annelids and some mollusks.

✔ CHECKPOINT *Why are closed circulatory systems more efficient than open circulatory systems?*

Excretion

Multicellular animals, whether they are aquatic or terrestrial, must control the amount of water in their tissues. At the same time, all animals must get rid of ammonia, a toxic nitrogenous (nitrogen-containing) waste produced as a result of metabolism. Ammonia (NH_3) results from the breakdown of amino acids. **Most animals have an excretory system that rids the body of metabolic wastes while controlling the amount of water in the tissues.** The excretory systems of invertebrates carry out these functions in a variety of ways, as shown in **Figure 29–11.**

Aquatic Invertebrates In aquatic invertebrates such as sponges, cnidarians, and some roundworms, ammonia diffuses from their body tissues into the surrounding water. The water immediately dilutes the ammonia and carries it away.

If freshwater invertebrates did not continually rid their bodies of excess water, they would swell up like water balloons. Flatworms use a network of flame cells to eliminate excess water. Fluid travels through execretory tubules and leaves the body through tiny pores in the animal's skin.

Terrestrial Invertebrates Terrestrial invertebrates must conserve body water while removing nitrogenous wastes from the body. To do this, many animals convert ammonia into a compound called urea, which is much less toxic than ammonia. Urea is eliminated from the body in urine. Urine is highly concentrated, so little water is lost. In annelids and mollusks, urine forms in tubelike structures called nephridia. Fluid enters the nephridia through openings called nephrostomes. Urine leaves the body through excretory pores.

Some insects and arachnids have Malpighian tubules, saclike organs that convert ammonia into uric acid. Uric acid is much less toxic than ammonia. Both uric acid and digestive wastes combine to form a thick paste that leaves the body through a structure called the rectum. Because the paste contains little water, this process also reduces water loss.

▼ **Figure 29–11** Most animals dispose of wastes through excretory systems. Excretory systems also control an organism's water levels. Flatworms excrete ammonia directly into the water and use flame cells to remove excess water. Annelids use nephridia to convert ammonia into urea and to concentrate it in urine. Some arthropods have Malpighian tubules, which convert ammonia into uric acid. Uric acid is eliminated from the body in a paste.

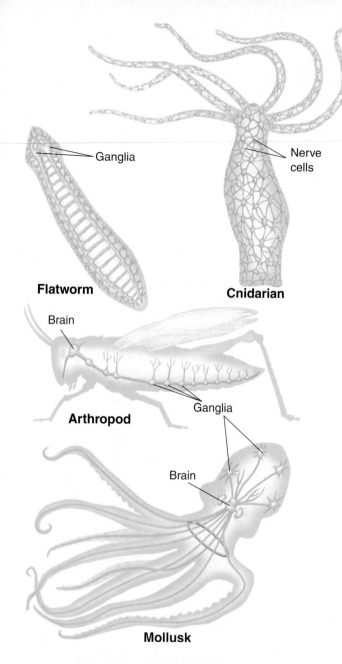

Ganglia

Nerve cells

Flatworm

Cnidarian

Brain

Arthropod

Ganglia

Brain

Mollusk

▲ **Figure 29–12** Invertebrate nervous systems have different degrees of centralization, cephalization, and specialization. Cnidarians have a simple nerve net. Flatworms, whose nervous systems are more centralized, have small ganglia in their heads. Arthropods and cephalopod mollusks have a centralized brain and specialized sensory organs.

Response

Nervous systems gather and process information from the environment and allow animals to respond appropriately. **Figure 29–12** shows the nervous system of four invertebrates. ⚷ **Invertebrates show three trends in the evolution of the nervous system: centralization, cephalization, and specialization.** Different nervous systems have various degrees of each of these characteristics.

Centralization and Cephalization
The simplest nervous systems, found in cnidarians, are called nerve nets. Nerve nets consist of individual nerve cells that form a netlike arrangement throughout the animal's body. In flatworms and roundworms, the nerve cells are more concentrated, or centralized. There are a few small clumps of nerve tissue, or ganglia, in the head. In cephalopod mollusks and arthropods, ganglia are organized into a brain that controls and coordinates the nervous system. This concentration of nerve tissue and organs in one end of the body is called cephalization.

Specialization
The more complex an animal's nervous system is, the more developed its sense organs tend to be. Flatworms, for example, have simple eyespots that detect only the presence of light. More complex animals, such as insects, have eyes that detect motion and color and form images. Complex animals may have a variety of specialized sense organs that detect light, sound, chemicals, movement, and even electricity to help them discover what is happening around them.

✓ **CHECKPOINT** *What is a nerve net?*

Movement and Support

Most animals use specialized tissues called muscles to move, breathe, pump blood, and perform other life functions. Muscles work by contracting, or becoming shorter. This is the only way that muscle tissue can generate force. When they are not stimulated, muscles relax. In most animals, muscles work together with some sort of skeletal system that provides firm support. ⚷ **Invertebrates have one of three main kinds of skeletal systems: hydrostatic skeletons, exoskeletons, or endoskeletons.**

Hydrostatic Skeletons
Some invertebrates, such as annelids and certain cnidarians, have **hydrostatic skeletons,** shown in **Figure 29–13.** In these animals, muscles surround a fluid-filled body cavity that supports the muscles. When the muscles contract, they push against fluid in the body cavity, causing the body to change shape.

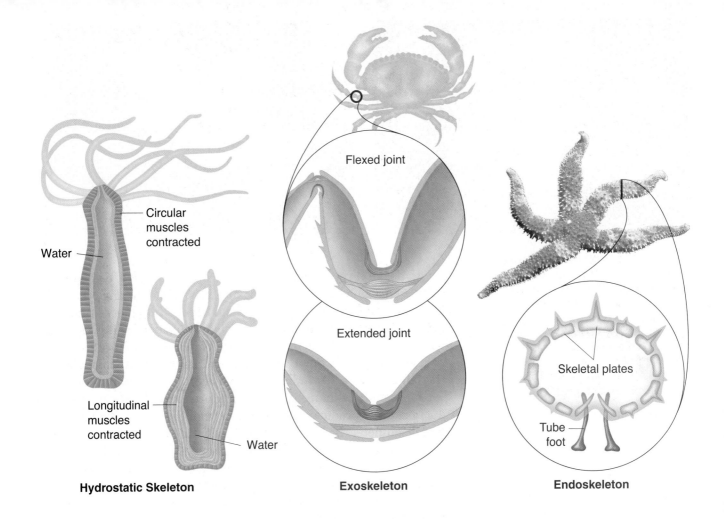

Hydrostatic Skeleton

Circular muscles contracted

Water

Longitudinal muscles contracted

Water

Exoskeleton

Flexed joint

Extended joint

Endoskeleton

Skeletal plates

Tube foot

Exoskeletons In arthropods, the **exoskeleton,** or external skeleton, is a hard body covering made of chitin. Arthropods move by using muscles that are attached to the inside of the exoskeleton. These muscles bend and straighten different joints. The shells of some mollusks can also be considered exoskeletons. Muscles attached to the shell make it possible for snails to withdraw into their shells and for bivalves to close.

Endoskeletons An **endoskeleton** is a structural support located inside the body. Sea stars and other echinoderms have an endoskeleton made of calcified plates. These plates function in support and protection, and also give these animals a bumpy and irregular texture. Vertebrates' bones are also endoskeletons.

Reproduction

Most invertebrates reproduce sexually during at least part of their life cycle. Depending on environmental conditions, however, many invertebrates may also reproduce asexually. Each form of reproduction has advantages and disadvantages. Asexual reproduction allows animals to reproduce rapidly and take advantage of favorable conditions in the environment. Sexual reproduction, however, maintains genetic diversity in a population by creating individuals with new combinations of genes.

▲ **Figure 29–13** The three main types of invertebrate skeletons are hydrostatic skeletons, exoskeletons, and endoskeletons. In animals with hydrostatic skeletons, muscles contract against a fluid-filled body cavity. In animals with exoskeletons, the muscles pull against the insides of the exoskeleton. Echinoderms and some sponges have endoskeletons.

Figure 29–14 Invertebrates may reproduce asexually or sexually. Note that the largest sea anemone in this group is undergoing asexual reproduction by splitting into two parts (left). The *Acorpora* coral (right) is releasing brown eggs into the water. The eggs will be fertilized externally. This is an example of sexual reproduction.

In asexual reproduction, all offspring produced are genetically identical to the parent. Asexual reproduction may occur by fragmentation, in which an organism breaks into pieces that grow into new individuals. It may also occur by budding, in which new individuals are produced from outgrowths of the parent's body wall. Some animals, such as the sea anemone on the left in **Figure 29–14,** reproduce asexually by dividing in two.

Most multicellular animals reproduce sexually. Sexual reproduction is the production of offspring from the fusion of male and female gametes. Most animals have separate sexes, meaning that an individual produces either sperm or eggs. But some animals, including certain mollusks and annelids, are hermaphrodites, or individual animals that can produce both sperm and eggs.

Sperm and eggs may meet in two different ways. In **external fertilization,** eggs are fertilized outside the female's body. Adults may release sperm and eggs into the surrounding water, and the sperm swim to the eggs and fertilize them. In **internal fertilization,** eggs are fertilized inside the female's body. Males typically use specialized organs to deposit sperm inside the female's reproductive tract.

29–2 Section Assessment

1. **Key Concept** In your own words, describe the evolution of three different body systems of invertebrates.

2. Compare circulation in annelids and arthropods.

3. What are the three main kinds of skeleton systems in invertebrates?

4. Compare asexual and sexual reproduction. What are the advantages and disadvantages of each?

5. **Critical Thinking Applying Concepts** List the three forms of nitrogenous wastes excreted by animals. How are the ways in which animals dispose of these wastes related to each animal's environment?

iTEXT Assessment Use iText to review the important concepts in Section 29–2.

Take It to the NET

Many invertebrates live in marine ecosystems. Choose one species of marine invertebrate to research. Then present your findings. Include a description and photograph of the animal, its species and common name, phylum, and habitat. Use the links provided in the Biology area at the Prentice Hall Web site for help in completing this activity: **www.phschool.com**

Comparing Invertebrate Responses to Stimuli

The responses of animals to stimuli depend on their nervous systems. In this investigation, you will design experiments to test the responses of three invertebrates to touch and food.

Problem   How do the responses of invertebrates relate to the structures of their nervous systems?

Materials

- dropper pipette
- hydra culture
- watch glass
- dissecting microscope
- blunt metal probe
- planarian
- petri dish
- crayfish
- brine shrimp
- cooked egg yolk
- slice of bologna

Skills   Formulating Hypotheses, Observing

Design Your Experiment

1. Use a dropper pipette to transfer a hydra and some water to the center of a watch glass or petri dish.

2. Place the watch glass or petri dish on the stage of a dissecting microscope and observe the hydra's movements for a few minutes.

3. With a blunt metal probe, gently touch one of the hydra's tentacles from several directions. Observe and record the hydra's responses. Return the hydra to its culture.

4. Design similar experiments to determine how a planarian and a crayfish respond to touch. Include touching both ends of each animal in your experimental plan.

5. Now design another set of experiments to determine how each animal will respond to food. Hydras will consume brine shrimp, planarians will eat cooked egg yolk, and crayfish will eat small pieces of bologna.

6. **Predicting** For each experiment you plan, write your prediction of the result. After your teacher approves your plan, carry out the experiments you have designed. Handle and touch the animals gently at all times. Record your observations. **CAUTION:** *Wash your hands before leaving the lab.*

Analyze and Conclude

1. **Comparing and Contrasting** Describe how each animal responded to touch. How were the responses of the animals related to the direction from which they were touched? What, if any, were the differences among the animals?

2. **Drawing Conclusions** Which animal displayed the most specific response to touch? Explain your answer in terms of the animals' nervous systems.

3. **Comparing and Contrasting** Describe how each animal responded to its food. Did your results support your hypothesis? How do each animal's responses relate to the structure of its nervous system?

4. **Drawing Conclusions** Which of these animals shows cephalization? Explain how your answer relates to each animal's behavior.

Go Further

Designing Experiments Design similar experiments using other invertebrates such as sponges, or earthworms. Obtain your teacher's permission before carrying out the experiments.

29–1 Invertebrate Evolution

 Key Concepts

- As animals became larger and more complex, specialized cells joined together to form tissues, organs, and organ systems that work together to carry out complex functions.

- All invertebrates except sponges exhibit some type of body symmetry—either radial symmetry or bilateral symmetry.

- Invertebrates with cephalization can respond to the environment more quickly and in more sophisticated ways than can simpler invertebrates.

- Most invertebrates with bilateral symmetry also have segmented bodies. Over the course of evolution, different segments have often become specialized for specific functions.

- Most animal phyla have a true coelom that is lined completely with mesoderm.

- Worms, arthropods, and mollusks are protostomes, and echinoderms are deuterostomes.

Vocabulary
radial symmetry, p. 748
bilateral symmetry, p. 748
cephalization, p. 748
coelom, p. 749

29–2 Form and Function in Invertebrates

Key Concepts

- The simplest animals break down food primarily through intracellular digestion, whereas more complex animals use extracellular digestion.

- Respiratory organs have large surface areas that are in contact with the air or water. In order for diffusion to occur, these respiratory surfaces must be kept moist.

- Most complex animals move fluid through their bodies using one or more hearts and an open or closed circulatory system.

- Most animals have an excretory system that rids the body of metabolic wastes and controls the amount of water in their tissues.

- Invertebrates show three trends in the evolution of the nervous system: centralization, cephalization, and specialization.

- Invertebrates have one of three main kinds of skeletal systems: hydrostatic skeletons, exoskeletons, and endoskeletons.

- Most invertebrates reproduce sexually during at least part of their life cycle. Depending on environmental conditions, however, many invertebrates may also reproduce asexually.

Vocabulary
intracellular digestion, p. 751
extracellular digestion, p. 751
open circulatory system, p. 754
closed circulatory system, p. 754
hydrostatic skeleton, p. 756
exoskeleton, p. 757
endoskeleton, p. 757
external fertilization, p. 758
internal fertilization, p. 758

Thinking Visually
Create two flowcharts describing the steps in the digestion of food. One flowchart should describe digestion in a hydra. The second flowchart should describe digestion in an earthworm.

Chapter 29

Part A

Multiple Choice

For each statement or question, select the number of the word or expression that, of those given, best completes the statement or answers the question.

1 Roundworms are classified as
(1) acoelomates   (3) deuterostomes
(2) coelomates   (4) pseudocoelomates

2 Which animal relies primarily on intracellular digestion?
(1) sponge   (3) dragonfly
(2) clam   (4) earthworm

3 Grasshoppers possess several organ systems that help them effectively perform the same essential tasks as all other animals. Which of these organ systems is shown in the illustration below?
(1) digestive   (3) excretory
(2) circulatory (4) nervous

4 In order for the exchange of oxygen and carbon dioxide to take place, an animal's respiratory surfaces must be
(1) thin and moist
(2) thick and dry
(3) thick and moist
(4) thin and dry

5 Which statement best describes a closed circulatory system?
(1) The blood comes in direct contact with tissues.
(2) The blood remains within blood vessels.
(3) The blood empties into body cavities called sinuses.
(4) The blood does not transport oxygen.

6 Malpighian tubules convert nitrogenous wastes into
(1) urine   (3) uric acid
(2) ammonia (4) urea

7 The simplest type of nervous system, found in cnidarians, is called
(1) nerve net   (3) ganglia network
(2) motor neurons (4) sensory neurons

8 Which term best describes an individual animal that produces both sperm and eggs?
(1) gamete
(2) hermaphrodite
(3) bud
(4) fragment

9 During invertebrate evolution, which trend did *not* occur?
(1) specialization of cells
(2) loss of a true coelom
(3) segmentation of bodies
(4) cephalization

10 All animals have some form of body symmetry *except* for
(1) sponges (3) worms
(2) jellyfishes (4) arthropods

11 Which activity is most closely associated with the excretory system?
(1) supplying cells with oxygen and nutrients
(2) ridding the body of metabolic wastes
(3) exchanging oxygen and carbon dioxide with the environment
(4) gathering information from the environment

12 The concentration of nerve tissue and organs in one end of an animal's body is called
(1) cephalization (3) body symmetry
(2) segmentation (4) diffusion

13 Which groups of invertebrates have a mesoderm?
(1) jellyfishes and arthropods
(2) earthworms and echinoderms
(3) echinoderms and jellyfishes
(4) sponges and roundworms

Test-Taking Tip Before taking a standardized test, it helps to become familiar with the format of the test, including the different question types. One method for this is to complete practice tests, such as this one. Even if you have practiced for a standardized test, be sure to read the direction lines carefully before you begin.

Preparing for the
Living Environment Exam

Parts B and C

Multiple Choice and Extended Response

For those questions that ask you to select a response, choose the one that best completes the statement or answers the question. For all others follow the directions given.

Base your answers to questions 14 and 15 on the information and diagram below and on your knowledge of biology.

A biology student wanted to find out if changing the temperature of an earthworm's environment would result in a corresponding change in heart rate. The student decided to set up two containers of worms kept at different temperatures, as shown below. To determine the number of heartbeats per minute, the student removed one worm at a time from each container and counted heartbeats through a stereomicroscope.

Sample A:
At temperature
of worms' soil environment

Sample B:
In ice water

14 After examining the two containers of worms, it can be concluded that
(1) Sample A is the control
(2) Sample B is the control
(3) either sample can serve as the control
(4) this is not a controlled experiment

15 The student found that the worms in Sample A have a faster heart rate than the worms in Sample B. Based on this observation, an appropriate conclusion would be that
(1) the worms in Sample A are healthier than the worms in Sample B
(2) there is no relationship between body temperature and heart rate
(3) with a decrease in body temperature, there is a corresponding increase in heart rate
(4) with a decrease in body temperature, there is a corresponding decrease in heart rate

16 How does the organ system shown in the figure below function?

Your answer should include the following
• the name of the organ system
• the name of important structures that make up the organ system
• a description of how the organ system carries out an essential function of the organism

17 Describe the effect the development of specialized cells had on the evolution of invertebrates.

18 What is one major advantage of cephalization?

19 Compare the processes of intracellular digestion and extracellular digestion.

20 Explain why the development of a one-way digestive system was important in the evolution of animals.

21 Describe the two types of circulatory systems. Give an example of an animal that has each type.

22 Name the three forms of nitrogenous wastes excreted by animals.

23 State the three major trends observed in the evolution of invertebrate nervous systems.

24 Compare and contrast internal and external fertilization.

25 The excretory systems of terrestrial invertebrates, such as earthworms, convert ammonia into less toxic components. Explain why this conversion is unnecessary in small aquatic invertebrates, such as planarians.

26 The external surface of slugs is slimy. Describe two adaptive advantages of this characteristic.

27 State two characteristics that all invertebrate respiratory structures have in common.

Base your answers to questions 28 and 29 on the illustration below and your knowledge of biology.

Circular muscles contracted

Longitudinal muscles contracted

28 Name the type of skeleton illustrated in the diagrams.

29 Describe how this type of skeleton functions.

30 No matter where they live, all animals need to control the amount of water within their bodies as well as eliminate ammonia—a toxic nitrogenous waste. How are invertebrates able to perform these functions, especially when they inhabit terrestrial environments?

31 What might have happened to the evolution of animals if segmentation had not occurred?

32 Predict what might happen if a flatworm's flame cells were damaged.

33 Write one or more paragraphs that compare the two methods of reproduction, asexual and sexual. Your answer should include
• one similarity between the two methods
• one difference between the two methods
• one example of an organism that reproduces by asexual reproduction
• one example of an organism that reproduces by sexual reproduction

34 Almost all animals exhibit some type of body symmetry. Describe the major forms of body symmetry seen in invertebrates. In your description, be sure to include
• the name of each type of symmetry
• a description of the advantages provided by each type of symmetry
• an example of an organism exhibiting each type of symmetry

35 The terms *acoelomate, pseudocoelomate,* and *coelomate* represent three different body plans of organisms. Compare these three body plans. In your comparison, be sure to
• describe how the body plans are similar
• describe how the body plans are different
• provide an example of a group of organisms that exhibits each body plan
• mention how the mesoderm is involved

36 A key concept in the study of biology is that respiratory organs must have large surface areas that are in contact with the air or water. These surfaces must be moist so that diffusion can occur. Describe two types of respiratory structures found in invertebrates. In your descriptions be sure to
• explain how gas exchange occurs
• explain whether organisms with each type of system are terrestrial or aquatic
• name a group of organisms that possesses each type of system

37 Animals with cephalization have sense organs concentrated in the anterior end. State two things these animals can do that would be impossible for animals that lack cephalization.

Take It to the NET

What kinds of organisms lived in the area of the Burgess Shale over 500 million years ago? Visit the Prentice Hall Web site at **www.phschool.com** to see artists' recreations of some Burgess Shale creatures, along with photographs of the fossils. Then, answer the following questions:
• Who discovered the Burgess Shale fossils, and when did the discovery occur?
• How do the Burgess Shale fossils differ from most other Cambrian deposits?
• What unique and unusual characteristics are attributed to the organisms called *Opabinia?*

► The greater bulldog bat (*Noctilio leporinus*), which is found in Mexico, Argentina, Brazil, and the Bahamas, is one of only a few bat species that catch and eat fish.

What do we know about chordates?

- There are more species of fishes than all other groups of chordates combined.

- The earliest mammals evolved at about the same time as the early dinosaurs but remained in the shadows until those great reptiles disappeared.

- The arms, legs, wings, and flippers of all four-limbed vertebrates are supported by different versions of the same bones.

What discoveries lie in the future?

- What, exactly, killed the dinosaurs?

- What combination of factors enabled the first vertebrates to leave the water for the land?

- What environmental factors are causing a decline in the populations of amphibians, reptiles, and birds? How can these organisms be protected?

- How do so many fishes, birds, and reptiles navigate thousands of kilometers in their migrations?

KEEP CURRENT WITH . . .

SCIENCE NEWS®

Find out more about topics in this unit:
www.phschool.com

30 Nonvertebrate Chordates, Fishes, and Amphibians

Many species of fish swim together in large groups called schools. This school of double-saddle butterflyfish lives in the tropical Pacific Ocean.

Inquiry Activity

Is a lancelet a fish?

Procedure

1. Closely examine a fish, using a hand lens if you like. Also look at a dissected fish. Record your observations. Make a list of what you think are the main characteristics of fishes.

2. Now, closely examine a preserved lancelet and a dissected lancelet. Make a list of the characteristics of lancelets.

Think About It

1. **Comparing and Contrasting** How are the fish and the lancelet similar? How are they different from each other?

2. **Classifying** Not all fishes have jaws or scales. Given this information, do you think the lancelet is a type of fish? Explain your answer.

30–1 The Chordates

At first glance, fishes, amphibians, reptiles, birds, and mammals appear to be very different from one another. Some have feathers; others have fins. Some fly; others swim or crawl. These variations are some of the characteristics that biologists use to separate these animals into different classes, yet all are members of the phylum Chordata (kawr-DAHT-uh).

What Is a Chordate?

Members of the phylum Chordata are called **chordates** (KAWR-dayts). To be classified as a chordate, an animal must have four key characteristics, although these characteristics need not be present during the entire life cycle. **A chordate is an animal that has, for at least some stage of its life, a dorsal, hollow nerve cord; a notochord; pharyngeal (fuh-RIN-jee-ul) pouches; and a tail that extends beyond the anus.** Refer to **Figure 30–1** as you read about each of these characteristics.

The hollow nerve cord runs along the dorsal (back) part of the body. Nerves branch from this cord at regular intervals and connect to internal organs, muscles, and sense organs.

The **notochord** is a long supporting rod that runs through the body just below the nerve cord. Most chordates have a notochord only when they are embryos.

Pharyngeal pouches are paired structures in the throat (pharynx) region. In some chordates—such as fishes and amphibians—slits develop that connect the pharyngeal pouches to the outside of the body. These slits may then develop into gills that are used for gas exchange.

At some point in their lives, all chordates have a tail that extends beyond the anus. The tail can contain bone and muscle and is used in swimming by many aquatic species.

CHECKPOINT *What is a notochord?*

Guide for Reading

Key Concepts
- What characteristics do all chordates share?
- What are the two groups of nonvertebrate chordates?

Vocabulary
chordate
notochord
pharyngeal pouch
vertebra

Reading Strategy: Building Vocabulary
Before you read, preview new vocabulary by skimming the section and making a list of the boldfaced terms. As you read, make notes next to each term.

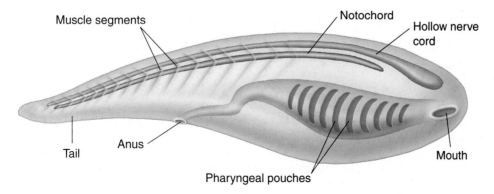

◀ **Figure 30–1** All chordates share four characteristics: a dorsal, hollow nerve cord; a notochord; pharyngeal pouches; and a tail that extends beyond the anus. Some chordates possess all these characteristics as adults; others, only as embryos.

Nonvertebrate Chordates, Fishes, and Amphibians **767**

Most Chordates Are Vertebrates

The diagram in **Figure 30–2** shows the current understanding of how chordates are related. More than 99 percent of all chordates are placed in the subphylum Vertebrata and are called vertebrates. A vertebrate is a chordate that has a strong supporting structure known as the vertebral column, or backbone. In vertebrates, the dorsal, hollow nerve cord is called the spinal cord. As a vertebrate embryo develops, the front end of the spinal cord grows into a brain. The backbone, which replaces the notochord in most developing vertebrates, is made of individual segments called **vertebrae** (singular: vertebra) that enclose and protect the spinal cord.

A vertebrate's backbone is part of an endoskeleton, or internal skeleton. Like an arthropod's exoskeleton, a vertebrate's endoskeleton supports and protects the animal's body and gives muscles a place to attach. However, unlike an arthropod's exoskeleton, a vertebrate's skeleton grows as the animal grows and does not need to be shed periodically. In addition, whereas an arthropod's skeleton is made entirely of nonliving material, a vertebrate's skeleton contains living cells as well as nonliving material. The cells produce the nonliving material in the skeleton.

✓**CHECKPOINT** *What is the function of the vertebral column?*

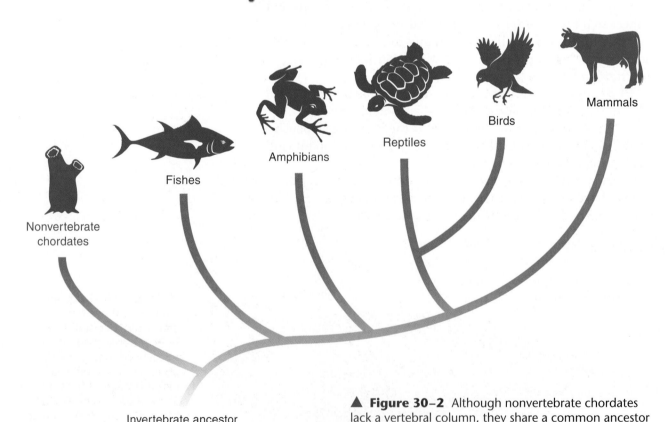

Nonvertebrate chordates

Fishes

Amphibians

Reptiles

Birds

Mammals

Invertebrate ancestor

▲ **Figure 30–2** Although nonvertebrate chordates lack a vertebral column, they share a common ancestor with vertebrates. **Interpreting Graphics** *To which other vertebrate group are birds most closely related?*

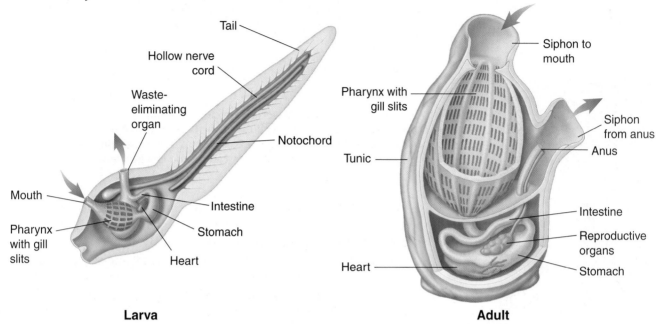

▼ Figure 30–3 ☀ Tunicates are one of two groups of nonvertebrate chordates. The tadpole-shaped tunicate larva (left) has all four chordate characteristics. When most tunicate larvae grow into adults, they lose their tails and attach to a solid surface. Adult tunicates (right) look nothing like the larvae, or even like other adult chordates. Both larvae and adults are filter feeders. The blue arrows show where water enters and leaves the tunicate's body.

Larva

Tail
Hollow nerve cord
Waste-eliminating organ
Notochord
Mouth
Intestine
Pharynx with gill slits
Stomach
Heart

Adult

Siphon to mouth
Pharynx with gill slits
Siphon from anus
Tunic
Anus
Intestine
Reproductive organs
Heart
Stomach

Nonvertebrate Chordates

There are two subphyla of chordates that do not have backbones. ☀ **The two groups of nonvertebrate chordates are tunicates and lancelets.** Both are soft-bodied marine organisms. Like all chordates, these animals have a hollow nerve cord, a notochord, pharyngeal pouches, and a tail at some stage of their life cycle.

In some ways, studying nonvertebrate chordates is like using a time machine to investigate the ancestors of our own subphylum, Vertebrata. Similarities in structure and embryological development indicate that vertebrates and nonvertebrate chordates evolved from a common ancestor. Fossil evidence from the Cambrian Period places this divergence at more than 550 million years ago. Although they seem to be simple animals, tunicates and lancelets are relatives of ours—very distant ones.

Tunicates Filter-feeding tunicates (subphylum Urochordata) certainly do not look as if they are related to us. **Figure 30–3** shows the body structure of a tunicate larva and an adult. Observe that the larval form has all of the chordate characteristics. In contrast, adult tunicates, like the ones in **Figure 30–4,** have neither a notochord nor a tail.

▲ Figure 30–4 Tunicates get their name from the adult's body covering—the tough, nonliving tunic. Most tunicates are commonly known as sea squirts, because of the stream of water they sometimes eject. **Inferring** *In what kind of ecosystem are you likely to find tunicates?*

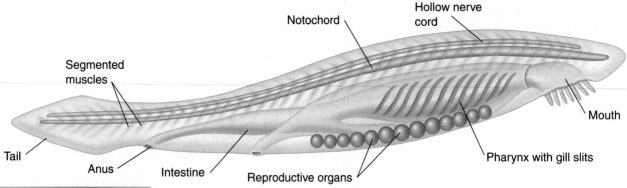

Notochord
Hollow nerve cord
Segmented muscles
Mouth
Tail
Anus
Intestine
Reproductive organs
Pharynx with gill slits

Figure 30–5 Lancelets are small nonvertebrate chordates that often live with their bodies half-buried in sand. Because lancelets do not have fins or legs, they can move only by contracting the paired muscles on their bodies. **Interpreting Graphics** *Which chordate characteristics do lancelets have?*

Lancelets The small, fishlike creatures called lancelets form the subphylum Cephalochordata. Lancelets live on the sandy ocean bottom. You can see a lancelet's body structure in **Figure 30–5.** Observe that, unlike an adult tunicate, an adult lancelet has a definite head region that contains a mouth. The mouth opens into a long pharynx with up to 100 pairs of gill slits. As water passes through the pharynx, a sticky mucus catches food particles. The lancelet then swallows the mucus into the digestive tract. Lancelets use gills in the pharynx for gas exchange. In addition, lancelets are thin enough to exchange gases through their body surface.

Lancelets have a closed circulatory system. They do not have a true heart. Instead, the walls of the major blood vessels contract to push blood through the body. The fishlike motion of lancelets results from contracting muscles that are organized into V-shaped units. The muscle units are paired on either side of the body.

30–1 Section Assessment

1. 🔑 **Key Concept** Describe four characteristics of chordates.

2. 🔑 **Key Concept** How do lancelets and tunicates differ?

3. What one characteristic distinguishes vertebrates from the other chordates?

4. Which characteristics of nonvertebrate chordates suggest that they developed from the same ancestor as vertebrates?

5. **Critical Thinking Inferring** How would a free-swimming larval stage be an advantage for tunicates?

🧍 **iTEXT Assessment** Use iText to review the important concepts in Section 30–1.

30–2 Fishes

If you think of Earth as land, then the name "Earth" is not particularly appropriate for the planet on which you live, for more than two thirds of its surface is water. And almost anywhere there is water—fresh or salt—there are fishes. At the edge of the ocean, blennies jump from rock to rock and occasionally dunk themselves in tide pools. Beneath the Arctic ice live fishes whose bodies contain a biological antifreeze that keeps them from freezing solid. In some shallow desert streams, pupfishes tolerate temperatures that would cook almost any other animal.

What Is a Fish?

You might think that with such extreme variations in habitat, fishes would be difficult to characterize. However, describing a fish is a rather simple task. **Fishes are aquatic vertebrates that are characterized by paired fins, scales, and gills.** Fins are used for movement, scales for protection, and gills for exchanging gases. You can observe most of those characteristics in **Figure 30–6.**

Fishes are so varied, however, that for almost every general statement there are exceptions. For example, some fishes, such as catfish, do not have scales. One reason for the enormous diversity among living fishes is that these chordates belong to very different classes. Thus, many fishes—sharks, lampreys, and perch, for example—are no more similar to one another than humans are to frogs!

✓ CHECKPOINT) *What are the basic functions of fins, scales, and gills?*

Guide for Reading

🔑 **Key Concepts**
• What are the basic characteristics of a fish?
• What were the important developments during the evolution of fishes?
• How are fishes adapted for life in water?
• What are the three main groups of fishes?

Vocabulary
• cartilage • atrium • ventricle
• cerebrum • cerebellum
• medulla oblongata
• lateral line system
• swim bladder • oviparous
• ovoviviparous • viviparous

Reading Strategy: Using Prior Knowledge
Before you read, make a list of the things you already know about fishes. After you have finished reading, check the list. Correct any errors and add new facts.

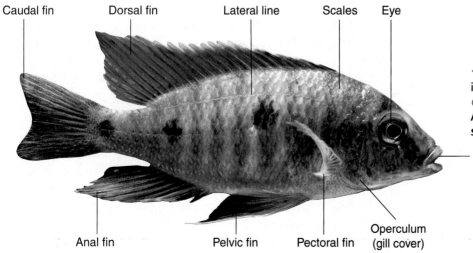

Caudal fin   Dorsal fin   Lateral line   Scales   Eye

◀ **Figure 30–6** Fishes come in many shapes and sizes. 🔑 Like most fishes, this African cichlid has paired fins, scales, and gills.

Mouth

Anal fin   Pelvic fin   Pectoral fin   Operculum (gill cover)

Pteraspis

Trilobite (an arthropod)

Doryaspis

Hemicyclaspis

▲ **Figure 30–7** Ancient jawless fishes swam in shallow seas during the early Devonian Period, about 400 million years ago. Lacking jaws, early jawless fishes were limited in their ability to feed and to defend themselves against predators. ⚷ The evolution of paired fins, however, gave these fishes more control over their movement in the water.

Evolution of Fishes

Fishes were the first vertebrates to evolve. They did not arise directly from tunicates or lancelets, but fishes and nonvertebrate chordates probably did evolve from common invertebrate ancestors. During the course of their evolution, fishes underwent several important changes. ⚷ **The evolution of jaws and the evolution of paired fins were important developments during the rise of fishes.**

The First Fishes The earliest fishes to appear in the fossil record were odd-looking, jawless creatures whose bodies were armored with bony plates. They lived in the oceans during the late Cambrian Period, about 510 million years ago. Fishes kept this armored, jawless body plan for 100 million years.

The Age of Fishes During the Ordovician and Silurian Periods, about 505 to 410 million years ago, fishes underwent a major adaptive radiation. The species to emerge from the radiation ruled the seas during the Devonian Period, which is often called the Age of Fishes. Some of these fishes were jawless species that had very little armor. These jawless fishes were the ancestors of modern hagfishes and lampreys. Others, such as those in **Figure 30–7,** were armored and ultimately became extinct at the end of the Devonian Period, about 360 million years ago.

The Arrival of Jaws and Paired Fins Still other ancient fishes kept their bony armor and possessed a feeding adaptation that would revolutionize vertebrate evolution: These fishes had jaws. Observe the powerful jaws of the ancient fish in **Figure 30–8.** Jaws are an extremely useful adaptation. Jawless fishes are limited to eating small particles of food that they filter out of the water or suck up like a vacuum cleaner. Because jaws can hold teeth and muscles, jaws make it possible for vertebrates to nibble on plants and munch on other animals. Thus, animals with jaws can eat a much wider variety of food. They can also defend themselves by biting.

The evolution of jaws in early fishes accompanied the evolution of paired pectoral (anterior) and pelvic (posterior) fins. These fins were attached to girdles—structures of cartilage (KAHR-tl-ij) or bone that support the fins. **Cartilage** is a strong tissue that supports the body and is softer and more flexible than bone. **Figure 30–9** shows the fins and fin girdles in one ancient fish species.

Paired fins gave fishes more control of body movement. In addition, tail fins and powerful muscles gave fishes greater thrust when swimming. The combination of accuracy and speed enabled fishes to move in new and varied patterns. This ability, in turn, helped fishes use their jaws in complex ways.

The Rise of Modern Fishes Although the early jawed fishes soon disappeared, they left behind two major groups that continued to evolve and still survive today. One group—the ancestors of modern sharks and rays—evolved a skeleton made of strong, resilient cartilage. The other group evolved skeletons made of true bone. A subgroup of bony fishes, called lobe-finned fishes, had fleshy fins from which the limbs of chordates would later evolve.

✓ CHECKPOINT *Which two groups of early jawed fishes still survive today?*

▲ **Figure 30–8** This photograph shows a reconstruction of an ancient armored fish called *Dunkleosteus,* an enormous predator that lived in the inland seas of North America during the late Devonian Period. **Drawing Conclusions** *What feature made this fish a successful predator in its time?*

▼ **Figure 30–9** This ancient Devonian fish is called *Eusthenopteron.* Although its skeleton differs from those of most modern fishes, its basic features—vertebral column, fins, and fin girdles—have been retained in many species. **Comparing and Contrasting** *How does this fish differ from the fishes in* **Figure 30–7?**

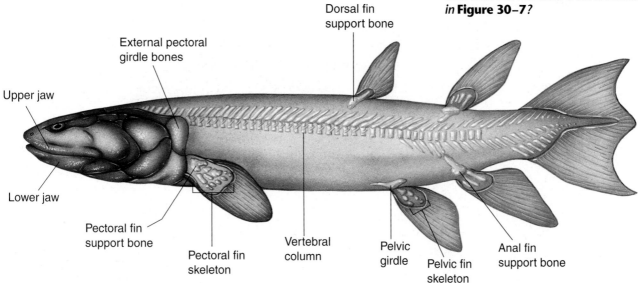

Dorsal fin
support bone

External pectoral
girdle bones

Upper jaw

Lower jaw

Pectoral fin
support bone

Pectoral fin
skeleton

Vertebral
column

Pelvic
girdle

Pelvic fin
skeleton

Anal fin
support bone

Nonvertebrate Chordates, Fishes, and Amphibians **773**

▲ **Figure 30–10** 🔵Adaptations to aquatic life include various modes of feeding. This deep-sea anglerfish has a built-in "fishing pole" that it uses to attract prey.

Form and Function in Fishes

Over time, fishes have evolved to survive in a tremendous range of aquatic environments. 🔵**Adaptations to aquatic life include various modes of feeding, specialized structures for gas exchange, and paired fins for locomotion.** Fishes have other types of adaptations, too, as you will learn.

Feeding Every mode of feeding is seen in fishes. There are herbivores, carnivores, parasites, filter feeders, and detritus feeders. In fact, a single fish may exhibit several modes of feeding, depending on what type of food happens to be available. Certain carp, for example, eat algae, aquatic plants, worms, mollusks, arthropods, dead fish, and detritus. Other fishes, such as barracuda, are highly specialized carnivores. A few fishes, such as some lampreys, are parasites. **Figure 30–10** shows a fish that even uses a fleshy bait to catch its meals!

Use **Figure 30–11** to locate the internal organs that are important during the fish's digestion of its food. From the fish's mouth, food passes through a short tube called the esophagus to the stomach, where it is partially broken down. In many fishes, the food is further processed in fingerlike pouches called pyloric ceca (py-LAWR-ik SEE-kuh; singular: cecum). The pyloric ceca secrete digestive enzymes and absorb nutrients from the digested food. Other organs, including the liver and pancreas, add enzymes and other digestive chemicals to the food as it moves through the digestive tract. The intestine completes the process of digestion and nutrient absorption. Any undigested material is eliminated through the anus.

▼ **Figure 30–11** The internal organs of a typical bony fish are shown here. **Applying Concepts** *What is the function of the pyloric cecum?*

Quick Lab

How do fishes use gills?

Materials fish food, food coloring, plastic cup, dropper pipette, live fish in an aquarium

Procedure

1. Mix some fish food and food coloring in a small volume of aquarium water in a plastic cup.
2. Use a dropper pipette to release the mixture near a fish in an aquarium. Release the mixture gently so that it does not scatter.
3. Observe what happens when the fish approaches the mixture. Watch the fish's gills especially closely.

Analyze and Conclude

1. **Drawing Conclusions** Describe what happened to the food coloring. What does this tell you about how water moves through a fish's body?
2. **Inferring** Why do most fishes seem to move or swallow continuously? What might happen if a fish were not able to move or stopped "swallowing"?

Respiration Most fishes exchange gases using gills located on either side of the pharynx. The gills are made up of feathery, threadlike structures called filaments. Each filament contains a network of fine capillaries that provides a large surface area for the exchange of oxygen and carbon dioxide. Fishes that exchange gases using gills do so by pulling oxygen-rich water in through their mouths, pumping it over their gill filaments, and then pushing oxygen-poor water out through openings in the sides of the pharynx.

Some fishes, such as lampreys and sharks, have several gill openings. Most fishes, however, have a single gill opening on each side of the body through which water is pumped out. This opening is hidden beneath a protective bony cover called the operculum.

A number of fishes—such as the lungfish in **Figure 30–12**—have an adaptation that allows them to survive in oxygen-poor water or in areas where bodies of water often dry up. These fishes have specialized organs that serve as lungs. A tube brings oxygen from the air to this organ through the fish's mouth. Some lungfishes are so dependent on getting oxygen from the air that they will suffocate if prevented from reaching the surface of the water.

✓**CHECKPOINT** *What structures do fishes use for gas exchange?*

▶ **Figure 30–12** This African lungfish has a breathing adaptation that allows it to survive in shallow waters that are subject to drought. It burrows into mud, covers itself with mucus, and becomes dormant. For several months until the rains fall, the lungfish breathes through its mouth and lungs. **Drawing Conclusions** *How is it an advantage for this lungfish to cover itself with mucus?*

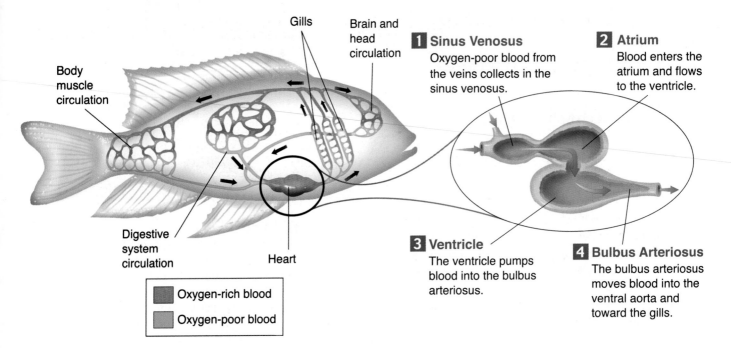

1 Sinus Venosus
Oxygen-poor blood from the veins collects in the sinus venosus.

2 Atrium
Blood enters the atrium and flows to the ventricle.

3 Ventricle
The ventricle pumps blood into the bulbus arteriosus.

4 Bulbus Arteriosus
The bulbus arteriosus moves blood into the ventral aorta and toward the gills.

Gills

Brain and head circulation

Body muscle circulation

Digestive system circulation

Heart

Oxygen-rich blood

Oxygen-poor blood

▲ **Figure 30–13** Blood circulates through a fish's body in a single loop—from the heart to the gills to the rest of the body, and then back to the heart again. **Interpreting Graphics** *Is the blood that flows from the heart to the gills rich in oxygen or does it lack oxygen?*

Circulation Fishes have closed circulatory systems with a heart that pumps blood around the body in a single loop—from the heart to the gills, from the gills to the rest of the body, and back to the heart. **Figure 30–13** shows the path of blood and the structure of the heart.

In most fishes, the heart consists of four parts: the sinus venosus (SYN-us vuh-NOH-sus), atrium (AY-tree-um), ventricle, and bulbus arteriosus (BUL-bus ahr-teer-ee-OH-sus). The sinus venosus is a thin-walled sac that collects blood from the fish's veins before it flows to the **atrium,** a large muscular chamber that serves as a one-way compartment for blood that is about to enter the ventricle. The **ventricle,** a thick-walled, muscular chamber, is the actual pumping portion of the heart. It pumps blood to a large, muscular tube called the bulbus arteriosus. At its front end, the bulbus arteriosus connects to a large blood vessel called the aorta, through which blood moves to the fish's gills.

Excretion Like many other aquatic animals, most fishes rid themselves of nitrogenous wastes in the form of ammonia. Some wastes diffuse through the gills into the surrounding water. Others are removed by kidneys, which are excretory organs that filter wastes from the blood.

Kidneys help fishes control the amount of water in their bodies. Fishes in salt water tend to lose water by osmosis. To solve this problem, the kidneys of marine fishes concentrate wastes and return as much water as possible to the body. In contrast, a great deal of water continually enters the bodies of freshwater fishes. The kidneys of freshwater fishes pump out plenty of dilute urine. Some fishes are able to move from fresh to salt water by adjusting their kidney function.

Response Fishes have well-developed nervous systems organized around a brain, which has several parts, as shown in **Figure 30–14.** The most anterior parts of a fish's brain are the olfactory bulbs, which are involved with the sense of smell, or olfaction. They are connected to the two lobes of the cerebrum (SEHR-uh-brum). In most vertebrates, the **cerebrum** is responsible for all voluntary activities of the body. However, in fishes, the cerebrum primarily processes the sense of smell. The optic lobes process information from the eyes. The **cerebellum** (sehr-uh-BEL-um) coordinates body movements. The **medulla oblongata** (mih-DUH-luh ahb-lahn-GAHT-uh) controls the functioning of many internal organs.

Most fishes have highly developed sense organs. Almost all fishes that are active in daylight have well-developed eyes and color vision that is at least as good as yours. Many fishes have specialized cells called chemoreceptors that are responsible for their extraordinary senses of taste and smell. Although most fishes have ears inside their head, they may not hear sounds well. Most fishes can, however, detect gentle currents and vibrations in the water with a sensitive receptor called the **lateral line system.** Fishes use this system to sense the motion of other fishes or prey swimming nearby. In addition to detecting motion, some fishes, such as catfish and sharks, have evolved sense organs that can detect low levels of electric current. Some fishes, such as the electric eel shown in **Figure 30–15,** can even generate their own electricity!

✓ **CHECKPOINT** *What are the parts of a fish's brain?*

Movement Most fishes move by alternately contracting paired sets of muscles on either side of the backbone. This creates a series of S-shaped curves that move down the fish's body. As each curve travels from the head toward the tail fin, it creates backward force on the surrounding water. This force, along with the action of the fins, propels the fish forward. The fins of fishes are also used in much the same way that airplanes use stabilizers, flaps, and rudders—to keep on course and adjust direction. Fins also increase the surface area of the tail, providing an extra boost of speed. The streamlined body shapes of most fishes help reduce the amount of drag (friction) as they move through the water.

Because their body tissues are more dense than the water they swim in, sinking is an issue for fishes. Many bony fishes have an internal, gas-filled organ called a **swim bladder** that adjusts their buoyancy. The swim bladder lies just beneath the backbone.

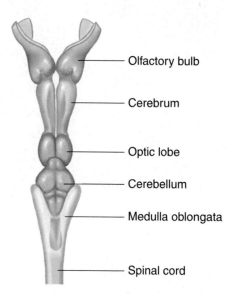

▲ **Figure 30–14** The brain of a fish, like all vertebrate brains, is situated at the anterior end of the spinal cord and has several different parts. **Inferring** *How might the size of the various parts of the brain differ in a blind cave fish that relies primarily on its sense of smell?*

Olfactory bulb

Cerebrum

Optic lobe

Cerebellum

Medulla oblongata

Spinal cord

▶ **Figure 30–15** The electric eel, *Electrophorus electricus,* can produce several hundred volts of electricity in brief bursts. **Formulating Hypotheses** *What function might such powerful electric bursts serve?*

▲ **Figure 30–16** Some newly hatched fishes, such as these coho salmon, are nourished by yolk sacs on their bellies. **Inferring** *What are the orange spheres at the bottom of the photograph?*

Reproduction The eggs of fishes are fertilized either externally or internally, depending on the species. In many fish species, the female lays the eggs and the embryos in the eggs develop and hatch outside her body. Fishes whose eggs hatch outside the mother's body are **oviparous** (oh-VIP-uh-rus). As the embryos of oviparous fishes develop, they obtain food from the yolk in the egg. The salmon in **Figure 30–16** are oviparous. In contrast, in **ovoviviparous** (oh-voh-vy-VIP-uh-rus) species, such as guppies, the eggs stay in the mother's body after internal fertilization. Each embryo develops inside its egg, using the yolk for nourishment. The young are then "born alive," the way the young of most mammals are. A few fish species, including several sharks, are viviparous. In **viviparous** (vy-VIP-uh-rus) animals, the embryos stay in the mother's body, as they do in ovoviviparous species. However, these embryos obtain the substances they need directly from the mother's body, not from material stored within an egg. The young of viviparous species are also born alive.

✓ CHECKPOINT *What are the three different modes of fish reproduction?*

Groups of Fishes

With over 24,000 living species, fishes are an extremely diverse group of chordates. These diverse species can be grouped according to body structure. 🔑 **When you consider their basic internal structure, all living fishes can be classified into three groups: jawless fishes, cartilaginous fishes, and bony fishes.**

Jawless Fishes As their name implies, jawless fishes have no true teeth or jaws. Their skeletons are made of fibers and cartilage. They lack vertebrae, and instead keep their notochords as adults. Modern jawless fishes are divided into two classes: lampreys and hagfishes.

Lampreys are typically filter feeders as larvae and parasites as adults. An adult lamprey's head is taken up almost completely by a circular sucking disk with a round mouth in the center, which you can see in **Figure 30–17.** Adult lampreys attach themselves to fishes, and occasionally to whales and dolphins. There, they scrape away at the skin with small toothlike structures that surround the mouth and with a strong, rasping tongue. The lamprey then sucks up the tissues and body fluids of its host.

Hagfishes have pinkish gray, wormlike bodies and four or six short tentacles around their mouths. Hagfishes lack eyes, although they do have light-detecting sensors scattered around their bodies. They feed on dead and dying fish by using a toothed tongue to scrape a hole into the fish's side. Hagfishes have other peculiar traits: They secrete incredible amounts of slime, have six hearts, possess an open circulatory system, and regularly tie themselves into knots!

Figure 30–17 🔎 Jawless fishes make up one of three major groups of living fishes. Modern jawless fishes are divided into two classes: lampreys (top) and hagfishes (bottom).

Sharks and Their Relatives The class Chondrichthyes (kahn-DRIK-theez) contains sharks, rays, skates, and a few uncommon fishes such as sawfishes and chimaeras. Some chondrichthyes are shown in **Figure 30–18.** *Chondros* is the Greek word for cartilage, so the name of this class tells you that the skeletons of these fishes are built entirely of cartilage, not bone. The cartilage of these animals is similar to the flexible tissue that supports your nose and your external ears. Most cartilaginous fishes also have toothlike scales covering their skin. These scales make shark skin so rough that it can be used as sandpaper.

Most of the 350 or so living shark species have large curved tails, torpedo-shaped bodies, and pointed snouts with the mouth underneath. One of the most noticeable characteristics of sharks is their enormous number of teeth. Many sharks have thousands of teeth arranged in several rows. As teeth in the front rows are worn out or lost, new teeth are continually replacing them. A shark goes through about 20,000 teeth in its lifetime!

Not all sharks have such fierce-looking teeth, however. Some, like the basking shark, are filter feeders with specialized feeding structures and teeth that are so small they are virtually useless. Other sharks have flat teeth adapted for crushing the shells of mollusks and crustaceans. Although there are a number of carnivorous sharks large enough to prey on humans, most sharks do not attack people.

Skates and rays are even more diverse in their feeding habits than their shark relatives. Some feed on bottom-dwelling invertebrates by using their mouths as powerful vacuums. However, the largest rays, like the largest sharks, are filter feeders that eat floating plankton. Skates and rays often glide through the sea with flapping motions of their large, winglike pectoral fins. When they are not feeding or swimming, many skates and rays cover themselves with a thin layer of sand and spend hours resting on the ocean floor.

▼ **Figure 30–18** Sharks and rays have skeletons that are made of cartilage. The large jaws and teeth of many sharks make them top predators in the world's oceans. **Applying Concepts** *How is the structure of a basking shark's mouth related to its diet?*

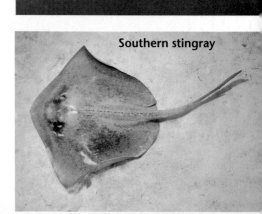
Basking shark

Southern stingray

Silky shark

FIGURE 30–19 DIVERSITY OF RAY-FINNED FISHES

Combtooth Blenny

Emperor Angelfish

Flying Fish

Peacock Flounder

Nearly all bony fishes belong to an enormous and diverse group called ray-finned fishes. These fishes have thin, bony spines that form the fins. **Observing** *What unusual adaptations do you see in each of these fishes?*

Leafy Sea Dragon

▲ **Figure 30–20** The coelacanth (genus *Latimeria*) is a lobe-finned fish that was thought to be extinct until one was caught in the Indian Ocean in 1938. Since then, many more specimens have been found. **Classifying** *Which group of living fishes is most closely related to the coelacanth?*

Bony Fishes Bony fishes make up the class Osteichthyes (ahs-tee-IK-theez). The skeletons of these fishes are made of hard, calcified tissue called bone. Almost all living bony fishes belong to a huge group called ray-finned fishes, some of which are shown in **Figure 30–19.** The name "ray-finned" refers to the slender bony spines, or rays, that are connected by a thin layer of skin to form the fins. The fin rays support the skin much as the thin rods in a handheld folding fan hold together the webbing of the fan.

Only seven living species of bony fishes are not classified as ray-finned fishes. These are the lobe-finned fishes, a subclass that includes lungfishes and the coelacanth (SEE-luh-kanth). Lungfishes live in fresh water, but the coelacanth, shown in **Figure 30–20,** lives in salt water. The fleshy fins of lobe-finned fishes have support bones that are more substantial than the rays of ray-finned fishes. Some of these bones are jointed, like the arms and legs of land vertebrates.

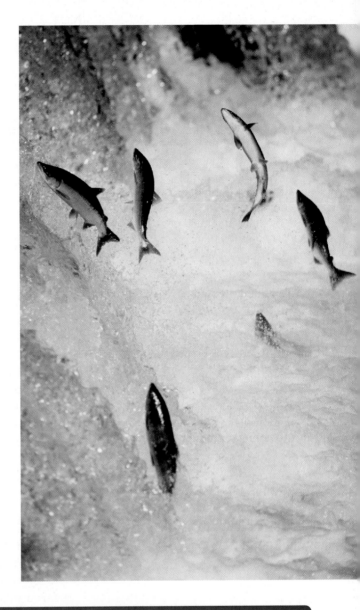

▶ **Figure 30–21** Adult salmon return from the sea to spawn in the stream or river in which they were born. Their journey is often long and strenuous. The salmon must swim upstream against the current and may even leap up waterfalls! **Applying Concepts** *What sense do the salmon use to find their home stream?*

Ecology of Fishes

Some fishes—such as lampreys, sturgeons, and salmon—spend most of their lives in the ocean but migrate to fresh water to breed. Fishes with this type of behavior are called anadromous (uh-NAH-druh-mus). Salmon, for example, begin their lives in rivers or streams but soon migrate to the sea. After one to four years at sea, mature salmon return to the place of their birth to spawn. This trip can take several months, covering as much as 3200 kilometers, and can involve incredible feats of strength, as shown in **Figure 30–21.** The adult salmon recognize their home stream using their sense of smell.

In contrast to anadromous fishes, some fishes live their lives in fresh water but migrate to the ocean to breed. These fishes are said to be catadromous (kuh-TAD-ruh-mus). European eels, for instance, live and feed in the rivers of North America and Europe. They travel up to 4800 kilometers to lay their eggs in the Sargasso Sea, in the North Atlantic Ocean. The eggs are carried by currents to shallow coastal waters. As they grow into young fish, the eels find their way to fresh water and migrate upstream.

30–2 Section Assessment

1. 🔑 **Key Concept** Identify the main characteristics of fishes.

2. 🔑 **Key Concept** What advantages do jaws and fins provide for fishes?

3. 🔑 **Key Concept** List four specific ways in which fishes are adapted for aquatic life.

4. 🔑 **Key Concept** Name the three main groups of fishes and give an example for each group.

5. Why might a scientist investigating evolutionary relationships study a coelacanth?

6. **Critical Thinking Applying Concepts** For fishes to survive in an aquarium, the water must be kept clean and well oxygenated. Explain why water quality is so important to a fish's survival.

🧍**TEXT** **Assessment** Use iText to review the important concepts in Section 30–2.

MAKING CONNECTIONS

Comparing and Contrasting In Chapter 27, you learned about the circulatory system of annelids. Create a Venn diagram comparing the circulatory system of an annelid with that of a fish. How are the two circulatory systems similar and different?

30–3 Amphibians

Guide for Reading

Key Concepts
- What is an amphibian?
- How are amphibians adapted for life on land?
- What are the main groups of living amphibians?

Vocabulary
cloaca
nictitating membrane
tympanic membrane

Reading Strategy:
Making Comparisons
As you read, write down similarities and differences between fishes and amphibians. Consider such characteristics as body structure, habitat, and method of reproduction.

Amphibians have survived for hundreds of millions of years, typically living in places where fresh water is plentiful. With over 4000 living species, amphibians are the only modern descendants of an ancient group that gave rise to all other land vertebrates.

What Is an Amphibian?

The word *amphibian* means "double life," emphasizing that these animals live both in water and on land. The larvae are fishlike aquatic animals that respire using gills. In contrast, the adults of most species of amphibians are terrestrial animals that respire using lungs and skin.

An amphibian is a vertebrate that, with some exceptions, lives in water as a larva and on land as an adult, breathes with lungs as an adult, has moist skin that contains mucus glands, and lacks scales and claws. In a sense, amphibians are to the animal kingdom what mosses and ferns are to the plant kingdom: They are descendants of ancestral organisms that evolved some—but not all—of the adaptations necessary for living entirely on land.

Evolution of Amphibians

The first amphibians to climb onto land probably resembled lobe-finned fishes similar to the modern coelacanth. However, the amphibians had legs, as shown in **Figure 30–22.** They appeared in the late Devonian Period, about 360 million years ago.

The transition from water to land involved more than just having legs and clambering out of the water. Vertebrates colonizing land habitats faced the same challenges that had to be overcome by invertebrates. Terrestrial vertebrates have to breathe air, protect themselves and their eggs from drying out, and support themselves against the pull of gravity.

◀ **Figure 30–22** Evolving in the swamplike tropical ecosystems of the Devonian Period, amphibians were the first chordates to live at least part of their lives on land. **Most amphibians live in water as larvae and on land as adults.**

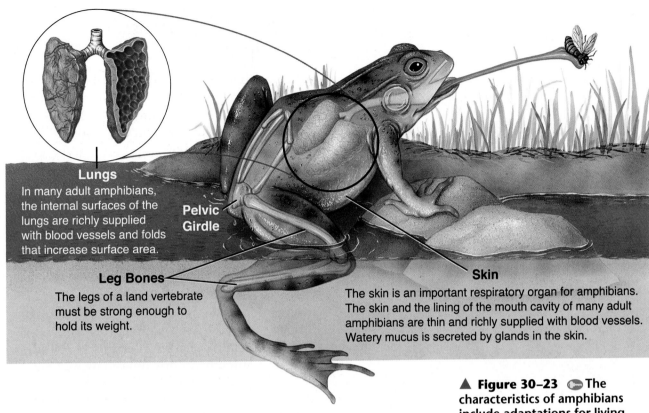

Lungs
In many adult amphibians, the internal surfaces of the lungs are richly supplied with blood vessels and folds that increase surface area.

Pelvic Girdle

Leg Bones
The legs of a land vertebrate must be strong enough to hold its weight.

Skin
The skin is an important respiratory organ for amphibians. The skin and the lining of the mouth cavity of many adult amphibians are thin and richly supplied with blood vessels. Watery mucus is secreted by glands in the skin.

▲ **Figure 30–23** The characteristics of amphibians include adaptations for living partially on land. For example, lungs enable adult amphibians to obtain oxygen from air.

Early amphibians evolved several adaptations that helped them live at least part of their lives out of water. Bones in the limbs and limb girdles of amphibians became stronger, permitting more-efficient movement. Lungs and breathing tubes enabled amphibians to breathe air. The sternum, or breastbone, formed a bony shield to support and protect internal organs, especially the lungs. Some of these adaptations are shown in **Figure 30–23.**

Soon after they first appeared, amphibians underwent a major adaptive radiation. Some of these ancient amphibians were huge. One early amphibian, *Eogyrinus,* is thought to have been about 5 meters long. Amphibians became the dominant form of animal life in the warm, swampy fern forests of the Carboniferous Period, about 360 to 286 million years ago. In fact, they were so numerous that the Carboniferous Period is sometimes called the Age of Amphibians. These animals gave rise to the ancestors of living amphibians and of vertebrates that live completely on land.

The great success of amphibians didn't last, however. Climate changes caused many of their low, swampy habitats to disappear. Most amphibian groups became extinct by the end of the Permian Period, about 245 million years ago. Only three orders of small amphibians survive today—frogs and toads, salamanders, and caecilians (see-SIL-ee-unz).

✓**CHECKPOINT** *Which geological period is called the Age of Amphibians?*

Word Origins

Carboniferous is a combination of two root words—*carbone* and *fer. Carbone* is a French word for coal; *fer* is a Latin suffix meaning "bearing or producing." *Carboniferous* is an adjective describing the coal-making period of the Paleozoic Era. **If *cone* refers to a reproductive structure of a tree, what do you think the word *coniferous* means?**

Mouth

Esophagus

Liver

Gallbladder

Pancreas

Stomach

Small
intestine

Large intestine
(colon)

Cloaca

▲ **Figure 30–24** This illustration shows the organs of a frog's digestive system. **Comparing and Contrasting** *Which digestive organs are found in both frogs and fishes?*

Form and Function in Amphibians

Although the class Amphibia is relatively small, it is diverse enough to make it difficult to identify a typical species. As you examine essential life functions in amphibians, you will focus on the structures found in frogs.

Feeding The double lives of amphibians are reflected in the feeding habits of frogs. Tadpoles are typically filter feeders or herbivores that graze on algae. Like other herbivores, the tadpoles eat almost constantly. Their intestines, whose long, coiled structure helps break down hard-to-digest plant material, are usually filled with food. However, when tadpoles change into adults, their feeding apparatus and digestive tract are transformed to strictly meat-eating structures, complete with a much shorter intestine.

Adult amphibians are almost entirely carnivorous. They will eat practically anything they can catch and swallow. Legless amphibians can only snap their jaws open and shut to catch prey. In contrast, many salamanders and frogs have long, sticky tongues specialized to capture insects.

Trace the path of food in a frog's digestive system in **Figure 30–24.** From the mouth, food slides down the esophagus into the stomach. The breakdown of food begins in the stomach and continues in the small intestine, where digestive enzymes are manufactured and food is absorbed. Tubes connect the intestine with organs such as the liver, pancreas, and gallbladder that secrete substances that aid in digestion. The small intestine leads to the large intestine, or colon. At the end of the large intestine is a muscular cavity called the **cloaca** (kloh-AY-kuh), through which digestive wastes, urine, and eggs or sperm leave the body.

Respiration In most larval amphibians, gas exchange occurs through the skin as well as the gills. Lungs typically replace gills when an amphibian becomes an adult, although some gas exchange continues through the skin and the lining of the mouth cavity. In frogs, toads, and many other adult amphibians, the lungs are reasonably well developed. In other amphibians, such as salamanders, the lungs are not as well developed. In fact, many terrestrial salamanders have no lungs at all! Lungless salamanders exchange gases through the thin lining of the mouth cavity as well as through the skin.

Circulation In frogs and other adult amphibians, the circulatory system forms what is known as a double loop. The first loop carries oxygen-poor blood from the heart to the lungs and skin, and takes oxygen-rich blood from the lungs and skin back to the heart. The second loop transports oxygen-rich blood from the heart to the rest of the body and oxygen-poor blood from the body back to the heart.

The amphibian heart, shown in **Figure 30–25,** has three separate chambers: left atrium, right atrium, and ventricle. Oxygen-poor blood circulates from the body into the right atrium. At the same time, oxygen-rich blood from the lungs and skin enters the left atrium. When the atria contract, they empty their blood into the ventricle. The ventricle then contracts, pumping blood out to a single, large blood vessel that divides and branches off into smaller blood vessels. Because of the pattern in which the blood vessels branch, most oxygen-poor blood goes to the lungs, and most oxygen-rich blood goes to the rest of the body. However, there is some mixing of oxygen-rich and oxygen-poor blood.

✓**CHECKPOINT** *How many chambers are in an amphibian's heart?*

Excretion Amphibians have kidneys that filter wastes from the blood. The excretory product of the kidneys—urine—travels through tubes called ureters into the cloaca. From there, urine can be passed directly to the outside, or it may be temporarily stored in a small urinary bladder just above the cloaca.

▼ **Figure 30–25** Like all vertebrates, amphibians have a circulatory system and an excretory system. An amphibian's heart has three chambers—two atria and one ventricle. Although some wastes diffuse across the skin, kidneys remove most wastes from the bloodstream. **Applying Concepts** *What excretory product do the kidneys produce?*

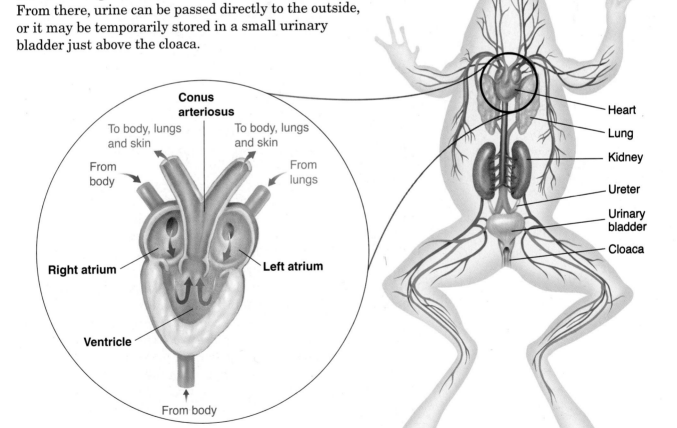

Conus arteriosus

To body, lungs and skin

To body, lungs and skin

From body

From lungs

Right atrium

Left atrium

Ventricle

From body

Heart

Lung

Kidney

Ureter

Urinary bladder

Cloaca

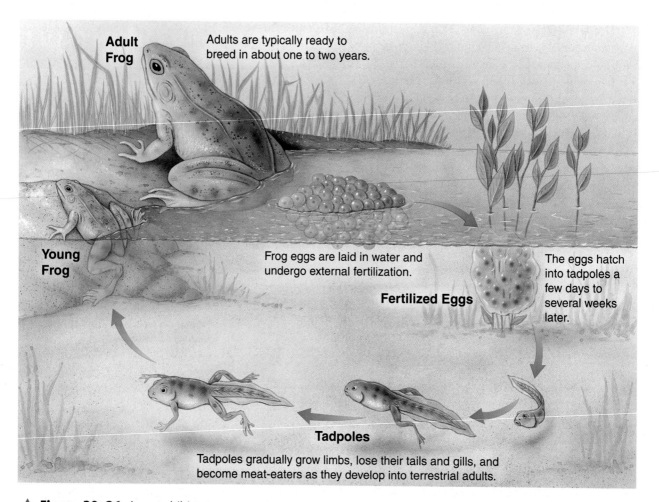

Adult Frog

Adults are typically ready to breed in about one to two years.

Young Frog

Frog eggs are laid in water and undergo external fertilization.

Fertilized Eggs

The eggs hatch into tadpoles a few days to several weeks later.

Tadpoles

Tadpoles gradually grow limbs, lose their tails and gills, and become meat-eaters as they develop into terrestrial adults.

▲ **Figure 30–26** An amphibian typically begins its life in the water, then moves onto land as an adult. This diagram shows the process of metamorphosis in a frog. **Comparing and Contrasting** *How are tadpoles similar to fish? How are they different?*

Reproduction Amphibian eggs do not have shells and tend to dry out if they are not kept moist. Thus, in most species of amphibians, the female lays eggs in water, then the male fertilizes them externally. In a few species, including most salamanders, eggs are fertilized internally.

When frogs reproduce, the male climbs onto the female's back and squeezes. In response to this stimulus, the female releases as many as 200 eggs that the male then fertilizes. Frog eggs are encased in a sticky, transparent jelly that attaches the egg mass to underwater plants and makes the eggs difficult for predators to grasp. The jelly nourishes the developing embryos until they hatch into larvae that are commonly called tadpoles. **Figure 30–26** shows the metamorphosis of tadpoles into frogs.

Most amphibians, including common frogs, abandon their eggs after they lay them. A few take great care of both eggs and young. Some amphibians incubate their young in highly unusual places, such as in the mouth, on the back, or even in the stomach! Male midwife toads wrap sticky strings of fertilized eggs around their hind legs and carry them about until the eggs are ready to hatch.

✔CHECKPOINT *What are the functions of the jelly surrounding frog eggs?*

Movement Amphibian larvae often move very much like fishes, by wiggling their bodies and using a flattened tail for propulsion. Most adult amphibians, like other four-limbed vertebrates, use their front and back legs to move in a variety of ways. Adult salamanders have legs that stick out sideways. These animals walk—or, in some cases, run—by throwing their bodies into S-shaped curves and using their legs to push backward against the ground. Other amphibians, including frogs and toads, have well-developed hind limbs that enable them to jump long distances. Some amphibians, such as tree frogs, have disks on their toes that serve as suction cups for climbing.

Response The brain of an amphibian has the same basic parts as that of a fish. Like fishes, amphibians have well-developed nervous and sensory systems. **Figure 30–27** points out some of these systems in a typical frog. An amphibian's eyes are large and can move around in their sockets. The surface of the eye is protected from damage under water and kept moist on land by a transparent **nictitating membrane** (NIK-tuh-tayt-ing). This movable membrane is located inside the regular eyelid, which can also be closed over the eye. Frogs have keen vision for spotting moving insects, but they probably do not see color as well as fishes do.

Amphibians hear through **tympanic membranes** (tim-PAN-ik), or eardrums, located on each side of the head. In response to sound, a tympanic membrane vibrates, sending sound waves deeper within the skull to the middle and inner ear. Many amphibian larvae and adults also have lateral line systems, like those of fishes, that detect water movement.

▼ **Figure 30–27** A frog's eyes and ears are among its most important sensory organs. Transparent eyelids called nictitating membranes protect the eyes underwater and keep them moist in air. Tympanic membranes receive sound vibrations from air as well as water. **Inferring** *What functions does hearing serve in frogs?*

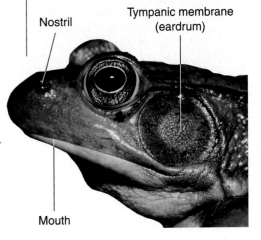

Nostril

Tympanic membrane (eardrum)

Mouth

Analyzing Data

Amphibian Population Trends

Over the past several decades, scientists have reported changes in amphibian populations worldwide. In 2000, a team of researchers analyzed data sets contributed by various amphibian population studies conducted in 37 different countries. The results of this analysis are shown in the table. Study the data table and answer the questions.

Numbers of Amphibian Populations

Region	Declining	Increasing	No Trend
Western Europe	309	248	29
North America	130	96	14
South America	31	19	1
Australia/NZ	17	6	1
Asia	10	10	1
Eastern Europe	4	5	0
Africa/Middle East	2	2	1

1. **Using Tables and Graphs** How many amphibian populations were studied?

2. **Predicting** If the trends presented in the data table continue, how do you expect amphibian populations in North America to change in the next two decades?

3. **Calculating** What percentage of worldwide amphibian populations is decreasing?

4. **Making Judgments** Do you think that regional population studies can be used to predict global population trends? Explain your answer.

FIGURE 30-28 DIVERSITY OF AMPHIBIANS

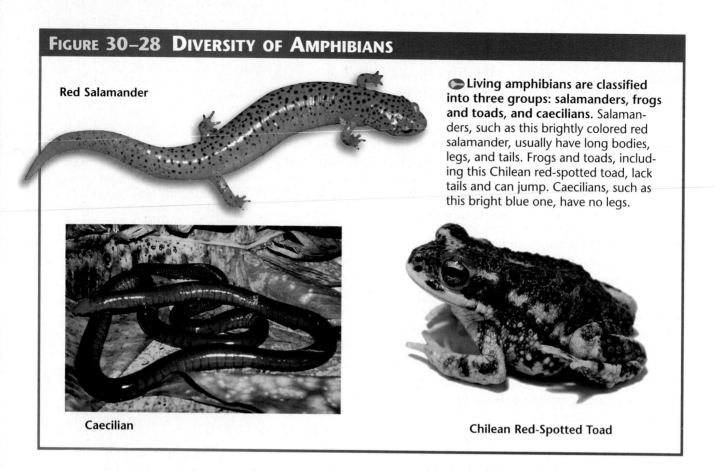

Red Salamander

Living amphibians are classified into three groups: salamanders, frogs and toads, and caecilians. Salamanders, such as this brightly colored red salamander, usually have long bodies, legs, and tails. Frogs and toads, including this Chilean red-spotted toad, lack tails and can jump. Caecilians, such as this bright blue one, have no legs.

Caecilian

Chilean Red-Spotted Toad

Groups of Amphibians

Modern amphibians can be classified into three categories. The three groups of amphibians alive today are salamanders, frogs and toads, and caecilians. Representative members are shown in **Figure 30–28.**

Salamanders Members of the order Urodela (yoor-oh-DEE-luh), including salamanders and newts, have long bodies and tails. Most also have four legs. Both adults and larvae are carnivores. The adults usually live in moist woods, where they tunnel under rocks and rotting logs. Some salamanders, such as the mud puppy, keep their gills and live in water all their lives.

Frogs and Toads The most obvious feature that members of the order Anura (uh-NOOR-uh) share is their ability to jump. Frogs tend to have long legs and make lengthy jumps, whereas the relatively short legs of toads limit them to short hops. Frogs are generally more closely tied to water—including ponds and streams—than toads, which often live in moist woods and even in deserts. Adult frogs and toads lack tails.

Caecilians The least known of the amphibians are the caecilians, members of the order Apoda (ay-POH-duh). Caecilians are legless animals that live in water or burrow in moist soil or sediment, feeding on small invertebrates such as termites. Many have fishlike scales embedded in their skin—which demonstrates that some amphibians don't fit the general definition.

Ecology of Amphibians

Because amphibians have no feathers, fur, or scales, many of them make an ideal meal for predators such as birds and mammals. However, amphibians have adaptations that protect them from predators. For example, many species have skin colors and markings that enable them to blend in with their surroundings. Most adult amphibians have skin glands that ooze an unpleasant-tasting and poisonous substance, or toxin.

Some amphibians that release toxins, like the toad in **Figure 30–29,** have bodies that are brightly colored and have bold patterns. The colors and patterns serve as a warning to potential predators. Other amphibian species that are nontoxic may have bodies that mimic, or resemble, those of the toxic amphibians. The mimicry protects the nontoxic species, because predators confuse them with the toxic species and avoid them.

Recently, scientists have noticed an alarming trend in amphibian populations worldwide. For the past several decades, the numbers of living species have been decreasing. The golden toad of Costa Rica, for example, seems to be extinct. In North America, the numbers of boreal toads have dwindled. Even the leopard frog—which is present throughout the world—is getting harder to find.

Scientists do not yet know what is causing the global amphibian population to decline. It is possible that amphibians are susceptible to a wide variety of environmental threats, such as decreasing habitat, depletion of the ozone layer, acid rain, water pollution, fungal infections, introduced aquatic predators, and an increasing human population.

To better understand this phenomenon, biologists worldwide have been focusing their efforts and sharing data about amphibian populations. In the late 1990s, a group of scientists set up monitoring programs that cover the entire area of North America. One such program relies mostly on the efforts of volunteers, who are trained to recognize the specific call of various species such as cricket frogs, bullfrogs, or spring peepers.

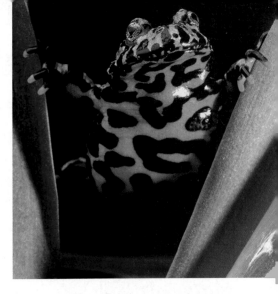

▲ **Figure 30–29** A European fire-bellied toad displays its brightly colored underside, which warns of a toxic and bad-tasting skin secretion. **Using Analogies** *How is the underside of this frog comparable to a dog showing its teeth?*

KEEP CURRENT WITH . . .
SCIENCE NEWS®

To find out more about the topics in this chapter, go to:
www.phschool.com

30–3 Section Assessment

1. **Key Concept** List the characteristics of amphibians.

2. **Key Concept** What adaptations helped amphibians evolve into land animals?

3. **Key Concept** List the three groups of amphibians.

4. What characteristics usually restrict amphibian reproduction to moist environments?

5. **Critical Thinking Formulating Hypotheses** Most caecilian species are totally blind as adults. How do you think this characteristic has evolved?

iTEXT Assessment Use iText to review the important concepts in Section 30–3.

Take It to the NET

Find out more about the different types of amphibian-monitoring programs that exist today. List the programs and indicate which, if any, are seeking volunteers in your area. Use the links provided in the Biology area at the Prentice Hall Web site for help in completing this activity: **www.phschool.com**

Investigating Homeostasis in Fishes and Amphibians

All living organisms must maintain homeostasis, or a controlled internal environment. Fishes are adapted to avoid gaining or losing excessive amounts of water or salts due to osmosis. Amphibians need to maintain a surface that can absorb oxygen from air and release carbon dioxide. In this investigation, you will examine these adaptations.

Green Frog

Problem How do fishes and amphibians maintain homeostasis?

Materials

- 5 g saltwater fish
- 5 g freshwater fish
- balance
- 4 test tubes
- test tube rack
- paper towels
- 2 glass rods
- 10-mL graduated cylinder
- 2 funnels
- 2 filter-paper circles

- silver nitrate solution
- 1000-mL beaker
- vinegar
- distilled water
- string
- scissors
- transparent tape
- blue litmus paper
- sodium bicarbonate (baking soda)
- glass-marking pencil

Warty Frog Fish

Skills Evaluating and Revising, Using Models

Procedure

Part A: Osmotic Homeostasis in Fishes

1. **Predicting** Predict whether saltwater fishes or freshwater fishes will have saltier flesh.

2. Obtain 5-g samples of freshwater fish and saltwater fish. Label 2 test tubes "salt" and "fresh" with a glass-marking pencil. Place each sample into the corresponding test tube and add 10 mL of distilled water. Put the test tubes in the rack.

3. Fold 2 paper towels in half 3 times to make 2 cushions. Place a paper towel cushion under each test tube. To make an extract of each fish sample, gently mash the sample with a glass rod until it becomes pasty. Use a separate glass rod for each sample. **CAUTION:** *Be careful not to break the rods or the test tubes.*

4. Label 2 more test tubes "salt filtered" and "fresh filtered." Put the test tubes in a rack and place a funnel in each of these test tubes. Fold 2 filter-paper circles in half, and then in half again. Open one layer of each folded filter paper to form a cone as shown. Insert a paper cone into each funnel.

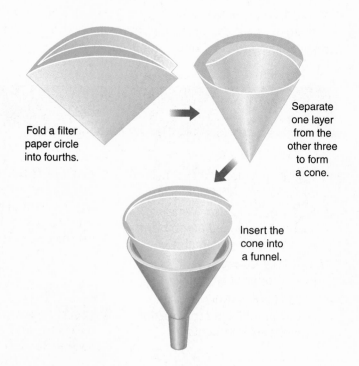

Fold a filter paper circle into fourths.

Separate one layer from the other three to form a cone.

Insert the cone into a funnel.

5. Pour the contents of the saltwater fish test tube into the funnel in the "salt filtered" test tube. Pour the contents of the freshwater fish test tube into the funnel in the "fresh filtered" test tube. Allow the liquid to filter through, and then remove the funnels.

6. Put on your safety goggles, plastic gloves, and lab apron. Silver nitrate is a chemical that is used to detect salt. A drop of silver nitrate turns cloudy when it is added to a solution that contains salt. **CAUTION:** *Silver nitrate is toxic and can stain skin.* Observe each filtered sample as you add 1 drop of silver nitrate solution. Record your observations.

Part B: Gas Exchange in Air

7. **Predicting** Amphibians need to exchange oxygen and carbon dioxide with the air around them. Record your prediction of whether gases will enter a dry surface or a moist one more quickly.

8. Place 100 mL of vinegar in a 1000-mL beaker. Cut a piece of paper large enough to cover the beaker and extend approximately 3 cm beyond the sides of the beaker.

9. Near the center of the paper, tape two 5-cm pieces of string approximately 3 cm apart. Then, tape a piece of blue litmus paper to the end of each string.

10. Use a drop of distilled water to moisten one of the strips of litmus paper, being sure to keep the other strip dry. The color of the litmus paper will change to red in the presence of carbon dioxide gas, which acts as an acid. The reaction between vinegar and sodium bicarbonate produces this gas.

11. Add 5 g of sodium bicarbonate to the beaker of vinegar. Quickly cover the beaker with the paper lid so that the filter strips hang down into the beaker as shown in the photograph. Record the time required for each strip of litmus paper to change color.

Analyze and Conclude

1. **Comparing and Contrasting** Compare the appearance of the saltwater and freshwater fish extracts after adding the silver nitrate.

2. **Inferring** What can you infer from this result about the ability of freshwater and saltwater fishes to maintain homeostasis?

3. **Drawing Conclusions** What must a freshwater fish do to maintain homeostasis? How would these activities differ in a saltwater fish?

4. **Inferring** What do your results in Part B indicate about the ability of gases to enter moist and dry surfaces?

5. **Inferring** Explain why it is important for amphibians to maintain a moist surface for gas exchange.

> **Go Further**
>
> **Researching** Salmon are fish that live their adult lives in the ocean but breed in freshwater rivers and streams. Do research in the library to find out how salmon regulate the water and salt content of their bodies as they move between fresh and salt water. Give an oral report to your class.

30–1 The Chordates

Key Concepts

- A chordate is an animal that has, for at least some stage of its life, a dorsal, hollow nerve cord; a notochord; pharyngeal pouches; and a tail that extends beyond the anus.
- The two groups of nonvertebrate chordates are tunicates and lancelets.

Vocabulary
chordate, p. 767
notochord, p. 767
pharyngeal pouch, p. 767
vertebra, p. 768

30–2 Fishes
Key Concepts

- Fishes are aquatic vertebrates that are character-ized by paired fins, scales, and gills.
- The evolution of jaws and the evolution of paired fins were important developments during the rise of fishes.
- Fishes' adaptations to aquatic life include various modes of feeding, specialized structures for gas exchange, and paired fins for locomotion.
- On the basis of their basic internal structure, all living fishes can be classified into three groups: jawless fishes, cartilaginous fishes, and bony fishes.

Vocabulary
cartilage, p. 773
atrium, p. 776
ventricle, p. 776
cerebrum, p. 777
cerebellum, p. 777
medulla oblongata, p. 777
lateral line system, p. 777
swim bladder, p. 777
oviparous, p. 778
ovoviviparous, p. 778
viviparous, p. 778

30–3 Amphibians
Key Concepts

- An amphibian is a vertebrate that, with some exceptions, lays eggs in water, lives in water as a larva and on land as an adult, breathes with lungs as an adult, has moist skin that contains mucus glands, and lacks scales and claws.
- Early amphibians evolved several adaptations that helped them live at least part of their lives out of water. Bones in the limbs and limb girdles of amphibians became stronger, permitting more-efficient movement. A set of lungs and breathing tubes enabled them to breathe air. Their sternum formed a bony shield that supports and protects the internal organs, especially the lungs.
- The three groups of living amphibians are salamanders, frogs and toads, and caecilians.

Vocabulary
cloaca, p. 784
nictitating membrane, p. 787
tympanic membrane, p. 787

Thinking Visually
Using information from this chapter, complete the following concept map:

Chapter 30

Part A

Multiple Choice

For each statement or question, select the number of the word or expression that, of those given, best completes the statement or answers the question.

1 Which is *not* a characteristic of all chordates?
   (1) hollow nerve cord
   (2) pharyngeal pouches
   (3) fins
   (4) notochord

2 The term that is *least* closely related to the others is
   (1) chordate   (3) nonvertebrate
   (2) cerebrum   (4) lancelet

3 The evolution of jaws and paired fins was an important development during the rise of
   (1) tunicates   (3) fishes
   (2) lancelets   (4) amphibians

4 Most fishes exchange gases by pumping water from their mouths
   (1) over the gill filaments
   (2) through the pyloric ceca
   (3) over the atrium
   (4) through the esophagus

5 A fish's body movements would be affected if which part of the brain were damaged?
   (1) olfactory lobe   (3) cerebrum
   (2) optic lobe   (4) cerebellum

6 Examine the diagrams below. Which of these is a jawed cartilaginous fish?

   (1)

   (2)

   (3)

   (4)

7 At the end of the large intestine of a frog is a muscular cavity called the
   (1) cloaca   (3) gallbladder
   (2) pancreas   (4) esophagus

8 An adult amphibian's heart typically has
   (1) one chamber   (3) three chambers
   (2) two chambers   (4) four chambers

9 Into which group can nonvertebrate chordates be classified?
   A Lancelets
   B Tunicates
   C Fishes
   (1) A, only   (3) A and C, only
   (2) A and B, only   (4) A, B, and C

10 Each organ serves as an organ of gas exchange in frogs *except* the
   (1) skin   (3) lungs
   (2) mouth cavity   (4) nictitating membrane

11 Which statement is *never* true of oviparous fishes?
   (1) Their eggs are fertilized externally.
   (2) Their eggs hatch outside the mother's body.
   (3) They have paired fins.
   (4) The embryos receive nourishment directly from the mother's body.

12 Most amphibian larvae are
   (1) carnivores
   (2) producers
   (3) filter feeders and herbivores
   (4) parasites and omnivores

13 Organisms that feed through the mouth with no jaws and breathe through thin skin are
   (1) lancelets   (3) salamanders
   (2) fishes   (4) caecilians

Complete the following analogy by selecting the correct number. In analogies, A : B :: C : means "A is to B as C is to ___?___."

14 Tadpole: gills :: frog :
   (1) atrium   (3) scales
   (2) lungs   (4) stomach

> **Test-Taking Tip** If a test question seems confusing, try rephrasing it in your own words. Often, rephrasing a question will allow you to better understand it.

Parts B and C

Multiple Choice and Extended Response

For those questions that ask you to select a response, choose the one that best completes the statement or answers the question. For all others follow the directions given.

15 Suppose you were visiting South America and you discovered an organism that reproduces by laying eggs and has a backbone, lungs, kidneys, and a two-chambered heart. Is the organism a fish, an amphibian, or something else? Support your answer with an explanation.

Base your answers to questions 16 through 18 on the information and data table below and on your knowledge of biology.

An ecologist collected data about the number of frogs that inhabit a certain pond each year. In addition, he collected data about the total amount of rainfall in that area each spring. The data are shown in the table below.

Rainfall and Frog Population in Pond		
Year	**Amount of Rainfall (centimeters)**	**Number of Frogs**
1995	13	45
1996	20	61
1997	8	33
1998	5	20
1999	23	63

16 In what year were the most frogs observed?
  (1) 1996   **(3)** 1998
  (2) 1997   **(4)** 1999

17 Which statement is best supported by the data?
  (1) The number of frogs increased each year.
  (2) The number of frogs decreased each year.
  (3) The number of frogs in the pond increased as the amount of rainfall increased.
  (4) The number of frogs in the pond decreased as the amount of rainfall increased.

18 Based on the data and your knowledge of the frog's life cycle, explain why the amount of rainfall might affect the number of frogs.

Base your answers to questions 19 through 22 on the information and chart below and on your knowledge of biology.

The chart below shows changes in five groups of vertebrates over the past 500 million years. The thickness of each band indicates changes in the relative number of species over geologic time.

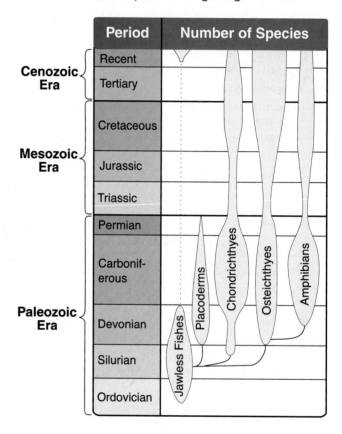

19 During which period did amphibians evolve?

20 Did the amphibians evolve from early jawless fishes or from early bony fishes (Osteichthyes)? Support your answer with an explanation.

21 In which groups of fishes have the numbers of species increased during recent times? Support your answer with an explanation.

22 Which group of fishes is extinct?

23 In order for amphibians to evolve from fishes, how did the circulatory system have to change? Explain why these changes were necessary.

Base your answers to questions 24 through 27 on the reading passage below and on your knowledge of biology.

Farm Ponds

Throughout New York state, there are many farm ponds on private land. The Department of Environmental Conservation provides guidelines for people interested in stocking a pond on their land.

Before beginning the process, individuals must obtain a stocking permit in order to have accurate records of what species of fish are being stocked. They must also determine whether the pond is "cold water" (the temperature stays below 72°F) or "warm water" (the temperature is above 72°F for long periods during summer). Coldwater ponds are generally stocked with trout. Warmwater ponds are stocked with largemouth bass.

Warmwater species can reproduce in the pond, whereas trout must be re-stocked every two years. A combination of largemouth bass/bluegill or bass/golden shiner is generally recommended for stocking. Minnows can be substituted for bluegill or golden shiner as the prey species.

Bluegills reproduce rapidly. If they are used to stock the pond, they must be heavily fished. In addition, only 11 bass per acre should be caught annually in the average bass/bluegill pond.

24 From an ecological point of view, why is it important for wildlife managers to have a record of the species of fish in a stocked pond?

25 Largemouth bass can reproduce in warm water ponds. They are oviparous. Explain the reproductive process characteristic to oviparous species.

26 When stocking ponds, people must understand the flow of energy in a pond ecosystem. According to the reading passage, draw a food chain for the pond.

27 Explain the importance of heavily fishing bluegills, as well as the importance of *not* heavily fishing bass each year.

Base your answers to questions 28 through 30 on the information below and on your knowledge of biology.

There are 18 salamander species in New York. A five-year survey was recently completed to document the distribution of these species throughout the state. Of particular interest is the eastern tiger salamander, which is on New York's endangered species list. Currently, the eastern tiger salamander lives only on Long Island, where most of its breeding colonies are in the eastern Pine Barrens. Heavy development on western Long Island has destroyed the salamander's habitat. In addition, pesticides and other contaminants threaten ponds and increased bullfrog populations disrupt the salamander's reproduction cycle.

28 Eastern tiger salamanders spend most of their lives underground and are often called "mole salamanders." This species does not live in lakes or ponds. Knowing this, explain why pollution levels in ponds affect the well-being of the tiger salamander.

29 The reproduction cycle of the tiger salamander begins with a brief courtship in spring. The female lays a mass of eggs, which are fertilized under water. Larvae hatch after about four weeks and remain in the pond until midsummer. They transform into air-breathing adults, leaving the pond and moving to land for their underground life. Compare this reproductive cycle with that of a frog.

30 Wildlife managers have suggested constructing "salamander tunnels" under roadways separating salamander habitat from breeding ponds. Predict what might happen to species diversity if the tunnels are not built.

Take It to the NET

The 1938 discovery of the first living coelacanth was a significant event in fish biology. Visit the Prentice Hall Web site at **www.phschool.com** to find out more about this rare and ancient fish. Then, answer the following questions:

• In what areas of the world have living coelacanths been sighted?

• What methods do scientists use to learn about the behavior of coelacanths?

• What is Project Splashback?

31 Reptiles and Birds

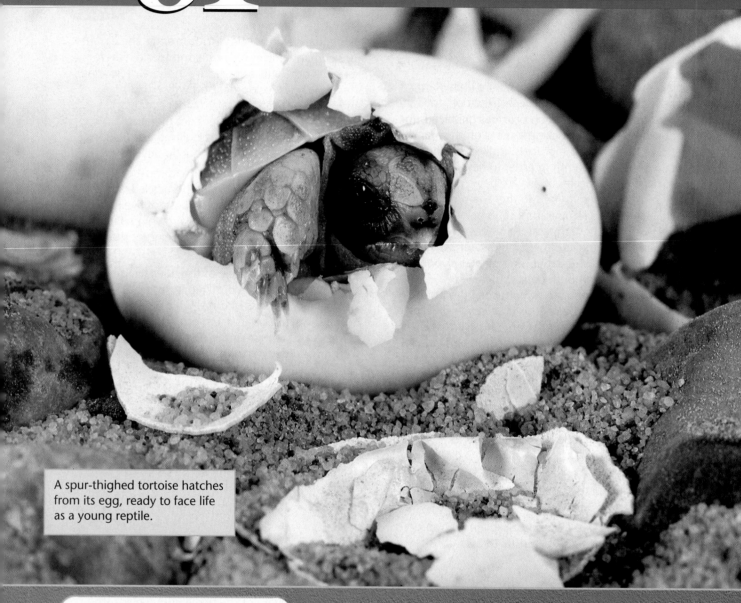

A spur-thighed tortoise hatches from its egg, ready to face life as a young reptile.

Inquiry Activity

How are bird eggs adapted for life on land?

Procedure

1. Put on plastic gloves. Examine a frog egg. Describe the characteristics of the egg.

2. Examine a chicken egg. Open the egg on a disposable plate. Describe the structures inside.
   CAUTION: *Do not eat raw egg. Wash your hands after completing this activity.*

Think About It

1. **Inferring** What conditions do frog eggs require to develop? How does this affect which types of habitats these animals can live in?

2. **Formulating Hypotheses** How do the characteristics of bird eggs affect which types of habitats birds can live in?

31–1 Reptiles

Humans have always been fascinated by—and sometimes frightened of—reptiles. Some people fear snakes because of their venomous bites or the way they crawl. Explorers' encounters with lizards and crocodiles inspired images of dragons in European folk tales. Turtles, too, are the subject of many a fable. The truth about reptiles is that they are as astonishing as any creatures of human imagination.

What Is a Reptile?

The basic body plan of a reptile is typical of land vertebrates: a well-developed skull, a backbone and tail, two limb girdles, and four limbs. The iguana in **Figure 31–1** exhibits this body plan. Two types of reptiles have slightly different body plans. Snakes are mostly limbless, while turtles have hard shells that are fused to their vertebrae.

What characteristics do snakes, turtles, and other reptiles share? **A reptile is a vertebrate that has dry, scaly skin, lungs, and terrestrial eggs with several membranes.** These characteristics enable reptiles to live their entire lives out of water, unlike their amphibious relatives.

Reptilian skin is dry and often covered with thick, protective scales. These scales may be smooth or rough. A reptile's body covering helps prevent the loss of body water in dry environments. But dry, waterproof skin can also be a disadvantage to reptiles. Because the tough, scaly layer of skin does not grow when the rest of a reptile grows, it must be shed periodically as the reptile increases in size.

Today, reptiles are widely distributed on Earth. Temperate and tropical areas contain populations of reptiles that are remarkably diverse in appearance and lifestyle. The only places on Earth that most reptiles cannot live in are very cold areas. The reason for this will soon be apparent.

✓**CHECKPOINT** *What are the advantages of dry, scaly skin for reptiles?*

▶ **Figure 31–1** Like all reptiles, this green iguana has lungs and dry, scaly skin. These characteristics help the iguana live on land.

Key Concepts
- What are the characteristics of reptiles?
- How are reptiles adapted to life on land?
- What are the four living orders of reptiles?

Vocabulary
ectotherm
amniotic egg
carapace
plastron

**Reading Strategy:
Outlining** Before you read, use the headings in this section to make an outline about reptiles. As you read, add phrases or a sentence about each topic and subtopic in your outline.

Evolution of Reptiles

To colonize permanently dry habitats, animals needed a way to reproduce that did not require depositing eggs into water. Reptiles were the first animals to evolve this adaptation. The fossil of the first known reptile dates back to the early Carboniferous Period, some 350 million years ago. However, reptiles did not become common until 40 or 50 million years later. As the Carboniferous Period came to a close and the Permian Period began, Earth's climate became cooler and less humid. Many lakes and swamps dried up, reducing the available habitat for water-dependent amphibians. Under these drier conditions, the first great adaptive radiation of reptiles began.

Mammal-like Reptiles   By the end of the Permian Period, about 245 million years ago, a great variety of reptiles roamed Earth. One early group was the mammal-like reptiles, which displayed a mix of reptilian and mammalian characteristics. These chordates eventually came to dominate many land habitats. However, the mammal-like reptiles went extinct in just a few million years. Toward the end of the Triassic Period, about 215 million years ago, they were replaced in the fossil record by another group of reptiles that had remained in the background for millions of years—the dinosaurs.

Enter the Dinosaurs   During the late Triassic and Jurassic periods, a great adaptive radiation of reptiles took place. The vast diversity and abundance of reptiles during that time are the main reasons why the Mesozoic Era is often called the Age of Reptiles. Two separate groups of large aquatic reptiles swam in the seas. Ancestors of modern turtles, crocodiles, lizards, and snakes populated many land habitats. And dinosaurs were everywhere. **Figure 31–2** shows two dinosaurs, *Plateosauras* and *Coelophysis*. The illustration also shows another kind of reptile, *Teratosaurus*.

Word Origins

Dinosaur is a combination of two Greek words: *deinos,* meaning "terrible" and *sauros,* meaning "lizard." The suffix *-ian* is used to turn a noun into an adjective. The adjective *dinosaurian,* for example, describes a dinosaur-like animal. **What do you think the adjective *saurian* describes?**

▼ **Figure 31–2** In the Triassic Period, reptiles such as these lived in the forests. The herbivorous *Plateosaurus* (left), nibbling on leaves, was a dinosaur, as were the group of carnivorous *Coelophysis* (center). The large carnivorous *Teratosaurus* (right) was a reptile but not a dinosaur. **Observing** *What characteristics did these reptiles have in common with modern reptiles?*

A Massive Controversy

Dinosaurs were the largest animals ever to walk on Earth. The plant-eating dinosaur *Brachiosaurus* reached lengths greater than 22 meters and had a mass of about 50,000 kilograms. It would take about 10 elephants to match the mass of one *Brachiosaurus*. How could the skeleton of such an animal support its immense mass? Imagine that you are a paleontologist searching for an answer to this question. Your job is to examine fossil skeletons of large dinosaurs for clues.

Defining the Problem Use your own words to describe the problem you face.

Organizing Information List the kinds of skeletal adaptations that would help a dinosaur support its mass.

Creating a Solution Carefully study the above illustration of a large dinosaur. Make a model of the part of the spinal column that is supported by the animal's legs. Include the legs in the model. Make another model of an alternative shape for the spinal column, one that is not curved.

Presenting Your Plan Describe what you might do to each model to discover which would support a greater mass. Show how you would test the models. Next to the models, place a card describing the steps in your test.

Dinosaurs ranged in size from small to enormous. They ran on two legs or lumbered along on four. Some, like *Plateosaurus*, ate leafy plants. *Coelophysis* and other hunters traveled in herds. Others, such as duckbilled *Maiasaura*, lived in small family groups, caring for their eggs and young in carefully constructed nests. Certain dinosaurs may even have had feathers, which may have evolved as a means of regulating body temperature. All of the dinosaurs, however, belonged to one of two major groups: the Ornithischia (awr-nuh-THISH-ee-uh), or "bird-hipped" dinosaurs, and the Saurischia (saw-RISH-ee-uh), or "lizard-hipped" dinosaurs. From one of these two branches of dinosaurs, probably the Saurischia, came the earliest members of evolutionary lines that would lead to modern birds.

Exit the Dinosaurs At the end of the Cretaceous Period, about 65 million years ago, a mass extinction occurred worldwide. This extinction was caused by a dramatic series of natural disasters. These disasters probably included a string of massive volcanic eruptions and lava flows, the dropping of sea level, and a huge asteroid or comet smashing into what is now the Yucatan Peninsula in Mexico. The asteroid or comet collision produced major forest fires and enormous dust clouds. After these events, dinosaurs, along with many other animal and plant groups, became extinct. The disappearance of these organisms during the late Cretaceous Period provided opportunities for other kinds of organisms to evolve on land and in the seas.

✓CHECKPOINT *How did the extinction of the dinosaurs pave the way for modern reptiles?*

KEEP CURRENT WITH . . .

SCIENCE NEWS®

To find out more about the topics in this chapter, go to:
www.phschool.com

Form and Function in Reptiles

Most reptiles have adapted to a fully terrestrial life. Tough, scaly skin is one adaptation to this type of life. **Well-developed lungs; a double-loop circulatory system; a water-conserving excretory system; strong limbs; internal fertilization; and shelled, terrestrial eggs are the other adaptations that have contributed to the success of reptiles on land.** In addition, reptiles can control their body temperature by changing their environments.

Body Temperature Control The ability to control their body temperature is an enormous asset for active animals. All the animals that you have read about so far are ectotherms (EK-toh-thurmz). **Ectotherms** rely on behavior to help control body temperature. Turtles, snakes, and other modern reptiles are all ectotherms. To warm up, they bask in the sun during the day or stay under water at night. To cool down, they move to the shade, go for a swim, or take shelter in underground burrows.

Feeding Reptiles eat a wide range of foods. Iguanas, which are herbivores, tear plants into shreds and swallow the tough, fibrous chunks. Their long digestive systems enable them to break down plant material. Many other reptiles are carnivores. Snakes, for example, prey on small animals, bird eggs, or even other snakes, grabbing them with their jaws and swallowing them whole as shown in **Figure 31–3**. Crocodiles and alligators eat fish and even land animals when they can catch them. Chameleons have sticky tongues as long as their bodies that flip out to catch insects.

Respiration The lungs of reptiles are spongy, providing more gas-exchange area than those of amphibians. This isn't surprising, because most reptiles cannot exchange gases through their skin the way many moist-skinned amphibians do. Many reptiles have muscles around their ribs that expand the chest cavity to inhale and collapse the cavity to force air out. Several species of crocodiles also have flaps of skin that can separate the mouth from the nasal passages, allowing these crocodiles to breathe through their nostrils while their mouth remains open. To exchange gases with the environment, reptiles have two efficient lungs or, in the case of certain species of snakes, one lung.

Circulation Reptiles have an efficient double-loop circulatory system. One of the loops brings blood to and from the lungs, and the other loop brings blood to and from the rest of the body. The heart diagram in **Figure 31–4** shows how blood flows through a turtle's heart. Reptile hearts contain two atria and either one or two ventricles. Most reptiles have a single ventricle with a partial septum, or wall, that helps separate oxygen-rich and oxygen-poor blood during the pumping cycle. Crocodiles and alligators, however, have the most developed hearts of living reptiles. The heart consists of two atria and two ventricles—an arrangement that is also found in birds and mammals.

▲ **Figure 31–3** The gaboon viper, like all snakes, is entirely carnivorous. It eats mice and other small mammals by stretching its jaws wide and swallowing its prey whole. **Inferring** *Besides feeding, what other function might fangs serve in snakes?*

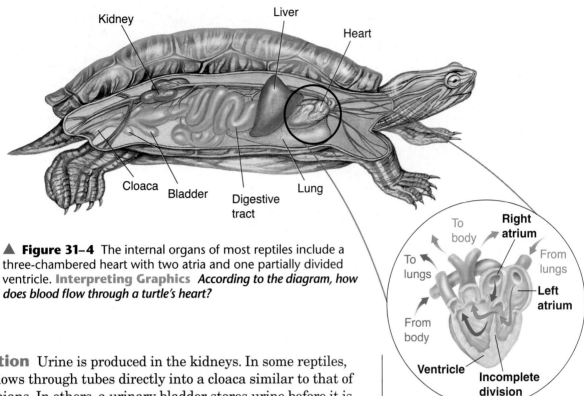

Kidney   Liver   Heart

Cloaca   Bladder   Digestive   Lung
                    tract

To body   **Right atrium**
To lungs   From lungs
                      Left atrium
From body
Ventricle   **Incomplete division**

▲ **Figure 31–4** The internal organs of most reptiles include a three-chambered heart with two atria and one partially divided ventricle. **Interpreting Graphics** *According to the diagram, how does blood flow through a turtle's heart?*

Excretion Urine is produced in the kidneys. In some reptiles, urine flows through tubes directly into a cloaca similar to that of amphibians. In others, a urinary bladder stores urine before it is expelled from the cloaca.

Reptiles' urine contains either ammonia or uric acid. Reptiles that live mainly in water, such as crocodiles and alligators, excrete most of their nitrogenous wastes in the form of ammonia, a toxic compound. Crocodiles and alligators drink a large amount of water, which dilutes the ammonia in the urine and helps carry it away. In contrast, many other reptiles—especially those that live entirely on land—do not excrete ammonia directly. Instead, they convert ammonia into a compound called uric acid. Uric acid is much less toxic than ammonia, so it does not have to be diluted as much. In these reptiles, excess water is absorbed in the cloaca, reducing urine to crystals of uric acid that form a pasty white solid. By eliminating wastes that contain little water, a reptile can conserve water.

Response The basic pattern of a reptile's brain is similar to that of an amphibian, although the cerebrum and cerebellum are considerably larger compared to the rest of the brain. Reptiles that are active during the day tend to have complex eyes and can see color well. Many snakes also have an extremely good sense of smell. In addition to a pair of nostrils, most reptiles have a pair of sensory organs in the roof of the mouth that can detect chemicals. Reptiles have simple ears with an external eardrum and a single bone that conducts sound to the inner ear. Snakes can also pick up vibrations in the ground through bones in their skulls. Some snakes, such as the viper in **Figure 31–5,** have the extraordinary ability to detect the body heat of their prey.

✔ CHECKPOINT *How does a reptile's brain compare to an amphibian's?*

▼ **Figure 31–5** The heat-sensitive pits above this eyelash viper's mouth enable it to locate prey, even in total darkness. Snakes that have these pits are commonly called pit vipers. **Inferring** *How would these organs give pit vipers an advantage over other reptiles?*

Figure 31–6 The shovel-snouted lizard (left) is not moving forward; rather, it lifts its feet to limit contact with the hot desert sand. The sidewinding adder propels itself forward by digging its ventral scales against the dunes while pushing its body into long curving waves. **Comparing and Contrasting** *How are the lizard's legs different from those of an amphibian?*

▼ **Figure 31–7** After a female box turtle digs a hole in the ground for her nest, she lays her eggs, dropping them one by one and gently lowering them into the hole with her hind feet. When she finishes, she will cover up her nest and leave without a backward glance. **Inferring** *Why would it be an advantage for turtles to lay a large number of eggs?*

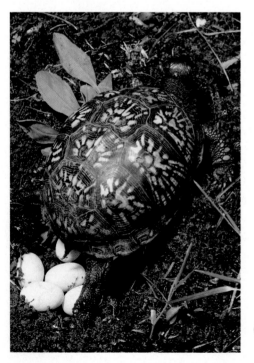

Movement Compared with most amphibians, reptiles with legs tend to have larger, stronger limbs that enable them to walk, run, burrow, swim, or climb. The legs of some reptiles are also rotated further under the body than those of amphibians, enabling reptiles to carry more body weight. The legs and feet of many aquatic turtles have developed into flippers. **Figure 31–6** shows some ways that reptiles can move. As with amphibians, the backbones of reptiles help accomplish much of their movement.

Reproduction All reptiles reproduce by internal fertilization, in which the male deposits sperm inside the body of the female. Most male reptiles have a penis that allows them to deliver sperm into the female's cloaca. After fertilization has occurred, the female's reproductive system covers the embryos with several membranes and a leathery shell.

Most reptiles are oviparous, laying eggs that develop outside the mother's body. Some species, such as the box turtle in **Figure 31–7,** lay their eggs in carefully prepared nests, then abandon them. Alligators also lay their eggs in nests, but they guard the eggs until they hatch, and provide some care after hatching. Some snakes and lizards are ovoviviparous, and the young are born alive. By carrying her eggs within her body, the female can protect the eggs and keep them warm.

Unlike an amphibian egg, which almost always needs to develop in water, the shell and membranes of a reptilian egg create a protected environment in which the embryo can develop without drying out. This type of egg is called an **amniotic egg** (am-nee-AHT-ihk), named after the amnion, one of the four membranes that surrounds the developing embryo. The other three membranes are the yolk sac, the chorion, and the allantois. Find each of these membranes in **Figure 31–8** and learn about their functions. The amniotic egg, also seen in birds, is one of the most important adaptations to life on land.

✓ CHECKPOINT *What are the four parts of an amniotic egg?*

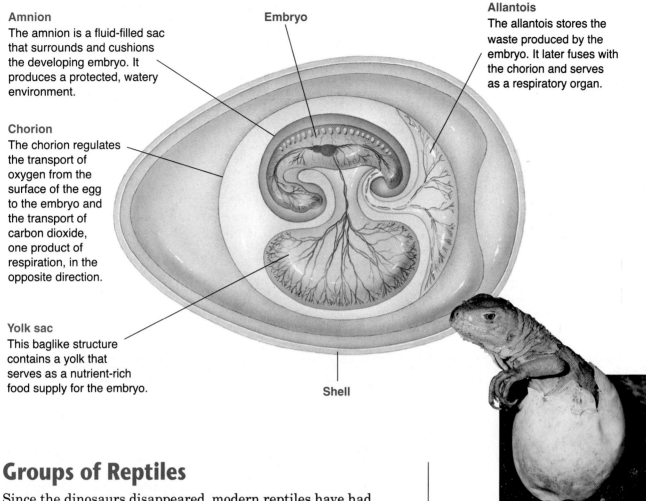

Amnion
The amnion is a fluid-filled sac that surrounds and cushions the developing embryo. It produces a protected, watery environment.

Chorion
The chorion regulates the transport of oxygen from the surface of the egg to the embryo and the transport of carbon dioxide, one product of respiration, in the opposite direction.

Yolk sac
This baglike structure contains a yolk that serves as a nutrient-rich food supply for the embryo.

Embryo

Allantois
The allantois stores the waste produced by the embryo. It later fuses with the chorion and serves as a respiratory organ.

Shell

▲ **Figure 31–8** An amniotic egg contains several membranes and an external shell. Although it is waterproof, the egg shell is porous, allowing gases to pass through. The shell of reptile eggs is usually soft and leathery. The photograph shows a hatching iguana leaving the broken shell of its amniotic egg. ⟶ **The amniotic egg is one of the most important adaptations to life on dry land.**

Groups of Reptiles

Since the dinosaurs disappeared, modern reptiles have had plenty of time and space to diversify. ⟶ **The four surviving groups of reptiles are lizards and snakes, crocodilians, turtles and tortoises, and the tuatara (too-uh-TAH-ruh).**

Lizards and Snakes Modern lizards and snakes belong to the order Squamata (skwah-MAH-tuh), or scaly reptiles. Most lizards have legs, clawed toes, external ears, and movable eyelids. Some lizards have evolved into highly specialized forms. For example, Gila (HEE-luh) monsters—large, stocky lizards that live in the southwestern United States and Mexico—have glands in the lower jaw that produce venom for defense against predators.

Snakes have lost both pairs of legs during the course of their evolution. Although they are legless, snakes are highly efficient predators, even in the ocean. Some snakes are so small that they resemble earthworms. Others, such as some species of python, can grow to more than 8 meters in length. The ability of certain snakes to produce venom has caused some people to harbor an unjustified fear of all snakes. More people in the United States die from bee stings than from snakebites. In fact, most snakes tend to avoid people, not to confront them!

Crocodilians Examples of crocodilians and other reptile groups are shown in **Figure 31–9.** Any member of the order Crocodilia—including alligators, crocodiles, caimans, and gavials—can easily be recognized by its long and typically broad snout and its squat appearance. Crocodilians are fierce carnivores that prey on animals such as fishes, deer, and even humans. Crocodilians are very protective of their young. The females guard their eggs from predators. After the eggs are hatched, the mother gently carries her young to a nursery area and watches over them.

Crocodilians live only in the tropics and subtropics, where the climate remains warm year-round. Alligators, and their relatives the caimans, live only in fresh water and are found almost exclusively in North and South America. Crocodiles, on the other hand, may live in either fresh or salt water and are native to Africa, India, and Southeast Asia.

Turtles and Tortoises Turtles and tortoises are members of the order Chelonia (kuh-LOH-nee-uh). The name *turtle* usually refers to members of this order that live in water; the name *tortoise* refers to those that live on land. A terrapin is a turtle that is found in water that is somewhat salty.

▼ **Figure 31–9** The four orders of living reptiles are the Squamata, Crocodilia, Testudines, and Sphenodonta. ◎ **The common names of these modern reptile groups are lizards and snakes, crocodilians, turtles and tortoises, and the tuatara.**

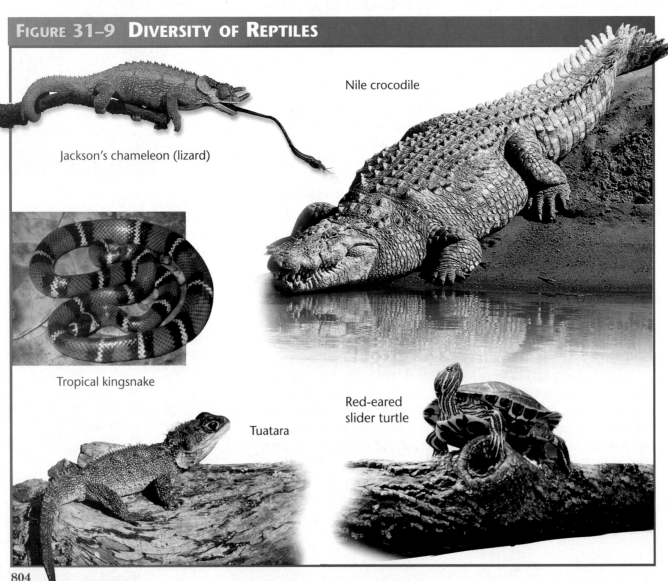

FIGURE 31–9 DIVERSITY OF REPTILES

Jackson's chameleon (lizard)

Nile crocodile

Tropical kingsnake

Tuatara

Red-eared slider turtle

Turtles and tortoises have a shell built into the skeleton, although in a few species the shell is not very hard. The shell consists of two parts: a dorsal part, or **carapace,** and a ventral part, or **plastron.** The animal's backbone forms the center of the carapace. The head, legs, and tail stick out through holes where the carapace and plastron join. Tortoises and most turtles pull into their shells to protect themselves.

Several other adaptations allow turtles and tortoises to live in a wide range of habitats—dry, wet, and in-between. Lacking teeth, these reptiles have horny ridges that cover the upper and lower jaws. The jaws are often powerful enough to deliver a damaging bite. All possess strong limbs to lift their body off the ground when walking or, in the case of sea turtles, to drag themselves across a sandy shore to lay eggs.

Tuataras The tuatara is the only surviving member of the order Rhynchocephalia (ring-koh-suh-FAY-lee-uh), or "beak-headed" reptiles. It is found only on a few small islands off the coast of New Zealand. Tuatura resemble lizards, but they differ from lizards in many ways. For example, they lack external ears and retain primitive scales. Tuatara also have a legendary "third eye," which is part of a complex organ located on top of the brain. The function of this organ, if any, is still unknown.

Ecology of Reptiles

Many reptiles are in danger because their habitats have been, and are being, destroyed. In addition, humans hunt reptiles for food, to sell as pets, and for their skins, from which bags, boots, and combs are made. Laws now protect some species, such as sea turtles, which were once numerous in both the Atlantic and Pacific oceans. Sea turtle recovery programs, such as the one shown in **Figure 31–10,** give many young turtles a head start on survival. Although there are many other programs in place that protect reptiles, more conservation efforts are needed worldwide to counteract their dwindling numbers.

▲ **Figure 31–10** This wildlife ranger is retrieving green sea turtle eggs on Turtle Island National Park in Borneo. He will bring the eggs to an incubation station, where they can hatch safe from harm. After hatching, the young turtles will be released to the sea. **Inferring** *What might harm sea turtle eggs that are left on a beach to hatch?*

31–1 Section Assessment

1. ⬤ **Key Concept** List the main characteristics of reptiles.

2. ⬤ **Key Concept** List five ways that reptiles are adapted to life on dry land.

3. ⬤ **Key Concept** Name the four orders of modern reptiles and give an example of each.

4. How is excretion carried out in animals that live on land?

5. How does a lizard control its body temperature?

6. **Critical Thinking** **Predicting** What might happen to reptiles if conditions on Earth became permanently warmer and much damper?

TEXT Assessment Use iText to review the important concepts in Section 31–1.

MAKING CONNECTIONS

Biodiversity
In Chapter 6, you learned about threats to biodiversity. Do research to find out what factors threaten a reptile such as the sea turtle, and what steps are taken to protect this reptile. Make a brochure that shows what you have learned.

31-2 Birds

Guide for Reading

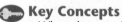

Key Concepts
• What characteristics do birds have in common?
• How are birds adapted for flight?

Vocabulary
feather
endotherm
crop
gizzard
air sac

**Reading Strategy:
Monitoring Your
Understanding**
As you read, make sure that you understand what you read. If you have difficulty, think of a strategy that might make the text clearer. For example, you might read the paragraph again, slowly; see whether an illustration helps you understand the printed text; or ask another student or your teacher for help.

Whether they are greeting the dawn with song or coloring the air with brilliant feathers, birds are among the most obvious and welcome of all animals. From common robins to the spectacular and rare quetzal of Central America, the nearly 10,000 modern bird species seem to live everywhere.

What Is a Bird?

In a group this diverse, it is difficult to find many characteristics that are shared by all members. But we can identify the features that most birds have in common. **Birds are reptilelike animals that maintain a constant internal body temperature. They have an outer covering of feathers; two legs that are covered with scales and are used for walking or perching; and front limbs modified into wings.** Most of these features are adaptations for flight.

The single most important characteristic that separates birds from living reptiles, and from all other living animals, is feathers. **Feathers** are made mostly of protein and develop from pits in the birds' skin. Feathers help birds fly and also keep them warm. **Figure 31–11** shows the two main types of feathers: contour feathers and down. Herons and some other birds that live on or in water also have powder down, which releases a fine powder that repels water.

▼ **Figure 31–11** Birds have different types of feathers that vary in structure and function. **An outer covering of feathers is the main characteristic that sets birds apart from other animals.**

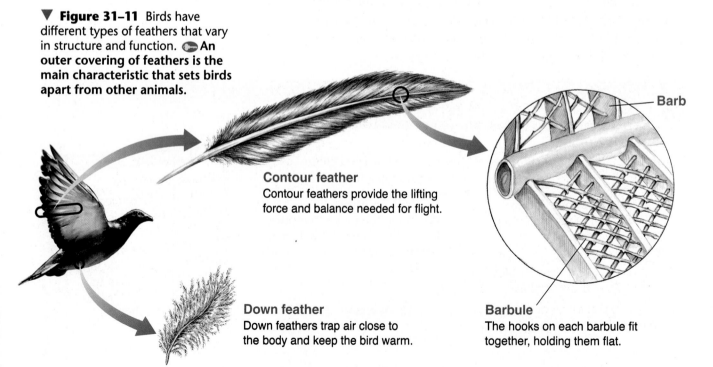

Contour feather
Contour feathers provide the lifting force and balance needed for flight.

Down feather
Down feathers trap air close to the body and keep the bird warm.

Barb

Barbule
The hooks on each barbule fit together, holding them flat.

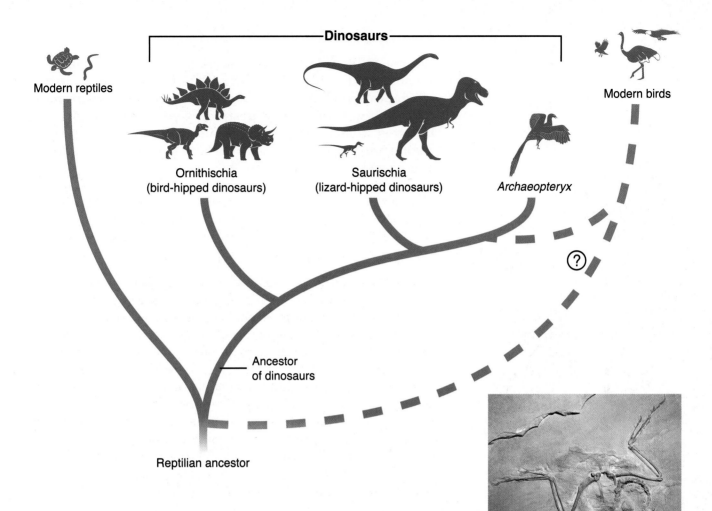

Dinosaurs

Modern reptiles

Ornithischia
(bird-hipped dinosaurs)

Saurischia
(lizard-hipped dinosaurs)

Archaeopteryx

Modern birds

(?)

Ancestor
of dinosaurs

Reptilian ancestor

Evolution of Birds

To many paleontologists a bird is a dinosaur with feathers. That definition may sound odd, but it makes sense. The first fossil ever found of an early birdlike animal is in the genus *Archaeopteryx* (ahr-kee-AHP-tur-iks) and dates from the late Jurassic Period, about 150 million years ago. *Archaeopteryx* looked like a small, running dinosaur. In fact, *Archaeopteryx* would be classified as a dinosaur except for one important feature: It had well-developed feathers covering most of its body. Because of this, the crow-sized *Archaeopteryx* is considered an early bird. Unlike modern birds, however, this creature had teeth in its beak, a bony tail, and toes and claws on its wings. Thus, *Archaeopteryx* is a transitional species with a combination of dinosaurlike and birdlike characteristics.

Scientists debate whether birds evolved directly from dinosaurs or both dinosaurs and birds evolved from a common ancestor. Today, most evidence suggests that birds and dinosaurs are close relatives. Although this relationship is shown in **Figure 31–12**, the evolutionary origin of birds is still not completely resolved.

✓ **CHECKPOINT** *What is* **Archaeopteryx?**

▲ **Figure 31–12** The diagram at the top shows the evolutionary tree of modern birds. None of the animals shown are direct ancestors of modern birds. But fossils such as *Archaeopteryx* (above) do show a mixture of characteristics of birds and dinosaurs. **Interpreting Graphics** *Based on the cladogram, what are the two alternative explanations for the evolution of modern birds?*

Form, Function, and Flight

One reason for the evolutionary success of birds is found in the adaptations that allow them to fly. 🗝 **Birds have a number of adaptations that enable them to fly. These adaptations include highly efficient digestive, respiratory, and circulatory systems; aerodynamic feathers and wings; and strong chest muscles.** Most birds have these characteristics, even though some birds cannot fly.

The ways in which birds carry out their life functions, such as obtaining food and oxygen, contribute to their ability to fly. For example, flight requires an enormous amount of energy, which birds obtain from the food they eat. Birds also require energy to maintain their body temperature.

Body Temperature Control Unlike reptiles, which must draw body warmth from their environment, birds can generate their own body heat. Animals that can generate their own body heat are called **endotherms.** Endotherms, which include birds, mammals, and some other animals, have a high rate of metabolism compared to ectotherms such as reptiles. Recall that metabolism is the sum of chemical and physical processes that go on inside the body. Metabolism produces heat. A bird's feathers insulate its body enough to conserve most of its metabolic energy, allowing the bird to warm its body more efficiently. The body temperature of most birds is about 41°C even on cold winter days.

✓CHECKPOINT *What is an endotherm?*

Feeding Any body heat that a bird loses must be regained by eating food. The more food a bird eats, the more heat energy its metabolism can generate. Because small birds lose heat relatively faster than large ones, small birds must eat more, relative to their body size. In fact, the phrase "eats like a bird" is quite misleading, because most birds are voracious eaters!

As you can see in **Figure 31–13,** birds' beaks, or bills, are adapted to the type of food they eat. Insect-eating birds have short, fine bills that can pick ants and other insects off leaves and branches, or can catch flying insects. Seed-eaters have short, thick bills. Carnivorous birds, such as eagles, shred their prey with strong hooked bills. Long, thin bills can be used for gathering nectar from flowers or probing soft mud for worms and shellfish. Large, long bills help birds to pick fruit from branches, while long, flat bills are used to grasp fish.

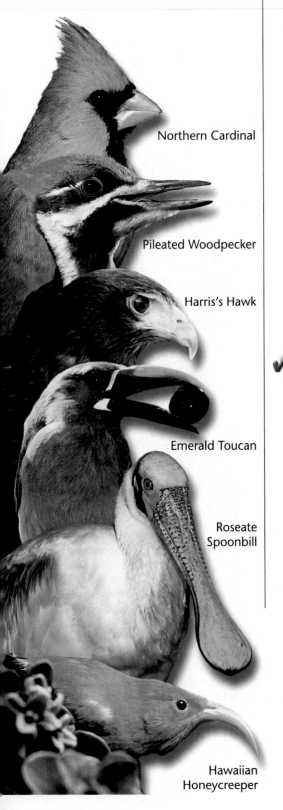

Northern Cardinal

Pileated Woodpecker

Harris's Hawk

Emerald Toucan

Roseate Spoonbill

Hawaiian Honeycreeper

Figure 31–13 Bird bills come in a variety of shapes and sizes. You can tell a good deal about a bird's feeding habits from its bill. **Drawing Conclusions** *Based on the size and shape of its bill, what does a roseate spoonbill feed on?*

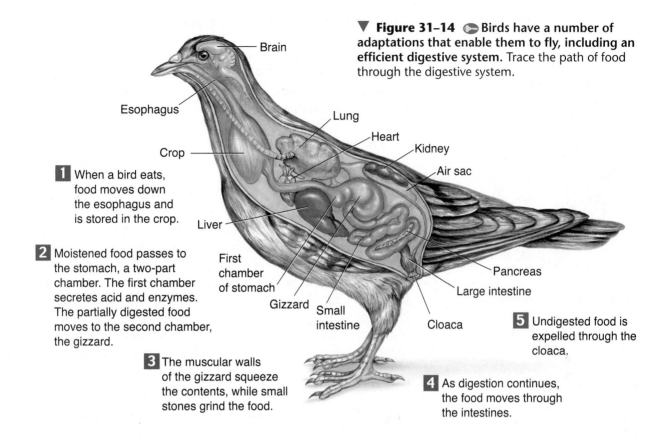

Figure 31–14 Birds have a number of adaptations that enable them to fly, including an efficient digestive system. Trace the path of food through the digestive system.

Brain

Esophagus

Lung

Heart

Crop

Kidney

Air sac

1 When a bird eats, food moves down the esophagus and is stored in the crop.

Liver

2 Moistened food passes to the stomach, a two-part chamber. The first chamber secretes acid and enzymes. The partially digested food moves to the second chamber, the gizzard.

First chamber of stomach

Gizzard

Small intestine

Pancreas

Large intestine

Cloaca

5 Undigested food is expelled through the cloaca.

3 The muscular walls of the gizzard squeeze the contents, while small stones grind the food.

4 As digestion continues, the food moves through the intestines.

The digestive system of a bird is shown in **Figure 31–14.** Birds lack teeth, and therefore they cannot break down food by chewing it. However, many birds have specialized structures to help digest food. One such structure is the **crop,** which is located at the lower end of the esophagus. Food is stored and moistened in the crop before it moves further in the digestive tract.

In some birds, such as pigeons, the crop has a second function. During nesting season, the breakdown of cells in the crop produces a substance that is rich in protein and fat. Parent birds regurgitate this substance and feed their newly hatched young with it. This substance provides the young birds with materials they need to grow.

From the crop, moistened food moves into the stomach. The form that a bird's stomach takes depends on the bird's feeding habits. Birds that eat meat or fish have an expandable area in which large amounts of soft food can be stored. Birds that eat insects or seeds, however, have a muscular organ called the **gizzard** that helps in the mechanical breakdown of food by grinding it. The gizzard forms part of the stomach. In many species of bird, the gizzard contains small pieces of stone and gravel that the bird has swallowed. The thick, muscular walls of the gizzard grind the gravel and food together, crushing food particles and making them easier to digest.

Food moves from the stomach to the small intestine, where the breakdown of food is completed and food is absorbed into the body. Digestive wastes leave the body through the cloaca.

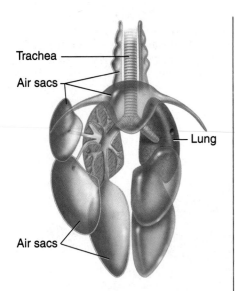

▲ **Figure 31–15** Birds have a unique respiratory system. Air sacs direct air through the lungs in an efficient, one-way flow. **Comparing and Contrasting** *How does this system differ from that of most land vertebrates?*

Labels on figure: Trachea, Air sacs, Lung, Air sacs

Respiration Birds have a unique and highly efficient way of taking in oxygen and eliminating carbon dioxide. When a bird inhales, most air first enters large posterior **air sacs** in the body cavity and bones. Observe the air sacs in **Figure 31–15.** The inhaled air then flows through the lungs. Air travels through the lungs in a series of small tubes. These tubes are lined with specialized tissue, where gas exchange takes place.

The complex system of air sacs and breathing tubes ensures that air flows into the air sacs and out through the lungs in a single direction. The one-way flow constantly exposes the lungs to oxygen-rich air. Contrast this to the system found in most land vertebrates, in which oxygen-rich air is inhaled, and oxygen-poor air is exhaled. The air travels in two directions, in and out. In an in-out system, the lungs are exposed to oxygen-rich air only during inhalation.

What advantage does the efficient respiratory system of birds provide? The constant, one-way flow of oxygen-rich air helps birds maintain their high metabolic rate. Birds need a high metabolism to maintain body temperature and provide the large amounts of energy required for flight. In addition, the abundant supply of oxygen enables birds to fly at high altitudes where there is little oxygen in the atmosphere.

✓ CHECKPOINT *How is their respiratory system advantageous to birds?*

Circulation Birds have four-chambered hearts and two separate circulatory loops. Notice in **Figure 31–16** that a bird's heart, unlike that of amphibians and most reptiles, has two separate ventricles, the right ventricle and the left ventricle. There is complete separation of oxygen-rich and oxygen-poor blood. One half of the heart receives oxygen-poor blood from the body and pumps this blood to the lungs. Oxygen-rich blood returns to the other side of the heart to be pumped to the rest of the body. This double-loop system ensures that oxygen collected by the lungs is distributed to the body tissue with maximum efficiency.

▼ **Figure 31–16** To keep blood moving rapidly, a bird's heart beats quickly—from 150 to more than 1000 beats per minute! **Applying Concepts** *Why is it important for a bird's heart to move blood so rapidly?*

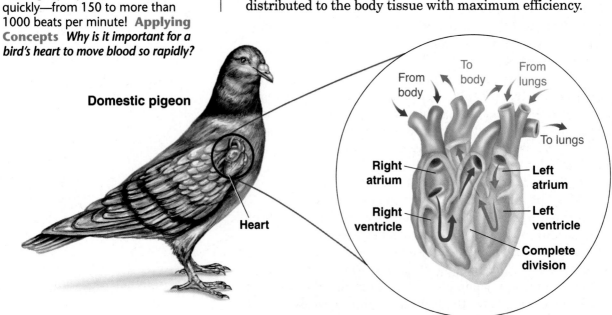

Domestic pigeon

Labels on figure: Heart, From body, To body, From lungs, To lungs, Right atrium, Left atrium, Right ventricle, Left ventricle, Complete division

Quick Lab

How do birds breathe?

Materials 6 round balloons, hand-powered balloon pump, measuring tape, clock with second hand

Procedure

1. Work in groups of three. Make a copy of the data table at right on a blank sheet of paper. One person will inflate a balloon by mouth, while a second person inflates a balloon with a hand-powered pump. The third person is the timekeeper.
2. Begin inflating both balloons at the same time. After 10 seconds, the timer will say "stop." Stop inflating the balloons and pinch the necks of the balloons to keep the air inside. **CAUTION:** *Do not try to inflate balloons if you have a condition that would make this dangerous for you.*
3. Measure and record the circumference of each balloon in your data table. **CAUTION:** *Discard all balloons that have been inflated.*

Data Table

Name	Balloon circumference (cm)		Difference
	Mouth	Pump	

Average difference _____

4. Repeat Steps 1–3 until each member of your group has inflated two balloons. In your data table, record the difference in balloon diameter for each person and the average difference for the group.

Analyze and Conclude

1. **Analyzing Data** Which method was faster? Which method required more effort?
2. **Using Models** Which method worked like reptile lungs? Which method worked like bird lungs? Explain your answers.
3. **Formulating Hypotheses** How is efficient respiration especially valuable to birds?

Excretion The excretory systems of many birds are similar to those of some reptiles. Nitrogenous wastes are removed from the blood by the kidneys, converted to uric acid, and deposited in the cloaca. There, most of the water is reabsorbed, leaving uric acid crystals in a white, pasty form that you may recognize as bird droppings.

Response To coordinate the movements required for flight, birds have well-developed sense organs. They also have a brain that can quickly interpret and respond to a lot of incoming signals. A bird's brain, shown in **Figure 31–17,** is relatively large for its body size. The cerebrum, which controls such behaviors as flying, nest building, care of young, courtship, and mating, is quite large. The cerebellum is also well developed, as you might expect in an animal that uses precise, coordinated movements. The medulla oblongata coordinates basic body processes, such as the heartbeat.

Birds have extraordinarily well-developed eyes and sizable optic lobes in the brain. Birds see color very well—in many cases, better than humans. Most bird species can also hear quite well. The senses of taste and smell, however, are not well developed in most birds, and the olfactory bulbs in a bird's brain are small.

▼ **Figure 31–17** Compared to reptiles, birds have an enlarged cerebellum that coordinates the movements of wings and legs. **Formulating Hypotheses** *Why would the cerebrum also be larger in birds than in reptiles?*

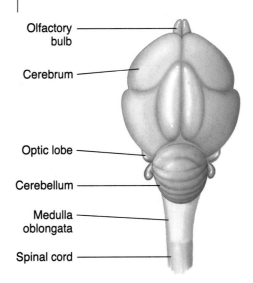

Olfactory bulb
Cerebrum
Optic lobe
Cerebellum
Medulla oblongata
Spinal cord

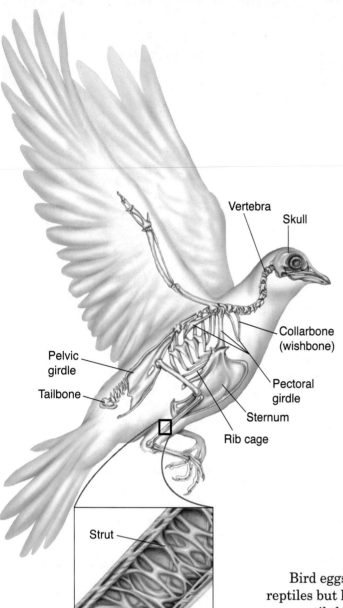

Movement Some birds cannot fly. Instead, they get around mainly by walking or running, like ostriches, or by swimming, like penguins. However, the vast majority of birds can fly.

Observe a bird's skeletal system in **Figure 31–18**. Although the bones in a bird's wings are homologous to the bones in the front limbs of other vertebrates, they have very different shapes and structures. In flying birds, many large bones, such as the collarbone, are fused together, making a bird's skeleton more rigid than a reptile's. These bones form a sturdy frame that anchors the muscles used for flight. The bones are strengthened by internal struts similar to those used in the framework of tall buildings and bridges. Birds also have large chest muscles that power the upward and downward wing strokes necessary for flight. The muscles attach to a long keel that runs down the front of an enlarged breastbone, or sternum.

Reproduction In birds, both male and female reproductive tracts open into the cloaca. The sex organs—which are internal in both sexes—often shrink in size when the birds are not breeding. As birds prepare to mate, the ovaries and testes grow larger until they reach functioning size. Mating birds press their cloacas together to transfer sperm from the male to the female. Some male birds have a penis that transfers sperm to the female's cloaca.

Bird eggs are amniotic eggs. They are similar to the eggs of reptiles but have hard outer shells. Most birds incubate their eggs until the eggs hatch. When a chick is ready to hatch, it uses a small tooth on its bill to make a hole in the shell. After much pushing, poking, and prodding by the chick, the eggshell breaks open. Once the exhausted bird has hatched, it collapses for a while and allows its feathers to dry. Both parents may be kept busy providing food for their hungry offspring.

CHECKPOINT *Do birds have external or internal fertilization?*

Groups of Birds

Birds fill the woods and fields with song. Flocks of birds are drawn to backyard feeders. Imagine how dull the world would be without the color, song, and variety of birds.

With nearly 30 different orders, it is impossible to present each type of bird here. Instead, **Figure 31–19** provides an overview of some of the better-known groups and their specific adaptations. By far, the largest order of birds is the passerines (pass-uh-REENZ), or perching birds. This group includes songbirds such as larks, sparrows, and finches. There are over 5000 species of perching birds.

▲ **Figure 31–18** Like most of its anatomy, a bird's skeleton is well adapted for flight, providing a sturdy attachment point for muscles. The long bones are exceptionally strong and light because of cross-bracing and air spaces. In strong flying birds, such as pigeons, the chest muscles may account for as much as 30 percent of the animal's mass. **Calculating** *If this pigeon has a mass of 200 grams, and 30 percent of its mass is chest muscles, what is the mass of its chest muscles?*

FIGURE 31-19 DIVERSITY IN BIRDS

Birds show remarkable diversity and inhabit many different environments. Some representative groups are shown below.

Applying Concepts *Which group of birds is the largest?*

◀ PELICANS AND THEIR RELATIVES

These birds are found in all types of aquatic ecosystems, from open ocean to lakes and rivers. All have four toes that are connected by a web. *Examples:* pelicans, cormorants, boobies, frigatebirds (shown here).

▲ BIRDS OF PREY

These birds, also known as raptors, are fierce predators with hooked bills, large wingspans, and sharp talons. *Examples:* condors, hawks, owls, eagles (shown above), falcons.

PARROTS ▶

Colorful and noisy, these birds use their feet to hold food. *Examples:* macaws, lovebirds, cockatoos.

▲ CAVITY-NESTING BIRDS

These multicolored birds live in holes that they make in trees, mounds, or underground tunnels. *Examples:* barbet (shown here), toucans, woodpeckers.

◀ PERCHING BIRDS

Also called passerines, this is by far the largest order of birds. Many are songbirds. *Examples:* sparrows, crows, mockingbirds, cardinals (shown here).

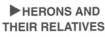 **▶ HERONS AND THEIR RELATIVES**

These birds are adapted to wading in a variety of aquatic habitats. *Examples:* storks, ibises, spoonbills, herons (shown here), cranes.

▶ OSTRICHES AND THEIR RELATIVES

These flightless birds must move by running or swimming. *Examples:* ostriches (shown here), rheas, emus, cassowaries, kiwis.

Ecology of Birds

Because birds are so numerous and diverse, they interact with natural ecosystems and human society in many different ways. For example, hummingbirds, like the one in **Figure 31–20,** pollinate flowers in both tropical and temperate zones. Fruit-eating birds swallow seeds but may not digest them, so their droppings disperse seeds over great distances. Insect-eating birds, such as swallows and chimney swifts, catch great numbers of mosquitoes and other insects, and therefore help control insect populations.

Many birds migrate long distances—often over hundreds of kilometers of open sea. Such migrations are usually seasonal. It can be startling during a winter visit to a tropical country to see Northern orioles or bright red cardinals flitting around banana trees with parrots and toucans! How do migrating birds find their way? Some species use stars and other celestial bodies as guides. Other species may use a combination of landmarks and cues from Earth's magnetic field.

Because birds are highly visible and are an important part of the biosphere, they can serve as indicators of environmental health. It is no accident that conservationist Rachel Carson chose songbirds for the focus of her pioneering campaign in the 1960s against the careless use of DDT and other pesticides. In her book *Silent Spring,* Carson described to the public for the first time how pesticides that stay in the environment can accumulate in food chains and cause harm to animals they were never intended to affect. Thanks to the efforts of Carson and other conservationists, many birds—especially predators such as eagles and ospreys—have returned from the brink of extinction.

▲ **Figure 31–20** This hummingbird uses its long, thin beak to draw nectar from a flower. While feeding, the bird may pick up pollen on its beak and carry it to the next flower it visits, thereby helping the flower to pollinate. **Applying Concepts** *Which type of ecological relationship is represented by the hummingbird and the flower: parasitism, mutualism, or commensalism?*

31–2 Section Assessment

1. **Key Concept** Describe the characteristics of a bird.

2. **Key Concept** List three ways in which birds are well adapted for flight.

3. What is the evolutionary relationship between birds and dinosaurs?

4. How does a chick get out of its eggshell?

5. **Critical Thinking Applying Concepts** Explain why crops and gizzards are especially common and well developed in seed-eating birds but less common in carnivorous birds.

iTEXT Assessment Use iText to review the important concepts in Section 31–2.

Take It to the NET

Find out more about the orders of birds. Then, create a poster that shows one representative from each order. Use the links provided in the Biology area at the Prentice Hall Web site for help in completing this activity: **www.phschool.com**

Examining Bird Bones

Birds have many adaptations that enable them to fly, including the structure and properties of their skeletons. In this investigation, you will compare bones from birds and mammals to determine how bird bones are adapted for flight.

Problem **How is a bird's skeleton adapted for flight?**

Materials

- cut sections of bird and mammal bones
- bird breastbone
- hand lens
- mammal bone
- bird wing bone
- balance
- 250-mL graduated cylinder
- dissecting probe
- calculator

Skills Observing, Measuring, Calculating

Procedure

Part A: Bone Structure

1. Use a hand lens to examine cut sections of bird and mammal bones. Look at the interiors of the bones and record your observations.

2. Look at a bird breastbone (sternum). Carefully observe its structure.

Part B: Bone Density

3. Make a copy of the data table on a separate sheet of paper. Use a balance to measure the mass of a bird wing bone.

4. Put 180 mL of water in the graduated cylinder. **CAUTION:** *Handle the graduated cylinder carefully. If it breaks, tell your teacher immediately.*

5. Use a dissecting probe to hold the bird wing bone under water in the graduated cylinder. In your data table, record the water level in the cylinder. Subtract the original water volume from this value to find the volume of the bone.

6. The density of an object is equal to its mass divided by its volume (D = M/V). Calculate the density of the bone by dividing its mass by its volume. Record the density of the bird bone in your data table.

7. Repeat steps 3 to 6 to find the density of the mammal bone.

Data Table					
Source of bone	Mass (g)	Volume (mL)			Density of bone (g/cm³)
		Water	Water + bone	Bone	
Bird					
Mammal					

Analyze and Conclude

1. **Comparing and Contrasting** How are the bird and mammal bones similar? Different? How is the bird bone adapted for flight?

2. **Inferring** What might be the function of the muscles that attach to a bird's sternum? How is the protruding bird sternum an adaptation for flight?

3. **Drawing Conclusions** How are the densities of bird and mammal bones related to the lives of these animals?

Go Further

Applying Concepts In addition to specialized bones, birds' adaptations to flight include several types of feathers. Use reference materials to find out how each type of feather contributes to birds' adaptations.

31–1 Reptiles
 Key Concepts

- A reptile is a vertebrate that has scaly skin, lungs, and eggs with several membranes.
- Well-developed lungs; a double-loop circulatory system; an efficient excretory system; strong limbs; internal fertilization; and shelled, terrestrial eggs are the main adaptations that have contributed to the success of reptiles on land.
- The four surviving groups of reptiles are lizards and snakes, crocodilians, turtles and tortoises, and the tuatara.

Vocabulary
ectotherm, p. 800
amniotic egg, p. 802
carapace, p. 805
plastron, p. 805

31–2 Birds
Key Concepts

- Birds are reptilelike animals that maintain a constant internal body temperature. They have an outer covering of feathers; two legs that are covered with scales and are used for walking or perching; and front limbs modified into wings.
- Birds have a number of adaptations that enable them to fly. These adaptations include highly efficient digestive, respiratory, and circulatory systems; aerodynamic feathers and wings; and strong chest muscles.

Vocabulary
feather, p. 806
endotherm, p. 808
crop, p. 809
gizzard, p. 809
air sac, p. 810

Thinking Visually
Using information from this chapter, complete the following concept map:

Chapter 31

Part A

Multiple Choice

For each statement or question, select the number of the word or expression that, of those given, best completes the statement or answers the question.

1 Feathers that provide lifting force and balance needed for flight are known as
  (1) down feathers
  (2) contour feathers
  (3) powder feathers
  (4) scale feathers

2 Which term best describes an animal that relies on interaction with the environment to help it control body temperature?
  (1) endotherm   **(3)** ectotherm
  (2) amnion   **(4)** endoderm

3 Which reptiles have both a carapace and a plastron for protection?
  (1) lizards and snakes
  (2) turtles and tortoises
  (3) crocodilians
  (4) tuataras

4 In the diagram below, what is the function of the structure labeled Y?
  (1) It stores wastes produced by the embryo.
  (2) It supplies nutrients to the embryo.
  (3) It enlarges the shell as the embryo grows.
  (4) It cushions the embryo from shock.

5 Which characteristic is an important adaptation that separates birds from other animals?
  (1) their lack of a bony skeleton
  (2) having only two legs
  (3) maintaining a constant body temperature
  (4) the presence of feathers

6 Which part of a bird's digestive tract is adapted for the storage of food before digestion takes place?
  (1) esophagus   **(3)** gizzard
  (2) crop   **(4)** cloaca

7 Which bird structure is especially adapted to support flight?
  (1) muscular gizzard
  (2) lightweight bill
  (3) strong legs
  (4) chest muscles

8 Which statement about reptiles is correct?
  (1) Water-dwelling reptiles produce eggs without shells.
  (2) Many reptiles have a single-loop circulatory system.
  (3) Land-dwelling reptiles convert ammonia to uric acid.
  (4) Most reptiles have internal mechanisms to regulate body temperature.

9 Birds are currently believed to have evolved from
  (1) mammal-like reptiles
  (2) flying amphibians
  (3) lizards
  (4) dinosaurs

10 Which group consists of organisms that are *all* reptiles?
  (1) tuataras, lizards, and dinosaurs
  (2) turtles, snakes, and passerines
  (3) crocodilians, condors, and cormorants
  (4) raptors, archaeopteryx, and tortoises

11 Amniotic eggs are a characteristic of
  (1) both amphibians and reptiles
  (2) both reptiles and birds
  (3) birds, only
  (4) reptiles, only

12 Reptiles carry on
  (1) internal fertilization and only external development
  (2) external fertilization and only external development
  (3) internal fertilization and either internal or external development
  (4) external fertilization and either internal or external development

Test-Taking Tip When presented with questions that are related to data in a table, study each column and row of the table for information you need to answer the questions.

Preparing for the
Living Environment Exam

Parts B and C

Multiple Choice and Extended Response

For those questions that ask you to select a response, choose the one that best completes the statement or answers the question. For all others follow the directions given.

13 State two adaptations that enable birds to live in environments that are colder than those typically supporting reptiles.

14 Explain why the amniotic egg is considered to be one of the most important adaptations to life on land.

15 Explain why a turtle cannot "crawl out of its shell."

16 Explain how a pigeon's crop helps it care for its young.

17 State two ways used by migrating birds to find their way.

Base your answers to questions 18 and 19 on the information and data table below and on your knowledge of biology.

Reptiles rely on their environment for body warmth. Studies have shown that there is a relationship between a turtle's body temperature and the ability of digestive enzymes to break down food, as shown in the following table.

The Effect of Body Temperature on Rate of Turtle Digestion

Body Temperature of Turtle	Rate of Digestion
35°C	Normal or slightly below normal
25°C	Proceeding normally
15°C	Very slow
5°C	No digestion occurring

18 Predict what environmental temperature would be best to produce the maximum growth in this species of turtle. Support your prediction with data from the table.

19 Explain why variations in the turtle's body temperature affect its rate of digestion.

Base your answers to questions 20 through 23 on the information and data table below and on your knowledge of biology.

An experiment was conducted to see how air temperature affects a snake's ability to move. The experimenter recorded the air temperature, then placed the snake a fixed distance away from a piece of food. Then, she recorded the time it took for the snake to reach the food. She repeated the experiment four times, each time at a different air temperature. The table shows the results of the five trials.

The Effect of Temperature on Snake Movement

Temperature (°C)	Time (seconds)
4	51
10	50
15	43
21	37
27	35

20 Graph the data in the table above on a separate sheet of graph paper. (*Hint:* Assign the manipulated, or independent, variable to the *x*-axis and the responding, or dependent, variable to the *y*-axis.)
    • Label each axis, including the units used, and indicate an appropriate scale on each axis.
    • Plot each data point. Surround each point with a circle, and then connect the points with a line.

21 At what air temperature did the snake reach the food the fastest?
    (1) 27°C   **(3)** 10°C
    (2) 21°C   **(4)** 4°C

22 State the relationship between air temperature and the time it took the snake to reach the food.

23 If this same experiment were conducted with a bird instead of a snake, would the experimenter be likely to obtain similar results? Support your answer with an explanation.

24 Predict how the ability of a bird egg to develop and hatch would be affected if the egg were coated with oil or wax. Support your prediction with information about the structures associated with bird eggs.

Base your answers to questions 25 through 27 on the reading passage below and on your knowledge of biology.

Bird Imports

Among the 1000 established species of birds in the United States, about 97 species were introduced. Of those, only about 5 percent are considered beneficial—chickens, for example—while most are pests. Peskiest of all is the ubiquitous pigeon, which racks up an estimated $1.1 billion a year in economic costs. Add in a few other imports, such as the starling, and the total comes to $2.1 billion.

The nonnative pigeons spend their time feeding on grain and fouling buildings, statues, cars, and sometimes people in most cities of the world. One study estimated the economic impact of fouling at $9 per pigeon per year. Assuming there are 0.5 pigeons per person in urban areas, scientists estimate that common pigeons cause at least $1.1 billion in damage each year. Pigeons are also reservoirs for over 50 diseases, including parrot fever, ornithosis, histoplasmosis, and encephalitis.

The English sparrow was imported to the United States in 1853 to control the cankerworm. Like other nonindigenous species, English sparrows didn't limit themselves to the intended food source. With none of their normal predators to keep their population in check, English sparrows cause extensive damage to decorative plants; devour wheat, corn, and buds of fruit trees; and harass robins, orioles, and other native bird species. They also have displaced many native species, such as bluebirds, wrens, and cliff swallows, by driving them from their nests, and they spread about 29 diseases of humans and domestic animals. Researchers estimate their damage at $200 million a year.

25 State three specific problems associated with imported birds that were probably not anticipated when the birds were originally brought into this country.

26 State one reason why nonnative species are able to build up such large populations in their new environments.

27 Since the English sparrow has become a major pest species in the United States, it has been suggested that we import a population of one of the natural predators of the sparrow from England and release these predators to help control the pest species. Explain how this suggestion could add to the problem, rather than solve it.

28 Most reptiles have dry skin covered with thick scales. Explain why this is both advantageous and disadvantageous to reptiles. Be sure to
- state one way reptilian skin is an advantage
- state one way reptilian skin is a disadvantage
- describe how reptiles overcome the disadvantage of having this type of body covering

29 Explain how the climate changes that occurred at the end of the Carboniferous Period affected the evolution of reptiles. In your explanation
- describe the climate changes that occurred
- describe how these changing conditions affected amphibians at the end of the Carboniferous Period
- state specifically why reptiles finally had a competitive advantage over amphibians

30 From the small size of its sternum, or breastbone, scientists infer that *Archaeopteryx* was a poor flier. Propose a hypothesis to explain how *Archaeopteryx* might have used its wings.

31 Compare the structure and function of down feathers to those of contour feathers.

Take It to the NET

One of the most interesting aspects of birds is their ability to migrate over long distances. Visit the Prentice Hall Web site at **www.phschool.com** to find out more about bird migration. Then, answer the following questions:
- How are migratory birds threatened by human activities?
- What are the four major migration routes in North America?
- What is bird-banding, and why is it done?

32 Mammals

A black bear nurses her two cubs in the Smoky Mountains of North Carolina.
🐾 Like all mammals, black bears have hair, breathe air, and nurse their young with milk.

Inquiry Activity

How are teeth adapted to processing different foods?

Procedure

1. Examine a mammal tooth. Describe the shape of the tooth.

2. Based on the tooth's structure, try to infer whether the mammal ate mainly plants or other animals.

3. Repeat steps 1 and 2 for other mammal teeth.

Think About It

1. **Classifying** Sort the teeth into different groups based on their structure. Explain how you classified the teeth.

2. **Inferring** Describe what type of food you think each type of tooth is adapted to processing. Explain your reasoning.

32–1 Introduction to the Mammals

It is late January in the Appalachian Mountains. In a rocky den beneath the snowdrifts, a black bear has just given birth. Two tiny cubs are nursing on their mother's rich milk. It is bitterly cold outside, but the mother's dense fur and thick layer of body fat keep her and her cubs comfortably warm. The mother and cubs will stay in the den for several more months. When spring arrives, the hungry bears will emerge from the den. For the next two years, the cubs will follow their mother as she teaches them to search for food and defend themselves.

Bears are mammals, members of the class Mammalia. All mammals are characterized by two notable features: hair and mammary glands. In female mammals, **mammary glands**—the feature for which mammals are named—produce milk to nourish the young. **In addition to having hair and the ability to nourish their young with milk, all mammals breathe air, have four-chambered hearts, and are endotherms that generate their body heat internally.**

Evolution of Mammals

Neither mammary glands nor hair are preserved in the fossil record. But mammals have several other characteristics that help scientists to identify mammalian fossils. These characteristics include a jaw joint that allows sideways movement, complex teeth that are replaced just once in a lifetime, and several distinctive features of the limbs and the backbone.

According to the fossil record, the first ancestors of mammals diverged from ancient reptiles during the Permian Period, from 290 to 250 million years ago. For millions of years, various mammal-like reptiles lived alongside dinosaurs.

The first true mammals appeared during the late Triassic Period, about 220 million years ago. These mammals were very small and probably resembled modern tree shrews, like the one in **Figure 32–1.** While dinosaurs ruled the Cretaceous Period, from about 145 to 65 million years ago, mammals were generally small and remained out of sight. These mammals were probably nocturnal, or active at night.

After the disappearance of the dinosaurs at the end of the Cretaceous Period, mammals underwent a burst of adaptive radiation. They increased in size and established many new niches. In fact, the Cenozoic Era, which followed the Cretaceous Period, is usually called the Age of Mammals. During the process of continental drift, three groups of mammals became isolated from one another around 60 million years ago. Surviving members of these groups, which include the monotremes, the marsupials, and the placental mammals, continue to inhabit Earth today.

Guide for Reading

Key Concepts
• What are the characteristics of mammals?
• When did mammals evolve?
• How do mammals maintain homeostasis?

Vocabulary
mammary gland
subcutaneous fat
rumen
diaphragm
cerebral cortex

**Reading Strategy:
Asking Questions** Before you read, rewrite the headings in the section as *how, why,* or *what* questions about mammals. As you read, write brief answers to these heading questions.

▼ **Figure 32–1** The first mammals appeared on Earth about 220 million years ago. They may have resembled this tree shrew from Madagascar, shown here clutching a beetle. Like this tree shrew, early mammals probably ate insects.

▲ **Figure 32–2** 🔑 As endotherms, mammals are capable of adjusting their body heat internally. When they get too warm, some mammals, such as this gray wolf puppy, pant to rid their bodies of excess heat.

Form and Function in Mammals

The mammalian body has adapted in varied ways to a great many habitats. As a member of this class of chordates, you may be familiar with some of these adaptations.

Body Temperature Control Like birds, mammals are endotherms. Because their bodies can generate heat internally, mammals do not rely on the sun to keep warm. Mammals—especially small ones—have a much higher metabolic rate than most other chordates. The high rate of metabolism helps mammals generate body heat. Mammals also have external body hair and subcutaneous (sub-kyoo-TAYN-ee-us) fat that help conserve body heat. **Subcutaneous fat** is a layer of fat cells located under the skin. Many mammals also have sweat glands that help cool the body. When the sweat produced by these glands evaporates from the skin, body temperature is lowered. Mammals that lack sweat glands, like the wolf in **Figure 32–2**, often pant to rid themselves of excess heat. 🔑 **The ability of mammals to regulate their body heat from within is an example of homeostasis.** This ability also allows mammals to move about after dark and in the cold, while most other animals would seek shelter.

✓CHECKPOINT) *What is the function of subcutaneous fat?*

Feeding Because of its high metabolic rate, a mammal must eat nearly ten times as much food as a reptile of the same size! Some mammals, such as rabbits and giraffes, eat only plants. Others, including cats and weasels, are meat-eaters. Bears and humans are omnivores, consuming all types of food. Certain whales, like the one in **Figure 32–3**, are filter feeders that eat plankton and small animals that they strain from the sea.

Early mammals ate insects. 🔑 **As mammals evolved, the form and function of their jaws and teeth became adapted to eat foods other than insects.** The joint between the skull and lower jaw became stronger than that of reptiles. This joint allowed mammals to evolve larger, more powerful jaw muscles and different ways of chewing.

▶ **Figure 32–3** The teeth of certain whales, such as this humpback, have been replaced by huge, stiffened plates called baleen. The fringed baleen acts like a filter to strain out small animals from the mouthfuls of water that the whale takes in.
Applying Concepts *What kind of animals do humpback whales eat?*

FIGURE 32–4 JAWS AND TEETH OF MAMMALS

The specialized jaws and teeth of mammals are adapted for different diets. Carnivorous mammals use sharp canines and incisors to grip and slice flesh from their prey. Their jaws usually move up and down as they chew. Herbivorous mammals use flat-edged incisors to grasp and tear vegetation, and flattened molars to grind the food. Their jaws generally move from side to side. Researchers often use tooth shape and structure to classify mammals.

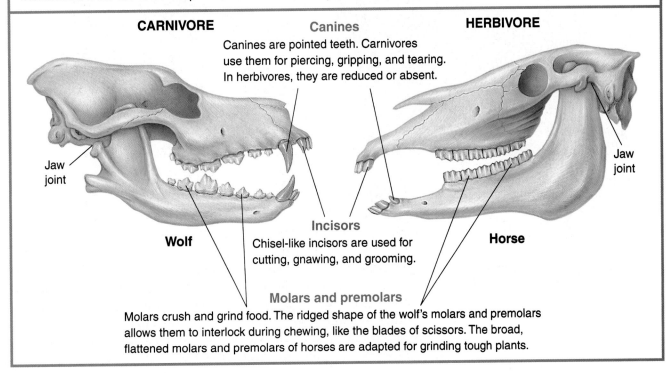

CARNIVORE

Canines
Canines are pointed teeth. Carnivores use them for piercing, gripping, and tearing. In herbivores, they are reduced or absent.

HERBIVORE

Jaw joint

Jaw joint

Wolf

Horse

Incisors
Chisel-like incisors are used for cutting, gnawing, and grooming.

Molars and premolars
Molars crush and grind food. The ridged shape of the wolf's molars and premolars allows them to interlock during chewing, like the blades of scissors. The broad, flattened molars and premolars of horses are adapted for grinding tough plants.

Modern mammals have specialized teeth—canines, incisors, molars, and premolars—which you can see in **Figure 32–4.** Observe that the structure of carnivores' teeth is different from that of herbivores' teeth. Mammals' teeth enable food to be processed efficiently. The more efficiently an animal can obtain and process its food, the more energy it can obtain.

A mammal's digestive tract is adapted to break down and absorb the type of food that it eats. Because digestive enzymes can quickly break down meat, carnivores have a relatively short intestine. Tough, fibrous plant tissues take much more time to digest, so most herbivores have a much longer intestine.

Many herbivores also have specialized digestive organs to break down plant matter. Cows and their relatives have a stomach chamber called the **rumen,** in which newly swallowed plant food is stored and processed. The rumen contains symbiotic bacteria that digest the cellulose of most plant tissues. After some time, the grazer regurgitates the food from the rumen into its mouth. The partially digested food is again chewed and mixed with saliva. The second time the food is swallowed, it moves through the rest of the stomach and into the intestines.

Word Origins

The word **incisor** comes from the Latin word *incisus,* meaning "to cut." **In surgery, what is an incision?**

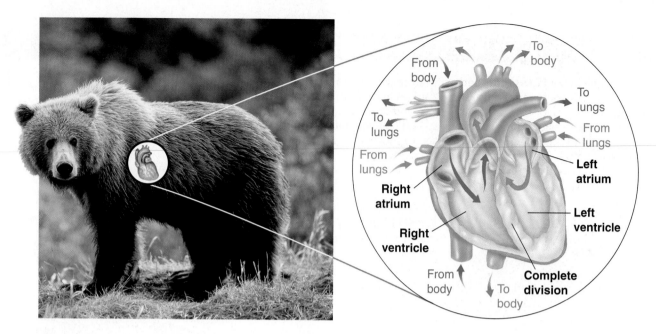

Figure 32–5 All mammals, including this brown bear, have a four-chambered heart that pumps blood in two separate circuits around the body.
Interpreting Graphics
According to the diagram, which chamber receives blood that is low in oxygen?

Respiration All mammals, even those that live in water, use lungs to breathe. These lungs are controlled by two sets of muscles. Mammals inhale when muscles in the chest lift the rib cage up and outward, increasing the volume of the chest cavity. At the same time, a powerful muscle called the **diaphragm** (DY-uh-fram) pulls the bottom of the chest cavity downward, which further increases its volume. As a result, air is pulled into the lungs. When the chest muscles lower the rib cage, and the diaphragm relaxes, the volume of the chest cavity decreases. This action pushes air out of the lungs.

Circulation The mammalian circulatory system is divided into two completely separate loops with a four-chambered heart, shown in **Figure 32–5.** The right side of the heart receives oxygen-poor blood from all over the body and pumps it to the lungs. After picking up oxygen in the lungs, blood returns to the left side of the heart. This oxygen-rich blood is then pumped through blood vessels to the rest of the body. The two separate circuits—one to and from the lungs, and the other to and from the rest of the body—efficiently transport materials throughout the body.

Excretion Mammals have highly developed kidneys that help control the composition of body fluids. Mammalian kidneys extract nitrogenous wastes from the blood in the form of urea. Urea, other wastes, and water combine to form urine. From the kidneys, urine flows to a urinary bladder, where it is stored until it is eliminated. ●━ **The kidneys of mammals help maintain homeostasis by filtering urea from the blood, as well as by excreting excess water or retaining needed water.** They also retain salts, sugars, and other compounds the body cannot afford to lose. Because they are so efficient at controlling and stabilizing the amount of water in the body, the kidneys enable mammals to live in many habitats, such as deserts, in which they could not otherwise survive.

Response Mammals have the most highly developed brains of any animals. As you can see in **Figure 32–6**, the brain consists of three main parts: the cerebrum, the cerebellum, and the medulla oblongata. The cerebrum makes possible such complicated behaviors as thinking and learning. The cerebellum controls muscular coordination. The medulla oblongata regulates involuntary body functions, or those that are not under conscious control, such as breathing and heart rate.

A mammal's cerebrum contains a well-developed outer layer called the **cerebral cortex**, which is the center of thinking and other complex behaviors. Some activities, such as reading this textbook, are possible only with the human cerebral cortex. However, mammals other than humans also exhibit complex behaviors, such as storing food for later use.

Mammals rely on highly developed senses to provide information about their external environment. Many mammals have well-developed senses of smell and hearing. You probably know, for example, that dogs can easily identify people by their particular scent. Although mammalian ears all have the same basic parts, they differ in their ability to detect sound. For example, dogs, bats, and dolphins can detect sounds at much higher frequencies than humans can. In fact, bats and dolphins can find objects in their environment using the echo of their own high-frequency sounds. Other mammals, such as elephants, can detect sounds at much lower frequencies.

Many mammals have some color-sensing structures in their eyes, yet the ability to distinguish colors may vary among different species. Color vision is most useful to diurnal animals—those that are active during daylight. Although mammals such as cats can detect color, they may not see the full range of colors that humans and some other primates can.

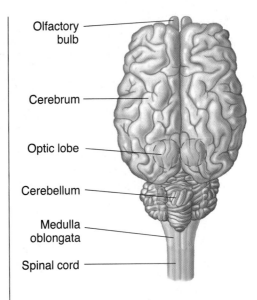

Olfactory bulb
Cerebrum
Optic lobe
Cerebellum
Medulla oblongata
Spinal cord

▲ **Figure 32–6** Mammals have large brains in proportion to their body size. Most of the brain is taken up by an enlarged cerebrum, which contains a well-developed cerebral cortex. **Inferring** *How would a large cerebrum be advantageous to a mammal?*

✓**CHECKPOINT** *What is the function of the cerebral cortex?*

Problem Solving

Breathless Divers

Many marine mammals have adaptations that allow them to do what no land mammal can do—live under water. A sperm whale, for example, can dive deeper than 1.5 km below the surface, holding its breath for more than an hour at a time. How can it go so long without inhaling? One clue lies in the amount of oxygen that whales can store in their bodies. During a dive, whales store, on average, 9 percent of oxygen in their lungs, 41 percent in their blood, 41 percent in muscles, and 9 percent in tissues. In contrast, human beings store an average of 34 percent of oxygen in their lungs, 41 percent in blood, 13 percent in muscles, and 12 percent in tissues.

Defining the Problem On the basis of what you have read, identify a question you would like answered.

Organizing Information Create a table that allows you to easily compare the percentages of oxygen stored in different parts of whales' and humans' bodies.

Creating a Solution Compare and contrast the data in your table. Then, formulate a hypothesis that might identify a characteristic shared by mammals that can hold their breath for a long time.

Presenting Your Plan Formulate a plan for evaluting your hypothesis. Identify the kinds of information you would need.

Figure 32–7 The limbs and digits (fingers and toes) of many mammals are adapted to their particular way of life. Note the variety of lengths and shapes of the limb bones that different mammals use for movement. Homologous bones are the same color in all the drawings. **Applying Concepts** *Which structure shown in this figure would most closely resemble the limbs and digits of a whale?*

Monkey

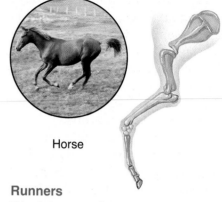

Horse

Climbers
Climbing mammals have long, flexible fingers and toes that can grasp vines and branches. They also have a flexible wrist joint.

Runners
Running mammals need long limbs that can absorb shock. These animals have lost the side digits on their front and back feet. They stand on the tips of their remaining toes, which are called hooves.

Movement Mammals have evolved a variety of adaptations that aid in movement, including a backbone that flexes both vertically and side to side. This flexibility allows mammals to move with a bouncing, leaping stride. Shoulder and pelvic girdles have become more streamlined and flexible, permitting both front and hind limbs to move in a variety of ways.

Compare the adaptations of mammalian limbs shown in **Figure 32–7.** Variations in the limb bones and muscles allow mammals to run, walk, climb, burrow, hop, pounce, swing, fly, leap, and swim. Depending on their lifestyle, mammals may use any number of these methods to move about.

Reproduction Mammals reproduce by internal fertilization. When mammals mate, the male deposits sperm inside the reproductive tract of the female, where fertilization occurs.

As you will learn in the next section, mammals are classified into three groups, based on their modes of development and birth. One group retains the reptilian characteristic of being oviparous, or egg-laying. The other two mammal groups are viviparous, or live-bearing. Their embryos develop within the mother for a time, and then are born alive. Most viviparous mammals nourish their embryos inside the mother's body before giving birth. Others deliver young that develop in a pouch on the outside of the mother's body. But, regardless of the mode of development, all newborn mammals feed on their mother's milk.

Many newborn mammals can stand up and move around on their own a short time after birth. The newborn wildebeest in **Figure 32–8** is awkward and barely able to stand. Within a few hours, however, it will be able to see and walk around on its own. On the other hand, the young of mammals such as mice and monkeys are helpless at birth and remain that way for some time. Such young depend on their mother for food and protection.

▼ **Figure 32–8** Still wobbly, a newborn wildebeest rises to its feet minutes after birth. Its mother will nurse and protect the calf until it is able to live on its own. **Classifying** *Is the wildebeest an oviparous or viviparous mammal?*

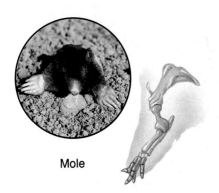

Mole

Diggers
Digging mammals have strong, thick claws, especially on their front feet. Their limbs are short and stocky, with large projections that anchor powerful muscles.

Bat

Flyers
The arms and hands of bats are modified to support flaps of skin that form wings.

Seal

Swimmers
Swimming mammals concentrate most of their movement between the arm and shoulder girdle. Their limbs are modified into broad, flat paddles, with the bones of their hands or feet extended to make a flipper, or fin.

Young mammals are generally helpless when they are born and for a long time afterward. During this period, they are cared for by one or both parents. Maternal care is an important mammalian characteristic, and the bond between mother and young is very close. Males of many species also play a role in caring for the young.

The duration and intensity of parental care varies among different species. Some mammals have a prolonged period when the young and the mother live together. The young may spend several years developing before they are able to live on their own. During that period, the juvenile learns from its caregiver the behaviors it needs to survive in its particular environment. Some mammal species, such as lions and elephants, live in groups in which the young may be cared for by adults other than the parents. Group living provides young mammals with the opportunity for complex social interaction among adults and juveniles.

32–1 Section Assessment

1. **Key Concept** Name the characteristics that are common to all mammals.

2. **Key Concept** When did mammalian ancestors diverge from the reptiles?

3. **Key Concept** List two ways in which mammals maintain homeostasis.

4. How are the teeth of mammals adapted to their different diets?

5. **Critical Thinking Inferring** Many humans have their wisdom teeth removed because their jaws are too small to accommodate those teeth. What might this suggest about the evolution of the human jaw?

iTEXT Assessment Use iText to review the important concepts in Section 32–1.

MAKING CONNECTIONS

Comparing and Contrasting Compare the structure of a mammal's brain to that of a fish, as shown in **Figure 30–14,** on page 777. What structures are more prominent in each animal's brain? How might these differences relate to the way the animals live?

32–2 Diversity of Mammals

Guide for Reading

 Key Concepts
- How do the three groups of living mammals differ from one another?
- How did convergent evolution cause mammals on different continents to be similar in form and function?

Vocabulary
monotreme
marsupial
placenta

**Reading Strategy:
Summarizing** As you read, make a list of the major groups of mammals. Write several sentences describing the characteristics of each group. Then, give an example for each.

The class Mammalia contains about 4500 species, and the diversity of these species is astonishing. From a tiny mouse nibbling its way along a corncob to an African elephant uprooting a gigantic tree with its tusks and trunk, mammals have the greatest range of size of any group of vertebrates.

As you have read, tooth structure is one characteristic that scientists use to classify mammals. Mammals are also classified by the number and kinds of bones in the head. But the most important way to categorize living mammals is by the way they reproduce and develop.

The three groups of living mammals are the monotremes (MAHN-oh-treemz), the marsupials (mahr-SOO-pee-ulz), and the placentals. These three groups differ greatly in their means of reproduction and development.

Monotremes and Marsupials

 Monotremes lay eggs. Marsupials bear live young that complete their development in a pouch. All monotremes are grouped in a single order, while marsupials are split into several different orders.

Monotremes Members of the **monotremes,** or egg-laying mammals, share two notable characteristics with reptiles. In monotremes, both the reproductive system and the urinary system open into a cloaca that is similar to the cloaca of reptiles. In fact, the name *monotreme* means "single opening." Reproduction in monotremes also resembles reproduction in reptiles more than other mammals. As in reptiles, a female monotreme lays soft-shelled eggs that are incubated outside her body. The eggs hatch into young animals in about ten days. Unlike young reptiles, however, young monotremes are nourished by their mother's milk, which they lick from pores on the surface of her abdomen.

Only three species of monotremes exist today: the duckbill platypus, shown in **Figure 32–9,** and two species of spiny anteaters, or echidnas. These animals are found in Australia and New Guinea.

◀ **Figure 32–9** Like all monotremes, the platypus lays eggs that hatch outside the body but nourishes its young with milk produced in mammary glands. The unusual snout of this duckbill platypus can sense electromagnetic signals put out by the muscles of other animals. The platypus uses its sensitive snout to locate prey, such as worms and mollusks, that burrow in the sediments.

Marsupials Kangaroos, koalas, and wombats are examples of **marsupials**—mammals bearing live young that complete their development in an external pouch. When marsupials reproduce, the fertilized egg develops into an embryo inside the mother's reproductive tract. There, it is nourished by a small yolk sac. When the food in the yolk sac is used up, the embryo leaves its mother's body. The tiny embryo crawls across its mother's fur into a pouch called the marsupium (mahr-SOO-pee-um) on the outside of her body. Marsupials are named after this structure. Once inside the marsupium, the embryo, looking much like the one in **Figure 32–10**, locates a nipple, attaches to it, and spends several months there. It will continue to drink milk in its mother's pouch until it grows large enough to survive on its own.

CHECKPOINT *How does a marsupial differ from a monotreme?*

Placental Mammals

Placental mammals are the mammals with which you are most familiar. Mice, cats, dogs, whales, elephants, humans, and the sea lions in **Figure 32–11** all fall within this category. This group gets its name from an internal structure called the **placenta,** which is formed when the embryo's tissues join with tissues from within the mother's body.
🔑 **In placental mammals, nutrients, oxygen, carbon dioxide, and wastes are exchanged between embryo and mother through the placenta.** The placenta allows the embryo to develop for a much longer time inside the mother—from a few weeks in mice and rats to as long as two years in elephants. After birth, most placental mammals care for their young and provide them with nourishment by nursing.
Figure 32–12, on the following pages, describes the main orders of placental mammals.

Figure 32–10 Most marsupials, including this wallaby, are originally from Australia and New Guinea. 🔑 **Marsupials bear live young that complete their development in a pouch.** The pink, newborn wallaby (inset) is still an embryo but will soon grow into a "joey" that resembles a small adult.

◀ **Figure 32–11** The California sea lion is an example of a placental mammal. 🔑 **In placental mammals, nutrients, oxygen, carbon dioxide, and wastes are exchanged between embryo and mother through the placenta.**

FIGURE 32–12 ORDERS OF PLACENTAL MAMMALS

The 12 orders of mammals shown on these pages contain the vast majority of living placental species. **Classifying** *How are perissodactyls similar to artiodactyls? How are the two orders different?*

◀ **INSECTIVORES**

These insect eaters have long, narrow snouts and sharp claws that are well suited for digging. *Examples:* shrews, hedgehogs (shown here), moles.

▼ **SIRENIANS**

Sirenians are herbivores that live in rivers, bays, and warm coastal waters scattered throughout most of the world. These large, slow-moving mammals lead fully aquatic lives. *Examples:* manatees, dugongs (shown here).

◀ **CHIROPTERANS**

Winged mammals—or bats—are the only mammals capable of true flight. Bats account for about one fifth of all mammalian species. They eat mostly insects or fruit and nectar, although three species feed on the blood of other vertebrates.

RODENTS ▶

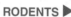

Rodents have a single pair of long, curved incisor teeth in both their upper and lower jaws, which they use for gnawing wood and other tough plant material. *Examples:* mice, rats (shown here), voles, squirrels, beavers, porcupines, gophers, chipmunks, gerbils, prairie dogs, chinchillas.

▲ **PERISSODACTYLS**

This order contains hoofed animals with an odd number of toes on each foot. *Examples:* horses, tapirs, rhinoceroses, and zebras (shown here).

▼ **CETACEANS**

Like sirenians, cetaceans—the order that includes whales and dolphins—are adapted to underwater life yet must come to the surface to breathe. Most cetaceans live and breed in the ocean. *Examples:* humpback whales (shown here), narwhals, sperm whales, beluga whales, river dolphins.

▲ XENARTHRANS

Most of the mammals in this order have no teeth. Some have very small teeth that are usually found in the back of the jaw. *Examples:* sloths, anteaters, armadillos (shown here).

▲ CARNIVORES

Many carnivores, or meat-eaters, such as tigers and hyenas, stalk and chase their prey by running and pouncing, then kill the prey with sharp teeth and claws. Some animals in this group eat plants as well as meat. Marine carnivores feed in the ocean but bear their young on land. *Examples:* dogs, foxes, bears, raccoons, walruses (shown here).

◄ ARTIODACTYLS

These hoofed mammals have an even number of digits on each foot. Like perissodactyls, this order contains mostly large, grazing animals. *Examples:* cattle, sheep, goats, pigs, ibex (shown here), giraffes, hippopotami, camels, antelope, deer, gazelles.

◄ PRIMATES

Members of this order are closely related to the ancient insectivores but have a highly developed cerebrum and complex behaviors. *Examples:* lemurs, tarsiers, apes, gibbons, macaques (shown here), humans.

▼ PROBOSCIDEANS

These are the mammals with trunks. Some time ago, this order went through an extensive adaptive radiation that produced many species, including mastodons and mammoths, which are now extinct. Only two species, the Asian elephant and this African elephant, survive today.

▲ LAGOMORPHS

Like rodents, members of this order are entirely herbivorous. They differ from rodents by having two pairs of incisors in the upper jaw. Most lagomorphs have hind legs that are adapted for leaping. *Examples:* Snowshoe hares (shown here), rabbits.

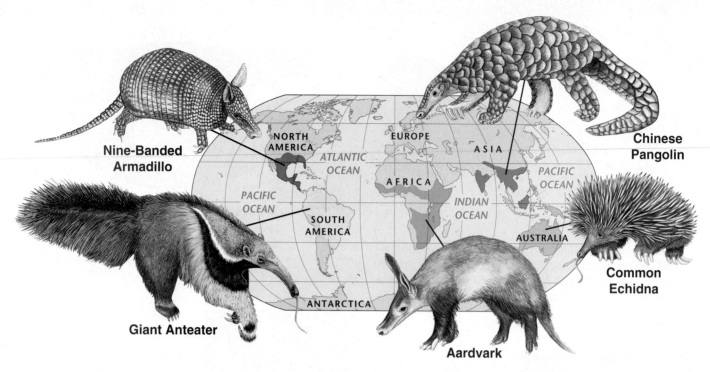

NORTH AMERICA · ATLANTIC OCEAN · EUROPE · ASIA · PACIFIC OCEAN · AFRICA · PACIFIC OCEAN · INDIAN OCEAN · SOUTH AMERICA · AUSTRALIA · ANTARCTICA

Nine-Banded Armadillo

Chinese Pangolin

Giant Anteater

Common Echidna

Aardvark

▲ **Figure 32–13** Similar ecological opportunities on different continents have resulted in convergent evolution among these and other mammals. Mammals that feed on ants and termites evolved not once but five times in different regions. Powerful front claws; a long, hairless snout; and a tongue covered with sticky saliva are common adaptations in these insect-eating animals.

Biogeography of Mammals

The history of Earth's geography has helped shape today's mammals. During the Paleozoic Era, the continents were one large landmass, and mammals could migrate freely across it. But when the continents drifted apart early in the Cenozoic Era, ancestors of different mammal groups were isolated from one another. Each landmass took with it a unique array of species.

🔑 **Similar ecological opportunities on the different continents have produced some striking examples of convergent evolution in mammals.** Thousands of kilometers apart, mammals such as those in **Figure 32–13** evolved similar adaptations in form and function. When some of the landmasses merged again in the late Cenozoic Era, mammals dispersed and intermingled in new habitats. Living mammals reflect the diversity that resulted from these events.

32–2 Section Assessment

1. 🔑 **Key Concept** Name the three groups of living mammals and describe the ways each develops.

2. 🔑 **Key Concept** With regard to mammals, what was the result of continental drift during the Cenozoic Era?

3. What is the function of the placenta?

4. List the major orders of placental mammals.

5. **Critical Thinking Inferring** How are powerful front claws and sticky tongues useful adaptations in mammals that feed on ants?

📱**TEXT** **Assessment** Use iText to review the important concepts in Section 32–2.

MAKING CONNECTIONS

Comparing and Contrasting Create a compare/contrast table that describes the characteristics of monotremes, marsupials, and placental mammals. Include characteristics that they share as well as ways in which they differ.

32–3 Primates and Human Origins

Our own species, *Homo sapiens,* belongs to the order that also includes lemurs, monkeys, and apes. Carolus Linnaeus named our order Primates, which means "first" in Latin.

What Is a Primate?

Just what are primates "first" in? When the first primates appeared, there was little to distinguish them from other mammals besides an increased ability to use their eyes and front limbs together to perform certain tasks. As primates evolved, however, several other characteristics became distinctive.

Primates share several important adaptations, many of which are extremely useful for a life spent mainly in trees. **In general, primates have binocular vision, a well-developed cerebrum, fingers and toes, and arms that can rotate around their shoulder joints.** The gibbon in **Figure 32–14** shows many of these primate characteristics.

Fingers, Toes, and Shoulders Primates normally have five flexible fingers that can curl around objects. Most also have flexible toes. Flexible digits enable many primates to run along tree limbs and swing from branch to branch with ease. Primates' arms are well adapted to climbing because they can rotate in broad circles around a strong shoulder joint. In most primates, the thumb and big toe can move against, or oppose, the other digits. The presence of opposable digits allows many primates to hold objects firmly in their hands or feet.

Well-Developed Cerebrum The large and intricate cerebrum of primates—including a well-developed cerebral cortex—enables them to display more complex behaviors than many other mammals. For example, many primate species have elaborate social behaviors that include adoption of orphans and even warfare between rival primate troops.

Guide for Reading

Key Concepts
- What characteristics do all primates share?
- What are the major evolutionary groups of primates?
- What hominids does the fossil record include?

Vocabulary
binocular vision
prosimian
anthropoid
prehensile
hominoid
hominid
bipedal
opposable thumb

Reading Strategy:
Finding Main Ideas Before you read, draw a line down the center of a sheet of paper. On the left side, write down the main topics about primates and human origins. On the right side, note supporting details and examples.

◀ **Figure 32–14** A white-handed gibbon displays several primate characteristics as it swings from tree to tree. Like all primates, the gibbon has flexible fingers and toes and has arms that can rotate in broad circles around the shoulder joint.

Binocular Vision Many primates have a flat face, so both eyes face forward with overlapping fields of view. This facial structure gives primates excellent binocular vision. **Binocular vision** is the ability to merge visual images from both eyes, thereby providing depth perception and a three-dimensional view of the world. This is a handy adaptation for judging the locations of tree branches, from which many primates swing.

Evolution of Primates

Humans and other primates evolved from a common ancestor that lived more than 65 million years ago. Very early in their history, primates split off into several groups. **Primates that evolved from two of the earliest branches look very little like typical monkeys and are called prosimians (proh-SIM-ee-unz). Members of the more familiar primate group that includes monkeys, apes, and humans are called anthropoids (AN-thruh-poydz).** Refer to **Figure 32–15** as you read about the relationships among these groups.

Prosimians With few exceptions, **prosimians** alive today are small, nocturnal primates with large eyes that are adapted to seeing in the dark. Many have doglike snouts. Living prosimians include the bush babies of Africa, the lemurs of Madagascar, and the lorises and tarsiers of Asia.

CHECKPOINT *What is a prosimian?*

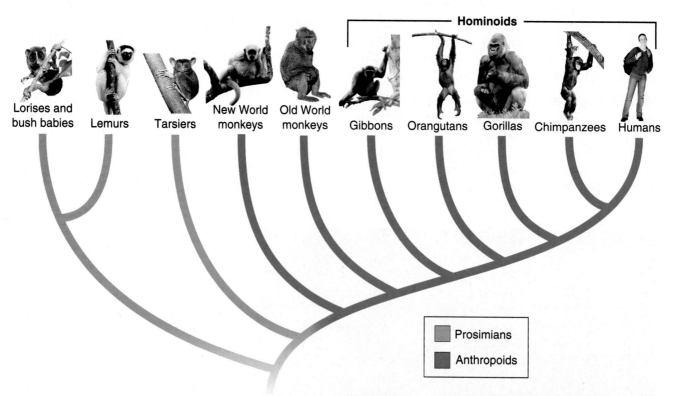

Hominoids

Lorises and bush babies — Lemurs — Tarsiers — New World monkeys — Old World monkeys — Gibbons — Orangutans — Gorillas — Chimpanzees — Humans

Prosimians
Anthropoids

Primate ancestor

▲ **Figure 32–15** Modern primates evolved from a common ancestor that lived more than 65 million years ago. **The two main groups of primates are prosimians and anthropoids.**

Anthropoids Humans, apes, and most monkeys belong to a group called **anthropoids,** which means humanlike primates. This group split very early in its evolutionary history into two major branches. These branches became separated from each other as drifting continents moved apart. One branch, found today in Central and South America, is called the New World monkeys. (After Columbus's voyage to America, Europeans began to use the term *New World* to refer to North and South America.) New World monkeys, which include squirrel monkeys and spider monkeys, live almost entirely in trees. They have long, flexible arms that enable them to swing from branch to branch. New World monkeys also have a long, prehensile tail. A **prehensile** tail is a tail that can coil tightly enough around a branch to serve as a "fifth hand."

The other anthropoid group, which evolved in Africa and Asia, includes the Old World monkeys and great apes. Old World monkeys, such as baboons and macaques (muh-KAHKS), spend time in trees but lack prehensile tails. Great apes, also called **hominoids,** include gibbons, orangutans, gorillas, chimpanzees, and humans. Recent molecular studies confirm that chimpanzees are humans' closest relatives among the great apes. Humans and chimps share an astonishing 98 percent of their DNA!

What Is a Hominid?

Around 6 million years ago, the hominoid line gave rise to a branch that ultimately led to the ancestors and closest relatives of modern humans. The **hominid** family, which includes modern humans, displayed several distinct evolutionary trends. Fossil evidence shows that as hominids evolved over millions of years, they became able to walk upright and developed thumbs adapted for grasping. They also developed large brains.

The skull, neck, spinal column, hipbones, and leg bones of early hominid species changed shape in ways that enabled later species to walk upright. **Figure 32–16** shows some ways in which the skeletons of modern humans differ from those of gorillas. The evolution of this **bipedal,** or two-foot, locomotion was very important, because it freed both hands to use tools. Meanwhile, the hominid hand evolved an **opposable thumb** that enabled grasping objects and using tools.

Modern Human

Modern Gorilla

Comparing Human and Gorilla Skeletons

Modern Human	Modern Gorilla
Skull atop S-shaped spine	Skull atop C-shaped spine
Spinal cord exits at bottom of skull	Spinal cord exits near back of skull
Arms shorter than legs; hands do not touch ground during walking	Arms longer than legs; hands touch ground during walking
Pelvis is bowl-shaped	Pelvis is long and narrow
Thigh bones angled inward, directly below body	Thigh bones angled away from pelvis

▲ **Figure 32–16** Modern hominids walk upright on two legs; gorillas use all four limbs. **Comparing and Contrasting** *According to the chart and illustration, what are the other differences between humans and gorillas?*

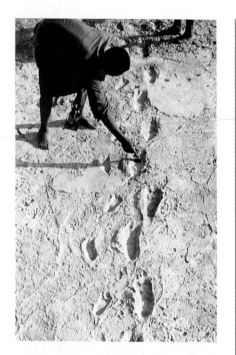

Hominids also displayed a remarkable increase in brain size. Chimpanzees, our closest living relatives among the apes, have a brain size of 280 to 450 cubic centimeters. The brain of *Homo sapiens*, on the other hand, ranges in size from 1200 to 1600 cubic centimeters! Most of the difference in brain size results from an enormously expanded cerebrum—the "thinking" area of the brain.

Early Hominids For years, paleontologists searched for a single fossil species that would link humans with their non-human primate ancestors. Recent discoveries have unearthed much more: a treasure trove of hominid species. **Today most paleontologists agree that the hominid fossil record includes 5 genera—*Ardipithecus, Australopithecus, Paranthropus, Kenyanthropus*, and *Homo*—and as many as 16 separate hominid species. This diverse group of fossils covers roughly 4.5 million years.** All of these species are relatives of modern humans, but they are not all human ancestors. To understand the distinction between relatives and ancestors, think of your own family. Your relatives may include aunts, uncles, cousins, grandparents, and great-grandparents. Of those, only your grandparents and great-grandparents are your ancestors.

Many questions remain about how hominid fossil species are related to one another and to humans. What once seemed to be a relatively simple pattern now looks like a dense, branching tree with many twigs. Let us examine some of those twigs.

▲ **Figure 32–17** Between 3.8 and 3.6 million years ago, members of a species of *Australopithecus* made these footprints. The footprints show that hominids walked upright millions of years ago. *Australopithecus* is one of the five known genera of hominids.

Biology and History

Human-Fossil Seekers

The study of human origins is an exciting search for our past. To piece together this complicated story requires the skills of many scientists.

Edouard Lartet
Henry Christy
French geologist Lartet and English banker Christy unearth several ancient human skeletons in a rock shelter called Cro-Magnon in France. These hominid fossils are the first to be classified as *Homo sapiens*.

Siege of the Alamo
1836

1868

1800

1812

Georges Cuvier
Cuvier, a French zoologist, rejects the idea of evolution based on a lack of evidence in the fossil record. He is noted for saying "Fossil man does not exist!" He believed species were static and unchanging.

1843

Wagons first leave on the Oregon Trail

1886

Marcel de Puydt
Max Lohest
De Puydt and Lohest, archaeologist and geologist, describe two Neanderthal skeletons found in a cave in Belgium. Their detailed description of the skeleton shows that Neanderthals were an extinct human form, not an abnormal form of modern human.

Australopithecus The earliest well-known group of hominids, members of the genus *Australopithecus,* lived from about 4 million to a million years ago. These hominids were bipedal apes that spent at least some time in trees. The structure of their teeth suggests a diet rich in fruit. Some *Australopithecus* species seem to have been human ancestors, while others formed separate branches off the main hominid line.

The best known species is *Australopithecus afarensis*—described from a remarkably complete female skeleton, nicknamed Lucy, who stood only about 1 meter tall. The humanlike footprints shown in **Figure 32–17,** which are between 3.8 and 3.6 million years old, were probably made by members of the same species as Lucy. Since *Australopithecus* fossils have small brains, the Laetoli footprints show that hominids walked bipedally long before large brains evolved.

Paranthropus Three later species, which grew to the size of well-fed football linebackers, were originally placed in the genus *Australopithecus.* However, they are now usually placed in their own genus, *Paranthropus.* The known *Paranthropus* species had huge, grinding back teeth. Their diets probably included coarse and fibrous plant foods like those eaten by modern gorillas. Most paleontologists now place *Paranthropus* on a separate, dead-end branch of our family tree.

✓CHECKPOINT *What are the characteristics of Australopithecus?*

To find out more about human history, view the videotape "Mummies: Ties to the Past."

Writing Activity

You have found Mary Leakey's journal and noticed that the entry for her discovery of the footprints at Laetoli is missing. Write an entry for the journal as she would have, describing the events of the day and her initial reaction to the find.

Donald Johanson
An American paleontologist and his team find a nearly complete skeleton of *Australopithecus,* which they call Lucy, in the Afar region of Ethiopia. The skeleton is about 3.2 million years old.

1974

Douglas Wallace
Wallace and fellow geneticists create a family tree of human evolution based on their studies of mitochondrial DNA, which is passed only from mother to child.

1999

2000

1924

Raymond Dart
Dart, an Australian anatomist, finds the first hominid fossil—a nearly complete skull of a young child—in South Africa. This specimen was placed in a new genus called *Australopithecus.*

1951

First color-television broadcast in the United States

1978

Mary Leakey
Leakey, a British anthropologist, discovers a set of 3.6 million-year-old fossil hominid footprints at Laetoli in Tanzania. The footprints provide evidence that early hominids walked erect on two legs.

Mammals **837**

Kenyanthropus Early in the year 2001, a team led by Meave Leakey announced a spectacular and puzzling discovery. On the western side of Lake Turkana in northern Kenya, they uncovered a well-preserved skull that has a confusing combination of characteristics. Its ear structures resemble those of chimpanzees, and its brain is rather small. Yet some of its facial features resemble those of fossils usually placed in the genus *Homo*.

The researchers decided that this skull should be placed in a new genus, *Kenyanthropus*, whose name comes from the country in which the fossil was found. Since the skull has a flat face, the researchers gave it the species name *Kenyanthropus platyops*. The word *platyops* comes from Greek words meaning "flat" and "face." *Kenyanthropus platyops* is one of the fossil skulls in **Figure 32–18.** Evidence indicates that *Kenyanthropus platyops* existed at the same time as *A. afarensis*.

The researchers further proposed that a specimen previously named *Homo rudolfensis* was similar enough to *Kenyanthropus platyops* that it should be renamed *Kenyanthropus rudolfensis*. This discovery raised many questions, not only about the two *Kenyanthropus* species, but about the evolutionary relationships of hominid species in general.

How Do the Branches Connect?

Kenyanthropus is the most recent hominid species to be described. It most certainly will not be the last. In the years between 1985 and the present time, paleontologists have more than doubled the number of recognized hominid species. It now seems clear that hominid evolution, like the evolution of other mammalian groups, did not involve the simple, straight-line transformation of one species into another. Rather, a series of complex adaptive radiations produced a large number of species whose relationships are tough to determine. Which species are true ancestors? Which are just relatives? And precisely how are those relatives related to each other and to us?

At the present time no one knows the answers to any of those questions for certain. **Figure 32–19** shows one recent attempt to chart the evolutionary relationships of known hominid species. The chart begins with the hominid descendants of a common ancestor shared by hominids and chimpanzees some time around 6 million years ago. The question mark indicates that this common ancestor has not yet been discovered. Note the many other question marks, each indicating *possible* lines of descent. It will probably take many years of work to more fully understand the fascinating and complex story of hominid evolution.

▲ **Figure 32–18** Paleontologists' interpretations of hominid evolution are based on the study of fossils such as these skulls—*Kenyanthropus platyops* (top), *Paranthropus robustus* (middle), and *Homo erectus* (bottom). **Observing** *Which of these skulls most closely resembles the skull of a modern human?*

✓**CHECKPOINT** *What is* **Kenyanthropus platyops***?*

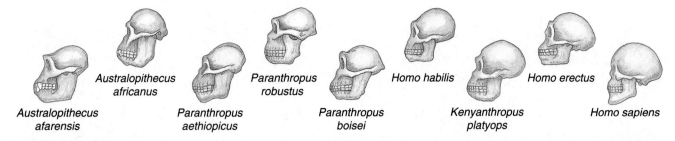

Australopithecus afarensis

Australopithecus africanus

Paranthropus aethiopicus

Paranthropus robustus

Paranthropus boisei

Homo habilis

Kenyanthropus platyops

Homo erectus

Homo sapiens

The Road to Modern Humans

Modern humans belong to the species *Homo sapiens.* As you can see from **Figure 32–19,** other species in the genus *Homo* existed before *Homo sapiens* appeared. The history and interrelationships of these species, and the path by which they led to modern humans, are fascinating and still not completely understood.

The Genus *Homo* About 2.5 million years ago, a new hominid appeared in Africa. Its fossils show that it resembled modern humans enough to be classified as a member of our own genus, *Homo.* Because this species was found with tools made of stone and bone, researchers called it *Homo habilis* (HAB-ih-lis), which means "handy man."

Homo habilis was the first of several members of our genus to arise in Africa. About 2 million years ago, a larger species appeared with bigger brains and downward-facing nostrils that resembled those of modern humans. Today, most researchers call the African fossils of this species *Homo ergaster.* Either *H. ergaster* or a closely related species, *Homo erectus,* soon began migrating out of Africa. By about 1.8 million years ago, these migrants had crossed Asia and reached China and Java. By a million years ago, populations of *Homo erectus* were living in several places across Asia.

Figure 32–19 The hominid fossil record includes five genera and several species. Only *Homo sapiens* survives today. However, several earlier hominid species lived at the same time as one another. The existence of these fossils is well established, but the diagram shows that paleontologists are debating just how they are related to one another and to modern humans. **Interpreting Graphics** *Trace two possible lines of descent from* **A. anamensis** *to* **H. sapiens.**

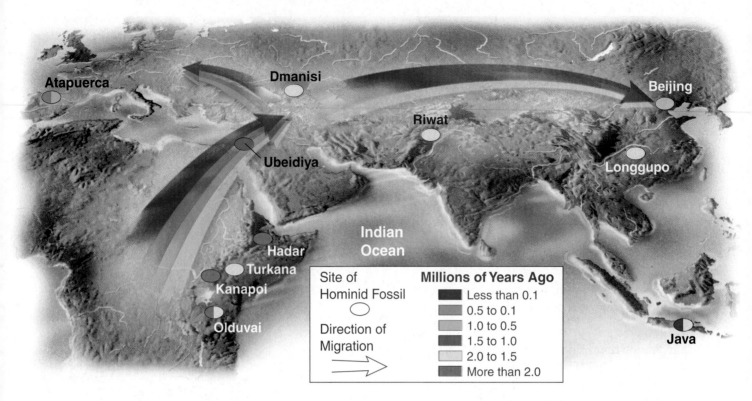

▲ **Figure 32–20** Data show that relatives and ancestors of modern humans left Africa several different times. But when did early hominids leave Africa, and how far did they travel? By comparing the mitochondrial DNA of indigenous human populations around the world, and by continuing to study the fossil record, scientists hope to improve our understanding of the complex history of *Homo sapiens*.

Out of Africa—But Who and When?

Precisely what happened next has been the subject of much scientific debate. How did modern *Homo sapiens* evolve from earlier members of the genus *Homo*? Two hypotheses describe two very different possible histories. One hypothesis, known as the multi-regional model, suggests that *Homo sapiens* could have evolved independently in several places around the world. This hypothesis proposes that modern humans descended directly from the far-flung populations of *H. erectus* that were already living outside of Africa more than a million years ago.

A second hypothesis, known as the out-of-Africa model, argues that the first true *Homo sapiens* evolved in Africa, probably between 200,000 and 150,000 years ago. This model further proposes that members of this species left Africa in one or more recent waves of migration, as shown in **Figure 32–20**. These migrants then replaced the descendants of *H. erectus* around the globe to found local populations of modern humans. This hypothesis has received powerful support from genetic analysis based on DNA found in the mitochondria of cells. The molecular data argue powerfully for a single African origin for all modern humans. For that reason, the out-of-Africa hypothesis is accepted by most researchers today.

Modern *Homo sapiens*

The story of modern humans over the past 500,000 years involves two main groups. The earliest of these species is now called *Homo neanderthalensis,* named after the Neander Valley in Germany where their remains were first found. Neanderthals, as they are commonly called, flourished from Europe through western Asia between about 200,000 and 30,000 years ago. Evidence from Neanderthal sites in Europe and the Middle East suggests that they not only made stone tools but also lived in organized social groups.

The other group is anatomically modern *Homo sapiens*—in other words, people whose skeletons look like those of modern humans. These *H. sapiens,* who probably arose in Africa, appeared in the Middle East around 100,000 years ago. They joined Neanderthals who had been living in that region for at least 100,000 years. As far as anyone can tell, Neanderthals and *Homo sapiens* lived side by side in what is now Israel, Lebanon, Syria, and Turkey for around 50,000 years, using similar tools and living in remarkably similar ways.

That situation changed dramatically around 50,000–40,000 years ago. That's when some populations of *H. sapiens* seem to have fundamentally changed their way of life. They used new technology to make more sophisticated stone blades, and made elaborately worked tools from bones and antlers. They produced spectacular cave paintings, such as the one in **Figure 32–21.** These *Homo sapiens* buried their dead with elaborate rituals. In other words, these people began to behave like modern humans. About 40,000 years ago, one such group, known as Cro-Magnons (kroh-MAG-nunz) appeared in Europe.

By 30,000 years ago, Neanderthals had disappeared from Europe—and from the Middle East as well. How and why they disappeared is not yet known. But since that time, our species has been Earth's only hominid.

▲ **Figure 32–21** This ancient cave painting from France shows the remarkable artistic abilities of Cro-Magnons. **Inferring** *How might these painted images be related to the lifestyle of these early humans?*

32–3 Section Assessment

1. 🔑 **Key Concept** List five characteristics that most primates share.

2. 🔑 **Key Concept** Describe the major primate groups and explain how they are related.

3. 🔑 **Key Concept** Name the genera that currently make up the hominid fossil record.

4. Compare and contrast hominids and hominoids. How are they similar? Different?

5. **Critical Thinking Applying Concepts** How did the separation of the continents contribute to the development of New World and Old World monkeys?

 Assessment Use iText to review the important concepts in Section 32–3.

Take It to the NET

Find out more about fossil hominids, including *Homo ergaster* and *Kenyanthropus rudolfensis*. Then, compare and contrast these two hominids. Use the links provided in the Biology area at the Prentice Hall Web site for help in completing this activity: **www.phschool.com**

Using Fibers as Forensic Evidence

Hair and other fibers are often used by police as evidence that a suspect was at the scene of a crime such as a burglary. In this investigation, you will examine a variety of hairs and other fibers to match unknown fibers to known reference fibers. The two human hairs represent hairs from two people who are suspected of having been at the crime scene. The unknown fibers represent fibers found at the crime scene.

DISCOVERY CHANNEL SCHOOL To find out more about how scientists use forensic evidence, view the videotape "Wrongly Accused: Science and Justice."

Problem How do forensic scientists identify unknown hairs and fibers?

Materials
- reference fibers
- unknown fibers
- microscope slides
- coverslips
- dropper pipette
- microscope
- glass-marking pencil
- facial tissues
- isopropyl alcohol
- rubber cement
- forceps
- test-tube rack
- 4 test tubes of biuret reagent
- 4 glass stirring rods
- hot water bath

Skills Observing, Inferring, Analyzing Data

Procedure

Part A: Observing Fibers

1. Place one of the reference fibers on a microscope slide. **CAUTION:** *Microscopes and slides are fragile. Handle them carefully. If you break any glass, inform your teacher immediately.* Add a drop of water and a coverslip. Label the slide with the name of the fiber. On a separate sheet of paper, make a copy of the data table shown with 10 blank lines.

2. Place the slide on the stage of a microscope and look at it under 100× magnification. Examine the fiber carefully, looking for features such as color, shape, texture, and whether or not a hair root is attached. Record your observations in your data table. Draw and label a sketch of the fiber.

3. Repeat steps 1 and 2 for each of the reference and unknown fibers.

4. Clean one of the reference fibers by pulling it through a folded tissue moistened with a small amount of alcohol. **CAUTION:** *Alcohol is flammable. Do not use it in the presence of an open flame or sparks.*

5. Smear a thin layer of rubber cement on the middle of a glass slide. Quickly place the fiber on the surface of the rubber cement.

Human Hairs
(magnification: 22×)

Polyester Threads
(magnification: 70×)

Silk Fibers
(magnification: about 50×)

6. Before the cement dries, lift the fiber off the slide with forceps. You should see an imprint of the fiber on the cement. Put the slide under a microscope and observe the surface texture of the fiber. Record your observations.

7. Repeat steps 4 to 6 for each of the other fibers.

Data Table

Fiber	General Observations	Surface Texture	Biuret Test Result

Part B: Testing for Protein

8. **Making Predictions** Hair contains protein. Synthetic and plant fibers do not contain protein. On the basis of the observations you have recorded in your data table, write a prediction of which unknown fibers contain protein. Include the reasons for your prediction, explaining what evidence supports your prediction about each fiber.

9. Label 4 test tubes of biuret reagent solution 1 through 4. **CAUTION:** *Wear safety goggles, a lab apron, and plastic gloves when working with biuret reagent solution. If any of the solution gets on your skin or clothing, wash it off immediately and inform your teacher.* Use forceps to place several strands of each unknown fiber in the test tube with the same number. Record the time.

10. Place a glass stirring rod in each test tube. Place the test tubes in the hot water bath. Stir each test tube occasionally. **CAUTION:** *Leave the stirring rods in the test tubes. Do not place the wet stirring rods on the table.*

11. Observe the color of each test tube. A change from blue to purple or reddish-brown within 5 minutes indicates the presence of protein. Add your observations to your data table. Follow your teacher's instructions for safe disposal of the biuret reagent.

Analyze and Conclude

1. **Comparing and Contrasting** How are hairs and synthetic fibers different?

2. **Observing** Did you observe any differences between human hair and other hair? If you did, describe the differences.

3. **Drawing Conclusions** Did your observations support the idea that one or both of the suspects may have been at the crime scene? Explain your answer.

4. **Making Judgments** Did your observations leave room for doubt about this conclusion? If so, what other evidence would provide a stronger test of your conclusion? Explain your answer.

Go Further

Additional Research Forensic science is the application of scientific knowledge to questions involving law. Do research to learn more about forensic science. Some topics you might investigate inculde the following:

• DNA evidence

• Evidence of poisoning

• Forensic dentistry

• Forensic anthropology

• Forensic pathology

• Ballistics

32–1 Introduction to the Mammals
Key Concepts

- In addition to having hair and the ability to nourish their young with milk, all mammals breathe air and are endotherms that generate their body heat internally.

- The first true mammals appeared during the late Triassic Period, about 220 million years ago.

- The ability of mammals to regulate their body heat from within is an example of homeostasis.

- As mammals evolved to eat foods other than insects, the form and function of their jaws and teeth became adapted to their diets.

- The kidneys of mammals help maintain homeostasis by excreting or retaining water.

Vocabulary
mammary gland, p. 821
subcutaneous fat, p. 822
rumen, p. 823
diaphragm, p. 824
cerebral cortex, p. 825

32–2 Diversity of Mammals
Key Concepts

- The three groups of living mammals are the monotremes, the marsupials, and the placentals. Marsupials bear live young that complete their development in a pouch. Monotremes lay eggs. In placental mammals, nutrients, oxygen, carbon dioxide, and wastes are exchanged between embryo and mother through the placenta.

- Similar ecological opportunities on the different continents have produced some striking examples of convergent evolution in mammals.

Vocabulary
monotreme, p. 828
marsupial, p. 829
placenta, p. 829

32–3 Primates and Human Origins
Key Concepts

- In general, primates have binocular vision, a well-developed cerebrum, fingers and toes, and arms that rotate in their joints.

- Primates that evolved from two of the earliest ancestral branches look very little like typical monkeys and are called prosimians. Members of the more familiar primate group that includes monkeys, apes, and humans are called anthropoids.

- Today most paleontologists agree that the hominid fossil record includes at least five genera—*Ardipithecus, Australopithecus, Paranthropus, Kenyanthropus,* and *Homo*—and as many as 16 separate hominid species. This diverse group of fossils covers roughly 4.5 million years.

Vocabulary
binocular vision, p. 834
prosimian, p. 834
anthropoid, p. 835
prehensile, p. 835
hominoid, p. 835
hominid, p. 835
bipedal, p. 835
opposable thumb, p. 835

Thinking Visually
Using information from this chapter, complete the following concept map:

Chapter 32

Part A

Multiple Choice

For each statement or question, select the number of the word or expression that, of those given, best completes the statement or answers the question.

1 Which structure in female mammals produces milk to nourish young?
(1) kidney   (3) cloaca
(2) mammary gland   (4) cerebral cortex

2 The first true mammals appeared during the late
(1) Permian Period   (3) Triassic Period
(2) Cretaceous Period   (4) Jurassic Period

3 Which of the animals shown below is a mammal?

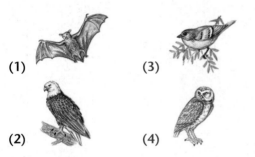

(1)   (3)

(2)   (4)

4 In mammals, the powerful muscle that aids in breathing is the
(1) diaphragm   (3) placenta
(2) cerebrum   (4) kidney

5 The composition and levels of body fluids in mammals are controlled by the
(1) lungs   (3) intestine
(2) kidneys   (4) heart

6 In the mammalian circulatory system, oxygen-poor blood moves from the heart to the
(1) stomach   (3) lungs
(2) diaphragm   (4) brain

7 A duckbill platypus is a monotreme because it
(1) lays eggs   (3) lives in Australia
(2) has only one lung   (4) bears only one young

8 Which animal is *not* an example of a placental mammal?
(1) cetacean   (3) rodent
(2) marsupial   (4) primate

9 Primates consist of two groups, anthropoids and
(1) monotremes   (3) apes
(2) hominids   (4) prosimians

10 How many hominid species exist today?
(1) one   (3) nine
(2) two   (4) twelve

11 Which is *not* a characteristic of all mammals?
(1) the ability to nourish young with milk
(2) giving birth to live young
(3) having hair
(4) the ability to generate body heat internally

12 Humans belong to the order
(1) Chiropterans   (3) Sirenians
(2) Carnivores   (4) Primates

13 Each characteristic belongs to primates *except*
(1) a well-developed cerebrum
(2) binocular visio
(3) flexible digits
(4) a small brain in proportion to body size

14 How are living mammals classified into groups?
(1) method of development
(2) structure of kidneys
(3) method of respiration
(4) method of regulating body temperature

15 What is the most likely food source of the animal whose skull is shown in the diagram below?
(1) grasses and vines
(2) insects
(3) trees and shrubs
(4) deer

Test-Taking Tip Take the time to read each question completely on a standardized test, including all of the answer choices. Consider each possible choice before determining which answer is correct.

Parts B and C

Multiple Choice and Extended Response

For those questions that ask you to select a response, choose the one that best completes the statement or answers the question. For all others follow the directions given.

16 Describe three adaptations mammals have to conserve body heat.

17 Describe an example of convergent evolution in mammals.

Base your answers to questions 18 through 21 on the information and graph below and on your knowledge of biology.

Radioactive substances found in living things decay at specific rates over time. The rate at which a substance decays is measured by its half-life. A half-life is the amount of time it takes for half a radioactive sample to decay. For example, the half-life of carbon-14 is 5770 years. Use the bar graph to answer the following questions.

Decay of Carbon-14

*Time of organism's death

18 How much carbon-14 would remain in an 11,540-year-old fossil?
(1) 25 percent (3) 50 percent
(2) 35 percent (4) 60 percent

19 A paleontologist determines that a particular fossil has $\frac{1}{8}$ of the amount of carbon-14 that was present at the time the organism died. How old is the fossil estimated to be?
(1) 11,540 years (3) 34,620 years
(2) 23,080 years (4) 46,160 years

20 Scientists cannot accurately detect the amount of carbon-14 in a fossil when more than $\frac{1}{16}$ of the carbon-14 has decayed. Which fossils could *not* be dated accurately using carbon-14?
(1) a 5000-year-old fossil
(2) a 10,000-year-old fossil
(3) a 25,000-year-old fossil
(4) a 75,000-year-old fossil

21 Explain why carbon-14 dating techniques are not used to provide information on the first hominid remains.

22 The following flowcharts show two proposed explanations for human evolution, beginning with the descent from *Australopithecus afarensis*. Describe how the two lines of descent differ.

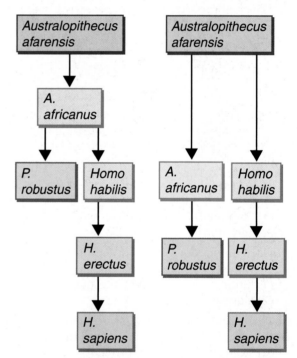

23 You are given the following descriptions of three placental mammals:
• Mammal A can fly, has sharp teeth, and consumes a liquid diet.

• Mammal B has a single pair of sharp, curved incisor teeth and eats only plant material.

• Mammal C is a filter feeder, mates and bears its young in water, but comes to the surface to breathe.

Place each mammal in its proper classification order, and explain your decision.

24 Are humans carnivores, herbivores, or omnivores? Give evidence to support your answer.

Base your answers to questions 25 through 28 on the reading passage below and on your knowledge of biology.

Neanderthal or Cro-Magnon?

A heated debate continues between archeologists as they try to determine the line of descent from ancient humans to modern humans, *Homo sapiens.* Many scientists believe that Neanderthals, whose remains were first found in the Neander Valley in Germany, should be classified as their own species because of their anatomical differences.

Neanderthals had a thick, squat body adapted to maintaining body temperature since they spent long periods in extremely cold climates. They had low, sloping foreheads and jaws that jutted forward.

Recently the skeletal remains of a four-year-old boy, buried 25,000 years ago, were discovered in a cave in Portugal. His chin, tooth size, and pelvic measurements identified him as Cro-Magnon (a group of *H. sapiens*). However, his stocky body and short legs showed that he had Neanderthal heritage. Scientists concluded that this was evidence of interbreeding between Neanderthals and Cro-Magnons.

Meanwhile, scientists in Scotland, along with their colleagues in Russia and Sweden, performed DNA analysis on the remains of a Neanderthal infant found in Russian mountains. The infant lived 30,000 years ago. By comparing regions of mitochondrial DNA that are known to evolve rapidly, they discovered that Neanderthals and modern humans diverged about 500,000 years ago. Scientists believe this discovery supports the "out-of-Africa" model of modern human evolution.

25 Recall that a species is a group of similar organisms that can breed and produce fertile offspring. What evidence suggests that Neanderthals and Cro-Magnons are not separate species?

26 The boy whose remains were found in Portugal lived 4000 years after Neanderthals were thought to have been extinct. He seemed to still have traits similar to his Neanderthal ancestors. Explain why he would still have these traits.

27 The Scottish scientists believe that their DNA analysis supports the out-of-Africa model. Describe this model, including why their DNA findings support it.

28 The Scottish findings indicate that Neanderthals and modern humans evolved separately beginning 500,000 years ago. Carbon dating indicates that the infant being studied lived 30,000 years ago. The Portuguese study gives evidence that Cro-Magnons interbred with Neanderthals about 25,000 years ago. During investigations such as these, what methods do scientists use as they analyze and report information that might seem to be conflicting?

29 Some species of mammals care for their young for many years. Explain how this adaptation might be advantageous compared to patterns shown by other chordates. How might it be disadvantageous?

30 Write definitions of "mammal" and "bird" that would help you explain why bats are classified as mammals even though they can fly.

31 Why is it important for paleontologists to estimate the age of a hominid fossil as well as analyze its structural characteristics?

32 Construct a chart comparing reproduction and development in monotremes, marsupials, and placental mammals. Include the following information
- development of young
- nourishment of young
- example of each type animal
- region found in world

Take It to the NET

The National Museum of Natural History houses one of the most important collections of mammals in the world. Visit the Prentice Hall Web site at **www.phschool.com** to find out more about this collection. Then, answer the following questions:
- How many voucher specimens are preserved at the National Museum of Natural History?
- During which two periods of history did the NMNH mammal collection grow the most? Why?
- What are the specialties of the mammal curators who work in the Department of Vertebrate Zoology?

33 Comparing Chordates

A cat-eyed snake is devouring some leaf frog eggs. Both the snake and the developing frogs are members of the chordate phylum.

Inquiry Activity

What are some adaptations of vertebrae?

Procedure

1. Put on plastic gloves. Use a hand lens to examine a chicken neck.
2. Bend the neck back and forth and from side to side.
3. Insert a dissecting probe into the opening at the top of the neck. What do you observe? **CAUTION:** *Use care with sharp instruments.*

Think About It

1. **Inferring** How is the structure of the chicken's neck related to its function?
2. **Predicting** What would happen if the chicken's neck vertebrae were one bone with no central opening?
3. **Drawing Conclusions** How would you expect the vertebrae to be different in an elephant's neck? Explain your answer.

33–1 Chordate Evolution

Ever since the first chordates appeared more than 500 million years ago, they have been evolving. During this continual process, chordates developed an incredible variety of adaptations. Some of these traits—scales or hair, for example—are relatively simple. Others—such as a four-chambered heart or an amniotic egg—are far more complex. All these adaptations were tested and shaped by natural selection.

Chordate Origins

Much of what scientists know about the origins of chordates comes from studying the embryos of living organisms. Such studies suggest that the most ancient chordates were closely related to echinoderms. Do scientists know what these early chordates looked like? Surprisingly, the answer is yes.

The variety of fossilized organisms preserved in the rich Cambrian deposits of Canada's Burgess Shale includes a peculiar organism called *Pikaia* (pih-KAY-uh), shown in **Figure 33–1.** When *Pikaia* was first discovered, it was thought to be a worm. On closer inspection, scientists determined that *Pikaia* had a **notochord**—a flexible, supporting structure that is found only in chordates. *Pikaia* also had paired serial muscles that were arranged in a manner similar to those of nonvertebrate chordates, such as lancelets. Scientists now consider *Pikaia* an early chordate.

To better understand the early evolution of chordates, biologists study a nonvertebrate chordate that is alive today—the tunicate. The tadpolelike larvae of tunicates are the simplest living animals to have a notochord, a dorsal hollow nerve cord, a tail that extends posterior to the anus, and pharyngeal pouches—key features common to all chordates. Today, biologists are studying the genes that control the development of these features.

Guide for Reading

 Key Concepts
- How are the different chordate groups related?
- What is a main trend in the evolution of chordates?

Vocabulary
notochord
adaptive radiation

**Reading Strategy:
Asking Questions** Before you read, study the cladogram in **Figure 33–2.** Make a list of questions about the cladogram. As you read, write down the answers to your questions.

Figure 33–1 This is a reconstruction of *Pikaia,* a soft-bodied animal that lived during the Cambrian Period. **Classifying** *Which features did* Pikaia *have that were characteristic of chordates?*

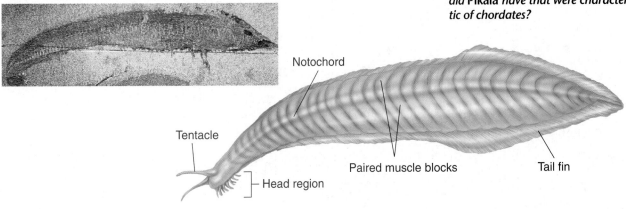

Notochord

Tentacle

Head region

Paired muscle blocks

Tail fin

The Chordate Family Tree

🔑 **The chordate family tree has its roots in ancestors that vertebrates share with tunicates and lancelets.** The cladogram in **Figure 33–2** shows how the different groups of living chordates are related to one another and to their invertebrate ancestors. It also shows the evolution of distinctly vertebrate features, such as jaws and limbs. As you study this cladogram, notice that the fishes—from hagfishes to lungfishes—include six different groups with long and separate evolutionary histories. On the other hand, modern amphibians, reptiles, birds, and mammals share much more recent common ancestors. Where do extinct groups, such as dinosaurs, fit into the chordate phylum? The answer may be found in the fossil record.

✓ **CHECKPOINT** *How many groups of fishes are alive today?*

Figure 33–2 🔵 The phylum Chordata includes both vertebrates and nonvertebrate chordates. All of these subphyla share a common invertebrate ancestor. This cladogram shows the relationship of modern chordate groups to that common ancestor. The different colored lines represent the traditional groupings of these animals, as listed in the key. The red circles indicate some of the important chordate adaptations.

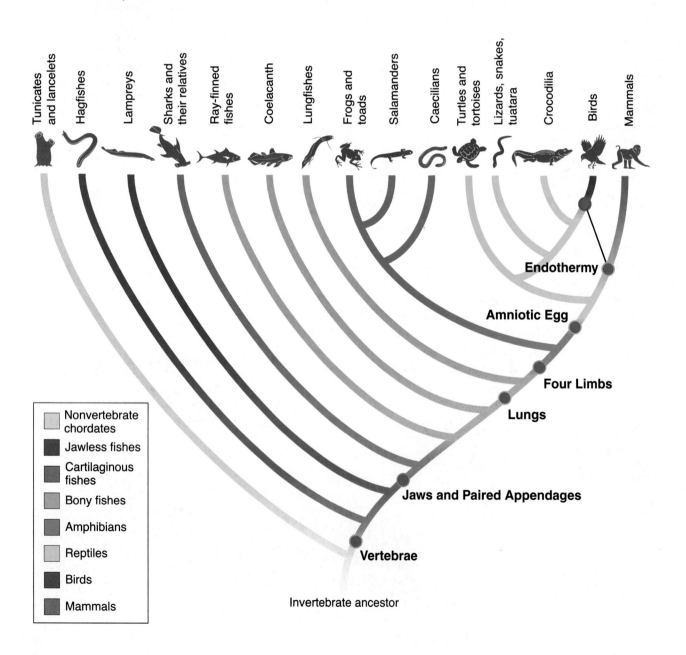

Key:
- Nonvertebrate chordates
- Jawless fishes
- Cartilaginous fishes
- Bony fishes
- Amphibians
- Reptiles
- Birds
- Mammals

Tunicates and lancelets · Hagfishes · Lampreys · Sharks and their relatives · Ray-finned fishes · Coelacanth · Lungfishes · Frogs and toads · Salamanders · Caecilians · Turtles and tortoises · Lizards, snakes, tuatara · Crocodilia · Birds · Mammals

Endothermy · Amniotic Egg · Four Limbs · Lungs · Jaws and Paired Appendages · Vertebrae · Invertebrate ancestor

Evolutionary Trends in Vertebrates

The hard body structures of many vertebrates have left behind an excellent fossil record. As a result, scientists know a great deal about vertebrates' evolutionary history. In addition, scientists infer evolutionary trends by studying the characteristics of chordates living today.

Adaptive Radiations The number of species within each chordate group has changed over geologic time. Look at the cladogram in **Figure 33–2** again. The red circles in that figure represent the origin of certain adaptive features. For example, one notable event in chordate evolution was the development of jaws. Another event was the development of paired appendages, including pectoral and pelvic fin or limb girdles. Paired appendages allowed chordates, such as the salamander in **Figure 33–3,** to move more efficiently. **Over the course of evolution, the appearance of new adaptations—such as jaws and paired appendages—has launched adaptive radiations in chordate groups.** An **adaptive radiation** is the rapid diversification of species as they adapt to new conditions.

Convergent Evolution Adaptive radiations sometimes produce species that are similar in appearance and behavior, even though they are not closely related. This trend is called convergent evolution. Convergent evolution occurred many times during chordate evolution when unrelated species encountered similar ecological conditions and evolved similar adaptations. For example, convergent evolution has produced flying vertebrates as different as birds and bats.

Chordate Diversity

Living chordates are extremely diverse, as shown in **Figure 33–4** on page 852. Yet, the species of chordates that are alive today are a small fraction of the total number of chordate species that have existed over time. Today, vertebrates make up about 96 percent of all living chordates and account for more than 50,000 species throughout the world. The six living groups of chordates are the nonvertebrate chordates, fishes, amphibians, reptiles, birds, and mammals. Of these, the largest group by far is the fishes.

Figure 33–3 Amphibians were the first chordates to have four limbs. Limbs allowed animals like this modern tiger salamander to crawl on land. **A rapid increase in the number and diversity of land vertebrates followed the evolution of four limbs.**

Comparing Chordates **851**

Figure 33–4 This pie chart shows the diversity of chordates. The area of each slice represents the relative number of living species in each group of chordates. The inner circle shows the six major chordate groups and gives the percentage of species contained in each. The outer circle breaks down each major group and shows the number of known species. **Calculating** *Of the total number of fish species, what percentage is represented by the ray-finned fishes?*

Nonvertebrate Chordates (4%)

Tunicates and lancelets (2022)

Hagfishes and lampreys (80)

Sharks and their relatives (900)

Mammals (4500)

Mammals (8%)

Birds (9650)

Birds (18%)

Fishes (47%)

Ray-finned fishes (23,700)

Crocodilians (22)

Lizards, snakes, tuatara (6850)

Reptiles (14%)

Amphibians (9%)

Frogs and toads (4100)

Turtles and tortoises (260)

Caecilians (165)

Salamanders (415)

Coelacanth and lungfishes (7)

33–1 Section Assessment

1. **Key Concept** To which groups of animals are vertebrates most closely related?

2. **Key Concept** Describe a major trend in chordate evolution.

3. Which characteristic appeared first: four limbs or jaws?

4. What is meant by adaptive radiation?

5. **Critical Thinking Inferring** Both frogs and ducks have webbed feet. However, ducks are more closely related to perching birds than to frogs. Explain the process that has resulted in both frogs and ducks having webbed feet.

iTEXT Assessment Use iText to review the important concepts in Section 33–1.

MAKING CONNECTIONS

Comparing and Contrasting
Recall what you learned about plant evolution in Chapter 22. In what ways are chordate adaptations to life on land similar to plant adaptations to life on land?

Should Marine Mammals Be Kept in Captivity?

December 26. A female beluga whale died today at a marine park in Canada. Two months ago, the park purchased nine beluga whales for a new exhibit. The whales had been caught in Russia's Sea of Okhotsk. Marine mammal experts attributed today's death to the stress of capture, transport, and confinement.

Many types of marine mammals, including dolphins, killer whales, and seals, are kept in captive display for educational, entertainment, and research purposes. Yet, there is strong debate about whether public display of such animals is ethical. Should we prohibit the capture of marine mammals for public display?

The Viewpoints

Pro: Captivity Should Be Allowed

Some people believe that we have an obligation to convey knowledge of the natural world to the public by displaying animals and educating ourselves about them. Information obtained by observing captive animals may be helpful in managing their populations in the wild. Many people argue that the adverse effects of captivity are outweighed by the benefits of conservation, an enhanced human appreciation for animals, and the advancement of scientific knowledge. There is also evidence that human interactions with captive dolphins may help people with disabilities, such as autism.

Con: Captivity Should Be Prohibited

Other people believe that because marine mammals are naturally social, with strong family bonds, they are not suited to capture or confinement. These people are concerned that the process of capture disrupts social groups.

Those opposed to the captivity of marine mammals also argue that confinement places the animals in an unnatural situation—one that is monotonous, limited, and unhealthy. In the wild, whales and dolphins travel long distances and dive much deeper than is possible in a shallow display tank. There is also a concern that human interaction with captive marine mammals increases the risk of transmitting diseases to the animals.

You Decide

1. **Defining the Issue** In your own words, explain the major issues surrounding public display of marine mammals.
2. **Analyzing the Viewpoints** List the options for education, entertainment, and research involving marine mammals. What are the benefits? The costs? Who is affected by each option?
3. **Forming Your Opinion** Should marine mammals be kept in captivity? Are there some instances when captivity is a good solution and other instances when it is not? Explain.
4. **Role-Playing** Suppose you are a wildlife biologist. Your job is to help manage a declining population of wild bottlenose dolphins living off the Florida coast. You need to learn about the lifestyle of this dolphin before you can recommend any solutions. You also want to increase public awareness to help protect the population. Write a proposal on how you will do all this.

33–2 Controlling Body Temperature

Guide for Reading

 Key Concepts
- How is the control of body temperature an important aspect of vertebrate life?
- What is the difference between ectotherms and endotherms?

Vocabulary
ectotherm
endotherm

Reading Strategy:
Finding Main Ideas Before you read, skim the section to identify the key-idea sentences about body temperature control. Then, carefully read the section, making a list of supporting details for each main idea.

On a spring morning, after a cold night, a tortoise lies on a rock basking in the sun. Nearby, a snake slides out of its burrow beneath a rotting stump. In a tree overhead, a young robin puffs up its downy feathers. As you walk out of the water after an early swim, your skin gets goose bumps and you shiver. All these activities are examples of the different ways that vertebrates control their body temperature.

Body Temperature and Homeostasis

Recall from Chapter 2 that many of the chemical reactions that are important in metabolism are influenced by temperature. For this reason, essential life functions can be carried out most efficiently when an animal's internal body temperature is within a particular "operating range." For muscles to operate quickly and efficiently, for example, their temperature can neither be too low nor too high. If muscles are too cold, they may contract slowly, making it difficult for the animal to respond quickly to events around it. If an animal gets too hot, on the other hand, its muscles may tire easily and other body systems may not function properly.

Because most chordates are vertebrates, and mechanisms for controlling body temperature are well developed among vertebrates, this section will focus exclusively on that group. **The control of body temperature is important for maintaining homeostasis in vertebrates, particularly in habitats where temperature varies widely with time of day and with season.** Vertebrates, such as the penguins in **Figure 33–5,** have a variety of ways to control their body temperature. All of these ways incorporate three important features: a source of heat for the body, a way to conserve that heat, and a method of eliminating excess heat when necessary. In terms of how they generate and control their body heat, vertebrates can be classified into two basic groups: ectotherms and endotherms.

◀ **Figure 33–5** Birds and other endotherms are able to generate their own body heat. ◗ **The internal control of body temperature allows these emperor penguins to live in cold Antarctic climates, where their feathers act as insulation.**

Analyzing Data

Comparing Ectotherms and Endotherms

Endotherms, such as humans, depend on their metabolism to maintain high body temperatures. Ectotherms, on the other hand, depend primarily on heat from the environment to regulate their body temperatures. The accompanying graph shows the internal body temperatures maintained by several ectotherms and endotherms at different environmental temperatures.

1. **Using Tables and Graphs** Which chordate has the highest body temperature when the environmental temperature is between 0° and 10°C? Which chordate has the lowest body temperature under those same conditions?

2. **Inferring** Which animals shown in the graph are ectotherms? Which are endotherms? Explain your answers.

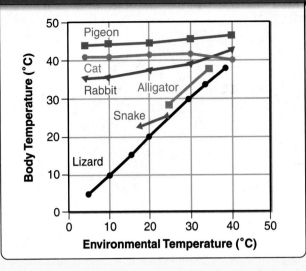

Temperature Control in Chordates

3. **Predicting** Describe the patterns of activity you would expect for the animals shown in this graph if they lived in your local environment. Would you expect all of the animals to be equally active year-round? If not, why not?

Ectothermy On cool, sunny mornings, lizards often bask in the sun. This doesn't mean that they are lazy! A lizard is an **ectotherm,** which means that its body temperature is mainly determined by the temperature of its environment. **Most reptiles, fishes, and amphibians are ectotherms—animals whose body temperatures are controlled primarily by picking up heat from, or losing heat to, their environment.** Ectotherms often warm up by basking in the sun, and may cool down by seeking shelter in underground burrows.

Ectotherms have relatively low rates of metabolism when they are resting. Thus, their bodies do not generate much heat. When active, an ectotherm's muscles generate heat, just as your muscles do. However, because its body lacks effective insulation, the heat is lost to the environment fairly easily.

Endothermy An **endotherm** is an animal that is able to control its body temperature from within. **Birds and mammals are endotherms, which means they can generate and retain heat inside their bodies.** Endotherms have relatively high metabolic rates that generate a significant amount of heat, even when they are resting. Birds conserve body heat primarily through insulating feathers, such as down. Mammals have body fat and hair for insulation. Mammals can get rid of excess heat by panting, as dogs do, or by sweating, as humans do.

Word Origins

Ectothermy and **endothermy** share the same suffix, which is derived from the Greek word *therme*, meaning "heat." The prefix *endo-* is a Greek word meaning "within." Therefore, the word *endotherm* literally means "heat from within." **What do you think the prefix *ecto-* means?**

✓**CHECKPOINT** *Give an example of an ectotherm and an endotherm.*

Comparing Ectotherms and Endotherms

In an absolute sense, neither endothermy nor ectothermy is superior. Each strategy has advantages and disadvantages in different environments. For example, endotherms move around easily during cool nights or in cold weather because they generate and conserve their own body heat. That's how musk ox live in the tundra and killer whales swim through polar seas. But the high metabolic rate that generates that heat requires a lot of fuel. The amount of food needed to keep a single cow alive would be enough to feed ten cow-sized lizards!

In environments where temperatures stay warm and fairly constant most of the time, ectothermy is a more energy-efficient strategy. Ectothermic animals, like the gila monster shown in **Figure 33-6,** need much less food than similarly-sized endotherms. But large ectotherms run into trouble in habitats where temperatures get cold at night or for long periods. It takes a long time for a large animal to warm up in the sun after a cold night. Most large lizards and amphibians live in the tropics and subtropics, and in sunny deserts.

▲ **Figure 33–6** Unlike birds and mammals, which can regulate their body temperature from within, lizards and other ectotherms rely on their surroundings to gain or lose body heat. The venomous gila monster, for example, makes its home in arid regions of the southwestern United States and Mexico, most often in desert and grassland biomes. To cool down, it burrows below the ground.

Evolution of Temperature Control

There is little doubt that the first land vertebrates were ectotherms. But there is some doubt as to when endothermy evolved. Although modern reptiles are ectotherms, some biologists hypothesize that dinosaurs were endotherms. Others hypothesize that endothermy evolved a long time after the appearance of the dinosaurs, so that at least some of the dinosaurs were ectotherms. Evidence suggests that endothermy has evolved more than one time—once along the evolutionary line of reptiles that led to birds and once along the evolutionary line of reptiles that led to mammals.

33–2 Section Assessment

1. **Key Concept** What important function does the control of body temperature serve in chordates?

2. **Key Concept** Compare and contrast ectotherms and endotherms.

3. What three features are needed to control an animal's body temperature?

4. How does endothermy affect an animal's need for food?

5. **Critical Thinking Inferring** Why is it unlikely that you would find a giant lizard living in the wild in North Dakota?

iTEXT **Assessment** Use iText to review the important concepts in Section 33–2.

ALTERNATIVE ASSESSMENT

Using Flashcards
Construct a set of 10 flash-cards showing a variety of endothermic and ectother-mic chordates. Draw an illustration of each animal on one side of the flashcard. On the other side of the flash-card, identify the animal as an endotherm or an ectotherm.

33-3 Form and Function in Chordates

The nonvertebrate chordates that are alive today represent a simple and ancient stage in the development of chordate body systems. However, the fact that the organ systems are simple does not mean they are inferior. After all, lancelets and tunicates have survived to the present day, so their body systems are well equipped to perform the essential functions of life.

Among vertebrates, organ systems exhibit a wider range of complexity than those of nonvertebrate chordates. In the hundreds of millions of years since chordates first appeared, the phylum has experienced many adaptive radiations. Each radiation produced a variety of specialized organ systems. The complexity of vertebrate organ systems can be seen in the different ways that vertebrates feed, breathe, respond, move, and reproduce.

Feeding

Most tunicates, and all lancelets, are filter feeders. These chordates remove small organisms called plankton from the water that passes through their pharynx. A few adult tunicates feed on deposited material from the surface of the sediments on which they dwell.

The skulls and teeth of vertebrates are adapted for feeding on a much wider assortment of foods, ranging from insects to large mammals, and from leaves to fruits and seeds. Some vertebrates—such as baleen whales, flamingoes, and manta rays—are filter feeders with sievelike mouth structures that enable them to strain small crustaceans and fish from the water. The long bill of the hummingbird and the narrow snout of the honey possum are both adaptations that enable them to feed on nectar. Other vertebrates, such as the crocodile in **Figure 33–7**, are adapted to eating meat. Many mammals have sharp canine teeth and incisors that they use to tear and slice their food.

Guide for Reading

🔑 **Key Concept**
• How do the organ systems of the different groups of chordates carry out essential life functions?

Vocabulary
alveolus

**Reading Strategy:
Using Graphic Organizers**
As you read, create a table that compares and contrasts the different life functions in non-vertebrate chordates, fishes, amphibians, reptiles, birds, and mammals.

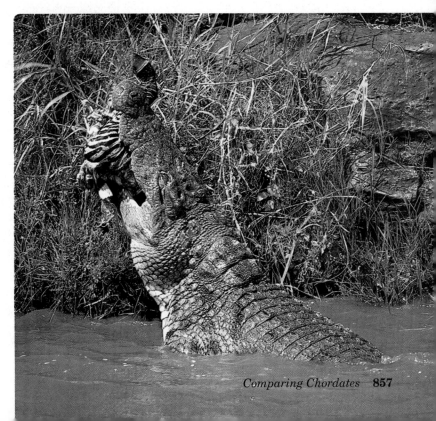

▶ **Figure 33–7** The blunt, broad jaws and numerous peglike teeth of this crocodile help it catch large prey—such as zebra—even in thick vegetation. **Comparing and Contrasting** *How do the mouth structures of a filter-feeding vertebrate differ from those of a carnivore like this reptile?*

| Shark | Salamander | Lizard | Pigeon | Cow |

Legend:
- Esophagus
- Stomach
- Intestine
- Liver
- Gallbladder
- Pancreas
- Cloaca
- Crop
- Gizzard
- Ceca
- Rectum

▲ **Figure 33–8** 🔑 The digestive systems of vertebrates are adapted for a variety of feeding modes. As you can see, these systems differ in their degree of complexity.

🔑 **The digestive systems of vertebrates have organs that are well adapted for different feeding habits.** Such variety is shown in **Figure 33–8.** Carnivores such as sharks typically have short digestive tracts that produce fast-acting, meat-digesting enzymes. Herbivores such as cows, on the other hand, often have long intestines that harbor colonies of bacteria. These bacteria are helpful in digesting the tough cellulose fibers in plant tissues.

✓**CHECKPOINT** *Compare the digestive tracts of herbivores and carnivores.*

Respiration

Chordates typically have one of two basic structures for respiration, or gas exchange. 🔑 **As a general rule, aquatic chordates—such as tunicates, fishes, and amphibian larvae—use gills for respiration. Land vertebrates, including adult amphibians, reptiles, birds, and mammals, use lungs.** However, some animals "break the rules." For example, several fishes, such as lungfishes, have both gills and lungs.

Some chordates have respiratory structures in addition to gills and lungs. Many bony fishes, for example, have accessory organs for respiration, such as simple air sacs, that are derived from the gut. All lancelets and some sea snakes respire by the diffusion of oxygen across their body surfaces. (Recall that diffusion is the process by which molecules move from an area of higher concentration to an area of lower concentration.) Many adult amphibians use their moist skins and the linings of their mouths and pharynxes to respire by diffusion.

Gills The diagram in **Figure 33–9** shows how gills function in chordates. As water passes over the gill filaments, oxygen molecules diffuse into blood in the capillaries. At the same time, carbon dioxide diffuses from blood into the water.

Lungs Although the structure of the lungs varies, the basic process of breathing is the same among land vertebrates. Inhaling brings oxygen-rich air from outside the body through the trachea (TRAY-kee-uh) and into the lungs. The oxygen diffuses into the blood inside the lung capillaries. At the same time, carbon dioxide diffuses out of the capillaries into the air within the lungs. Oxygen-poor air is then exhaled.

As you move from amphibians to mammals, the surface area of the lungs increases. Observe this trend in **Figure 33–10.** The typical amphibian lung is little more than a sac with ridges. Reptilian lungs are often divided into a series of large and small chambers that increase the surface area available for gas exchange. In mammals, the lungs branch extensively, and their entire volume is filled with thousands of bubblelike structures called **alveoli** (al-VEE-uh-ly; singular: alveolus). Alveoli provide an enormous surface area for gas exchange. This lung structure enables mammals to take in the large amounts of oxygen required by their endothermic metabolism. However, because air must move in and out through the same passageways, there is always stale, oxygen-poor air trapped in the lungs of mammals.

In contrast, in the lungs of birds, air flows in only one direction. A system of tubes in a bird's lungs, plus air sacs, enables this one-way air flow. Thus, gas exchange surfaces are constantly in contact with fresh air that contains a lot of oxygen. This supply of oxygen enables birds to fly at high altitudes, where there is less oxygen in the atmosphere than at lower altitudes.

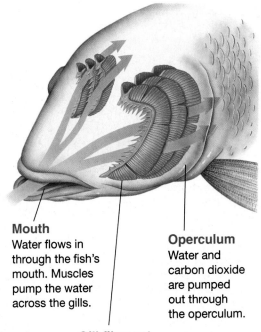

▼ **Figure 33–9** Fishes and many other aquatic chordates use gills for respiration. **Interpreting Graphics** *Describe the path of water as it flows into and out of the fish.*

Mouth
Water flows in through the fish's mouth. Muscles pump the water across the gills.

Operculum
Water and carbon dioxide are pumped out through the operculum.

Gill filament
Each gill contains thousands of filaments that absorb oxygen from the water.

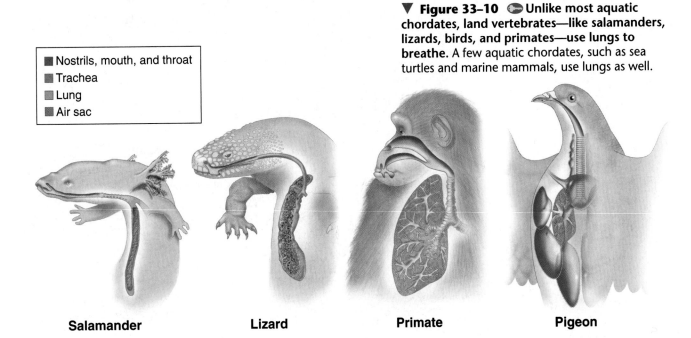

▼ **Figure 33–10** Unlike most aquatic chordates, land vertebrates—like salamanders, lizards, birds, and primates—use lungs to breathe. A few aquatic chordates, such as sea turtles and marine mammals, use lungs as well.

■ Nostrils, mouth, and throat
■ Trachea
■ Lung
■ Air sac

Salamander   **Lizard**   **Primate**   **Pigeon**

Circulation

Like modern tunicates and lancelets, the first chordates probably had simple circulatory systems. Tunicates, for example, have short, tubelike hearts with a simple pump. There are no true chambers in the heart. Lancelets have a fairly well-developed circulatory system but no specialized heart.

Single- and Double-Loop Circulation

As chordates evolved, more complex organ systems and more efficient channels for internal transport developed. **Figure 33–11** shows the main transport systems in vertebrates. Those that use gills for respiration have a single-loop circulatory system. In this system, blood travels from the heart to the gills, then to the rest of the body, and back to the heart in one circuit.

Vertebrates that use lungs for respiration have a double-loop circulatory system. The first loop carries blood between the heart and lungs. Oxygen-poor blood from the heart is pumped to the lungs, while oxygen-rich blood from the lungs returns to the heart. The second loop carries blood between the heart and the body. Oxygen-rich blood from the heart is pumped to the body, while oxygen-poor blood from the body returns to the heart.

✓ **CHECKPOINT** *What is a single-loop circulatory system?*

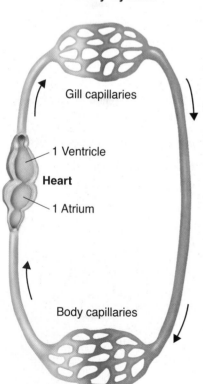

▼ **Figure 33–11** Most vertebrates that use gills for respiration have a single-loop circulatory system that forces blood around the body in one direction. Vertebrates that use lungs have a double-loop system. **The hearts of fishes have two chambers. Amphibians and most reptiles have three-chambered hearts. Crocodilians, birds, and mammals have hearts with four separate chambers.**

Single-Loop Circulatory System

Gill capillaries

1 Ventricle

Heart

1 Atrium

Body capillaries

FISHES

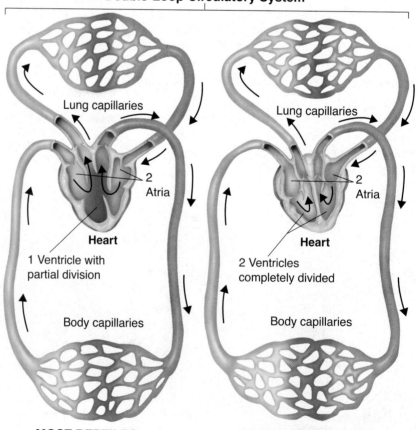

Double-Loop Circulatory System

Lung capillaries

2 Atria

Heart

1 Ventricle with partial division

Body capillaries

MOST REPTILES

Lung capillaries

2 Atria

Heart

2 Ventricles completely divided

Body capillaries

CROCODILIANS, BIRDS, AND MAMMALS

Heart Chambers Chordate hearts are adapted to the complexity of internal transport for each of the different groups. 🔑 **During the course of chordate evolution, the heart developed chambers and partitions that help separate oxygenated and deoxygenated blood traveling in the circulatory system.** In vertebrates that use gills for respiration, such as fishes and larval amphibians, the heart consists of two chambers: an atrium that receives blood from the body, and a ventricle that pumps blood to the gills and then on to the rest of the body.

The hearts of most amphibians have three chambers: two atria and one ventricle. The left atrium receives oxygen-rich blood from the lungs. The right atrium receives oxygen-poor blood from the body. Both atria empty into the ventricle. There is some mixing of oxygen-rich and oxygen-poor blood in the ventricle. However, the internal structure of the ventricle directs the flow of blood so that most oxygen-poor blood goes to the lungs, and most oxygen-rich blood goes to the rest of the body.

Most reptiles have a three-chambered heart. However, unlike amphibians, most reptiles have a partial partition in their ventricle. Because of this partition, there is even less mixing of oxygen-rich and oxygen-poor blood than there is in amphibian hearts.

Birds, mammals, and crocodilians have hearts that are completely partitioned into four chambers. This type of heart is sometimes described as a double pump. One pump moves blood through the lung loop and the other moves blood through the body loop. The two loops of the circulatory system are completely separated. There is no mixing of oxygen-rich and oxygen-poor blood.

Excretion

Excretory systems eliminate nitrogenous wastes from the body. In nonvertebrate chordates and fishes, gills and gill slits play an important role in excretion. However, most vertebrates rely on kidneys—excretory organs composed of small filtering tubes that remove wastes from the blood.

Nitrogenous wastes—formed from the breakdown of proteins—are first produced in the form of ammonia. Ammonia is a highly toxic compound that must quickly be eliminated from the body or changed into a less poisonous form. In tunicates, ammonia leaves the body through the outflow siphons. Other waste byproducts, such as uric acid, are stored within the tunicate's body and released only when the animal dies.

In vertebrates, excretion is carried out mostly by the kidneys. Aquatic amphibians and most fishes also excrete ammonia directly from the gills into the surrounding water through simple diffusion. In mammals, land amphibians, and cartilaginous fishes, ammonia is changed into urea, a less-toxic compound, before it is excreted. In most reptiles and birds, ammonia is changed into uric acid. Besides filtering wastes, vertebrate kidneys help maintain homeostasis by regulating the amounts of water, salt, and other substances dissolved in body fluids.

Response

Compared with invertebrates, most chordates have elaborate systems that allow them to respond to stimuli in their environment. ◯ **Nonvertebrate chordates have a relatively simple nervous system with a mass of nerve cells that form a brain. Vertebrates have a more complex brain with distinct regions, each with a different function.**

Nonvertebrate chordates do not have specialized sensory organs. In tunicates, however, sensory cells in and on the siphons and other internal surfaces may help control the amount of water passing through the pharynx. Lancelets—which have a more defined head region—have a small, hollow brain with a pair of eyespots that detect light.

Vertebrates display a high degree of cephalization, or concentration of sense organs and nerve cells at the front of the body. The head contains a well-developed brain, which is situated on the end of the spinal cord. The vertebrate brain is divided into several parts, including the cerebrum, cerebellum, medulla oblongata, optic lobes, and olfactory bulbs. The medulla oblongata controls the functioning of many internal organs. The optic lobes are involved in vision and the olfactory bulbs in the sense of smell.

Figure 33–12 shows how the size and complexity of the cerebrum and cerebellum increase from fishes to mammals. The cerebrum is the "thinking" region of the brain. It receives, interprets, and determines the response to sensory information. The cerebrum is also involved in learning, memory, and conscious thought. In fishes, amphibians, and reptiles, the cerebrum is relatively small. In birds and mammals, especially primates, the cerebrum is greatly enlarged and may contain folds that increase its surface area. The cerebellum, which coordinates movement and controls balance, is also most developed in birds and mammals.

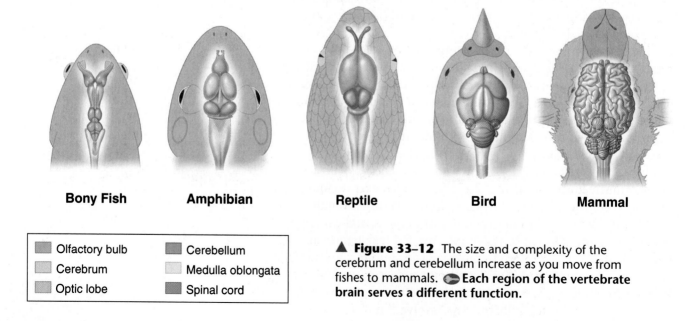

Bony Fish   **Amphibian**   **Reptile**   **Bird**   **Mammal**

■ Olfactory bulb   ■ Cerebellum
■ Cerebrum   ☐ Medulla oblongata
■ Optic lobe   ■ Spinal cord

▲ **Figure 33–12** The size and complexity of the cerebrum and cerebellum increase as you move from fishes to mammals. ◯ **Each region of the vertebrate brain serves a different function.**

Movement

Unlike most other chordates, nonvertebrate chordates lack bones. They do, however, have muscles. Lancelets and larval tunicates swim with a fishlike movement of their muscular tails. Some adult tunicates use their siphons to swim by jet propulsion. However, most adult tunicates lose their tails and attach to a hard surface on the ocean floor for life.

The skeletal and muscular systems support a vertebrate's body and make it possible to control movement. Vertebrates are much more mobile than nonvertebrate chordates. With the exception of hagfishes, all vertebrates have an internal skeleton of bone—as shown in **Figure 33–13**—or, in the case of certain fishes, cartilage. The skeleton includes a backbone made up of individual bones called vertebrae. In most vertebrates, tough yet flexible tissues called ligaments connect the vertebrae and allow the backbone to bend without falling apart. Most vertebrates have fin girdles or limb girdles that support the fins or limbs.

In many fishes and snakes, the main body muscles are arranged in blocks on either side of the backbone. These muscle blocks contract in waves that make the body bend back and forth, generating forward thrust. In many amphibians and reptiles, the limbs stick out sideways from the body in a position resembling a push-up. Most mammals stand with their legs straight under them, whether they walk on two legs or on four. In this position, the legs can support the body weight efficiently.

▼ **Figure 33–13** Like the skeletons of most vertebrates, this lizard's skeleton has two pairs of appendages. Muscles and ligaments attach the appendages to the backbone and help control movement.

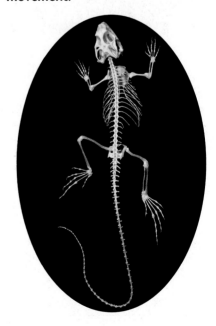

✓ **CHECKPOINT** What three structures support a vertebrate's body and allow it to move?

Comparing Chordates **863**

▲ **Figure 33–14** Chordates differ enormously in the way they reproduce and develop. The male band-tailed cardinalfish (left) carries externally fertilized eggs in his mouth while the eggs incubate. Like most birds, the female emperor goose (center) actively defends her nest, which contains eggs that were internally fertilized. After bearing live young, this female mountain lion (right) nurses her cubs with milk. **Applying Concepts** *Which of these animals is viviparous?*

Reproduction

You can see in **Figure 33–14** that chordates show tremendous diversity in the ways they reproduce and develop. Almost all chordates reproduce sexually.

Vertebrate evolution shows a general trend from external to internal fertilization. The eggs of most nonvertebrate chordates are fertilized externally. Many fishes and amphibians also have external fertilization, while the eggs of reptiles, birds, and mammals are fertilized internally.

After fertilization, the development of chordates can be oviparous, ovoviviparous, or viviparous. In oviparous species, which include most fishes and amphibians and all birds, the eggs develop outside the mother's body. In ovoviviparous animals, such as sharks, the eggs develop within the mother's body and the embryos receive nutrients from the yolk in the egg. The young of ovoviviparous species are born alive. The developing embryos of viviparous species—including most mammals—obtain nutrients directly from the mother's body. As with ovoviviparous species, the young of viviparous animals are born alive.

33–3 Section Assessment

1. 🔑 **Key Concept** List the various organ systems that chordates use to perform essential life functions. How does each system vary between nonvertebrate chordates and vertebrates?

2. Compare and contrast the respiratory systems of a frog, a gorilla, and a sparrow.

3. Describe the parts of the body that most vertebrates use in movement.

4. Explain the difference between oviparous, ovoviviparous, and viviparous modes of development. Give an example of each.

5. **Critical Thinking Applying Concepts** What advantage does a double-loop circulatory system with a three-chambered heart provide that a single-loop system with a two-chambered heart does not?

Assessment Use iText to review the important concepts in Section 33–3.

Take It to the NET

Read about the chordates that lived during the Permian, Jurassic, Cretaceous, and Eocene Periods. Then, construct a table that shows the time period and environment in which each group of chordates lived. Use the links provided in the Biology area at the Prentice Hall Web site for help in completing this activity: **www.phschool.com**

Comparing Chordate Family Trees

Differences in the amino acid sequence of a protein can indicate how long ago two or more species diverged from a common ancestor. In this investigation, you will compare the family trees of several chordate species based on their anatomy and amino acid sequences.

Problem   How can you use anatomical and molecular evidence to determine the evolutionary relationships among chordates?

Species	Amino Acid Sequence of Cytochrome C											
Human	GDVEK	GKKIF	IMKCS	QCHTV	EKGGK	HKTGP	NLHGL	FGRKT	GQAPG	YSYTA	ANKNK	GIIWG
Donkey	GDVEK	GKKIF	VQKCA	QCHTV	EKGGK	HKTGP	NLHGL	FGRKT	GQAPG	FSYTD	ANKNK	GITWK
Horse	GDVEK	GKKIF	VQKCA	QCHTV	EKGGK	HKTGP	NLHGL	FGRKT	GQAPG	FTYTD	ANKNK	GITWK
Chicken	GDIED	GKKIF	VQKCS	QCHTV	EKGGK	HKTGP	NLHGL	FGRKT	GQAEG	FSYTD	ANKNK	GITWG
Turkey	GDIEK	GKKIF	VQKCS	QCHTV	EKGGK	HKTGP	NLHGL	FGRKT	GQAEG	FSYTD	ANKNK	GITWG
Rattlesnake	GDVEK	GKKIF	TMKCS	QCHTV	EKGGK	HKTGP	NLHGL	FGRKT	GQAVG	YSYTA	ANKNK	GITWG

G=glycine, A=alanine, V=valine, L=leucine, I=isoleucine, M=methionine, F=phenylalanine, W=tryptophan, P=proline, S=serine, T=threonine, C=cysteine, Y=tyrosine, N=asparagine, Q=glutamine, D=aspartate, E=glutamate, K=lysine, R=arginine, H=histidine

Materials

- scissors
- toothpicks
- modeling clay
- masking tape
- drinking straws

Skills   Using Models, Analyzing Data

Procedure

1. Use your knowledge of chordate anatomy to decide how to arrange humans, donkeys, horses, chickens, turkeys, and rattlesnakes on a cladogram. The more closely two species are related, the shorter you should make the branches that connect them.

2. Cut pieces of soda straws to form the main branches of the family tree. Use balls of modeling clay to connect the straws.

3. Break toothpicks into appropriate lengths to represent branches within the main groups. Use clay to attach the toothpicks to your model.

4. Write the name of each species on a piece of masking tape. Attach these labels to your model to represent the position of each species.

5. Cytochrome c is a protein found in most eukaryotic cells. The table above the Materials list shows the first 60 amino acids that make up this protein in each species listed in step 1.

6. Construct a data table with the headings "Donkey," "Horse," and "Chicken." Count the number of amino acids that differ in the sequences of chicken and horse cytochrome c. Record this number in your data table.

7. Complete your data table by comparing the amino acid sequences of each pair of species.

8. Make a family tree based on differences among species in cytochrome c.

Analyze and Conclude

1. **Comparing and Contrasting** Did your two cladograms agree? Explain your answer.

2. **Using Models** With which species do horses share the most recent ancestor? Explain.

3. **Evaluating** Could a cladogram based on anatomy differ from one based on amino acid sequences? Why or why not?

Go Further

Comparing and Contrasting What advantages would comparing the nucleotide sequences of DNA have over comparing amino acid sequences?

33–1 Chordate Evolution
Key Concepts

- The chordate family tree has its roots in ancestors that vertebrates share with tunicates and lancelets.
- Over the course of evolution, the appearance of new adaptations—such as jaws and paired appendages—has launched adaptive radiation in chordate groups.

Vocabulary
notochord, p. 849
adaptive radiation, p. 851

33–2 Controlling Body Temperature
Key Concepts

- The control of body temperature is important for maintaining homeostasis in many vertebrates, particularly in habitats where temperature varies widely with time of day and with season.
- Most fishes, amphibians, and reptiles are ectotherms—organisms that obtain heat from outside their bodies. Birds and mammals are endotherms, which means they can generate heat inside their bodies.

Vocabulary
ectotherm, p. 855
endotherm, p. 855

33–3 Form and Function in Chordates
Key Concepts

- The digestive systems of vertebrates have organs that are well adapted for different feeding habits.
- Aquatic chordates—such as tunicates, fishes, and amphibian larvae—use gills for respiration. Land vertebrates, including adult amphibians, reptiles, birds, and mammals, use lungs.
- During the course of chordate evolution, the heart developed chambers and partitions that help separate the blood traveling in the circulatory system.
- Nonvertebrate chordates have a relatively simple nervous system with a mass of nerve cells that form a brain. Vertebrates have a more complex brain with distinct regions, each with a different function.
- Muscular and skeletal systems support a vertebrate's body and make it possible to control movement.

Vocabulary
alveolus, p. 859

Thinking Visually
Using information from this chapter, fill in the following concept map:

Chapter 33

Part A

Multiple Choice
For each statement or question, select the number of the word or expression that, of those given, best completes the statement or answers the question.

1 Which characteristic is unique to chordates?
   (1) ectothermy   (3) response to light
   (2) diffusion   (4) a notochord

2 Which animals have an amniotic egg?
   (1) birds   (3) fishes
   (2) tunicates   (4) amphibians

3 Which animal does not belong with the others?

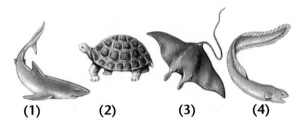

   (1)   (2)   (3)   (4)

4 The main source of heat in ectotherms is their
   (1) high metabolism   (3) own bodies
   (2) environment   (4) food

5 A characteristic of endotherms is that they
   (1) control body temperature through behavior
   (2) control body temperature from within
   (3) obtain heat from outside their bodies
   (4) have relatively low rates of metabolism

6 Aquatic chordates such as tunicates, fishes, and amphibian larvae typically breathe using
   (1) lungs   (3) alveoli
   (2) skin   (4) gills

7 Most chordates that use gills for respiration have a(an)
   (1) double-loop circulatory system
   (2) accessory lung
   (3) single-loop circulatory system
   (4) four-chambered heart

8 An excretory organ composed of small tubes that filter wastes from the blood is the
   (1) kidney   (3) gill
   (2) ureter   (4) cloaca

9 The "thinking" region of the chordate brain is the
   (1) optic lobe   (3) cerebellum
   (2) cerebrum   (4) spinal cord

10 Most vertebrates have
    (1) an inflexible backbone
    (2) a flexible backbone
    (3) a backbone made of cartilage
    (4) no backbone

11 Rapid growth in the diversity of a group of organisms is called
    (1) adaptive radiation
    (2) convergent evolution
    (3) evolutionary history
    (4) rapid extinction

12 Which is *not* a characteristic of breathing?
    (1) inhalation of oxygen-rich air into the lungs
    (2) diffusion of oxygen into the blood within the lung capillaries
    (3) diffusion of carbon dioxide out of the blood within the lung capillaries
    (4) exhalation of oxygen-rich air

13 In chordates with four-chambered hearts, there is
    (1) a partial mixing of oxygen-rich and oxygen-poor blood
    (2) a partial partition in the ventricle
    (3) a partial partition in the atrium
    (4) no mixing of oxygen-rich and oxygen-poor blood

14 In oviparous species, the eggs
    (1) develop internally
    (2) obtain nutrients directly from the mother's body
    (3) obtain nutrients from the external environment
    (4) develop outside the body

15 Which features are common to *all* chordates?
    A A series of connected vertebrae
    B A notochord
    C Pharyngeal pouches
    (1) A, only
    (2) B, only
    (3) B and C
    (4) A, B, and C

Test-Taking Tip Before you answer questions about a diagram, study the diagram and ask yourself what the diagram is about and what it tells you.

Preparing for the Living Environment Exam

Parts B and C

Multiple Choice and Extended Response

For those questions that ask you to select a response, choose the one that best completes the statement or answers the question. For all others follow the directions given.

16 Write a paragraph that compares and contrasts how ectotherms and endotherms control their body temperature. For each type of temperature control, be sure to
- identify the source of heat for the body
- describe a method of conserving body heat
- describe a method of eliminating excess heat

Base your answers to questions 17 through 19 on the diagram below and on your knowledge of biology.

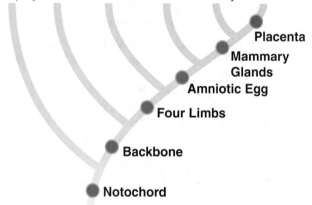

17 Which characteristic is shared by humans, wallabies, and trout?
(1) placenta   (3) four limbs
(2) notochord   (4) mammary glands

18 Which have the closest evolutionary relationship?
(1) humans and wallabies
(2) humans and lizards
(3) humans and lampreys
(4) humans and salamanders

19 A valid conclusion from this cladogram is that
(1) salamanders, trout, and lampreys all have a backbone
(2) four limbs appeared in vertebrate evolution before the notochord
(3) humans and lampreys share a common ancestor
(4) salamanders have amniotic eggs

Base your answers to questions 20 through 23 on the information and illustrations below and on your knowledge of biology.

These diagrams show three kinds of circulatory systems.

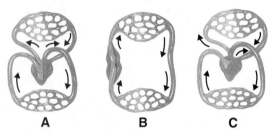

20 Which diagram(s) illustrates a heart with blood containing carbon dioxide but little oxygen?

21 Which diagram(s) shows a circulatory system with a four-chambered heart?

22 Which diagram(s) illustrates a heart that has oxygen-rich and oxygen-poor blood in the same ventricle?

23 Which diagram(s) illustrates a double-loop circulatory system?

24 Write a paragraph comparing the digestive tracts of a horse and a wolf. Be sure to include
- how the types of foods eaten are digested
- how the structure of the digestive tract is specialized for a particular diet

For questions 25 through 27, read the following descriptions of animals and identify the chordate group to which each animal belongs.

25 Two-chambered heart; single-loop circulatory system; excretes ammonia; vertebral column

26 Three-chambered heart; feet not directly beneath the body when standing; oviparous; ectothermic

27 Endothermic; well-developed lungs; excretes uric acid; four-chambered heart

28 Groups of animals that have evolved more recently are sometimes called "advanced," whereas earlier groups are called "primitive." Do you agree with these descriptions? Use examples from the chordates to explain your position.

29 In what way(s) do vertebrates display a high degree of cephalization?

30 Fishes and whales are not closely related, but they share a number of similarities, such as overall body shape and the absence of legs. How can their similarities be explained?

31 Explain how the position of the legs of mammals is different from those of amphibians and most reptiles. How is this characteristic an adaptive advantage?

Base your answers to questions 32 through 34 on the reading passage below and on your knowledge of biology.

Rescue at Sea

The call came to the Coast Guard dispatch officer. The fishing boat, *RubiJewel,* was fully engulfed in flames and was losing electrical power. The lone fisherman on board was about to abandon ship. The dispatcher broadcasted a mayday relay to any vessels in the area. The *Island Transporter* radioed back. It was in the area and was on its way.

   Guided by the emergency beacon on the fisherman's survival suit, the rescuers found him in the bone-chilling seawater. His suit had filled with gallons of the icy water. He had been floating for 40 minutes and was hypothermic and unresponsive. They hauled him aboard and began emergency procedures.

32 Evaluation of the fisherman's vital signs showed his body temperature was 90°F (32.2°C), both his pulse and respiration were very slow, and he was barely conscious. He was severely hypothermic. Why would his vital signs have changed in this situation?

33 In hypothermia cases, patients must be kept warm on the outside and their core body temperature must also be raised. "Inhalation re-warming therapy" is a new treatment that delivers warm, moist oxygen to the lungs of hypothermia patients. The oxygen is warmed to 43°C (normal human body temperature is 37°C). From your knowledge of the double-loop circulatory system of mammals, explain how this therapy could be so successful.

34 Before his accident, the fisherman saw seabirds floating on the water and seals playing on rocks and in the sea. How are those animals able to survive in the same icy water?

Base your answers to questions 35 through 37 on the information below and on your knowledge of biology.

On cool days, a student notices that a duck sits on a sunny lawn with its wings outspread. On hot days, he sees the same duck sitting in the shade of a tree with its bill open.

35 Explain how each of these behaviors might help maintain the duck's body temperature.

36 The student thinks he sees a pattern in the duck's behavior. He decides that he would like to do a scientific study. Develop a hypothesis that the student might investigate and create the data table he would use to gather data that would prove or disprove the hypothesis.

37 Identify whether the duck is endothermic or exothermic. Explain the advantages and disadvantages of each.

---

38 North American hummingbirds and Hawaiian honeycreepers have long, thin bills adapted for drinking nectar from flowers. Recall from Chapter 18 that organisms' DNA can be used to infer evolutionary relationships. Explain how you could determine whether the similarities between these two birds are the result of convergent evolution or adaptive radiation.

 Take It to the NET

An ongoing controversy in the area of paleontology is whether dinosaurs were endotherms or ectotherms. Visit the Prentice Hall Web site at **www.phschool.com** to find out more about this debate. Then, answer the following questions:
- What are three lines of evidence that support the hypothesis that dinosaurs were endotherms?
- What are three lines of evidence that support the hypothesis that dinosaurs were ectotherms?
- What are the main current hypotheses concerning temperature control in dinosaurs? Do you agree with any of them? Explain your answer.

34 Animal Behavior

Two elk bulls lock antlers in a battle for access to a female elk.

Inquiry Activity

What is learning?

Procedure

1. Your teacher will give you a noisemaker and read a paragraph out loud. Each time your teacher reads the word "and," sound your noisemaker once. Record a mark on a piece of paper each time you sound your noisemaker.

2. Observe when other students are sounding their noisemakers.

3. Compare the number of times that you and other students sounded the noisemakers.

Think About It

1. **Observing** Did all students sound their noisemakers the same number of times? Explain any differences.

2. **Drawing Conclusions** What did you and your classmates learn as you performed the activity? How do you think this learning affected the number of times students sounded their noisemakers?

34–1 Elements of Behavior

Do you wash your vegetables before you eat them? If so, you have something in common with a troop of Japanese macaque (muh-KAHK) monkeys that live on the Pacific island of Koshima. Many years ago, biologists in Koshima began leaving sweet potatoes on a sandy beach to entice the resident monkeys into the open. The monkeys ate their potatoes with sand still stuck to them. One day, a young female member of the troop dunked her potato into a nearby pool and scrubbed the sand off it with her hand. The young monkey, apparently preferring the taste of a washed potato, repeated this technique each day. Soon, another monkey in the troop started to imitate her. Months later, her mother began to copy her, too. Eventually, all troop members came to wash their potatoes in the pool. To this day, the descendants of the monkeys on the island of Koshima wash their sweet potatoes before eating them.

Stimulus and Response

The macaque monkey in **Figure 34–1** is exhibiting a learned behavior. Biologists define **behavior** as the way an organism reacts to changes in its internal condition or external environment. A behavior can be simple, such as turning your head in the direction of a noise, or complex, such as washing food. Usually, behaviors are performed when an animal reacts to a stimulus. A **stimulus** (plural: stimuli) is any kind of signal that carries information and can be detected. If you are hungry, your body is providing you with an internal stimulus that might prompt you to eat. The sound of your phone ringing on a Friday night is an external stimulus that might result in your running to answer it!

A single, specific reaction to a stimulus—such as waking up when you hear an alarm—is called a **response.** A behavior may consist of more than one response. For example, a tiger shark might respond to the movements of a potential prey by swimming toward the stimulus, attacking the source of the movement, and swallowing the prey. What stimuli are you responding to right now?

Key Concepts
- What produces behavior in animals?
- What is an innate behavior?
- What are the major types of learning?

Vocabulary
behavior
stimulus
response
innate behavior
learning
habituation
classical conditioning
operant conditioning
insight learning
imprinting

**Reading Strategy:
Using Prior Knowledge**
Before you read, write a definition of behavior based on what you already know. After reading this section, use what you have learned to revise your definition and give examples to support it.

▶ **Figure 34–1** On the island of Koshima, Japanese macaques like this one rinse their sweet potatoes in water. **Inferring** *How did this monkey acquire this behavior?*

▲ **Figure 34–2** 🔵 Behavior is produced by the interaction of body systems. This frog detected a noise with its ears and is now using its brain and muscles to leap out of the water.

Figure 34–3 Moths of the genus *Automeris* normally rest with their front wings over their hind wings (left). If disturbed, the moth will lift its front wings and hold them up to expose a striking circular pattern on its hind wings (right). As one scientist has suggested, this behavior may scare off predators when they mistake the moth's hind-wing pattern for the eyes of predatory owls. **Inferring** *If the scientist's hypothesis is correct, how might you explain the evolution of wing-lifting behavior in this moth?*

Types of Stimuli Animals respond to many types of stimuli, such as light, sound, odors, and heat. However, not every animal can detect all of these stimuli. Humans perceive the world through many senses—including sight, smell, touch, taste, and hearing. Other animals have different senses and may, therefore, respond to stimuli that you are not equipped to sense. The Mexican bulldog bat, for instance, uses high-pitched sounds, which humans cannot hear, to detect the ripples made by a fish breaking the surface of a lake. Some birds can detect Earth's magnetic field and use it to navigate over complex terrain.

How Animals Respond Because of the differences in animals' sensory abilities, responses can vary greatly. 🔵 **When an animal responds to a stimulus, body systems—including the sense organs, nervous system, and muscles—interact to produce the resultant behavior.** Once an animal's senses have detected a stimulus, that information is passed along nerve cells to the brain. The brain and other parts of the nervous system process the information and direct the body's response. Animals with very simple nervous systems are capable of only very simple behaviors, such as moving toward a stimulus or away from it. For example, an earthworm will move away from bright light. Animals with more complex nervous systems, such as the frog in **Figure 34–2,** are better equipped to respond with more complicated and precise behaviors.

Behavior and Evolution

Animal behavior is as important to survival and reproduction as any physical characteristic, such as teeth or claws. Recall that physical traits develop according to a specific set of genetic instructions. Many behaviors are also influenced by genes. Therefore, some behaviors can be inherited by an animal's offspring. Behaviors, like physical characteristics, may evolve under the influence of natural selection. A behavior that is directed by genes may help an individual to survive and reproduce. For example, the genes that code for behavior of the moth in **Figure 34–3** may help the moth escape predators. Organisms with an adaptive behavior will survive and reproduce better than organisms that lack the behavior. After natural selection has operated for many generations, most individuals in the population will exhibit the adaptive behavior.

Innate Behavior

Why do newly hatched birds beg for food within moments after hatching? How do spiders know how to build their first web? These animals are exhibiting an **innate behavior,** also called an instinct, or inborn behavior. 🔑 **Innate behaviors appear in fully functional form the first time they are performed, even though the animal may have had no previous experience with the stimuli to which it responds.** One of the simplest innate behaviors is the suckling of a newborn mammal. Other innate behaviors, such as the weaving of a spider web like the one in **Figure 34–4,** or the building of hanging nests by weaver birds, can be quite complex. All innate behaviors depend on internal mechanisms that develop as a result of complex interactions between an animal's genes and its environment. Biologists do not yet fully understand just how these kinds of interactions occur.

✓ CHECKPOINT) *What is innate behavior?*

Learned Behavior

Animals often live in unpredictable environments, so their behavior must be flexible enough to deal with uncertainty and change. Many animals can alter their behavior as a result of experience. Such changes are called **learning.** Acquired behavior is another name for learning, because these behaviors develop over time.

Many animals have the ability to learn. Organisms with simple nervous systems, such as most invertebrates, may learn only rarely. Among a few invertebrates, and many chordates, learning is common and occurs under a wide range of circumstances. In organisms that care for their young, for example, offspring can learn behaviors from their parents or other caretakers. Scientists have identified several different ways of learning. 🔑 **The four major types of learning are habituation, classical conditioning, operant conditioning, and insight learning.**

▲ **Figure 34– 4** 🔑 Innate behaviors appear in fully functional form the first time they are performed. Because web building is an innate behavior, a spider weaves a web correctly the first time it performs the behavior.

1 Before Conditioning
When a dog sees or smells food, it produces saliva. Food is the stimulus and the dog's response is salivation. Dogs do not usually salivate in response to nonfood stimuli.

2 During Conditioning
By ringing a bell every time he fed the dog, Pavlov trained the dog to associate the sight and smell of food with the ringing bell.

3 After Conditioning
When Pavlov rang a bell in the absence of food, the dog still salivated. The dog was conditioned to salivate in response to a stimulus that it did not normally associate with food.

Habituation The simplest type of learning is habituation. **Habituation** is a process by which an animal decreases or stops its response to a repetitive stimulus that neither rewards nor harms the animal. By ignoring a nonthreatening or unrewarding stimulus, animals can spend their time and energy more efficiently.

Consider the common shore ragworm. This animal lives in a sandy tube that it leaves only to feed. If a shadow passes overhead, the worm will instantly retreat to the safety of its burrow. Yet, if repeated shadows pass within a short time span, this response quickly subsides. When the worm has learned that the shadow is neither food nor threat, it will stop responding. At this point the worm has habituated to the stimulus.

Classical Conditioning When a dog sees its owner approaching with a leash, it may wag its tail and bark, eager to go for a walk. The dog has learned to associate the sight of the leash with a walk. Any time an animal makes a mental connection between a stimulus and some kind of reward or punishment, it has learned by **classical conditioning.** In the case of the dog and its owner, the stimulus of the leash is associated with a pleasant reward—a brisk walk. Now, think of what happens if a dog tries to attack a skunk. The skunk sprays the dog with a substance that stings and smells awful. In the future, that dog is likely to avoid skunks, because it associates the stimulus of the sight and scent of the skunk with the punishment of its foul spray.

The most famous example of classical conditioning is the work of the Russian physiologist Ivan Pavlov, around 1900. Pavlov was studying salivation—an innate behavior—in dogs. He discovered that if he always rang a bell at the same time he fed his dog, the dog would eventually begin to salivate whenever it heard a bell, even if no food was present. **Figure 34–5** shows how the dog in Pavlov's experiment learned to associate the bell (stimulus) with the arrival of food (reward).

◀ **Figure 34–5** Ivan Pavlov taught his dog to expect food whenever a bell was rung. **Pavlov's experiment is an example of classical conditioning, one of the four major types of learning.**

Operant Conditioning Conditioning is often used to train animals. **Operant conditioning** occurs when an animal learns to behave in a certain way through repeated practice, in order to receive a reward or avoid punishment. Operant conditioning is also called trial-and-error learning because it begins with a random behavior that is rewarded in an event called a trial. Most trials result in errors, but occasionally a trial will lead to a reward or punishment.

Operant conditioning was first described in the 1940s by the American psychologist B. F. Skinner. Skinner invented a testing procedure that used a certain type of box—the "Skinner box" shown in **Figure 34–6.** A Skinner box contains a colored button or lever that, when pressed, delivers a food reward. After an animal is rewarded several times, it learns that it gets food whenever it presses the button or lever. At this point, the animal has learned by operant conditioning how to obtain food.

CHECKPOINT *What is operant conditioning?*

Insight Learning The most complicated form of learning is **insight learning,** or reasoning. Insight learning occurs when an animal applies something it has already learned to a new situation, without a period of trial and error. For instance, if you are given a new math problem on an exam, you may apply principles you have already learned in the class in order to solve the problem. Insight learning is common among humans and other primates. In one experiment, a hungry chimpanzee used insight learning to figure out how to reach a bunch of bananas hanging overhead: it stacked some boxes on top of one another and climbed to the top of the stack. In contrast, if a dog accidentally wraps its leash around a tree, the dog is usually unable to free itself.

▲ **Figure 34–6** Notice the pigeon in the Skinner box. Sooner or later, a laboratory animal placed in a Skinner box will accidentally press a button or lever that delivers a food reward. In time, this pigeon will learn how to obtain food whenever it wants. **Applying Concepts** *Which type of learning occurs in a Skinner box?*

Quick Lab

What kind of learning is practice?

Materials paper, ruler, scissors

Procedure
1. Draw straight lines on a piece of paper to divide it into several sections of different sizes and shapes. Then cut the paper into sections along those lines.
2. Shuffle the pieces and then have another student time you as you try to reassemble the pieces. Record how long it takes you to do this task.
3. Repeat step 2 three times. Construct a graph showing how the time you needed to assemble the puzzle changed with repeated practice.

Analyze and Conclude
1. **Analyzing Data** Explain the shape of your graph. How did the time you needed to reassemble the pieces change as you repeated the task?
2. **Drawing Conclusions** What kind of learning did you display in this activity? Was it classical conditioning, operant conditioning, habituation, or some other kind of learning? Explain your answer.

Instinct and Learning Combined

Most behaviors result from a combination of innate ability and learning. Young white-crowned sparrows, for example, have an innate ability to recognize their own species' song. To sing the complete version, however, the young birds must first hear it sung by the adults.

Some very young animals, such as ducks and geese, learn to recognize and follow the first moving object that they see during a critical time early in their lives. Usually, this object is their mother. This process is called **imprinting.** Imprinting keeps young animals close to their mother, who protects them and leads them to food sources. Once imprinting has occurred, the behavior cannot be changed.

Imprinting involves both innate and learned behavior. The young animals have an innate urge to follow the first moving object they see, but they are not born knowing what that object will look like. The young animal must learn from experience what object to follow. In fact, the object on which the young animal imprints does not have to be its mother, or even a living organism. The birds in **Figure 34–7** have imprinted on an aircraft!

Imprinting can occur through scent as well as sight. Newly hatched salmon, for example, imprint on the odor of the stream in which they hatch. Young salmon then head out to sea. Years later, when they mature, the salmon remember the odor of their home stream and return there to spawn.

▲ **Figure 34–7** These young Canada geese were trained to migrate behind this ultralight aircraft in an experiment called Operation Migration. The geese followed the craft as closely as they would their own parents. This type of conditioning is now being used to help endangered species, such as whooping cranes, learn a migration route. **Inferring** *Why would these birds follow this aircraft?*

34–1 Section Assessment

1. 🔑 **Key Concept** Which body systems interact to produce a behavioral response?

2. 🔑 **Key Concept** Compare and contrast innate and learned behavior.

3. 🔑 **Key Concept** Define the four major types of learning.

4. Explain the difference between a stimulus and a response.

5. How does natural selection affect animal behavior?

6. **Critical Thinking Applying Concepts** Give an example of how humans learn through classical conditioning.

iTEXT Assessment Use iText to review the important concepts in Section 34–1.

ALTERNATIVE ASSESSMENT

Creating a Graphic Organizer
Create a graphic organizer to compare innate behavior with the different forms of learned behavior discussed in this section. Include at least one example of each kind of behavior in your graphic organizer.

Using Remote Sensing to Study Animal Behavior

Studying any animal in the wild is difficult. But following elephants as they travel through a jungle or blue whales as they swim through the open ocean is almost impossible. Or is it? The first efforts at such studies involved hands-on techniques that required the capture, banding, release, and recapture of individual animals. Researchers would mark or band an animal with a tag that included a unique way of identifying the individual. If that animal was seen again or recaptured, the identification tag would be recorded and compared to the original field notes. Using this method, scientists could get an idea of the places their subjects visited. But they had few clues to the routes that animals traveled or where they went between capture points.

Remote Sensing

Today, small radio tags or transmitters, whose signals can be located by orbiting satellites, are used to track the positions of some animals as they travel in the wild. As with banding, the lightweight transmitters are attached to individual animals. Satellites that orbit Earth are programmed to locate the transmitter signal and record the position—latitude, longitude, and even depth—of the animal as it moves. Some transmitters even contain computer chips that can record the animal's body temperature, rate of breathing, and other physiological characteristics. These data can be made available to researchers over periods of days, weeks, or even months. This method, called satellite telemetry (tehl-EHM-uh-tree), can be expensive, but the data it provides are extremely valuable.

In the Jungle

Scientists are using remote sensing techniques to track elephants through the dense jungles of Thailand and Malaysia. Preliminary data suggest that elephants can move across long distances within a home range of almost 7000 square kilometers. Such a large area would have been impossible for researchers to cover from the ground, or even by airplane or helicopter.

In the Ocean

Researchers also use remote sensing to study marine animals—particularly sea turtles. Because sea turtles spend most of their lives at sea and come ashore only during breeding season, little is known about their daily habits or migration routes. To get that information, scientists are using satellite telemetry to track the behavior of sea turtles. A transmitter about the size of a portable CD player is glued to the back of the turtle's carapace, where it remains for up to 8 to 10 months. Over time, the information that scientists gain from this technology will help in efforts to protect turtles, elephants, and other endangered species.

On Your Own

Find out more about the use of remote sensing in studies of animal behavior. Log on to the Prentice Hall Web site at **www.phschool.com**.

34–2 Patterns of Behavior

Guide for Reading

 Key Concepts
• How do environmental changes affect animal behavior?
• How do courtship and social behavior increase an animal's evolutionary fitness?
• How do animals communicate?

Vocabulary
migration
circadian rhythm
courtship
territory
aggression
communication
language

Reading Strategy:
Using Visuals As you read, write a sentence explaining how each diagram or photograph reinforces or enhances the content of this section.

At this very moment, somewhere in an African grassland, elephants are calling to one another. Elephants communicate with sounds that they use to locate each other across distances more than 2 kilometers away. When they are not calling long-distance, elephants may spar with each other to test their strength or greet each other by wrapping their trunks together. These behaviors are patterns that have evolved in elephants. In this section, you will investigate some common patterns of animal behavior.

Behavioral Cycles

The environment is full of natural cycles. Night follows day, seasons change, the moon has phases, the tides rise and fall. **Many animals respond to periodic changes in the environment with daily or seasonal cycles of behavior.** For example, several species of reptiles and mammals are active during warm seasons but enter into a sleeplike state, or dormancy, during cold seasons. Dormancy allows an animal to survive periods when food and other resources may not be available.

Another type of behavior that is influenced by changing seasons is **migration,** the periodic movement from one place to another and then back again. Animals that migrate include species of birds, butterflies, and whales. **Figure 34–8** shows the migratory pattern of green sea turtles. Migration usually allows animals to take advantage of favorable environmental conditions. For example, when birds fly south for the winter, they go to regions where food is more plentiful than in northern areas.

Behavioral cycles that occur in daily patterns are called **circadian rhythms** (sur-KAY-dee-un). The fact that you sleep at night and attend school during the day is an example of a circadian rhythm.

▶ **Figure 34–8** Each year, between December and June, green sea turtles migrate from their feeding grounds along the coast of Brazil to mate and nest on Ascension, a tiny island more than 2000 kilometers away. **Like many animals, sea turtles migrate in response to seasonal changes in their environment.**

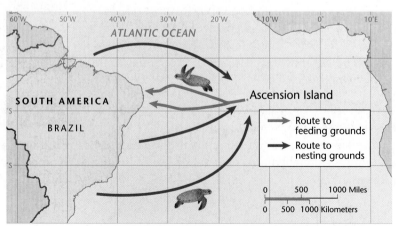

Caring for Eggs

Reproduction is vital to animal survival. Humans can learn child-rearing skills. Is there evidence that other animals learn to care for their young?

The data at right are from field studies of the short-tailed shearwater, *Puffinus tenuirostris.* Each pair of parents produces only one egg a year. If that egg breaks or if the chick dies, the egg is not replaced. The graph shows the percentage of eggs that hatch and develop into free-flying young, in relation to the number of years that the parents have been breeding. This variable is referred to as reproductive success. The purple line indicates the success rate of female parents. The green line indicates the success rate of male parents.

Reproductive Success of Short-Tailed Shearwaters

y-axis: Average Percentage of Eggs Producing Young (0, 20, 40, 60, 80, 100)

x-axis: Breeding Experience (years) (0, 5, 10, 15, 20, 25)

Males
Females

1. **Using Tables and Graphs** What is the approximate success rate of a female shearwater with 5 years of breeding experience?

2. **Using Tables and Graphs** Are there obvious differences in reproductive success between male and female shearwaters?

3. **Drawing Conclusions** Do older shearwaters have better reproductive success than younger birds? Explain your answer.

4. **Formulating Hypotheses** Do you think these birds learn to raise young more successfully over time? Is there an alternative hypothesis that could explain these data?

Courtship

Animal behavior is geared toward reproduction as well as survival. 🔑 **To pass along its genes to the next generation, any animal that reproduces sexually needs to locate and mate with another member of its species at least once. Courtship behavior helps many animals identify healthy mates.**

In **courtship,** an individual sends out stimuli—such as sounds, visual displays, or chemicals—in order to attract a member of the opposite sex. For example, fireflies flash a distinct series of light signals to indicate their readiness to mate. The musical trill of a tree frog and the sheeplike bleat of a narrowmouth toad are among the many distinctive breeding calls of amphibians.

In some species, courtship involves an elaborate series of behaviors called rituals. A ritual is a series of behaviors performed the same way by all members of a population for the purpose of communicating. Most rituals consist of specific signals and individual responses that continue until mating occurs. For example, newly paired cranes, such as those in **Figure 34–9,** engage in intense periods of dancing before they mate.

✔**CHECKPOINT** *What is the function of courtship behavior?*

▼ **Figure 34–9** 🔵 **Courtship behavior helps many animals identify healthy mates.** The courtship ritual of this pair of Japanese cranes consists of head bobbing, deep bows, leaps, grasping and tossing objects, short flights, and several other moves. If a potential mate does not perform the parts of this dance in the proper sequence, it will be rejected and must locate a different mate.

The origin of the adjective **social** is the Latin word *socialis,* meaning "companionship." Animals that are social spend most of their time in a group. **What does a socio-biologist do?**

Social Behavior

Whenever animals interact with members of their own species, as in courtship, they are exhibiting social behavior. For some species, social behavior offers great survival advantages. Zebras and other grazers, for example, band together when searching for food. They are safer from predators when they are part of a group than when alone.

Some animals—including ants, certain shrimps, and some mammals—go a step further in their social behavior and form societies. A society is a group of closely related animals of the same species that work together for the benefit of the group. It takes millions of termites, for example, to build a single termite mound. Animal societies also use strength in numbers to improve their ability to hunt, to protect their territory, to guard their young, and to fight with rivals if necessary. In wild African dog packs, for instance, adult females take turns guarding all the pups in the pack, while the other adults hunt together for prey.

🔑 **Usually, members of a society are related to one another. Related individuals share a large proportion of each other's genes. Therefore, helping a relative survive increases the chance that the genes an individual shares with that relative will be passed along to offspring.** Thus, social behavior that helps a relative survive and reproduce improves an individual's evolutionary fitness.

Primates form some of the most complex animal societies known. Macaque, baboon, and other primate societies hunt together, travel in search of new territory, and interact with neighboring societies. A great deal of what we know about primate societies comes from the work of Jane Goodall, the animal behaviorist pictured in **Figure 34–10,** who spent thousands of hours observing chimps in their natural habitat.

✓CHECKPOINT *What is an animal society?*

▶ **Figure 34–10** 🔵Animal societies enhance the reproductive success of individual members. The work of the British behaviorist Jane Goodall, at right, laid the foundation for modern primate studies. Goodall observed chimpanzees in their natural habitat, as shown here. Goodall's methodology and profound scientific discoveries revolutionized the field of animal behavior.

Competition and Aggression

Some animals have behaviors that help prevent others from using limited resources. Often, such patterns involve a specific area, or **territory,** that is occupied and protected by an animal or group of animals. Territories contain resources, such as food, water, nesting sites, shelter, and potential mates, that are necessary for an animal's survival and reproduction. By claiming a territory, an animal keeps others at a distance. If a rival enters a territory, the "owner" of the territory may attack the rival and drive it away. Algae-eating damselfish are notorious for such attacks. An algae-eating damselfish can distinguish other algae-feeding species from species that do not eat algae. The damselfish chases the other algae-eaters away, but ignores the fish that do not eat algae.

When two or more animals try to claim limited resources, such as a territory or food, competition occurs. Many animals, such as the giraffes in **Figure 34–11,** use rituals and displays when they compete. During competition, animals may also show **aggression,** a threatening behavior that one animal uses to gain control over another. For instance, before a pride of lions settles down to eat, individuals may snap, claw, and snarl at one another. The most aggressive members will get to eat their fill of prey. The less aggressive lions will have to wait for their chance to feed.

Communication

Often, when animal behavior involves more than one individual, some form of **communication**—the passing of information from one organism to another—is involved. 🔑 **Animals may use visual, sound, touch, or chemical signals to communicate with one another.** The specific techniques that animals use depend on the types of stimuli their senses can detect.

Visual Signals Animals with good eyesight often use visual signals involving movement and color. Cuttlefish, for example, have large eyes that are as sophisticated as those of vertebrates. In a matter of seconds, a single cuttlefish, like the one in **Figure 34–12,** can undergo changes in the colors and patterns on its body. Its skin will pucker into bumps and spines, then suddenly become smooth as stone. These visual displays—as fascinating as any computer screen saver—function in defense, hunting, mating, warning, and perhaps other forms of communication that are not yet known.

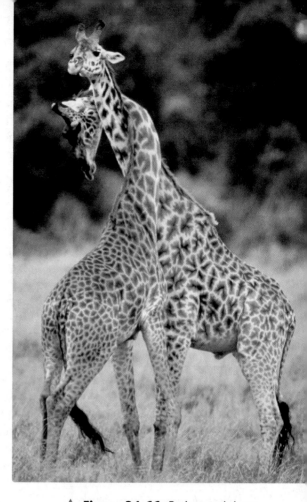

▲ **Figure 34–11** By intertwining their long necks, these two giraffes compete for resources on an African savanna. **Inferring** *What resources might these giraffes compete for?*

▶ **Figure 34–12** 🔑 Animals use visual, sound, touch, and chemical signals to communicate. Like many animals with good eyesight, this Pacific giant cuttlefish uses visual signals in displaying a variety of bright colors and patterns on its body.

Chemical Signals Animals with well-developed senses of smell, including insects, fishes, and many mammals, may communicate with chemicals. For example, some animals release pheromones (FEHR-uh-mohnz), chemical messengers that affect the behavior of other individuals of the same species, to mark a territory or to signal their readiness to mate.

Sound Signals Animals with strong vocal abilities, including crickets, toads, and birds, communicate with sound. Some animals that use sound have evolved elaborate communication systems. Dolphins, for example, rely mainly on sound signals in the dark and often murky ocean depths where vision is not very useful. Scientists have discovered that bottlenose dolphins each have their own unique "signature" whistle that is used for recognition, like the ones whose patterns are shown on the graph in **Figure 34–13.** The dolphins' whistles function something like your signature on a letter, letting others know who is sending the communication.

Language The most complicated form of communication is language. **Language** is a system of communication that combines sounds, symbols, or gestures according to sets of rules about word order and meaning, such as grammar and syntax. Many animals, like dolphins, elephants, and gorillas, have fairly complex ways of communicating. However, outside of experiments in which they were trained by humans, none of those animals have been shown to use language. Only humans are known to use language.

Vocal Signatures of Four Dolphins

Frequency (kiloHertz)

Time (seconds)

◀ **Figure 34–13** Individual bottlenose dolphins use vocal "signatures" during communication. The spectrograms at left show the signature signals of four different dolphins. **Interpreting Graphics** *What two variables are plotted in a spectrogram?*

34–2 Section Assessment

1. 🔑 **Key Concept** Name two ways in which animal behavior is related to environmental cycles.

2. 🔑 **Key Concept** Explain how an animal society can contribute to the survival of an individual animal.

3. 🔑 **Key Concept** What are the main ways in which animals communicate with each other?

4. Define "courtship ritual," and give an example of an animal's courtship ritual.

5. **Critical Thinking Inferring** Suppose you discover a new type of animal that is very different in appearance from other animals you have seen. How could observing the sense organs of this animal help you to understand if and how it communicates?

🧍**iTEXT** **Assessment** Use iText to review the important concepts in Section 34–2.

Take It to the NET

Read about the behavior of bears. Then, prepare a multimedia presentation that includes photographs or drawings showing the behavior and habitat of bears, along with any sounds that they make. Use the links provided in the Biology area at the Prentice Hall Web site for help in completing this activity.
www.phschool.com

Observing Behavior in Fish

Animals of the same species often use aggressive behavior to signal others to retreat, but rarely do they hurt each other. In this investigation, you will examine some stimuli that provoke aggressive behavior.

Problem What triggers the aggressive behavior of male betta fish?

Materials

- male betta fish
- aquarium net
- clear plastic box of aquarium water
- small mirror
- construction paper
- colored pencils or markers
- transparent tape
- popsicle sticks
- watch with a second hand

Skills Posing Questions, Designing Experiments

Design Your Experiment

Part A: Observing Aggressive Displays

1. Use an aquarium net to transfer a male betta from the aquarium to a clear plastic box of aquarium water. **CAUTION:** *Do not touch the fish with your hands. Fish are easily injured.*

2. Observe the betta's behavior.

3. Place a mirror against the side of the box so that the fish can see its reflection. Observe and record the betta's behavior. Remove the mirror within 1 minute so that the fish does not habituate to its reflection.

Part B: Identifying the Stimulus for Aggression

4. **Predicting** What feature of a betta provokes aggressive behavior in other bettas? Is it color, size, movement, or something else? Record a prediction of what provokes aggressive displays by bettas.

5. Design an experiment that will use paper models of bettas to test your prediction. You can tape the models to popsicle sticks and use colored pencils or markers to add details. Have your teacher check your plan before you begin your experiment.

6. Carry out your experiment. Record your observations of the betta's behavior. **CAUTION:** *To avoid exhausting the betta, always allow it at least 1 minute of rest between stimuli.*

Analyze and Conclude

1. **Observing** Did the male betta exhibit aggressive behavior? If so, how did it show aggression?

2. **Evaluating** What stimuli provoked the most aggression? Did your observations support your prediction?

3. **Inferring** Male bettas are more aggressive toward other males when a female betta is present. How can such behavior be an advantage to the male? How does it help the species survive?

Go Further

Designing Experiments Male bettas use aggression to defend their territory against invasion from other male bettas. Design an experiment to investigate what traits determine which male bettas will be successful in conflicts with other males.

34–1 Elements of Behavior
🔑 Key Concepts

- When an animal responds to a stimulus, body systems—including the sense organs, nervous system, and muscles—interact to produce the resultant behavior.

- Innate behaviors appear in fully functional form the first time they are performed, even though the animal may have had no previous experience with the stimuli to which it responds.

- The four major types of learning are habituation, classical conditioning, operant conditioning, and insight learning.

Vocabulary
behavior, p. 871
stimulus, p. 871
response, p. 871
innate behavior, p. 873
learning, p. 873
habituation, p. 874
classical conditioning, p. 874
operant conditioning, p. 875
insight learning, p. 875
imprinting, p. 876

34–2 Patterns of Behavior
🔑 Key Concepts

- Many animals respond to periodic changes in the environment with daily or seasonal cycles of behavior.

- To pass along its genes to the next generation, any animal that reproduces sexually needs to locate and mate with another member of its species at least once. Courtship behavior helps many animals identify healthy mates.

- Usually, members of a society are related to one another. Related individuals share a large proportion of each other's genes. Therefore, helping a relative survive increases the chance that the genes an individual shares with that relative will be passed along to the next generation of offspring.

- Animals may use visual, sound, touch, or chemical signals to communicate with one another.

Vocabulary
migration, p. 878
circadian rhythm, p. 878
courtship, p. 879
territory, p. 881
aggression, p. 881
communication, p. 881
language, p. 882

Thinking Visually
Using information from this chapter, complete the following concept map:

Chapter 34

Part A

Multiple Choice

For each statement or question, select the number of the word or expression that, of those given, best completes the statement or answers the question.

1 The set of reactions of an organism to changes in its internal condition or external environment is called
(1) behavior   (3) learning
(2) conditioning   (4) stimuli

2 Which type of behavior is demonstrated when a dog learns to expect food whenever a bell is rung?
(1) insight learning
(2) classical conditioning
(3) operant conditioning
(4) instinct habituation

3 Light, sound, and temperature are examples of
(1) responses   (3) circadian rhythms
(2) stimuli   (4) conditioned behaviors

4 A decrease in response to a stimulus that neither rewards nor harms an animal is called
(1) instinct
(2) operant conditioning
(3) habituation
(4) classical conditioning

5 Insight learning is common among
(1) dogs   (3) insects
(2) primates   (4) geese

6 What type of learning is being demonstrated by the baby birds in the illustration below?
(1) imprinting   (3) classical conditioning
(2) habituation   (4) operant conditioning

7 The fact that you sleep at night and attend school during the day is an example of a(an)
(1) migration
(2) circadian rhythm
(3) aggressive behavior
(4) social behavior

8 Each year, a bird called the American redstart travels from its winter home in South America to its nesting area in New York. Which term best describes this behavior?
(1) migration   (3) imprinting
(2) competition   (4) courtship

9 A system of communication that uses meaningful sounds, symbols, or gestures according to specific rules is called
(1) competition
(2) language
(3) vision
(4) parenting

10 Which kind of behavior does *not* involve learning?
(1) habituation
(2) trial and error
(3) imprinting offspring
(4) instinct

11 A male three-spined stickleback fish will attack male red-bellied sticklebacks and models of fishes that have a red underside. It will not attack males or models that do not have a red underside. What is the best conclusion that can be drawn from the behavior of this fish?
(1) The stimulus for an attack is a fish with red fins.
(2) The stimulus for an attack is a red underside.
(3) The stickleback fish will defend its territory against all other fish.
(4) The stickleback fish will not attack red-colored fish.

For questions 12 and 13, complete each analogy by selecting the correct number. In analogies, A : B :: C : means "A is to B as C is to ___?___."

12 Stimulus : cold temperatures :: response :
(1) sweating   (3) shivering
(2) egg laying   (4) warm weather

13 Finding a mate : courtship behavior :: protecting a territory:
(1) feeding   (3) migration
(2) aggression   (4) habituation

Test-Taking Tip When you are asked to analyze a graph showing experimental data, first look at the shape of the line. Identify the variables and try to determine how they are related.

Parts B and C

Multiple Choice and Extended Response
For those questions that ask you to select a response, choose the one that best completes the statement or answers the question. For all others follow the directions given.

14 Identify each of the following as a stimulus or a response: laughter, thirst, cold air, eating, baseball being thrown at you, a sneeze, light, flying.

15 The survival of an animal often depends on making the appropriate response to a stimulus. For each of the following stimuli, state an appropriate response.
- A deer sees a predator nearby.
- A person feels something hot touching his hand.
- A female fly detects the smell of rotting meat.

16 State the brain's role in an animal's response to a stimulus.

17 The social behavior shown by some species can help them survive. Name two species that demonstrate some form of social organization, and, for each species, give an example of how this behavior aids its survival.

18 Although the members of many animal species derive benefits from living in social groups, members of other species live alone. State one adaptive advantage of solitary living that would not be true for a species living in social groups.

For questions 19 through 22, select the number of the behavior chosen from the list below, that is best described by that statement. A choice may be used once, more than once, or not at all.

Behaviors
(1) Insight learning
(2) Operant conditioning
(3) Classical conditioning
(4) Habituation

19 A rat learns to press a button to get food.

20 A dog always salivates at the ringing of a bell.

21 A chimpanzee stacks boxes in order to reach a banana hanging from the ceiling.

22 A bird stops responding to a repeated warning call when it is not followed by an attack.

Base your answers to questions 23 through 25 on the information and graph below and on your knowledge of biology.

A researcher observed sedge warblers during breeding season. She charted the number of different songs each male bird sang compared to the time it took him to pair with a mate. The graph illustrates her data.

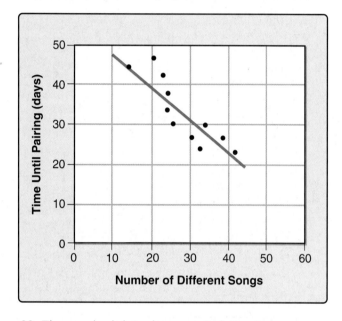

23 The graphed data show a correlation between
(1) the number of a male bird's songs and the time to sing them
(2) the number of a male bird's songs and his attractiveness to females
(3) which songs a male bird sings on different days
(4) which songs a male bird sings for each female

24 State the conclusion that would most likely be made based on the data shown in the graph. In your answer, be sure to
- name the two variables in the study
- explain how the two variables are related

25 Over time, natural selection could lead to changes in the courtship behavior of these birds. State one environmental condition that would favor the reproductive success of male birds that sing a greater variety of songs over those with less song variety. Support your answer with an explanation.

26 In an effort to repopulate once-polluted rivers with salmon, scientists take fertilized salmon eggs from a clean river and place them in the once-polluted river. The salmon will hatch from the eggs, move to the ocean for several years, and then return to the river where they hatched—instead of the river from which the eggs were obtained. Explain how imprinting is specifically involved in this process.

27 Animals in captivity often behave differently than they would in nature. Jane Goodall is a scientist who has contributed much to our knowledge of primate societal structure. Describe what Goodall did to obtain her data that made them especially valuable and accurate.

28 Explain how aggression and territorial behavior are related.

29 Compare animal communication with the use of language. In your answer be sure to include
- an explanation of the difference between communication and the use of language
- an example of an animal that communicates without language, and how it communicates
- an example of an animal that communicates with language

30 A classmate suggests that German shepherd dogs are more easily trained than poodles. Describe the steps in an experiment that would determine which breed of dog is more easily trained to respond correctly to the command "stay." In your description, be sure to include the following
- how many dogs of each breed you should attempt to train, and why it is necessary to use this many
- what procedure should be followed with each dog
- how you will know if one breed is easier to train than the other

Base your answers to questions 31 and 32 on the information below and on your knowledge of biology.

In a particular species of insect, the females each release small quantities of a certain pheromone to attract males. Once a male of the species detects the pheromone scent released by a female, it flies toward the scent to locate and mate with that particular female.

31 Predict what would happen to the ability of the males to find females in a field if a farmer released large quantities of the pheromone to form a "cloud of pheromone" over the entire area. Support your answer with an explanation.

32 Explain why this method to control the population of insects is less damaging to other organisms in the environment than the use of pesticides to control insect pests.

33 When temperatures are low and food is scarce, some mammals enter into a state of dormancy. Dormancy is an energy-saving adaptation in which metabolism decreases, and as a result, body temperature declines. The graph below tracks a ground squirrel's body temperature over the course of a year.

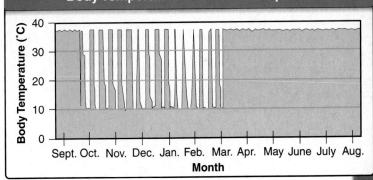

Body Temperature of a Ground Squirrel

Describe the pattern that you observe, and explain what can be inferred about the squirrel's behavior at different times of the year.

Take It to the NET

What kinds of animal behavior studies are currently being conducted? Visit the Prentice Hall Web site at **www.phschool.com** to find out about current projects. Then, answer the following questions:
- What are three scientific projects that are currently underway in animal behavior?
- Who is working on these projects?
- Where is the research conducted?
- What do scientists hope to learn from the projects?

▶ Each body system performs its function and works with other systems to keep the bodies of these hurdlers in perfect working order.

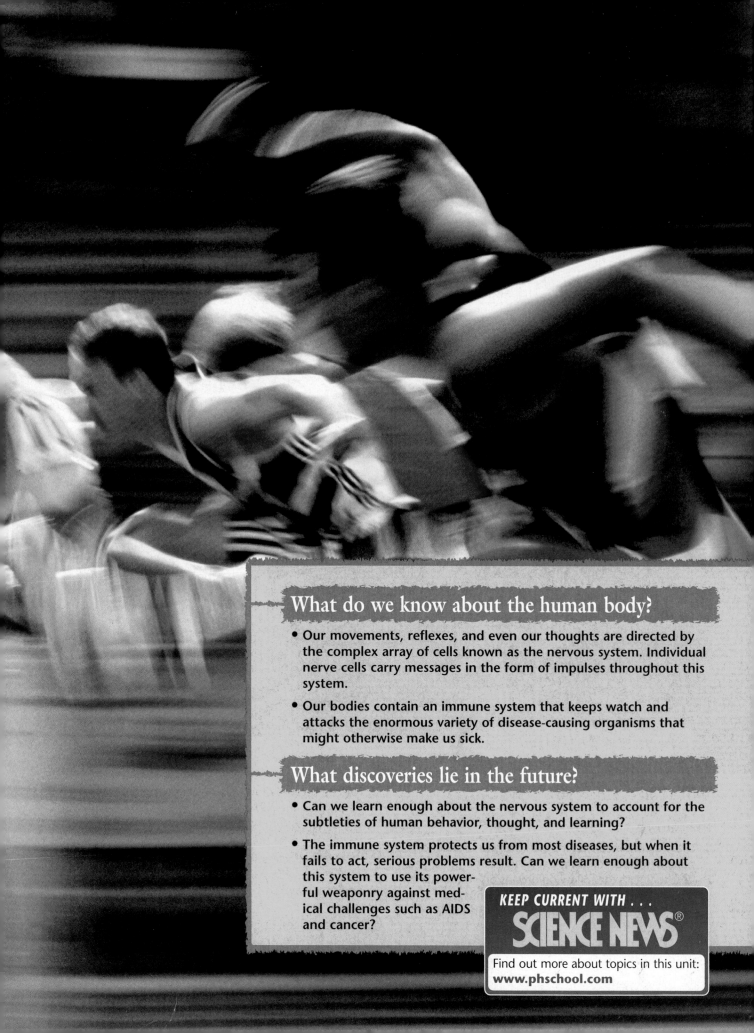

What do we know about the human body?

- Our movements, reflexes, and even our thoughts are directed by the complex array of cells known as the nervous system. Individual nerve cells carry messages in the form of impulses throughout this system.

- Our bodies contain an immune system that keeps watch and attacks the enormous variety of disease-causing organisms that might otherwise make us sick.

What discoveries lie in the future?

- Can we learn enough about the nervous system to account for the subtleties of human behavior, thought, and learning?

- The immune system protects us from most diseases, but when it fails to act, serious problems result. Can we learn enough about this system to use its powerful weaponry against medical challenges such as AIDS and cancer?

35 Nervous System

This scanning electron micrograph shows part of an eye. The dark blue on the upper left is the edge of the pupil, the opening through which light enters. The mauve object is the iris, which controls the size of the pupil. The yellow and green objects are fibers that suspend the lens in the eyeball.

Inquiry Activity

What are the organ systems?

Procedure

1. Draw an outline of the human body on a sheet of paper. Without referring to any illustrations, do your best to locate the following organs on your outline: brain, stomach, kidneys, heart, and lungs. Pay attention to the shapes of the organs and their relative sizes.

2. Make a second drawing using **Figure 35–2** on pages 892 and 893 as a reference. Indicate which organs belong to which organ systems.

Think About It

1. **Predicting** Can an organ belong to more than one organ system? Explain.

2. **Evaluating and Revising** Compare your two drawings. Describe any misconceptions you had about the size, shape, or location of the organs.

35–1 Human Body Systems

As the missed shot bounces high in the air, one of the defenders decides to take a chance. She breaks for the other end of the court. Another defender grabs the rebound, glances upcourt, and throws a long, arching pass toward the basket. Wide open, her teammate grabs the pass, dribbles, and leaps into the air, laying the basketball carefully off the backboard and into the unguarded basket. The buzzer goes off, and the game is over.

Organization of the Body

Teamwork is a wonderful thing! Anyone watching the end of this game would be impressed at the way these two players worked together to make the winning play. But the real teamwork on this play involved a much larger number of players— nearly a hundred trillion cells that make up the human body.

Every cell in the human body is both an independent unit and an interdependent part of a larger community—the entire organism. To make a winning basket, a basketball player has to use her eyes to watch the play and her brain to figure out how to score. With the support of her bones, her muscles propel her body up the court. As she sprints for a pass, her lungs absorb oxygen, which her blood carries to her cells. Her brain monitors the sensation of the ball on her fingertips and sends signals that guide her body into the air for the final play.

Levels of Organization How does the body get so many individual cells to work together so beautifully? You can begin to answer this question by studying the organization of the human body. Recall the levels of organization in a multicellular organism—cells, tissues, organs, and organ systems. Tissues are groups of similar cells that perform a single function, such as connecting a muscle to a bone. An organ is a group of tissues that work together to perform a complex function, such as sight. An organ system is a group of organs that perform closely related functions.

The eleven organ systems of the human body work together to maintain homeostasis. The organ systems are shown in **Figure 35–2** on pages 892 and 893.

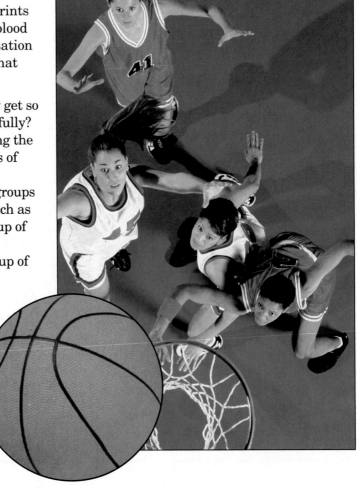

▶ **Figure 35–1** Each player on a basketball team has a different role, but together the team works toward a common goal—winning the game.

Guide for Reading

🔑 **Key Concepts**
• How does the human body maintain homeostasis?

Vocabulary
muscle tissue
epithelial tissue
connective tissue
nervous tissue
feedback inhibition

Reading Strategy:
Predicting Before you read, use **Figure 35–2** to predict how many organ systems help to regulate body temperature. As you read, look for evidence to support your prediction.

FIGURE 35–2 HUMAN ORGAN SYSTEMS

Each of the eleven organ systems shown here has a different set of functions. 🔑 The organ systems work together to maintain a stable internal environment.

Nervous System
Structures: Brain, spinal cord, peripheral nerves
Function: Coordinates the body's response to changes in its internal and external environments

Integumentary System
Structures: Skin, hair, nails, sweat and oil glands
Function: Serves as a barrier against infection and injury; helps to regulate body temperature; provides protection against ultraviolet radiation from the sun

Skeletal System
Structures: Bones, cartilage, ligaments, tendons
Function: Supports the body; protects internal organs; allows movement; stores mineral reserves; provides a site for blood cell formation

Muscular System
Structures: Skeletal muscle, smooth muscle, cardiac muscle
Function: Works with skeletal system to produce voluntary movement; helps to circulate blood and move food through the digestive system

Circulatory System
Structures: Heart, blood vessels, blood
Function: Brings oxygen, nutrients, and hormones to cells; fights infection; regulates body temperature

Respiratory System
Structures: Nose, pharynx, larynx, trachea, bronchi, bronchioles, lungs
Function: Provides oxygen needed for cellular respiration and removes excess carbon dioxide from the body

Digestive System
Structures: Mouth, pharynx, esophagus, stomach, small and large intestines
Function: Converts foods into simpler molecules that can be used by the cells of the body; absorbs food

Excretory System
Structures: Skin, lungs, kidneys, ureters, urinary bladder, urethra
Function: Eliminates waste products of metabolism from the body; maintains homeostasis

Endocrine System
Structures: Hypothalamus, pituitary, thyroid, parathyroids, adrenals, pancreas, ovaries (in females), testes (in males)
Function: Controls growth, development, metabolism, and reproduction

Reproductive System
Structures: Testes, epididymis, vas deferens, urethra, and penis (in males); ovaries, Fallopian tubes, uterus, vagina (in females)
Function: Produces reproductive cells; in females, nurtures and protects developing embryo

Lymphatic System
Structures: White blood cells, thymus, spleen, lymph nodes, lymph vessels
Function: Helps protect the body from disease; collects fluid lost from blood vessels and returns the fluid to the circulatory system

Epithelial Tissue (magnification: 6000×)

Connective Tissue (magnification: about 50×)

Nervous Tissue (magnification: 1100×)

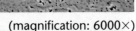

Muscle Tissue (magnification: 150×)

▲ **Figure 35–3** The four major types of tissues in the human body are epithelial tissue, connective tissue, nervous tissue, and muscle tissue. **Inferring** *What kind of tissue is bone?*

Types of Tissues Different tissue types work together within organs. **Muscle tissue** is the most abundant tissue in most animals. Muscle tissue controls the internal movement of materials such as blood through the circulatory system and food through the digestive system. Muscle tissue also controls the external movements of the entire body or parts of the body, such as your hands when you type on a computer keyboard.

The heart is mainly muscle tissue, but three other types of tissues are needed for the heart to function. The closely packed cells in **epithelial tissue** cover the surface of the body and line internal organs. Epithelial tissue lining the chambers of the heart prevents leakage of blood. Glands are made from epithelial tissue. A gland is a structure that makes and secretes, or releases, a particular product such as saliva, sweat, or milk.

Connective tissue does more than its name implies. It holds organs in place and binds different parts of the body together. The tendons that connect bones to muscles and the ligaments that join bones to bones are examples of connective tissue. This type of tissue also provides support for the body. Connective tissue keeps the walls of the heart flexible, but strong. Some connective tissue pads and insulates the body.

Nervous tissue receives messages from the body's external and internal environments, analyzes the data, and directs the response. Nervous tissue in the heart controls the rate at which the heart beats.

✓CHECKPOINT) *What is the role of nervous tissue?*

Maintaining Homeostasis

You can get a glimpse of the functions of your organ systems when you breathe deeply after climbing a steep hill or your blood clots to seal a cut. Behind the scenes, your organ systems are working constantly to do something that few people appreciate—maintain a controlled, stable internal environment. Recall from Chapter 1 that this process is called homeostasis. The cells of the body must be kept at a temperature within a certain narrow range, supplied with energy through cellular respiration, bathed in fluid, and cleansed of their waste products. Failure at any of these tasks, even for a few minutes, could lead to permanent injury or death of the entire organism.

A Nonliving Example One way to understand homeostasis is to look at a nonliving system that also keeps environmental conditions within a certain range. The heating system of a house is a perfect example. In most houses, heat is supplied by a furnace that burns oil or natural gas. When the temperature within the house drops below a set point, a sensor in a device called a thermostat switches the furnace on. Heat produced by the furnace warms the house. When the temperature rises above the set point, the thermostat switches the furnace off. Because the furnace runs only when it is needed, the temperature of the house is kept within a narrow range.

A heating system like the one described is said to be controlled by feedback inhibition. **Feedback inhibition** is the process by which the product of a system shuts down the system or limits its operation. **Figure 35–4** summarizes the feedback inhibition process in a home heating system. When the furnace is switched on, it produces a product (heat) that changes the environment of the house (by raising the air temperature). This environmental change then "feeds back" to "inhibit" the operation of the furnace. In other words, heat from the furnace eventually raises the temperature enough to send a feedback signal to switch the furnace off. Systems controlled by feedback inhibition are generally fully automated and very stable. That is why a house with a good heating system is a comfortable place to be, even on the coldest of days.

▼ **Figure 35–4** A home heating system uses feedback inhibition to maintain a stable, comfortable environment within a house. **Predicting** *In which organ system is the thermostat for the human body located?*

Thermostat senses temperature change and switches off heating system

Room temperature decreases

Thermostat senses temperature change and switches on heating system

Heating system turns on

In the Body Could biological systems achieve homeostasis through feedback inhibition? Absolutely. All that is needed is a system that regulates some aspect of the cellular environment and that can respond to feedback from its own activities by switching on or off as needed.

For the body to maintain a stable temperature, there must be a balance between heat production and heat loss. The body regulates temperature by a mechanism that is remarkably similar to that of a household heating system. A part of the brain called the hypothalamus contains nerve cells that monitor both the temperature of the skin at the surface of the body and the temperature of organs in the body's core. The temperature of the core is generally higher than the temperature of the skin.

If the nerve cells sense that the core temperature has dropped much below 37°C, the hypothalamus produces chemicals that signal cells throughout the body to speed up their activities. Heat produced by this increase in cellular activity causes a gradual rise in body temperature, which is detected by nerve cells in the hypothalamus. This feedback inhibits the production of the chemicals that speed up cellular activity and keeps body temperature from rising to a dangerous level.

Have you ever been so cold that you began to shiver? If your body temperature drops well below its normal range, the hypothalamus releases chemicals that signal muscles just below the surface of the skin to contract involuntarily—to "shiver." These muscle contractions release heat, which helps the body temperature to rise back toward the normal range.

If body temperature rises too far above 37°C, the hypothalamus slows down cellular activities, minimizing the production of heat. This is one of the main reasons you may feel tired and sluggish on a hot day. The body also responds to high temperatures by producing sweat, which helps to cool the body surface by evaporation. Because heat from the body's core is carried by the blood to the skin, evaporation at the body surface also helps to lower the temperature of the core. When this temperature returns to its set point, the body stops producing sweat.

Word Origins

Thermometer comes from the Greek words *therme,* meaning "heat," and *metron,* meaning "measure." So, thermometer means an instrument used to measure heat. **If** *hypo-* is Greek for "under," what does *hypothermia* mean?

35–1 Section Assessment

1. **Key Concept** Explain the role the nervous system plays in maintaining homeostasis.

2. What are the four types of tissue?

3. Which organ systems help to maintain body temperature?

4. Explain why the hypothalamus can be compared to a thermostat.

5. **Critical Thinking Classifying** Would you classify blood as a cell, a tissue, or an organ? Explain your answer.

iTEXT **Assessment** Use iText to review the important concepts in Section 35–1.

35-2 The Nervous System

Play any team sport—basketball, softball, soccer—and you will discover that communication is one of the keys to success. Coaches call plays, players signal to one another, and the very best teams communicate in a way that enables them to play as a single unit. Communication can make the difference between winning and losing.

The same is true for living organisms. Nearly all multicellular organisms have communication systems. Specialized cells carry messages from one cell to another so that communication among all body parts is smooth and efficient. In humans, these cells are in the nervous system. **The nervous system controls and coordinates functions throughout the body and responds to internal and external stimuli.**

Neurons

The messages carried by the nervous system are electrical signals called impulses. The cells that transmit these impulses are called **neurons**. Neurons can be classified into three types according to the direction in which an impulse travels. Sensory neurons carry impulses from the sense organs to the spinal cord and brain. Motor neurons carry impulses from the brain and the spinal cord to muscles and glands. Interneurons connect sensory and motor neurons and carry impulses between them. Although neurons come in all shapes and sizes, they have certain features in common. **Figure 35–5** shows a typical neuron. The largest part of a typical neuron is the **cell body.** The cell body contains the nucleus and much of the cytoplasm. Most of the metabolic activity of the cell takes place in the cell body.

Guide for Reading

Key Concepts
- What is the function of the nervous system?
- How is a nerve impulse transmitted?

Vocabulary
neuron • cell body
dendrite • axon
myelin sheath
resting potential
action potential
threshold • synapse
neurotransmitter

Reading Strategy:
Summarizing As you read, find the key ideas for each paragraph. Write down a few key words from each main idea. Then, use the key words in your summary.

▼ **Figure 35–5** ⊂⊃ **The nervous system controls and coordinates functions throughout the body.** The basic units of the nervous system are neurons.

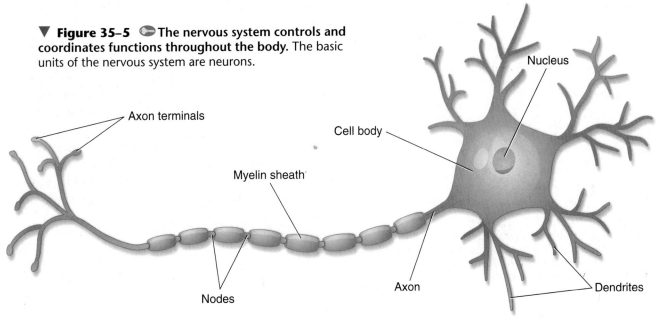

Spreading out from the cell body are short, branched extensions called **dendrites.** Dendrites carry impulses from the environment or from other neurons toward the cell body. The long fiber that carries impulses away from the cell body is called the **axon.** The axon ends in a series of small swellings called axon terminals, located some distance from the cell body. Neurons may have dozens of dendrites but usually have only one axon. In most animals, axons and dendrites are clustered into bundles of fibers called nerves. Some nerves contain only a few neurons, but many others have hundreds or even thousands of neurons.

In some neurons, the axon is surrounded by an insulating membrane known as the **myelin sheath** (MY-uh-lin). The myelin sheath that surrounds a single long axon leaves many gaps, called nodes, where the axon membrane is exposed. As an impulse moves along the axon, it jumps from one node to the next, which increases the speed at which the impulse can travel.

The Nerve Impulse

As the Italian scientist Luigi Galvani discovered more than 200 years ago, nerve impulses are electrical. There are important differences, however, between the movement of a nerve impulse and the flow of electrical current through a metal wire. The best way to understand these differences is to look first at a neuron at rest, one that is not carrying an impulse.

Resting Potential A neuron has an electrical potential, or voltage, across its cell membrane of approximately 70 millivolts (mV). This might not seem like much, but it means that this tiny cell produces a voltage roughly equal to one twentieth that of a flashlight battery (1.5 volts). Where does this voltage come from? The potential is produced by the actions of a cell membrane pump, powered by the energy of ATP. As shown in **Figure 35–6,** this membrane protein forces sodium ions (Na^+) out of the cell and pumps potassium ions (K^+) in.

As a result of this active transport, the cytoplasm of the neuron contains more K^+ ions and fewer Na^+ ions than the surrounding medium. However, K^+ ions leak out across the cell membrane more easily than Na^+ ions leak in. As a result, K^+ ions leak out of the cell to produce a negative charge on the inside of the membrane. This charge difference is known as the **resting potential** of the neuron. The neuron, of course, is not actually "resting," because it must produce a constant supply of ATP to fuel active transport.

✓ CHECKPOINT *What is resting potential?*

▼ **Figure 35–6** At rest, the inside of the neuron's membrane has a negative charge. **Predicting** *Is the distribution of positive ions shown the result of diffusion or of active transport?*

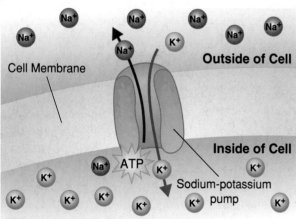

A A protein pump in the neuron cell membrane uses the energy of ATP to pump Na+ out of the cell, and at the same time to pump K+ in.

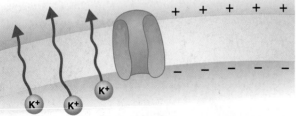

B The cell membrane is leakier to K+ than it is to Na+. Because more positive charges leak out of the cell than leak in, the inside of the cell becomes negatively charged with respect to the outside.

The Moving Impulse A nerve impulse is similar to a ripple passing along the surface of a pond. Instead of a ripple, the impulse causes a movement of ions across the cell membrane.

⚷ **An impulse begins when a neuron is stimulated by another neuron or by the environment.** Once it begins, the impulse travels rapidly down the axon away from the cell body and toward the axon terminals. As **Figure 35–7** shows, an impulse is a sudden reversal of the membrane potential. What causes the reversal?

The cell membrane of a neuron contains thousands of protein channels, or gates, that allow ions to pass through. Generally, these gates are closed. At the leading edge of an impulse, however, the sodium gates open, allowing positively charged Na^+ ions to flow inside the cell membrane. The inside of the membrane temporarily becomes more positive than the outside, reversing the resting potential. This reversal of charges is called an **action potential.** As the impulse passes, the potassium gates open, allowing positively charged K^+ ions to flow out. This restores the resting potential so that the neuron is once again negatively charged on the inside of the cell membrane and positively charged on the outside.

A nerve impulse is self-propagating; that is, an impulse at any point on the membrane causes an impulse at the next point along the membrane. We might compare the flow of an impulse to the fall of a row of dominoes. As each domino falls, it causes its neighbor to fall.

Threshold The strength of an impulse is always the same—either there is an impulse in response to a stimulus or there is not. In other words, a stimulus must be of adequate strength to cause a neuron to transmit an impulse. The minimum level of a stimulus that is required to activate a neuron is called the **threshold.** Any stimulus that is stronger than the threshold will produce an impulse. Any stimulus that is weaker than the threshold will produce no impulse. Thus, a nerve impulse follows the all-or-none principle: either the stimulus will produce an impulse, or it won't produce an impulse.

The all-or-none principle can be illustrated by using a row of dominoes. If you were to gently press the first domino in a row, it might not move at all. A slightly harder push might make the domino teeter back and forth but not fall. A slightly stronger push would cause the first domino to fall into the second. You have reached the threshold at which the row of dominoes would fall.

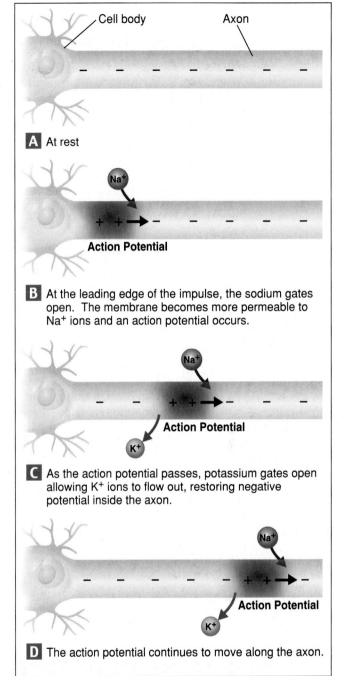

A At rest

B At the leading edge of the impulse, the sodium gates open. The membrane becomes more permeable to Na^+ ions and an action potential occurs.

C As the action potential passes, potassium gates open allowing K^+ ions to flow out, restoring negative potential inside the axon.

D The action potential continues to move along the axon.

▲ **Figure 35–7** ⚬ **A nerve impulse is self-propagating.** At the leading edge of an action potential, sodium gates open, allowing Na^+ ions to flow into the cell. This flow of ions triggers more sodium gates to open, causing the action potential to move. At the trailing edge of an action potential, potassium gates open, allowing positive ions to flow out, restoring the resting potential of the neuron.

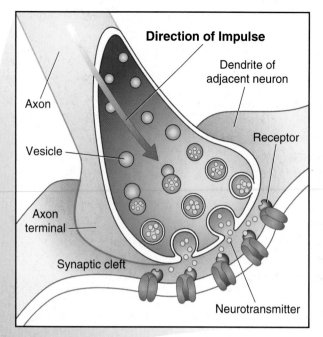

Direction of Impulse

Dendrite of
adjacent neuron

Axon

Receptor

Vesicle

Axon
terminal

Synaptic cleft

Neurotransmitter

▲ **Figure 35–8** When an impulse reaches the end of the axon of one neuron, neurotransmitters are released into the synaptic cleft. The neurotransmitters bind to receptors on the membrane of an adjacent neuron. **Predicting** *Is the adjacent cell always another neuron?*

The Synapse

At the end of the neuron, the impulse reaches an axon terminal. Usually the neuron makes contact with another cell at this location. The neuron may pass the impulse along to the second cell. Motor neurons, for example, pass their impulses to muscle cells.

The location at which a neuron can transfer an impulse to another cell is called a **synapse** (SIN-aps). As shown in **Figure 35–8,** a small cleft, or gap, separates the axon terminal from the dendrites of the adjacent cell, in this case a neuron. The terminals contain tiny sacs, or vesicles, filled with neurotransmitters (noo-roh-TRANZ-mit-urs). **Neurotransmitters** are chemicals used by a neuron to transmit an impulse across a synapse to another cell.

When an action potential arrives at an axon terminal, the sacs release the neurotransmitters into the small gap between the two cells. The neurotransmitter molecules diffuse across the gap and attach themselves to receptors on the membrane of the neighboring cell. This stimulus causes positive sodium ions to rush across the cell membrane, stimulating the second cell. If the stimulation exceeds the cell's threshold, a new impulse begins.

Only a fraction of a second after binding to their receptors, the neurotransmitter molecules are released from the cell surface. They may then be broken down by enzymes, or taken up and recycled by the axon terminal.

35–2 Section Assessment

1. **Key Concept** Describe the functions of the nervous system.
2. **Key Concept** What happens when a neuron is stimulated by another neuron?
3. What are the three types of neurons?
4. Describe the role of the myelin sheath.

5. **Critical Thinking Applying Concepts** How can the level of pain you feel vary if a stimulus causes an all-or-none response?

TEXT Assessment Use iText to review the important concepts in Section 35–2.

ALTERNATIVE ASSESSMENT

Creating a Flowchart
Create a flowchart to show the events that occur as a nerve impulse travels from one neuron to the next. Include as much detail as you can. Use your flowchart to explain the process to a classmate.

35-3 Divisions of the Nervous System

Neurons do not act alone. Instead, they are joined together to form a complex network—the nervous system. The human nervous system is separated into two major divisions: the central nervous system and the peripheral nervous system.

The central nervous system is the control center of the body. The functions of the central nervous system are similar to those of the central processing unit of a computer. **The central nervous system relays messages, processes information, and analyzes information.** The peripheral nervous system receives information from the environment and relays commands from the central nervous system to organs and glands.

The Central Nervous System

The **central nervous system** consists of the brain, shown in **Figure 35-9,** and the spinal cord. The skull and vertebrae in the spinal column protect the brain and spinal cord. Both the brain and spinal cord are wrapped in three layers of connective tissue known as **meninges** (muh-NIN-jeez). Between two of these layers is a space filled with cerebrospinal fluid. **Cerebrospinal fluid** (sehr-uh-broh-SPY-nul) bathes the brain and spinal cord and acts as a shock absorber that protects the central nervous system. The fluid also allows for the exchange of nutrients and waste products between blood and nervous tissue.

Guide for Reading

🔑 Key Concepts
• What are the functions of the central nervous system?
• What are the two divisions of the peripheral nervous system?

Vocabulary
central nervous system
meninges • cerebrospinal fluid
cerebrum • cerebellum
brain stem • thalamus
hypothalamus • reflex

Reading Strategy:
Asking Questions Before you read, rewrite the headings in the section as *how, why,* or *what* questions about the nervous system. As you read, write down the answers to your questions.

▼ **Figure 35-9** 🔑 The brain—the main switching area of the central nervous system—helps to relay messages, process information, and analyze information. The brain consists of the cerebrum, cerebellum, and brain stem.

Cerebrum

Hypothalamus

Pituitary gland

Pons

Medulla oblongata

Thalamus

Pineal gland

Cerebellum

Spinal cord

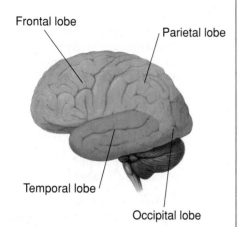

Frontal lobe

Parietal lobe

Temporal lobe

Occipital lobe

▲ **Figure 35–10** Each hemisphere of the cerebrum is divided into four lobes. Different functions of the body are controlled by different lobes of the brain. **Drawing Conclusions** *The frontal lobe controls voluntary muscle movements. What might happen if this part of the brain became injured?*

The Brain

The brain contains approximately 100 billion neurons. The neurons in the brain are mainly interneurons. The brain has a mass of about 1.4 kilograms. It is the main switching unit of the central nervous system.

The Cerebrum The largest and most prominent region of the human brain is the **cerebrum.** The cerebrum is responsible for the voluntary, or conscious, activities of the body. It is the site of intelligence, learning, and judgment. A deep groove divides the cerebrum into right and left hemispheres. The hemispheres are connected by a band of tissue called the corpus callosum.

Folds and grooves on the surface of each hemisphere greatly increase the surface area of the cerebrum. Each hemisphere of the cerebrum is divided into regions called lobes. The lobes are named for the skull bones that cover them. The locations of four lobes of the brain are shown in **Figure 35–10.**

Remarkably, each half of the cerebrum deals mainly with the opposite side of the body. Sensations from the left side of the body go to the right hemisphere of the cerebrum, and those from the right side of the body go to the left hemisphere. Commands to move muscles are generated in the same way. The left hemisphere controls the body's right side and the right hemisphere controls the body's left side.

There is more than a simple left-right division of labor between the hemispheres. For example, some studies have suggested that the right hemisphere may be associated with creativity and artistic ability, whereas the left hemisphere may be associated with analytical and mathematical ability.

The cerebrum consists of two surfaces. The outer surface of the cerebrum is called the cerebral cortex and consists of gray matter. Gray matter consists mainly of densely packed nerve cell bodies. The cerebral cortex processes information from the sense organs and controls body movements. The inner surface of the cerebrum consists of white matter, which is made up of bundles of axons with myelin sheaths. The myelin sheaths give the white matter its characteristic color.

The Cerebellum The second largest region of the brain is the **cerebellum.** The cerebellum is located at the back of the skull. Although the commands to move muscles come from the cerebral cortex, the cerebellum coordinates and balances the actions of the muscles so that the body can move gracefully and efficiently.

The Brain Stem The **brain stem** connects the brain and spinal cord. Located just below the cerebellum, the brain stem includes two regions known as the pons and the medulla oblongata (ahb-lahn-GAHT-uh). Each of these regions acts as a neural "switchboard," regulating the flow of information between the brain and the rest of the body. Some of the body's most important functions—including blood pressure, heart rate, breathing, and swallowing—are controlled in the brain stem.

The Thalamus and Hypothalamus The thalamus and hypothalamus are found between the brain stem and the cerebrum. The **thalamus** receives messages from the sense organs. It relays the information to the proper region of the cerebrum for further processing. The hypothalamus is just below the thalamus. The **hypothalamus** is the control center for recognition and analysis of hunger, thirst, fatigue, anger, and body temperature.

The Spinal Cord

Like a major telephone line that carries thousands of calls at once, the spinal cord is the main communications link between the brain and the rest of the body. Thirty-one pairs of spinal nerves branch out from the spinal cord, connecting the brain to the body. **Figure 35–11** shows a cross section of the spinal cord.

Certain kinds of information, such as reflexes, are processed directly in the spinal cord. A **reflex** is a quick, automatic response to a stimulus. Sneezing and blinking are two examples of reflexes. A reflex allows your body to respond to danger immediately, without spending time thinking about a response. Animals rely heavily on reflex behaviors for survival.

✓ CHECKPOINT *What is a reflex?*

The Peripheral Nervous System

The peripheral nervous system lies outside of the central nervous system. It consists of all of the nerves and associated cells that are not part of the brain and the spinal cord. Included here are cranial nerves that pass through holes in the skull and stimulate regions of the head and neck, spinal nerves, and ganglia. Ganglia are collections of nerve cell bodies.

The peripheral nervous system can be divided into the sensory division and the motor division. ☞ **The sensory division of the peripheral nervous system transmits impulses from sense organs to the central nervous system. The motor division transmits impulses from the central nervous system to the muscles or glands.** The motor division is further divided into the somatic nervous system and the autonomic nervous system.

The Somatic Nervous System The somatic nervous system regulates activities that are under conscious control, such as the movement of the skeletal muscles. Every time you lift your finger or wiggle your toes, you are using the motor neurons of the somatic nervous system. Some somatic nerves are also involved with reflexes and can act with or without conscious control.

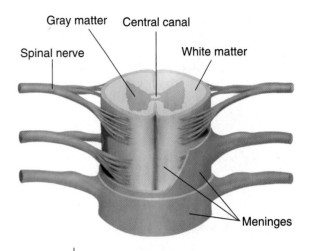

Gray matter   Central canal

Spinal nerve   White matter

Meninges

▲ **Figure 35–11** The spinal cord—the major nerve pathway to and from the brain—is protected by the vertebral column and meninges. **Comparing and Contrasting** *What is the difference between the white and gray matter?*

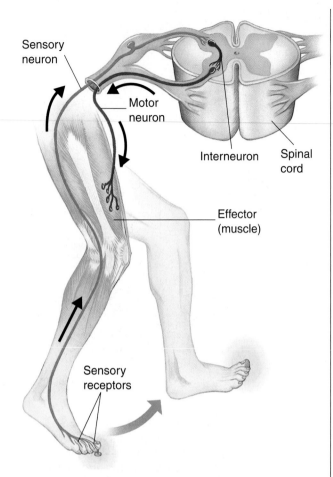

▲ **Figure 35–12** 🌐 **The peripheral nervous system transmits impulses from sense organs to the central nervous system and back to muscles or glands.** When you step on a tack, sensory receptors stimulate a sensory neuron, which relays the signal to an interneuron within the spinal cord. The signal is then sent to a motor neuron, which in turn stimulates a muscle in your leg to lift your leg.

Sensory neuron

Motor neuron

Interneuron

Spinal cord

Effector (muscle)

Sensory receptors

If you accidentally step on a tack with your bare foot, your leg may recoil before you are aware of the pain. This rapid response is possible because receptors in your skin stimulate sensory neurons, which carry the impulse to your spinal cord. Even before the information is relayed to your brain, a group of neurons in your spinal cord automatically activates the appropriate motor neurons. These motor neurons cause the muscles in your leg to contract, pulling your foot away from the tack.

The pathway that an impulse travels from your foot back to your leg is known as a reflex arc. As shown in **Figure 35–12,** a reflex arc includes a sensory receptor (in this case, a receptor in your toe), sensory neuron, motor neuron, and effector (leg muscle). Some reflex arcs include interneurons. In other reflex arcs, a sensory neuron communicates directly with a motor neuron.

✓ CHECKPOINT **What is a reflex arc?**

The Autonomic Nervous System The autonomic nervous system regulates activities that are automatic, or involuntary. The nerves of the autonomic nervous system control functions of the body that are not under conscious control. For example, the autonomic nervous system regulates the heartbeat and controls the contraction of smooth muscles in the digestive system and in blood vessels.

The autonomic nervous system is further subdivided into two parts that have opposite effects on the organs they control. The two parts are known as the sympathetic nervous system and the parasympathetic nervous system. Most organs controlled by the autonomic nervous system are under the control of both sympathetic and parasympathetic neurons.

Why is it important to have two systems that control the same organs? The sympathetic and parasympathetic nervous systems have opposite effects on the same organ system. For example, heart rate is increased by the sympathetic nervous system, but decreased by the parasympathetic nervous system. The process can be compared to the process of controlling the speed of a car. One system is like the gas pedal and the other is like the brake. Because there are two different sets of neurons, the autonomic nervous system can quickly speed up the activities of major organs in response to a stimulus, or slam on the brakes if necessary.

How do reflexes occur?

Mousetrap

Tape

String

Materials string, scissors, 3 plastic mousetraps, packing tape, 30-cm ruler

Procedure

1. To model a synapse, cut a 30-cm piece of string. **CAUTION:** *Handle scissors carefully.*
2. Hold a mousetrap open. Pull the string through the bait platform as shown. **CAUTION:** *Do not let the mousetrap snap on your fingers.* Slide a piece of tape under the bait platform and tape the trap to the table as shown. Label the trap "sensory neuron."
3. Hold one end of the string in each hand. Gently pull one end without setting off the trap. Now gradually pull harder.
4. To model a reflex arc, cut two more 30-cm pieces of string. Tie one end of each piece of string to the bait platform of a separate trap.
5. Tape the 2 new traps to the table, 20 cm from the first trap. Label one new trap "motor neuron," and the other "brain."
6. Reset the first trap, then set the new ones. Tape both ends of the strings attached to the new traps to the top of the first trap. Leave these strings slightly slack.

7. Pull the strings attached to the bait platform of the "sensory neuron."

Analyze and Conclude

1. **Drawing Conclusions** What was required for the trap to close in step 3? How does this behavior compare to the transmission of a nerve impulse?
2. **Applying Concepts** Does a stronger stimulus produce a stronger nerve impulse? Explain your answer.
3. **Using Analogies** Use your observations from step 7 to explain how your hand withdraws from a hot stove before you feel pain.

35–3 Section Assessment

1. **Key Concept** Discuss the overall function of the central nervous system.
2. **Key Concept** What are the functions of the two divisions of the peripheral nervous system?
3. Compare the central nervous system to the central processing unit of a computer.
4. Is a reflex part of the central nervous system, the peripheral nervous system, or both? Explain your answer.

5. **Critical Thinking Inferring** Why do you think the cerebrum is larger and more developed in humans than it is in other vertebrates?

Assessment Use iText to review the important concepts in Section 35–3.

MAKING CONNECTIONS

Animal Behavior
Using Section 34–1, decide which parts of the nervous system are most likely to be involved with innate behaviors. Which parts are likely to be involved with learned behaviors? Explain your reasoning.

35–4 The Senses

Guide for Reading

 Key Concept
- What are the five types of sensory receptors?

Vocabulary
sensory receptor
pupil
lens
retina
rod
cone
cochlea
semicircular canal
taste bud

Reading Strategy:
Outlining Before you read, use the headings of the section to make an outline about the five senses. As you read, fill in the subtopics and smaller topics. Then, add phrases or a sentence after each to provide key information.

The body contains millions of neurons that react directly to stimuli from the environment, including light, sound, motion, chemicals, pressure, or changes in temperature. These neurons, known as **sensory receptors,** react to light, sound, or other specific stimuli by sending impulses to other neurons, and eventually to the central nervous system. Sensory receptors are located throughout the body but are concentrated in the sense organs. These sense organs include the eyes, the inner ears, the nose, the mouth, and the skin. Sensory receptors within each organ enable it to respond to a particular stimulus.

 There are five general categories of sensory receptors: pain receptors, thermoreceptors, mechanoreceptors, chemoreceptors, and photoreceptors. Pain receptors are located throughout the body except in the brain. Pain receptors respond to chemicals released by damaged cells. Pain is important to recognize because it usually indicates danger, injury, or disease. Thermoreceptors are located in the skin, body core, and hypothalamus. Thermoreceptors detect variations in temperature. Mechanoreceptors are found in the skin, skeletal muscles, and inner ears. They are sensitive to touch, pressure, stretching of muscles, sound, and motion. Chemoreceptors, located in the nose and taste buds, are sensitive to chemicals in the external environment. Photoreceptors, found in the eyes, are sensitive to light. **Figure 35–13** shows the type of photoreceptor that distinguishes the color of objects.

Vision

The world around us is bathed in light. The sense organs that we use to sense light are the eyes. The structures of the eye are shown in **Figure 35–14.** Light enters the eye through the cornea, a tough transparent layer of cells. The cornea helps to focus the light, which then passes through a small chamber called the anterior chamber. This chamber is filled with a fluid called aqueous (AY-kwee-uhs) humor. At the back of the chamber is a disklike structure called the iris. The iris is the colored part of the eye. In the middle of the iris is a small opening called the **pupil.** Tiny muscles in the iris adjust the size of the pupil to regulate the amount of light that enters the eye. In dim light, the pupil becomes larger so that more light can enter the eye. In bright light, the pupil becomes smaller so that less light enters the eye.

(magnification: 2000×)

◀ **Figure 35–13** ◉ **There are two types of light-sensitive photoreceptor cells in the retina—rods and cones.** This color-enhanced scanning electron micrograph shows the rod cells of an eye.

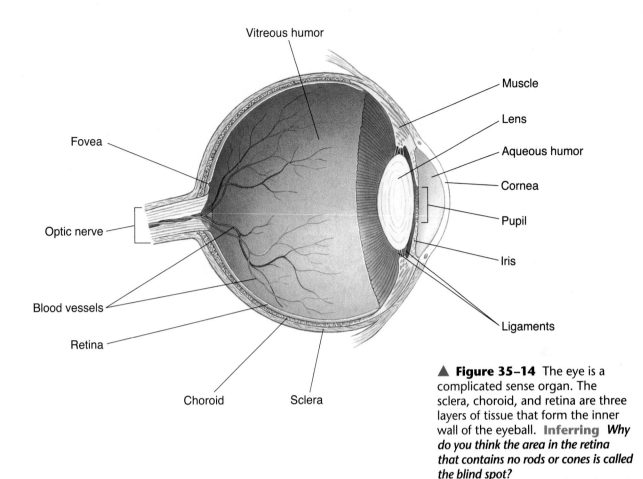

Vitreous humor

Fovea

Optic nerve

Blood vessels

Retina

Choroid   Sclera

Muscle

Lens

Aqueous humor

Cornea

Pupil

Iris

Ligaments

▲ **Figure 35–14** The eye is a complicated sense organ. The sclera, choroid, and retina are three layers of tissue that form the inner wall of the eyeball. **Inferring** *Why do you think the area in the retina that contains no rods or cones is called the blind spot?*

Just behind the iris is the **lens.** Small muscles attached to the lens change its shape to help you adjust your eyes' focus to see near or distant objects. Behind the lens is a large chamber filled with a transparent, jellylike fluid called vitreous (VIH-tree-uhs) humor.

The lens focuses light onto the **retina.** Photoreceptors are arranged in a layer in the retina. The photoreceptors convert light into nerve impulses that are carried to the central nervous system. There are two types of photoreceptors: rods and cones. **Rods** are extremely sensitive to light, but they do not distinguish different colors. **Cones** are less sensitive than rods, but they do respond to light of different colors, producing color vision. Cones are concentrated in the fovea. The fovea is the site of sharpest vision.

The impulses assembled by this complicated layer of interconnected cells leave each eye by way of an optic nerve. The optic nerves then carry the impulses to the appropriate regions of the brain. The brain interprets them as visual images and provides information about the external world.

✓ **CHECKPOINT** *Where are the photoreceptors located in the eye?*

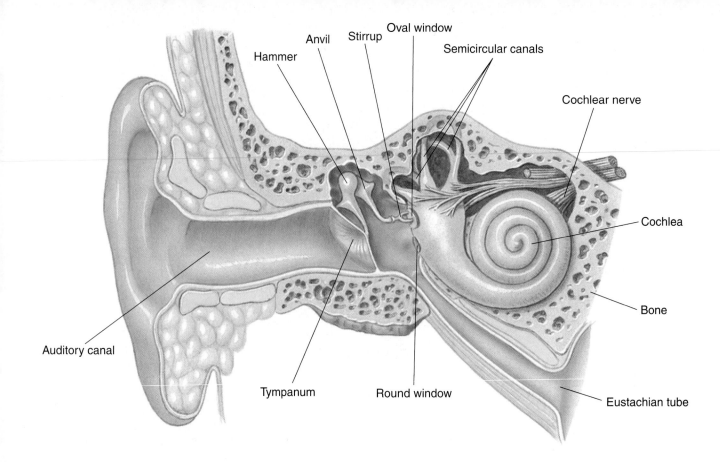

Hammer Anvil Stirrup Oval window Semicircular canals Cochlear nerve

Cochlea

Bone

Auditory canal

Tympanum Round window Eustachian tube

(magnification: about 3500×)

▲ **Figure 35–15** The diagram shows structures in the ear that transmit sounds. The scanning electron micrograph shows hair cells (yellow) in the inner ear. The motion of these hairs produces a nerve impulse that travels to the brain through the cochlear nerve. **Predicting** *How would frequent exposure to loud noise affect a person's threshold for detecting sound?*

Hearing and Balance

The human ear has two sensory functions. One of these functions is hearing. The other function is maintaining balance.

Hearing Sound is nothing more than vibrations in the air around us. The ears are the sensory organs that can distinguish both the pitch and loudness of those vibrations. The structure of the ear is shown in **Figure 35–15.**

Vibrations enter the ear through the auditory canal. The vibrations cause the tympanum (TIM-puh-num), or eardrum, to vibrate. These vibrations are picked up by three tiny bones, commonly called the hammer, anvil, and stirrup. The last of these bones, the stirrup, transmits the vibrations to the oval window. Vibrations of the oval window create pressure waves in the fluid-filled **cochlea** (KAHK-lee-uh) of the inner ear.

The cochlea is lined with tiny hair cells that are pushed back and forth by these pressure waves. In response to these movements, the hair cells produce nerve impulses that are sent to the brain through the cochlear nerve.

Balance Your ears contain structures that help your central nervous system maintain your balance, or equilibrium. Within the inner ear just above the cochlea are three tiny canals at right angles to each other. They are called **semicircular canals** because each forms a half circle. The semicircular canals and the two tiny sacs located behind them monitor the position of your body, especially your head, in relation to gravity.

The semicircular canals and the sacs are filled with fluid and lined with hair cells. As the head changes position, the fluid in the canals also changes position. This causes the hair on the hair cells to bend. This action, in turn, sends impulses to the brain that enable it to determine body motion and position.

Smell and Taste

You may never have thought of it this way, but your sense of smell is actually an ability to detect chemicals. Chemoreceptors in the lining of the nasal passageway respond to specific chemicals and send impulses to the brain through sensory nerves.

Your sense of smell is capable of producing thousands of different sensations. In fact, much of what we commonly call the "taste" of food and drink is actually smell. To prove this to yourself, eat a few bites of food while holding your nose. You'll discover that much of the taste of food disappears until you open your nose and breathe freely.

Like the sense of smell, the sense of taste is a chemical sense. The sense organs that detect taste are the **taste buds.** Most of the taste buds are on the tongue, but a few are found at other locations in the mouth. The surface of the tongue is shown in **Figure 35–16.** The tastes detected by the taste buds are classified as salty, bitter, sweet, and sour. Sensitivity to these different categories varies on different parts of the tongue.

Touch and Related Senses

The sense of touch, unlike the other senses you have just read about, is not found in one particular place. All of the regions of the skin are sensitive to touch. In this respect, your largest sense organ is your skin. Skin contains sensory receptors that respond to temperature, touch, and pain. Not all parts of the body are equally sensitive to touch, because not all parts have the same number of receptors. The greatest density of touch receptors is found on your fingers, toes, and face.

(magnification: 86×)

▲ **Figure 35–16** This color-enhanced scanning electron microgram shows the surface of the tongue. The large pink objects are the taste buds. ⬤ **Chemoreceptors found in the taste buds are sensitive to chemicals in food.**

35–4 Section Assessment

1. 🔑 **Key Concept** Name the five types of sensory receptors and list where they are found in the body.

2. Identify the parts of the eye and the function of each part.

3. What parts of the ear are responsible for hearing? For balance?

4. Explain why you can't "taste" food when you have a bad cold.

5. **Critical Thinking Applying Concepts** Why do you feel dizzy after spinning around? How can a dancer or ice skater do lengthy spins?

   iTEXT Assessment Use iText to review the important concepts in Section 35–4.

35–5 Drugs and the Nervous System

Guide for Reading

Key Concepts
- What are the different classes of drugs that directly affect the central nervous system?
- What is the effect of alcohol on the body?

Vocabulary
drug
stimulant
depressant
addiction
fetal alcohol syndrome
drug abuse

Reading Strategy:
Using Graphic Organizers
As you read, create a table that lists each of the drugs in this section and the effects that each drug has on the body.

By definition, a **drug** is any substance, other than food, that changes the structure or function of the body. Some drugs, such as cocaine and heroin, are so powerful and dangerous that their possession is illegal. Other drugs, including penicillin and codeine, are prescription drugs and can be used only under the supervision of a doctor. Still other drugs, including cough and cold medicines, are sold over the counter. All drugs, both legal and illegal, have the potential to do harm if they are used improperly or abused.

Drugs differ in the ways in which they affect the body. Some drugs kill bacteria and are useful in treating disease. Other drugs affect a particular system of the body, such as the digestive or circulatory systems. Among the most powerful drugs, however, are the ones that cause changes in the nervous system, especially to the brain and the synapses between neurons.

Drugs That Affect the Synapse

The nervous system performs its regulatory functions through the transmission of information along pathways from one part of the body to another. Synapses are key relay stations along the way. The nervous system depends on neurotransmitters to bridge the gap between neurons or between a neuron and an effector. A drug that interferes with the action of neurotransmitters can disrupt the functioning of the nervous system.

Stimulants A number of drugs, called **stimulants,** increase the actions regulated by the nervous system. **Stimulants increase heart rate, blood pressure, and breathing rate. In addition, stimulants increase the release of neurotransmitters at some synapses in the brain.** This release leads to a feeling of energy and well-being. When the effects of stimulants wear off, however, the brain's supply of neurotransmitters has been depleted. The user quickly falls into fatigue and depression. Long-term use can cause circulatory problems, hallucinations, and psychological depression.

Figure 35–17 Common stimulant drugs include amphetamines, cocaine, nicotine (found in cigarettes), and caffeine (found in coffee, tea, chocolate, and cola products). Stimulants increase heart rate, blood pressure, and breathing rate.

Depressants Some drugs, called **depressants,** decrease the rate of functions regulated by the brain. 🔑 **Depressants slow down heart rate and breathing rate, lower blood pressure, relax muscles, and relieve tension.** Some depressants enhance the effects of neurotransmitters that prevent some nerve cells from starting action potentials. This calms parts of the brain that sense fear and relaxes the individual. As a result, the user comes to depend on the drug to relieve the anxieties of everyday life, which may seem unbearable without the drug. When depressants are used in combination with alcohol, the results are often fatal because the central nervous system can become so depressed that breathing stops.

✓ CHECKPOINT *What is the general function of a depressant?*

Cocaine Even stronger effects are produced by drugs that act on neurons in what are known as the pleasure centers of the brain. The effects of cocaine and opiate drugs are so strong that they produce **addiction**—an uncontrollable craving for more of the drug. Cocaine is obtained from the leaves of coca plants like the one shown in **Figure 35–18.** 🔑 **Cocaine causes the sudden release in the brain of a neurotransmitter called dopamine.** Normally, this compound is released when a basic need, such as hunger or thirst, is fulfilled. By fooling the brain into releasing dopamine, cocaine produces intense feelings of pleasure and satisfaction. So much dopamine is released when the drug is used that the supply of dopamine is depleted when the drug wears off. Users quickly discover that they feel sad and depressed without the drug. The psychological dependence that cocaine produces is difficult to break.

Cocaine also acts as a powerful stimulant, increasing heart rate and blood pressure. The stimulation can be so powerful that the heart is damaged. Sometimes, even a first-time user may experience a heart attack after using cocaine.

Crack is a particularly potent and dangerous form of cocaine. Crack becomes addictive after only a few doses. The intense "high" produced by crack wears off quickly and leaves the brain with too little dopamine. As a result, the user suddenly feels sad and depressed, and quickly seeks another dose of the drug. In time, the urge to seek this drug can be so strong that it leads users to commit serious crimes and to abandon their families and children.

Opiates The opium poppy produces a powerful class of painkilling drugs called opiates. 🔑 **Opiates mimic natural chemicals in the brain known as endorphins, which normally help to overcome sensations of pain.** The first doses of these drugs produce strong feelings of pleasure and security, but the body quickly adjusts to the higher levels of endorphins. Once this happens, the body cannot do without the drug. A user who tries to stop taking these drugs will suffer from uncontrollable pain and sickness because the body cannot produce enough of the natural endorphins.

Figure 35–18 Many illegal drugs are found in nature. Cocaine comes from the South American *Erythroxylum coca* plant (top). The centers of opium poppies (below) contain pods from which opiate drugs are derived. 🔑 **Opiates mimic endorphins, which help overcome pain.** For this reason, opiates are often used medically as painkillers.

Commonly Abused Drugs			
Drug Type	Medical Use	Examples	Effects on the Body
Stimulants	Used to increase alertness, relieve fatigue	Amphetamines	Increases heart and respiratory rates, elevates blood pressure, dilates pupils, and decreases appetite
Depressants	Used to relieve anxiety, irritability, tension	Barbiturates Tranquilizers	Slows down the actions of the central nervous system; small amounts cause calmness and relaxation; larger amounts cause slurred speech and impaired judgment
Opiates	Used to relieve pain	Morphine Codeine	Acts as a depressant; causes drowsiness, restlessness, nausea

▲ **Figure 35–19** Many abused drugs are legal and used for medical purposes. **Applying Concepts** *Do you think a person can become addicted to a legal drug?*

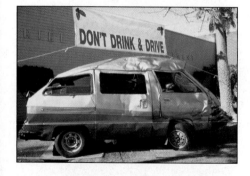

▲ **Figure 35–20** 🔊 Alcohol is a depressant that slows down the rate at which the nervous system functions. It slows down reflexes, disrupts coordination, and impairs judgment. For this reason, you should never get into a car with a driver who has been drinking.

Because many users inject drugs for maximum effect, there is another important consequence of drug use—the increased transmission of the HIV virus that causes AIDS. The virus can be spread rapidly from person to person when drug users share contaminated needles. Many of the new AIDS cases reported in the United States can be traced back to the use of injected drugs.

Marijuana Statistically, the most widely abused illegal drug is marijuana. Marijuana comes from *Cannabis sativa,* a species of hemp plant. Marijuana is commonly called grass or pot. Hashish, or hash, is a potent form of marijuana made from the flowering parts of the plant. The active ingredient in all forms of marijuana is tetrahydrocannabinol (THC). Smoking or ingesting THC can produce a temporary feeling of euphoria and disorientation. Smoking marijuana is bad for the lungs. In fact, smoking marijuana is even more destructive to the lungs than smoking tobacco. Long-term use of marijuana can also result in loss of memory, inability to concentrate, and reduced levels of the hormone testosterone in males.

✓CHECKPOINT) *What are the long-term effects of marijuana use?*

Alcohol One of the most dangerous and abused depressant drugs is alcohol. The most immediate effects of alcohol are on the central nervous system. 🔊 **Alcohol is a depressant, and even small amounts of alcohol slow down the rate at which the central nervous system functions.** Alcohol slows down reflexes, disrupts coordination, and impairs judgment. Heavy drinking fills the blood with so much alcohol that the central nervous system cannot function properly. People who have two or three drinks in the span of an hour may feel relaxed and confident, but their blood contains as much as 0.10 percent alcohol, making them legally drunk in most states. They usually cannot walk or talk properly, and they are certainly not able to safely control an automobile, as shown in **Figure 35–20.**

Alcohol is the drug most commonly abused by teenagers. The abuse of alcohol has a frightening social price. About 40 percent of the 50,000 people who die on American highways in a typical year are victims of accidents in which at least one driver had been drinking. One third of all homicides can be attributed to the effects of alcohol. When health care, property damage, and lost productivity are considered, alcohol abuse costs the U.S. economy at least $150 billion per year.

But the toll of alcohol abuse does not stop there! Women who are pregnant and drink on a regular basis run the risk of having a child with fetal alcohol syndrome. **Fetal alcohol syndrome** (FAS) is a group of birth defects caused by the effects of alcohol on the fetus. Babies born with FAS can suffer from heart defects, malformed faces, delayed growth, and poor motor development. More than 50,000 babies are born in this country every year with alcohol-related birth defects, many of which are irreversible.

Alcohol and Disease People who have become addicted to alcohol suffer from a disease called alcoholism. Some alcoholics feel the need to have a drink before work or school—every day! They may drink so heavily that they black out and cannot remember what they have done while drinking. Some alcoholics, however, do not drink to the point where it is obvious that they have an alcohol-abuse problem. If a person cannot function properly without satisfying the need or craving for alcohol, that person is considered to have an alcohol-abuse problem.

Analyzing Data

Blood Alcohol Concentration

Blood alcohol concentration (BAC) is a measure of the amount of alcohol in the bloodstream per 100 mL of blood. A BAC of 0.1 percent means that one tenth of 1.0 percent of the fluid in the blood is alcohol. In some states, if a driver has a BAC of 0.08 percent, he or she is considered legally drunk. In other states, drivers with a BAC of 0.10 percent are considered drunk. The graph shows the relative risk of being involved in a fatal accident as a result of the blood alcohol concentration of the driver.

1. **Interpreting Data** What trends do you see in the number of fatal crashes from age 17 to age 66+ based on the two ranges of BAC?

2. **Interpreting Data** How does the consumption of alcohol affect driving risk for the average driver?

3. **Drawing Conclusions** Is the effect of alcohol consumption on driving independent of the age of the driver? Are young drivers more affected by alcohol or less affected by it than older drivers?

4. **Making Judgments** All levels of alcohol consumption affect driving skills, although the effect increases dramatically as more drinks are consumed. To minimize accidents and fatalities due to drunk driving, what should be the legal limit of blood alcohol for drivers?

Long-term alcohol use also destroys cells in the liver, where alcohol is broken down. As liver cells die, the liver becomes less able to handle large amounts of alcohol. The formation of scar tissue, known as cirrhosis of the liver, occurs next. The scar tissue blocks the flow of blood through the liver and interferes with its other important functions. Eventually, a heavy drinker may die from liver failure.

As with other drugs, dealing with alcohol abuse is not simply a matter of willpower. Alcoholics often need special help and support to quit their drinking habit. Organizations such as Alcoholics Anonymous are available in most communities to help individuals and families deal with the problems created by alcohol abuse.

Drug Abuse

Each of the drugs discussed so far presents a danger to users. The misuse of either a legal or an illegal drug is a serious problem in modern society. **Drug abuse** can be defined as using any drug in a way that most doctors could not approve. With some drugs, such as cocaine, drug abuse causes serious physical damage to the body. With other drugs, such as marijuana, drug abuse produces psychological dependence that can be strong enough to disrupt family life and schoolwork.

An uncontrollable dependence on a drug is known as a drug addiction. Some drugs cause a strong psychological dependence. People who are psychologically dependent on a drug have a mental craving, or need, for the drug. Other drugs cause a strong physical dependence. Physical dependence occurs when the body cannot function without a constant supply of the drug.

The best way to avoid the effects of drugs is to avoid drugs. The decision not to use drugs can be difficult when you are faced with pressure to take them. By deciding not to take drugs, you are acting to take control of your life.

35–5 Section Assessment

1. **🔑 Key Concept** Describe the effects of stimulants, cocaine, depressants, and opiates on the central nervous system.

2. **🔑 Key Concept** Explain the effects of alcohol on the body.

3. What is a drug?

4. Based on alcohol's effects on the central nervous system, why is drinking and driving an extremely dangerous behavior?

5. **Critical Thinking Inferring** Which do you think is a more difficult addiction to break: one in which a person is physically dependent on a drug, or one in which a person is psychologically dependent on a drug? Explain your answer.

TEXT Assessment Use iText to review the important concepts in Section 35–5.

Take It to the NET
Read about the effects of different drugs. Then, create a chart listing five different drugs and their short-term and long-term effects on the body. Use the links provided in the Biology area at the Prentice Hall Web site for help in completing this activity:
www.phschool.com

Correcting Vision With Lenses

The lenses of your eyes focus light on the retina. The lenses of people who are nearsighted focus images in front of the retina, making distant objects appear blurry. The lenses of people who are farsighted focus behind the retina, making nearby objects difficult to see. To see more clearly, these people wear glasses or contact lenses. The shapes of these artificial lenses depend on the type of correction needed.

Problem
What types of corrective lenses are needed by near-sighted individuals and by farsighted individuals?

Materials

- tape
- 2 cardboard photo easels
- black construction paper
- unruled white index card
- 6-V light bulb and socket
- 6-V battery and wires with alligator clips
- 2 convex lenses
- modeling clay
- meter stick
- concave lens

Skills
Analyzing Data, Using Models

Procedure

1. Set up your equipment as shown. Place the white index card about 50 to 60 cm in front of the bulb.

2. Place a convex lens in front of the bulb and move the lens until an image of the bulb focuses clearly on the index card. Secure the lens in this position with modeling clay or tape. The distance between the fixed lens and the index card is the focal length of the lens.

3. Move the index card about 5 to 8 cm away from the fixed lens to simulate the formation of an image in front of the retina. Observe the image and record your observations.

4. Hold the concave lens between the light bulb and the fixed lens. Try to focus the image by moving the concave lens between the light bulb and the fixed lens.

5. Repeat step 4, but this time use the second convex lens. Record your observations.

6. Move the index card about 10 to 16 cm closer to the fixed lens to simulate image formation behind the retina. Record your observations.

7. Repeat steps 4 and 5.

Analyze and Conclude

1. **Drawing Conclusions** Does the lens in your eye focus an image right side up or upside down on your retina? Why does an image appear right side up when you look at objects?

2. **Drawing Conclusions** Which lens sharpened the image that formed in front of the retina? Behind the retina?

3. **Using Models** Which condition—long-focal length or short-focal length—do you think models the problem of nearsightedness? Which condition models farsightedness? Explain your answers.

Battery
Wires
Black paper taped to photo easel
Alligator clip
Convex lens
Clay
Meter stick
Index card taped to photo easel

35–1 Human Body Systems
 Key Concepts

• The eleven organ systems of the human body work together to maintain homeostasis.

Vocabulary
muscle tissue, p. 894
epithelial tissue, p. 894
connective tissue, p. 894
nervous tissue, p. 894
feedback inhibition, p. 895

35–2 The Nervous System
Key Concepts

• The nervous system controls and coordinates functions throughout the body and responds to internal and external stimuli.

• A nerve impulse begins when a neuron is stimulated by another neuron or by its environment.

Vocabulary
neuron, p. 897 • cell body, p. 897
dendrite, p. 898 • axon, p. 898
myelin sheath, p. 898 • resting potential, p. 898
action potential, p. 899 • threshold, p. 899
synapse, p. 900 • neurotransmitter, p. 900

35–3 Divisions of the Nervous System
Key Concepts

• The central nervous system relays messages, processes information, and analyzes information.

• The sensory division of the peripheral nervous system transmits impulses from sense organs to the central nervous system. The motor division transmits impulses from the central nervous system to the muscles or glands.

Vocabulary
central nervous system, p. 901
meninges, p. 901 • cerebrospinal fluid, p. 901
cerebrum, p. 902 • cerebellum, p. 902
brain stem, p. 902 • thalamus, p. 903
hypothalamus, p. 903 • reflex, p. 903

35–4 The Senses
Key Concept

• There are five general categories of sensory receptors: pain receptors, thermoreceptors, mechanoreceptors, chemoreceptors, and photoreceptors.

Vocabulary
sensory receptor, p. 906 • pupil, p. 906
lens, p. 907 • retina, p. 907 • rod, p. 907
cone, p. 907 • cochlea, p. 908
semicircular canal, p. 908 • taste bud, p. 909

35–5 Drugs and the Nervous System
Key Concepts

• Stimulants increase heart rate, blood pressure, and breathing rate. In addition, stimulants increase the release of neurotransmitters at some synapses in the brain.

• Depressants slow down heart rate and breathing rate, lower blood pressure, relax muscles, and relieve tension.

• Cocaine causes the sudden release of a neurotransmitter in the brain called dopamine.

• Opiates mimic natural chemicals in the brain known as endorphins, which normally help to overcome sensations of pain.

• Alcohol is a depressant, and even small amounts of alcohol slow down the rate at which the nervous system functions.

Vocabulary
drug, p. 910 • stimulant, p. 910
depressant, p. 911 • addiction, p. 911
fetal alcohol syndrome, p. 913
drug abuse, p. 914

Thinking Visually
Develop a graphic organizer to show the relationship between the different divisions of the nervous system.

Preparing for the Living Environment Exam

Chapter 35

Part A

Multiple Choice

For each statement or question, select the number of the word or expression that, of those given, best completes the statement or answers the question.

1 The type of tissue that covers the body, lines internal surfaces, and forms glands is
(1) muscle tissue
(2) connective tissue
(3) epithelial tissue
(4) nervous tissue

2 The process of maintaining a relatively constant internal environment despite changes in the external environment is called
(1) regulation   (3) homeostasis
(2) synapse   (4) stimulation

3 The basic units of structure and function of the nervous system are
(1) neurons
(2) axons
(3) neurotransmitters
(4) dendrites

4 The place where a nerve cell transfers an impulse to another cell is the
(1) synapse   (3) axon
(2) sheath   (4) receptor

5 Two organs are considered to be part of the same body system if the organs
(1) are located next to each other
(2) work independently of each other
(3) work together to carry out a life function
(4) are made up of cells with organelles

6 A hawk sees a field mouse and then captures it for food. In this activity, the eyes of the hawk function as
(1) dendrites
(2) receptors
(3) stimuli
(4) neurotransmitters

7 Which term is correctly paired with examples of that term?
(1) receptors: leg muscles and testes
(2) stimuli: temperature and light
(3) impulses: skin and eyes
(4) depressants: neurotransmitters and hormones

8 The central nervous system consists of
(1) sense organs
(2) reflexes
(3) brain and spinal cord
(4) sensory and motor neurons

9 Which division of the nervous system controls voluntary activities, such as walking the dog or singing a song?
(1) somatic   (3) autonomic
(2) central   (4) reflex

10 Which part of the brain controls conscious thought?
(1) medulla oblongata
(2) cerebellum
(3) cerebrum
(4) brain stem

11 The sympathetic nervous system and the parasympathetic nervous system are divisions of the
(1) peripheral nervous system
(2) central nervous system
(3) somatic nervous system
(4) autonomic nervous system

12 The semicircular canals and the two tiny sacs located behind them help the body to maintain
(1) vision
(2) respiratory rate
(3) equilibrium
(4) body temperature

13 The division of the nervous system that controls cardiac muscle is the
(1) autonomic
(2) somatic
(3) cerebellum
(4) hypothalamus

14 Drugs that increase heart rate, blood pressure, and breathing rate are called
(1) stimulants   (3) depressants
(2) opiates   (4) barbiturates

Test-Taking Tip Questions that begin with a list of lettered choices (A–E) followed by numbered statements are essentially multiple-choice questions. To solve these questions, use the same process that you use to solve standard multiple-choice questions.

Parts B and C

Multiple Choice and Extended Response
For those questions that ask you to select a response, choose the one that best completes the statement or answers the question. For all others follow the directions given.

Base your answers to questions 15 and 16 on the diagram below and on your knowledge of biology.

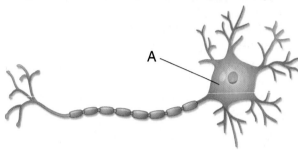

A

15 Letter A is pointing to the
(1) myelin sheath (3) axon
(2) dendrite (4) cell body

16 Copy the diagram on a sheet of paper. Then, circle the part of the cell that secretes a neurotransmitter.

Base your answers to questions 17 through 19 on the information and graph below and on your knowledge of biology.

A student surveyed 200 students who each had an overall grade point average of A or B. The results of the survey are summarized in the graph.

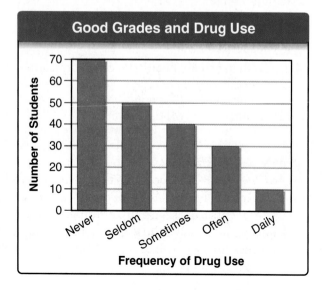

Good Grades and Drug Use

Number of Students

Frequency of Drug Use (Never, Seldom, Sometimes, Often, Daily)

17 What is the manipulated (independent) variable in the study?
(1) good grades
(2) student age
(3) popularity at school
(4) frequency of drug use

18 What percentage of students with good grades say they never use drugs?
(1) 10% (3) 50%
(2) 30% (4) 70%

19 The student conducting the survey concluded that students with good grades use drugs less frequently than students with poor grades. Why might this conclusion not be valid?
(1) There are no data on students with poor grades.
(2) Students with good grades use drugs 70 percent of the time.
(3) The researcher did not survey enough students.
(4) Only students in one school were surveyed.

Base your answers to questions 20 through 23 on the reading passage below and on your knowledge of biology.

What Did You Say?

There are three types of hearing loss: conductive, sensorineural, and mixed. In conductive hearing loss, problems in the outer or middle ear block the transmission of vibrations to the inner ear. Conductive hearing loss can result from ear infections, excessive earwax, fluid in the middle ear, or a perforated eardrum. Sensorineural hearing loss, or "nerve deafness," is most often due to changes with aging or to long-term exposure to loud noises. For example, over a 6-year period a rock band player developed a 40 percent hearing loss because he did not use ear protection during performances. The use of personal listening devices, such as headphones, can also cause sensorineural hearing loss, as can high fevers, birth defects, and certain drugs. Mixed hearing loss is a combination of both other types.

Tests to determine the cause and extent of hearing loss include: tympanometry, which examines the middle ear, eardrum, and possible blockage of the ear canal; pure-tone and speech reception testing, which determines the lowest level at which tones and speech can be heard; and word discrimination testing, which measures the ability to distinguish words at a comfortable volume.

20 Which of the graphs below best represents a common relationship between age and nerve deafness?

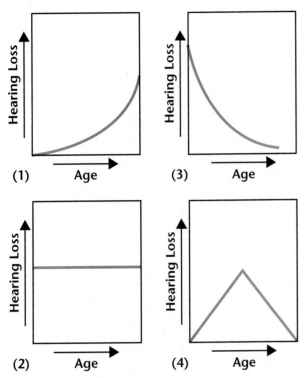

21 A prolonged body temperature of 105°F (40.4°C) may result in
(1) an inner ear infection
(2) conductive hearing loss
(3) sensorineural hearing loss
(4) a perforated eardrum

22 Which test is used to determine the presence of excessive wax in the ear canal?
(1) sensorineural assessment
(2) word discrimination testing
(3) pure-tone and speech reception testing
(4) tympanometry

23 Explain how a personal listening device can be controlled to decrease the risk of hearing damage.

24 Arrange the following terms in order from simplest to most complex: organ system, tissue, organ, organism, cell.

25 Explain why depressant drugs and alcohol are a life-threatening combination.

26 Explain why it is important for an organism to be able to maintain homeostasis.

27 Describe the changes that occur in a neuron as it carries out its normal functions. In your answer be sure to
• explain the changes that occur during action potential
• explain the changes that occur during resting potential
• discuss the ions involved
• discuss the role of the cell membrane

28 Explain how the all-or-none principle relates to the transmission of a nerve impulse.

29 Describe how the central nervous system is protected from injury.

30 Describe the advantage of a reflex response in the survival of an organism.

31 Describe the functions of rods and cones in the human eye.

32 Explain why a pregnant woman should avoid drinking alcohol.

33 A routine examination by a doctor usually includes a knee-jerk test. What might the absence of a response to this test indicate?

34 Multiple sclerosis (MS) is a disease characterized by the patchy destruction of myelin. Based on your knowledge of neuron structure and the function of various cell parts, predict the symptoms this destruction of myelin might produce.

 Take It to the NET

You can visit the Prentice Hall Web site at **www.phschool.com** to explore the many facts and figures about the human nervous system. Then, answer the following questions:
• How many synapses does a typical neuron have?
• What is the average weight of the human brain? Which species have average brain weights greater than the average weight of the human brain?
• How many taste buds does a typical human have? How many of these are on the tongue?
• Compare the number of olfactory (smell) receptors in a human with the number found in a dog.

Chapter 36 Skeletal, Muscular, and Integumentary Systems

Osteocytes are cells that maintain bone tissue. An osteocyte is shown in this color-enhanced scanning electron micrograph (magnification: 18,000×).

Inquiry Activity

How do your joints move?

Procedure

1. Look at the examples of a hinge and a ball-and-socket joint provided by your teacher. Determine how each moves.
2. Based on your observations, identify joints in your body that are hinge joints and joints that are ball-and-socket joints.

Think About It

1. **Classifying** What type of movement does a hinge joint allow?
2. **Inferring** What type of movement does a ball-and-socket joint allow?
3. **Inferring** Your body also has joints called pivot joints and saddle joints. Based on their names, what type of movement might these joints allow? *Hint:* Consider how a rider might move in a saddle.

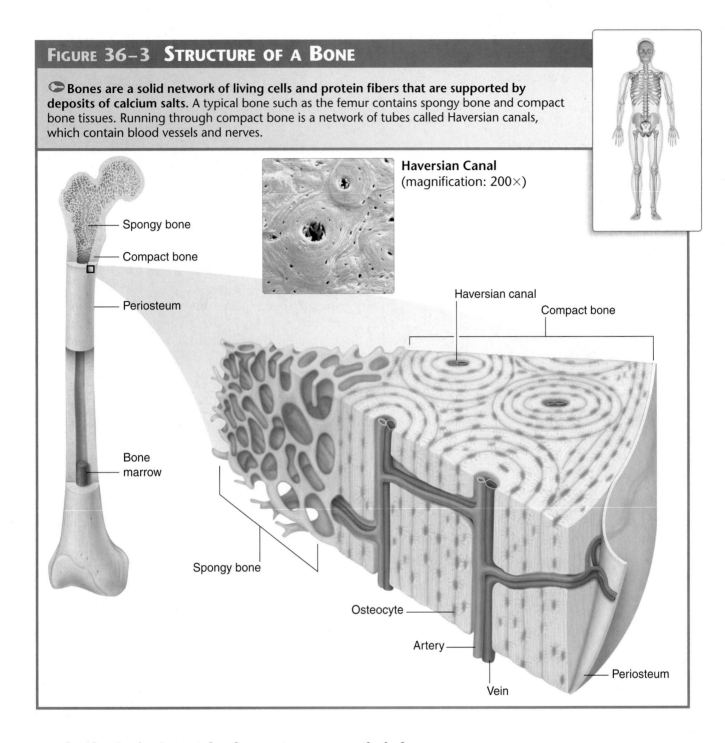

Figure 36–3 Structure of a Bone

🔑 **Bones are a solid network of living cells and protein fibers that are supported by deposits of calcium salts.** A typical bone such as the femur contains spongy bone and compact bone tissues. Running through compact bone is a network of tubes called Haversian canals, which contain blood vessels and nerves.

Spongy bone

Compact bone

Periosteum

Bone marrow

Haversian Canal (magnification: 200×)

Haversian canal

Compact bone

Spongy bone

Osteocyte

Artery

Vein

Periosteum

Ossification begins to take place up to seven months before birth. Bone tissue forms as osteoblasts secrete mineral deposits that replace the cartilage in developing bones. When the osteoblasts become surrounded by bone tissue, they mature into osteocytes. Many long bones, including those of the arms and legs, have growth plates at either end. The growth of cartilage at these plates causes the bones to lengthen. Gradually, this new growth of cartilage is replaced by bone tissue, and the bones become larger and stronger. During late adolescence or early adulthood, the cartilage in the growth plates is replaced by bone, the bones become completely ossified, and the person "stops growing."

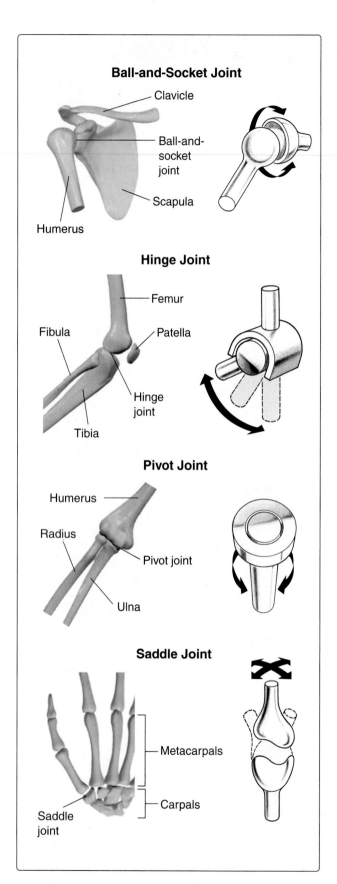

Ball-and-Socket Joint

- Clavicle
- Ball-and-socket joint
- Scapula
- Humerus

Hinge Joint

- Femur
- Fibula
- Patella
- Hinge joint
- Tibia

Pivot Joint

- Humerus
- Radius
- Pivot joint
- Ulna

Saddle Joint

- Metacarpals
- Carpals
- Saddle joint

▲ **Figure 36–4** Freely movable joints are classified by the type of movement they permit. The joints illustrated are in the hip, knee, elbow, and hand.

Bone formation also occurs when a bone is broken. Osteoclasts remove damaged bone tissue. Osteoblasts produce new bone tissue. The repair of a broken bone can take months because the process is slow and gradual.

In adults, cartilage is found in those parts of the body where flexibility is needed, such as the tip of the nose and the external ears. Cartilage also is found where the ribs are attached to the sternum, which allows the rib cage to move during breathing.

Types of Joints

A place where one bone attaches to another bone is called a **joint.** Joints permit bones to move without damaging each other. Some joints, such as those of the shoulder, allow extensive movement. Others, like the joints of the fully developed skull, allow no movement at all. 🔑 **Depending on its type of movement, a joint is classified as immovable, slightly movable, or freely movable.**

Immovable Joints Immovable joints, often called fixed joints, allow no movement. The bones at an immovable joint are interlocked and held together by connective tissue, or they are fused. The places where the bones in the skull meet are examples of immovable joints.

Slightly Movable Joints Slightly movable joints permit a small amount of restricted movement. The bones of slightly movable joints are separated from each other. The joints between the two bones of the lower leg and the joints between adjacent vertebrae are examples of slightly movable joints.

Freely Movable Joints Freely movable joints permit movement in one or more directions. Freely movable joints are grouped according to the shapes of the surfaces of the adjacent bones. The most common types of freely movable joints are shown in **Figure 36–4.**

Ball-and-socket joints permit circular movement—the widest range of movement. Hinge joints permit back-and-forth motion, like the opening and closing of a door. Pivot joints allow one bone to rotate around another. Saddle joints permit one bone to slide in two directions.

✔ **CHECKPOINT** *What are the four common types of freely movable joints?*

Structure of Joints

In freely movable joints, the ends of the bones are covered with a smooth surface layer of cartilage that protects the bones as they move against each other. The joints are also surrounded by a fibrous joint capsule that helps hold the bones together while still allowing them to move.

The joint capsule consists of two layers. One layer forms strips of tough connective tissue called **ligaments.** Ligaments are attached to the membranes that surround bones and hold the bones together. Cells in the other layer of the joint capsule produce a substance called synovial (sin-OH-vee-ul) fluid, which forms a thin film within the bone surfaces of a joint. This lubricating film enables the ends of the bones to slip past each other smoothly.

In some freely movable joints, such as the knee in **Figure 36–5,** small sacs of synovial fluid called bursae (BUR-see; singular: bursa) form. A bursa reduces the friction between the bones of a joint and also acts as a tiny shock absorber.

When a tissue is damaged, the body's response is called inflammation. Symptoms include swelling, redness, heat, and pain. Inflammation of a bursa is called bursitis. Too much fluid fills the bursa, resulting in a painful swelling. A more serious disorder is arthritis, which involves inflammation of one or more joints. There are over 100 different types of arthritis, which as a group affect approximately 10 percent of the world's population.

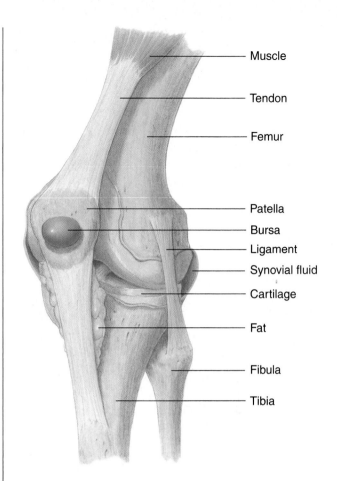

Muscle
Tendon
Femur
Patella
Bursa
Ligament
Synovial fluid
Cartilage
Fat
Fibula
Tibia

▲ **Figure 36–5** The knee joint is protected by cartilage and bursae. The ligaments hold the bones associated with the knee joint—femur, patella, tibia, and fibula—together. **Inferring** *How do the cartilage and bursae help reduce friction?*

36–1 Section Assessment

1. **Key Concept** List the different functions of the skeletal system.

2. **Key Concept** Describe the structure of a typical bone.

3. **Key Concept** What is a joint? List the three types of joints.

4. How does compact bone differ from spongy bone?

5. **Critical Thinking Inferring** Why do you think the amount of cartilage decreases and the amount of bone increases as a person develops?

TEXT **Assessment** Use iText to review the important concepts in Section 36–1.

Take It to the NET

Read about the wrist joint. Then, draw the wrist joint, labeling the adjacent bones and ligaments. Describe what kind of movement the wrist joint permits. Use the links provided in the Biology area at the Prentice Hall Web site for help in completing this activity:
www.phschool.com

36-2 The Muscular System

Guide for Reading

 Key Concepts
- What are the three types of muscle tissue?
- How do muscles contract?

Vocabulary
myosin
actin
neuromuscular junction
acetylcholine
tendon

Reading Strategy:
Summarizing As you read, find the main ideas for each paragraph. Write down a few key words from each main idea. Then, use the key words in your summary. Reread your summary, keeping only the most important ideas.

Despite the fantasies of Hollywood horror films, a skeleton cannot move by itself. Muscles provide the forces that put the body into motion. More than 40 percent of the mass of the average human body is muscle. The muscular system includes the large muscles that athletes display as signs of physical development. It also includes thousands of tiny muscles throughout the body that help to regulate blood pressure, move food through the digestive system, and power every movement of the body—from the blink of an eye to the hint of a smile.

Types of Muscle Tissue

Muscle tissue is found everywhere in the body—not only just beneath the skin but also deep within the body. **There are three different types of muscle tissue: skeletal, smooth, and cardiac.** Each type of muscle has a different structure and plays a different role in the body. Refer to **Figure 36–6** as you read about the different types of muscles.

Skeletal Muscles Skeletal muscles are usually attached to bones. Skeletal muscles are responsible for such voluntary movements as typing on a computer keyboard, dancing, or winking an eye. When viewed under a microscope at high magnification, skeletal muscle appears to have alternating light and dark bands or stripes called striations. For this reason, skeletal muscle is sometimes called striated muscle. Most skeletal muscles are controlled by the central nervous system.

Skeletal muscle cells are large, have many nuclei, and vary in length from 1 millimeter to about 30 centimeters. Because skeletal muscle cells are long and slender, they are often called muscle fibers. Complete skeletal muscles consist of muscle fibers, connective tissues, blood vessels, and nerves. **Figure 36–7** shows the structure of a skeletal muscle in the leg.

Figure 36–6 There are three types of muscle tissue: skeletal, smooth, and cardiac. Skeletal muscle cells have striations, or stripes, and many nuclei. Smooth muscle cells are spindle-shaped, and have one nucleus and no striations. Cardiac muscle cells have striations and usually only one nucleus.

Skeletal Muscle (150×)

Smooth Muscle (400×)

Cardiac Muscle (500×)

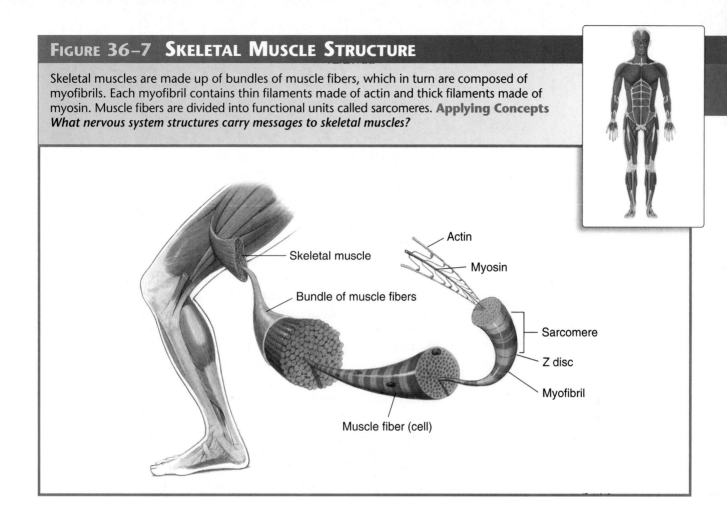

FIGURE 36–7 SKELETAL MUSCLE STRUCTURE

Skeletal muscles are made up of bundles of muscle fibers, which in turn are composed of myofibrils. Each myofibril contains thin filaments made of actin and thick filaments made of myosin. Muscle fibers are divided into functional units called sarcomeres. **Applying Concepts** *What nervous system structures carry messages to skeletal muscles?*

Skeletal muscle

Bundle of muscle fibers

Actin

Myosin

Sarcomere

Z disc

Myofibril

Muscle fiber (cell)

Smooth Muscles Smooth muscles are usually not under voluntary control. A smooth muscle cell is spindle-shaped, has one nucleus, and is not striated. Smooth muscles are found in hollow structures such as the stomach, blood vessels, and the small and large intestines. Smooth muscles move food through your digestive tract, control the way blood flows through your circulatory system, and decrease the size of the pupils of your eyes in bright light. Most smooth muscle cells can function without nervous stimulation. They are connected to one another by gap junctions that allow electrical impulses to travel directly from one muscle cell to a neighboring muscle cell.

Cardiac Muscle Cardiac muscle is found in just one place in the body—the heart. The prefix *cardio-* comes from a Greek word meaning "heart." Cardiac muscle shares features with both skeletal muscle and smooth muscle. Cardiac muscle is striated like skeletal muscle, although its cells are smaller. Cardiac muscle cells usually have one nucleus, but they may have two. Cardiac muscle is similar to smooth muscle because it is usually not under the direct control of the central nervous system and cardiac cells are connected to their neighbors by gap junctions. You will learn more about cardiac muscle in Chapter 37.

✓**CHECKPOINT** *What kind of muscle tissue lines the blood vessels?*

Skeletal, Muscular, and Integumentary Systems **927**

Muscle Contraction

The muscle fibers in skeletal muscles are composed of smaller structures called myofibrils. Each myofibril is made up of even smaller structures called filaments. The striations in skeletal muscle cells are formed by an alternating pattern of thick and thin filaments. The thick filaments contain a protein called **myosin** (MY-uh-sin). The thin filaments are made up mainly of a protein called **actin.** The filaments are arranged along the muscle fiber in units called sarcomeres, which are separated from each other by regions called Z discs. As **Figure 36–8** shows, when a muscle is relaxed, there are no thin filaments in the center of a sarcomere.

The tiny myosin and actin filaments are the force-producing engines that cause a muscle to contract. **A muscle contracts when the thin filaments in the muscle fiber slide over the thick filaments.** This process is called the sliding-filament model of muscle contraction. For a muscle to contract, the thick myosin filament must form a cross-bridge with the thin actin filament. As the cross-bridge changes shape, it pulls on the actin filament, which slides toward the center of the sarcomere. The distance between the Z discs decreases. The cross-bridge detaches from the actin filament. The cycle is repeated when the myosin binds to another site on the actin filament.

When hundreds of thousands of myosin cross-bridges change shape in a fraction of a second, the muscle fiber shortens with considerable force. **The energy for muscle contraction is supplied by ATP.** Because one molecule of ATP supplies the energy for one interaction between a myosin cross-bridge and an actin filament, the cell needs plenty of ATP molecules for a strong contraction. Recall that the cell can produce ATP in two ways—by cellular respiration and by fermentation.

CHECKPOINT *What is actin? What is myosin?*

Relaxed Muscle

Z disc — Myosin — Actin — Z disc

Sarcomere

Contracted Muscle

Cross-bridges — Z disc

Figure 36–8 During muscle contraction, the actin filaments slide over the myosin filaments, decreasing the distance between the Z discs.

Movement of Actin Filament

Actin

Binding sites — Cross-bridge

Myosin

During muscle contraction, the knoblike head of a myosin filament attaches to a binding site on actin, forming a cross-bridge.

ATP

Powered by ATP, the myosin cross-bridge changes shape and pulls the actin filament toward the center of the sarcomere.

The cross-bridge is broken, the myosin binds to another site on the actin filament, and the cycle begins again.

Control of Muscle Contraction

Skeletal muscles are useful only if they contract in a controlled fashion. Remember that motor neurons connect the central nervous system to skeletal muscle cells. Impulses from motor neurons control the contraction of skeletal muscle fibers.

Figure 36–9 is a photo of a **neuromuscular junction** (noo-roh-MUS-kyoo-lur), which is the point of contact between a motor neuron and a skeletal muscle cell. Vesicles, or pockets, in the axon terminals of the motor neuron release a neurotransmitter called **acetylcholine** (as-ih-til-KOH-leen). Acetylcholine molecules diffuse across the synapse, producing an impulse in the cell membrane of the muscle fiber. The impulse causes the release of calcium ions (Ca^{2+}) within the fiber. The calcium ions affect regulatory proteins that allow actin and myosin filaments to interact. From the time a nerve impulse reaches a muscle cell, it is only a few milliseconds before these events occur and the muscle cell contracts.

A muscle cell remains contracted until the release of acetylcholine stops and an enzyme produced at the axon terminal destroys any remaining acetylcholine. Then, the cell pumps calcium ions back into storage, the cross-bridges stop forming, and contraction ends.

The contraction of a single muscle fiber is an all-or-none process. A stimulated fiber will contract to its full extent. So how can there be strong and weak contractions? Each muscle contains hundreds of cells. A single motor neuron may form synapses with more than one muscle fiber.

▲ **Figure 36–9** This photograph shows a neuromuscular junction—the point of contact between a motor neuron and a skeletal muscle. The threadlike structure is a motor neuron with its knoblike axon terminals. **Applying Concepts** *How does the neurotransmitter produced by the motor neuron cause the skeletal muscle to contract?*

▼ **Figure 36–10** Because this rock climber exercises regularly, her muscles have remained firm and also have increased in size. **Predicting** *What do you think would happen to this rock climber's muscles if she stopped exercising regularly?*

How Muscles and Bones Interact

Skeletal muscles generate force and produce movement by contracting, or pulling on body parts. Individual muscles can only pull in one direction. Yet, you know from experience that your legs bend when you sit and extend when you stand up. How is this possible?

Skeletal muscles are joined to bones by tough connective tissues called **tendons.** Tendons are attached in such a way that they pull on the bones and make them work like levers. The joint functions as a fulcrum—the fixed point around which the lever moves. The muscles provide the force to move the lever. Usually, there are several muscles surrounding each joint that pull in different directions.

Most skeletal muscles work in opposing pairs. When one muscle contracts, the other relaxes. The muscles of the upper arm shown in **Figure 36–11** are a good example of this dual action. When the biceps muscle contracts, it bends, or flexes, the elbow joint. When the triceps muscle contracts, it opens, or extends, the elbow joint. A controlled movement, however, requires contraction by both muscles. To hold a tennis racket or a violin, both the biceps and triceps must contract in balance. This is why the training of athletes and musicians is so difficult. The brain must learn how to work opposing muscle groups in just the right ways to make the joint move precisely.

Quick Lab

Biceps

Tendon

What do tendons do?

Materials plastic gloves, raw chicken wing treated with bleach, paper towels, forceps, scissors, scalpel

Procedure

1. Put on the plastic gloves. **CAUTION:** *Do not touch your face with your hands during the lab. Be careful with the scissors and scalpel.*
2. Put a chicken wing on a paper towel. Peel back or cut away the skin and fat of the largest wing segment to expose the large muscle. This muscle is called the biceps. Find the tendon that attaches the biceps to the bones of the middle segment of the wing. Tendons are the tough, shiny white cords that join the muscles to the bones.
3. Use forceps to pull on the tendon of the biceps and observe what happens to the chicken wing.

4. Clean your tools and dispose of the chicken wing and gloves according to your teacher's instructions. Wash your hands with soap and warm water.
5. Observe the back of your hand as you move each of your fingers in turn. Compare what you see to how the chicken wing moved.

Analyze and Conclude
1. **Applying Concepts** What happened when you pulled on the tendon? In a live chicken, what structure would pull on the tendon to move the wing?
2. **Comparing and Contrasting** How is the way the wing moves similar to the way your fingers move?

▼ **Figure 36–11** By contracting and relaxing, the triceps and biceps in the upper arm enable you to bend or straighten your elbow. **Applying Concepts** *Which skeletal muscle must contract in order for you to straighten your elbow?*

Movement

Biceps (relaxed)

Triceps (contracted)

Movement

Biceps (contracted)

Triceps (relaxed)

Skeletal muscles generally remain in a state of partial contraction. At any given time, a few muscle cells are being stimulated while others are not. This limited stimulation causes a tightening of some muscles called resting muscle tone. Muscle tone is responsible for keeping the back and legs straight and the head upright, even when you are relaxed. Regular exercise is good for your body because it increases muscle tone. Muscles that are exercised regularly stay firm and increase in size by adding more material to the inside of the muscle cells. Regular exercise also helps your body systems become more efficient. For example, some types of exercise increase the efficiency of your heart and lungs. Muscles that are not used at all become weak and can visibly decrease in size.

36–2 Section Assessment

1. 🔑 **Key Concept** List the three types of muscle tissue and explain the function of each.
2. 🔑 **Key Concept** Explain how a muscle contracts.
3. How do bones and muscles work together to move the body?
4. What is acetylcholine, and what is its role in muscle contraction?

5. **Critical Thinking** **Predicting** If a muscle cell receives a second stimulus while it is contracting, will it respond to the second stimulus? Explain.

*i***TEXT** **Assessment** Use iText to review the important concepts in Section 36–2.

ALTERNATIVE ASSESSMENT

Making a Model
Create your own model to show how actin filaments slide over myosin filaments during a muscle contraction. Include as much detail in your model as possible.

Manufacturing Artificial Skin

The skin is not only the largest organ in the body, it is also one of the most easily injured, especially by fire. More than 2 million Americans suffer burn injuries every year, and more than 10,000 die from such injuries. The skin is the body's most important barrier against infection, but burns can destroy that barrier, leaving tissues exposed and vulnerable.

The best way to protect badly burned tissue is to cover it with a layer of fresh skin. If the burned region is small, this can be done with skin grafts taken from other parts of the body. For larger burns, however, this isn't possible. Scientists have now developed a way to help many victims of serious burns—they have developed artificial skin.

Constructing a Scaffold

Skin is a complex organ. For this reason, researchers realized that the best way to replace skin would be with an artificial skin that the body's own cells could grow into. After the outer layer of burned tissue is removed from a severely burned patient, surgeons can apply artificial skin made from a biodegradable meshwork of protein fibers similar to those in human skin. Cells from the dermis migrate upward and gradually "take over" the artificial layer, replacing the meshwork with human proteins. Thus, a new layer of dermis is produced. A very thin layer of the patient's own epidermal cells, grown in culture, is then applied to the surface of the artificial skin.

Perfecting the Technique

Artificial skin is used only in the treatment of burns so severe that normal healing is not possible. One of its main drawbacks is that the migration of cells into the artificial layer may take as long as three weeks, enough time for infection and other complications to develop. Researchers are trying to speed up the process by placing cell-growth signal chemicals in the artificial layer. If they succeed, the successful treatment of even serious burns may become routine.

On Your Own

1. Use reference materials to find information on the treatment of serious burns. Design a brochure that explains and illustrates the steps in the treatment of third-degree burns.
2. Visit or telephone your local hospital to see if it has a burn clinic that uses artificial skin. If it does, arrange to either visit the hospital or have information sent to you. Write a brief summary of what you find out.

36–3 The Integumentary System

"Good fences make good neighbors," wrote the American poet Robert Frost as he explained the importance of property boundaries. Living things have their own "fences," and none is as important as the skin—the boundary that separates the human body from the outside world.

The skin, the single largest organ of the body, is part of the integumentary (in-teg-yoo-MEN-tuh-ree) system. The word *integument* comes from a Latin word that means "to cover," reflecting the fact that the skin and its related structures form a covering over the entire body. Skin and its related structures—the hair, nails, and a variety of glands—make up the integumentary system.

The Skin

The skin has many different functions, but its most important function is protection. **The integumentary system serves as a barrier against infection and injury, helps to regulate body temperature, removes waste products from the body, and provides protection against ultraviolet radiation from the sun.** Because the largest component of the integumentary system—the skin—contains several types of sensory receptors, it serves as the gateway through which sensations such as pressure, heat, cold, and pain are transmitted to the nervous system.

The skin is made up of two main layers—the epidermis and the dermis. Beneath the dermis is a subcutaneous layer of fat and loose connective tissue that helps to insulate the body.

Guide for Reading

Key Concept
• What are the functions of the integumentary system?

Vocabulary
epidermis
keratin
melanin
dermis
hair follicle

**Reading Strategy:
Building Vocabulary**
Before you read, preview **Figure 36–13** to identify vocabulary with which you are unfamiliar. As you read, look for the meaning of these terms.

(magnification: 340×)

Figure 36–12 After strenuous exercise, the skin produces sweat, which decreases the temperature of the body and rids the body of wastes. Sweat is secreted by sweat glands and leaves the body through sweat pores.

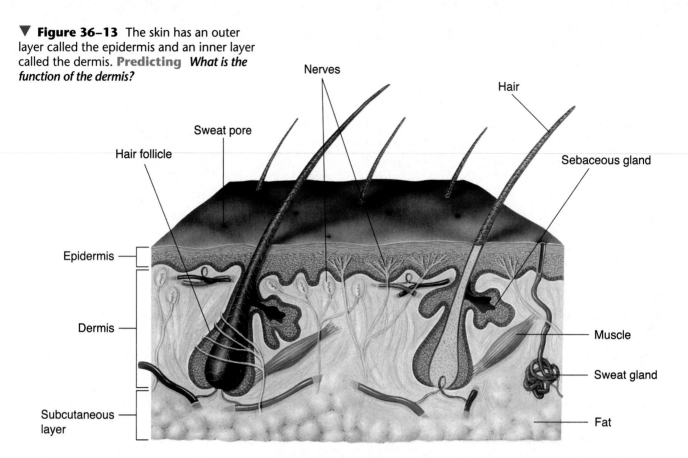

▼ **Figure 36–13** The skin has an outer layer called the epidermis and an inner layer called the dermis. **Predicting** *What is the function of the dermis?*

Nerves

Hair

Sweat pore

Hair follicle

Sebaceous gland

Epidermis

Dermis

Muscle

Sweat gland

Subcutaneous layer

Fat

Word Origins

Epidermis comes from two Greek words: *epi,* meaning "on the outside," and *derma,* meaning "skin." **If the Greek word** *phyton* **means "plant," what does the term** *epiphyte* **mean?**

Epidermis The outer layer of the skin is the **epidermis.** The epidermis itself has two layers. The outside of the epidermis—the part that comes in contact with the environment—is made up of dead cells. The inner layer of the epidermis is made up of living cells.

Cells in the inner layer of the epidermis undergo rapid cell division, producing new cells that push older cells to the surface of the skin. As they move upward, the older cells become flattened and their organelles disintegrate. They also begin making **keratin,** a tough, fibrous protein.

Eventually, the keratin-producing cells die and form a tough, flexible, waterproof covering on the surface of the skin. This outer layer of dead cells is shed or washed away at a surprising rate—once every four to five weeks.

The epidermis also contains melanocytes (MEL-uh-noh-syts). Melanocytes are cells that produce **melanin,** a dark brown pigment. Although most people have roughly the same number of melanocytes in their skin, differences in skin color are caused by the different amount of melanin the melanocytes produce and where these cells are distributed.

Look closely at **Figure 36–13** and you will see that there are no blood vessels in the epidermis. This explains why a slight scratch will not cause bleeding.

✓ CHECKPOINT *What is melanin?*

Dermis The inner layer of the skin is the **dermis.** It lies beneath the epidermis and contains collagen fibers, blood vessels, nerve endings, glands, sense organs, smooth muscles, and hair follicles. When the body needs to conserve heat on a cold day, the blood vessels in the dermis narrow, helping to limit heat loss. On hot days, the blood vessels widen, bringing heat from the body's core to the skin and increasing heat loss.

The dermis contains two major types of glands: sweat glands and sebaceous (suh-BAY-shus), or oil, glands. These glands have openings in the epidermis at the surface of the skin through which they release their products. If your body gets too hot, sweat glands produce perspiration, or sweat. When sweat evaporates, it takes heat away from your body. Perspiration contains water, salts, and other compounds. The release of these secretions is stimulated by nerve impulses when the temperature of the body rises above the normal range.

Sebaceous glands produce an oily secretion called sebum that spreads out along the surface of the skin and helps to keep the keratin-rich epidermis flexible and waterproof.

Analyzing Data

The UV Index and Sunburn

Ultraviolet (UV) radiation is one type of energy from the sun. UV rays cause sunburn, some cataracts, and skin cancer. There are many factors that affect the amount of UV radiation to which you are exposed. These include the time of day, the season, the weather conditions, and your location. Recently, the National Weather Service, the Environmental Protection Agency, and the Centers for Disease Control agreed upon a national UV index. The UV index is issued daily to advise you of conditions in your region of the country. Use the information in the chart to answer the questions that follow.

1. **Interpreting Graphics** Describe the trend in the amount of time it takes to sunburn, from a minimal UV index level to a very high UV index level.

2. **Applying Concepts** Why do you think applying sunscreen is always recommended?

3. **Drawing Conclusions** Why should a hat worn as protection against UV rays have a brim?

4. **Predicting** The minutes to burn data apply to most people. What variable could cause the time for a particular person to burn to be shorter or longer?

Protection From Sunburn		
UV Index Level	How to Protect Yourself	Minutes to Burn
Minimal (0–2)	Apply sunscreen Wear sunglasses near snow and water	60
Low (3–4)	Apply sunscreen Wear sunglasses and hat	45
Moderate (5–6)	Apply sunscreen Wear sunglasses and hat Apply lip balm	30
High (7–9)	Apply sunscreen Wear sunglasses and hat Seek shade from 10 AM to 4 PM	15
Very High (10+)	Apply sunscreen Wear sunglasses and hat Avoid sun from 10 AM to 4 PM	10

5. **Making a Graph** Use the data in the table to construct a bar graph. Place the UV index levels on the x-axis and the minutes to burn on the y-axis.

▲ **Figure 36–14** In this color-enhanced scanning electron micrograph of a hair shaft, the scalelike structures are layers of skin cells. The part of the hair that is above the skin is made up of dead cells that become filled with keratin. **Observing** *What layer of the skin contains the hair follicle?*

Hair and Nails

The basic structure of human hair and nails is keratin. In other animals, keratin forms a variety of structures, including bull horns, reptile scales, bird feathers, and porcupine quills.

Hair Hair covers almost every exposed surface of the body and has important functions. Hair on the head protects the scalp from ultraviolet light from the sun and provides insulation from the cold. Hairs in the nostrils, external ear canals, and around the eyes (eyelashes) prevent dirt and other particles from entering the body.

Hair is produced by cells at the base of structures called hair follicles. **Hair follicles** are tubelike pockets of epidermal cells that extend into the dermis. The individual hair shown in **Figure 36–14** is actually a large column of cells that have filled with keratin and then died. Rapid cell growth at the base of the hair follicle causes the hair to grow longer. Hair follicles are in close contact with sebaceous glands. The oily secretions of these glands help maintain the condition of each individual hair. Hair follicles also contain clusters of stem cells that give rise to epidermal cells.

Nails Nails protect the tips of the fingers and toes. Nails grow from an area of rapidly dividing cells known as the nail root. The nail root is located near the tips of the fingers and toes. During cell division, the cells of the nail root fill with keratin and produce a tough, platelike nail that covers and protects the tips of the fingers and toes. Nails grow at an average rate of 3 millimeters per month, with fingernails growing more rapidly than toenails—about four times as fast.

36–3 Section Assessment

1. 🔑 **Key Concept** List the functions of the integumentary system.
2. What organs and tissues make up the integumentary system?
3. Compare the structures of the epidermis and dermis.
4. In what way is the growth of hair and nails similar?

5. **Critical Thinking Applying Concepts** Why does cutting your skin hurt, while cutting your hair or nails does not?

📱**TEXT** **Assessment** Use iText to review the important concepts in Section 36–3.

MAKING CONNECTIONS

Plant Structure
Compare the structure and function of the dermal tissue in plants discussed in Section 23–1 with the structures in human skin.

Making a Model of a Transdermal Patch

Some medications are introduced into the body using a patch attached to the skin, rather than by mouth or by injection. This is especially useful for medications that need to be continuously released in very small quantities over an extended period of time. In this investigation, you will model how these patches, called transdermal patches, work.

Problem How can some medications be given through the skin?

Materials
- dialysis tubing
- plastic cup
- phenolphthalein solution
- 50-mL graduated cylinder
- paper towels
- scissors
- metric ruler
- filter paper
- dropper pipette
- sodium bicarbonate solution

Skills Using Models, Observing

Procedure

1. Soak a piece of dialysis tubing in a cup of water until it is soft (about 1 minute).

2. Tie a knot in one end of the dialysis tubing. Use a graduated cylinder to fill the tubing with phenolphthalein solution. **CAUTION:** *Phenolphthalein is toxic. Do not rub your eyes during this investigation.*

3. Squeeze as much air out of the tubing as you can, then tie a knot in the open end of the tubing to seal it off. The tubing represents the cell membrane of a skin cell.

4. Lay the model skin cell down on a paper towel. Use another paper towel to wipe dry the outside of the tubing.

5. Carefully cut out four 1-cm squares of filter paper. **CAUTION:** *Scissors are sharp. Handle them carefully.* Stack the filter-paper squares on top of the model skin cell. The filter paper represents a patch that will be saturated with the medication to be delivered.

6. Using a dropper pipette, carefully soak the filter paper, 1 drop at a time, with sodium bicarbonate solution. Try not to let the solution run down the sides of the tubing. The sodium bicarbonate solution represents the medication.

7. Observe the model cell for 10 to 15 minutes and record your observations.

Analyze and Conclude

1. **Observing** What happened when you added the sodium bicarbonate solution to the filter paper?

2. **Inferring** What property did the "cell membrane" (dialysis tubing) need to possess for you to observe these changes?

3. **Drawing Conclusions** What kinds of substances would be absorbed most easily in this way? Explain your answer.

Go Further

Additional Research Research transdermal patches in the library or on the Internet. Write a brief report describing at least two uses of transdermal patches. Describe the advantages and disadvantages of transdermal patches compared with injections and oral medications.

36–1 The Skeletal System
Key Concepts

- The human skeleton supports the body, protects internal organs, provides for movement, stores mineral reserves, and provides a site for blood cell formation.
- Bones are a solid network of living cells and protein fibers that are surrounded by deposits of calcium salts.
- Depending on its type of movement, a joint is classified as immovable, slightly movable, or freely movable.

Vocabulary
periosteum, p. 922
Haversian canal, p. 922
bone marrow, p. 922
cartilage, p. 922
ossification, p. 922
joint, p. 924
ligament, p. 925

36–2 The Muscular System
Key Concepts

- There are three different types of muscle tissue: skeletal muscle, smooth muscle, and cardiac muscle.

- A muscle fiber contracts when the thin filaments in the muscle fiber slide over the thick filaments.
- The energy for muscle contraction is supplied by ATP.

Vocabulary
myosin, p. 928
actin, p. 928
neuromuscular junction, p. 929
acetylcholine, p. 929
tendon, p. 930

36–3 The Integumentary System
Key Concept

- The integumentary system serves as a barrier against infection and injury, helps to regulate body temperature, removes waste products from the body, and provides protection against ultraviolet radiation from the sun.

Vocabulary
epidermis, p. 934
keratin, p. 934
melanin, p. 934
dermis, p. 935
hair follicle, p. 936

Thinking Visually

Using the information in this chapter, complete the following concept map:

Chapter 36

Part A

Multiple Choice

For each statement or question, select the number of the word or expression that, of those given, best completes the statement or answers the question.

1 The tough connective tissue layer surrounding bone is called
   (1) tendon   (3) periosteum
   (2) ligament   (4) cartilage

2 The network of tubes running through compact bone is called the
   (1) periosteum
   (2) joint
   (3) Haversian canals
   (4) bone marrow

3 Cartilage is replaced by bone during the process of
   (1) ossification
   (2) calcification
   (3) ligamentation
   (4) puberty

4 Strips of tough connective tissue that hold bones together are known as
   (1) tendons
   (2) smooth muscles
   (3) striated muscles
   (4) ligaments

5 Small sacs of synovial fluid that help reduce friction between the bones of a joint are called
   (1) bursae   (3) tendons
   (2) ligaments   (4) striations

6 Which figure shows smooth muscle tissue?

(1)

(3)

(2)

(4)

7 Joints that allow circular movement are referred to as
   (1) gliding joints
   (2) ball-and-socket joints
   (3) hinge joints
   (4) pivot joints

8 Two proteins that are involved in the contraction of muscle are
   (1) sarcomere and myofibril
   (2) actin and myosin
   (3) periosteum and cartilage
   (4) ATP and acetylcholine

9 The point of contact between a motor neuron and a skeletal muscle cell is called a
   (1) cross-bridge site
   (2) periosteum
   (3) tendon
   (4) neuromuscular junction

10 The outermost layer of skin is the
   (1) dermis   (3) epidermis
   (2) keratin   (4) melanin

11 What determines differences in skin color among individuals?
   (1) number of melanocytes in the skin
   (2) amount of melanin produced by each melanocyte
   (3) amount of keratin in the skin
   (4) amount of sebum produced in the dermis

12 Smooth muscle is found in the
   (1) walls of blood vessels
   (2) heart
   (3) skeletal muscles
   (4) joints

13 All are important roles of the skeletal system *except*
   (1) protection of internal organs
   (2) movement of the body
   (3) production of red blood cells
   (4) regulation of body temperature

Test-Taking Tip When evaluating multiple-choice answers, be sure to read all the choices, even if the first choice seems to be correct. When you consider all the choices, you are more likely to choose the best one.

Parts B and C

Multiple Choice and Extended Response

For those questions that ask you to select a response, choose the one that best completes the statement or answers the question. For all others follow the directions given.

14 What is released by the motor neuron at the neuromuscular junction?
  (1) actin   (3) ADP
  (2) ATP   (4) acetylcholine

15 The thick filaments of striated muscle are composed of
  (1) myosin   (3) ADP
  (2) actin   (4) ATP

Base your answers to questions 16 through 18 on the information and graphs below and on your knowledge of biology.

Osteoporosis is a disease characterized by the loss and weakening of bone tissue. One possible explanation for this condition is that, as people age, the calcium content of their bones decreases. To assess this hypothesis, the bone mineral content of 250 men and 250 women was measured. The data are shown in the graph below.

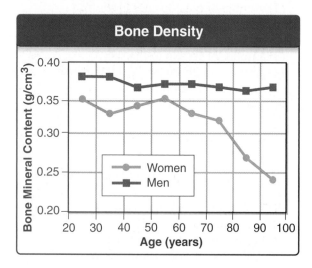

16 At which age range do women show the lowest bone mineral content?
  (1) 60–69 years   (3) 80–89 years
  (2) 70–79 years   (4) 90–95 years

17 A valid conclusion that can be drawn from this graph is that, on average,
  (1) women lose more bone mineral content as they age than men do
  (2) men lose more bone mineral content as they age than women do
  (3) women gain bone mineral content as they age
  (4) men gain bone mineral content as they age

18 A possible way of slowing osteoporosis is to
  (1) add calcium to the diet
  (2) strengthen the ligaments
  (3) receive a bone marrow transplant
  (4) reduce salt in the diet

19 Lever is to bone as fulcrum is to
  (1) muscle   (3) tendon
  (2) ligament   (4) joint

20 On the diagram of a long bone shown below, identify the following structures: spongy bone, osteocyte, periosteum, Haversian canal, compact bone, artery, and vein. (Do not write in this book.) Which of these structures contains blood vessels and nerves?

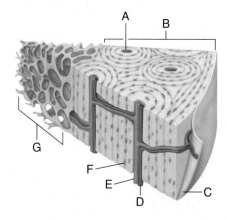

21 Which structures in skin make it flexible and waterproof?
  (1) sweat glands
  (2) sebaceous glands
  (3) hairs
  (4) pores

22 Sweat glands begin their work when the
  (1) muscles tire
  (2) body becomes overheated
  (3) epidermis releases moisture
  (4) blood vessels narrow

23 Because cartilage does not appear on X-ray film, it is seen as a clear area between the shaft and the ends of the individual bones. Examine the X-rays below.

Which hand belongs to the youngest person? Explain how you determined this.

24 Certain bacteria produce a toxin that prevents the release of acetylcholine from the motor neurons. Explain why this can result in a fatal loss of muscle movement.

25 Assume you have a habit of leaning on your elbow while reading. One day, you notice that you have developed a painful swelling on your elbow. Explain what might have caused this.

26 Compare the roles of ligaments and tendons.

27 Disks of rubbery cartilage are found between the individual bones in the spinal column. What function would you predict these disks serve?

28 Suppose that you want to design a robotic arm that works the way the human elbow works. State three facts about the elbow that you would have to consider in your design.

29 Blood vessels bring oxygen and nutrients to all parts of the body. Ligaments contain fewer blood vessels than some other kinds of tissues. How might this affect the rate of healing in injured ligaments? Support your answer with an explanation.

30 A skin callus is a thickening of the epidermis caused by repeated rubbing. Explain why people often get calluses on their feet.

31 Use the sliding filament model to describe how skeletal muscles work.

32 Explain the statement: "Most skeletal muscles work in opposing pairs."

33 Which of the joints shown below is a pivot joint?

34 On the drawing of skin shown below, identify each of the following structures: muscle, epidermis, hair follicle, sweat gland, sebaceous gland, dermis, and nerves. (Do not write in this book.)

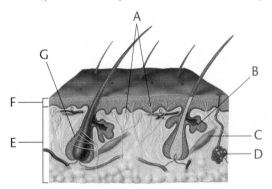

35 Describe the primary function of the three types of muscle.

36 Explain why spongy bone tissue is found in the ends of long bones.

 Take It to the NET

One common bone disorder among adolescents is scoliosis, or curvature of the spine. Visit the Prentice Hall Web site at **www.phschool.com** to find out more about scoliosis. Then, answer the following questions:

• What is idiopathic scoliosis?

• How does nonstructural scoliosis differ from structural scoliosis?

• What treatments are available for scoliosis?

This scanning electron micrograph shows individual red and white blood cells flowing through a vein (magnification 3850×).

Inquiry Activity

What factors affect your heart rate?

Procedure

1. While sitting still, measure your heart rate. To do this, find the pulse in one of your wrists using the first two fingers of your other hand.

2. Count the number of beats you feel in 15 seconds and multiply this number by 4. This will give you the number of beats per minute.

3. What do you think would happen if you stood up? Would your heart rate decrease, increase, or stay the same? Stand up and measure your heart rate to find out.

Think About It

Formulating Hypotheses Propose an explanation for any difference between your sitting heart rate and your standing heart rate.

37–1 The Circulatory System

Your heartbeat is a sign of life itself. Even when you drift off to sleep, your heart continues to beat at a steady rhythm. Why is this process so important that it must keep going even when you sleep?

Each breath you take brings air into your respiratory system. The oxygen in that air is needed by the trillions of cells in your body. Your heart is essential in delivering that oxygen. Its beating produces the force to move oxygen-rich blood through the circulatory system. Working together, your circulatory and respiratory systems supply cells throughout the body with the nutrients and oxygen that they need to stay alive.

Functions of the Circulatory System

Organisms composed of a small number of cells don't need a circulatory system. Most cells in such organisms are in direct contact with the environment. Oxygen, nutrients, and waste products can easily diffuse back and forth across cell membranes.

Larger organisms, however, cannot rely on diffusion. Most of their cells are not in direct contact with the environment, and substances made in one part of the organism may be needed in another part. In a way, this same problem is faced by the millions of people living in a large city. Cities have transportation systems that move people, goods, and waste material from one place to another. The transportation system of a city is its streets, highways, and rail lines. The transportation system of a living organism is its circulatory system.

Humans and other vertebrates have closed circulatory systems. This means that a circulating fluid called blood is pumped through a system of vessels. **The human circulatory system consists of the heart, a series of blood vessels, and the blood that flows through them.**

Guide for Reading

🔑 **Key Concepts**
• What are the structures of the circulatory system?
• What are the three types of blood vessels in the circulatory system?

Vocabulary
myocardium
atrium
ventricle
pulmonary circulation
systemic circulation
valve
pacemaker
aorta
artery
capillary
vein
atherosclerosis

**Reading Strategy:
Using Visuals** Before you read, preview **Figure 37–3.** Make a list of questions about the illustration. As you read, write down the answers to the questions.

◀ **Figure 37–1** These roads form a transportation system. **Using Analogies** *How is the human circulatory system like the streets and highways of a large city?*

Word Origins

The word **myocardium** comes from two Greek words: *myo,* meaning "muscle," and *kardia,* meaning "heart." **If** *itis* **means an "inflammation," what does** *myocarditis* **mean?**

The Heart

As you can feel with your hand, your heart is located near the center of your chest. The heart, which is composed almost entirely of muscle, is a hollow organ that is about the size of your clenched fist. The heart is enclosed in a protective sac of tissue called the pericardium (pehr-ih-KAHR-dee-um). In the walls of the heart, there are two thin layers of epithelial and connective tissue that form a sandwich around a thick layer of muscle called the **myocardium**. The powerful contractions of the myocardium pump blood through the circulatory system.

The heart contracts roughly 72 times a minute, pumping about 70 milliliters of blood with each contraction. This means that during one year, an average person's heart pumps more than enough blood to fill an Olympic-sized swimming pool. (An Olympic-sized swimming pool is about 2,000,000 liters: 0.07 liters × 4320 beats per hour × 24 hours × 365 days = 2,649,024 liters.)

Dividing the right side of the heart from the left side of the heart is a septum, or wall. The septum prevents the mixing of oxygen-poor and oxygen-rich blood. On each side of the septum are two chambers. The upper chamber, which receives the blood, is the **atrium** (plural: atria). The lower chamber, which pumps blood out of the heart, is the **ventricle.** The heart has a total of four chambers—two atria and two ventricles.

Circulation Through the Body The heart functions as two separate pumps. **Figure 37–2** shows that the right side of the heart pumps blood from the heart to the lungs. This pathway is known as **pulmonary circulation.** In the lungs, carbon dioxide leaves the blood while oxygen is absorbed. The oxygen-rich blood flows into the left side of the heart and is pumped to the rest of the body. This pathway is called **systemic circulation.** Blood that returns to the right side of the heart is oxygen-poor because cells have absorbed much of the oxygen and loaded the blood with carbon dioxide. At this point, it is ready for another trip to the lungs.

Oxygen-rich and oxygen-poor blood are both shades of red. Often, oxygen-poor blood is shown as blue in art to make it easier to tell where each type of blood is found in the circulatory system.

Blood Flow Through the Heart Blood enters the heart through the right and left atria, as shown in **Figure 37–3.** As the heart contracts, blood flows into the ventricles and then out from the ventricles.

▼ **Figure 37–2** The circulatory system is divided into two pathways. The pulmonary circulation carries blood between the heart and the lungs. The systemic circulation carries blood between the heart and the rest of the body. **Observing** *What kind of blood—oxygen-rich or oxygen-poor—leaves the lungs and returns to the heart?*

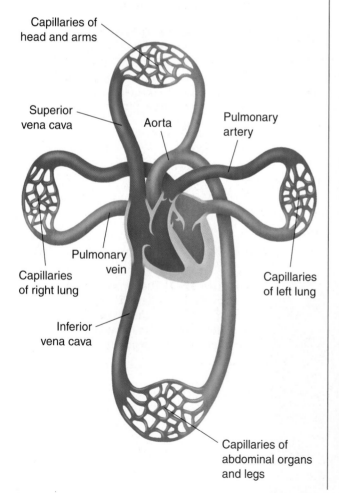

Capillaries of head and arms

Superior vena cava

Aorta

Pulmonary artery

Pulmonary vein

Capillaries of right lung

Capillaries of left lung

Inferior vena cava

Capillaries of abdominal organs and legs

FIGURE 37-3 STRUCTURES OF THE HEART

👄 The circulatory system consists of the heart, a series of blood vessels, and the blood that flows through them. Notice the valves between the atria and ventricles and those between the ventricles and the blood vessels leaving the heart. The valves prevent blood from flowing backward.

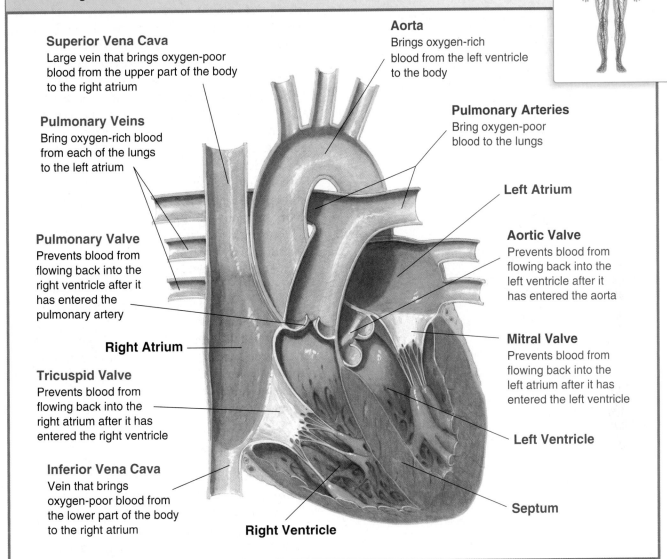

Superior Vena Cava
Large vein that brings oxygen-poor blood from the upper part of the body to the right atrium

Pulmonary Veins
Bring oxygen-rich blood from each of the lungs to the left atrium

Pulmonary Valve
Prevents blood from flowing back into the right ventricle after it has entered the pulmonary artery

Right Atrium

Tricuspid Valve
Prevents blood from flowing back into the right atrium after it has entered the right ventricle

Inferior Vena Cava
Vein that brings oxygen-poor blood from the lower part of the body to the right atrium

Right Ventricle

Aorta
Brings oxygen-rich blood from the left ventricle to the body

Pulmonary Arteries
Bring oxygen-poor blood to the lungs

Left Atrium

Aortic Valve
Prevents blood from flowing back into the left ventricle after it has entered the aorta

Mitral Valve
Prevents blood from flowing back into the left atrium after it has entered the left ventricle

Left Ventricle

Septum

There are flaps of connective tissue called **valves** between the atria and the ventricles. Blood moving from the atria holds the valves open. When the ventricles contract, the valves close, which prevents blood from flowing back into the atria.

At the exits from the right and left ventricles, there are valves that prevent blood that flows out of the heart from flowing back in. This system of valves keeps blood moving through the heart in one direction, like traffic on a one-way street. The one-way flow increases the pumping efficiency of the heart. The valves are so important to heart function that surgeons often attempt to repair or replace a damaged valve.

✓ **CHECKPOINT** *What is the function of the heart valves?*

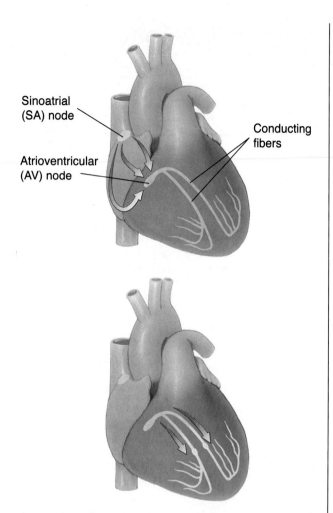

Sinoatrial (SA) node

Atrioventricular (AV) node

Conducting fibers

▲ **Figure 37–4** The signal to contract spreads from the sinoatrial node to the cardiac muscle cells of the atria, causing the atria to contract. The impulse is picked up by the atrioventricular node, which transmits the impulse to muscle fibers in the ventricles, causing the ventricles to contract.
Predicting *In times of stress, does the heart beat faster or slower?*

Heartbeat There are two networks of muscle fibers in the heart, one in the atria and one in the ventricles. When a single fiber in either network is stimulated, all the fibers are stimulated and the network contracts as a unit. Each contraction begins in a small group of cardiac muscle cells located in the right atrium—the sinoatrial node. Because these cells "set the pace" for the heart as a whole, they are also called the **pacemaker**.

As shown in **Figure 37–4**, the impulse spreads from the pacemaker to the network of fibers in the atria. It is picked up by a bundle of fibers called the atrioventricular node and carried to the network of fibers in the ventricles. When the network in the atria contracts, blood flows into the ventricles. When the network in the ventricles contracts, blood flows out of the heart. This two-step pattern of contraction makes the heart a more efficient pump.

Your heart can beat faster or more slowly, depending on your body's need for oxygen-rich blood. During vigorous exercise, your heart rate may increase to about 200 beats per minute. Although the heartbeat is not directly controlled by the nervous system, the autonomic nervous system does influence heart rate. Neurotransmitters released by neurons in the sympathetic nervous system can increase heart rate. Those released by neurons in the parasympathetic nervous system can decrease heart rate.

Blood Vessels

Blood leaving the left side of the heart is loaded with oxygen from the lungs. When it leaves the left ventricle, the blood passes into a large blood vessel known as the **aorta.** The aorta is the first of a series of blood vessels that carry the blood on its round trip through the body and back to the heart. 🔑 **As blood flows through the circulatory system, it moves through three types of blood vessels—arteries, capillaries, and veins.**

Arteries Large vessels that carry blood from the heart to the tissues of the body are called **arteries.** Arteries are the superhighways of the circulatory system. Except for the pulmonary arteries, all arteries carry oxygen-rich blood. Arteries have thick walls that help them withstand the powerful pressure produced when the heart contracts and pushes blood into the arteries.

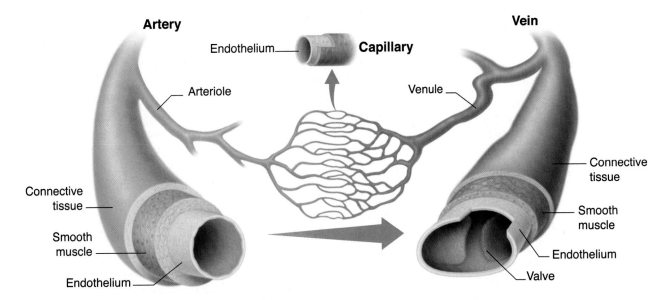

Artery

Endothelium — **Capillary**

Arteriole

Venule

Connective tissue

Connective tissue

Smooth muscle

Smooth muscle

Endothelium

Endothelium

Valve

Vein

▲ **Figure 37–5** 🔵 **In the circulatory system, there are three types of blood vessels—arteries, capillaries, and veins.** The walls of these vessels contain connective, muscle, and epithelial tissue.

Figure 37–5 shows that the walls contain connective tissue, smooth muscle, and epithelial cells. The elastic connective tissue allows an artery to expand under pressure. Contractions of the smooth muscle regulate the diameter of an artery.

Capillaries The smallest of the blood vessels are the **capillaries.** Capillaries are the side streets and alleys of the circulatory system. The walls of capillaries are only one cell thick, and most are so narrow that blood cells must pass through them in single file. The real work of the circulatory system—bringing nutrients and oxygen to the tissues and absorbing carbon dioxide and other waste products—is done in the capillaries.

Veins Once blood has passed through the capillary system, it must be returned to the heart. This is the job of the **veins.** As with arteries, the walls of veins contain connective tissue and smooth muscle. As shown in **Figure 37–6,** the largest veins contain one-way valves that keep blood flowing toward the heart. Many veins are located near skeletal muscles. When these muscles contract, they help to force blood through the veins. Blood flow through the veins of the arms and legs often occurs against the force of gravity. Exercise helps to keep blood from accumulating in the limbs and stretching the veins out of shape.

✓**CHECKPOINT** *What happens in the capillaries?*

Valve open

Valve closed

Valves closed

▶ **Figure 37–6** Contraction of skeletal muscles helps move blood in veins toward the heart. **Drawing Conclusions** *What role do valves play in large veins?*

Blood Pressure

Like any pump, the heart produces pressure. When the heart contracts, it produces a wave of fluid pressure in the arteries. The force of the blood on the arteries' walls is known as blood pressure. Blood pressure decreases when the heart relaxes, but the system still remains under pressure. It's a good thing, too. Without that pressure, blood would stop flowing through the body.

Medical workers can measure blood pressure with a device called a sphygmomanometer (sfig-moh-muh-NAHM-uh-tur). A cuff is wrapped around the upper arm. Air is pumped into the cuff until blood flow through an artery is blocked. As the pressure is released, the worker listens to the pulse and records two numbers from a pressure gauge. The first number is the systolic pressure—the force felt in the arteries when the ventricles contract. The second number is the diastolic pressure—the force of the blood felt in the arteries when the ventricles relax. An average adult's blood pressure is 120/80.

The body normally regulates blood pressure in two ways. Sensory neurons at several places in the body detect the level of blood pressure, sending impulses to the medulla oblongata region of the brain stem. When blood pressure is too high, the autonomic nervous system releases neurotransmitters that cause the smooth muscles around blood vessels to relax, lowering blood pressure. When blood pressure is too low, neurotransmitters are released that elevate blood pressure by causing these smooth muscles to contract.

Biology and History

Cardiovascular Advances

William Harvey, the father of cardiovascular medicine, correctly described the role of the heart in the circulation of blood more than three centuries ago. Since then, modern advances in this area have improved the lives of many people with heart disease.

Willem Einthoven
Einthoven wins a Nobel Prize for his invention of the electrocardiograph (EKG), a device used to measure tiny electric currents produced by the heart.

The *Titanic* sinks

1912

1924

1900

1902

Alexis Carrel
Carrel paves the way for organ transplantation by developing techniques for rejoining severed blood vessels.

1929

Worldwide economic depression begins

The kidneys, which remove water from the blood, also help to regulate blood pressure. Hormones produced by the heart and other organs cause the kidneys to remove more water from the blood when blood pressure is high. This action reduces blood volume, thereby lowering the blood pressure.

✓ **CHECKPOINT** *What instrument measures blood pressure?*

Disorders of the Circulatory System

Unfortunately, disorders of the circulatory system are all too common. Many of them stem from a condition known as **atherosclerosis** (ath-ur-oh-skluh-ROH-sis), in which fatty deposits called plaque build up on the walls of arteries. If these deposits get too large, they obstruct the flow of blood and may cause an increase in blood pressure. The plaque buildup also increases the risk of blood clots. If a clot breaks free, it can get stuck in an artery and obstruct blood flow to tissues beyond the clot.

High Blood Pressure If blood pressure is too high, medical problems may result. High blood pressure, or hypertension, forces the heart to work harder, which may weaken or damage the heart muscle and blood vessels. People with high blood pressure are more likely to develop heart disease and to suffer from other diseases of the circulatory system. Hypertension increases the risk of heart attack and stroke.

Writing Activity

Use the Internet or a library to find out more about the research conducted by one of these scientists. Then, write a summary of the scientist's experiments.

Christiaan Barnard
Barnard performs the first partially successful human heart transplant. The patient lived for 18 days.

1967

Wilson Greatbatch
Greatbatch wins a Lifetime Achievement Award for his invention, the implantable pacemaker. The mechanical device emits electrical signals that keep the heart beating normally.

1996

2000

1977

Andreas Gruentzig
Gruentzig performs the first angioplasty by inserting a hollow tube containing a tiny uninflated balloon into a patient's coronary artery. The balloon is inflated, opening up the blocked area and restoring blood flow to the heart.

1982

William DeVries
DeVries leads a team of doctors to implant the Jarvik-7 artificial heart in a patient, who lives for 112 days.

Heart Attack Atherosclerosis is particularly dangerous in the coronary arteries, the set of small arteries that bring oxygen and nutrients to the heart muscle itself. If one of these arteries becomes blocked, part of the heart muscle may begin to die for lack of oxygen—a condition known as a heart attack.

The symptoms of a heart attack include nausea, shortness of breath, and severe, crushing chest pain. People who show these symptoms need immediate medical attention. New drugs are available that can increase blood flow enough to save heart cells. These drugs must be given in the early stages of a heart attack to save the heart muscle and prevent cell death.

Stroke Blood clots formed as a result of atherosclerosis may break free and get stuck in one of the blood vessels leading to a part of the brain. This event is known as a stroke. Brain cells served by that blood vessel gradually die from a lack of oxygen, and brain function in that region may be lost. A stroke can also occur when a weakened artery in the brain bursts, flooding the area with blood. Depending on what part of the brain they affect, strokes may cause paralysis, loss of the ability to speak, and even death.

Prevention of Circulatory System Disorders Like most other disorders, cardiovascular disorders are easier to prevent than to cure. Exercise, weight control, sensible diet, and not smoking seem to be the keys to avoiding cardiovascular disorders. Exercise increases your respiratory system's efficiency. It helps control your weight, reduces body fat, and reduces stress. It also strengthens your muscles, including your heart. A diet low in saturated fat can reduce your risk of developing heart disease.

37–1 Section Assessment

1. **Key Concept** List the structures of the circulatory system.
2. **Key Concept** Compare the functions of the three types of blood vessels in the circulatory system.
3. Describe the path of blood circulation through the body.
4. How is heartbeat controlled?

5. **Critical Thinking Relating Concepts** Explain how regular exercise can promote good circulation.

iTEXT Assessment Use iText to review the important concepts in Section 37–1.

Take It to the NET

Exercise and weight control are important factors in heart disease prevention. Research current recommendations for diet and exercise and develop a brochure stressing healthy behaviors. Use the links provided in the Biology area at the Prentice Hall Web site for help in completing this activity:
www.phschool.com

37–2 Blood and the Lymphatic System

Just as a plumbing system carries water through a series of pipes to different parts of a house, the circulatory system carries blood through a series of blood vessels to different parts of the body. Blood is a type of connective tissue containing both dissolved substances and specialized cells. Blood collects oxygen from the lungs, nutrients from the digestive tract, and waste products from tissues. Blood helps to regulate factors in the body's internal environment, such as body temperature. In addition, components in blood help to fight infections. Blood can even form clots to repair damaged blood vessels.

Blood Plasma

The human body contains 4 to 6 liters of blood, which is about 8 percent of the total mass of the body. As **Figure 37–7** shows, about 45 percent of the volume of blood consists of cells, which are suspended in the other 55 percent—a straw-colored fluid called **plasma.** Plasma is about 90 percent water and 10 percent dissolved gases, salts, nutrients, enzymes, hormones, waste products, and proteins called plasma proteins.

Plasma proteins, which perform a variety of functions, are divided into three groups: albumins, globulins, and fibrinogen. Albumins and globulins transport substances such as fatty acids, hormones, and vitamins. Albumins also help to regulate osmotic pressure and blood volume. Some globulins fight viral and bacterial infections. Fibrinogen is the protein responsible for the ability of blood to clot.

Guide for Reading

 Key Concepts
- What is the function of each type of blood cell?
- What is the role of the lymphatic system?

Vocabulary
plasma
hemoglobin
phagocyte
platelet
lymph

Reading Strategy:
Asking Questions Before you read, rewrite the headings in the sections as *how, why,* or *what* questions about blood and the lymphatic system. As you read, write brief answers to the heading questions.

▼ **Figure 37–7** Blood consists of plasma, blood cells, nutrients, hormones, waste products, and plasma proteins. **Interpreting Graphics** *What happens when a whole blood sample is placed in a centrifuge?*

Whole Blood Sample   Sample Placed in Centrifuge

Plasma

Platelets
White blood cells

Red blood cells

Blood Sample That Has Been Centrifuged

(magnification: 6000×)

▲ **Figure 37–8** 🔑 Red blood cells transport oxygen. White blood cells fight invasions of foreign substances, cells, and organisms. Red blood cells and a single white blood cell are shown in this scanning electron micrograph.

▼ **Figure 37–9** This table shows five types of white blood cells and their functions. **Interpreting Graphics** *Which white blood cells produce antibodies?*

Blood Cells

The cellular portion of blood consists of red blood cells, white blood cells, and platelets. Red blood cells transport oxygen, white blood cells perform a variety of protective functions, and platelets help in the clotting process.

Red Blood Cells The most numerous cells in the blood are the red blood cells, or erythrocytes (eh-RITH-roh-syts). One milliliter of blood contains about 5 million red blood cells.

🔑 **Red blood cells transport oxygen.** They get their color from hemoglobin. **Hemoglobin** is the iron-containing protein that binds to oxygen in the lungs and transports it to tissues throughout the body where the oxygen is released.

Red blood cells, like those shown in **Figure 37–8**, are shaped like disks that are thinner in the center than along the edges. These cells are produced from cells in red bone marrow. As these cells gradually become filled with hemoglobin, their nuclei and other organelles are forced out. Thus, mature red blood cells do not have nuclei. Red blood cells circulate for an average of 120 days before they are worn out from squeezing through narrow capillaries. They are destroyed in the liver and spleen.

White Blood Cells White blood cells, or leukocytes (LOO-koh-syts), are much less abundant than red blood cells, which outnumber them about 700 to 1. White blood cells also are produced in red bone marrow, but they are released into blood with nuclei and do not contain hemoglobin. Some white blood cells live for months, but most live for just a few days.

White blood cells are the "army" of the circulatory system. 🔑 **White blood cells attack foreign substances or organisms.** These include cancer cells, substances that cause allergic reactions, and transplanted organs. White blood cells called **phagocytes,** or "eating cells," engulf and digest foreign cells. Other white blood cells can slip across capillary walls and attack invading organisms in body tissues. Still others release chemicals that help the body fight disease and resist infection. **Figure 37–9** lists different types of white blood cells.

White Blood Cells	
Cell Type	**Function**
Neutrophils	Engulf and destroy small bacteria and foreign substances
Eosinophils	Attack parasites; limit inflammation associated with allergic reactions
Basophils	Release histamines that cause inflammation; release anticoagulants, which prevent blood clots
Monocytes	Give rise to leukocytes that engulf and destroy large bacteria and substances
Lymphocytes	Some destroy foreign cells by causing their membranes to rupture; some develop into cells that produce antibodies, which target specific foreign substances

Like an army with units in reserve, the body is able to increase the number of white blood cells dramatically when a "battle" is underway. A sudden increase in the number of white cells is one of the ways by which physicians can tell that the body is fighting a serious infection.

Platelets and Blood Clotting Blood is essential to life. An injury can cause the body to lose this essential fluid. Fortunately, blood has an internal mechanism to slow bleeding and begin healing. A minor cut or scrape may bleed for a few seconds or minutes, but then it stops. Clean it up with soap and water, cover it with a bandage, and it begins to heal. Have you ever wondered why the bleeding stops?

The answer is that blood has the ability to form a clot. **Figure 37–10** summarizes the process. 🔑 **Blood clotting is made possible by plasma proteins and cell fragments called platelets.** There are certain large cells in bone marrow that can break into thousands of small pieces. Each fragment of cytoplasm is enclosed in a piece of cell membrane and released into the bloodstream as a **platelet**.

When platelets come into contact with the edges of a broken blood vessel, their surfaces become very sticky, and a cluster of platelets develops around the wound. These platelets then release proteins called clotting factors. The clotting factors start a series of chemical reactions that are quite complicated. In one reaction, a clotting factor called thromboplastin (thrahm-boh-PLAS-tin) converts prothrombin, which is found in blood plasma, into thrombin. Thrombin is an enzyme that helps convert the soluble plasma protein fibrinogen into a sticky mesh of fibrin filaments. These filaments stop the bleeding by producing a clot. **Figure 37–11** shows the tangle of microscopic fibers in an actual blood clot.

✓ **CHECKPOINT** *What are platelets?*

Break in Capillary Wall
Blood vessels injured.

Clumping of Platelets

Platelets clump at the site and release thromboplastin. Thromboplastin converts prothrombin into thrombin.

Clot Forms

Thrombin converts fibrinogen into fibrin, which causes a clot. The clot prevents further loss of blood.

▲ **Figure 37–10** 🔑 Blood clotting is made possible by a number of plasma proteins and cell fragments called platelets. Calcium and vitamin K aid in converting prothrombin into thrombin.

(magnification: 3000×)

▶ **Figure 37–11** Strands of fibrin trap blood cells, forming a net that prevents blood from leaving a damaged blood vessel. **Using Analogies** *How is a blood clot similar to a screened-in porch?*

Predicting the Success of Blood Transfusions

The first successful transfusions of human blood were performed by the British physician James Blundell between 1825 and 1830. Blundell's records indicated that at least half of his patients benefited from the transfusions, but many others had severe reactions to the transfused blood, and several of these patients died. In 1900, Karl Landsteiner, an Austrian physician, discovered why some of Blundell's patients had such severe reactions and why others died.

Landsteiner discovered the ABO blood group, which has four blood types: A, B, AB, and O. When the blood type of a donor and recipient matched, the transfusion was almost always successful. Sometimes, transfusions were successful even when the blood types of donor and recipient did not match. Use the table showing successful and unsuccessful blood transfusions to answer the following questions.

Blood Transfusions

Blood Type of Donor	Blood Type of Recipient			
	A	B	AB	O
A	✓	X	✓	X
B	X	✓	✓	X
AB	X	X	✓	X
O	✓	✓	✓	✓

X = Unsuccessful transfusion   ✓ = Successful transfusion

1. **Drawing Conclusions** One blood type is sometimes referred to as the "universal donor." Which blood type is it and why? Another blood type is known as the "universal recipient." Which blood type is it and why?

2. **Drawing Conclusions** In a transfusion involving the A and O blood types, does it make a difference which blood type belongs to the recipient and which to the donor?

3. **Formulating Hypotheses** Propose a hypothesis about the effect of differences in blood type on the success of transfusions.

If the wound is small, within a few minutes the mesh of platelets and fibrin seals the wound, and bleeding stops. Most of the time, this clotting reaction works so well that we take it for granted. However, if one of the clotting factors is missing or defective, the clotting process does not work well. Hemophilia is a genetic disorder that results from a defective protein in the clotting pathway. People with hemophilia cannot produce blood clots that are firm enough to stop even minor bleeding. They must take great care to avoid injury. Fortunately, hemophilia can be treated by injecting extracts containing the missing clotting factor.

The Lymphatic System

As blood circulates, some fluid leaks from the blood into the surrounding tissues. This isn't an altogether bad thing. A steady flow of fluid helps to maintain an efficient movement of nutrients and salts from the blood into the tissues. However, more than 3 liters of fluid leak from the circulatory system into surrounding tissues every day! If this leakage continued unchecked, the body would begin to swell with fluid—not a very pleasant prospect.

Fortunately, this does not happen. **A network of vessels called the lymphatic system (lim-FAT-ik) collects the fluid that is lost by the blood and returns it to the circulatory system.** The fluid is known as **lymph** (LIMF).

It collects in lymphatic capillaries and slowly flows into larger and larger lymph vessels. Like large veins, lymph vessels contain valves that prevent lymph from flowing backward. Ducts collect the lymph and return it to the circulatory system through two openings in the superior vena cava. The openings are under the left and right clavicle bones just below the shoulders. **Figure 37–12** shows the lymphatic system.

Along the length of the lymph vessels are small bean-shaped enlargements called lymph nodes. Lymph nodes act as filters, trapping bacteria and other microorganisms that cause disease. When large numbers of microorganisms are trapped in the lymph nodes, the nodes become enlarged. If you have ever had "swollen glands," you actually had swollen lymph nodes. The lymph nodes also house specialized white blood cells called lymphocytes, which protect the body from infection.

Lymph vessels do not merely return excess fluid to the circulation. They also play a very important role in nutrient absorption. Lymph vessels lie near the cells that line the intestines, where they absorb fats and fat-soluble vitamins (A, D, E, and K) from the digestive tract and carry them to the blood. Lymph moves through the lymphatic system under osmotic pressure from the blood and is pushed along by the contractions of nearby skeletal muscles. It is important that there is a steady flow of lymph. Edema, a swelling of the tissues due to the accumulation of excess fluid, can occur when lymphatic vessels are blocked due to injury or disease.

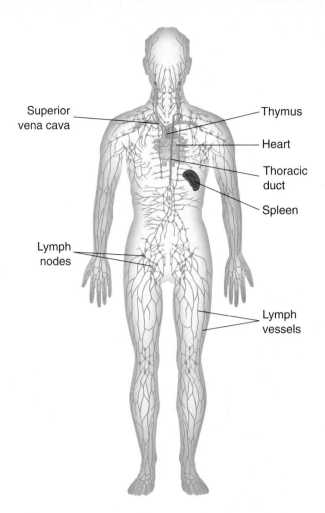

▲ **Figure 37–12** 🔑 **The lymphatic system collects and returns fluid that leaks from blood vessels.** The spleen is a mass of lymphatic tissue whose main function is to destroy damaged red blood cells and platelets. Certain white blood cells called T cells mature in the thymus gland, which produces hormones that promote their development.

37–2 Section Assessment

1. 🔑 **Key Concept** List the main function of red blood cells, white blood cells, and platelets.

2. 🔑 **Key Concept** Describe the role of the lymphatic system.

3. What types of materials are dissolved in plasma?

4. Explain how blood clots.

5. **Critical Thinking Relating Cause and Effect** Infections sometimes cause severe swelling in the tissues. Explain why this happens.

🧍 **TEXT** Assessment Use iText to review the important concepts in Section 37–2.

ALTERNATIVE ASSESSMENT

Constructing a Concept Map
Construct a concept map that shows the components of blood. Be sure to include the different types of white blood cells.

37–3 The Respiratory System

Guide for Reading

 Key Concepts
- What are the structures of the respiratory system?
- How does smoking affect the respiratory system?

Vocabulary
- pharynx • trachea
- larynx • bronchus
- alveolus • diaphragm
- nicotine • emphysema

**Reading Strategy:
Monitoring Your
Understanding** Make
a table with three columns
labeled *K, W,* and *L.* Before
you read, write what you know
about respiration in Column K
and what you want to learn in
Column W. After you read,
write what you have learned
in Column L.

When paramedics rush to the aid of an injured person, they check to see if the person is breathing. If the person's chest is not rising and falling and they cannot feel or hear air being exhaled from the mouth or nose, the person is not breathing. Paramedics will ignore broken bones or burns to focus on breathing because there is no time to lose! If breathing stops for more than a few minutes, a life may be lost.

Paramedics can do mouth-to-mouth rescue breathing to force air into the lungs. They can do chest compressions to keep the blood circulating. Cardiopulmonary resuscitation, or CPR, is rescue breathing combined with chest compressions.

What Is Respiration?

In biology, the word *respiration* is used in two slightly different ways. At the cellular level, respiration is defined as the release of energy from the breakdown of molecules in food in the presence of oxygen. Without oxygen, cells lose much of their ability to produce ATP. Without ATP, cells cannot synthesize new molecules, pump ions, and carry nerve impulses.

The blood carries oxygen and carbon dioxide—a waste product of cellular respiration—between the lungs and the trillions of cells throughout the body. The process by which oxygen and carbon dioxide are exchanged between cells, the blood, and air in the lungs is also known as respiration.

The Human Respiratory System

The basic job performed by the human respiratory system is remarkably simple—to bring about the exchange of oxygen and carbon dioxide. With each breath, air enters the body through the air passageways and fills the lungs, where gas exchange takes place. **The respiratory system consists of the nose, pharynx, larynx, trachea, bronchi, and lungs.**

Figure 37–14 shows the structures of the respiratory system. Air moves through the nose to a tube at the back of the mouth called the pharynx, or throat. The **pharynx** serves as a passageway for both air and food. Air moves from the pharynx into the **trachea**, or windpipe. A piece of cartilage called the epiglottis covers the entrance to the trachea when you swallow.

(magnification: 5600×)

◀ **Figure 37–13** In this cross section of the trachea, the cilia have been colored green. **Inferring** *What is the role of cilia in the respiratory system?*

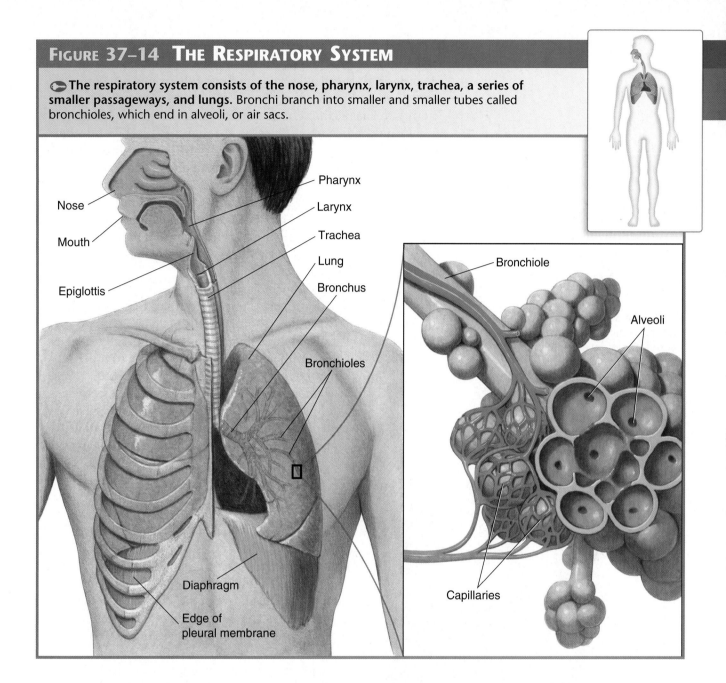

FIGURE 37–14 THE RESPIRATORY SYSTEM

The respiratory system consists of the nose, pharynx, larynx, trachea, a series of smaller passageways, and lungs. Bronchi branch into smaller and smaller tubes called bronchioles, which end in alveoli, or air sacs.

Nose

Mouth

Epiglottis

Pharynx

Larynx

Trachea

Lung

Bronchus

Bronchioles

Diaphragm

Edge of pleural membrane

Bronchiole

Alveoli

Capillaries

The respiratory passageways allow air to pass directly into some of the most delicate tissues in the body. To keep the lung tissue healthy, air entering the respiratory system must be warmed, moistened, and filtered. Large dust particles get trapped by the hairs lining the entrance to the nasal cavity. Some of the cells that line the respiratory system produce a thin layer of mucus. The mucus moistens the air and traps inhaled particles of dust or smoke. Cilia sweep the trapped particles and mucus away from the lungs toward the pharynx. The mucus and trapped particles are either swallowed or spit out. These protective measures help keep the lungs clean and open for the important work of gas exchange.

✓**CHECKPOINT** *What is the pharynx?*

At the top of the trachea is the larynx. The **larynx** contains two highly elastic folds of tissue known as the vocal cords. When muscles pull the vocal cords together, the air moving between them causes the cords to vibrate and produce sounds. Your ability to speak, shout, and sing comes from these tissues.

From the larynx, air passes through the trachea into two large passageways in the chest cavity called **bronchi** (singular: bronchus). Each bronchus leads to one of the lungs. Within each lung, the large bronchi subdivides into smaller bronchi, which lead to even smaller passageways called bronchioles. Air moving along this path can be compared to a motorist who takes an exit off an eight-lane highway onto a four-lane highway, makes a turn onto a two-lane road, and ends up on a narrow country lane.

The bronchi and bronchioles are surrounded by smooth muscle that helps to support them and enables the autonomic nervous system to regulate the size of the air passageways. The bronchioles continue to subdivide until they reach a series of dead ends—millions of tiny air sacs called **alveoli** (al-VEE-uh-ly; singular: alveolus). Alveoli are grouped in little clusters, like bunches of grapes. A delicate network of thin-walled capillaries surrounds each alveolus. The real work of the respiratory system takes place here, where blood and air are side by side.

Gas Exchange

There are about 350 million alveoli in a healthy lung, providing an enormous surface area for gas exchange. Oxygen dissolves in the moisture on the inner surface of the alveoli and then diffuses across the thin-walled capillaries into the blood. Carbon dioxide in the bloodstream diffuses in the opposite direction, across the membrane of an alveolus and into the air within it. This process is illustrated in **Figure 37-15.**

The process of gas exchange in the lungs is very efficient. The air that you inhale usually contains 21 percent oxygen and 0.04 percent carbon dioxide. Exhaled air usually contains less than 15 percent oxygen and 4 percent carbon dioxide. The lungs remove about one third of the oxygen in the air that you inhale and increase the carbon dioxide content of that air by a factor of 100.

Because oxygen dissolves easily, you may wonder why hemoglobin, the oxygen-carrying protein in blood, is needed at all. The reason is efficiency. Hemoglobin binds with so much oxygen that it increases the oxygen-carrying capacity of the blood more than 60 times. Without hemoglobin to carry the oxygen that it uses, your body might need as much as 300 liters of blood to get the same result!

▼ **Figure 37-15** Gas exchange occurs by diffusion across the membrane of an alveolus and a capillary. **Drawing Conclusions** *Where is oxygen more concentrated, in an alveolus or in a capillary?*

Alveoli

Bronchiole

O_2

CO_2

Capillary

Careers in Biology

Respiratory Care Practitioner

Job Description: provide care for patients with respiratory problems in hospitals, clinics, nursing homes, schools, and at home

Education: a two-year or four-year training program; certification exams; individual states have additional licensing requirements

Skills: good communication skills; enjoy working with people; capable of working independently; good decision-making skills; knowledge of anatomy, physiology, microbiology

Highlights: You provide quick responses in emergency situations. You work as a member of a team.

Aaron Koseki left his career as an Asian philosophy professor to start all over as a Respiratory Care Practitioner (RCP). "My oldest son received the help of Respiratory Care Practitioners at birth . . . . The work fascinated me so much that I just had to find out more about breathing . . . in a more scientific sense. That's why I became an RCP."

Take It to the NET

For more career information, visit the Prentice Hall Web site at **www.phschool.com**.

Breathing

Breathing is the movement of air into and out of the lungs. Surprisingly, there are no muscles connected to the lungs. The force that drives air into the lungs comes from ordinary air pressure. How does the body use this force to inflate the lungs? The lungs are sealed in two sacs, called the pleural membranes, inside the chest cavity. At the bottom of the cavity is a large, flat muscle known as the **diaphragm** (DY-uh-fram).

As **Figure 37–16** shows, when you breathe in, or inhale, the diaphragm contracts and expands the volume of the chest cavity. Because the chest cavity is tightly sealed, this creates a partial vacuum inside the cavity. Atmospheric pressure does the rest, filling the lungs as air rushes into the breathing passages.

The system works only because the chest cavity is sealed. A puncture wound to the chest—even if it does not touch the lungs—may allow air to leak into the chest cavity and make breathing impossible. This is one of the reasons chest wounds are always serious.

CHECKPOINT *Why are chest wounds so serious?*

Inhalation

Exhalation

▶ **Figure 37–16** During inhalation, the diaphragm contracts, increasing the size of the chest cavity. This causes the pressure inside the lungs to decrease, and air enters. **Interpreting Graphics** *What happens as the diaphragm relaxes?*

Most of the time, exhaling is a passive event. When the diaphragm muscle relaxes, the pressure in the chest cavity becomes greater than atmospheric pressure. Air rushes back out of the lungs. To blow out a candle, you need a greater force. Muscles surrounding the chest cavity provide that extra force, contracting vigorously just as the diaphragm relaxes.

How Breathing Is Controlled

You can control your breathing almost anytime you want, whether it's to blow up a balloon or to play a musical instrument. But this doesn't mean that breathing is purely voluntary. If you hold your breath for a minute or so, you'll see what happens. Your chest begins to feel tight, your throat begins to burn, and the muscles in your mouth and throat struggle to keep from breathing. Eventually your body takes over. It "forces" you to breathe!

Breathing is such an important function that your nervous system will not let you have complete control over it. The brain controls breathing in a center located in the medulla oblongata. Autonomic nerves from the medulla oblongata to the diaphragm and chest muscles produce the cycles of contraction that bring air into the lungs. How does the medulla oblongata "know" when it's time to breathe? Cells in its breathing center monitor the amount of carbon dioxide in the blood. As the carbon dioxide level rises, nerve impulses from the breathing center cause the diaphragm to contract, bringing air into the lungs. The higher the carbon dioxide level, the stronger the impulses. If the carbon dioxide level reaches a critical point, the impulses become so powerful that you cannot keep from breathing.

Quick Lab

Does oxygen or carbon dioxide regulate breathing?

Materials seltzer tablet, plastic cup

Procedure
1. **Formulating Hypotheses** Which do you think is more important in regulating breathing, the level of oxygen in the air or the level of carbon dioxide? Write a hypothesis about how your breathing will be affected if the level of carbon dioxide increases.
2. Place approximately 100 mL of water in the cup and add a seltzer tablet. The bubbles in the water are carbon dioxide. Bring the cup up to your face and inhale deeply.

Analyze and Conclude
1. **Drawing Conclusions** Describe what happened when you inhaled the carbon dioxide.
2. **Drawing Conclusions** Air is about 21 percent oxygen and about 0.04 percent carbon dioxide. Did your oxygen intake or your carbon dioxide intake change more during step 2?
3. **Drawing Conclusions** Did your results support your hypothesis or not? Explain your answer.

▲ **Figure 37–17** This pilot must use an oxygen mask because there is not enough oxygen available in the air at high altitudes. **Applying Concepts** *How would a mountain climber decide when to carry a supply of oxygen?*

That the breathing center responds primarily to carbon dioxide can have dangerous consequences. Consider a plane flying at high altitude. Although the amount of oxygen in the air decreases as the altitude increases, the passengers do not need oxygen masks because the cabin is pressurized. Oxygen is available for use in an emergency, but the passengers often have to be told to begin breathing the oxygen. Although their bodies may be starving for oxygen, they have no more carbon dioxide in their blood than usual, so the breathing center does not sense a problem. The pilot in **Figure 37–17** is not in a pressurized cabin and must use an oxygen mask at high altitudes.

✓ CHECKPOINT *What does the breathing center do?*

Tobacco and the Respiratory System

The upper part of the respiratory system is generally able to filter out dust and foreign particles that could damage the lungs. Millions of people engage in an activity—smoking tobacco—that damages and eventually destroys this protective system.

Substances in Tobacco Tobacco smoke contains many substances that affect the body. Three of the most dangerous substances are nicotine, carbon monoxide, and tar. **Nicotine** is a stimulant drug that increases the heart rate and blood pressure. Carbon monoxide is a poisonous gas that blocks the transport of oxygen by hemoglobin in the blood. It decreases the blood's ability to supply oxygen to its tissues, depriving the heart and other organs of the oxygen they need to function. Tar contains a number of compounds that have been shown to cause cancer.

Circulatory and Respiratory Systems **961**

Smoking tobacco brings nicotine and carbon monoxide into the upper respiratory system. These compounds paralyze the cilia. With the cilia out of action, the inhaled particles stick to the walls of the respiratory tract or enter the lungs.

Without cilia to sweep it along, smoke-laden mucus becomes trapped along the airways. This explains why smokers often cough. Irritation from the accumulated mucus triggers a cough that helps to clear the airways. Smoking also causes the lining of the respiratory tract to swell, which reduces the air flow to the alveoli.

Diseases Caused by Smoking Only 30 percent of male smokers live to age 80, but 55 percent of male nonsmokers live to that age. Clearly, smoking reduces life expectancy.
Smoking can cause such respiratory diseases as chronic bronchitis, emphysema, and lung cancer. In chronic bronchitis, the bronchi become swollen and clogged with mucus. Even smoking a moderate number of cigarettes on a regular basis can produce bronchitis. People with this disease often find simple activities, such as climbing stairs, difficult.

Long-term smoking can also cause a respiratory disease called emphysema (em-fuh-SEE-muh). **Emphysema** is the loss of elasticity in the tissues of the lungs. This condition makes breathing very difficult. People who have emphysema cannot get enough oxygen to the body tissues or rid the body of excess carbon dioxide.

Smoking is an important, but preventable, cause of lung cancer. **Figure 37–18** shows the effects of smoking on the lungs. Lung cancer is particularly deadly because its cells can spread to other locations. By the time lung cancer is detected, it usually has spread to dozens of other places. About 160,000 people in the United States are diagnosed with lung cancer each year. Few will survive for five years after the diagnosis.

▶ **Figure 37–18** Smoking can cause respiratory diseases such as chronic bronchitis, emphysema, and lung cancer. The lung on the left is from a smoker. The lung on the right is from a nonsmoker.

Smoking is also a major cause of heart disease. Smoking constricts, or narrows, the blood vessels. This causes blood pressure to rise and makes the heart work harder. The effects of smoking on the circulatory system can be seen in **Figure 37–19.** There is a drastic change in body temperature and in circulation immediately after smoking a cigarette. Smoking doubles the risk of death from heart disease for men between 45 and 65. Moreover, for men and women of all ages, the risk of death from heart disease is greater among smokers than among nonsmokers.

Smoking and the Nonsmoker In recent years, evidence has shown that tobacco smoke is damaging to anyone who inhales it, not just the smoker. For this reason, many states have restricted smoking in restaurants and other public places.

Passive smoking, or inhaling the smoke of others, is particularly damaging to young children because their lungs are still developing. Studies now indicate that the children of smokers are twice as likely as children of nonsmokers to develop respiratory problems, such as asthma.

Dealing With Tobacco Whatever the age of a smoker, and no matter how long that person has smoked, his or her health can be improved by quitting. Nicotine is a powerful drug with strong addictive qualities that make it very difficult to quit smoking. Thus, considering the cost, the medical dangers, and the powerful addiction, the best solution is not to begin smoking.

▲ **Figure 37–19** These thermograms provide a color-coded map of temperature distribution over the body surface, with blue = cold and white = hot. The top thermogram shows the forearm and hand area prior to smoking a cigarette. The bottom thermogram shows the same area after smoking. **Interpreting Graphics** *Do you think circulation is increased or decreased after smoking?*

37–3 Section Assessment

1. 🔑 **Key Concept** List in order the structures of the respiratory system through which air passes from the outside to the alveoli.

2. 🔑 **Key Concept** Describe some of the health problems caused by smoking tobacco.

3. Explain the process of gas exchange in the lungs.

4. Describe how breathing is controlled.

5. **Critical Thinking Inferring** As you have read, the breathing center in the brain responds to the level of carbon dioxide in the blood—not the level of oxygen. What consequences does this have for people at high altitudes?

TEXT Assessment Use iText to review the important concepts in Section 37–3.

MAKING CONNECTIONS

Comparative Anatomy Compare what you learned in Units 8 and 9 about respiration in terrestrial arthropods, fish, and flatworms with human respiration. What do these methods have in common? How do they differ?

Modeling Breathing

As you breathe, your body moves air into and out of your lungs. All body movements depend on muscles, which work only by contracting. How does your body use muscles to cause air to flow into and out of your lungs? In this investigation, you will make a working model of human lungs that will help you answer this question.

Problem How do muscle contractions move air into and out of the lungs?

Materials
• small, clear plastic bottle
• large round balloon
• small round balloon
• one-hole rubber stopper
• scissors

Skills Using Models

Design Your Experiment

Part A: A Model of Normal Lungs

1. Place a clear plastic bottle on its side. Press one point of a pair of scissors through the side of the bottle about 1 cm from the bottom.

2. Using the scissors, cut off the bottom of the bottle by cutting all the way around. Trim off any rough spots from the edge.

3. Stretch a small balloon, and blow it up several times to make it pliable.

4. Pull the opening of the small balloon over the bottom of a one-hole rubber stopper.

5. Insert the balloon through the mouth of the bottle. Press the stopper tightly into the bottle so that it holds the lip of the balloon in place.

6. Stretch a large balloon, and blow it up several times to make it pliable.

7. Using the scissors, cut off about 1 cm from the rounded, closed end of the large balloon. Tie the other end closed.

8. Stretch the large balloon far enough over the cut end of the bottle to keep the balloon from slipping off, as shown.

9. As you watch the small balloon, pull down on the knot of the large balloon. Then, still watching the small balloon, press up on the large balloon.

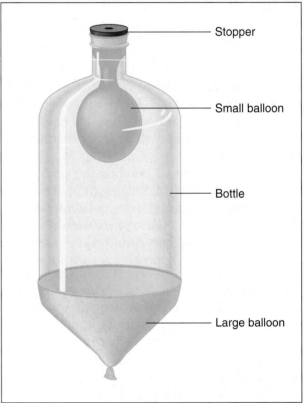

Stopper

Small balloon

Bottle

Large balloon

Part B: A Model of a Chest Injury

10. **Formulating Hypotheses** If a person receives an injury that punctures the skin and muscles of the chest, outside air can come into direct contact with the outer surfaces of the lungs. How would such an event affect a person's ability to breathe? Record your hypothesis.

11. Think of a way you could modify your model of human lungs to represent the lungs in a person with a punctured chest. Write a description of your plan, including your prediction of how the model will behave and how the model will test your hypothesis.

12. Show your plan to your teacher. If your teacher approves, make a model of a punctured chest. Use your model to test your hypothesis.

Analyze and Conclude

1. **Observing** What happened to the small balloon in your first model when you pulled down on the large balloon?

2. **Observing** What happened to the small balloon when you pressed up on the large balloon?

3. **Inferring** What happened to the pressure inside the bottle when you moved the large balloon up and down?

4. **Formulating Hypotheses** What caused the small balloon to expand and contract?

5. **Using Models** How is the first model you constructed similar to the human respiratory system? How is it different from the human respiratory system?

6. **Evaluating** Was your prediction in Part B correct? Did the behavior of your second model support your hypothesis? Explain your answer.

7. **Drawing Conclusions** How do muscles cause air to flow into and out of human lungs?

8. **Drawing Conclusions** What did your second model demonstrate about the importance of the chest wall in breathing? Give reasons for your answer.

Go Further

Making Models Obtain information from a hospital, doctor's office, or county health department about the mechanics of breathing and diseases such as asthma and emphysema that make breathing difficult. Find out what causes these diseases, how they affect breathing, and how they are prevented and treated. Then, make a new model that demonstrates the effects of one of these diseases.

Chapter 37 Study Guide

37-1 The Circulatory System
🔑 Key Concepts

- The human circulatory system consists of the heart, a series of blood vessels, and the blood that flows through them.
- As the blood flows through the circulatory system, it moves through three types of blood vessels—arteries, capillaries, and veins.

Vocabulary
myocardium, p. 944
atrium, p. 944
ventricle, p. 944
pulmonary circulation, p. 944
systemic circulation, p. 944
valve, p. 945
pacemaker, p. 946
aorta, p. 946
artery, p. 946
capillary, p. 947
vein, p. 947
atherosclerosis, p. 949

37-2 Blood and the Lymphatic System
🔑 Key Concepts

- Red blood cells transport oxygen.
- White blood cells attack foreign substances or organisms.
- Blood clotting is made possible by plasma proteins and cell fragments called platelets.
- A network of vessels called the lymphatic system collects the fluid that is lost by the blood and returns it to the circulatory system.

Vocabulary
plasma, p. 951
hemoglobin, p. 952
phagocyte, p. 952
platelet, p. 953
lymph, p. 954

37-3 The Respiratory System
🔑 Key Concepts

- The respiratory system consists of the nose, pharynx, larynx, trachea, bronchi, and lungs.
- Smoking can cause such respiratory diseases as chronic bronchitis, emphysema, and lung cancer.

Vocabulary
pharynx, p. 956
trachea, p. 956
larynx, p. 958
bronchus, p. 958
alveolus, p. 958
diaphragm, p. 959
nicotine, p. 961
emphysema, p. 962

Thinking Visually
On a separate sheet of paper, complete the following flowchart tracing the flow of air through the respiratory system.

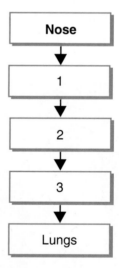

Nose
↓
1
↓
2
↓
3
↓
Lungs

Chapter 37

Part A

Multiple Choice

For each statement or question, select the number of the word or expression that, of those given, best completes the statement or answers the question.

1 Which group of structures best describes the circulatory system?
(1) arteries, veins, capillaries
(2) lungs, air passages, alveoli
(3) lungs, blood vessels, heart
(4) heart, blood, blood vessels

2 Blood leaving the heart for the body passes through a large blood vessel known as the
(1) aorta
(2) vena cava
(3) pulmonary vein
(4) pulmonary artery

3 Which cells are able to protect the body by engulfing foreign cells or producing antibodies?
(1) red blood cells
(2) plasma cells
(3) platelets
(4) white blood cells

4 Exchange of nutrients and wastes with the body cells takes place by diffusion through the walls of
(1) veins   (3) arteries
(2) capillaries   (4) atria

5 The process shown below is made possible by a number of plasma proteins and cell fragments called
(1) fibrinogens   (3) platelets
(2) basophils   (4) lymphocytes

6 Which substance is the iron-containing protein found in red blood cells?
(1) hemoglobin
(2) fibrinogen
(3) prothrombin
(4) thrombin

7 To aid the process of breathing, the diaphragm
(1) increases blood flow from the heart to the lungs
(2) moves up and down to alter the volume of the chest cavity
(3) inflates and deflates to force air in and out of the lungs
(4) moves the rib cage in and out as air is inhaled

8 Which group consists entirely of materials found in human blood?
(1) plasma, alveoli, proteins
(2) platelets, mucus, red blood cells
(3) phagocytes, platelets, proteins
(4) hemoglobin, capillaries, white blood cells

9 Nicotine affects the body by
(1) paralyzing cilia
(2) decreasing blood pressure
(3) blocking transport of oxygen by hemoglobin
(4) decreasing heart rate

10 The upper chambers of the heart are the
(1) ventricles   (3) myocardia
(2) vena cava   (4) atria

For questions 11 and 12, complete each analogy by selecting the correct number. In analogies, A : B :: C : means "A is to B as C is to ___?___ ."

11 Platelets : clotting :: red blood cells :
(1) inhalation
(2) exhalation
(3) oxygen transport
(4) cellular respiration

12 Tree branch : bronchus :: leaf :
(1) pharynx   (3) diaphragm
(2) alveolus   (4) trachea

Test-Taking Tip When you are asked questions about structures in a diagram, first identify each structure. Then, try to answer the questions.

Preparing for the Living Environment Exam

Parts B and C

Multiple Choice and Extended Response

For those questions that ask you to select a response, choose the one that best completes the statement or answers the question. For all others follow the directions given.

13 Explain how the circulatory system protects the human body against invading microorganisms.

14 Describe the process by which the human respiratory system provides oxygen to the body.

15 You have learned about the circulatory system and the respiratory system. Which statement best describes an interaction between these two systems that helps maintain homeostasis?
- **(1)** Blood plasma transports salts, sugars, fats, and dissolved proteins through the body to keep it healthy.
- **(2)** The diaphragm and rib cage work together to move air into and out of the lungs.
- **(3)** The lymphatic system contains nodes that act as filters to remove bacteria that could otherwise cause disease.
- **(4)** Blood cells pick up and carry oxygen from the lungs to the body's cells.

16 Name the three most dangerous substances in tobacco smoke, and state how each substance affects the body.

17 Explain the role of valves in the functioning of the circulatory system. In your explanation be sure to
- identify the function of a valve in relation to the flow of blood
- identify two places in the circulatory system where valves are found
- identify one specific valve by name and describe its specific function

18 Describe the sequence of events that regulates the rate of the heartbeat. In your description, be sure to
- explain why the rate of heartbeat needs to be regulated
- name the specific group of cells that begins the process
- describe the specific pathway along which the impulses travel

Base your answers to questions 19 through 22 on the diagram and on your knowledge of biology.

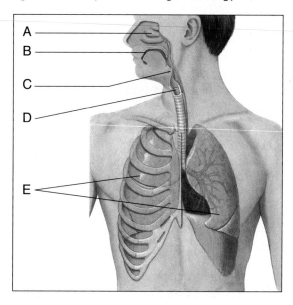

19 Which structure's primary function is to warm and moisten the air?
- **(1)** A
- **(2)** B
- **(3)** C
- **(4)** D

20 Which structure contains the vocal cords?
- **(1)** A
- **(2)** B
- **(3)** C
- **(4)** D

21 Which structure is altered by emphysema?
- **(1)** E
- **(2)** B
- **(3)** C
- **(4)** D

22 Which structure contains alveoli?
- **(1)** E
- **(2)** B
- **(3)** C
- **(4)** D

23 Explain how pulmonary circulation differs from systemic circulation.

24 Compare the wall thickness and diameter of the three different types of blood vessels.

25 Describe what happens in the body to result in "involuntary breathing" if you hold your breath for too long. In your answer, be sure to
- name the region of the brain responsible for this action
- identify the substance that the body actually monitors to determine when this action is needed

26 Make a copy of the chart below. Then, fill in the missing structures and functions. (Do not write in this book.)

Structure	Function
	Chamber where blood enters heart from the body
Right ventricle	
	Carry blood from the heart to the lungs
	Carry blood back to the heart from the lungs
Left atrium	
	Chamber that pumps blood to the body
Aorta	

27 Distinguish between systolic pressure and diastolic pressure.

Base your answers to questions 28 and 29 on the table below and on your knowledge of biology.

Blood Flow Through Human Organs

Organ	Percentage of Total Flow
Brain	14%
Heart	5%
Kidneys	22%
Liver	13%
Lungs	100%
Skeletal muscles	18%
Skeletal muscles during exercise	75%

28 Name the organ through which all the blood flows each time it passes through the body.

29 Explain the reason for the differences indicated in blood flow to skeletal muscles (normal vs. during exercise).

30 A student undertook an investigation involving three subjects. The results of the investigation are shown in the table.

Person Tested	Resting Pulse Rate (beats per minute)	Time After Exercise for Pulse to Return to Resting Level
Subject A	75	8 minutes
Subject B	84	6 minutes
Subject C	67	2 minutes

Based on the information provided, discuss the purpose and usefulness of the investigation. In your answer, be sure to
- state what question the investigator was most likely attempting to answer
- state two reasons why a valid conclusion cannot be reached, based on the data provided
- state one way the investigation should be modified so a valid conclusion about the interaction between the variables could be reached

31 Predict what might happen if a blood clot formed inside the circulatory system and lodged in a major blood vessel.

32 Explain why a person with a low red blood cell count is likely to experience fatigue.

33 Explain why even minor injuries can be serious for people with hemophilia.

34 State the four primary functions of the lymphatic system.

 Take It to the NET

Lung disease is the number three cause of death in the United States. Visit **www.phschool.com** to find out more about lung disease. Then, answer the following questions:
- List five different chronic lung diseases.
- How much does smoking cost Americans each year in terms of health care and loss of productivity?
- How many people die from smoking related illnesses each year in the United States?
- How does air quality affect lung health?

38 Digestive and Excretory Systems

The surface of your small intestine is covered with microvilli (magnification: 100×).

Inquiry Activity

What's in a chip?

Procedure

1. Place a regular potato chip on a brown paper towel and fold the towel over the chip. Repeat using a similarly sized, baked potato chip and another towel. **CAUTION:** *Do not eat the potato chips.*

2. Press down on the towels for 1 minute, then unfold them. Hold the towels up to the light. A bright spot indicates the presence of fat.

3. Observe as your teacher burns the potato chips.

Think About It

1. **Observing** Which type of potato chip contains more fat?

2. **Inferring** Which potato chip has more stored chemical energy?

3. **Drawing Conclusions** How are the results from burning the potato chips related to the fat and Calorie contents listed on the package labels?

38–1 Food and Nutrition

How important is food in your life? Before you answer, think of two uniquely American holidays: Independence Day and Thanksgiving Day. What comes to mind? No matter where you live, chances are that a meal is the centerpiece of that special day. To most of us, food is more than just nourishment—it is an important part of our culture. Human societies throughout the world organize meetings and family gatherings around food.

Food and Energy

Have you ever wondered why you need to eat food? The most obvious answer is to obtain energy—the ability to do work. You need energy to climb stairs, lift books, run, and even to think. Just as a car needs gasoline, your body needs fuel for all that work, and food is your fuel. Cells convert the chemical energy stored in the sugar glucose and other molecules into ATP.

The energy available in food can be measured in a surprisingly simple way—by burning the food! The amount of heat given off is measured and expressed in terms of calories. One calorie is the amount of heat needed to raise the temperature of one gram of water by one Celsius degree. Scientists refer to the energy stored in food as dietary Calories with a capital *C*. One **Calorie** is equal to 1000 calories, or 1 kilocalorie (kcal).

The energy needs of an average-sized teenager are about 2200 Calories per day for females and about 2800 Calories per day for males. If you engage in vigorous physical activity, however, your energy needs may be higher.

Chemical pathways in your body's cells can extract energy from almost any type of food. Why then does it matter which foods you eat? Although most of the food you eat is used as fuel, a certain amount of the food you eat has other important functions. Food supplies the raw materials used to build and repair body tissues. Some of these raw materials are used to manufacture new macromolecules. These include the proteins that regulate cellular reactions, the phospholipids in cell membranes, and DNA—your genetic material. Food also contains at least 45 substances that the body needs but cannot manufacture.

The science of nutrition—the study of food and its effects on the body—tries to determine how food helps the body meet all of its various needs. Based on their research, nutritionists recommend balanced diets that include many different types of food. They also plan diets for people with particular needs, such as diabetics.

Guide for Reading

 Key Concepts
- What are the nutrients your body needs?
- Why is water such an important nutrient?

Vocabulary
Calorie
carbohydrate
fat
protein
vitamin
mineral

**Reading Strategy:
Finding Main Ideas** Before you read, skim the section to identify the key ideas. Then, carefully read the section, making a list of supporting details for each main idea.

▼ **Figure 38–1** Holidays and other celebrations often center around food.

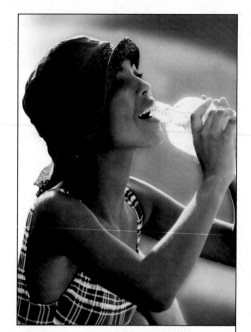

▲ **Figure 38–2** 🔑 Every cell in the body needs water because many of the body's processes take place in water. On hot days, or when you exercise, you need to drink more water to replace the water that is lost in sweat.

▲ **Figure 38–3** Breads, pastas, and cereals are foods rich in carbohydrates. Simple carbohydrates do not have to be digested or broken down. Complex carbohydrates must be broken down before they can be used by the body. **Inferring** *Which type of carbohydrate—simple or complex—provides the body with quick energy?*

Nutrients

Nutrients are substances in food that supply the energy and raw materials your body uses for growth, repair, and maintenance. 🔑 **The nutrients that the body needs are water, carbohydrates, fats, proteins, vitamins, and minerals.**

Water The most important of all nutrients is water. 🔑 **Every cell in the human body needs water because many of the body's processes, including chemical reactions, take place in water.** Water makes up the bulk of blood, lymph, and other bodily fluids. On hot days, or when you take part in strenuous exercise, sweat glands remove water from your tissues and release it as sweat on the surface of your body. As the water in sweat evaporates, it cools the body. Water vapor is also lost from the body with every breath you exhale and in urine.

Humans need to drink at least a liter of water a day. If enough water is not taken in to replace what is lost, dehydration can result. This condition leads to problems with the circulatory, respiratory, and nervous systems. Drinking plenty of clean water, as the woman is doing in **Figure 38–2,** is one of the best things you can do to help keep your body healthy.

✓**CHECKPOINT**) *What does sweat do?*

Carbohydrates Simple and complex **carbohydrates** are the main source of energy for the body. The sugars found in fruits, honey, and sugar cane are simple carbohydrates, or mono- and disaccharides. The starches found in grains, potatoes, and vegetables are complex carbohydrates, or polysaccharides. Starches are broken down by the digestive system into simple sugars. These molecules are absorbed into the bloodstream and carried to cells throughout the body. Sugars that are not immediately used to supply energy are converted into the complex carbohydrate glycogen, which is stored in the liver and skeletal muscles.

Many foods contain the complex carbohydrate cellulose, often called fiber. Although the human digestive system cannot break down cellulose, you need fiber in your diet. The bulk supplied by fiber helps muscles to keep food and wastes moving through your digestive and excretory systems. Foods like the breads, pasta, and cereals in **Figure 38–3** are rich in fiber. So are many fruits and vegetables.

Fats Fats, or lipids, are an important part of a healthy diet. **Fats** are formed from fatty acids and glycerol. Your body cannot manufacture all of the fatty acids it needs. These fatty acids, which are known as essential fatty acids, are found in vegetable oils. Deposits of fats protect body organs, insulate the body, and store energy. Fats are used to produce cell membranes, myelin sheaths, and certain hormones. They also help the body absorb fat-soluble vitamins.

Figure 38–4 Fats and proteins are two of the six nutrients the body needs. The foods on the left contain essential fatty acids. The foods below are good sources of proteins.

Based on the structure of their fatty acid chains, fats are classified as saturated or unsaturated. When there are only single bonds between the carbon atoms in the fatty acids, they have the maximum number of hydrogen atoms per carbon atom and the fat is said to be saturated. Most saturated fats are solids at room temperature—including butter and other animal fats.

Unsaturated fats have at least one double bond in a fatty acid chain. Unsaturated fats are usually liquids at room temperature. Because many vegetable oils contain more than one double bond, they are called polyunsaturated. **Figure 38–4** shows foods containing both saturated and unsaturated fats.

People often consume more fat than they actually need. The American Heart Association recommends a diet with a maximum of 30 percent of Calories from fat, of which only 10 percent should be from saturated fats. The health consequences of a diet high in fat are serious. They include an increased risk of high blood pressure, heart disease, obesity, and diabetes.

Proteins Proteins have a wide variety of roles. **Proteins** supply raw materials for growth and repair of structures such as skin and muscle. Proteins have regulatory and transport functions. For example, insulin controls the level of sugar in the blood. Hemoglobin transports oxygen. The enzymes that make biochemical reactions possible are proteins.

Proteins are polymers of amino acids. The body is able to produce only 12 of the 20 amino acids used to make proteins. The other 8, which are listed in **Figure 38–5,** are called essential amino acids because it is essential that they are included in the foods that you eat. Meat, fish, eggs, and milk generally contain all 8 essential amino acids. Plant foods do not. People who don't eat animal products must eat a combination of plant foods, such as beans and rice, to obtain all of the essential amino acids.

▼ **Figure 38–5** When plant foods are eaten in the right combination, they provide all of the essential amino acids. **Interpreting Graphics** *Which amino acids are found in both grains and legumes?*

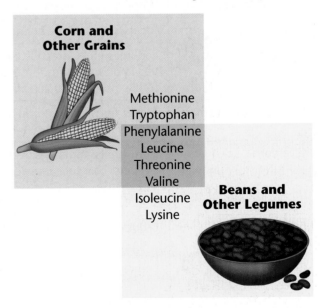

Corn and Other Grains

Methionine
Tryptophan
Phenylalanine
Leucine
Threonine
Valine
Isoleucine
Lysine

Beans and Other Legumes

Vitamins If you think of carbohydrates, fats, and proteins as the fuel and parts of an automobile engine, then vitamins are the ignition. **Vitamins** are organic molecules that help regulate body processes, often working with enzymes. Some are made by bacteria that live in the digestive tract. Most vitamins must be obtained from food. Vitamin deficiencies, or the absence of certain vitamins, can have serious, even fatal, consequences.

The 14 vitamins listed in **Figure 38–6** are generally recognized as essential to human health. There are two types of vitamins: fat-soluble and water-soluble. The fat-soluble vitamins—vitamins A, D, E, and K—can be stored in the fatty tissues of the body. The body can build up small stores of

▼ **Figure 38–6** This table lists the food sources and functions of 14 essential vitamins. The fat-soluble vitamins are listed in the blue rows, and the water-soluble vitamins in the white rows.
Interpreting Graphics *What is the function of vitamin K?*

Vitamins		
Vitamin	**Sources**	**Function**
A (retinol)	Yellow, orange, and dark green vegetables; dairy products	Important for growth of skin cells; important for night vision
D (calciferol)	Fish oils, eggs; made by skin when exposed to sunlight; added to dairy products	Promotes bone growth; increases calcium and phosphorus absorption
E (tocopherol)	Green leafy vegetables, seeds, vegetable oils	Antioxidant; prevents cellular damage
K	Green leafy vegetables; made by bacteria that live in human intestine	Needed for normal blood clotting
B_1 (thiamine)	Whole grains, pork, legumes, milk	Normal metabolism of carbohydrates
B_2 (riboflavin)	Dairy products, meats, vegetables, whole-grain cereal	Normal growth; part of electron transport chain; energy metabolism
Niacin	Liver, milk, whole grains, nuts, meats, legumes	Important in energy metabolism
B_6 (pyridoxine)	Whole grains, meats, vegetables	Important for amino acid metabolism
Pantothenic acid	Meats, dairy, whole grains	Needed for energy metabolism
Folic acid	Legumes, nuts, green leafy vegetables, oranges, broccoli, peas, fortified bread and cereal	Coenzyme involved in nucleic acid metabolism; prevents neural-tube defects in developing fetuses
B_{12} (cyanocobalamin)	Meats, eggs, dairy products, enriched cereals	Coenzyme in nucleic acid metabolism; maturation of red blood cells
C (ascorbic acid)	Citrus fruits, tomatoes, red or green peppers, broccoli, cabbage, strawberries	Maintenance of cartilage and bone; antioxidant; improves iron absorption; important for healthy gums, tissue repair, and wound healing
Biotin	Legumes, vegetables, meat	Coenzyme in synthesis of fat; glycogen formation; amino acid metabolism
Choline	Egg yolk, liver, grains, legumes	Required for phospholipids and neurotransmitters

Important Minerals		
Mineral	**Sources**	**Function**
Calcium	Dairy products; salmon; sardines; kale; tofu; collard greens; legumes	Bone and tooth formation; blood clotting; nerve and muscle function
Phosphorus	Dairy products; meats; poultry; grains	Bone and tooth formation; acid-base balance
Potassium	Meats; dairy products; many fruits and vegetables; grains	Acid-base balance; body water balance; nerve function
Chlorine	Table salt; processed foods	Acid-base balance; formation of gastric juice
Sodium	Table salt; processed foods	Acid-base balance; body water balance; nerve function
Magnesium	Whole grains; green leafy vegetables	Activation of enzymes in protein synthesis
Iron	Meats; eggs; legumes; whole grains; green leafy vegetables; dried fruit	Component of hemoglobin and of electron carriers used in energy metabolism
Fluorine	Fluoridated drinking water; tea; seafood	Maintenance of tooth structure; maintenance of bone structure
Iodine	Seafood; dairy products; iodized salt	Component of thyroid hormones
Zinc	Meats; seafood; grains	Component of certain digestive enzymes

▲ **Figure 38–7** Minerals are often called trace elements because they are needed by the body in such small amounts. **Inferring** *Why do you think some cities and towns add fluoride to their water supply?*

these vitamins for future use. The water-soluble vitamins, which include vitamin C and the B vitamins, dissolve in water and cannot be stored. Therefore, they should be included in the foods you eat each day. Eating a diet containing a variety of foods will supply the daily vitamin needs of nearly everyone.

As you probably are aware, food stores and pharmacies sell vitamin supplements. Taking extra-large doses of vitamin supplements does not benefit the body, and in some cases, it may cause harm. Excessive amounts of vitamins A, D, E, and K can be toxic.

CHECKPOINT *Why is it important to not take more than the recommended amount of fat-soluble vitamins?*

Minerals Inorganic nutrients that the body needs, usually in small amounts, are called **minerals.** Some examples of minerals are calcium, iron, and magnesium. Calcium is a major component of bones and teeth, and iron is needed to make hemoglobin, the oxygen-carrying protein in red blood cells. Magnesium is required for normal functioning of nerves and muscle tissue. **Figure 38–7** lists some of the minerals needed by the body.

Although the body does not digest the minerals it takes in, it does lose many of them in sweat, urine, and other waste products. How are these important chemicals replaced? Many of these elements are found in the living tissues of plants and other animals. By eating a variety of foods, you can meet your daily requirement of minerals.

Balancing the Diet

It's no easy task to figure out the best balance of nutrients for the human diet, but nutritionists have tried to do exactly that. The result is the Food Guide Pyramid shown in **Figure 38–8.**

The Food Guide Pyramid classifies foods into six groups. It also indicates how many servings from each group should be eaten every day to maintain a healthy diet. Carbohydrate-rich foods such as bread, cereal, rice, and grains are at the base of the pyramid. At the top of the pyramid are foods such as fats and sweets, which should be used sparingly. Foods in the other groups already contain fats and sugars, so you should limit your intake of additional fats and sugars. The basic idea behind the pyramid is sound and simple—you should eat a variety of foods each day, and limit your intake of fatty, sugary foods.

▼ **Figure 38–8** The Food Guide Pyramid illustrates the main characteristics of a balanced diet. Carbohydrate-rich foods should make up the major portion of the diet, whereas foods containing fats and sugars should be eaten sparingly. **Interpreting Graphics** *Why do you think nutritionists recommend that you limit your intake of fats, oils, and sweets?*

Fats, Oils, and Sweets (use sparingly)
Soft drinks, candy, ice cream, mayonnaise, and other foods in this group have relatively few valuable nutrients.

Milk, Yogurt, and Cheese Group (2–3 servings)
Milk and other dairy products are rich in proteins, carbohydrates, vitamins, and minerals.

Meat, Poultry, Fish, Dry Beans, Eggs, and Nut Group (2–3 servings)
These foods are high in protein. They also supply vitamins and minerals.

Vegetable Group (3–5 servings)
Vegetables are a low-fat source of carbohydrates, fiber, vitamins, and minerals.

Fruit Group (2–4 servings)
Fruits are good sources of carbohydrates, fiber, vitamins, and water.

Bread, Cereal, Rice, and Pasta Group (6–11 servings)
The foods at the base of the pyramid are rich in complex carbohydrates and also provide proteins, fiber, vitamins, and some minerals.

○ Fats
▼ Sugars

Reading Food Labels

Nutrients are substances your body needs for energy, growth, repair, and maintenance. Federal regulations require that labels on packaged foods display the nutrients each food contains, the percentage of daily value each nutrient represents for a person, as well as serving size, number of servings per container, and Calories per serving.

Carefully examine the nutritional information on the food label shown. Based on the information on the label, answer the questions that follow.

1. **Calculating** Calculate the daily value in grams for total carbohydrate and dietary fiber.

2. **Calculating** If you ate 2 cups of this product, how many grams of fat would you eat? How many grams of protein?

3. **Drawing Conclusions** Based on the data, which food do you think has more Calories: one with 8 g of fat or one with 8 g of carbohydrate? Explain your answer.

4. **Going Further** People with hypertension, or high blood pressure, often are advised to restrict their intake of sodium. Those who also are overweight are advised to lose excess pounds by following a diet lower in fat and in total Calories. Visit a local food store and look at the labels on 10 types of packaged foods. From this information, recommend which of the foods would be healthful for people who are overweight and have hypertension.

Nutrition Facts

| Serving Size | 1 cup (30g) |
| Servings Per Container | About 10 |

Amount Per Serving

| **Calories** 110 | Calories from Fat 15 |

	% Daily Value*
Total Fat 2g	**3%**
Saturated Fat 0g	**0%**
Cholesterol 0mg	**0%**
Sodium 280mg	**12%**
Total Carbohydrate 22g	**7%**
Dietary Fiber 3g	**12%**
Sugars 1g	
Protein 3g	

| Vitamin A | 10% | • | Vitamin C | 20% |
| Calcium | 4% | • | Iron | 45% |

* Percent Daily Values are based on a 2,000 Calorie diet. Your daily values may be higher or lower depending on your caloric needs:

	Calories	2,000	2,500
Total Fat	Less than	65g	80g
Sat. Fat	Less than	20g	25g
Cholesterol	Less than	300mg	300mg
Sodium	Less than	2,400mg	2,400mg
Total Carbohydrate		300g	375g
Fiber		25g	30g

Calories per gram:
Fat 9 • Carbohydrate 4 • Protein 4

Ingredients: Whole grain oats, sugar, salt, milled corn, oat fiber, dried whey, hon~~ey~~ almonds, d~~...~~

38–1 Section Assessment

1. 🔑 **Key Concept** List the six nutrients needed by the body.

2. 🔑 **Key Concept** What is the importance of water in the body?

3. Why is fiber an important part of your diet?

4. How are vitamins and minerals similar? How are they different?

5. **Critical Thinking Interpreting Graphics** Which vitamins and minerals promote healthy bones? (See **Figures 38–6** and **38–7.**)

🄸**TEXT** Assessment Use iText to review the important concepts in Section 38–1.

38–2 The Process of Digestion

Guide for Reading

 Key Concepts
- What are the organs of the digestive system?
- What is the function of the digestive system?

Vocabulary
amylase
esophagus
peristalsis
stomach
peptic ulcer
chyme
small intestine
pancreas
liver
villus
large intestine

Reading Strategy:
Asking Questions Before you read, rewrite the headings in the section as *how*, *why*, or *what* questions. As you read, write brief answers to the heading questions.

Food presents every animal with at least two challenges. The first is how to obtain it. Once an animal has caught, gathered, or engulfed its food, it faces a new challenge—how to break that food down into small molecules that can be passed to the cells that need them. This is the job of the digestive system. As food passes through the digestive system, it gets disassembled, distributing its nutrient value to the body along the way.

The human digestive system, like those of other chordates, is built around an alimentary canal—a one-way tube that passes through the body. **The digestive system includes the mouth, pharynx, esophagus, stomach, small intestine, and large intestine. Several major accessory structures, including the salivary glands, the pancreas, and the liver, add secretions to the digestive system.**

The Mouth

As you take a forkful of food into your mouth, the work of the digestive system begins. The teeth tear and crush the moistened food into a fine paste until it is ready to be swallowed. Chewing begins the process of mechanical digestion—the physical breakdown of large pieces of food into smaller pieces. But there is a great deal more to it than that. As you chew your food, digestive enzymes begin to break food molecules down into smaller molecules. This process is called chemical digestion. During chemical digestion, large food molecules are broken down into smaller food molecules. **The function of each organ of the digestive system is to help convert foods into simpler molecules that can be absorbed and used by the cells of the body.**

Teeth The teeth shown in **Figure 38–9** are anchored in the bones of the jaw. The surfaces of the teeth, which are much tougher than ordinary bone, are protected by a coating of mineralized enamel. Teeth do much of the mechanical work of digestion by cutting, tearing, and crushing food into small fragments.

✓ CHECKPOINT *What do the teeth do?*

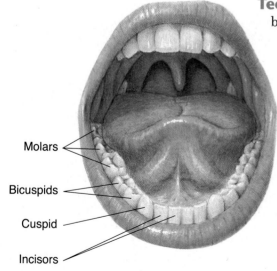

Molars
Bicuspids
Cuspid
Incisors

◀ **Figure 38–9** Human teeth include sharp incisors; cuspids and bicuspids, which grasp and tear food; and large, flat molars. **Inferring** *How do human teeth reflect an omnivorous diet?*

FIGURE 38–10 THE DIGESTIVE SYSTEM

The digestive system includes the mouth, pharynx, esophagus, stomach, small intestine, and large intestine.

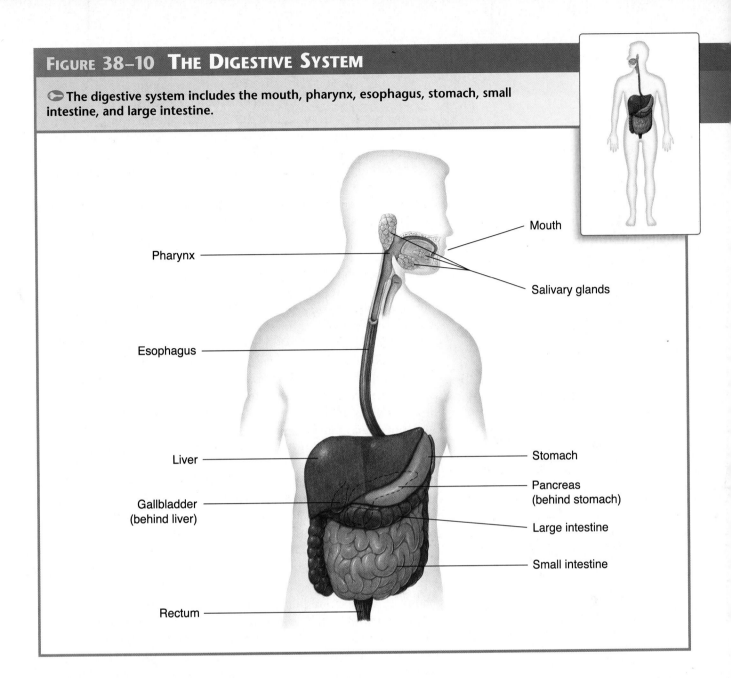

- Mouth
- Pharynx
- Salivary glands
- Esophagus
- Liver
- Stomach
- Pancreas (behind stomach)
- Gallbladder (behind liver)
- Large intestine
- Small intestine
- Rectum

Saliva As the teeth cut and grind the food, the salivary glands secrete saliva, which helps to moisten the food and make it easier to chew. The release of saliva is under the control of the nervous system, and can be triggered by the scent of food—especially when you are hungry!

Saliva not only helps ease the passage of food through the digestive system. It begins the process of chemical digestion. Saliva contains an enzyme called **amylase** that breaks chemical bonds between the sugar monomers in starches. If you chew on a starchy food like crackers long enough, it will begin to taste sweet. This sweet taste is a sign that sugar has been released from starch by the action of amylase. Saliva also contains lysozyme, an enzyme that fights infection by digesting the cell walls of many bacteria that may enter the mouth with food.

The Esophagus

The combined actions of the tongue and throat muscles push the chewed clump of food, called a bolus, down the throat. Recall that a flap of connective tissue called the epiglottis closes over the opening to the trachea as you swallow. This action prevents food from clogging the air passageways to the lungs.

From the throat, the bolus passes through the **esophagus,** or food tube, into the stomach. You might think that gravity draws food down through the esophagus, but this is not correct. You are able to swallow food just fine while lying down or standing on your head. Astronauts are even able to swallow food in the weightless environment of space! The reason food travels through the esophagus into the stomach is that it is moved along by contractions of smooth muscle surrounding the esophagus. Known as **peristalsis** (pehr-uh-STAL-sis), these contractions squeeze the food through the 25-centimeter length of the esophagus into the stomach. Peristalsis is illustrated in **Figure 38–11.**

A thick ring of muscle, called the cardiac sphincter, closes the esophagus after food has passed into the stomach, and prevents the contents of the stomach from moving back up into the esophagus. Have you ever suffered from "heartburn"? Heartburn is a painful, burning sensation that feels as if it is coming from the center of the chest, just above the stomach. The sensation is usually caused by stomach acid that moves past the cardiac sphincter and splashes against the lining of the esophagus. Overeating or an excess of caffeinated drinks can cause the cardiac sphincter muscles to open, allowing stomach acid to back up into the esophagus.

The Stomach

Food from the esophagus empties into a large muscular sac called the **stomach.** The size of the stomach enables you to eat a few large meals a day, rather than having to nibble all the time. The stomach continues the mechanical digestion of food. Contractions of its smooth muscles thoroughly churn and mix the food you swallow.

Chemical Digestion The lining of the stomach contains millions of microscopic gastric glands that release a number of substances into the stomach. Some of these glands produce mucus, a fluid that lubricates and protects the stomach wall. Other glands produce hydrochloric acid, which makes the contents of the stomach very acidic. The acid activates an enzyme called pepsin, which is secreted by a third set of glands. Pepsin works best under the acidic conditions present in the stomach. The combination of pepsin and hydrochloric acid begins the complex process of protein digestion. Pepsin breaks proteins into smaller polypeptide fragments. Some other enzymes that help in digestion are shown in **Figure 38–12.**

✓ CHECKPOINT *What is the role of pepsin?*

▲ **Figure 38–11** Muscles in the walls of the esophagus contract in waves. Each wave pushes the bolus in front of it. Eventually, the bolus is pushed into the stomach. **Applying Concepts** *What kind of muscle surrounds the esophagus?*

Esophagus
Bolus
Muscles contracted
Stomach

Ulcers The powerful acids released into the stomach sometimes damage the organ's own lining, producing a hole in the stomach wall known as a **peptic ulcer.** For years, physicians assumed that the primary cause of ulcers was too much stomach acid. They prescribed drugs that suppressed acid production, and recommended bland, easily digested diets.

Scientists have discovered that peptic ulcers are usually caused by the bacterium *Helicobacter pylori*. Doctors around the world now know that many peptic ulcers are caused by an infectious disease that can be cured. Thanks to powerful antibiotics, cure rates for peptic ulcers are as high as 90 percent.

Mechanical Digestion As digestion proceeds, stomach muscles contract to churn and mix stomach fluids and food, gradually producing a mixture known as **chyme** (KYM). After an hour or two, the pyloric valve, which is located between the stomach and small intestine, opens and chyme begins to flow into the small intestine.

The Pancreas and Liver

As chyme is pushed through the pyloric valve, it enters the duodenum (doo-oh-DEE-num). The duodenum is the first of three parts of the small intestine. The **small intestine** is the location where most of chemical digestion takes place. As chyme enters the duodenum from the stomach, it mixes with enzymes and digestive fluids from the pancreas, the liver, and even the lining of the duodenum itself. The pancreas and liver are shown in **Figure 38–13.**

Digestive Enzymes		
Site	**Enzyme**	**Role in Digestion**
Mouth	Salivary amylase	Breaks down starches into disaccharides
Stomach	Pepsin	Breaks down proteins into large peptides
Small intestine (from pancreas)	Amylase	Continues the breakdown of starch
	Trypsin	Continues the breakdown of protein
	Lipase	Breaks down fat
Small intestine	Maltase, sucrase, lactase	Breaks down remaining disaccharides into monosaccharides
	Peptidase	Breaks down dipeptides into amino acids

▲ **Figure 38–12** Digestive enzymes break down foods and make nutrients available to the body. **Interpreting Graphics** *Where in the body does the digestion of carbohydrates begin?*

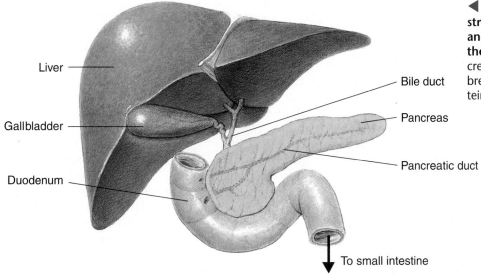

◀ **Figure 38–13** ⬠ Accessory structures, including the liver and pancreas, add secretions to the digestive system. The pancreas secretes enzymes that help break down carbohydrates, proteins, and fats.

Liver

Gallbladder

Duodenum

Bile duct

Pancreas

Pancreatic duct

To small intestine

Just below the stomach is the **pancreas.** The pancreas is a gland that serves three important functions. One function is to produce hormones that regulate blood sugar levels. Within the digestive system, the pancreas plays two key roles. It produces enzymes that break down carbohydrates, proteins, lipids, and nucleic acids. The pancreas also produces sodium bicarbonate, a base that neutralizes stomach acid so that these enzymes can be effective. Why is this neutralization necessary? Stomach acid can change the shapes of protein molecules and enzymes are proteins. If the shape of an enzyme's active site does not match the shape of its substrate, the enzyme will not be effective.

Assisting the pancreas is the **liver,** a large organ located just above the stomach. The liver produces bile, a fluid loaded with lipids and salts. Bile acts like a detergent, dissolving and dispersing the droplets of fat found in fatty foods. This action makes it possible for enzymes to reach the fat molecules and break them down. Bile is stored in a small, pouchlike organ called the gallbladder.

✓**CHECKPOINT** *What is bile?*

Quick Lab

How do villi help the small intestine absorb nutrients?

Materials 2 paper towels, scissors, 2 cardboard tubes, metric ruler, 30-mL graduated cylinder, 2 plastic cups

Procedure
1. Cut and roll up a single sheet of paper towel so that it fits in a cardboard tube without overlapping itself. **CAUTION:** *Scissors are sharp.* The tube represents the small intestine and the paper towel represents an intestinal lining without villi.
2. Spread the paper towel out flat and use the ruler to determine the area of the towel (area = width × length). Put the paper towel back in the tube.
3. Fold the second paper towel back and forth on itself in a zigzag pattern as if you are making a fan. Then, roll up the crinkled paper to fit in the second tube without overlapping itself. Cut off any excess. The folds represent an intestinal lining with villi.
4. **Predicting** Repeat step 2 for the second towel. Predict which model will absorb more water.

5. Stand each tube in a plastic cup. Slowly pour 30 mL of water down the inside of each tube. Remove the tubes. Then, measure and record the quantity of water in each cup.

Analyze and Conclude
1. **Observing** Which model had more surface area? How does surface area affect the ability to absorb substances? Was your prediction in step 4 correct?
2. **Applying Concepts** How do folds and finger-like projections affect the area of an absorbing surface? How do villi help the intestine absorb nutrients?
3. **Inferring** Your kidneys contain about 1 million microscopic structures that filter waste products from your blood. What advantage does this arrangement have over filtering the waste products out of one large blood vessel?

FIGURE 38–14 THE SMALL INTESTINE

The lining of the small intestine consists of folds that are covered with tiny projections called villi. Within each villus there is a network of blood capillaries and lymph vessels that absorb and carry away nutrients. **Applying Concepts** *How do the folds in the small intestine help in absorption?*

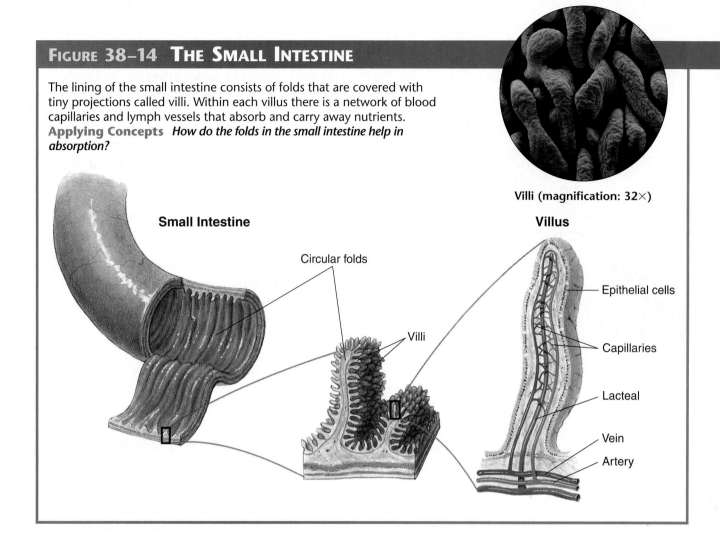

Villi (magnification: 32×)

Small Intestine

Circular folds

Villi

Villus

Epithelial cells

Capillaries

Lacteal

Vein

Artery

The Small Intestine

The duodenum is much shorter than the remaining parts of the small intestine—the jejunum and the ileum, which are about three meters long. By the time chyme enters these parts of the small intestine, much of the chemical digestion has been completed. The chyme is now a rich mixture of medium and small nutrient molecules.

The small intestine is specially adapted to absorb nutrients. The folded surfaces of the small intestine are covered with projections called **villi** (VIL-eye; singular: villus). The villi are illustrated in **Figure 38–14.** The surfaces of the cells of the villi are covered with thousands of fingerlike projections known as microvilli. These folds and projections mean that the small intestine has an enormous surface area available to absorb nutrient molecules. Slow, wavelike contractions of smooth muscles move the chyme along this surface.

Nutrient molecules are rapidly absorbed into the cells lining the small intestine. Most of the products of carbohydrate and protein digestion are absorbed into the capillaries in the villi. Molecules of undigested fat and some fatty acids are absorbed by lymph vessels called lacteals.

▲ **Figure 38–15** This barium X-ray shows the large intestine. **Applying Concepts** *What is the role of the large intestine?*

The Large Intestine

By the time food leaves the small intestine, it is basically nutrient-free. The complex organic molecules have been digested and absorbed, leaving only water, cellulose, and other undigestible substances behind. The chyme enters the large intestine, or colon. The primary job of the **large intestine** is to remove water from the undigested material that is left. The large intestine is shown in **Figure 38–15.**

Just below the entry to the colon is a small organ called the appendix. Some animals have appendixes in which cellulose is digested by bacteria. In humans, the appendix appears to do little to promote digestion. The only time people pay attention to the appendix is when it becomes inflamed, causing appendicitis. The remedy for acute appendicitis is to surgically remove the infected organ as quickly as possible.

Water is moved quickly across the large intestine wall. Rich colonies of bacteria grow on the undigested material left in the colon. These intestinal bacterial help the digestive process. Some of the bacteria produce compounds that the body can use, such as vitamin K. The concentrated waste material that remains after the water has been removed passes through the rectum and is eliminated from the body. When something happens that interferes with the removal of water by the large intestine, you usually become aware of it right away. The condition that is produced is known as diarrhea. The loss of salts and water due to diarrhea can be life threatening, especially for an infant. Diarrhea resulting from bacterial infections and contaminated drinking water is the leading cause of childhood death in many developing countries around the world.

38–2 Section Assessment

1. 🔑 **Key Concept** List the organs of the digestive system and give the function of each.

2. 🔑 **Key Concept** Explain the role of the digestive system.

3. How do mechanical and chemical digestion work together to break down foods?

4. How does bile help in the digestion of fats?

5. **Critical Thinking Inferring** What can you infer about the diet of an animal that has a large appendix?

🅣 **Assessment** Use iText to review the important concepts in Section 38–2.

Take It to the NET

Read about diseases of the digestive system. Then, create a table that lists the cause or contributing factors for five digestive diseases. Use the links provided in the Biology area at the Prentice Hall Web site for help: **www.phschool.com**

38–3 The Excretory System

The chemistry of the human body is a marvelous thing. An intricate system of checks and balances controls everything from your blood pressure to your body temperature. Nutrients are absorbed, stored, and carefully released when they are needed. However, every living system, including the human body, produces chemical waste products that are not useful to the body. Some waste products are even so toxic that the body needs a system to eliminate them.

Excretion

You might think that homeostasis involves the body's efforts to respond only to changes in the external environment. Homeostasis, however, also requires the body to deal with internal processes that might upset the internal cellular environment. For example, as a normal consequence of being alive, every cell in the body produces metabolic wastes, such as excess salts, carbon dioxide, and urea. Urea is a toxic compound that is produced when amino acids are used for energy. The process by which these metabolic wastes are eliminated is called excretion. Excretion is one part of the many processes that maintain homeostasis.

You have already learned about two organs of excretion—the skin and the lungs. The skin excretes excess water and salts, as well as a small amount of urea, in the form of sweat. The lungs excrete carbon dioxide, a gas produced when energy is captured from compounds in foods. The remaining organs of excretion are the kidneys. **Together, the skin, lungs, and kidneys—along with their associated organs—make up the excretory system.**

The Kidneys

The main organs of the excretory system are the two kidneys. The **kidneys** are located on either side of the spinal column near the lower back. Each kidney is about the size of a clenched fist. A tube, called the **ureter** yoo-REET-ur), leaves each kidney, carrying urine to the urinary bladder. The **urinary bladder** is a saclike organ where urine is stored before being excreted.

What does a kidney do? Waste-laden blood enters the kidney through the renal artery. As blood travels through the kidney, urea, excess water, and other waste products are removed and collected as urine. The clean, filtered blood is returned to circulation through the renal vein.

Guide for Reading

🔑 **Key Concepts**
• What are the organs of the excretory system?
• How do the kidneys maintain homeostasis?

Vocabulary
• kidney • ureter
• urinary bladder
• nephron • glomerulus
• Bowman's capsule
• filtration • reabsorption
• loop of Henle • urethra

Reading Strategy:
Building Vocabulary
Before you read, preview **Figure 38–17** to identify vocabulary with which you are unfamiliar. Look for the meanings of these terms as you read.

▼ **Figure 38–16** 🔑 The skin is an organ of the excretory system. The skin excretes water, salts, and urea in sweat.

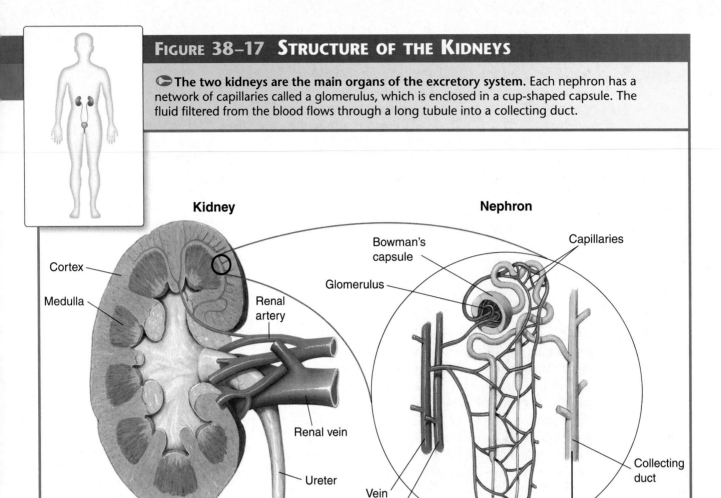

FIGURE 38–17 STRUCTURE OF THE KIDNEYS

The two kidneys are the main organs of the excretory system. Each nephron has a network of capillaries called a glomerulus, which is enclosed in a cup-shaped capsule. The fluid filtered from the blood flows through a long tubule into a collecting duct.

Kidney

Cortex

Medulla

Renal artery

Renal vein

Ureter

To the bladder

Nephron

Bowman's capsule

Glomerulus

Capillaries

Vein

Artery

Loop of Henle

Collecting duct

To the ureter

Kidney Structure If a kidney is cut in half, two distinct regions can be seen. The inner part is called the renal medulla. The outer part is called the renal cortex. The functional units of the kidney are called nephrons (NEF-rahnz). Each **nephron** is a small, independent processing unit. There are about 1 million nephrons in each kidney. The parts of a nephron are shown in **Figure 38–17**. Nephrons are in the renal cortex, except for their loops of Henle, which descend into the renal medulla.

Each nephron has its own blood supply: an arteriole, a venule, and a network of capillaries connecting them. Blood enters the nephron through the arteriole. As the blood passes through the capillaries, it is filtered. Waste products removed from the blood end up in the collecting duct, which leads to the ureter. The purified blood exits the nephron through the venule. The mechanism of blood purification is extremely complex. It involves three distinct processes: filtration, reabsorption, and secretion. These processes are summarized in **Figure 38–18**.

✓ CHECKPOINT *What are the two parts of the kidney?*

Filtration As the blood enters a nephron, it flows into the glomerulus (gloh-MUR-yoo-lus). The **glomerulus** is a small network of capillaries encased in the upper end of the nephron by a cup-shaped structure called **Bowman's capsule.**

Because the blood is under pressure and the walls of the capillaries and Bowman's capsule are permeable, fluid flows from the blood into Bowman's capsule. This process is known as **filtration.** The materials that are filtered from the blood are collectively called the filtrate. The filtrate contains water, urea, glucose, salts, amino acids, and some vitamins. Because plasma proteins, cells, and platelets are too large to pass through the capillary walls, they remain in the blood.

Reabsorption and Secretion The kidneys filter the entire volume of blood approximately every 45 minutes. Needless to say, not all of the filtrate is excreted. Most of the material removed from the blood at Bowman's capsule makes its way back into the blood by a process known as **reabsorption.** Nutrients, such as amino acids and glucose, are removed from the filtrate by active transport and reabsorbed by the capillaries. Because water follows these materials by osmosis, almost 99 percent of the water that enters Bowman's capsule is reabsorbed into the blood.

While water and nutrients are being returned to the blood from the renal tubules, other materials are being secreted into the filtrate from the capillaries. The secreted materials include hydrogen ions. Remember that the concentration of hydrogen ions affects the pH of a solution such as blood plasma.

▼ **Figure 38–18** ⬛ The kidneys play an important part in maintaining homeostasis. Nephrons control the composition, volume, and pH of blood through the processes of filtration, reabsorption, and secretion.

Filtration

Most filtration occurs in the glomerulus. Blood pressure forces water, salt, glucose, amino acids, and urea into Bowman's capsule. Proteins and blood cells are too large to cross the membrane; they remain in the blood. The fluid that enters the renal tubule is called the filtrate.

Reabsorption

As the filtrate flows through the renal tubule, most of the water and nutrients are reabsorbed into the blood. The concentrated fluid that remains is called urine.

Secretion

Substances such as hydrogen ions are transferred from the blood to the filtrate.

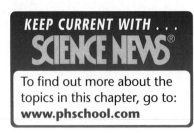
Word Origins

Absorb comes from the Latin *ab-* meaning "from" or "away," and *sorbere,* meaning "to draw in." **If the Latin word *radere* means "to scrape," what does the word *abrade* mean?**

The material that remains after reabsorption, called urine, is emptied into a collecting duct. Urine, which contains urea, excess salts, and water, among other substances, is primarily concentrated in the loop of Henle. The **loop of Henle** is a section of the nephron tubule in which water is conserved and the volume of urine minimized.

As the kidney works, purified blood is returned to circulation while urine is collected in the urinary bladder. Urine is stored in the urinary bladder until it can be released from the body through a tube called the **urethra** (yoo-REE-thruh).

Control of Kidney Function

The kidneys play an important role in maintaining homeostasis. They regulate the water content of the blood and, therefore, blood volume, maintain blood pH, and remove waste products from the blood. How are these activities controlled?

To a large extent, the activity of the kidneys is controlled by the composition of blood itself. In addition, regulatory hormones are released in response to the composition of blood. These mechanisms combine to ensure that the kidneys will maintain the proper composition of blood.

When you drink glass after glass of liquid, the liquid is quickly absorbed into the blood through the digestive system. As a result, the concentration of water in the blood increases. If it were not for your kidneys, this increased concentration of water in the blood would force water into cells and tissues by osmosis, causing your body to swell.

As the amount of water in the blood increases, the rate of water reabsorption in the kidneys decreases. Less water is returned to the blood, and the excess water is sent to the urinary bladder to be excreted as urine.

If you eat salty food, your kidneys will respond to the increased level of salt in your blood. When your kidneys detect an increase in salt, they respond by returning less salt to the blood by reabsorption. The excess salt the kidneys retain is excreted in urine, thus maintaining the composition of the blood.

CHECKPOINT *How do the kidneys respond to salty foods?*

Homeostasis by Machine

The kidneys are the master chemists of the blood supply. If anything goes wrong with the kidneys, serious medical problems soon follow. Fortunately, humans have two kidneys and can survive with only one. If both kidneys are damaged by disease or injury, there are only two ways to keep an individual alive. The first way is to transplant a kidney from a healthy and compatible donor to the person in need of the kidney.

Blood in tubing flows
through dialysis fluid

Blood pump

Vein

Artery

Shunt

Used dialysis fluid

Air detector

Dialysis
machine

Fresh
dialysis
fluid

Compressed
air

In many cases, a donor is not available or surgery is not advisable. In these instances, a kidney dialysis machine becomes a lifesaver. In one type of dialysis, blood is removed from the body through a tube inserted in the arm and pumped through special tubing that acts like nephrons. Tiny pores in the tubing allow salts and small molecules, including nitrogen wastes, to pass through. Wastes—urea and excess salts—diffuse out of the blood into the fluid-filled chamber, allowing purified blood to be returned to the body. This process of dialysis is shown in **Figure 38–19.** Dialysis is not only expensive, but it also is time-consuming, occupying several hours a day as often as three times a week. The ideal solution, assuming a kidney transplant is not possible, would be the implantation of an artificial kidney. Medical science is working toward developing such an artificial kidney.

▲ **Figure 38–19** For people with damaged kidneys, dialysis machines can perform many of the functions of the kidneys. **Applying Concepts** *Why is dialysis such an important lifesaving technique?*

38–3 Section Assessment

1. 🔑 **Key Concept** What are the parts of the excretory system?

2. 🔑 **Key Concept** What is the kidney's role in maintaining homeostasis?

3. Describe the structures of the kidney.

4. Describe the processes of filtration and reabsorption.

5. **Critical Thinking Drawing Conclusions** Explain why a person may temporarily lose weight after changing to a low-salt diet even without reducing Caloric intake.

🧍 **TEXT** **Assessment** Use iText to review the important concepts in Section 38–3.

ALTERNATIVE ASSESSMENT

Constructing a Flowchart
Construct a flowchart that illustrates how wastes are removed by the kidneys.

Testing the Specificity of Digestive Enzymes

In this investigation, you will test the ability of the digestive enzyme pepsin to break down egg white, which is mostly protein. You will also design your own experiments to test the effect of pepsin on starch, and the effects of amylase on proteins and starch.

Problem
Do different digestive enzymes act only on specific types of compounds?

Materials
- heat-resistant gloves
- Benedict's solution
- boiling water bath
- cooked egg white
- scalpel or single-edged razor blade
- metric ruler
- 6 large test tubes
- 6 stoppers for test tubes
- glass-marking pencil
- test-tube rack
- 10-mL graduated cylinder
- 1% pepsin solution
- 0.2% hydrochloric acid
- cooked potato
- 1% amylase solution
- test-tube holder

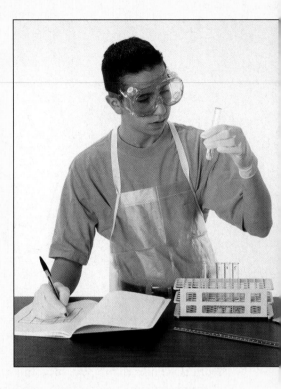

Skills
Formulating Hypotheses, Controlling Variables, Forming Operational Definitions

Design Your Experiment

Part A: The Basic Procedure

1. **Predicting** Predict whether pepsin can break down protein.

2. Put on an apron and safety goggles. Label three test tubes 1, 2, and 3 and put them in a test-tube rack. Cut three 5-mm cubes of cooked egg white and add one to each test tube.

3. Put on plastic gloves. Use a graduated cylinder to add 6 mL of water to test tube 1, and 3 mL of water and 3 mL 0.2% hydrochloric acid to test tube 2. **CAUTION:** *Hydrochloric acid can damage skin and clothing. If hydrochloric acid spills, notify your teacher. Wash the affected area with large amounts of cool water.* Carefully rinse the graduated cylinder.

4. To test tube 3, add 3 mL 1% pepsin solution and 3 mL 0.2% hydrochloric acid. Carefully rinse the graduated cylinder.

5. Put a stopper in each test tube and gently turn the tubes upside down several times to mix the contents. Put the tubes back in the test-tube rack. Make a copy of the data table. Set your test-tube rack where it will not be disturbed.

6. After 2 days, examine the contents of each test tube. Record your observations in your copy of the data table.

Part B: Design Your Own Experiments

7. **Predicting** Do you think pepsin will digest potato, which is rich in starch? Write down your prediction. Now, design an experiment to test your prediction. You can use the test for sugars described in Part C to determine whether starch has been broken down. Write down your procedure. What is your manipulated variable? Your responding variable? Make sure to control all other variables. **CAUTION:** *Before you perform your experiment, have your teacher approve your procedure.*

8. Design two experiments to test whether amylase can digest protein or starch. Make sure you control your variables. Record in your copy of the data table what you put in each test tube. **CAUTION:** *Before you perform your experiments, have your teacher approve your procedures.*

Data Table

Test Tube	Compound Tested	Liquid(s) Added	Observations
1	protein (egg white)	6 mL water	
2	protein (egg white)	3 mL water, 3 mL hydrochloric acid	
3	protein (egg white)	3 mL pepsin, 3 mL hydrochloric acid	

9. Set your test-tube rack aside where it will not be disturbed for 2 days.

10. After 2 days, examine each test tube. Record your observations in your data table.

Part C: Testing for Sugar

11. To test for the presence of sugar in the liquid in the tubes that contained potato: Put 1 mL of the liquid in a test tube. Add 2 mL of water and mix.

12. Add 3 mL Benedict's solution to the same tube.

13. Your teacher will provide a boiling water bath. Put on the heat-resistant gloves and use a test-tube holder to put the test tubes from step 12 in the boiling water bath. **CAUTION:** *Be careful when working with boiling water.* Observe the test tube for about 5 minutes. A change in color from blue to yellow (or green, or orange, or red) is a positive test for sugar. Record your observations in your data table.

Analyze and Conclude

1. **Applying Concepts** Why was hydrochloric acid included with the pepsin in step 4? Did you add hydrochloric acid to the amylase solution? Why or why not?

2. **Observing** What effect did pepsin have on the egg white? Was your prediction correct? Explain your answer.

3. **Observing** What effect did water, and water with hydrochloric acid, have on the egg white? What was the purpose of including these tests?

4. **Drawing Conclusions** Describe the results of the experiments you designed. Do the enzymes you tested act only on specific compounds? Explain your answer.

Go Further

Designing Experiments What factors affect the rates of the reactions you tested? How could you increase these rates? Design one or more experiments to test the effects of changing one of these factors. Remember to write a prediction and to control variables. After obtaining approval from your teacher, carry out your experiment(s).

38–1 Food and Nutrition

🔑 Key Concepts

- The nutrients that the body needs are water, carbohydrates, fats, proteins, vitamins, and minerals.
- Every cell in the human body needs water because many of the body's processes, including chemical reactions, take place in water.

Vocabulary
Calorie, p. 971
carbohydrate, p. 972
fat, p. 972
protein, p. 973
vitamin, p. 974
mineral, p. 975

38–2 The Process of Digestion

🔑 Key Concepts

- The digestive system includes the mouth, pharynx, esophagus, stomach, small intestine, and large intestine. Several accessory structures, including the salivary glands, the pancreas, and the liver, add secretions to the digestive system.
- The function of each organ of the digestive system is to help convert foods into simpler molecules that can be absorbed and used by the cells of the body.

Vocabulary
amylase, p. 979
esophagus, p. 980
peristalsis, p. 980
stomach, p. 980
peptic ulcer, p. 981
chyme, p. 981
small intestine, p. 981
pancreas, p. 982
liver, p. 982
villus, p. 983
large intestine, p. 984

38–3 The Excretory System

🔑 Key Concepts

- Together, the skin, lungs, and kidneys—along with their associated organs—make up the excretory system.
- The kidneys play an important role in maintaining homeostasis. They regulate the water content of the blood and, therefore, blood volume, maintain blood pH, and remove waste products from the blood.

Vocabulary
kidney, p. 985
ureter, p. 985
urinary bladder, p. 985
nephron, p. 986
glomerulus, p. 987
Bowman's capsule, p. 987
filtration, p. 987
reabsorption, p. 987
loop of Henle, p. 988
urethra, p. 988

Thinking Visually
Create a flowchart that shows the path of food through the organs of the digestive system.

Chapter 38

Part A

Multiple Choice

For each statement or question, select the number of the word or expression that, of those given, best completes the statement or answers the question.

1 If equal masses of nutrients are oxidized, the largest amount of energy will be released by
   (1) fats   (3) carbohydrates
   (2) proteins   (4) vitamins

2 Inorganic nutrients that your body needs, usually in small amounts, are called
   (1) vitamins   (3) proteins
   (2) minerals   (4) lipids

3 The mechanical breakdown of food
   (1) occurs mainly in the large intestine
   (2) exposes a larger surface area for chemical digestion
   (3) produces the soluble end products of digestion
   (4) is brought about by digestive enzymes

4 The diagram below represents a portion of the esophagus.

Food

   Which statement is correct about the process shown in the diagram?
   (1) It transports food through the digestive tract.
   (2) It must occur prior to the mechanical digestion of food in the oral cavity.
   (3) It breaks down fats into fatty acids for digestion in the small intestine.
   (4) It increases water absorption in the stomach.

5 An enzyme in saliva that breaks the chemical bonds in starch, releasing sugar, is
   (1) pepsin   (3) bile
   (2) chyme   (4) amylase

6 Most absorption of the end products of digestion into the circulatory system in humans occurs
   (1) in the large intestine
   (2) in the stomach
   (3) through the lining of the esophagus
   (4) through the villi of the small intestine

7 The main function of the human digestive system is to
   (1) break down large, insoluble molecules into smaller, soluble molecules
   (2) excrete oxygen and carbon dioxide
   (3) synthesize minerals and vitamins needed for a healthy body
   (4) add essential vitamins to blood

8 The basic functional unit of the kidney is the
   (1) nephron   (3) glomerulus
   (2) loop of Henle (4) Bowman's capsule

9 Urine is excreted from the body through the
   (1) ureter   (3) urethra
   (2) urinary bladder (4) renal vein

10 Which is *not* a function of the kidneys?
   (1) maintenance of blood pH
   (2) regulation of the water content of blood
   (3) maintenance of homeostasis
   (4) excretion of carbon dioxide

For questions 11 and 12, complete each analogy by selecting the correct number. In analogies, A : B :: C : means "A is to B as C is to __?__."

11 Energy : carbohydrates :: structural material :
   (1) proteins   (3) water
   (2) minerals   (4) fat

12 Lung : carbon dioxide :: kidney :
   (1) oxygen   (3) urea
   (2) nutrients   (4) cellulose

Test-Taking Tip To complete an analogy, write a sentence that clearly describes the relationship between the first pair of terms. Then, rewrite the sentence with the third term and fill in the blank with the answer choice that best completes the analogy.

Preparing for the
Living Environment Exam

Parts B and C

Multiple Choice and Extended Response

For those questions that ask you to select a response, choose the one that best completes the statement or answers the question. For all others follow the directions given.

13 Going without food affects the amount of urea in the urine, as shown in the graph below.

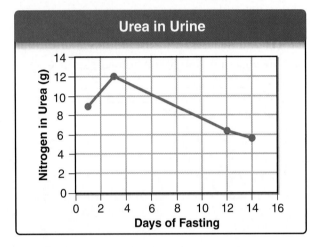

Urea in Urine

The graph shows that the amount of nitrogen excreted in the urea
(1) increases steadily during 14 days of fasting
(2) decreases steadily during 14 days of fasting
(3) increases for the first few days of fasting
(4) will be 6 grams after 16 days of fasting

14 Describe the two primary functions of food in the human body.

15 Describe three ways proteins are important to the body.

16 Explain why swallowed food does not usually enter the airway leading to the lungs.

Base your answers to questions 17 and 18 on the information below and on your knowledge of biology.

Your kidneys, along with your skin and lungs and their associated organs, make up your excretory system. All of these organs are vital in maintaining the chemical balance of your blood.

17 List the materials that healthy kidneys remove from the blood.

18 List the materials that remain in the blood as it passes through healthy kidneys.

19 What information is provided by the Food Guide Pyramid?

20 Describe the function of enzymes during the process of chemical digestion.

Base your answers to questions 21 through 24 on the information and table below and on your knowledge of biology.

A student is studying the effect of temperature on the action of an enzyme in stomach fluid. The enzyme digests protein. An investigation was set up using five identical test tubes, each containing 40 mL of stomach fluid and 20 mm of glass tubing filled with gelatin. After 48 hours, the amount of gelatin digested in each tube was measured in millimeters. The results for the five test tubes are shown in the table below.

Test Tube	Temperature (°C)	Amount of Digestion After 48 Hours
1	2	0.0 mm
2	10	3.0 mm
3	22	4.5 mm
4	37	8.0 mm
5	100	0.0 mm

21 Which is the manipulated (independent) variable in this investigation?
(1) gastric fluid
(2) length of glass tubing
(3) temperature
(4) time

22 An additional test tube was set up that was identical to the other test tubes and placed at a temperature of 15°C for 48 hours. What amount of digestion would you expect to occur in this test tube?
(1) less than 3.0 mm
(2) between 3.0 mm and 4.5 mm
(3) between 4.5 mm and 8.0 mm
(4) more than 8.0 mm

23 The experiment was repeated a third time, using apple instead of gelatin. There was no evidence of any digestion after 48 hours at any temperature. Explain why no digestion occurred.

24 Which set of axes below should be used to plot the data?

(1) Gastric Fluid

(2) Temperature (°C)

(3) Amount of Digestion (mm)

(4) Temperature (°C)

25 Individuals who have had part, or even all, of their stomachs removed can survive if fed predigested food. Could individuals with a stomach survive without a small intestine if they were fed predigested food? Support your answer with an explanation.

26 Fad diets that boast of rapid weight loss often become popular. Many of these diets involve eating only a limited variety of foods. Explain why these diets are an unhealthy way to lose weight.

27 In some countries, people have diets that contain more complex carbohydrates and fewer fats and proteins than the typical American diet. What are two reasons such diets might be healthier than the typical American diet?

28 Suppose your doctor prescribed an antibiotic that killed all the bacteria in your body. What effect would this have on your digestive system?

29 Explain why kidney failure can be fatal.

Base your answers to questions 30 through 32 on the information and graph below and on your knowledge of biology.

Pancreatic juice contains sodium bicarbonate and digestive enzymes. The juice is secreted by the pancreas in response to the specific composition of chyme in the upper portion of the small intestine. The graph below shows secretions of the pancreas in response to the presence of three different substances.

30 Each pair of bars on the graph represents the response of the pancreas to a different variable. What are the three variables?

31 Describe how the presence of protein affects the amounts of bicarbonate and digestive enzymes secreted.

32 How does the presence of fat affect the composition of pancreatic juice?

Take It to the NET

How can you tell which snack foods are healthy? Visit the Prentice Hall Web site at **www.phschool.com** to find out what you can learn by reading the labels on food packages. Then, answer the following questions:

• Suppose you read the label "low fat" on a carton of ice cream. What does this label tell you?

• How are "low fat" crackers different from crackers with "reduced" fat?

• Why is it important to limit fat in your diet?

39 Endocrine and Reproductive Systems

This photomicrograph, which was artificially colored, shows sperm (yellow objects) trying to break through the outer membrane of an egg.

Inquiry Activity

Where in cells do hormones go?

Procedure

1. Fill 2 test tubes one third full of water. Add the same amount of vegetable oil (a lipid) to each test tube.
2. Add a few drops of food coloring to one of the test tubes. Stopper the test tube and turn it upside down to mix the contents.
3. Repeat step 2 using a drop of annatto coloring and the second test tube.

Think About It

1. **Observing** Did the food coloring dissolve in water or oil? Do you think food coloring can pass through cell membranes? (*Hint:* Cell membranes are composed of lipids.)
2. **Observing** Did the annatto coloring dissolve in water or oil? Do you think this dye can pass through cell membranes?

39-1 The Endocrine System

If you had to get a message to just one or two of your friends, what would you do? You might use the telephone. Wires running from your house to theirs would carry the message almost instantaneously. The telephone is a good way to reach a small number of people, but what if you wanted to get that same message to thousands of people? You might decide to broadcast it on the radio, sending the message in a way that made it possible to contact thousands of people at once.

Your nervous system works much like the telephone: Many impulses move swiftly over a system of wirelike neurons that carry specific messages from one cell to another. But another system, the endocrine system, does what the nervous system generally cannot. **The endocrine system is made up of glands that release their products into the bloodstream. These products broadcast messages throughout the body.** In the same way that a radio broadcast can reach thousands or even millions of people in a large city, the chemicals released by the endocrine system can affect almost every cell in the body.

Hormones

The chemicals that "broadcast" messages from the endocrine system are called hormones. **Hormones** are chemicals that travel through the bloodstream and affect the activities of other cells. Hormones do this by binding to specific chemical receptors on those cells. Cells that have receptors for a particular hormone are called **target cells.** If a cell does not have receptors or the receptors do not respond to a particular hormone, the hormone has no effect on it.

In general, the body's responses to hormones are slower and longer-lasting than the responses to nerve impulses. It may take several minutes, several hours, or even several days for a hormone to have its full effect on its target cells. A nerve impulse, on the other hand, may take only a fraction of a second to reach and affect its target cells.

Guide for Reading

🔑 **Key Concepts**
• What is the function of the endocrine system?
• How does the endocrine system maintain homeostasis?

Vocabulary
hormone
target cell
exocrine gland
endocrine gland
prostaglandin

Reading Strategy:
Making Comparisons
As you read, list the differences and similarities between types of glands, and between types of hormones.

▶ **Figure 39–1** 🔑 **The endocrine system releases hormones that affect the activities of other cells.** Much of the increase in heart rate and breathing that the people are experiencing on this ride is due to the actions of hormones.

Glands

A gland is an organ that produces and releases a substance, or a secretion. **Exocrine glands** release their secretions through tubelike structures called ducts. Exocrine glands include those that release sweat, tears, and digestive juices. Unlike exocrine glands, **endocrine glands** release their secretions (hormones) directly into the bloodstream. **Figure 39–2** shows the location of the major endocrine glands in the human body.

✓CHECKPOINT *What are exocrine glands?*

▼ **Figure 39–2** Endocrine glands produce hormones that affect many parts of the body. **Interpreting Graphics** *What is the function of the pituitary gland?*

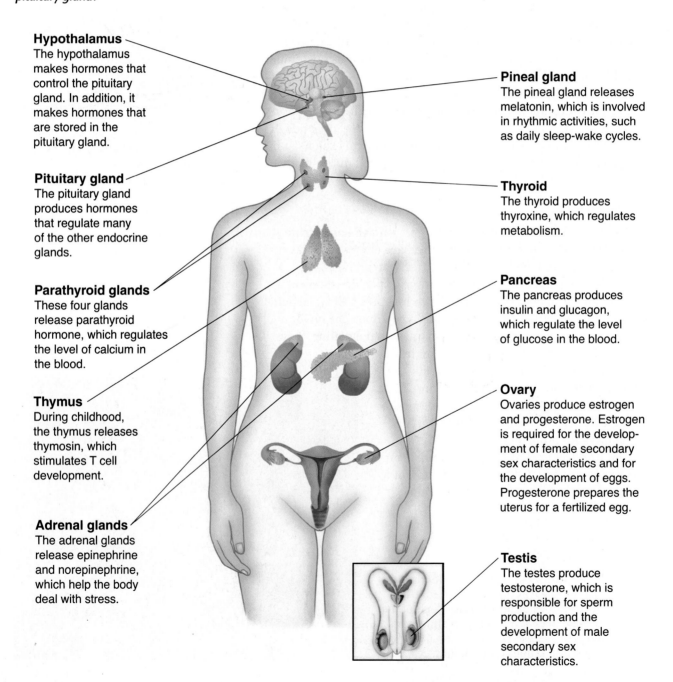

Hypothalamus
The hypothalamus makes hormones that control the pituitary gland. In addition, it makes hormones that are stored in the pituitary gland.

Pituitary gland
The pituitary gland produces hormones that regulate many of the other endocrine glands.

Parathyroid glands
These four glands release parathyroid hormone, which regulates the level of calcium in the blood.

Thymus
During childhood, the thymus releases thymosin, which stimulates T cell development.

Adrenal glands
The adrenal glands release epinephrine and norepinephrine, which help the body deal with stress.

Pineal gland
The pineal gland releases melatonin, which is involved in rhythmic activities, such as daily sleep-wake cycles.

Thyroid
The thyroid produces thyroxine, which regulates metabolism.

Pancreas
The pancreas produces insulin and glucagon, which regulate the level of glucose in the blood.

Ovary
Ovaries produce estrogen and progesterone. Estrogen is required for the development of female secondary sex characteristics and for the development of eggs. Progesterone prepares the uterus for a fertilized egg.

Testis
The testes produce testosterone, which is responsible for sperm production and the development of male secondary sex characteristics.

Hormone Action

Hormones fall into two general groups—steroid hormones and nonsteroid hormones. Steroid hormones are produced from a lipid called cholesterol. Nonsteroid hormones include proteins, small peptides, and modified amino acids. The two basic patterns of hormone action are shown in **Figure 39–3**.

Steroid Hormones Because they are lipids, steroid hormones can cross cell membranes easily, passing directly into the cytoplasm and even into the nuclei of target cells.

1. A steroid hormone enters a cell by passing directly across its cell membrane.
2. Once inside, it binds to a steroid receptor protein (found only in its target cells) to form a hormone-receptor complex.
3. The hormone-receptor complex enters the nucleus of the cell, where it binds to a DNA control sequence.
4. This binding initiates the transcription of specific genes to messenger RNA (mRNA).
5. The mRNA moves into the cytoplasm and directs protein synthesis.

Hormone-receptor complexes work as regulators of gene expression—they can turn on or turn off whole sets of genes. Because steroid hormones affect gene expression directly, they can produce dramatic changes in cell and organism activity.

Nonsteroid Hormones Nonsteroid hormones generally cannot pass through the cell membrane of their target cells.

1. A nonsteroid hormone binds to receptors on the cell membrane.
2. The binding of the hormone activates an enzyme on the inner surface of the cell membrane.
3. This enzyme activates secondary messengers that carry the message of the hormone inside the cell. Calcium ions, cAMP (cyclic adenosine monophosphate), nucleotides, and even fatty acids can serve as second messengers.
4. Once released, these second messengers can activate or inhibit a wide range of other cell activities.

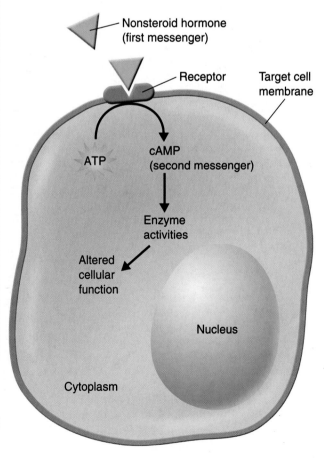

Figure 39–3 The two main types of hormones are steroid hormones and nonsteroid hormones. **Comparing and Contrasting** *How are steroid hormones different from nonsteroid hormones?*

Prostaglandins

Until recently, the glands of the endocrine system were thought to be the only organs that produced hormones. However, except for red blood cells, all cells have been shown to produce small amounts of hormonelike substances called **prostaglandins** (prahs-tuh-GLAN-dinz). Prostaglandins get their name from a gland in the male reproductive system, the prostate, in which they were first discovered. Prostaglandins are modified fatty acids that are produced by a wide range of cells. They generally affect only nearby cells and tissues, and thus are known as "local hormones."

Some prostaglandins cause smooth muscles, such as those in the uterus, bronchioles, and blood vessels, to contract. One group of prostaglandins causes the sensation of pain in most headaches. Aspirin helps to stop the pain of a headache because it inhibits the synthesis of these prostaglandins.

Control of the Endocrine System

As powerful as they are, hormones must be closely monitored in order to keep the functions of different organs in balance. Even though the endocrine system is one of the master regulators of the body, it too must be controlled. 🔑 **Like most systems of the body, the endocrine system is regulated by feedback mechanisms that function to maintain homeostasis.**

Recall that feedback inhibition occurs when an increase in any substance "feeds back" to inhibit the process that produced the substance in the first place. Heating and cooling systems, controlled by thermostats, are examples of mechanical feedback systems. The hormones of the endocrine system are biological examples of the same process.

Controlling Metabolism To see how a feedback mechanism regulates the activity of the endocrine system, let's look at one of the body's most important endocrine glands, the thyroid gland. Thyroxine, the gland's principal hormone, affects the activity of cells throughout the body. Increased levels of thyroxine in the blood stimulate cells to become more active. A drop in thyroxine decreases the metabolic activity of cells.

Does the thyroid gland determine how much thyroxine to release on its own? Not at all. The activity of the thyroid gland is controlled by the hypothalamus and the anterior pituitary gland. When the hypothalamus senses that the thyroxine level in the blood is low, it secretes a hormone known as thyroid-releasing hormone (TRH), which stimulates the anterior pituitary to secrete thyroid-stimulating hormone (TSH). TSH stimulates the release of thyroxine by the thyroid gland, which sets up the feedback loop shown in **Figure 39–4.** This feedback mechanism keeps the level of thyroxine in the blood relatively constant.

▼ **Figure 39–4** 🖲 Like most body systems, the endocrine system is regulated by feedback controls that function to maintain homeostasis. Notice how an increase in TSH causes the release of thyroxine. As the level of thyroxine increases in the blood, the level of TSH decreases. This action causes a decrease in thyroxine, which causes an increase in TSH, and the cycle begins again.

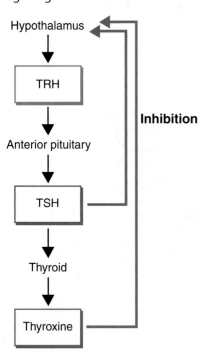

Recall that the hypothalamus is also sensitive to temperature. When core body temperature begins to drop, even if the level of thyroxine is normal, the hypothalamus produces extra TRH. The release of TRH stimulates the release of TSH, which stimulates the release of additional thyroxine. The increase in metabolic activity that results helps the body maintain its core temperature despite colder air temperatures.

Maintaining Water Balance Homeostatic mechanisms regulate the levels of a wide variety of materials dissolved in the blood and in extracellular fluids. These include minerals such as sodium, potassium, and calcium, and soluble proteins such as serum albumin, which is found in blood plasma. Most of the time, homeostatic systems operate so smoothly that we are scarcely aware of their existence. However, that is not the case with one of the most important homeostatic processes, the one that regulates the amount of water in the body.

When you exercise strenuously, you lose water as you sweat. If this water loss continued, your body would soon become dehydrated. Generally, that doesn't happen because your body's homeostatic mechanisms swing into action.

The hypothalamus contains cells that are sensitive to the concentration of water in the blood. As you lose water, the concentration of dissolved materials in the blood rises. The hypothalamus responds in two ways. First, the hypothalamus signals the pituitary gland to release a hormone called antidiuretic hormone (ADH). ADH molecules are carried by the bloodstream to the kidneys, where the removal of water from the blood is quickly slowed down. Later, you experience a sensation of thirst, a signal that you should take a drink to restore lost water.

When you finally get around to taking that drink, you might take in as much as 1 or 2 liters of fluid. Most of that water is quickly absorbed across the walls of the digestive system into the bloodstream. But this volume of water added to the blood would dilute it so much that the equilibrium between the blood and the cells of the body would be disturbed. Large amounts of water would diffuse across blood vessel walls into the tissues. The cells of the body would swell with the excess water.

Needless to say, this doesn't happen, because the same homeostatic mechanism intervenes. When the water content of the blood rises, the pituitary releases less ADH. In response to lower ADH levels, the kidneys remove water from the bloodstream, restoring the blood to its original concentration. The water homeostatic system sets both upper and lower limits for blood water content: A water deficit stimulates the release of ADH, causing the kidneys to conserve water; an oversupply of water causes the kidneys to eliminate the excess.

CHECKPOINT *What process does thyroxine control?*

▼ **Figure 39–5** When exercising on a hot day, it is important to replenish lost liquid. **Applying Concepts** *Explain why people who are exercising should drink fluids before they are thirsty.*

Complementary Hormone Action

Sometimes two hormones with opposite effects act to regulate part of the body's internal environment. Why are two hormones necessary? Think about driving a car. A good driver might be able to control a car on an open highway by using only the accelerator pedal. But driving around town, even a good driver would get into trouble using just the accelerator. There are too many situations in which the brake is needed to slow the car down.

In the same way, many endocrine functions depend on the complementary effects of two opposing hormones. Such a system regulates the level of calcium ions in the bloodstream.

The level of calcium dissolved in the bloodstream is kept within a narrow range. Two hormones regulate calcium concentration: calcitonin from the thyroid gland and parathyroid hormone (PTH) from the parathyroid glands. When blood calcium levels are too high, calcitonin helps to reduce the level. Calcitonin signals the kidneys to retain less calcium in the bloodstream. The release of calcitonin also reduces the amount of calcium absorbed in the intestine and stimulates calcium deposition in the bones.

If calcium levels drop too low, PTH is released by the parathyroids. PTH, together with vitamin D, stimulates the intestine to absorb more calcium from food. PTH also causes the kidneys to retain more calcium, and it stimulates bone cells to release some of the calcium stored in bone tissue into the bloodstream.

You may be surprised that the body regulates calcium levels so carefully. This careful regulation is necessary because calcium is one of the most important minerals in the body. If calcium levels drop below their normal range, blood cannot clot, muscles cannot contract, and the transport of materials across cell membranes may fail.

39–1 Section Assessment

1. **Key Concept** Describe the role of the endocrine system in the body.

2. **Key Concept** Explain how the endocrine system helps maintain homeostasis.

3. Compare endocrine glands and exocrine glands.

4. What are prostaglandins and why are they called "local hormones"?

5. **Critical Thinking Applying Concepts** What are the advantages of having both a nervous system and an endocrine system?

TEXT **Assessment** Use iText to review the important concepts in Section 39–1.

MAKING CONNECTIONS

Cell Structure
Use what you learned in Chapter 7 about cell membranes to explain the actions of steroid hormones and nonsteroid hormones.

39–2 Human Endocrine Glands

The endocrine glands are scattered throughout the body. Generally, they do not have direct connections to one another. Like signals that are beamed throughout the country from a broadcast station, the hormones released from the endocrine glands travel throughout the body, reaching almost every cell.

The human endocrine system regulates a wide variety of activities. Any improper functioning of an endocrine gland may result in a disease or a disorder. The major glands of the endocrine system include the pituitary gland, the hypothalamus, the thyroid gland, the parathyroid glands, the adrenal glands, the pancreas, and the reproductive glands.

Pituitary Gland

The **pituitary gland** is a bean-sized structure that dangles on a slender stalk of tissue at the base of the skull. As you can see in **Figure 39–6,** the gland is divided into two parts: the anterior pituitary and the posterior pituitary. **The pituitary gland secretes nine hormones that directly regulate many body functions and controls the actions of several other endocrine glands.**

Normal function of the pituitary gland is essential to good health. For example, if the pituitary gland produces too much growth hormone (GH), the body grows too quickly and a condition called gigantism results. Too little GH during childhood causes a condition known as pituitary dwarfism, which can be treated by administering growth hormone.

Guide for Reading

🔑 **Key Concept**
• What are the functions of the major endocrine glands?

Vocabulary
pituitary gland
diabetes mellitus
ovary
testis

Reading Strategy: Finding Main Ideas Before you read, skim the text paragraphs in this section to find the seven boldfaced sentences. Copy each sentence onto a note card. As you read, note supporting details on the cards.

▼ **Figure 39–6** 🔑 The pituitary gland, which controls many other endocrine glands, is located below the hypothalamus in the brain. The pituitary gland has two lobes: an anterior lobe and a posterior lobe.

Hypothalamus

Anterior pituitary   Posterior pituitary

Pituitary gland

Hypothalamus

The hypothalamus is the part of the brain above and attached to the posterior pituitary. **The hypothalamus controls the secretions of the pituitary gland.** The activity of the hypothalamus is influenced by the levels of hormones in the blood and by sensory information collected by other parts of the central nervous system. Interactions between the nervous system and the endocrine system take place at the hypothalamus.

The posterior pituitary is made up of axons belonging to cells called neurosecretory cells, whose cell bodies are in the hypothalamus. When these cell bodies are stimulated, the axons in the posterior pituitary release their hormones into the bloodstream. In a way, the posterior pituitary is an extension of the hypothalamus.

In contrast, the hypothalamus has indirect control of the anterior pituitary. The hypothalamus produces small amounts of chemicals called releasing hormones, which are secreted directly into blood vessels. The releasing hormones are carried by the circulatory system to the anterior pituitary, where they control the production and release of hormones.

The close connection between the hypothalamus and the pituitary gland means that the nervous and endocrine systems can act together to help coordinate body activities. Hormones released by the pituitary gland are listed in **Figure 39–7.**

✓ CHECKPOINT *What is the role of releasing hormones?*

▼ **Figure 39–7** **The hypothalamus controls the secretions of the pituitary gland.** Notice the effect that each hormone produced by the pituitary gland has on the body.

Pituitary Gland Hormones

Pituitary Gland	Hormone	Action
Posterior pituitary	Antidiuretic hormone (ADH)	Stimulates the kidneys to reabsorb water from the collecting tubules
	Oxytocin	Stimulates contractions of uterus during childbirth; releases milk in nursing mothers
Anterior pituitary	Follicle-stimulating hormone (FSH)	Stimulates production of eggs and sperm
	Luteinizing hormone (LH)	Stimulates ovaries and testes; prepares uterus for implantation of fertilized egg
	Thyroid-stimulating hormone (TSH)	Stimulates the synthesis and release of thyroxine from the thyroid gland
	Adreno-corticotropic hormone (ACTH)	Stimulates release of some hormones from the adrenal cortex
	Growth hormone (GH)	Stimulates protein synthesis and growth in cells
	Prolactin	Stimulates milk production in nursing mothers
	Melanocyte-stimulating hormone (MSH)	Stimulates the melanocytes of the skin, increasing their production of the skin pigment melanin

Thyroid Gland

If you look at **Figure 39–8**, you can see that the thyroid gland is located at the base of the neck and wraps around the upper part of the trachea.

🔑 **The thyroid gland has the major role in regulating the body's metabolism.** Cells in the thyroid gland produce thyroxine, which is made up of the amino acid tyrosine and the mineral iodine. Remember that thyroxine affects nearly all of the cells of the body by regulating their metabolic rates. Increased levels of thyroxine can increase the cellular respiration rate, which means that the cells release more energy. Decreased levels of thyroxine can decrease the cellular respiration rate and the amount of energy released. Other cells in the thyroid gland secrete calcitonin—the hormone that decreases the level of calcium in the blood.

The homeostatic activities of the thyroid gland are so well controlled that you may never become aware of them. However, if the thyroid gland produces too much thyroxine, a condition called hyperthyroidism occurs. Hyperthyroidism results in nervousness, elevated body temperature, increased heart and metabolic rates, increased blood pressure, and weight loss. Too little thyroxine causes a condition called hypothyroidism. Lower metabolic rates and body temperature, lack of energy, and weight gain are characteristics of this condition. In some cases, hypothyroidism is associated with goiter, an enlargement of the thyroid gland.

The importance of proper thyroid activity can be seen in parts of the world where food lacks enough iodine for the thyroid to produce normal amounts of thyroxine. Unable to produce the thyroxine needed for normal development, iodine-deficient infants suffer from a condition called cretinism (KREE-tuh-niz-um) in which neither the skeletal system nor the nervous system develops properly. Two effects of cretinism are dwarfism and severe mental retardation. Cretinism usually can be prevented by the addition of small amounts of iodine to table salt or other items in the food supply.

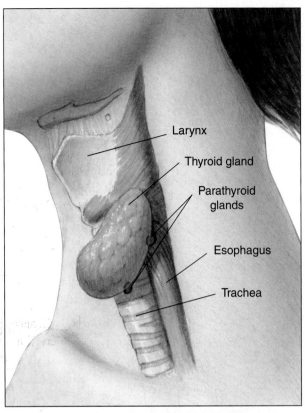

▲ **Figure 39–8** 🔑 Hormones **produced by the thyroid gland and the parathyroid glands maintain the level of calcium in the blood.** The thyroid gland wraps around the trachea.

Parathyroid Glands

The four parathyroid glands are found on the back surface of the thyroid gland. 🔑 **Hormones from the thyroid gland and the parathyroid glands maintain homeostasis in blood calcium levels.** Parathyroid glands secrete parathyroid hormone (PTH). PTH regulates the calcium levels in the blood by increasing the reabsorption of calcium in the kidneys and by increasing the uptake of calcium from the digestive system. Parathyroid hormone is also important for promoting proper nerve and muscle function and bone structure.

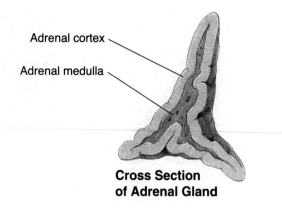

Adrenal cortex

Adrenal medulla

**Cross Section
of Adrenal Gland**

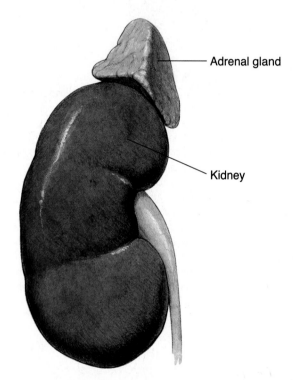

Adrenal gland

Kidney

▲ **Figure 39–9** 🔑 **The adrenal glands help the body prepare for and deal with stress.** The adrenal gland is divided into two parts: the adrenal cortex and the adrenal medulla.

Adrenal Glands

The adrenal glands are two pyramid-shaped structures that sit on top of the kidneys, one gland on each kidney, as shown in **Figure 39–9**. 🔑 **The adrenal glands help the body prepare for and deal with stress.** An adrenal gland has an outer part called the adrenal cortex and an inner part called the adrenal medulla. These parts contain different types of tissues.

Adrenal Cortex About 80 percent of an adrenal gland is its adrenal cortex. The cortex produces more than two dozen hormones called cortico-steroids (kawr-tih-koh-STEER-oydz). The hormone aldosterone (al-DAHS-tuh-rohn) regulates the reabsorption of sodium ions and the excretion of potassium ions by the kidneys. Another hormone, called cortisol, helps control the rate of metabolism of carbohydrates, fats, and proteins.

Adrenal Medulla The release of hormones from the adrenal medulla is regulated by the sympathetic nervous system. The two hormones released by the adrenal medulla are epinephrine and norepinephrine. Epinephrine, which is more powerful than norepinephrine, makes up about 80 percent of the total secretions of the adrenal medulla.

The adrenal medulla produces the "fight or flight" response to stress. This response is the feeling you get when you are excited or fright-ened. Nerve impulses from the sympathetic nervous system stimulate cells of the adrenal medulla. This stimulation causes the cells to release large amounts of epinephrine and norepi-nephrine. These hormones increase heart rate, blood pressure, and blood flow to the muscles. They cause air passageways to open wider, allowing for an increase in the intake of oxygen. They also stimulate the release of extra glucose into the blood to help produce a sudden burst of energy. The result of all these actions is a general increase in body activity, which can serve as preparation for intense physical activity. If your heart rate speeds up and your hands begin to perspire when you take a test, you are feeling the effects of your adrenal medulla!

✓ CHECKPOINT *Which hormones are released from the adrenal cortex? From the adrenal medulla?*

Pancreas

The pancreas is an unusual organ. Located along the right side of and behind the stomach, the pancreas seems to be a single gland—but appearances can be deceiving! Recall that the pancreas is a digestive organ whose enzyme secretions help to break down food. This makes the pancreas an exocrine gland. However, different cells in the pancreas release hormones into the blood, making the pancreas an endocrine gland as well.

The hormone-producing portion of the pancreas consists of clusters of cells that resemble islands. These clusters of cells are called islets of Langerhans after their discoverer, the German anatomist Paul Langerhans. Each islet includes beta cells, which secrete a hormone called insulin, and alpha cells, which secrete another hormone called glucagon. 🔑 **Insulin and glucagon released from the pancreas help to keep the level of glucose in the blood stable.** Insulin stimulates cells in the liver and muscles to remove sugar from the blood and store it as glycogen or fat. Glucagon stimulates the liver to break down glycogen and release glucose back into the blood. The actions of insulin and glucagon are summarized in **Figure 39–10.**

▼ **Figure 39–10** 🔑 Insulin and glucagon from the pancreas help keep the level of glucose in the blood stable. The top half of the flowchart shows what happens when the level of glucose in the blood increases. The bottom half shows what happens when the level of glucose in the blood decreases.

Normal Coronary Artery

Coronary Artery Totally Blocked

▲ **Figure 39–11** Uncontrolled diabetes can increase the risk of blocked arteries. **Applying Concepts** *What effect do blocked arteries have on blood pressure?*

When the pancreas produces too little insulin, a condition known as **diabetes mellitus** occurs. In diabetes mellitus, the amount of glucose in the blood may rise so high that the kidneys actually excrete glucose in the urine. Very high blood glucose levels can damage many organs and tissues, including the coronary artery shown in **Figure 39–11.**

There are two types of diabetes mellitus. Juvenile-onset diabetes, also known as Type I, most commonly develops in people before the age of 15. In this type of diabetes, there is little or no secretion of insulin. People with this type of diabetes must follow a strict diet and get daily injections of insulin. Adult-onset diabetes, or Type II, most commonly develops in people after the age of 40. People with adult-onset diabetes produce low to normal amounts of insulin. However, their cells are unable to properly respond to the hormone because the interaction of the insulin receptors and the insulin is inefficient. Adult-onset diabetes, especially in its early stages, can often be controlled through diet and exercise.

Reproductive Glands

The gonads are the body's reproductive glands.
🔑 **The gonads serve two important functions: the production of gametes and the secretion of sex hormones.** The female gonads—the **ovaries**—produce eggs (ova). The male gonads—the **testes** (singular: testis)—produce sperm. The gonads also produce sex hormones. You will read more about these hormones in the next section.

39–2 Section Assessment

1. 🔑 **Key Concept** Describe the role of each major endocrine gland.
2. Why is the hypothalamus an important part of both the nervous system and the endocrine system?
3. What are the two types of diabetes mellitus?
4. What endocrine gland goes to work when you are surprised with a pop quiz?

5. **Critical Thinking Predicting** Suppose the secretion of a certain hormone causes an increase in the concentration of substance X in the blood. What is the effect on the rate of hormone secretion if an abnormal condition causes the level of X in the blood to remain very low?

📱 **Assessment** Use iText to review the important concepts in Section 39–2.

📱 *Take It to the NET*

Read about the hormone leptin and write a paragraph about its relationship to body weight, new blood vessel growth, and the immune system. Use the links provided in the Biology area at the Prentice Hall Web site for help in completing this activity:
www.phschool.com

39–3 The Reproductive System

Reproduction is the formation of new individuals. This makes the reproductive system unique among the systems of the body. If any other body system, such as the nervous or circulatory system, failed to function, the result would be fatal in most animals. This is not the case for the reproductive system because an individual can lead a healthy life without reproducing. However, the reproductive system could be thought of as the single most important system for the continuation of a species—without it, no species could produce another generation.

In humans, as in other vertebrates, the reproductive system produces, stores, and releases specialized sex cells known as gametes. These cells are released in ways that make possible the fusion of sperm and egg to form a zygote, the single cell from which all cells of the human body develop.

Sexual Development

For the first six weeks of development, human male and female embryos are identical in appearance. Then, during the seventh week, major changes occur. The primary reproductive organs—the testes in males and the ovaries in females—begin to develop. The testes produce testosterone, a male sex hormone. Testosterone is required for sperm production and the development of male physical characteristics. The ovaries produce the female sex hormones estrogen and progesterone. Estrogen is required for the development of eggs and for the formation of female physical characteristics. Progesterone prepares the uterus for the arrival of a developing embryo. Although the male and female reproductive organs develop from the same tissues in the embryo, these hormones determine whether the embryo will develop into a male or a female.

After birth, the gonads produce small amounts of sex hormones that continue to influence the development of the reproductive organs. However, neither the testes nor the ovaries are capable of producing active reproductive cells until puberty. **Puberty** is a period of rapid growth and sexual maturation during which the reproductive system becomes fully functional. At the completion of puberty, the male and female reproductive organs are fully developed. The onset of puberty varies considerably among individuals. It may occur any time between the ages of 9 and 15, and, on average, begins about a year earlier in females than in males.

Guide for Reading

 Key Concepts
- What are the roles of the male and female reproductive systems?
- What are the four phases of the menstrual cycle?

Vocabulary
puberty • scrotum
seminiferous tubule
epididymis • vas deferens
urethra • penis • follicle
ovulation • Fallopian tube
uterus • vagina
menstrual cycle
corpus luteum • menstruation

Reading Strategy:
Outlining Before you read, use the headings in this section to make an outline about the reproductive system. As you read, fill in subtopics. Then, add phrases or a sentence after each subtopic to provide key information showing how the reproductive system is important.

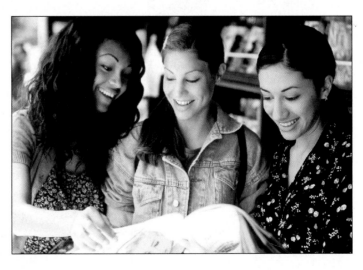

▼ **Figure 39–12** Many changes in your life—both social and physical—are dependent on your age.

Puberty begins when the hypothalamus signals the pituitary to produce increased levels of two hormones that affect the gonads. These hormones are follicle-stimulating hormone (FSH) and luteinizing hormone (LH).

The Male Reproductive System

The release of FSH and LH stimulates cells in the testes to produce testosterone (tes-TAHS-tuh-rohn), a steroid that is the principal male sex hormone. Target cells for testosterone are found all over the body. Testosterone produces a number of secondary sex characteristics that appear in males at puberty. These characteristics include the growth of facial and body hair, increase in body size, and deepening of the voice.

FSH and testosterone stimulate the development of sperm. Once large numbers of sperm have been produced in the testes, the developmental process of puberty is completed. The reproductive system is now functional, meaning that the male can produce and release active sperm.

👁 **The main structures of the male reproductive system are the testes, the epididymis, the vas deferens, the urethra, and the penis. These structures work together to produce and deliver sperm.** Just before birth (or sometimes just after), the testes descend from the abdomen through a canal into an external sac called the **scrotum.** The testes remain in the scrotum, outside the body cavity, where the temperature is about one to three degrees lower than the internal temperature of the body (37°C). The lower temperature is important for proper sperm development. Within each testis are clusters of hundreds of tiny tubules called **seminiferous tubules** (sem-uh-NIF-ur-us). The seminiferous tubules are tightly coiled and twisted together. Sperm are produced in the seminiferous tubules.

✓**CHECKPOINT** *What is the role of testosterone?*

Sperm Development Sperm are derived from special cells in the testes that undergo the process of meiosis to form the haploid nuclei of mature sperm. A sperm cell is illustrated in **Figure 39–13.** A sperm cell consists of a head, which contains a highly condensed nucleus; a midpiece, which is packed with energy-releasing mitochondria; and a tail, or flagellum, which propels the cell forward. At the tip of the head is a small cap that contains an enzyme vital to the process of fertilization.

Figure 39–14 shows the structures of the male reproductive system. Sperm produced in the seminiferous tubules are moved into the **epididymis** (ep-uh-DID-ih-mis). This is the structure in which sperm fully mature and are stored. From the epididymis, some sperm are moved into a tube called the **vas deferens.**

▼ **Figure 39–13** The sperm is the male gamete, or sex cell. **Interpreting Graphics** *What are the three sections of a sperm cell?*

Nucleus

Head

Neck

Mitochondria

Midpiece

Tail

The vas deferens extends upward from the scrotum into the abdominal cavity. Eventually, the vas deferens merges with the **urethra,** the tube that leads to the outside of the body through the **penis.**

Glands lining the reproductive tract—including the seminal vesicles, the prostate, and the bulbourethral (bul-boh-yoo-REE-thrul) glands—produce a nutrient-rich fluid called seminal fluid. The combination of sperm and seminal fluid is known as semen. The number of sperm present in even a few drops of semen is astonishing. Between 50 and 130 million sperm are present in 1 milliliter of semen. That's about 2.5 million sperm per drop!

Sperm Release When the male is sexually excited, the autonomic nervous system prepares the male organs to deliver sperm. Sperm are ejected from the penis by the contractions of smooth muscles lining the glands in the reproductive tract. This process is called ejaculation. Because ejaculation is regulated by the autonomic nervous system, it is not completely voluntary. About 2 to 6 milliliters of semen, containing more than 200 to 600 million sperm, are released in an average ejaculation. If these hundreds of millions of sperm are released in the reproductive tract of a female, the chances of a single sperm fertilizing an egg, if one is available, are quite good.

▼ **Figure 39–14** ⬤ The main structures of the male reproductive system are the testes, epididymis, vas deferens, urethra, and penis. The testes descend into the scrotum just before or just after birth.

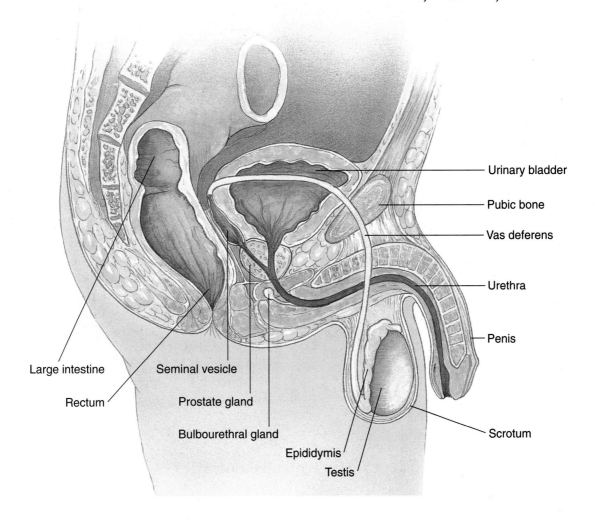

Urinary bladder

Pubic bone

Vas deferens

Urethra

Penis

Scrotum

Large intestine

Rectum

Seminal vesicle

Prostate gland

Bulbourethral gland

Epididymis

Testis

The Female Reproductive System

As in males, puberty in females starts when the hypothalamus signals the pituitary gland to release FSH and LH. FSH stimulates cells within the ovaries to produce estrogen, the female steroid sex hormone. Interactions of estrogen with target cells produce female secondary sex characteristics. These characteristics include the development of the female reproductive system, widening of the hips, and development of the breasts.

🔑 **The main structures of the female reproductive system are the ovaries, the Fallopian tubes, the uterus, and the vagina. In addition to producing eggs, the female reproductive system prepares the female's body to nourish a developing embryo.** The structures of the female reproductive system are shown in **Figure 39–15.** In contrast to the millions of sperm produced each day in the male reproductive system, the ovaries usually produce only one mature ovum (plural: ova), or egg, between them each month.

Egg Development Each ovary contains about 400,000 primary **follicles,** which are clusters of cells surrounding a single egg. The function of a follicle is to help an egg mature for release into the reproductive tract, where it can be fertilized. Eggs mature within their follicles. Although a female is born with about 400,000 immature eggs (primary follicles)—and does not produce any new eggs during her lifetime—only about 400 eggs will actually be released.

▼ **Figure 39–15** 🔑 **The main structures of the female reproductive system are the ovaries, Fallopian tubes, uterus, and vagina.** After puberty, a mature egg is released from an ovary about once a month.

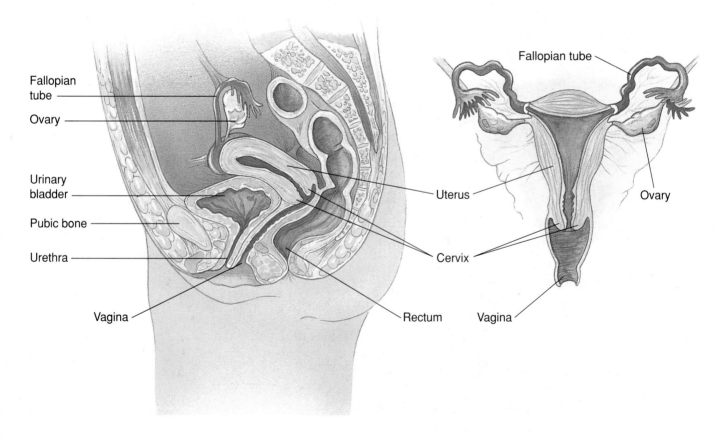

Fallopian tube

Ovary

Urinary bladder

Pubic bone

Urethra

Vagina

Uterus

Cervix

Rectum

Fallopian tube

Ovary

Vagina

Roughly once a month, under the influence of FSH, a follicle gets larger and the egg passes through the early stages of meiosis. When meiosis is complete, a single large haploid egg and three smaller cells called polar bodies will be produced. The polar bodies have very little cytoplasm and soon disintegrate.

✓ CHECKPOINT *Where do eggs develop?*

Egg Release When a follicle has completely matured, its egg is released in a process called **ovulation.** The follicle breaks open, and the egg is swept from the surface of the ovary into the opening of one of the two **Fallopian tubes,** as shown in **Figure 39–16.** The egg moves through the fluid-filled Fallopian tube, pushed along by microscopic cilia lining the walls of the tube. During its journey through the Fallopian tube, an egg can be fertilized. After a few days, the egg passes from the Fallopian tube into the cavity of an organ known as the **uterus.** The lining of the uterus is ready to receive a fertilized egg, if fertilization has occurred. The outer end of the uterus is called the cervix. Beyond the cervix is a canal—the **vagina**—that leads to the outside of the body.

▲ **Figure 39–16** This photograph shows an ovum being released from an ovary. **Applying Concepts** *What is this process called?*

The Menstrual Cycle

After puberty, the interaction of the reproductive system and the endocrine system in females takes the form of a complex series of periodic events called the menstrual cycle. The cycle takes an average of about 28 days. The word *menstrual* comes from the Latin word *mensis,* meaning "month." The menstrual cycle is regulated by hormones that are controlled by negative-feedback mechanisms.

During the **menstrual cycle,** an egg develops and is released from an ovary. In addition, the uterus is prepared to receive a fertilized egg. If the egg is fertilized after ovulation, it is implanted in the uterus and embryonic development begins. If an egg is not fertilized, it is discharged, along with the lining of the uterus. ⚷ **The menstrual cycle has four phases: follicular phase, ovulation, luteal phase, and menstruation.** Refer to **Figure 39–17** on page 1014 as you read about what happens during each phase.

Follicular Phase The follicular phase begins when the level of estrogen in the blood is relatively low. The hypothalamus reacts to low estrogen levels by producing a releasing hormone that acts on the pituitary gland. The releasing hormone stimulates the anterior pituitary to secrete FSH and LH. These two hormones travel through the circulatory system to the ovaries, where they cause a follicle to develop to maturity. Generally, just a single follicle develops, but sometimes two or even three mature during the same cycle.

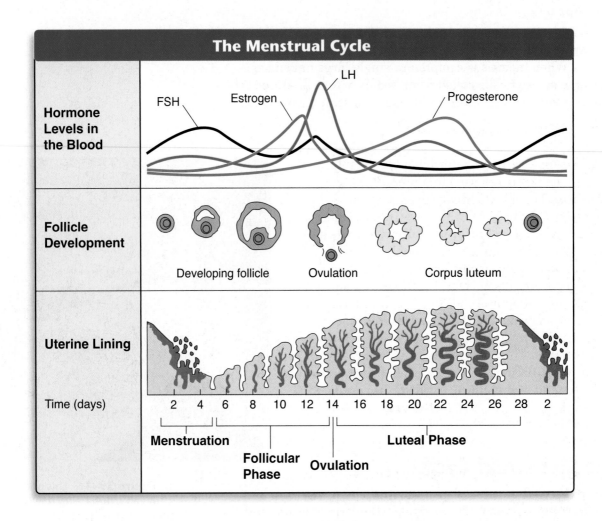

The Menstrual Cycle

Hormone Levels in the Blood

FSH Estrogen LH Progesterone

Follicle Development

Developing follicle   Ovulation   Corpus luteum

Uterine Lining

Time (days)   2 4 6 8 10 12 14 16 18 20 22 24 26 28 2

Menstruation

Follicular Phase   Ovulation   Luteal Phase

▲ **Figure 39–17** The menstrual cycle is divided into four phases: menstruation, follicular phase, ovulation, and luteal phase. Notice the changes in hormone levels in the blood, the development of the follicle, and the changes in the uterine lining during the menstrual cycle.

As the follicle develops, the cells surrounding the egg enlarge and begin to produce increased amounts of estrogen. As the follicle produces more and more of the hormone, the estrogen levels in the blood rise dramatically. Estrogen causes the lining of the uterus to thicken in preparation for receiving a fertilized egg. The development of an egg in this stage of the cycle takes about 10 days.

Ovulation This phase is the shortest in the cycle. It occurs about midway through the cycle and lasts three to four days. During this phase, something (no one is certain what) causes the hypothalamus to send a large amount of releasing hormone to the pituitary gland. This in turn causes the pituitary gland to produce a sudden rush of FSH and LH. The release of these hormones has a dramatic effect on the follicle: It ruptures, and a mature egg is released into one of the Fallopian tubes.

✓ CHECKPOINT *What happens during ovulation?*

Luteal Phase The luteal phase of the cycle begins after the egg is released. As the egg moves through the Fallopian tube, the cells of the ruptured follicle undergo a change. The follicle turns yellow and is now known as the **corpus luteum** (KAWR-pus LOOT-ee-um), which means "yellow body" in Latin. The corpus luteum not only continues to release estrogen but also begins to release progesterone. During the first 14 days of the cycle, rising estrogen levels stimulate cell growth and tissue development in the lining of the uterus. Progesterone adds the finishing touches to that lining. Blood supply increases, the tissue matures, and the lining is fully prepared to accept a fertilized egg.

During the first two days of the luteal phase, immediately following ovulation, the chances that an egg will be fertilized are the greatest. This is usually from 10 to 14 days after the completion of the last menstrual cycle. If an egg is fertilized by a sperm, it will start to divide. After several divisions, a ball of cells will form and implant itself in the lining of the uterus. Within a few days of implantation, the uterus and the growing embryo will release hormones that keep the corpus luteum functioning for several weeks. This allows the lining of the uterus to nourish and protect the developing embryo.

Menstruation What happens if fertilization does not occur? Within two to three days of ovulation, the egg will pass through the uterus without implantation. The corpus luteum will begin to disintegrate. As the old follicle breaks down, it releases less and less estrogen and progesterone. The result is a decrease in the level of these hormones in the blood.

When the level of estrogen falls below a certain point, the lining of the uterus begins to detach from the uterine wall. This tissue, along with blood and the unfertilized egg, are discharged through the vagina. This phase of the cycle is called **menstruation.** Menstruation lasts about three to seven days on average. A new cycle begins with the first day of menstruation.

A few days after menstruation ends, levels of estrogen in the blood are once again low enough to stimulate the hypothalamus. The hypothalamus produces a releasing hormone that acts on the pituitary gland, which then starts to secrete FSH and LH, and the menstrual cycle begins again.

39–3 Section Assessment

1. **Key Concept** Describe the functions of the male and female reproductive systems.

2. **Key Concept** What happens during each of the four phases of the menstrual cycle?

3. What is puberty?

4. What is the function of testosterone? What is the function of progesterone?

5. **Critical Thinking Interpreting Graphics** Which hormone is at its peak during ovulation? (*Hint:* You may wish to refer to **Figure 39–17.**)

TEXT Assessment Use iText to review the important concepts in Section 39–3.

MAKING CONNECTIONS

Chromosomes
How many chromosomes are there in a human egg cell or in a sperm? How many are there in a fertilized egg? (*Hint:* You may wish to refer back to Section 14–1.)

39–4 Fertilization and Development

Guide for Reading

Key Concepts
• What is fertilization?
• What is the function of the placenta?

Vocabulary
zygote
implantation
gastrulation
placenta
fetus

**Reading Strategy:
Using Graphic Organizers**
As you read, draw a flowchart that shows the steps from fertilized egg to newborn baby.

When an egg is fertilized, the remarkable process of human development begins. In this process, a single cell no larger than the period at the end of this sentence undergoes a series of cell divisions that results in the formation of a new human being.

Fertilization

If an egg is to become fertilized, sperm must be present in the female reproductive tract—more specifically, in a Fallopian tube. Sperm are released during sexual intercourse, when semen is ejaculated through the penis into the vagina. The penis generally enters the vagina to a point just below the cervix, which is the opening that connects the vagina to the uterus. Sperm swim actively through the uterus into the Fallopian tubes. Although hundreds of millions of sperm are released during an ejaculation, only about one percent will reach the upper region of each Fallopian tube. If an egg is present in one of the Fallopian tubes, its chances of being fertilized by a sperm are very good.

The egg is surrounded by a thick protective layer that contains binding sites to which sperm can attach. When a sperm attaches to a binding site, as shown in **Figure 39–18,** a sac in the sperm head ruptures and releases powerful enzymes that break down the protective layer of the egg. Once the sperm enters the egg, the membranes around the egg and sperm nuclei rupture and the nuclei are joined. **The process of a sperm joining an egg is called fertilization.**

The fertilized egg, called a **zygote** (ZY-goht), undergoes cell division to produce a two-celled embryo. These cells divide again and again to form a ball of cells. The ball of cells attaches itself to the wall of the uterus and continues to divide.

▶ **Figure 39–18** Once the sperm nucleus enters the egg, the egg's cell membrane changes, preventing other sperm from entering. **The process by which a sperm joins an egg is called fertilization.**

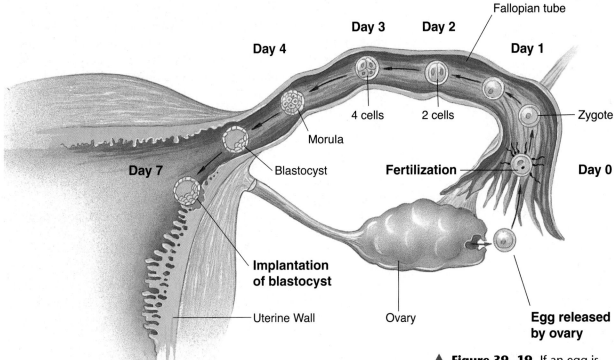

Day 4   Day 3   Day 2   Fallopian tube   Day 1

4 cells   2 cells   Zygote

Morula

Blastocyst   Fertilization   Day 0

Day 7

Implantation of blastocyst

Uterine Wall   Ovary   **Egg released by ovary**

▲ **Figure 39–19** If an egg is fertilized, a zygote forms and begins to undergo cell division as it travels to the uterus. (The size of the egg has been greatly exaggerated.) **Interpreting Graphics** *How much time passes before the blastocyst is attached to the uterine wall?*

Early Development

The first few cell divisions take place while the zygote is still in the Fallopian tube, as shown in **Figure 39–19.** Four days after fertilization, the embryo is a solid ball of about 50 cells called a morula (MAWR-yoo-luh). As the embryo grows, a fluid-filled cavity forms in the center, transforming the embryo into a hollow structure called a blastocyst. About six or seven days after fertilization, the blastocyst attaches itself to the wall of the uterus. The embryo secretes enzymes that digest a path into the soft tissue. This process is known as **implantation.**

Gastrulation A cluster of cells gradually forms within the cavity of the blastocyst. This cluster sorts itself into two layers, which then produce a third layer by a process of cell migration known as **gastrulation** (gas-troo-LAY-shun). The result of gastrulation is the formation of three cell layers known as the ectoderm, mesoderm, and endoderm. These three layers are referred to as the primary germ layers, because all of the organs and tissues of the embryo will be formed from them.

Shortly after implantation, the outer layer of cells of the blastocyst produces important membranes that surround, protect, and nourish the developing embryo. Two of these membranes are the amnion and the chorion.

✓ **CHECKPOINT** *What is gastrulation?*

Word Origins

Zygote comes from the Greek word *zygon,* meaning "yoke." A yoke is a frame used to harness a pair of oxen together. **Why is zygote an appropriate name for a fertilized egg?**

Endocrine and Reproductive Systems **1017**

The Placenta By the end of the third week of development, the nervous and digestive systems have begun to form. The chorion has grown into the uterine tissue to form a vital organ called the **placenta.** The placenta is the connection between mother and developing embryo. The developing embryo needs a supply of nutrients and oxygen. It also needs a means of eliminating carbon dioxide and other metabolic wastes. At first thought, it seems that this task could be accomplished by having the blood supply of the embryo joined to that of the mother. But such an arrangement would allow disease to spread from mother to embryo. It would also cause a problem if the mother and embryo had different blood types.

Figure 39–20 shows that the blood of the mother and that of the embryo flow past each other, but they do not mix. They are separated by the placenta. Across this thin barrier, gases are exchanged and food and waste products diffuse. **The placenta is the embryo's organ of respiration, nourishment, and excretion.** Almost everything that the mother takes into her body passes through the placenta to the embryo.

This early period of development is particularly important because a number of external factors can disrupt development at this time. The placenta acts as a barrier to some harmful or disease-causing organisms. Others, such as rubella (German measles), can penetrate the placenta and affect development. So can drugs—including alcohol and prescription medications.

▼ **Figure 39–20** The placenta is the connection between the mother and the developing embryo. **It is through the placenta that the embryo gets its oxygen and nutrients and excretes its waste products.**

Amniotic sac

Placenta

Umbilical cord

Uterus

Amnion

Fetal portion of placenta

Maternal portion of placenta

Villus in chorion

Amnion

Umbilical cord

Maternal artery

Maternal vein

Umbilical arteries

Umbilical vein

After eight weeks of development, the embryo is called a **fetus.** By the end of three months of development, most of the major organs and tissues of the fetus are fully formed. During this time, the umbilical cord also forms. The umbilical cord connects the fetus to the placenta. The muscular system of the fetus is by now well developed, and the fetus may begin to move and show signs of reflexes. After three months the average fetus is about 8 centimeters long and has a mass of about 28 grams. The amnion has developed into a fluid-filled amniotic sac, which cushions and protects the developing fetus.

✓ CHECKPOINT **What is the umbilical cord?**

Later Development

During the fourth, fifth, and sixth months after fertilization, the tissues of the fetus become more complex and specialized, and more tissues begin to function. A skeleton forms, and the fetal heartbeat becomes strong enough to be heard with a stethoscope. A layer of soft hair grows over the fetus's skin. As the fetus increases in size, the mother's abdomen swells to accommodate it. The developing fetus is about 35 centimeters long and has a mass of about 850 grams after seven months.

After six months, the fetus may be able to survive outside the uterus if life-supporting equipment is available. However, its chances of survival are much better after three more months in the uterus. The fetus doubles in mass, and the lungs and other organs undergo a series of changes that prepare them for life outside the uterus. Premature babies—those born before eight months of development—often have severe breathing problems because of incomplete lung development. **Figure 39–21** shows an embryo and a fetus at different stages of development.

Embryo at 7 Weeks

Fetus at 14 Weeks

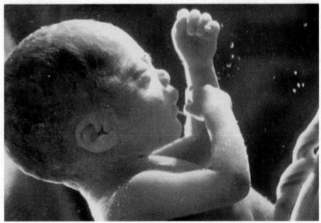

Fetus at Full Term

Figure 39–21 At 7 weeks, most of the organs have begun to form. The heart—the dark rounded structure—is beating. By 14 weeks, the hands, feet, and legs have reached their birth proportions. The eyes, ears, and nose are well developed. When the fetus is full-term, it is fully developed and capable of living on its own. **Interpreting Graphics** *What significant changes do you see from 7 weeks to 14 weeks?*

How do embryos develop?

Frog Embryos

Materials dropper pipette, early-stage frog embryos, depression slide, dissecting microscope, prepared slides of frog embryos

Procedure

1. Use a dropper pipette to transfer several early-stage frog embryos in water to a depression slide.
   CAUTION: *Microscopes and slides are fragile. Handle them carefully. Tell your teacher if you break any glass.*
2. Look at the embryos under the dissecting microscope at low power. Sketch what you see.
3. Look at prepared slides of the early embryonic stages of a frog. Make sketches of what you see.

Analyze and Conclude

1. **Observing** Describe any differences you saw among the cells. At what stage is cell differentiation visible?
2. **Observing** Were you able to see a distinct body plan? At what stage did the body plan become visible?
3. **Drawing Conclusions** Describe any organs you saw. At what stage did specific organs form?

Childbirth

About nine months after fertilization, the fetus is ready for birth. A complex set of factors affect the onset of childbirth. One factor is the release of the hormone oxytocin from the posterior pituitary gland. Oxytocin affects a group of large involuntary muscles in the uterine wall. As these muscles are stimulated, they begin a series of rhythmic contractions known as labor. The contractions become more frequent and more powerful. The opening of the cervix expands until it is large enough for the head of the baby to pass through it. At some point, the amniotic sac breaks, and the fluid it contains rushes out of the vagina. Contractions of the uterus force the baby, usually head first, out through the vagina.

As the baby meets the outside world, he or she may begin to cough or cry, which rids the lungs of fluid. Breathing starts almost immediately, and the blood supply to the placenta begins to dry up. The umbilical cord is clamped and cut, leaving a small piece attached to the baby. This piece will soon dry up and fall off, leaving a scar known as the navel—or in its more familiar term, the belly button. In a final series of uterine contractions, the placenta itself and the now-empty amniotic sac are expelled from the uterus as the afterbirth.

The baby now begins to lead an independent existence. Most newborn babies are remarkably hardy. Their systems quickly switch over to life outside the uterus, supplying their own oxygen, excreting wastes on their own, and maintaining their own body temperatures.

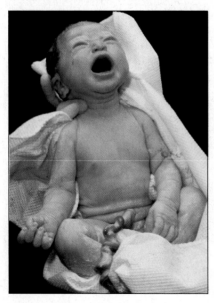

▼ **Figure 39–22** A newborn baby takes its first breath of air.

Within a few hours after birth, the pituitary hormone prolactin stimulates the production of milk in the breast tissues of the mother. Nutrients packed into that milk contain everything the baby needs for growth and development during the first few months of life.

Sometimes more than one baby develops during a pregnancy. Multiple births can happen for one of two reasons: (1) When two eggs are released and fertilized during the same cycle, fraternal twins result. Such twins are not identical because each has been formed by the fusion of a different sperm and egg cell. (2) Identical twins are formed when a single zygote splits apart to produce two embryos. Identical twins are formed by the fusion of the same sperm and egg cell and, therefore, are genetically identical.

✓CHECKPOINT *What is oxytocin?*

Early Years

Although the most spectacular developments of the human body occur before birth, development is a continuing process—it lasts throughout the life of an individual. In the first weeks of a baby's life, the systems that developed before birth move into high gear, supporting rapid growth that generally triples a baby's birth weight within 12 months.

Infancy Infancy, the period from four weeks after birth until about two years of age, is a period of rapid growth and development. The nervous system develops coordinated body movements as the infant begins to crawl and then to walk. A baby's first teeth appear and he or she begins to eat solid food. Infants also begin to understand and use language. Growth in the skeletal and muscular systems is especially rapid, demanding good nutrition to support proper development.

Childhood Childhood lasts from infancy until the onset of puberty, typically around the age of 12 or 13. During this time language is acquired and motor coordination is perfected. Permanent teeth begin to appear and the long bones of the skeletal system reach 80 percent of their adult length. The key elements of personality and human social skills are formed, and reasoning skills are developed to a high level.

Figure 39–23 During infancy, an infant learns to stand, walk, speak a few words, and imitate others. From ages 5 to 12, children grow to about 70 percent of their adult height and weight.

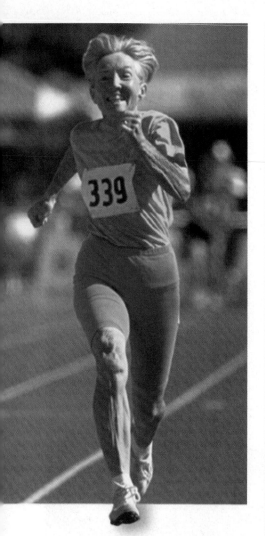

▲ **Figure 39–24** By maintaining a healthy lifestyle, you may be able to slow the aging process. **Applying Concepts** *What factors contribute to a healthy life cycle?*

Adolescence Adolescence begins with puberty and ends with adulthood. The surge in sex hormones that starts at puberty produces a growth spurt that will conclude in mid-adolescence as the long bones of the arms and legs stop growing and complete their mineralization. The continuing development of intellectual skills is associated with personality changes that come with adult maturity.

Adulthood

Development continues during adulthood. By most measures, adults reach their highest levels of physical strength and development between the ages of 25 and 35. Peak childbearing years are those of early adulthood. During these years, most individuals assume the responsibilities of adulthood, including establishing careers.

In most individuals, the first signs of physiological aging appear in the 30s. Joints begin to lose some of their flexibility, muscle strength plateaus, and several body systems show slight declines in efficiency. By age 50, these changes, although generally still minor, are apparent to most individuals. In women, menopause greatly reduces estrogen levels. After menopause, ovulation stops, marking the end of the childbearing years. At around age 65, most systems of the body become less efficient, making homeostasis more difficult to maintain.

Although there are some changes in mental functioning during older adulthood, these changes usually have little effect on thinking, learning, or long-term memory. The brain remains open to change and to learning. In fact, evidence suggests that the aging process can be slowed by keeping the mind active and challenged. Most older adults are fully capable of continuing stimulating intellectual work. By practicing the habits of good health and regular exercise, as the woman is doing in **Figure 39–24,** every person can hope to be happy and productive at every stage of human development.

39–4 Section Assessment

1. **Key Concept** Describe the process of fertilization.

2. **Key Concept** Describe the role of the placenta.

3. What are the three germ layers that result from gastrulation?

4. Describe the early years of development.

5. **Critical Thinking Applying Concepts** Why do you think doctors recommend that women avoid most medications and alcohol during pregnancy?

iTEXT **Assessment** Use iText to review the important concepts in Section 39–4.

Modeling Blood Glucose Regulation

Regulating the level of blood glucose is one of the body's most important jobs. Two hormones, insulin and glucagon, help to regulate the level of glucose in blood. Because these two hormones have opposite effects, it is important that a proper balance between them is maintained. In this investigation, you will simulate how this regulatory mechanism works.

Problem How does the body regulate blood glucose levels?

Materials
- 3 pieces of construction paper of different colors
- scissors

Skills Using Models, Posing Questions

Procedure

1. Work in groups of three students. Give each member of the group a number from 1 to 3.

2. Cut 15 cards out of construction paper of one color. On each card, print "10 mg glucose/100 mL blood" on the front and "glycogen" on the back. These are your glucose cards. Turning over a glucose card represents converting glucose into glycogen, or vice versa.

3. Cut out 2 cards of a second color. On each of these cards print "insulin." One of these insulin cards can convert 1 glucose card into glycogen.

4. Cut out 2 more cards of a third color. On each of these cards print "glucagon." One glucagon card can convert 1 glucose card from glycogen into glucose.

5. Place 9 glucose cards face up on the table. This represents the normal level of glucose in blood (90 mg glucose/100 mL blood). Student 1 should keep 2 more glucose cards face up.

6. Student 2 should keep the insulin and glucagon cards. Student 3 should keep the remaining 4 glucose cards face down, to represent stored glycogen.

7. To simulate the effect of a meal, student 1 should add a glucose card to the 9 on the table. Discuss how the body responds to this change.

8. Students 2 and 3 should use the cards to model how the body restores the normal blood glucose level after a meal.

9. To simulate the effect of exercise, student 1 should remove a glucose card from the 9 on the table. Repeat step 8.

10. To simulate what happens when a person has Type I diabetes, repeat steps 7 and 8 without using the insulin cards.

Analyze and Conclude

1. **Applying Concepts** What organ does student 2 represent? Explain your answer.

2. **Using Models** How did students 2 and 3 respond in step 8? In step 9? In step 10? Describe what happens in the body in each situation.

3. **Predicting** What do you think would happen if a person with diabetes ate a lot of sugar?

Go Further

Making a Model What do you think would happen if the body did not produce enough glucagon? Use your cards to model what would happen in this situation.

39–1 The Endocrine System
Key Concepts

- The endocrine system is made up of glands that release their products into the bloodstream. These products broadcast messages throughout the body.
- Like most systems of the body, the endocrine system is regulated by feedback mechanisms that function to maintain homeostasis.

Vocabulary
hormone, p. 997
target cell, p. 997
exocrine gland, p. 998
endocrine gland, p. 998
prostaglandin, p. 1000

39–2 Human Endocrine Glands
Key Concepts

- The pituitary gland secretes nine hormones that directly regulate many body functions and control the actions of several other endocrine glands.
- The hypothalamus controls the secretions of the pituitary gland.
- The thyroid gland has the major role in regulating the body's metabolism.
- Hormones from the thyroid gland and the parathyroid glands maintain homeostasis in blood calcium levels.
- The adrenal glands help the body prepare for and deal with stress.
- Insulin and glucagon released from the pancreas help to keep the level of glucose in the blood stable.
- The gonads serve two important functions: the production of gametes and the secretion of sex hormones.

Vocabulary
pituitary gland, p. 1003
diabetes mellitus, p. 1008
ovary, p. 1008
testis, p. 1008

39–3 The Reproductive System
Key Concepts

- The main structures of the male reproductive system are the testes, the epididymis, the vas deferens, the urethra, and the penis. These structures work together to produce and deliver sperm.
- The main structures of the female reproductive system are the ovaries, the Fallopian tubes, the uterus, and the vagina. In addition to producing eggs, the female reproductive system prepares the female's body to nourish a developing embryo.
- The menstrual cycle has four phases: follicular phase, ovulation, luteal phase, and menstruation.

Vocabulary
puberty, p. 1009 • scrotum, p. 1010
seminiferous tubule, p. 1010
epididymis, p. 1010 • vas deferens, p. 1011
urethra, p. 1011 • penis, p. 1011
follicle, p. 1012 • ovulation, p. 1013
Fallopian tube, p. 1013 • uterus, p. 1013
vagina, p. 1013 • menstrual cycle, p. 1013
corpus luteum, p. 1014 • menstruation, p. 1015

39–4 Fertilization and Development
Key Concepts

- The process of a sperm joining with an egg is called fertilization.
- The placenta is the embryo's organ of respiration, nourishment, and excretion.

Vocabulary
zygote, p. 1016
implantation, p. 1017
gastrulation, p. 1017
placenta, p. 1018
fetus, p. 1019

Thinking Visually
Use the information in this chapter to construct a chart listing the actions of each hormone discussed. Your chart should include three headings: Endocrine Gland, Hormone, and Action of Hormone.

Chapter 39

Part A

Multiple Choice

For each statement or question, select the number of the word or expression that, of those given, best completes the statement or answers the question.

1 Glands that release hormones into the blood are part of the
 (1) digestive system
 (2) endocrine system
 (3) circulatory system
 (4) nervous system

2 Hormones produced from cholesterol are called
 (1) protein hormones
 (2) steroid hormones
 (3) nonsteroid hormones
 (4) peptide hormones

3 Hormonelike substances produced by nearly all cells are known as
 (1) thyroxines
 (2) steroids
 (3) prostaglandins
 (4) androgens

4 Hormones that help regulate blood calcium levels are produced by the
 (1) adrenal gland
 (2) pancreas
 (3) thymus gland
 (4) parathyroid glands

5 The rate of body metabolism is regulated by
 (1) PTH   (3) aldosterone
 (2) thyroxine   (4) calcitonin

6 The diagram below shows the female reproductive system.

 Which structure is indicated by the X?
 (1) cervix   (3) ovary
 (2) Fallopian tube (4) uterus

7 The principal male sex hormone is
 (1) FSH   (3) insulin
 (2) estrogen   (4) testosterone

8 Fertilization usually occurs in the
 (1) uterus   (3) vagina
 (2) Fallopian tube (4) ovary

9 After the eighth week of development, the human embryo is known as a(an)
 (1) zygote   (3) infant
 (2) fetus   (4) blastula

10 Which sequence correctly describes the route that sperm take through the male reproductive system?
 (1) vas deferens, urethra, epididymis
 (2) epididymis, vas deferens, urethra
 (3) vas deferens, epididymis, urethra
 (4) urethra, epididymis, vas deferens

11 Each of these terms refers to a stage in the human menstrual cycle *except*
 (1) ovulation
 (2) follicular phase
 (3) luteal phase
 (4) corpus phase

12 Which is *not* an endocrine gland?
 (1) thyroid gland   (3) pituitary gland
 (2) sweat gland   (4) adrenal gland

13 The part of the sperm that contains genetic information is the
 (1) nucleus   (3) mitochondria
 (2) neck   (4) tail

14 Development of sperm is stimulated by
 (1) LH and estrogen
 (2) FSH and testosterone
 (3) the corpus luteum
 (4) adrenalin

15 Structures that have receptors for a particular hormone are called
 (1) target cells
 (2) endocrine glands
 (3) enzymes
 (4) steroids

Test-Taking Tip For questions containing words like *not* or *except*, first rule out any choice that does fit the characteristic in question. Use this approach to eliminate three out of four choices. To check if your answer is correct, confirm that it does not fit the characteristic in question.

Preparing for the
Living Environment Exam

Parts B and C

Multiple Choice and Extended Response

For those questions that ask you to select a response, choose the one that best completes the statement or answers the question. For all others follow the directions given.

Base your answers to questions 16 through 19 on the diagram below and on your knowledge of biology.

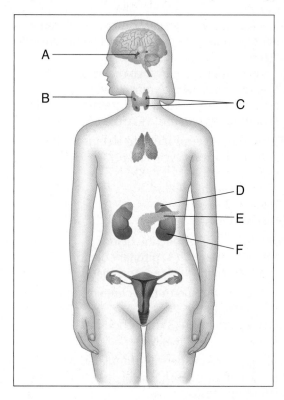

16 Which gland helps the body deal with stress?
- (1) A
- (3) C
- (2) B
- (4) D

17 Which gland is both an endocrine and an exocrine gland?
- (1) E
- (3) C
- (2) B
- (4) D

18 Which gland secretes growth hormone?
- (1) A
- (3) E
- (2) B
- (4) F

19 Which gland secretes thyroxine?
- (1) A
- (3) D
- (2) B
- (4) F

20 Predict the effects that insufficient amounts of FSH and LH will have on the menstrual cycle.

21 Which structure is correctly matched with its function?
- (1) cervix: prepares egg for release into female reproductive tract
- (2) follicle: secretes fluid into semen
- (3) hypothalamus: controls secretions of pituitary gland
- (4) epididymis: produces estrogen and progesterone

Base your answers to questions 22 and 23 on the information and graph below and on your knowledge of biology.

Levels of glucose in the blood of two people were measured repeatedly during a 5-hour period, immediately following the ingestion of a typical meal. One of the people has diabetes. The other one does not. The data are shown in the graph.

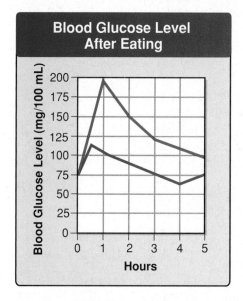

22 Which line represents the person with diabetes? Which line represents the person without diabetes? Support your answers with an explanation.

23 Describe how the graph might be different if the person with diabetes had received insulin after the meal.

24 Explain what is meant by the "fight-or-flight" response. In your answer, describe the role played by the endocrine system, the physical changes that take place in the body, and how the changes help the individual fight or flee.

25 Describe how each of the following is an adaptation that helps ensure successful fertilization: seminal fluid, production and release of millions of sperm, cilia lining the Fallopian tubes, long tails of sperm.

Base your answers to question 26 and 27 on the information below and on your knowledge of biology.

In many areas during rush hour, radio and television stations broadcast traffic reports. The reports inform the listening public where accidents and construction have interrupted normal traffic patterns so that drivers can plan their routes accordingly.

26 Explain how traffic reports are similar to hormones. What part of traffic reporting is similar to a target cell?

27 Explain how a traffic report acts as a feedback mechanism to control the flow of traffic.

28 Explain how the placenta prevents the mother's blood from mixing with the blood of the developing fetus.

29 Describe what happens if blood glucose levels are not kept stable.

30 Explain what puberty is.

31 State the two hormones that stimulate the gonads to produce their hormones.

32 Identify the secondary sex characteristics that appear in males at puberty.

33 Describe the structure of sperm.

34 State two functions of estrogen.

35 Describe the path of an unfertilized egg from a follicle until it leaves the body.

36 Explain why the menstrual cycle is an example of a feedback mechanism.

37 Trace the development of a zygote from fertilization through implantation.

38 Describe gastrulation, and explain the importance of the primary germ layers.

39 Explain why some hormones can be taken orally, whereas others, such as insulin, are injected directly into the body.

40 The heartbeat of a swimmer increases significantly both before and during a swim meet. Explain why this happens.

Base your answers to questions 41 through 43 on the information below and on your knowledge of biology.

Fetal Alcohol Syndrome

Pregnant women subject themselves to the same risks caused by alcohol use and abuse as the general population. In addition, they place their fetuses at risk of developing fetal alcohol syndrome, or FAS.

Although the placenta provides an effective barrier for most substances in the mother's blood, it does not keep out alcohol. Alcohol may damage the fetus and cause problems such as heart defects and facial abnormalities. Alcohol may also cause the fetus to grow and develop slowly, leading to low birth weight, small head circumference, delayed development, and mental retardation.

The fetus is particularly sensitive to the adverse effects of alcohol during the first three months of development because all the major organs and tissues are forming then. Alcohol may cause problems at other times as well. The only sure way to prevent the fetus from being harmed is to avoid alcohol throughout pregnancy.

41 Explain what causes fetal alcohol syndrome, and describe how it affects the fetus. How can it be prevented?

42 Explain why the fetus is especially sensitive to the adverse effects of alcohol during the first three months of development.

43 How do you predict the use of other drugs, such as cocaine or heroin, might affect fetal development?

 Take It to the NET

Who is at risk for diabetes? Visit the Prentice Hall Web site at **www.phschool.com** to find out the risk factors for the disease. Then, answer the following questions:

• What types of questions are included in the risk test?

• What can a person do to maintain or lower his or her risk?

• Why are questions about symptoms of diabetes left off the risk test?

• What data are the test questions based on?

Chapter 40

The Immune System and Disease

White blood cells help protect the body from disease. Here, one type of white blood cell—a macrophage—engulfs a parasite (magnification: 1950×).

Discovery CHANNEL SCHOOL

To find out more about transmission of a virus, view the videotape "Influenza: Tracking a Virus."

Inquiry Activity

How do diseases spread?

Procedure

1. Your teacher has placed a fluorescent material in the classroom to simulate a virus. The material glows when exposed to ultraviolet radiation (UV). Use a UV lamp to check for "virus" on your hands and objects you touched since entering the classroom. **CAUTION:** *Ultraviolet light can harm your eyes. Do not look directly at the ultraviolet light.*

2. Exchange results with your classmates to determine how the "virus" spread through the classroom. Wash your hands with soap and water.

Think About It

1. **Inferring** What can you infer about how the "virus" spread through the classroom?

2. **Drawing Conclusions** How does thorough hand washing help prevent the spread of diseases?

40–1 Infectious Disease

Good health is something that you might take for granted—until you, or someone close to you, gets sick. Then, the value of good health becomes all too obvious. Why do you get sick? How do you get better? What is the best way for you to avoid getting sick in the first place? These are questions that people have been asking for centuries. Today, in most cases, these questions can be answered.

A **disease** is any change, other than an injury, that disrupts the normal functions of the body. **Some diseases, such as hemophilia, are inherited. Others are caused by materials in the environment, such as cigarette smoke. Still others are produced by agents such as bacteria, viruses, and fungi.** Disease-causing agents such as bacteria are called **pathogens,** which means "sickness-makers." Diseases caused by pathogens are generally called infectious diseases because the agents that cause them usually enter, or infect, the body of the person who gets sick.

The Germ Theory of Disease

For thousands of years, people believed that diseases were caused by curses, evil spirits, or night vapors. In the mid-nineteenth century, a new explanation based on the work of the French chemist Louis Pasteur and the German bacteriologist Robert Koch was put forth. The observations of Pasteur and Koch led them to conclude that infectious diseases were caused by microorganisms, or germs. This conclusion is now known as the **germ theory of disease.** The world is filled with microorganisms of every shape and description. How can scientists be sure which organism causes a particular disease?

In 1975, Allen Steere of Yale University got a chance to ask exactly that question. In a small area of Connecticut, Steere found 39 children and several adults suffering from pain and joint inflammation. Their symptoms looked like a rare form of childhood arthritis. However, Steere thought that there were far too many cases for such a small population. The rural location of the outbreak, and the fact that most of the cases had started in summer or early fall, made Steere suspect that this could be an infectious disease carried by an insect.

Guide for Reading

🔑 **Key Concepts**
- What causes disease?
- How are infectious diseases transmitted?

Vocabulary
disease
pathogen
germ theory of disease
Koch's postulates
toxin
vector
antibiotic

**Reading Strategy:
Using Prior Knowledge**
Before you read, make a list of diseases that you have had. As you read, decide whether or not these diseases were infectious.

Figure 40–1 🔑 **Diseases can be inherited, caused by materials in the environment, or produced by pathogens.** Ticks often carry bacteria, so when they come in contact with human skin, they often transmit pathogens.

(magnification: about 30×)

Pathogen (*Borrelia burgdorferi*) identified

Pathogen grown in pure culture

Pathogen injected into healthy lab mouse

Healthy mouse becomes sick

Pathogen (*Borrelia burgdorferi*) identified

▲ **Figure 40–2** Allen Steere followed Koch's postulates to test his theory that the bacterium *Borrelia burgdorferi* caused Lyme disease. **Inferring** *Why must the pathogen be grown in a pure culture?*

Sure enough, many of the children reported that their problems had begun with what they thought was an insect bite. The bite was followed by an expanding skin rash. Steere called the infection Lyme disease after the town of Lyme, Connecticut, where it was first discovered.

Steere and his colleagues were able to link the skin rash to the bite of the tiny deer tick (*Ixodes scapularis*). One of Steere's colleagues, Dr. Willy Burgdorfer, found an unusual spiral-shaped bacterium *(Borrelia burgdorferi)* in the ticks. Steere found the same bacterium in patients with Lyme disease. Could this bacterium be the cause of Lyme disease?

For ethical reasons, Steere did not try to infect healthy children with the bacterium. However, when the bacterium was injected into laboratory mice, they developed arthritis and other symptoms, just like the children. From the sick mice, Steere recovered the bacteria, which were then able to pass the infection along to healthy mice. Steere and his colleagues had found the organism that caused Lyme disease. The process Steere used is shown in **Figure 40–2.**

Koch's Postulates

The groundwork for Allen Steere's work with Lyme disease was actually laid more than a hundred years earlier by Robert Koch. From his studies with other bacteria, Koch developed a series of guidelines still used today to identify the microorganism that causes a specific disease. These rules are known as **Koch's postulates.** Koch's postulates state the following:

1. The pathogen should always be found in the body of a sick organism and should not be found in a healthy one.

2. The pathogen must be isolated and grown in the laboratory in pure culture.

3. When the purified pathogens are placed in a new host, they should cause the same disease that infected the original host.

4. The injected pathogen should be reisolated from the second host. It should be identical to the original pathogen.

With these rules, disease did not seem to be an unavoidable consequence of being alive. If a particular pathogen could be identified, maybe the disease it caused could be prevented or cured.

✓ CHECKPOINT *What are Koch's postulates?*

Agents of Disease

For many pathogens, the human body provides just the right conditions for growth—the right temperature, a watery environment, and an abundance of nutrients. The large intestine, for example, harbors dense colonies of bacteria. Bacteria and yeast are found in the mouth, throat, and in the tissues surrounding the eyeball. Fortunately, most of these organisms are harmless and many are actually beneficial.

If this is true, then exactly how do pathogens cause disease? Recall the pathogens you studied in Units 6 and 8. Bacteria can either break down the tissues in an infected organism or release toxins into the body. **Toxins** are poisons that produce illness by disrupting bodily functions. Some protists, fungi, and worms are parasites that live and feed inside an infected organism. Some remove nutrients from the digestive system. Others destroy blood cells and neurons. A virus, which is a nonliving pathogen, can use the materials of a host cell to make copies of the virus until the cell bursts. **Figure 40–3** gives examples of pathogens, the diseases they cause, and how the pathogens are transmitted.

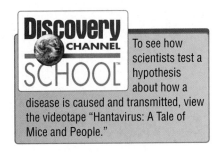

To see how scientists test a hypothesis about how a disease is caused and transmitted, view the videotape "Hantavirus: A Tale of Mice and People."

▼ **Figure 40–3** This table lists some of the viruses, bacteria, protists, worms, and fungi that cause disease. **Using Tables and Graphs** *What kind of pathogen causes athlete's foot?*

Pathogens and Disease

Pathogen Types	Disease	Agent That Causes Disease	Method of Transmission
Viruses	Common cold	Rhinovirus	Airborne; direct contact with infected person
	Influenza	Two types (A, B), plus subtypes	Airborne; droplet infection; direct contact with infected person
	Chicken pox	Varicella	Airborne; direct contact with infected person
	Measles	Paramyxovirus	Droplets in air; direct contact with secretions of infected person
Bacteria	Tuberculosis	*Mycobacterium tuberculosis*	Droplets in air; contaminated milk and dairy products
	Meningitis	*Neisseria meningitidis*	Direct contact with a carrier
	Cholera	*Vibrio cholerae*	Contaminated drinking water
	Tetanus	*Clostridium tetani*	Contaminated wound; usually puncture wound
Protists	African sleeping sickness	*Trypanosoma*	Spread by tsetse fly
	Malaria	*Plasmodium*	Spread by *Anopheles* mosquitoes
	Amoebic dysentery	*Entamoeba histolytica*	Contaminated drinking water
Worms	Schistosomiasis	*Schistosoma*	Freshwater streams and rice paddies
	Beef tapeworm	*Taenia saginata*	Contaminated meat
Fungi	Athlete's foot	Imperfect fungi	Contact with infected person; shower stalls
	Ringworm	Imperfect fungi	Exchange of hats, combs, or athletic head gear with infected person

How Diseases Are Spread

The best method for fighting any disease is to avoid it. Once a pathogen has been identified, biologists search for clues as to how it is passed from one person to the next. If a disease is thoroughly understood, how to prevent it usually becomes clear.

Infectious diseases are transmitted in a number of ways. 🔑 **Some infectious diseases are spread from one person to another through coughing, sneezing, or physical contact. Other infectious diseases are spread through contaminated water or food. Still others are spread by infected animals.**

▲ **Figure 40–4** 🔑 Some infectious diseases are spread by insects. This *Anopheles* mosquito may be a carrier of the protist that causes malaria.

Vectors Animals, such as ticks or the mosquito in **Figure 40–4,** spread many diseases. Animals that carry disease-causing organisms from person to person are called **vectors.** Vectors are often the key to stopping the diseases they spread. Avoiding tall grass and wooded areas where deer are present will limit your exposure to the ticks that carry Lyme disease. **Figure 40–5** shows another method of limiting people's exposure to vectors—spraying insecticides. Mosquito breeding areas can be sprayed with insecticides to fight malaria and West Nile virus.

The common cold, mumps, measles, and influenza are diseases that can spread from one person to another through coughing, sneezing, or even through hand-to-hand contact. Some habits can help to control transmission of these diseases. Simple measures such as covering your mouth with a tissue when you cough are often enough to limit infection. Washing your hands thoroughly helps to prevent the spread of many pathogens. You probably have noticed the signs in restaurant bathrooms reminding employees to wash their hands. This reminder is one way that restaurant owners try to prevent contamination of food.

Sexually Transmitted Diseases Some of the most dangerous pathogens are spread from one person to another by sexual contact. Sexually transmitted diseases, or STDs, are a serious health problem in the United States, infecting millions of people each year and accounting for thousands of deaths. Many of the most serious STDs—including syphilis and gonorrhea—are caused by bacteria. Others, including hepatitis B, hepatitis C, genital herpes, and AIDS, are caused by viruses. The consequences of infection can be severe. Gonorrhea and a disease called chlamydia, for example, can permanently damage the reproductive system. Other STDs, including syphilis and AIDS, can be fatal.

Fighting Infectious Diseases

If prevention fails, drugs have been developed for use against all sorts of pathogens. Perhaps the most useful single class of infection-fighting drugs are the antibiotics. **Antibiotics** are compounds that kill bacteria without harming the cells of humans or animals. Antibiotics work by interfering with the cellular processes of microorganisms. Many antibiotics are produced naturally by living organisms. Others are produced synthetically. Penicillin is, perhaps, the most well-known antibiotic.

Penicillin, the first antibiotic to be discovered, was found accidently in 1928 by the Scottish bacteriologist Alexander Fleming. Fleming had been growing *Staphylococcus* bacteria in a culture dish. One day, Fleming noticed that the culture of bacteria had been contaminated by a species of green mold called *Penicillium notatum*. This might simply have been annoying. However, Fleming noticed something exciting. The bacteria were not growing near the mold. Something produced by the mold was inhibiting the growth of the bacteria. Later, researchers discovered that penicillin—the name given to the antibiotic by Fleming—interferes with the synthesis of cell walls by bacteria, crippling fast-growing, walled bacteria.

Another antibiotic, streptomycin, interferes with the growth of bacteria by blocking protein synthesis on their ribosomes. Streptomycin was discovered by Russian American microbiologist Selman Waksman in 1943.

Antibiotics have no effect on viruses. However, antiviral drugs have been developed to fight certain viral diseases. These drugs generally inhibit the ability of viruses to invade cells and to multiply once inside of cells.

▲ **Figure 40–5** Spraying insecticides helps prevent the spread of disease. Because most insecticides can harm more than the target organism, they must be used with caution. Spraying is usually done at night when contact with humans and other animals is limited. **Applying Concepts** *How do insecticides help prevent the spread of disease?*

40–1 Section Assessment

1. 🔑 **Key Concept** Describe some of the causes of disease.

2. 🔑 **Key Concept** What are the ways in which infectious diseases are spread?

3. List Koch's postulates.

4. Give two examples each of diseases caused by viruses, bacteria, fungi, and protists.

5. How do vectors spread disease?

6. What are antibiotics?

7. **Critical Thinking Inferring** Louis Pasteur once stated, "In the fields of observation, chance favors only the mind that is prepared." How does this statement apply to the discovery of the antibiotic properties of penicillin?

📱 **TEXT** Assessment Use iText to review the important concepts in Section 40–1.

ALTERNATIVE ASSESSMENT

Designing a Graphic Organizer
Create a graphic organizer to show the different ways that infectious diseases are spread. Include at least four different routes of transmission in your graphic organizer.

40–2 The Immune System

Guide for Reading

 Key Concepts
• What are the body's non-specific defenses against invading pathogens?
• What is immunity?

Vocabulary
inflammatory response
fever
interferon
immune response
antigen
humoral immunity
antibody
cell-mediated immunity
permanent immunity
vaccination
active immunity

**Reading Strategy:
Finding Main Ideas** Before you read, skim the section to identify the key ideas. Then, carefully read the section, making a list of supporting details for each main idea.

W̶ith pathogens all around us, it might seem like a miracle that you aren't sick all of the time. There's a reason, of course, why most of us enjoy good health. Our bodies have a protective system—a series of defenses that guard against disease. Some of these defenses, like the wall around a fortress, are simple barriers that keep all invaders out. Others, like security guards, are trained to spot invaders that have somehow slipped through the fortress walls. Once identified, such invaders can be rounded up and kept from doing damage.

Nonspecific Defenses

The immune system is the body's primary defense against pathogens. It consists of nonspecific and specific defenses against infection. Nonspecific defenses are the fortress walls of the system. They keep everything out and guard against all infections. Specific defenses work like security guards. They track down harmful pathogens that have managed to break through the body's nonspecific defenses.

First Line of Defense The job of the body's first line of defense is to keep pathogens out. This role is carried out by skin, mucus, sweat, and tears. 🔑 **Your body's most important nonspecific defense is the skin.** Very few pathogens can penetrate the layers of dead cells at the skin's surface. Oil and sweat glands in the skin produce an acidic environment that kills many bacteria. The importance of the skin as a barrier against infection becomes obvious as soon as the skin is broken. As you know, even a small scrape or cut can become infected if it is not taken care of. The infections are caused by microorganisms normally present on the unbroken surface of your skin. When your skin is broken, pathogens can enter your body and multiply. As they grow, they cause the symptoms of an infection, such as swelling, redness, and pain.

Pathogens can also enter your body through your mouth and nose. Your body has other nonspecific defenses that protect these openings. Mucus in your nose and throat traps viruses and bacteria and cilia push them away from your lungs. Stomach acid and digestive enzymes destroy many pathogens that make their way to your stomach. Finally, many secretions of the body, including mucus, saliva, sweat, and tears, contain lysozyme, an enzyme that breaks down the cell walls of many bacteria.

(magnification: 1100×)

◀ **Figure 40–6** 🔎 **Mucus is another of your body's nonspecific defenses against infection.** Pathogens can get trapped in mucus the way the long brown strand of dirt in the photograph is trapped.

Skin

Wound

Bacteria enter the wound

Phagocytes move into the area and engulf the bacteria and cell debris

Capillary

Second Line of Defense If pathogens do manage to enter your body, they may multiply quickly, releasing toxins into your tissues. When this happens, the **inflammatory response**—a second line of defense—is activated. 🔑 **The inflammatory response is a nonspecific defense reaction to tissue damage caused by injury or infection.** Blood vessels near the wound expand, and white blood cells leak from the vessels to enter the infected tissues. Many of these white blood cells are phagocytes, which engulf and destroy bacteria. The infected tissue may become swollen and painful. The battle between pathogens and phagocytes is illustrated in **Figure 40–7.**

When pathogens are detected, the immune system produces millions of white blood cells, which fight the infection. If a blood test reveals an increase in the number of white blood cells, the body is dealing with a serious infection. The immune system also releases chemicals that increase the core body temperature. You may have experienced this elevated body temperature, called a **fever**. Many pathogens can only survive within a narrow temperature range. An elevated temperature slows down or stops the growth of such pathogens. The higher temperature increases heart rate so that the white blood cells get to the sites of infection faster. An increased temperature also speeds the activities of the white blood cells and the rate of the chemical reactions that help repair damaged tissues.

Interferon In 1957, scientists discovered that virus-infected cells produce a group of proteins that help other cells resist viral infection. Scientists named these proteins **interferons** because they "interfere" with the virus. Interferons inhibit the synthesis of viral proteins in infected cells and help block viral replication. This slows down the progress of infection and often gives the specific defenses of the immune system time to respond.

✓ **CHECKPOINT** *How do interferons help fight infection?*

▲ **Figure 40–7** 💬 The inflammatory response is a nonspecific defense reaction to tissue damage caused by injury or infection. When pathogens enter the body, phagocytes move into the area and engulf the pathogens. In addition, platelets and clotting factors leak from the capillaries.

Word Origins

Phagocyte comes from the Greek *phag*, meaning "eat," and *kutos*, meaning "cell." Thus, a phagocyte is a cell that eats or engulfs. If the Greek prefix *macro-* means "large," what might the word *macrophage* mean?

Specific Defenses

If a pathogen is able to get past the body's nonspecific defenses, the immune system reacts with a series of specific defenses that attack the disease-causing agent. These defenses are called the **immune response.** A substance that triggers this response is known as an **antigen.** Carbohydrates, proteins, and lipids on the surfaces of viruses, bacteria, and other pathogens may serve as antigens that trigger responses by the immune system. The body can produce two different immune responses: humoral immunity and cell-mediated immunity.

Humoral Immunity   **Humoral immunity** is immunity against pathogens in the body fluids (blood and lymph). This immune response is produced by the actions of lymphocytes, a type of white blood cell. B lymphocytes, or B cells, are responsible for producing antibodies.

An antibody molecule is the basic functional unit of the humoral immune response. An **antibody** is a protein that helps destroy pathogens. As shown in **Figure 40–8,** an antibody is shaped like the letter Y and has two identical antigen-binding sites. These sites allow each antibody to bind to two antigens. Suppose the antigen is a protein found on the surface of the flu virus. Each flu virus particle is covered with many protein antigens. By attaching to the viral antigens, a group of antibody molecules can link the viruses together in a large mass. The clump of viruses and antibodies attracts phagocytes, which engulf and destroy the whole mass. If the immune system produces enough antibodies to a particular virus, it can prevent that virus from infecting cells.

Antibodies can fight bacterial infections as well. When antibodies bind to the surfaces of bacteria, they mark the cells for destruction by phagocytes and other white blood cells.

How does the immune system produce the specific antibodies that bind to antigens on the surface of pathogens? In a sense, they are custom made. As B cells develop early in life, the genes that code for antibodies rearrange themselves in slightly different ways in each B cell. When the development of B cells is complete, the immune system contains millions of B cells. Each of these B cells is capable of producing a slightly different antibody.

When a pathogen invades the body, its antigens are recognized by a small fraction of the body's B cells. These activated B cells grow and divide rapidly, producing large numbers of specialized B cells called plasma cells. Plasma cells release antibodies into the bloodstream to attack the pathogen that is causing the infection. Millions of plasma cells may form from just a few dozen B cells as a result of exposure to an antigen. The activation of plasma cells is assisted and regulated by lymphocytes known as T lymphocytes, or T cells. **Figure 40–9** summarizes the process of humoral immunity.

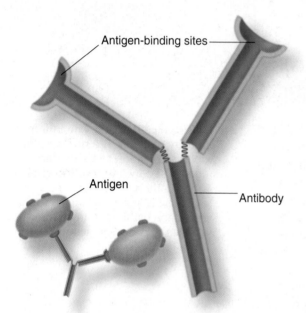

Antigen-binding sites

Antigen

Antibody

▲ **Figure 40–8** An antibody molecule has two identical antigen-binding sites. It is at these sites that one or two specific antigens bind to the antibody. **Applying Concepts** *How do antibodies help in the immune response?*

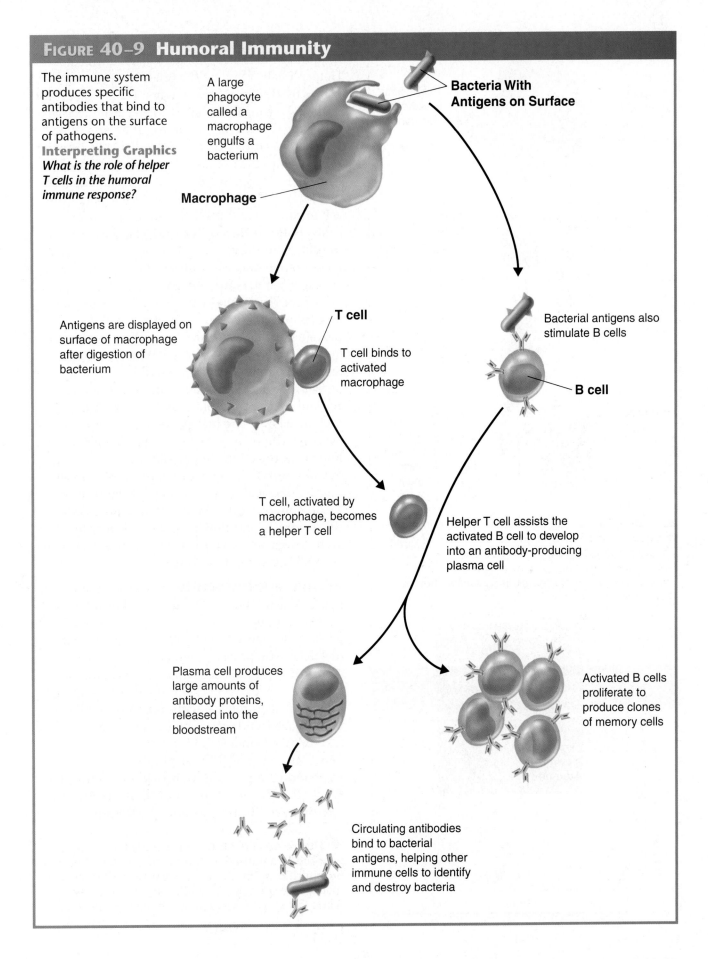

FIGURE 40–9 Humoral Immunity

The immune system produces specific antibodies that bind to antigens on the surface of pathogens.

Interpreting Graphics
What is the role of helper T cells in the humoral immune response?

A large phagocyte called a macrophage engulfs a bacterium

Macrophage

Bacteria With Antigens on Surface

Antigens are displayed on surface of macrophage after digestion of bacterium

T cell

T cell binds to activated macrophage

Bacterial antigens also stimulate B cells

B cell

T cell, activated by macrophage, becomes a helper T cell

Helper T cell assists the activated B cell to develop into an antibody-producing plasma cell

Plasma cell produces large amounts of antibody proteins, released into the bloodstream

Activated B cells proliferate to produce clones of memory cells

Circulating antibodies bind to bacterial antigens, helping other immune cells to identify and destroy bacteria

The Immune System and Disease **1037**

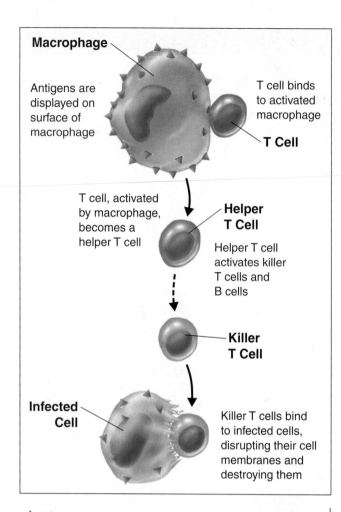

Macrophage

Antigens are displayed on surface of macrophage

T cell binds to activated macrophage

T Cell

T cell, activated by macrophage, becomes a helper T cell

Helper T Cell

Helper T cell activates killer T cells and B cells

Killer T Cell

Infected Cell

Killer T cells bind to infected cells, disrupting their cell membranes and destroying them

▲ **Figure 40–10** During the cell-mediated immune response, helper T cells stimulate killer T cells to divide. The killer T cells then attack the pathogen.
Comparing and Contrasting *How are humoral immunity and cell-mediated immunity similar? How are they different?*

Primary and Secondary Immune Responses

Antibody Concentration

First exposure

Interval between exposures

Second exposure

Time

Cell-Mediated Immunity Sometimes immunity relies on lymphocytes, not antibodies. Helper T cells regulate the production of antibodies by B cells. However, other T cells can attack antigen-bearing cells directly. The most effective attacking cells in the immune system are killer T cells, or cytotoxic T cells. These killer cells transfer proteins into the cell membrane of a pathogen, causing fluid from inside the cell to leak out of the membrane. The rapid loss of material causes the cell to rupture and die. This immune response, called **cell-mediated immunity,** is particularly important in the case of diseases caused by eukaryotic pathogens. Cell-mediated immunity is summarized in **Figure 40–10.**

Killer T cells make it difficult to do organ transplants. Body cells have a set of marker proteins on their surfaces that allow the immune system to recognize the cells. When an organ from one person is transplanted into another person, the second person's immune system recognizes the transplanted organ as foreign, and attacks it. The immune system damages and destroys the transplanted organ. This process is known as rejection. To prevent organ rejection, doctors search for a donor whose markers are nearly identical to the markers of the recipient. Recipients must take drugs that suppress the cell-mediated immune response, usually for the rest of their lives. These drugs include cyclosporine and the steroid prednisone.

Permanent Immunity The growth of B cells and T cells in response to infection has an important consequence—one that people have been aware of for more than 2000 years. The Greek physician Hippocrates noted that people who survived certain diseases, such as measles and smallpox, never developed those diseases again. They had acquired a **permanent immunity** to the disease that had previously infected them.

Today we understand the nature of permanent immunity. 🔑 **Once the body has been exposed to a pathogen, millions of memory B and T cells remain capable of producing specific antibodies to that pathogen.**

◀ **Figure 40–11** 🔑 Once the body has been exposed to a pathogen, it remains capable of producing specific antibodies to that pathogen. Notice how much more strongly and quickly the immune system reacts to a second infection by the same pathogen.

How does cell-mediated immunity work?

Materials 3 red balloons; 3 yellow balloons; 3 blue balloons; red, yellow, and white adhesive notes; toothpick

Procedure
1. Partially inflate and tie the balloons. The balloons represent pathogens. The different colors represent different surface antigens. Put the inflated balloons on the table.
2. The adhesive notes represent antibodies that can bind to antigens on the surface of a pathogen of the same color. Use the adhesive notes to model the binding of antibodies to antigens on pathogens.
3. The toothpick represents a killer T cell. Use the toothpick to burst any balloons marked by adhesive notes.

Analyze and Conclude
1. **Using Models** How did you model the binding of antibodies to matching antigens in step 2?
2. **Using Models** What signals a killer T cell to attack a pathogen?

These memory B cells ensure that the disease never gets a chance to develop a second time. **Figure 40–11** shows how antibody production differs between the first and second exposures.

✓ CHECKPOINT *What is cell-mediated immunity?*

Active Immunity

More than 200 years ago, the English physician Edward Jenner wondered if it might be possible to produce permanent immunity against one of the deadliest diseases of the day—smallpox. Jenner knew of a mild disease called cowpox that was often contracted by milkmaids. Once they had contracted cowpox, the milkmaids were immune to smallpox. Was there a way, Jenner wondered, to deliberately infect a person with cowpox, thus protecting them from getting smallpox?

To answer this question, Jenner took fluid from one of the sores of a cowpox patient and put the fluid into a small cut that he made on the arm of a young farm boy named Jamie Phipps. As expected, Jamie developed a cowpox infection. Two months later, Jenner performed a daring experiment. He inoculated Jamie with fluid from a smallpox infection. Fortunately for Jamie, the experiment was a success—the boy did not develop smallpox. His cowpox infection had protected him from getting smallpox.

▲ **Figure 40–12** Vaccines are an important weapon in fighting disease. **Applying Concepts** *How do vaccines work?*

The injection of a weakened or mild form of a pathogen to produce immunity is known as a **vaccination.** *Vacca* is the Latin word for "cow," reflecting the history of Jenner's first vaccination experiment. The immunity produced by a vaccine is known as **active immunity** because the body of the recipient has the ability to mount an immediate active immune response against the pathogen.

Today, more than 20 serious human diseases can be prevented by vaccination. Like the vaccines developed by Jenner, modern vaccines stimulate the immune system to create millions of plasma cells ready to produce specific types of antibodies.

When you were very young, you were probably vaccinated against polio. Weakened polio viruses were used to stimulate the B cells in your body capable of making antipolio antibodies. As a result, should you ever be exposed to polio, your body is prepared to fight the virus with millions of plasma cells ready to make antipolio antibodies.

Passive Immunity

In active immunity, the body makes its own antibodies in response to an antigen. The body can also be protected from disease in another way. If antibodies produced by other animals for a pathogen are injected into the bloodstream, the antibodies produce a passive immunity against the pathogen as long as they remain in the circulation, usually for several weeks. Travelers are sometimes given antibodies against tropical diseases before they leave home. Passive immunity lasts only a short time because the body destroys the borrowed antibodies.

Another type of passive immunity is called maternal immunity. It occurs when antibodies from the mother are passed to the fetus through the placenta or to the infant in mother's milk. Maternal immunity protects a child against most infectious diseases for the first few months of its life, or longer if the infant is breast-fed.

40–2 Section Assessment

1. 🔑 **Key Concept** Describe the body's nonspecific defenses against pathogens.
2. 🔑 **Key Concept** Describe the process of immunity.
3. How do interferons protect the body against viruses?
4. How are antigens related to antibodies?

5. **Critical Thinking Comparing and Contrasting** How are active and passive immunity similar? How are they different?

📱 **iTEXT** Assessment Use iText to review the important concepts in Section 40–2.

40–3 Immune System Disorders

Although the immune system defends the body from a wide range of potential pathogens, sometimes disorders occur. There are two main types of disorders. In the first type, the immune system may overreact to an antigen, producing discomfort or even disease. In the second type, the cellular nature of the immune response is a potential weak point. What would happen if a disease attacked the lymphocytes, which are the heart of the immune system? As you will learn, the consequences can be disastrous.

Allergies

The most common overreactions of the immune system are known as allergies. **Allergies** result when antigens from allergens, such as those in **Figure 40–13,** bind to mast cells. Mast cells are a type of immune cell. They are especially common in the linings of the nasal passages.

When allergy-causing antigens attach themselves to mast cells, the activated mast cells release chemicals known as **histamines.** Histamines increase the flow of blood and fluids to the surrounding area. Histamines produce the sneezing, runny eyes and nose, and other irritations that make a person with allergies so uncomfortable. If you have allergies, you may have taken antihistamines. Antihistamines are drugs that are used to counteract the effects of histamines.

Guide for Reading

Key Concept
• What is an autoimmune disease?

Vocabulary
allergy
histamine
asthma

**Reading Strategy:
Using Prior Knowledge**
Do you or someone you know have allergies? As you read this section, use what you learn to explain the cause and symptoms of allergies.

Figure 40–13 Many common objects including ragweed pollen, dust, and dust mites are allergens. In the SEM of the dust ball, notice the insect parts, gray spider webbing, and other dirt. Dust mites live in furniture, mattresses, and even pillows. **Inferring** *Why do you think it is recommended that people wash their sheets and bedding in hot water?*

Ragweed Pollen (magnification: 770×)   **Dust Ball** (magnification: 760×)   **Dust Mite** (magnification: 900×)

Allergic reactions can create a dangerous condition called **asthma** in which smooth muscle contractions reduce the size of air passageways in the lungs and make breathing very difficult. A particular antigen usually triggers an asthma attack. For people prone to asthma, the best way to avoid an attack is to avoid the antigen that produces the attack. Scientists do not fully understand the reasons why some individuals become oversensitive to certain antigens. Drugs that are inhaled or injected make it possible to provide immediate relief. These drugs relax the smooth muscles to make breathing easier.

✓ CHECKPOINT   *What happens in the lungs during an asthma attack?*

Autoimmune Disease

The immune system could not defend your body against a host of invading pathogens unless it was able to distinguish those pathogens from the cells and tissues that are part of your body. In other words, the immune system has the ability to distinguish "self" from "nonself." 🔑 **When the immune system makes a mistake and attacks the body's own cells, it produces an autoimmune disease.**

Sometimes an infection can produce an autoimmune disease. This can happen when *Streptococcus* bacteria produce an infection known as strep throat. If the strep throat is left untreated, the immune system produces antibodies that destroy the bacteria. Because antigens on the surface of the bacteria are so similar to proteins on the surface of some cardiac cells, the immune system may attack the heart as well. This results in a condition known as rheumatic fever. In this disease, antibodies and killer T cells kill and scar cells of the heart lining and valves. Rheumatic fever can be prevented if the *Streptococcus* infection is promptly treated with antibiotics.

Other autoimmune diseases include juvenile-onset diabetes, myasthenia gravis, and multiple sclerosis. In juvenile-onset diabetes, an autoimmune reaction attacks the insulin-producing cells of the pancreas. In myasthenia gravis, antibodies attack neuromuscular junctions. Multiple sclerosis, or MS, is an autoimmune disease of the nervous system that results from the destruction of the myelin sheath that surrounds nerve fibers. The first symptoms of multiple sclerosis usually appear between the ages of 20 and 40. There is some evidence that suggests that this disease may be triggered by a viral infection.

AIDS

A dramatic example of what happens when cells of the immune system are weakened by infection is the disease called Acquired Immune Deficiency Syndrome, or AIDS. In the early 1980s, physicians began to see a number of unusual infections. The infections included protozoa in the lungs, severe fungal infections in the mouth and throat, and a rare form of skin cancer.

▼ **Figure 40–14** 🔑 When the immune system makes a mistake and attacks the body's own cells, it produces an autoimmune disease. Multiple sclerosis is one example of an autoimmune disease.

HIV Infection Among Women

Since the beginning of the AIDS epidemic, researchers at the Centers for Disease Control (CDC) in Atlanta have closely monitored the number of new AIDS cases each year. When an AIDS case is reported, investigators do their best to determine the source of the infection and report it along with the case itself. The data shown below are taken from a CDC report showing the number of new AIDS cases in adult and teenage women in the United States.

1. **Interpreting Graphics** From 1996 through 1998, did the overall number of AIDS cases among women increase, decrease, or remain the same?

2. **Drawing Conclusions** Which source of infection presents the greatest risk of AIDS for American women?

3. **Applying Concepts** If you were asked to design an educational program to decrease the risk of AIDS among women, which sources of infection would you stress? Which behaviors or activities seem to carry the greatest danger to women?

4. **Going Further** Use the library or the Internet and find the latest statistics on infections in men and adolescent boys. Analyze the differences between male and female patterns of HIV infection.

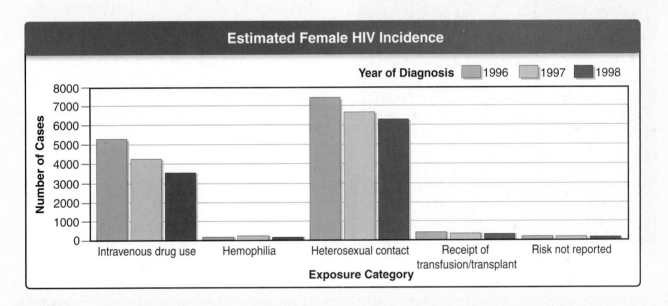

Estimated Female HIV Incidence

Normally, such infections are prevented by the immune system. Individual doctors realized that the symptoms were a signal that the immune systems of their patients had been weakened. However, doctors needed to see many similar cases before they were able to conclude that these weakened immune systems were characteristic of a new autoimmune disease.

The spread of the disease made scientists suspect that it was caused by a virus. In 1983, that virus—now known as HIV (human immunodeficiency virus)—was identified. Once HIV enters the body, it attaches to receptors on the surfaces of the T cells that help other lymphocytes respond to infection. The body does produce antibodies against HIV, but HIV replicates within cells of the immune system. Thus, it is less likely to bind to antibodies. Gradually, HIV kills off most of the helper T cells.

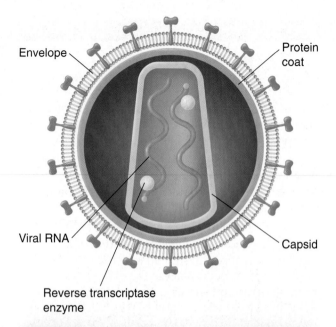

Envelope

Protein coat

Viral RNA

Reverse transcriptase enzyme

Capsid

(magnification: about 5000×)

By the year 2000, more than 350,000 Americans had died from AIDS. The death toll worldwide was more than 10 times as great. At present, there is no cure for AIDS. Some progress has been made in developing drugs that make it more difficult for HIV to infect cells and to reproduce. Fortunately, HIV does not spread easily from person to person. The way in which the virus is transmitted is now well understood.

To help slow down the spread of this deadly epidemic, people need to know how HIV is transmitted. HIV is spread only by contact with infected blood and other bodily fluids. It is not spread by casual contact. One way HIV is spread is by intravenous drug users who share needles, which is reason enough to avoid using drugs.

HIV is also spread by sexual contact. Any sexual contact carries some risk of contracting HIV. Some people may not know that they have the virus, or they may know but not tell. The safest course of conduct people can follow is to abstain from sexual contact before marriage and for both partners in a committed relationship to remain faithful. The next safest course is to use a latex condom, but even a latex condom does not provide 100 percent protection.

Figure 40–15 HIV is an example of a retrovirus, which contains RNA as its genetic material. Retroviruses get their name because their genetic information is first copied backward from RNA to DNA. **Interpreting Graphics** *In the photograph, what type of blood cell are the red HIV particles attacking?*

40–3 Section Assessment

1. 🔑 **Key Concept** What happens in an autoimmune disease?

2. What are the two main types of immune system disorders?

3. What produces an allergy attack?

4. Why is it difficult for a person with HIV to fight off infections?

5. What are three ways in which HIV is spread?

6. **Critical Thinking Relating Concepts** In treating asthma, the first thing many physicians do is to ask a patient to make a list of times and places he or she has experienced asthmatic reactions. Why do you suppose doctors do this?

iTEXT Assessment Use iText to review the important concepts in Section 40–3.

Take It to the NET

Find out about three other autoimmune diseases. Then, construct a chart that contains the name of the disease, a description, symptoms, and treatments. Use the links provided in the Biology area at the Prentice Hall Web site for help in completing this activity: **www.phschool.com**

Slowing the AIDS Epidemic

AIDS is a threat on every continent in the world, but nowhere has its effect been more devastating than in Africa. Seventy percent of the world's HIV-infected population lives in sub-Saharan Africa. Thirteen million Africans have already died of AIDS and another ten million are expected to die within the next 5 years. In some African countries, the HIV-infection rate is as high as one in three people.

Leaders from around the world disagree on how the AIDS epidemic should be handled. Some argue that anti-AIDS drugs should be distributed. Other leaders argue that the people should be given AIDS education in order to prevent future AIDS cases.

The Viewpoints

Spend Money for Treatment
Pharmaceutical companies holding patents on anti-HIV drugs should provide the drugs to those countries with high HIV-infection rates. In countries such as the United States, these drugs have dramatically cut the death rate from AIDS. In addition, these drugs have improved the lives of people living with HIV infection. If African countries had access to these drugs, the effects of this epidemic would be dramatically lessened. Therefore, money should be spent on treating those who are already HIV-infected.

Spend Money for Education
Intensive efforts to prolong the lives of HIV-infected people will only prolong the effects of the epidemic. Many people in the HIV-infected population do not have basic knowledge about AIDS, including how HIV is spread. Thus, what is really needed is an intensive program of public health and education to stop the spread of the virus. If people are educated about risk factors and modes of transmission, they will take some responsibility in the prevention of the disease. For this reason, the money should be spent on AIDS education.

You Decide

1. **Making Judgments** Given limited resources to fight HIV, how would you decide if those resources would be better spent on treatment or prevention education?
2. **Interpreting Graphics** Look at the world map showing the number of adults and children living with HIV/AIDS. What three regions have the highest number of people living with HIV/AIDS? Which three areas have the lowest?

Adults and Children Living With HIV/AIDS

NORTH AMERICA
920,000

WESTERN EUROPE
540,000

EASTERN EUROPE and CENTRAL ASIA
700,000

NORTH AFRICA and MIDDLE EAST
400,000

CARIBBEAN
390,000

EAST ASIA and PACIFIC ISLANDS
640,000

SUB-SAHARAN AFRICA
25.3 million

CENTRAL and SOUTH AMERICA
1.4 million

SOUTH and SOUTHEAST ASIA
5.8 million

AUSTRALIA and NEW ZEALAND
15,000

40–4 Cancer

Guide for Reading

 Key Concepts
- What is the basic mechanism of cancer?
- How is cancer treated?

Vocabulary
tumor
malignant
metastasis
chemotherapy

Reading Strategy:
Predicting Before you read, hypothesize about how radiation can be both a cause and a treatment for cancer. As you read, list evidence that supports or rejects your hypothesis.

Cancer is a life-threatening disease in which cells multiply uncontrollably and destroy healthy tissue. Cancer is a unique disease because the cells that cause it are not foreign cells but the body's own cells. This fact has made cancer difficult to treat and to understand.

A Cellular Disease

Cancers begin when something goes wrong with the controls that normally regulate cell growth and division. A single cell or a group of cells begins to grow and divide uncontrollably, often resulting in the formation of a mass of growing tissue known as a **tumor.** Not all tumors are cancerous. Some tumors are benign, or noncancerous. A benign tumor does not spread to surrounding healthy tissue or to other parts of the body.

Cancerous tumors, on the other hand, are **malignant,** which means that they can invade and destroy surrounding healthy tissue. In some cases, cells from a malignant tumor break away and are carried by blood or lymph to other parts of the body. The spread of cancerous tumors beyond their original site is called **metastasis** (muh-TAS-tuh-sis).

As cancer cells like the one in **Figure 40–16** spread, they absorb the nutrients needed by other cells, block nerve connections, and prevent the organs they invade from functioning properly. Soon, the delicate balance of processes in the body is disrupted and a life-threatening illness results.

✓ **CHECKPOINT** *What are benign tumors?*

Causes of Cancer

Cancers are caused by defects in the genes that regulate cell growth and division. There are several sources of such defects: They may be inherited, they may be caused by viruses, or they may result from mutations in DNA. These mutations in DNA may occur spontaneously, or they may be produced by radiation or chemicals.

Viral Cancers Certain viruses cause cancer when the genes they inject into cells disrupt the normal process of mitosis. The result is uncontrolled cell division in the injured cell and its descendants. Although many cancer-causing viruses have been discovered in animals, only a few have been found in humans. One of these is the human papilloma virus (HPV), which is passed from person to person by sexual contact. Chronic HPV infections can lead to cancer of the reproductive organs.

▼ **Figure 40–16** ⬤ **Cancers involve a breakdown in the control of cell growth.** The body recognizes cancer cells as foreign and tries to destroy them. In this color-enhanced SEM, a killer T cell (orange) is attacking a cancer cell (purple).

(magnification: about 3000×)

Figure 40–17 Radiation from sunlight and chemicals in tobacco smoke can lead to two of the most common forms of cancer. **Inferring** *How might applying sunscreen help reduce your risk of skin cancer?*

Radiation Most forms of radiation—including sunlight, X-rays, and nuclear radiation—can cause cancer by producing mutations in DNA. If mutations occur in genes that control cell growth, a normal cell may be transformed into a cancer cell. Most cases of skin cancer, for example, are caused by the ultraviolet radiation in sunlight. For this reason, it is important to use sunscreen and avoid prolonged exposure to the sun.

Chemicals Chemical compounds can also cause cancer, usually by triggering mutations in the DNA of normal cells. Chemical compounds that are known to cause cancer are called carcinogens. Some carcinogens are produced in nature. Others, such as chloroform and benzene, are synthetic compounds. Some of the most powerful chemical carcinogens are found in tobacco smoke. Cigarette smoking is responsible for at least 80 percent of all cases of lung cancer. Lung cancer is the most common fatal cancer in the United States.

Fighting Cancer

As with other diseases, the best way to fight cancer is to prevent it. The best way to do that is by protecting your DNA from agents that cause cancer. For example, you can dramatically reduce your risk of developing lung cancer by not smoking. In addition, regular exercise and a balanced diet with plenty of fruits and vegetables also can help to lower your cancer risk.

Physicians also stress that, if a cancer is detected early, the chances of treating it successfully may be as high as 90 percent. Regular checkups and tests are an important preventive measure. These tests depend on a person's age, gender, and family history. Self-examinations for skin, breast, or testicular cancer are also helpful when combined with regular checkups. Your doctor can give you instructions for performing these self-examinations.

🔑 **Treatments for cancer fall into three general categories: surgery, radiation therapy, and drug therapy.** In many cases, treatment consists of two or sometimes all three of these methods.

KEEP CURRENT WITH . . .

SCIENCE NEWS®

To find out more about the topics in this chapter, go to: **www.phschool.com**

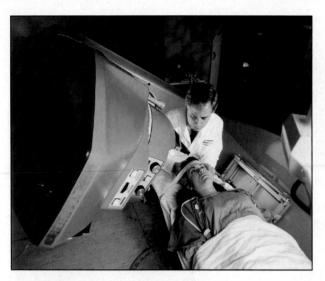

▲ **Figure 40–18** 🔊 Radiation is used to treat some cancers, as are surgery and chemotherapy. The high-energy beam of radiation is focused on the cancer cells.

Localized cancerous tumors, or those that do not spread quickly, are often removed by surgery. If this can be done before the cancer has spread, the patient may be completely cured. **Figure 40–18** shows radiation therapy being used to attack cancer cells. Perhaps this seems confusing after you just learned that radiation is also a cause of cancer. However, controlled amounts of properly directed radiation destroy fast-growing cancer cells more quickly than normal cells, making this method a useful form of therapy.

Drug therapy, or **chemotherapy,** is the use of a combination of chemicals to destroy cancer cells. Although most anticancer drugs destroy cancer cells, many of these drugs also harm normal cells. In addition, patients undergoing chemotherapy may experience nausea, headaches, and hair loss.

Progress Against Cancer

In the last decade, genuine progress has been made in the war on cancer. In the United States since 1990, both the incidence of cancer and the rate of cancer deaths have declined steadily. Earlier detection, better treatment, and fewer people using tobacco have all been behind the decline. Researchers, however, still dream of a "magic bullet" that could destroy cancer cells the way that antibiotics kill bacteria. That day is not yet here, but there are hopeful indications that it may not be too far away. A number of researchers have found compounds that can block the growth of new blood vessels into tumors, thereby causing many tumors to shrink and disappear. Other researchers have sought ways to block the signals that cause cancer cells to grow, and still others have tried to stimulate the body's own immune system to attack cancer cells directly. We can all hope that sooner or later one of these approaches will be successful and cancer will join the list of other diseases that medical science has overcome.

40–4 Section Assessment

1. 🔑 **Key Concept** Describe how cancer starts.
2. 🔑 **Key Concept** What are three methods of treating cancer?
3. List some of the causes of cancer.
4. Why are regular medical check-ups and self-examinations important?

5. **Critical Thinking Classifying** Is cancer an infectious disease? Explain your answer.

📱 **TEXT** Assessment Use iText to review the important concepts in Section 40–4.

MAKING CONNECTIONS

The Cell Cycle
Recall the cell cycle from Section 10–2. In which phase would cells be most vulnerable to damage from radiation? Explain your choice. What characteristic of cancer cells might make them especially vulnerable?

Testing the Specificity of Antibodies

Antibodies are very selective. They will bind only to specific antigens. An antibody that binds strongly to a certain protein or carbohydrate may not bind at all to another molecule that has a very similar structure. In this investigation, you will determine the specificity of an antibody.

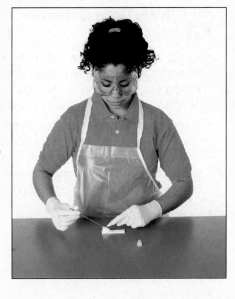

Problem How specific is the binding of antibodies to antigens?

Materials

- Strep A diagnostic kits with control samples (materials for three tests)
- sterile water

Skills Predicting, Posing Questions

Procedure

1. Make a copy of the data table shown. To see how the antibody-based Strep A diagnostic kit reacts to an antigen found in the cell wall of *Streptococcus* group A (the bacterium that causes the infection known as "strep throat"), follow the instructions in the kit to test the positive control sample. Record the result of this test.

2. **Predicting** *Streptococcus* group C is closely related to *Streptococcus* group A, but does not cause disease. Record your prediction of how the diagnostic kit will react to antigens from the cell wall of *Streptococcus* group C.

3. Test the *Streptococcus* group C sample as you did the *Streptococcus* group A sample in step 1. Record the result of this test.

4. **Predicting** Record your prediction of whether *Streptococcus* group A is present on the tabletops in your lab.

5. Use sterile water to moisten the tip of one of the test swabs supplied with your diagnostic kit and rub it on the tabletop. Then, test the sample on the swab and record your results.

Analyze and Conclude

1. **Observing** Did the antibody-based test react to the antigen of *Streptococcus* group A? To the antigen of group C?

2. **Analyzing Data** Did your results support the idea that an antibody can be used to distinguish between two similar antigens, such as those of *Streptococcus* group A and group C?

3. **Evaluating** Did the diagnostic kit detect any *Streptococcus* on the tabletop? Did your results in steps 1 through 3 support the idea that this is a reliable result? Explain your answer.

4. **Drawing Conclusions** Use what you have learned about the specificity of antibodies to explain what happens in autoimmune diseases such as rheumatic fever.

Go Further

Interviewing a Professional Interview a health professional to find out how antibody-based tests are used to determine blood types and to diagnose diseases.

Data Table	
Sample	Result (positive or negative)
Streptococcus group A	
Streptococcus group C	
Tabletop swab	

40–1 Infectious Disease

 Key Concepts

- Some diseases are inherited. Others are caused by materials in the environment. Still others are produced by organisms such as bacteria and fungi.

- Some infectious diseases are spread from one person to another through coughing, sneezing, or physical contact. Other infectious diseases are spread through contaminated water or food. Still others are spread by infected animals.

Vocabulary
- disease, p. 1029
- pathogen, p. 1029
- germ theory of disease, p. 1029
- Koch's postulates, p. 1030
- toxin, p. 1031
- vector, p. 1032
- antibiotic, p. 1033

40–2 The Immune System

 Key Concepts

- Your body's most important nonspecific defense is the skin.

- The inflammatory response is a nonspecific defense reaction to tissue damage caused by injury or infection.

- Once the body has been exposed to a pathogen, millions of memory B and T cells remain capable of producing specific antibodies to that pathogen.

Vocabulary
- inflammatory response, p. 1035 • fever, p. 1035
- interferon, p. 1035 • immune response, p. 1036
- antigen, p. 1036 • humoral immunity, p. 1036
- antibody, p. 1036
- cell-mediated immunity, p. 1038
- permanent immunity, p. 1038
- vaccination, p. 1040 • active immunity, p. 1040

40–3 Immune System Disorders

 Key Concept

- When the immune system makes a mistake and attacks the body's own cells, it produces an autoimmune disease.

Vocabulary
- allergy, p. 1041 • histamine, p. 1041
- asthma, p. 1042

40–4 Cancer

 Key Concepts

- Cancers begin when something goes wrong with the controls that normally regulate cell growth and division.

- Treatments for cancer fall into three general categories: surgery, radiation therapy, and drug therapy.

Vocabulary
- tumor, p. 1046 • malignant, p. 1046
- metastasis, p. 1046 • chemotherapy, p. 1048

Thinking Visually

Using the information in this chapter, complete the following concept map:

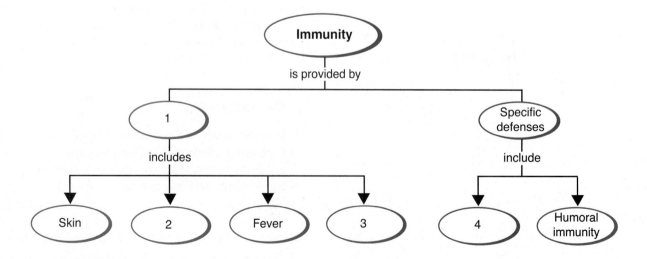

Chapter 40

Part A

Multiple Choice

For each statement or question, select the number of the word or expression that, of those given, best completes the statement or answers the question.

1 Any change, other than an injury, that disrupts the normal functions of the body is a(an)
(1) disease   (3) allergy
(2) pathogen   (4) vaccine

2 Which term best describes disease-causing organisms such as viruses, bacteria, and worms?
(1) antibodies   (3) pathogens
(2) antigens   (4) toxins

3 Which scientist's observations led to the germ theory of disease?
(1) Steere   (3) Koch
(2) Hooke   (4) Salk

4 The body's most important nonspecific defense against pathogens is
(1) tears   (3) saliva
(2) mucus   (4) skin

5 In the illustration below, the label X indicates the
(1) antibodies   (3) antigen-binding sites
(2) antigens   (4) interferon parts

6 A substance that triggers an immune response is an
(1) antibody   (3) allergy
(2) antigen   (4) antibiotic

7 A nonspecific defense reaction to tissue damage caused by injury or infection is known as
(1) the inflammatory response
(2) active immunity
(3) cell-mediated immunity
(4) permanent immunity

8 A protein that helps cells resist viruses is
(1) interferon   (3) plasma
(2) penicillin   (4) histamine

9 Swelling and pain associated with inflammation are caused by the
(1) secretion of antibodies
(2) narrowing of local blood vessels
(3) secretion of antigens
(4) destruction of bacteria by white blood cells

10 Which is *not* a sign of an inflammatory response?
(1) white blood cells rushing to infected tissues
(2) blood vessels narrowing near a wound
(3) phagocytes engulfing pathogens
(4) infected tissues swelling

11 Which body defense does *not* prevent pathogens from entering the body?
(1) macrophages   (3) mucus
(2) tears   (4) skin

12 Mast cells release chemicals known as
(1) antibodies   (3) histamines
(2) antigens   (4) pathogens

13 Which statement describes one effect of a fever?
(1) It increases the growth of pathogens.
(2) It decreases the rate of chemical reactions.
(3) It increases the heart rate.
(4) It decreases the number of white blood cells.

14 White blood cells that can engulf pathogens are referred to as
(1) antibodies   (3) B cells
(2) antigens   (4) phagocytes

15 Proteins that bind to specific chemicals on the surface of foreign cells are called
(1) phagocytes   (3) T cells
(2) antigens   (4) antibodies

16 White blood cells that produce pathogen-destroying proteins are known as
(1) T cells   (3) B cells
(2) antigens   (4) phagocytes

Test-Taking Tip   When evaluating multiple choice answers, be sure to read all of the answer choices, even if the first answer choice seems to be the correct one. By doing so, you can make sure that the answer you chose is the best one.

Preparing for the
Living Environment Exam

Parts B and C
Multiple Choice and Extended Response

For those questions that ask you to select a response, choose the one that best completes the statement or answers the question. For all others follow the directions given.

Base your answers to questions 17 through 20 on the information and graph below and on your knowledge of biology.

The graph shows concentrations of HIV and T cells in 120 HIV-infected patients over ten years.

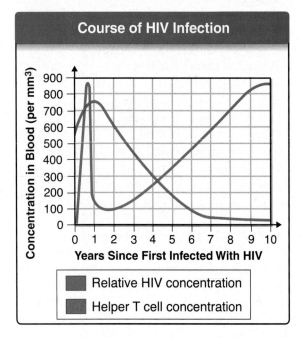

Course of HIV Infection

17 Which statement best explains why the T-cell concentration increases after two years?
   (1) HIV dies off after two years.
   (2) HIV attacks T-cells.
   (3) T-cells produce toxins.
   (4) B-cells increase.

18 Which statement best describes the change in the HIV concentration from years 2 through 10?
   (1) It increased, then decreased, then gradually increased.
   (2) It increased, then gradually decreased.
   (3) It steadily increased, then began to level off.
   (4) It steadily decreased, then began to level off.

19 What is most likely responsible for the change in HIV concentration during the first year?
   (1) an immune response
   (2) an inflammatory response
   (3) an HIV vaccination
   (4) HIV stopped replicating

20 What is the most likely result of the changes shown?
   (1) The body will be unable to deal with infections caused by pathogens.
   (2) Antibodies against the AIDS virus will eventually be released.
   (3) Cancer cells in the body will be replaced by AIDS cells.
   (4) The damage to the immune system will be repaired by vaccinations.

21 Explain why the fourth step of Koch's postulates is necessary to prove that a disease is caused by a specific pathogen.

22 List the five types of pathogens that are responsible for the spread of infectious disease. Give an example of a disease caused by each type of pathogen.

23 Explain what is meant by the term *vectors* in the statement: Mosquitoes and flies are often vectors of human disease.

24 State one specific way penicillin and streptomycin kill bacteria.

25 State three ways that a fever may be beneficial to a person who is sick.

26 Antibodies and antibiotics are both useful in combating disease. Compare these two methods of attacking pathogens. In your answer be sure to
   • identify the source of both antibodies and antibiotics
   • describe the way antibodies work to combat pathogens
   • describe the way antibiotics combat pathogens
   • identify the types of pathogens that antibodies and antibiotics can be used against successfully

27 Distinguish between humoral immunity and cell-mediated immunity.

28 Explain why allergies are not classified as autoimmune diseases.

29 Immunity to a disease can be acquired either by getting the disease and recovering or by receiving a vaccination. Compare these two methods of becoming immune to a specific disease. In your answer be sure to

- explain why getting a disease and recovering can leave a person immune to that disease for life

- explain how getting a vaccination results in the same type of immunity to the disease, but is safer

30 Describe how passive immunity to a disease is obtained, and explain why it does not last very long.

31 Describe the specific action of HIV that makes the body unable to cope with other infections.

32 State the difference between a malignant tumor and a benign tumor.

Base your answers to questions 33 through 35 on the chart below, which shows the relative 5-year cancer survival rates in the United States, and on your knowledge of biology.

Relative 5-year Cancer Survival Rates (in %)			
Site	1974–76	1980–82	1989–95
All sites	50	51	59
Brain	22	25	30
Breast (female)	75	76	85
Colon	50	55	62
Lung and bronchus	13	13	14
Leukemia	34	39	43
Prostate	67	73	92

33 Name the type of cancer that has the highest survival rate.

34 Name the type of cancer that has the lowest survival rate.

35 Describe the trend in survival rates that is evident from the data.

36 Compare and contrast the roles of B cells and T cells in the immune response.

37 Cancer results from errors in the genetic information that regulates cell division. Explain the connection between cancer and environmental conditions. In your answer be sure to

- name two environmental conditions that can lead to cancer

- explain how such environmental conditions can specifically lead to unregulated cell division

38 What are the possible risks and benefits associated with gaining immunity to a disease by entential exposure to it?

39 Explain why a second bee sting is more dangerous than the first for a person who is allergic to bee stings.

40 Bone marrow transplants are a method of treatment being considered for some AIDS patients. How might a bone marrow transplant benefit an AIDS patient? What might be some problems with this treatment?

41 The virus that causes influenza mutates rapidly. Explain why this makes it necessary for people to receive flu shots repeatedly in order to remain immune to the disease.

 Take It to the NET

The Internet is an excellent source of current information on cancer. Visit the Prentice Hall Web site at **www.phschool.com** to find out more about cancer prevention and awareness. Then, answer the following questions:

- What is a risk factor?

- What is the difference between prevention and early detection?

- How can you affect your risk of cancer by changing your diet?

- What are the two main steps in an environmental risk assessment?

Basic Process Skills

During a biology course, you often carry out short lab activities as well as lengthier experiments. Here are some skills that you will use.

30 cm

20 cm

Comparing Observations and Inferences

Sample Observations	Sample Inferences
The footprints in the soil each have five toes.	An animal made the footprints.
The larger footprints are about 20 cm long.	A bear made the footprints.
The space between each pair of footprints is about 30 cm.	The animal was walking, not running.

Observing

In every science activity, you make a variety of observations. Observing is using one or more of the five senses to gather information. Many observations involve the senses of sight, hearing, touch, and smell. On rare occasions in a lab—but only when explicitly directed by your teacher—you may use the sense of taste to make an observation.

Sometimes you will use tools that increase the power of your senses or make observations more precise. For example, hand lenses and microscopes enable you to see things in greater detail. Rulers, balances, and thermometers help you measure key variables. Besides expanding the senses or making observations more accurate, tools may help eliminate personal opinions or preferences.

In science, it is customary to record your observations at the time they are made, usually by writing or drawing in a notebook. You may also make records by using computers, cameras, videotapes, and other tools. As a rule, scientists keep complete accounts of their observations, often using tables to organize their observations.

Inferring

In science, as in everyday life, observations are usually followed by inferences. Inferring is interpreting an observation or statement based on prior knowledge. For example, suppose you're on a mountain hike and you see footprints in wet soil. Based on their size and shape, you might infer that a large mammal had passed by. In making that inference, you would use your knowledge about the shape of animals' feet. Someone who knew more about mammals might infer that a bear left the footprints. You can compare examples of observations and inferences in the table above.

Notice that an inference is an act of reasoning, not a fact. An inference may be logical but not true. It is often necessary to gather further information before you can be confident that an inference is correct. For scientists, that information may come from further observations or from research done by others.

As you study biology, you may make different types of inferences. For example, you may generalize about all cases based on information about some cases: *All the plant roots I've observed grow downward, so I infer that all roots grow downward.* You may determine that one factor or event was caused by another factor or event: *The bacteria died after I applied bleach, so I infer that bleach kills bacteria.* Predictions may be another type of inference.

Predicting

People often make predictions, but their statements about the future could be either guesses or inferences. In science, a prediction is an inference about a future event based on evidence, experience, or knowledge. For example, you can say, *On the first day next month, it will be sunny.* If your statement is based on evidence of weather patterns in the area, then the prediction is scientific. If the statement was made without considering any evidence, it's just a guess.

Predictions play a major role in science because they provide a way to test ideas. If scientists understand an event or the properties of a particular object, they should be able to make accurate predictions about that event or object. Some predictions can be tested simply by making observations. At other times, carefully designed experiments are needed. You'll read more about the relationship between predictions and experiments on the next two pages.

Classifying

If you have ever heard people debate whether a tomato is a fruit or a vegetable, you've heard an argument about classification. Classifying is the process of grouping items that are alike according to some organizing idea or system. Classifying occurs in every branch of science, but it is especially important in biology because living things are so numerous and diverse.

You may have the chance to practice classifying in different ways. Sometimes you will place objects into groups using an established system. At other times, you may create a system of your own by examining a variety of objects and identifying their properties.

Classification can have different purposes. Sometimes it's done just to keep things organized, for example, to make lab supplies easy to find. More likely, though, classification helps scientists understand living things better and discover relationships among them. For example, biologists classify certain animal parts as bone or muscle and investigate how they work together. One way biologists determine how groups of vertebrates are related is to compare their bones.

Using Models

Some cities refuse to approve any new buildings that could cast shadows on a popular park. As architects plan buildings in such locations, they use models that can show where a proposed building's shadow will fall at any time of day at any season of the year. A model is a mental or physical representation of an object, process, or event. In science, models are usually made to help people understand natural objects and processes.

Model of a Glucose Molecule

$$CH_2OH$$

Models can be varied. Mental models, such as mathematical equations, can represent some kinds of ideas or processes. For example, the equation for the surface area of a sphere can model the surface of Earth, enabling scientists to determine its size. Physical models can be made of a huge variety of materials; they can be two-dimensional (flat) or three-dimensional (having depth). In biology, a drawing of a molecule or a cell is a typical two-dimensional model. Common three-dimensional models include a representation of a DNA molecule and a plastic skeleton of an animal.

Physical models can also be made "to scale," which means they are in proportion to the actual object. Something very large, such as an area of land being studied, can be shown at 1/100 of its actual size. A tiny organism can be shown at 100 times its size.

Conducting an Experiment

A science experiment is a procedure designed to test a prediction. Some types of experiments are fairly simple to design. Others may require ingenious problem solving.

Starting With Questions or Problems

A gardener collected seeds from a favorite plant at the end of the summer, stored them indoors for the winter, then planted them the following spring. None of the stored seeds developed into plants, yet uncollected seeds from the original plant germinated in the normal way. The gardener wondered: *Why didn't the collected seeds germinate?*

An experiment may have its beginning when someone asks a specific question or wants to solve a particular problem. Sometimes the original question leads directly to an experiment, but often researchers must restate the problem before they can design an appropriate experiment. The gardener's question about the seeds, for example, is too broad to be tested by an experiment, because there are so many possible answers. To narrow the topic, the gardener might think about related questions: *Were the seeds I collected different from the uncollected seeds? Did I try to germinate them in poor soil or with insufficient light or water? Did storing the seeds indoors ruin them in some way?*

Developing a Hypothesis

In science, a question about an object or event is answered by developing a possible explanation called a **hypothesis.** The hypothesis may be developed after long thought and research, or it may come to a scientist "in a flash." How a hypothesis is formed doesn't matter; it can be useful as long as it leads to predictions that can be tested.

The gardener decided to focus on the fact that the nongerminating seeds were stored in the warm conditions of a heated house. That led the person to propose this hypothesis: *Seeds require a period of low temperatures in order to germinate.* The next step is to make a prediction based on the hypothesis, for example: *If seeds are stored indoors in cold conditions, they will germinate in the same way as seeds left outdoors during the winter.* Notice that the prediction suggests the basic idea for an experiment.

Designing an Experiment

A carefully designed experiment can test a prediction in a reliable way, ruling out other possible explanations. As scientists plan their experimental procedures, they pay particular attention to the factors that must be controlled.

The gardener decided to study three groups of seeds: (1) some that would be left outdoors throughout the winter, (2) some that would be brought indoors and kept at room temperature, and (3) some that would be brought indoors and kept cold.

Controlling Variables

As researchers design an experiment, they identify the **variables,** factors that can change. Some common variables include mass, volume, time, temperature, light, and the presence or absence of specific materials. An experiment involves three categories of variables. The factor that scientists purposely change is called the **manipulated variable.** A manipulated variable is also known as an **independent variable**. The factor that may change because of the manipulated variable and that scientists want to observe is called the **responding variable.** A responding variable is also known as a **dependent variable.** Factors that scientists purposely keep the same are called **controlled variables.** Controlling variables enables researchers to conclude that the changes in the responding variable are due exclusively to changes in the manipulated variable.

For the gardener, the manipulated variable is whether the seeds were exposed to cold conditions. The responding variable is whether or not the seeds germinate. Among the variables that must be controlled are whether the seeds remain dry during storage, the time of year the seeds are planted, the amount of water the planted seeds receive, and the type of soil used.

Forming Operational Definitions

In an experiment, it is often necessary to define one or more variables explicitly so that any researcher could measure or control the variable in exactly the same way. An **operational definition** describes how a particular variable is to be measured or how a term is to be defined. ("Operational" means "describing what to do.")

The gardener, for example, had to decide exactly what the indoor "cold" conditions of the experiment would involve. Would the seeds be kept in a refrigerator or in a freezer? Since winter temperatures often fell below freezing, the gardener decided that "cold" meant keeping the seeds in a freezer.

Interpreting Data

The observations and measurements that are made in an experiment are called **data.** Scientists usually record data in an orderly way. When an experiment is finished, the researcher analyzes the data for trends or patterns, often by doing calculations or making graphs, to determine whether the results support the hypothesis.

For example, after planting the seeds in the spring, the gardener counted the seeds that germinated and found these results: None of the seeds kept at room temperature germinated, 80 percent of the seeds kept in the freezer germinated, and 85 percent of the seeds left outdoors germinated. The overall trend was clear: The gardener's prediction was correct.

Drawing Conclusions

Based on whether the results support or refute the hypothesis, researchers make a final statement summing up the results of the experiment. That final statement is called the conclusion of the experiment. For example, the gardener's conclusion was: *Some seeds must undergo a period of freezing in order to germinate.*

Following Up an Experiment

When an experiment has been completed, one or more events often follow. Researchers may repeat the experiment to verify the results. They may publish the experiment so that others can evaluate and replicate their procedures. They may compare their conclusion with the discoveries made by other scientists. And they may raise new questions that lead to new experiments. For example, *Are the spores of fungi affected by temperature as these seeds were?*

Researching other discoveries about seeds would show that certain other plants in temperate zones require periods of freezing before they germinate. This pattern makes it less likely that the seeds will germinate before winter, so it increases the chances that the young plants will survive.

Organizing Information

When you study or want to communicate facts and ideas, you may find it helpful to organize information visually. Here are some common graphic organizers you can use. Notice that each type of organizer is useful for specific types of information.

Concept Maps

Concept maps can help you organize a broad topic having many subtopics. A concept map begins with a main idea and shows how it can be broken down into specific topics. It makes the ideas easier to understand by presenting their relationships visually.

You construct a concept map by placing the concept words (usually nouns) in ovals and connecting the ovals with linking words. The most general concept usually is placed at the top of the map or in the center. The content of the other ovals becomes more specific as you move away from the main concept. The linking words, which describing the relationship between the linked concepts, are written on a line between two ovals. If you follow any string of concepts and linking words down through a map, they should sound approximately like a sentence.

Some concept maps may also include linking words that connect a concept in one branch to another branch. Such connections, called cross-linkages, show more complex interrelationships.

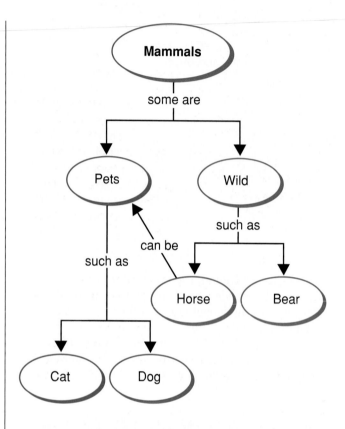

Compare-and-Contrast Tables

Compare-and-contrast tables are useful for showing the similarities and differences between two or more objects or processes. The table provides an organized framework for making comparisons based on specific characteristics.

To create a compare-and-contrast table, list the items to be compared across the top of the table. List the characteristics that will form the basis of your comparison in the column on the left. Complete the table by filling in information for each item.

Comparing Baseball and Basketball		
Characteristic	Baseball	Basketball
Number of Players	9	5
Playing Field	Baseball diamond	Basketball court
Equipment	Bat, baseball, mitts	Basket, basketball

Venn Diagrams

Another way to show similarities and differences between items is with a Venn diagram. A Venn diagram consists of two or more circles or ovals that partially overlap. Each circle or oval represents a particular object or idea. Characteristics that the objects share are written in the area of overlap. Differences or unique characteristics are written in the areas that do not overlap.

To create a Venn diagram, draw two overlapping circles or ovals. Label them with the names of the objects or the ideas they represent. Write the unique characteristics in the part of each circle or oval that does not overlap. Write the shared characteristics within the area of overlap.

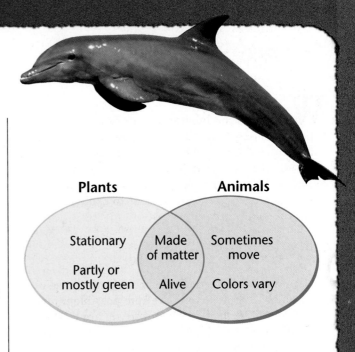

Plants   **Animals**

Stationary — Made of matter — Sometimes move

Partly or mostly green — Alive — Colors vary

Flowcharts

A flowchart can help you represent the order in which a set of events have occurred or should occur. Flowcharts are useful for outlining the steps in a procedure or stages in a process with a definite beginning and end.

To make a flowchart, list the steps in the process you want to represent, and count the steps. Then, create the appropriate number of boxes, starting at the top of a page or on the left. Write a brief description of the first event in the first box, then fill in the other steps, box by box. Link each box to the next event in the process with an arrow. Then, add a title to the flowchart.

Preparing Pasta

Boil water → Cook pasta → Drain water → Add sauce

Cycle Diagrams

A cycle diagram shows a sequence of events that is continuous, or cyclical. A continuous sequence does not have a beginning or an end; instead, each event in the process leads to another event. The diagram shows the order of the events.

To create a cycle diagram, list the events in the process and count them. Draw one box for each event, placing the boxes around an imaginary circle. Write one of the events in a box, then draw an arrow to the next box, moving clockwise. Continue to fill in the boxes and link them with arrows until the descriptions form a continuous circle. Then, add a title.

The Moon as Seen From Earth

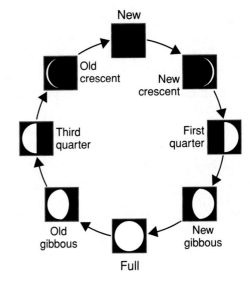

New
Old crescent
New crescent
Third quarter
First quarter
Old gibbous
New gibbous
Full

Science Safety Rules

Working in the laboratory can be an exciting experience, but it can also be dangerous if proper safety rules are not followed at all times. To prepare yourself for a safe year in the laboratory, read the following safety rules. Make sure that you understand each rule. Ask your teacher to explain any rules you don't understand.

Dress Code

1. Many materials in the laboratory can cause eye injury. To protect yourself from possible injury, wear safety goggles whenever you are working with chemicals, burners, or any substance that might get into your eyes. Avoid wearing contact lenses in the laboratory. Tell your teacher if you need to wear contact lenses to see clearly, and ask if there are any safety precautions you should observe.

2. Wear a laboratory apron or coat whenever you are working with chemicals or heated substances.

3. Tie back long hair to keep it away from any chemicals, burners, candles, or other laboratory equipment.

4. Before working in the laboratory, remove or tie back any article of clothing or jewelry that can hang down and touch chemicals and flames.

General Safety Rules and First Aid

5. Read all directions for an experiment several times. Follow the directions exactly as they are written. If you are in doubt about any part of the experiment, ask your teacher for assistance.

6. Never perform investigations your teacher has not authorized.

7. Never handle equipment unless you have specific permission.

8. Take care not to spill any material in the laboratory. If spills occur, ask your teacher immediately about the proper cleanup procedure. Never pour chemicals or other substances into the sink or trash container.

9. Never eat, drink, or bring food into the laboratory.

10. Immediately report all accidents, no matter how minor, to your teacher.

11. Learn what to do in case of specific accidents, such as getting acid in your eyes or on your skin. (Rinse acids off your body with lots of water.)

12. Be aware of the location of the first-aid kit. Your teacher should administer any required first aid due to injury. Your teacher may send you to the school nurse or call a physician.

13. Know where and how to report an accident or fire. Find out the location of the fire extinguisher, fire alarm, and phone. Report any fires to your teacher at once.

Heating and Fire Safety

14. Never use a heat source such as a candle or burner without wearing safety goggles.

15. Never heat a chemical you are not instructed to heat. A chemical that is harmless when cool can be dangerous when heated.

16. Maintain a clean work area and keep all materials away from flames. Be sure that there are no open containers of flammable liquids in the laboratory when flames are being used.

17. Never reach across a flame.

18. Make sure you know how to light a Bunsen burner. (Your teacher will demonstrate the proper procedure for lighting a burner.) If the flame leaps out of a burner toward you, turn the gas off immediately. Do not touch the burner. It may be hot. Never leave a lighted burner unattended!

19. When you are heating a test tube or bottle, point the opening away from yourself and others. Chemicals can splash or boil out of a heated test tube.

20. Never heat a closed container. The expanding hot air, vapors, or other gases inside may blow the container apart, causing it to injure you or others.

21. Never pick up a container that has been heated without first holding the back of your hand near it. If you can feel the heat on the back of your hand, the container may be too hot to handle. Use a clamp or tongs when handling hot containers.

Using Chemicals Safely

22. Never mix chemicals for "the fun of it." You might produce a dangerous, possibly explosive substance.

23. Many chemicals are poisonous. Never touch, taste, or smell a chemical that you do not know for certain is harmless. If you are instructed to smell fumes in an experiment, gently wave your hand over the opening of the container and direct the fumes toward your nose. Do not inhale the fumes directly from the container.

24. Use only those chemicals needed in the investigation. Keep all container lids closed when a chemical is not being used. Notify your teacher whenever chemicals are spilled.

25. Dispose of all chemicals as instructed by your teacher. To avoid contamination, never return chemicals to their original containers.

26. Be extra careful when working with acids or bases. Pour such chemicals from one container to another over the sink, not over your work area.

27. When diluting an acid, pour the acid into water. Never pour water into the acid.

28. If any acids or bases get on your skin or clothing, rinse them with water. Immediately notify your teacher of any acid or base spill.

Using Glassware Safely

29. Never heat glassware that is not thoroughly dry. Use a wire screen to protect glassware from any flame.

30. Keep in mind that hot glassware will not appear hot. Never pick up glassware without first checking to see if it is hot.

31. Never use broken or chipped glassware. If glassware breaks, notify your teacher and dispose of the glassware in the proper trash container.

32. Never eat or drink from laboratory glassware. Thoroughly clean glassware before putting it away.

Using Sharp Instruments

33. Handle scalpels or razor blades with extreme care. Never cut material toward you; cut away from you.

34. Notify your teacher immediately if you cut yourself when in the laboratory.

Working With Live Organisms

35. No experiments that will cause pain, discomfort, or harm to animals should be done in the classroom or at home.

36. Your teacher will instruct you how to handle each species that is brought into the classroom. Animals should be handled only if necessary. Special handling is required if an animal is excited or frightened, pregnant, feeding, or with its young.

37. Clean your hands thoroughly after handling any organisms or materials, including animals or cages containing animals.

End-of-Experiment Rules

38. When an experiment is completed, clean up your work area and return all equipment to its proper place.

39. Wash your hands before and after every experiment.

40. Turn off all burners before leaving the laboratory. Check that the gas line leading to the burner is off as well.

Safety Symbols

These symbols appear in laboratory activities to alert you to possible dangers and to remind you to work carefully.

Safety Goggles Always wear safety goggles to protect your eyes in any activity involving chemicals, flames or heating, or the possibility of broken glassware.

Lab Apron Wear a laboratory apron to protect your skin and clothing from injury.

Breakage Handle breakable materials such as thermometers and glassware with care. Do not touch broken glass.

Heat-Resistant Gloves Use an oven mitt or other hand protection when handling hot materials. Heating plates, hot water, and glassware can cause burns. Never touch hot objects with your bare hands.

Plastic Gloves Wear disposable plastic gloves to protect yourself from contact with chemicals or organisms that could be harmful. Keep your hands away from your face, and dispose of the gloves according to your teacher's instructions at the end of the activity.

Heating Use a clamp or tongs to hold hot objects. Do not touch hot objects with your bare hands.

Sharp Object Scissors, scalpels, pins, and knives are sharp. They can cut or puncture your skin. Always direct sharp edges and points away from yourself and others. Use sharp instruments only as directed.

Electric Shock Avoid the possibility of electric shock. Never use electrical equipment around water, or when the equipment or your hands are wet. Be sure cords are untangled and cannot trip anyone. Disconnect equipment when it is not in use.

Corrosive Chemical This symbol indicates the presence of an acid or other corrosive chemical. Avoid getting the chemical on your skin or clothing, or in your eyes. Do not inhale the vapors. Wash your hands when you are finished with the activity.

Poison Do not let any poisonous chemical get on your skin, and do not inhale its vapor. Wash your hands when you are finished with the activity.

Physical Safety This activity involves physical activity. Use caution to avoid injuring yourself or others. Follow instructions from your teacher. Alert your teacher if there is any reason that you should not participate in the activity.

Animal Safety Treat live animals with care to avoid injuring the animals or yourself. Working with animal parts or preserved animals may also require caution. Wash your hands when you are finished with the activity.

Plant Safety Handle plants only as your teacher directs. If you are allergic to any plants used in an activity, tell your teacher before the activity begins. Avoid touching poisonous plants and plants with thorns.

Flames Tie back loose hair and clothing, and put on safety goggles before working with fire. Follow instructions from your teacher about lighting and extinguishing flames.

No Flames Flammable materials may be present. Make sure there are no flames, sparks, or exposed sources of heat present.

Fumes Poisonous or unpleasant vapors may be produced. Work in a ventilated area. Avoid inhaling a vapor directly. Test an odor only when directed to do so by your teacher, using a wafting motion to direct the vapor toward your nose.

Disposal Chemicals and other materials used in the activity must be disposed of safely. Follow the instructions from your teacher.

Hand Washing Wash your hands thoroughly when finished with the activity. Use antibacterial soap and warm water. Lather both sides of your hands and between your fingers. Rinse well.

General Safety Awareness You may see this symbol when none of the symbols described earlier applies. In this case, follow the specific instructions provided. You may also see this symbol when you are asked to design your own experiment. Do not start your experiment until your teacher has approved your plan.

The Metric System

The metric system of measurement is used by scientists throughout the world. It is based on units of ten. Each unit is ten times larger or ten times smaller than the next unit. The most commonly used units of the metric system are given below. After you have finished reading about the metric system, try to put it to use. How tall are you in meters? What is your mass? What is your normal body temperature in degrees Celsius?

Metric Ruler

Commonly Used Metric Units

Length The distance from one point to another

meter (m)	A meter is slightly longer than a yard.
	1 meter = 1000 millimeters (mm)
	1 meter = 100 centimeters (cm)
	1000 meters = 1 kilometer (km)

Volume The amount of space an object takes up

liter (L)	A liter is slightly more than a quart.
	1 liter = 1000 milliliters (mL)

Mass The amount of matter in an object

gram (g)	A paper clip has a mass equal to about one gram.
	1000 grams = 1 kilogram (kg)

Temperature The measure of hotness or coldness

degrees Celsius (°C)	0°C = freezing point of water
	100°C = boiling point of water

Triple-Beam Balance

Metric–English Equivalents

2.54 centimeters (cm) = 1 inch (in.)
1 meter (m) = 39.37 inches (in.)
1 kilometer (km) = 0.62 miles (mi)
1 liter (L) = 1.06 quarts (qt)
236 milliliters (mL) = 1 cup (c)
1 kilogram (kg) = 2.2 pounds (lb)
28.3 grams (g) = 1 ounce (oz)
$°C = 5/9 \times (°F-32)$

Thermometer

Graduated Cylinder

The Compound Microscope

The microscope used in most biology classes, the compound microscope, contains a combination of lenses. The eyepiece lens is located in the top portion of the microscope. This lens usually has a magnification of 10×. Other lenses, called objective lenses, are at the bottom of the body tube on the revolving nosepiece. By rotating the nosepiece, you can select the objective through which you will view your specimen.

The shortest objective is a low-power magnifier, usually 10×. The longer ones are of high power, usually up to 40× or 43×. The magnification is marked on the objective. To determine the total magnification, multiply the magnifying power of the eyepiece by the magnifying power of the objective. For example, with a 10× eyepiece and a 40× objective, the total magnification is $10 \times 40 = 400\times$.

Learning the name, function, and location of each of the microscope's parts is necessary for proper use. Use the following procedures when working with the microscope.

1. Carry the microscope by placing one hand beneath the base and grasping the arm of the microscope with the other hand.

2. Gently place the microscope on the lab table with the arm facing you. The microscope's base should be resting evenly on the table, approximately 10 cm from the table's edge.

3. Raise the body tube by turning the coarse adjustment knob until the objective lens is about 2 cm above the opening of the stage.

4. Rotate the nosepiece so that the low-power objective (10×) is directly in line with the body tube. A click indicates that the lens is in line with the opening of the stage.

5. Look through the eyepiece and switch on the lamp or adjust the mirror so that a circle of light can be seen. This is the field of view. Moving the lever of the diaphragm permits a greater or smaller amount of light to come through the opening of the stage.

6. Place a prepared slide on the stage so that the specimen is over the center of the opening. Use the stage clips to hold the slide in place.

7. Look at the microscope from the side. Carefully turn the coarse adjustment knob to lower the body tube until the low-power objective almost touches the slide or until the body tube can no longer be moved. Do not allow the objective to touch the slide.

PARTS OF THE MICROSCOPE AND THEIR FUNCTION

1. **Eyepiece** Contains a magnifying lens
2. **Arm** Supports the body tube
3. **Stage** Supports the slide being observed
4. **Opening of the stage** Permits light to pass up to the eyepiece
5. **Fine adjustment knob** Moves the body tube slightly to sharpen the image
6. **Coarse adjustment knob** Moves the body tube to focus the image
7. **Base** Supports the microscope
8. **Illuminator** Produces light or reflects light up toward the eyepiece
9. **Diaphragm** Regulates the amount of light passing up toward the eyepiece
10. **Diaphragm lever** Opens and closes the diaphragm
11. **Stage clips** Hold the slide in place
12. **Low-power objective** Provides a magnification of 10× and is the shortest objective
13. **High-power objective** Provides a magnification of 40× and is the longest objective
14. **Nosepiece** Holds the objectives and can be rotated to change the magnification
15. **Body tube** Maintains the proper distance between the eyepiece and the objectives

8. Look through the eyepiece and observe the specimen. If the field of view is out of focus, use the coarse adjustment knob to raise the body tube while looking through the eyepiece. **CAUTION:** *To prevent damage to the slide and the objective, do not lower the body tube using the coarse adjustment while looking through the eyepiece.* Focus the image as best you can with the coarse adjustment knob. Then use the fine adjustment knob to focus the image more sharply. Keep both eyes open when viewing a specimen. This helps prevent eyestrain.

9. Adjust the lever of the diaphragm to allow the right amount of light to enter.

10. To change the magnification, rotate the nosepiece until the desired objective is in line with the body tube and clicks into place.

11. Look through the eyepiece and use the fine adjustment knob to bring the image into focus.

12. After every use, remove the slide. Return the low-power objective into place in line with the body tube. Clean the stage of the microscope and the lenses with lens paper. Do not use other types of paper to clean the lenses; they may scratch the lenses.

Preparing a Wet-Mount Slide

1. Obtain a clean microscope slide and a coverslip. A coverslip is very thin, permitting the objective lens to be lowered very close to the specimen.

2. Place the specimen in the middle of the microscope slide. The specimen must be thin enough for light to pass through it.

Drop of water — Dropper pipette

Slide

Needle or probe

Coverslip

3. Using a dropper pipette, place a drop of water on the specimen.

4. Lower one edge of the coverslip so that it touches the side of the drop of water at about a 45° angle. The water will spread evenly along the edge of the coverslip. Using a dissecting needle or probe, slowly lower the coverslip over the specimen and water as shown in the drawing. Try not to trap any air bubbles under the coverslip. If air bubbles are present, gently tap the surface of the coverslip over the air bubble with a pencil eraser.

5. Remove any excess water at the edge of the coverslip with a paper towel. If the specimen begins to dry out, add a drop of water at the edge of the coverslip.

Staining Techniques

1. Obtain a clean microscope slide and coverslip.

2. Place the specimen in the middle of the microscope slide.

3. Using a dropper pipette, place a drop of water on the specimen. Place the coverslip so that its edge touches the drop of water at a 45° angle. After the water spreads along the edge of the coverslip, use a dissecting needle or probe to lower the coverslip over the specimen.

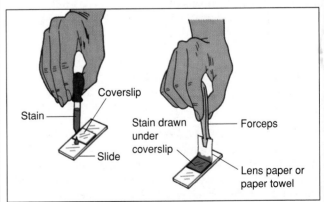

Stain

Coverslip

Slide

Stain drawn under coverslip

Forceps

Lens paper or paper towel

4. Add a drop of stain at the edge of the coverslip. Using forceps, touch a small piece of lens paper or paper towel to the opposite edge of the coverslip, as shown in the drawing. The paper causes the stain to be drawn under the coverslip and to stain the cells in the specimen.

DOMAIN ARCHAEA
Kingdom Archaebacteria

Single-celled prokaryotic organisms that lack peptidoglycan cell walls and have distinctive ribosomal RNA sequences.

The Archaebacteria include methanogens (organisms that produce methane gas, such as *Methanobacterium*), salt-loving bacteria (*Halococcus*), and thermoacidophilic bacteria (*Thermoplasma*), which grow in extremely high temperatures.

DOMAIN BACTERIA
Kingdom Eubacteria

Single-celled prokaryotic organisms; most have peptidoglycan cell walls. Sometimes form colonies of clumps or filaments.

The Eubacteria include the blue-green bacteria (cyanobacteria such as *Anabaena*), chemoautotrophs (*Nitrobacter*), spirochetes (*Treponema*), prochlorobacteria (*Prochloron*), spore-forming bacteria (*Bacillus*), and obligate internal parasites, such as the rickettsiae (*Rickettsia*).

DOMAIN EUKARYA
Kingdom Protista

Eukaryotic; usually unicellular; some multicellular or colonial; heterotrophic or autotrophic organisms.

ANIMALLIKE PROTISTS
Unicellular; heterotrophic; usually motile; also known as protozoa.

PHYLUM CILIOPHORA (ciliates) All have cilia at some point in development; almost all use cilia to move; characterized by two types of nuclei: macronuclei and micronuclei; most have a sexual process known as conjugation. Examples: *Paramecium, Didinium, Stentor.*

PHYLUM ZOOMASTIGINA (zooflagellates) Possess one or more flagella (some have thousands). Examples: *Trichomonas, Trichonympha.*

PHYLUM SPOROZOA Nonmotile parasites; produce small infective cells called sporozoites; life cycles usually complex, involving more than one host species; cause a number of diseases, including malaria. Example: *Plasmodium.*

PHYLUM SARCODINA Sarcodines use pseudopods for feeding and movement; some produce elaborate shells that contain silica or calcium carbonate; most free-living; a few parasitic; some involved in formation of sedimentary rock. Examples: *Amoeba,* foraminiferans.

PLANTLIKE PROTISTS
Mostly unicellular photosynthetic autotrophs that have characteristics similar to those of plants. A few species are multicellular or heterotrophic.

PHYLUM EUGLENOPHYTA (euglenophytes) Primarily photosynthetic; most live in fresh water; possess two unequal flagella; lack cell walls. Example: *Euglena.*

PHYLUM PYRROPHYTA (dinoflagellates) Two flagella; most live in salt water, are photosynthetic, and have rigid cell walls that contain cellulose; some are luminescent; many are symbiotic. Examples: *Gonyaulux, Noctilucans scintillans.*

PHYLUM CHRYSOPHYTA (chrysophytes) Mostly photosynthetic; aquatic; mostly unicellular; contain yellow-brown pigments. Example: *Thallasiosira.*

PHYLUM BACILLARIOPHYTA (diatoms) Photosynthetic; live in fresh and salt water; have unique glasslike cell walls; among the most abundant organisms on Earth. Example: *Navicula.*

PHYLUM CHLOROPHYTA (green algae) Live in fresh water and salt water; unicellular or multicellular; chlorophylls and accessory pigments similar to those in vascular plants; food stored as starch. Examples: *Ulva, Chlamydomonas, Spirogyra.*

PHYLUM PHAEOPHYTA (brown algae) Live almost entirely in salt water; multicellular; contain brown pigment fucoxanthin. Examples: *Fucus* (rockweed), kelp, *Sargassum.*

PHYLUM RHODOPHYTA (red algae) Live almost entirely in salt water; multicellular; contain red pigment phycobilins. Examples: *Chondrus* (Irish moss), coralline algae.

FUNGUSLIKE PROTISTS

Heterotrophs that have some characteristics similar to those of fungi, though they have centrioles and lack cell walls of chitin.

PHYLUM ACRASIOMYCOTA (cellular slime molds) Spores develop into independent free-living amoeba-like cells that may come together to form a multicellular structure; this structure forms a fruiting body that produces spores. Example: *Dictyostelium*.

PHYLUM MYXOMYCOTA (acellular slime molds) Spores develop into haploid cells that can switch between flagellated and amoeba-like forms; these haploid cells fuse to form a zygote that grows into a plasmodium, which ultimately forms spore-producing fruiting bodies. Example: *Physarum*.

PHYLUM OOMYCOTA (water molds) Unicellular or multicellular; mostly aquatic; cell walls contain cellulose. Example: *Phytophthora infestans*.

Kingdom Fungi

Eukaryotic; heterotrophic; unicellular or multicellular; cell walls typically contain chitin; mostly decomposers; some parasites; some commensal or mutualistic symbionts; asexual reproduction by spore formation, budding, or fragmentation; sexual reproduction involving mating types; classified according to structure and method of reproduction.

PHYLUM ZYGOMYCOTA (common molds) Cell walls of chitin; hyphae generally lack cross walls; sexual reproduction by conjugation produces diploid zygospores; asexual reproduction produces haploid spores; most parasites; some decomposers. Example: *Rhizopus stolonifer* (black bread mold).

PHYLUM ASCOMYCOTA (sac fungi) Cell walls of chitin; hyphae have perforated cross walls; most multicellular; yeasts unicellular; sexual reproduction produces ascospores; asexual reproduction by spore formation or budding; some cause plant diseases such as chestnut blight and Dutch elm disease. Examples: *Neurospora* (red bread mold), baker's yeast, morels, truffles.

PHYLUM BASIDIOMYCOTA (club fungi) Cell walls of chitin; hyphae have cross walls; sexual reproduction involves basidiospores, which are borne on club-shaped basidia; asexual reproduction by spore formation. Examples: mushrooms, puffballs, shelf fungi, rusts.

PHYLUM DEUTEROMYCOTA (imperfect fungi) Cell walls of chitin; sexual reproduction never observed; members resemble ascomycetes, basidiomycetes, or zygomycetes. Example: *Penicillium*.

Kingdom Plantae

Eukaryotic; multicellular and nonmotile; photosynthetic autotrophs; possess chlorophylls *a* and *b* and other pigments in organelles called chloroplasts; cell walls contain cellulose; food stored as starch; reproduce sexually; alternate haploid (gametophyte) and diploid (sporophyte) generations.

PHYLUM BRYOPHYTA (mosses) Generally small; multicellular plants; live on land in moist habitats; lack vascular tissue; lack true roots, leaves, and stems; gametophyte dominant; water required for reproduction.

PHYLUM HEPATICOPHYTA (liverworts) Generally small, flat, lobe-shaped; multicellular plants; live on land in moist habitats; lack vascular tissue and true roots, leaves, and stems; gametophyte dominant; water required for reproduction.

PHYLUM ANTHCEROPHYTA (hornworts) Generally small; multicellular plants; live on land in moist habitats; lack vascular tissue and true roots, leaves, and stems; gametophyte dominant; named for horn-shaped sporophyte; water required for reproduction.

PHYLUM LYCOPHYTA (club mosses) Primitive vascular plants; usually small; sporophyte dominant; possess roots, stems, and leaves; water required for reproduction. Examples: club moss, quillwort.

PHYLUM ARTHROPHYTA (horsetails) Primitive vascular plants; stems comprise most of mature plants and contain silica; produce only one kind of spore; motile sperm must swim in water. Only one living genus. Example: *Equisetum*.

PHYLUM PTEROPHYTA (ferns) Vascular plants well-adapted to live in predominantly damp or seasonally wet environments; sporophyte dominant and well adapted to terrestrial life; gametophyte inconspicuous; reproduction still dependent on water for free-swimming gametes. Examples: cinnamon fern, Boston fern, tree fern, maidenhair fern.

PHYLUM CYCADOPHYTA (cycads) Evergreen, slow-growing, tropical and subtropical shrubs; many resemble small palm trees; palmlike or fernlike compound leaves; sexes are separate—individuals have either male pollen-producing cones or female seed-producing cones.

PHYLUM GINKGOPHYTA (ginkgoes) Deciduous trees with fan-shaped leaves; sexes separate; outer skin of ovule develops into a fleshy, fruitlike covering. Only one living species: *Ginkgo biloba* (ginkgo).

PHYLUM GNETOPHYTA (gnetophytes) Few species; mostly desert-living. Examples: *Welwitschia*, Mormon tea (*Ephedra*).

PHYLUM CONIFEROPHYTA (conifers) Seeds born on cones; predominantly wind-pollinated; most are evergreen; most are temperate and subarctic shrubs and trees; many have needlelike leaves; in most species, sexes are not separate. Examples: pine, spruce, cedar, cypress, yew, fir, larch, sequoia.

PHYLUM ANTHOPHYTA (angiosperms: flowering plants) Seeds develop enclosed within ovaries; leaves modified into flowers; flowers pollinated by wind or by animals, including insects, birds, and bats; occur in many different forms; found in most land and freshwater habitats; a few species found in shallow saltwater and estuarine areas.

CLASS MONOCOTYLEDONAE (monocots) Embryo with a single cotyledon; leaves with predominantly parallel venation; flower parts in multiples of three; vascular bundles scattered throughout stem. Examples: lily, corn, grasses, iris, palm, tulip.

CLASS DICOTYLEDONAE (dicots) Embryo with two cotyledons; leaves with venation in netlike patterns; flower parts in multiples of fours or fives; vascular bundles arranged in rings in stem. Examples: rose, maple, oak, daisy, apple.

Kingdom Animalia

Multicellular; eukaryotic; typical heterotrophs that ingest their food; lack cell walls; in most phyla, cells are organized into tissues that make up organs; most reproduce sexually; development involves formation of a hollow ball of cells called a blastula.

PHYLUM PORIFERA (sponges) Aquatic; lack true tissues and organs; motile larvae and sessile adults; filter feeders; internal skeleton made up of spongin and/or spicules of calcium carbonate or silica. Examples: Venus' flower basket, bath sponge, tube sponge.

PHYLUM CNIDARIA (cnidarians) Previously known as coelenterates; aquatic; mostly carnivorous; two layers of true tissues; radial symmetry; tentacles bear stinging nematocysts; many alternate between polyp and medusa body forms; gastrovascular cavity.

CLASS HYDROZOA Spend most of their time as polyps; colonial or solitary; life cycle typically includes a medusa generation that reproduces sexually and a polyp generation that reproduces asexually. Examples: hydra, Portuguese man-of-war.

CLASS SCYPHOZOA Spend most of their time as medusas; some species bypass polyp stage. Examples: lion's mane jellyfish, moon jelly, sea wasp.

CLASS ANTHOZOA Colonial or solitary polyps; no medusa stage. Examples: reef coral, sea anemone, sea pen, sea fan.

PHYLUM PLATYHELMINTHES (flatworms) Three layers of tissues (endoderm, mesoderm, ectoderm); bilateral symmetry; some cephalization; acoelomate; free-living or parasitic.

CLASS TURBELLARIA (turbellarians) Free-living carnivores and scavengers; live in fresh water, in salt water, or on land; move with cilia. Example: planarians.

CLASS TREMATODA (flukes) Parasites; life cycle typically involves more than one host. Examples: *Schistosoma*, liver fluke.

CLASS CESTODA (tapeworms) Internal parasites; lack digestive tract; body composed of many repeating sections (proglottids). Example: tapeworms.

PHYLUM NEMATODA (roundworms)
Digestive system has two openings—a mouth and an anus; pseudocoelomates. Examples: *Ascaris lumbricoides*, hookworms, *Trichinella*.

PHYLUM ANNELIDA (segmented worms) Body composed of segments separated by internal partitions; digestive system has two openings; coelomate; closed circulatory system.

CLASS POLYCHAETA (polychaetes) Live in salt water; pair of bristly, fleshy appendages on each segment; some live in tubes. Examples: sandworm, fanworm, feather-duster worm.

CLASS OLIGOCHAETA (oligochaetes) Lack appendages; few bristles; terrestrial or fresh water. Examples: *Tubifex*, earthworm.

CLASS HIRUDINEA (leeches) Lack appendages; carnivores or blood-sucking external parasites; most live in fresh water. Example: medicinal leech (*Hirudo medicinalis*).

PHYLUM MOLLUSCA (mollusks) Soft-bodied; often possess a hard, calcified shell secreted by a mantle; muscular foot; digestive system with two openings; coelomates.

CLASS BIVALVIA (bivalves) Two-part hinged shell; wedge-shaped foot; typically sessile as adults; primarily aquatic; some burrow in mud or sand. Examples: clam, oyster, scallop, mussel.

CLASS GASTROPODA (gastropods) Use broad, muscular foot in movement; most have spiral, chambered shell; some lack shell; distinct head; some terrestrial, others aquatic; many are cross-fertilizing hermaphrodites. Examples: snail, slug, nudibranch, sea hare, sea butterfly.

CLASS CEPHALOPODA (cephalopods) Foot is divided into tentacles; live in salt water; closed circulatory system. Examples: octopus, squid, nautilus, cuttlefish.

PHYLUM ARTHROPODA (arthropods) Exoskeleton of chitin; jointed appendages; segmented body; many undergo metamorphosis during development; open circulatory system; largest animal phylum.

Subphylum Trilobita (trilobites) Two furrows running from head to tail divide body into three lobes; one pair of unspecialized appendages on each body segment; each appendage divided into two branches—a gill and a walking leg; all extinct.

Subphylum Chelicerata (chelicerates) First pair of appendages specialized as feeding structures called chelicerae; body composed of two parts—cephalothorax and abdomen; lack antennae; most terrestrial. Examples: horseshoe crab, tick, mite, spider, scorpion.

Subphylum Crustacea (crustaceans) Most aquatic; most live in salt water; two pairs of antennae; mouthparts called mandibles; appendages consist of two branches; many have a carapace that covers part or all of the body. Examples: crab, crayfish, pill bug, water flea, barnacle.

Subphylum Uniramia Almost all terrestrial; one pair of antennae; mandibles; unbranched appendages.

CLASS CHILOPODA (centipedes) Long body consisting of many segments; one pair of legs per segment; poison claws for feeding; carnivorous.

CLASS DIPLOPODA (millipedes) Long body consisting of many segments; two pairs of legs per segment; mostly herbivorous.

CLASS INSECTA (insects) Body divided into three parts—head, thorax, and abdomen; three pairs of legs and usually one or two pairs of wings attached to thorax; some undergo complete metamorphosis. Examples: termite, ant, beetle, dragonfly, fly, moth, grasshopper.

PHYLUM ECHINODERMATA (echinoderms) Live in salt water; larvae have bilateral symmetry; adults typically have radial symmetry; endoskeleton; tube feet; water vascular system used in respiration, excretion, feeding, and locomotion; deuterostomes.

CLASS CRINOIDEA (crinoids) Filter feeders; feathery arms; mouth and anus on upper surface of body disk; some sessile. Examples: sea lily, feather star.

CLASS ASTEROIDEA (sea stars) Star-shaped; carnivorous; bottom dwellers; mouth on lower surface. Examples: crown-of-thorns sea star, sunstar.

CLASS OPHIUROIDEA Small body disk; long armored arms; most have only five arms; lack an anus; most are filter feeders or detritus feeders. Examples: brittle star, basket star.

CLASS ECHINOIDEA Lack arms; body encased in rigid, box-like covering; covered with spines; most grazing herbivores or detritus feeders. Examples: sea urchin, sand dollar, sea biscuit.

CLASS HOLOTHUROIDEA (sea cucumbers) Cylindrical body with feeding tentacles on one end; lie on their side; mostly detritus or filter feeders; endoskeleton greatly reduced.

PHYLUM CHORDATA (chordates) Dorsal hollow nerve cord, notochord, pharyngeal pouches, and a muscular tail during at least part of development.

Subphylum Urochordata (tunicates) Live in salt water; tough outer covering; display chordate features during larval stages; many adults sessile, some free-swimming. Examples: sea squirt, sea peach, salp.

Subphylum Cephalochordata (lancelets) Fishlike; live in salt water; filter feeders; no internal skeleton. Example: Branchiostoma.

Subphylum Vertebrata Most possess a vertebral column (backbone) that supports and protects dorsal nerve chord; endoskeleton; distinct head with a skull and brain.

CLASS MYXINI (hagfishes) Mostly scavengers; live in salt water; short tentacles around mouth; rasping tongue; extremely slimy; open circulatory system.

CLASS CEPHALASPIDOMORPHI (lampreys) Larvae filter feeders; adults are parasites whose circular mouth is lined with rasping toothlike structures; many live in both salt water and fresh water during the course of their lives.

CLASS CHONDRICHTHYES (cartilaginous fishes) Have jaws, fins, and endoskeleton of cartilage; most live in salt water; typically several gill slits; tough small scales with spines; ectothermic; two-chambered heart; males possess structures for internal fertilization. Examples: shark, ray, skate, chimaera, sawfish.

CLASS OSTEICHTHYES (bony fishes) Bony endoskeleton; aquatic; ectothermic; well-developed respiratory system, usually involving gills; possess swim bladder; paired fins; divided into two groups—ray-finned fishes, which include most living species, and lobe-finned fishes, which include lungfishes and the coelocanth. Examples: salmon, perch, sturgeon, tuna, goldfish, eel.

CLASS AMPHIBIA (amphibians) Adapted primarily to life in wet places; ectothermic; most carnivorous; smooth, moist skin; typically lay eggs that develop in water; usually have gilled larvae; most have three-chambered heart; adults either aquatic or terrestrial; terrestrial forms respire using lungs, skin, and/or lining of the mouth.

Order Urodela (salamanders) Possess tail as adults; carnivorous; usually have four legs; usually aquatic as larvae and terrestrial as adults.

Order Anura (frogs and toads) Adults in almost all species lack tail; aquatic larvae called tadpoles; well-developed hind legs adapted for jumping.

Order Apoda (legless amphibians) Wormlike; lack legs; carnivorous; terrestrial burrowers; some undergo direct development; some viviparous. Example: caecilians.

CLASS REPTILIA (reptiles) As a group, adapted to fully terrestrial life, some live in water; dry, scale-covered skin; ectothermic; most have three-chambered hearts; internal fertilization; amniotic eggs typically laid on land; extinct forms include dinosaurs and flying reptiles.

Order Sphenodonta (tuataras) Lack internal ears; primitive scales; found only in New Zealand; carnivorous. One species: *Sphenodon punctatus*.

Order Squamata (lizards and snakes) Most carnivorous; majority terrestrial; lizards typically have legs; snakes lack legs. Examples: iguana, gecko, skink, cobra, python, boa.

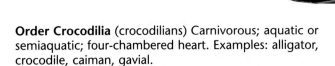

Order Crocodilia (crocodilians) Carnivorous; aquatic or semiaquatic; four-chambered heart. Examples: alligator, crocodile, caiman, gavial.

Order Testudines (turtles and tortoises) Bony shell; ribs and vertebrae fused to upper part of shell; some terrestrial, others semiaquatic or aquatic; all lay eggs on land. Examples: snapping turtle, tortoise, hawksbill turtle, box turtle.

CLASS AVES (birds) Endothermic; feathered over much of body surface; scales on legs and feet; bones hollow and lightweight in flying species; four-chambered heart; well-developed lungs and air sacs for efficient air exchange. Examples: owl, eagle, duck, chicken, pigeon, penguin, sparrow, stork.

CLASS MAMMALIA (mammals) Endothermic; subcutaneous fat; hair; most viviparous; suckle young with milk produced in mammary glands; four-chambered heart; most have four legs; use lungs for respiration.

Order Monotremata (monotremes) Exhibit features of both mammals and reptiles; possess a cloaca; lay eggs that hatch externally; produce milk from primitive nipple-like structures. Examples: duckbill platypus, short-beaked echidna.

Order Marsupialia (marsupials) Young develop in the female's uterus but emerge at very early state of development; development completed in mother's pouch. Examples: opossum, kangaroo, koala.

Order Insectivora (insectivores) Have long, narrow snouts and sharp claws for digging. Examples: shrew, mole, hedgehog.

Order Chiroptera (bats) Flying mammals, with forelimbs adapted for flight; most nocturnal; most navigate by echolocation; most species feed on insects, nectar, or fruits; some species feed on blood. Examples: fruit bat, flying fox, vampire bat.

Order Primates (primates) Highly developed brain and complex social behavior; excellent binocular vision; quadrupedal or bipedal locomotion; five digits on hands and feet. Examples: lemur, monkey, chimpanzee, human.

Order Edentata (edentates) Teeth reduced or absent; feed primarily on social insects, such as termites and ants. Examples: anteater, armadillo.

Order Lagomorpha (lagomorphs) Small herbivores with chisel-shaped front teeth; generally adapted to running and jumping. Examples: rabbit, pika, hare.

Order Rodentia (rodents) Mostly herbivorous but some omnivorous; sharp front teeth. Examples: rat, beaver, guinea pig, hamster, gerbil, squirrel.

Order Cetacea (cetaceans) Fully adapted to aquatic existence; feed, breed, and give birth in water; forelimbs specialized as flippers; external hindlimbs absent; many species capable of long, deep dives; some use echolocation to navigate; communicate using complex auditory signals. Examples: whale, porpoise, dolphin.

Order Carnivora (carnivores) Mostly carnivorous; live in salt water or on land; aquatic species must return to land to breed. Examples: seal, bear, raccoon, weasel, skunk.

Order Proboscidea (elephants) Herbivorous; have trunks; largest land animal. Examples: Asian elephant, African elephant.

Order Sirenia (sirenians) Aquatic herbivores; slow-moving; front limbs modified as flippers; hindlimbs absent; little body hair. Examples: manatee, sea cow.

Order Perissodactyla (odd-toed ungulates) Hoofed herbivores; odd number of digits on each foot; teeth, jaw, and digestive system adapted to plant material. Examples: horse, donkey, rhinoceros, tapir.

Order Artiodactyla (even-toed ungulates) Hoofed herbivores; hoofs derived from two digits on each foot; digestive system adapted to thoroughly process tough plant material. Examples: sheep, cow, hippopotamus, antelope, camel, giraffe, pig.

GLOSSARY

A

abdomen posterior part of an arthropod's body (p. 721)

abiotic factor physical, or nonliving, factor that shapes an ecosystem (p. 90)

abscission layer layer of cells at the petiole that seals off a leaf from the vascular system (p. 642)

accessory pigment compound other than chlorophyll that absorbs light at different wavelengths than chlorophyll (p. 506)

acellular slime mold slime mold that passes through a stage in which its cells fuse to form large cells with many nuclei (p. 516)

acetylcholine neurotransmitter that diffuses across a synapse and produces an impulse in the cell membrane of a muscle cell (p. 929)

acid compound that forms hydrogen ions (H^+) in solution (p. 43)

acid rain rain containing nitric and sulfuric acids (p. 148)

acoelomate animal lacking a coelom, or body cavity (p. 683)

actin a protein that mainly makes up the thin filaments in striations in skeletal muscle cells (p. 928)

action potential reversal of charges across the cell membrane of a neuron (p. 899)

activation energy energy needed to get a reaction started (p. 50)

active immunity immunity produced by a vaccine; so-called because the body has the ability to mount an active immune response against the pathogen (p. 1040)

active transport energy-requiring process that moves material across a cell membrane against a concentration difference (p. 189)

adaptation inherited characteristic that increases an organism's chance of survival (p. 380)

adaptive radiation process by which a single species or small group of species evolves into several different forms that live in different ways; rapid growth in the diversity of a group of organisms (pp. 437, 851)

addiction uncontrollable craving for more of a drug (p. 911)

adenosine triphosphate (ATP) one of the principal chemical compounds that living things use to store energy (p. 202)

adhesion attraction between molecules of different substances (p. 41); in plants: attraction between unlike molecules (p. 599)

aerobic process that requires oxygen (p. 226)

age-structure diagram graph of the numbers of males and females within different age groups of a population (p. 131)

aggression threatening behavior that one animal uses to gain control over another (p. 881)

agriculture the practice of farming (p. 141)

air sac one of several sacs attached to a bird's lungs into which air moves when a bird inhales; allows for the one-way flow of air through the respiratory system (p. 810)

algal bloom an immediate increase in the amount of algae and other producers that results from a large input of a limiting nutrient (p. 80)

allele one of a number of different forms of a gene (p. 265)

allergy overreaction of the immune system that results when antigens bind to mast cells (p. 1041)

alternation of generations process in which many algae switch back and forth between haploid and diploid stages of their life cycles (p. 512)

alveolus tiny air sac at the end of a bronchiole in the lungs that provides surface area for gas exchange to occur (pp. 859, 958)

amino acid compound with an amino group ($—NH_2$) on one end and a carboxyl group ($—COOH$) on the other end (p. 47)

amniotic egg egg composed of shell and membranes that create a protected environment in which the embryo can develop out of the water (p. 802)

amoeboid movement type of locomotion used by amoebas (p. 498)

amphibian vertebrate that, with some exceptions, lives in water as a larva and on land as an adult, breathes with lungs as an adult, has moist skin that contains mucus glands, and lacks scales and claws (p. 782)

amylase enzyme in saliva that breaks the chemical bonds between the sugar monomers in starches (p. 979)

anaerobic process that does not require oxygen (p. 224)

anal pore region of the cell membrane of a ciliate where waste-containing food vacuoles fuse and are then emptied into the environment (p. 500)

anaphase the third phase of mitosis, during which the chromosome pairs separate and move toward opposite poles (p. 248)

angiosperm flowering plant; bears its seeds within a layer of tissue that protects the seed (p. 564)

Animalia kingdom of multicellular eukaryotic heterotrophs whose cells do not have cell walls (p. 461)

annual flowering plant that completes a life cycle within one growing season (p. 572)

anther flower structure in which haploid male gametophytes are produced (p. 612)

antheridium male reproductive structure in some algae and plants (pp. 519, 559)

anthropoid humanlike primate (p. 835)

antibiotic compound that blocks the growth and reproduction of bacteria (pp. 480, 1033)

antibody specialized protein that helps destroy disease-causing organisms (p. 1036)

anticodon group of three bases on a tRNA molecule that are complementary to an mRNA codon (p. 304)

antigen substance that triggers an immune response (p. 1036)

anus opening through which wastes leave the digestive tract (pp. 661, 689)

aorta large blood vessel in mammals through which blood travels from the left ventricle to all parts of the body except the lungs (p. 946)

aphotic zone permanently dark layer of the oceans below the photic zone (p. 109)

apical dominance phenomenon in which the closer a bud is to the stem's tip, the more its growth is inhibited (p. 636)

apical meristem group of undifferentiated cells that divide to produce increased length of stems and roots (p. 580)

appendage structure, such as a leg or antenna, that extends from the body wall (p. 715)

aquaculture farming of aquatic organisms (p. 147)

Archaea domain of unicellular prokaryotes that have cell walls that do not contain peptidoglycan (p. 459)

Archaebacteria kingdom of unicellular prokaryotes whose cell walls do not contain peptidoglycan (p. 459)

archaeocyte specialized cell in a sponge that makes spicules (p. 665)

archegonium female reproductive structure in some plants, including mosses and liverworts (p. 559)

artery large blood vessel that carries blood from the heart to the tissues of the body (p. 946)

artificial selection selection by humans for breeding of useful traits from the natural variation among different organisms (p. 379)

ascospore haploid spore produced within the ascus of ascomycetes (p. 532)

ascus structure within the fruiting body of an ascomycete in which two nuclei of different mating types fuse (p. 532)

asexual reproduction process by which a single parent reproduces by itself (p. 17)

asthma allergic reaction in which smooth muscle contractions reduce the size of air passageways in the lungs and make breathing very difficult (p. 1042)

atherosclerosis condition in which fatty deposits called plaque build up on the walls of the arteries (p. 949)

atom basic unit of matter (p. 35)

ATP synthase large protein that uses energy from H+ ions to bind ADP and a phosphate group together to produce ATP (p. 210)

atrium large muscular upper chamber of the heart that receives and holds blood that is about to enter the ventricle (pp. 776, 944)

autosome autosomal chromosome; chromosome that is not a sex chromosome (p. 341)

autotroph organism that can capture energy from sunlight or chemicals and use it to produce its own food from inorganic compounds; also called a producer (pp. 67, 201)

auxin substance produced in the tip of a seedling that stimulates cell elongation (p. 635)

axon long fiber that carries impulses away from the cell body of a neuron (p. 898)

bacillus rod-shaped prokaryote (p. 473)

Bacteria domain of unicellular prokaryotes that have cell walls containing peptidoglycans (p. 459)

bacteriophage virus that infects bacteria (pp. 289, 484)

bark tree structure that includes all tissues outside the vascular cambium, including phloem, the cork cambium, and cork (p. 593)

base compound that produces hydroxide ions (OH⁻) in solution (p. 43)

base-pairing principle that bonds in DNA can form only between adenine and thymine and between guanine and cytosine (p. 294)

basidiospore spore in basidiomycetes that germinates to produce haploid primary mycelia (p. 535)

basidium spore-bearing structure of a basidiomycete (p. 534)

behavior the way an organism reacts to changes in its internal condition or external environment (p. 871)

behavioral isolation form of reproductive isolation in which two populations have differences in courtship rituals or other types of behavior that prevent them from interbreeding (p. 404)

benthos organisms that live attached to or near the ocean floor (p. 112)

biennial flowering plant that completes its life cycle in two years (p. 572)

bilateral symmetry body plan in which only a single, imaginary line can divide the body into two equal halves; characteristic of worms, arthropods, and chordates (pp. 662, 748)

binary fission type of asexual reproduction in which a prokaryote replicates its DNA, and divides in half, producing two identical daughter cells (p. 476)

binocular vision ability to merge visual images from both eyes, which provides depth perception and a three-dimensional view of the world (p. 834)

binomial nomenclature classification system in which each species is assigned a two-part scientific name (p. 448)

biodiversity biological diversity; the sum total of the variety of organisms in the biosphere (p. 150)

GLOSSARY

biogeochemical cycle process in which elements, chemical compounds, and other forms of matter are passed from one organism to another and from one part of the biosphere to another (p. 74)

biological magnification increasing concentration of a harmful substance in organisms at higher trophic levels in a food chain or food web (p. 152)

biology science that seeks to understand the living world (p. 16)

biomass total amount of living tissue within a given trophic level (p. 72)

biome group of ecosystems that have the same climate and similar dominant communities (pp. 64, 98)

biosphere part of Earth in which life exists including land, water, and air or atmosphere (p. 63)

biotic factor biological influence on organisms within an ecosystem (p. 90)

bipedal term used to refer to two-footed locomotion (p. 835)

bird endothermic animal that has an outer covering of feathers, two legs covered with scales that are used for walking or perching, and front limbs modified into wings (p. 800)

blade thin, flattened section of a plant leaf that collects sunlight (p. 595)

blastula hollow ball of cells formed when a zygote undergoes a series of divisions (p. 661)

bone marrow soft tissue inside cavities within bones; two types are yellow marrow and red marrow (p. 922)

book lung organ that has layers of respiratory tissue stacked like the pages of a book; used by some terrestrial arthropods to exchange gases (p. 717)

Bowman's capsule cup-shaped structure in the upper end of a nephron that encases the glomerulus (p. 987)

brain stem structure that connects the brain and spinal cord; includes the medulla oblongata and the pons (p. 902)

bronchus passageway leading from the trachea to a lung (p. 958)

bryophyte nonvascular plant; examples are mosses and their relatives (p. 556)

bud plant structure containing undeveloped tissue that can produce new stems and leaves (p. 589)

budding process of attaching a bud to a plant to produce a new branch (p. 623)

buffer weak acid or base that can react with strong acids or bases to help prevent sharp, sudden changes in pH (p. 43)

calorie amount of energy required to raise the temperature of 1 gram of water by 1 Celsius degree (p. 221)

Calorie term used by scientists to measure the energy stored in foods; 1000 calories (p. 971)

Calvin cycle reactions of photosynthesis in which energy from ATP and NADPH is used to build high-energy compounds such as sugars (p. 212)

cancer disorder in which some of the body's own cells lose the ability to control growth (p. 252)

canopy dense covering formed by the leafy tops of tall rain trees (p. 100)

capillary smallest blood vessel; brings nutrients and oxygen to the tissues and absorbs carbon dioxide and waste products (p. 947)

capillary action tendency of water to rise in a thin tube (p. 599)

capsid outer protein coat of a virus (p. 483)

carapace in crustaceans, the part of the exoskeleton that covers the cephalothorax (p. 721); in turtles and tortoises, the dorsal part of the shell (p. 805)

carbohydrate compound made up of carbon, hydrogen, and oxygen atoms; major source of energy for the human body (pp. 45, 972)

carnivore organism that obtains energy by eating animals (p. 69)

carpel innermost part of a flower that produces the female gametophytes (p. 612)

carrying capacity largest number of individuals of a population that a given environment can support (p. 122)

cartilage strong connective tissue that supports the body and is softer and more flexible than bone (pp. 773, 922)

Casparian strip waterproof strip that surrounds plant endodermis cells (p. 587)

caste group of individual insects specialized to perform particular tasks, or roles (p. 732)

catalyst substance that speeds up the rate of a chemical reaction (p. 51)

cell collection of living matter enclosed by a barrier that separates the cell from its surroundings; basic unit of all forms of life (pp. 17, 170)

cell body largest part of a typical neuron; contains the nucleus and much of the cytoplasm (p. 897)

cell culture group of cells grown in a nutrient solution from a single original cell (p. 27)

cell cycle series of events that cells go through as they grow and divide (p. 245)

cell division process by which a cell divides into two new daughter cells (p. 243)

cell fractionation technique in which cells are broken into pieces and the different cell parts are separated (p. 27)

cell-mediated immunity an immune response in which killer T cells attack antigen-bearing cells directly (p. 1038)

cell membrane thin, flexible barrier around a cell; regulates what enters and leaves the cell (p. 171)

cell specialization separate roles for each type of cell in multicellular organisms (p. 191)

cell theory idea that all living things are composed of cells, cells are the basic units of structure and function in living things, and new cells are produced from existing cells (p. 170)

cellular respiration process that releases energy by breaking down food molecules in the presence of oxygen; made up of glycolysis, the Krebs cycle, and the electron transport chain (p. 222)

cellular slime mold slime mold whose individual cells remain separated during every phase of the mold's life cycle (p. 516)

cell wall strong layer around the cell membrane in plants, algae, and some bacteria (p. 171)

central nervous system the brain and the spinal cord (p. 901)

centriole one of two tiny structures located in the cytoplasm of animal cells near the nuclear envelope (p. 246)

centromere area where the chromatids of a chromosome are attached (p. 244)

cephalization concentration of sense organs and nerve cells at the front of an animal's body (pp. 663, 748)

cephalothorax region of a crustacean formed by the fusion of the head with the thorax (p. 721)

cerebellum region of the brain that coordinates body movements (pp. 777, 902)

cerebral cortex outer layer of the cerebrum of a mammal's brain; center of thinking and other complex behaviors (p. 825)

cerebrospinal fluid fluid in the space between the meninges that acts as a shock absorber that protects the central nervous system (p. 901)

cerebrum area of the brain responsible for all voluntary activities of the body (pp. 777, 902)

chelicerae pair of mouthparts in chelicerates that contain fangs and are used to stab and paralyze prey (p. 722)

cheliped one of the first pair of legs of decapods (p. 721)

chemical bond link that holds together atoms in compounds (p. 38)

chemical reaction process that changes one set of chemicals into another set of chemicals (p. 49)

chemoautotroph prokaryote that obtains energy directly from inorganic molecules using chemical reactions (p. 474)

chemosynthesis process by which some organisms use chemical energy to produce carbohydrates (p. 68)

chemotherapy drug therapy; the use of a combination of chemicals to destroy cancer cells (p. 1048)

chitin complex carbohydrate that makes up the cell walls of fungi; also found in the external skeletons of arthropods (pp. 527, 715)

chlorophyll principal pigment of plants and other photosynthetic organisms; captures light energy (p. 207)

chloroplast organelle found in cells of plants and some other organisms that uses energy from sunlight to make energy-rich food molecules by photosynthesis (p. 180)

choanocyte specialized cell in sponges that uses a flagellum to move a steady current of water through the sponge (p. 665)

chordate member of the phylum Chordata; animal that has, for at least some stage of its life, a dorsal, hollow nerve cord; a notochord; pharyngeal pouches; and a muscular tail (p. 767)

chromatid one of two identical "sister" parts of a duplicated chromosome (p. 244)

chromatin granular material visible within the nucleus; consists of DNA tightly coiled around proteins (pp. 175, 297)

chromosome threadlike structure within the nucleus containing the genetic information that is passed from one generation of cells to the next (p. 175)

chyme mixture of stomach fluids and food produced in the stomach by contracting stomach muscles (p. 981)

cilium short hairlike projection similar to a flagellum; produces movement in many cells (p. 499)

circadian rhythm behavioral cycle that occurs in a daily pattern (p. 878)

cladogram diagram that shows the evolutionary relationships among a group of organisms (p. 453)

class group of similar orders (p. 449)

classical conditioning learning process in which an animal makes a mental connection between a stimulus and some kind of reward or punishment (p. 874)

climate average, year-after-year conditions of temperature and precipitation in a particular region (p. 87)

clitellum band of thickened, specialized segments in annelids that secretes a mucus ring into which eggs and sperm are released (p. 696)

cloaca a muscular cavity at the end of the large intestine through which digestive wastes, urine, and eggs or sperm leave the body (p. 748)

clone member of a population of genetically identical organisms produced from a single cell (p. 333)

closed circulatory system system in which blood is contained within a network of blood vessels (pp. 695, 754)

cnidocyte stinging cell located along the tentacles of cnidarians; used for defense and to capture prey (p. 669)

coastal ocean marine zone that extends from the low-tide mark to the end of the continental shelf (p. 110)

coccus spherical prokaryote (p. 473)

cochlea fluid-filled part of the inner ear; sends nerve impulses to the brain through the cochlear nerve (p. 908)

codominance situation in which both alleles of a gene contribute to the phenotype of the organism (p. 272)

codon three-nucleotide sequence on messenger RNA that codes for a single amino acid (p. 302)

coelom fluid-filled body cavity lined with mesoderm (pp. 683, 749)

coevolution process by which two species evolve in response to changes in each other (p. 437)

cohesion attraction between molecules of the same substance (p. 41)

collenchyma type of ground tissue cell with a strong, flexible cell wall; helps support larger plants (p. 583)

commensalism symbiotic relationship in which one member of the association benefits and the other is neither helped nor harmed (p. 93)

common descent principle that all living things have a common ancestor (p. 382)

communication passing of information from one organism to another (p. 881)

community assemblage of different populations that live together in a defined area (p. 64)

companion cell phloem cell that surrounds sieve tube elements (p. 583)

competitive exclusion principle ecological rule that states that no two species can occupy the same exact niche in the same habitat at the same time (p. 92)

complete metamorphosis type of insect development in which the larvae look and act nothing like their parents and also feed in completely different ways (p. 729)

compound substance formed by the chemical combination of two or more elements in definite proportions (p. 37)

compound light microscope microscope that allows light to pass through a specimen and uses two lenses to form an image (p. 26)

concentration the mass of solute in a given volume of solution, or mass/volume (p. 185)

cone in gymnosperms, a seed-bearing structure (p. 564); in the retina of the eye, a photoreceptor that responds to light of different colors, producing color vision (p. 907)

conidium tiny fungal spore that forms at the tips of specialized hyphae in ascomycetes (p. 532)

coniferous term used to refer to trees that produce seed-bearing cones and have thin leaves shaped like needles (p. 103)

conjugation form of sexual reproduction in which paramecia and some prokaryotes exchange genetic information (pp. 476, 500)

connective tissue tissue that holds organs in place and binds different parts of the body together (p. 894)

conservation wise management of natural resources, including the preservation of habitats and wildlife (p. 154)

consumer organism that relies on other organisms for its energy and food supply; also called a heterotroph (p. 68)

contractile vacuole cavity in the cytoplasm of some protists that collects water and discharges it from the cell (p. 500)

controlled experiment a test of the effect of a single variable by changing it while keeping all other variables the same (p. 9)

controlled variable factor in an experiment that a scientist purposely keeps the same (p. 1056)

convergent evolution process by which unrelated organisms independently evolve similarities when adapting to similar environments (p. 437)

coral reef diverse and productive environment named for the coral animals that makes up its primary structure (p. 111)

cork cambium lateral meristematic tissue that produces the outer covering of stems (p. 591)

corpus luteum name given to a follicle after ovulation because of its yellow color (p. 1014)

cortex spongy layer of ground tissue just inside the epidermis of a root (p. 585)

cotyledon seed leaf in a plant embryo (p. 570)

courtship type of behavior in which an animal sends out stimuli—such as sounds, visual displays, or chemicals—in order to attract a member of the opposite sex (p. 879)

covalent bond bond formed by the sharing of electrons between atoms (p. 38)

crop in earthworms, part of the digestive system in which food can be stored (p. 695); in birds, structure at the lower end of the esophagus in which food is stored and moistened (p. 809)

crossing-over process in which homologous chromosomes exchange portions of their chromatids during meiosis (p. 277)

cuticle in plants, a thick, waxy layer on exposed outer surfaces of cells that protects them against water loss and injury (p. 581)

cyclin one of a family of closely related proteins that regulate the cell cycle in eukaryotic cells (p. 251)

cytokinesis division of the cytoplasm during cell division (p. 248)

cytoplasm material inside the cell membrane—but not including the nucleus (p. 171)

cytoskeleton network of protein filaments within some cells that helps the cell maintain its shape and is involved in many forms of cell movement (p. 176)

D

data evidence; information gathered from observations (pp. 4, 1057)

deciduous term used to refer to a tree that sheds its leaves during a particular season each year (p. 100)

decomposer organism that breaks down and obtains energy from dead organic matter (p. 69)

deforestation destruction of forests (p. 146)

demographic transition change in a population from high birth and death rates to low birth and death rates (p. 130)

demography scientific study of human populations (p. 130)

dendrite extension of the cell body of a neuron that carries impulses from the environment or from other neurons toward the cell body (p. 898)

denitrification conversion of nitrates into nitrogen gas (p. 78)

density-dependent limiting factor limiting factor that depends on population size (p. 125)

density-independent limiting factor limiting factor that affects all populations in similar ways, regardless of population size (p. 127)

deoxyribonucleic acid (DNA) nucleic acid that contains the sugar deoxyribose (p. 47)

dependent variable factor in an experiment that a scientist wants to observe, which may change because of the manipulated variable; also known as a responding variable (p. 1056)

depressant drug that decreases the rate of functions regulated by the brain (p. 911)

derived character characteristic that appears in recent parts of a lineage, but not in its older members (p. 453)

dermis innermost layer of the skin (p. 935)

descent with modification principle that each living species has descended, with changes, from other species over time (p. 381)

desertification in areas with dry climates, a process caused by a combination of poor farming practices, overgrazing, and drought that turns productive land into desert (p. 145)

detritivore organism that feeds on plant and animal remains and other dead matter (p. 69)

detritus particles of organic material that provide food for organisms at the base of an estuary's food web (p. 108)

deuterostome animal whose anus is formed from the blastopore of a blastula (p. 661)

diabetes mellitus condition that occurs when the pancreas produces too little insulin, resulting in an increase in the amount of glucose in the blood (p. 1008)

diaphragm large, flat muscle at the bottom of the chest cavity that contracts during breathing, pulling the bottom of the chest cavity down and increasing its volume (pp. 824, 959)

dicot angiosperm whose seeds have two cotyledons (p. 570)

diffusion process by which molecules tend to move from an area where they are more concentrated to an area where they are less concentrated (p. 185)

diploid term used to refer to a cell that contains both sets of homologous chromosomes (p. 275)

directional selection form of natural selection in which the entire curve moves; occurs when individuals at one end of a distribution curve have higher fitness than individuals in the middle or at the other end of the curve (p. 398)

disease any change, other than an injury, that disrupts the normal functions of the body (p. 1029)

disruptive selection form of natural selection in which a single curve splits into two; occurs when individuals at the upper and lower ends of a distribution curve have higher fitness than individuals near the middle (p. 399)

DNA fingerprinting analysis of sections of DNA that have little or no known function, but vary widely from one individual to another, in order to identify individuals (p. 357)

DNA polymerase enzyme that "proofreads" new DNA strands, helping to ensure that each molecule is a nearly perfect copy of the original DNA (p. 299)

domain most inclusive taxonomic category; larger than a kingdom (p. 458)

dormancy period of time during which a plant embryo is alive but not growing (pp. 620, 641)

double fertilization fertilization in angiosperms, in which two distinct fertilization events take place between the male and female gametophytes (p. 616)

drug any substance, other than food, that causes a change in the structure or function of the body (p. 910)

drug abuse use of any drug in a way that most doctors would not approve (p. 914)

E

ecological pyramid diagram that shows the relative amounts of energy or matter within each trophic level in a food chain or food web (p. 72)

ecological succession gradual change in living communities that follows a disturbance (p. 94)

ecology scientific study of interactions among organisms and between organisms and their environment (p. 63)

ecosystem collection of all the organisms that live in a particular place, together with their nonliving environment (p. 64)

ecosystem diversity variety of habitats, living communities, and ecological processes in the living world (p. 150)

ectoderm outermost germ layer of most animals; gives rise to outer layer of the skin, sense organs, and nerves (p. 661)

ectotherm animal that relies on interactions with the environment to help it control body temperature (pp. 800, 855)

electron negatively charged particle; located outside the atomic nucleus (p. 35)

electron microscope microscope that forms an image by focusing beams of electrons onto a specimen (p. 26)

electron transport chain a series of proteins in which the high-energy electrons from the Krebs cycle are used to convert ADP into ATP (p. 228)

element substance consisting entirely of one type of atom (p. 36)

embryo early developmental stage of a sporophyte plant (p. 565)

embryo sac female gametophyte within the ovule of a flowering plant (p. 615)

emigration movement of individuals out of a population (p. 120)

emphysema disease in which the tissues of the lungs lose elasticity, making breathing very difficult (p. 962)

endangered species species whose population size is rapidly declining and will become extinct if the trend continues (p. 151)

endocrine gland gland that releases its secretions directly into the bloodstream (p. 998)

endocytosis process by which a cell takes material into the cell by infolding of the cell membrane (p. 189)

endoderm innermost germ layer of most animals; develops into the linings of the digestive tract and much of the respiratory system (p. 661)

endodermis layer of cells that completely encloses vascular tissue (p. 585)

endoplasmic reticulum internal membrane system in cells in which components of the cell membrane are assembled and some proteins are modified (p. 177)

endoskeleton structural support located inside the body of an animal (pp. 734, 757)

endosperm food-rich tissue that nourishes a seedling as it grows (p. 616)

endospore type of spore formed when a bacterium produces a thick internal wall that encloses its DNA and a portion of its cytoplasm (p. 476)

endosymbiotic theory theory that eukaryotic cells formed from a symbiosis among several different prokaryotic organisms (p. 427)

endotherm animal that generates its own body heat and controls its body temperature from within (pp. 808, 855)

enzyme protein that acts as a biological catalyst (p. 51)

epidermal cell cell that makes up the dermal tissue, which is the outer covering of a plant (p. 581)

epidermis outer layer of the skin (p. 934)

epididymis structure in the male reproductive system in which sperm fully mature and are stored (p. 1010)

epiphyte plant that grows directly on the body of another plant (p. 645)

epithelial tissue tissue that covers the surface of the body and lines internal organs (p. 894)

era one of several subdivisions of the time between the Precambrian and the present (p. 421)

esophagus food tube connecting the mouth to the stomach (p. 980)

estuary wetlands formed where rivers meet the ocean (p. 108)

ethylene plant hormone that stimulates fruits to ripen (p. 638)

Eubacteria kingdom of unicellular prokaryotes whose cell walls are made up of peptidoglycan (p. 459)

Eukarya domain of all organisms whose cells have nuclei, including protists, plants, fungi, and animals (p. 460)

eukaryote organism whose cells contain nuclei (p. 172)

evaporation process by which water changes from a liquid into an atmospheric gas (p. 75)

evolution change in a kind of organism over time; process by which modern organisms have descended from ancient organisms (pp. 20, 369)

evolutionary classification method of grouping organisms together according to their evolutionary history (p. 452)

exocrine gland gland that releases its secretions through tubelike structures called ducts (p. 998)

exocytosis process by which a cell releases large amounts of material (p. 189)

exon expressed sequence of DNA; codes for a protein (p. 302)

exoskeleton external skeleton; tough external covering that protects and supports the body of many invertebrates (pp. 715, 757)

exponential growth growth pattern in which the individuals in a population reproduce at a constant rate (p. 121)

external fertilization process in which eggs are fertilized outside the female's body (pp. 672, 758)

extinct term used to refer to a species that has died out (p. 417)

extinction disappearance of a species from all parts of its geographical range (p. 151)

extracellular digestion process in which food is broken down outside the cells in a digestive tract (p. 751)

eyespot group of cells that can detect changes in the amount of light in the environment (pp. 506, 685)

facilitated diffusion movement of specific molecules across cell membranes through protein channels (p. 188)

Fallopian tube one of two fluid-filled tubes in human females through which an egg passes after its release from an ovary (p. 1013)

family group of genera that share many characteristics (p. 449)

fat lipid; made up of fatty acids and glycerol (p. 972)

feather structure made mostly of protein that develops from a pit in a bird's skin (p. 806)

feedback inhibition process by which the product of a system shuts down the system or limits its operation (p. 895)

fermentation process by which cells release energy in the absence of oxygen (p. 224)

fetal alcohol syndrome group of birth defects caused by the effects of alcohol on a fetus (p. 913)

fetus name given to a human embryo after eight weeks of development (p. 1019)

fever elevated body temperature that occurs in response to infection (p. 1035)

fibrous root part of a root system in which roots branch to such an extent that no single root grows larger than the rest (p. 584)

filament in algae, a long threadlike colony formed by many green algae (p. 512); in plants, a long, thin structure that supports an anther (p. 612)

filtration process by which fluid from the blood filters into Bowman's capsule in the kidneys (p. 987)

fish aquatic vertebrate characterized by paired fins, scales, and gills (p. 771)

fission form of asexual reproduction in which an organism splits into two, and each half grows new parts to become a complete organism (p. 686)

fitness ability of an organism to survive and reproduce in its environment (p. 380)

flagellum whiplike structure on some cells that is used for movement (p. 473)

flame cell specialized cell that filters and removes excess water from the body of a flatworm (p. 684)

flower seed-bearing structure of an angiosperm (p. 564)

follicle cluster of cells surrounding a single egg in the human female reproductive system (p. 1012)

food chain series of steps in an ecosystem in which organisms transfer energy by eating and being eaten (p. 69)

food vacuole small cavity in the cytoplasm of protists that temporarily stores food (p. 498)

food web network of complex interactions formed by the feeding relationships among the various organisms in an ecosystem (p. 70)

foot muscular part of a mollusk (p. 702)

fossil preserved remains or evidence of an ancient organism (p. 371)

fossil record information about past life, including the structure of organisms, what they ate, what ate them, in what environment they lived, and the order in which they lived (p. 417)

founder effect change in allele frequencies as a result of the migration of a small subgroup of a population (p. 400)

frameshift mutation mutation that shifts the "reading" frame of the genetic message by inserting or deleting a nucleotide (p. 307)

frond large leaf of a fern (p. 562)

fruit thick wall of tissue surrounding an angiosperm seed (p. 569)

fruiting body reproductive structure of fungus that develops from a mycelium (p. 528)

Fungi kingdom composed of heterotrophs; many obtain energy and nutrients from dead organic matter (p. 460)

gametangium gamete-forming structure produced when the hyphae of opposing mating types of fungi meet (p. 529)

gamete specialized cell involved in sexual reproduction (p. 266)

gametophyte haploid, or gamete-producing, phase of an organism (pp. 514, 552)

ganglion group of nerve cells (p. 685)

gastrovascular cavity digestive chamber with a single opening, in which cnidarians, flatworms, and echinoderms digest food (p. 671)

gastrulation process of cell migration by which a third layer of cells is formed within the cavity of a blastocyst (p. 1017)

gel electrophoresis procedure used to separate and analyze DNA fragments by placing a mixture of DNA fragments at one end of a porous gel and applying an electrical voltage to the gel (p. 323)

gemma small cup-shaped structure in liverworts that contains many haploid cells; used for asexual reproduction (p. 557)

gemmule group of archaeocytes surrounded by a tough layer of spicules; produced by some sponges (p. 667)

gene sequence of DNA that codes for a protein and thus determines a trait (p. 265)

gene map diagram showing the relative locations of each known gene on a particular chromosome (p. 280)

gene pool combined genetic information of all the members of a particular population (p. 394)

genetic diversity sum total of all the different forms of genetic information carried by all organisms living on Earth today (p. 150)

genetic drift random change in allele frequencies that occurs in small populations (p. 400)

genetic engineering process of making changes in the DNA code of living organisms (p. 322)

genetic equilibrium situation in which allele frequencies remain constant (p. 401)

genetic marker gene that makes it possible to distinguish bacteria that carry a plasmid with foreign DNA from those that don't (p. 328)

genetics scientific study of heredity (p. 263)

genotype genetic makeup of an organism (p. 268)

genus group of closely related species, first part of the scientific name in binomial nomenclature (p. 448)

geographic isolation form of reproductive isolation in which two populations are separated physically by geographic barriers such as rivers, mountains, or stretches of water (p. 405)

geologic time scale scale used by paleontologists to represent evolutionary time (p. 421)

germ theory of disease idea that infectious diseases are caused by microorganisms, or germs (p. 1029)

germination early growth stage of a plant embryo (p. 621)

gibberellin growth-promoting substance produced by plants (p. 637)

gill filamentous organ in aquatic animals specialized for the exchange of gases with water (p. 696)

gizzard in earthworms, part of the digestive system in which food is ground into smaller pieces (p. 695); in birds, a muscular organ that helps in the mechanical breakdown of food (p. 809)

global warming increase in the average temperatures on Earth (p. 159)

glomerulus small network of capillaries encased in the upper end of a nephron (p. 987)

glycolysis first step in releasing the energy of glucose, in which a molecule of glucose is broken into two molecules of pyruvic acid (p. 221)

Golgi apparatus stack of membranes in the cell in which enzymes attach carbohydrates and lipids to proteins (p. 178)

grafting use of a stem as a scion (p. 623)

gravitropism tendency of a plant to grow in a direction in response to the force of gravity (p. 635)

green revolution introduction of intensive farming practices that lead to a substantial increase in crop yields (p. 142)

greenhouse effect natural situation in which heat is retained in Earth's atmosphere by carbon dioxide, methane, water vapor, and other gases (p. 87)

guard cell specialized cell in the epidermis of plants that controls the opening and closing of stomata by responding to changes in water pressure (p. 596)

gullet indentation in one side of a ciliate that allows food to enter the cell (p. 500)

gymnosperm seed plant that bears its seeds directly on the surfaces of cones (p. 564)

habitat the area where an organism lives, including the biotic and abiotic factors that affect the organism (p. 90)

habitat fragmentation splitting of ecosystems into small fragments (p. 151)

habituation learning process by which an animal decreases or stops its response to a repetitive stimulus that neither rewards nor harms it (p. 874)

hair follicle tubelike pocket of epidermal cells that extends into the dermis; cells at the base of hair follicles produce hair (p. 936)

half-life length of time required for half of the radioactive atoms in a sample to decay (p. 420)

haploid term used to refer to a cell that contains only a single set of chromosomes and therefore only a single set of genes (p. 275)

Hardy-Weinberg principle principle that allele frequencies in a population will remain constant unless one or more factors cause the frequencies to change (p. 401)

Haversian canal one of a network of tubes running through compact bone that contains blood vessels and nerves (p. 922)

heartwood older xylem near the center of a woody stem that no longer conducts water (p. 592)

hemoglobin iron-containing protein in red blood cells that transports oxygen from the lungs to the tissues of the body (p. 952)

herbicide compound that is toxic to plants (p. 636)

herbivore organism that obtains energy by eating only plants (p. 69)

hermaphrodite individual that has both male and female reproductive organs (p. 686)

heterotroph organism that obtains energy from the foods it consumes; also called a consumer (pp. 68, 201)

heterozygous term used to refer to an organism that has two different alleles for the same trait (p. 268)

histamine chemical released by activated mast cells that increases the flow of blood and fluids to the surrounding area (p. 1041)

histone globular protein molecule around which DNA is tightly coiled in chromatin (p. 297)

homeostasis process by which organisms maintain a relatively stable internal environment (p. 19)

hominid primate that walks upright, has opposable thumbs, and possesses a large brain; only living members are humans (p. 835)

hominoid member of a group of primates that includes apes and humans (p. 835)

homologous term used to refer to chromosomes that each have a corresponding chromosome from the opposite-sex parent (p. 275)

homologous structures structures that have different mature forms in different organisms but develop from the same embryonic tissues (p. 384)

homozygous term used to refer to an organism that has two identical alleles for a particular trait (p. 268)

hormone substance produced in one part of an organism that affects another part of the same individual (pp. 634, 997)

host organism that provides a source of nutritional needs for a parasite (p. 658)

hox genes series of genes that controls the organs and tissues that develop in various parts of an embryo (p. 312)

humoral immunity immunity against pathogens in the body fluids (p. 1036)

humus material formed from decaying leaves and other organic matter (p. 103)

hybrid offspring of crosses between parents with different traits (p. 264)

hybridization breeding technique that involves crossing dissimilar individuals to bring together the best traits of both organisms (p. 319)

hydrostatic skeleton layers of circular and longitudinal muscles, together with the water in the gastrovascular cavity, that enable movement (p. 671)

hypha tiny filament that makes up a multicellular fungus or a water mold (pp. 518, 527)

hypothalamus brain structure that acts as a control center for recognition and analysis of hunger, thirst, fatigue, anger, and body temperature (p. 903)

hypothesis possible explanation for a set of observations or possible answer to a scientific question (pp. 5, 1056)

immigration movement of individuals into an area occupied by an existing population (p. 120)

immune response the body's specific defenses that attack a disease-causing agent (p. 1036)

implantation process in which a blastocyst attaches itself to the wall of the uterus (p. 1017)

imprinting learning based on early experience; once imprinting has occurred, the behavior cannot be changed (p. 876)

inbreeding continued breeding of individuals with similar characteristics (p. 320)

incomplete dominance situation in which one allele is not completely dominant over another (p. 272)

incomplete metamorphosis type of insect development characterized by a similar appearance throughout all stages of the life cycle (p. 729)

independent assortment independent segregation of genes during the formation of gametes (p. 271)

independent variable factor in an experiment that a scientist purposely changes; also known as a responding variable (p. 1056)

index fossil distinctive fossil used to compare the relative ages of fossils (p. 419)

inference logical interpretation based on prior knowledge and experience (p. 4)

inflammatory response nonspecific defense reaction to tissue damage caused by injury or infection (p. 1035)

innate behavior instinct, or inborn behavior; behavior that appears in a fully functional form the first time it is performed (p. 873)

insight learning also called reasoning; learning process in which an animal applies something it has already learned to a new situation without a period of trial and error (p. 875)

interferon one of a group of proteins that help cells resist viral infection (p. 1035)

internal fertilization process in which eggs are fertilized inside the female's body (pp. 666, 690, 758)

internode region between nodes on plant stems (p. 589)

interphase period of the cell cycle between cell divisions (p. 245)

intracellular digestion process in which food is digested inside cells (p. 751)

intron intervening sequence of DNA; does not code for a protein (p. 302)

invasive species plants and animals that have migrated to places where they are not native (p. 153)

invertebrate animal that does not have a backbone or vertebral column (p. 657)

ion atom that has a positive or negative charge (p. 38)

ionic bond bond formed when one or more electrons are transferred from one atom to another (p. 38)

isotope atom of an element that has a number of neutrons different from that of other atoms of the same element (p. 36)

joint place where one bone attaches to another (p. 924)

karyotype set of photographs of chromosomes grouped in order in pairs (p. 341)

kelp forest coastal ocean community named for its dominant organism—kelp (p. 110)

keratin tough, fibrous protein found in skin (p. 934)

kidney organ that removes urea, excess water, and other waste products from the blood and passes them to the ureter (p. 985)

kingdom largest taxonomic group, consisting of closely related phyla (p. 449)

Koch's postulates series of guidelines used to identify the microorganism that causes a specific disease (p. 1030)

Krebs cycle second stage of cellular respiration, in which pyruvic acid is broken down into carbon dioxide in a series of energy-extracting reactions (p. 226)

language system of communication that combines sounds, symbols, or gestures according to a set of rules about word order and meaning (p. 882)

large intestine colon; organ that removes water from the undigested materials that pass through it (p. 984)

larva immature stage of an organism that looks different from the adult form (p. 666)

larynx structure in the throat containing the vocal cords (p. 958)

lateral bud meristematic area on the side of a stem that gives rise to side branches (p. 636)

lateral line system sensitive receptor system that enables fish to detect gentle currents and vibrations in the water (p. 777)

leaf photosynthetic organ that contains one or more bundles of vascular tissue (p. 561)

learning alterations in behavior as a result of experience (p. 873)

lens transparent object behind the iris that changes shape to help adjust the eye's focus to see near or distant objects (p. 907)

lichen symbiotic association between a fungus and a photosynthetic organism (p. 540)

ligament strip of tough connective tissue in a joint that holds bones together (p. 925)

light-dependent reactions reactions of photosynthesis that use energy from light to produce ATP and NADPH (p. 210)

lignin substance in vascular plants that makes cell walls rigid (p. 560)

limiting factor factor that causes the growth of a population to decrease (p. 124)

limiting nutrient single nutrient that either is scarce or cycles very slowly, limiting the growth of organisms in an ecosystem (p. 80)

lipid macromolecule made mainly from carbon and hydrogen atoms; includes fats, oils, and waxes (p. 46)

lipid bilayer double-layered sheet that forms the core of nearly all cell membranes (p. 184)

liver large organ just above the stomach that produces bile, a fluid loaded with lipids and salts (p. 982)

logistic growth growth pattern in which a population's growth rate slows or stops following a period of exponential growth (p. 122)

long-day plant plant that flowers when days are long (p. 641)

loop of Henle section of the nephron tubule that conserves water and minimizes the volume of urine (p. 988)

lymph fluid lost by the blood into surrounding tissue (p. 954)

lysogenic infection process by which a virus embeds its DNA into the DNA of the host cell and is replicated along with the host cell's DNA (p. 485)

lysosome cell organelle filled with enzymes needed to break down certain materials in the cell (p. 178)

lytic infection process in which a virus enters a cell, makes a copy of itself, and causes the cell to burst (p. 485)

macroevolution large-scale evolutionary changes that take place over long periods of time (p. 435)

macronucleus the larger of a ciliate's two nuclei, contains multiple copies of most of the genes that the cell needs in its day-to-day existence (p. 499)

madreporite sievelike structure through which the water vascular system of an echinoderm opens to the outside (p. 735)

malignant term used to describe cancerous tumors, which can invade and destroy surrounding healthy tissue (p. 1046)

Malpighian tubule saclike organ in most terrestrial arthropods that extracts wastes from the blood and adds them to feces that move through the gut (p. 717)

mammary gland gland in mammals that produces milk to nourish the young (p. 821)

mandible mouthpart adapted for biting and grinding food (p. 721)

mangrove swamp coastal wetland dominated by mangroves, salt-tolerant woody plants (p. 108)

manipulated variable factor in an experiment that a scientist purposely changes; also known as independent variable (pp. 9, 1056)

mantle thin layer of tissue that covers most of a mollusk's body (p. 702)

marsupial mammal which bears live young that complete their development in an external pouch (p. 829)

mass extinction event in which many types of living things become extinct at the same time (p. 431)

medulla oblongata area of the brain that controls the functioning of many internal organs (p. 777)

medusa motile stage of the life cycle of a cnidarian that has a bell-shaped body (p. 670)

meiosis process by which the number of chromosomes per cell is cut in half through the separation of homologous chromosomes in a diploid cell (p. 276)

melanin dark-brown pigment found in skin (p. 934)

meninges three layers of connective tissue in which the brain and spinal cord are wrapped (p. 901)

menstrual cycle cycle during which an egg develops and is released from an ovary and the uterus is prepared to receive a fertilized egg (p. 1013)

menstruation last phase of the menstrual cycle, during which the lining of the uterus, along with blood and the unfertilized egg, is discharged through the vagina (p. 1015)

meristematic tissue plant tissue found only in the tips of shoots and roots; responsible for plant growth (p. 580)

mesoderm middle germ layer of most animals; gives rise to muscles and much of the circulatory, reproductive, and excretory systems (p. 661)

mesophyll specialized ground tissue that makes up the bulk of most leaves; performs most of a plant's photosynthesis (p. 596)

messenger RNA (mRNA) RNA molecule that carries copies of instructions for the assembly of amino acids into proteins from DNA to the rest of the cell (p. 301)

metabolism set of chemical reactions through which an organism builds up or breaks down materials as it carries out its life processes (p. 18)

metaphase second phase of mitosis, during which the chromosomes line up across the center of the cell (p. 248)

metastasis spread of a cancerous tumor beyond its original site (p. 1046)

metric system decimal system of measurement based on certain physical standards and scaled on multiples of 10 (p. 24)

microclimate climate within a small area that differs significantly from the climate of the surrounding area (p. 98)

microfilament long, thin fiber that functions in the movement and support of the cell (p. 176)

microfossil microscopic fossil (p. 426)

micronucleus the smaller of a ciliate's two nuclei; contains a "reserve copy" of all of the cell's genes (p. 499)

microscope device that produces magnified images of structures that are too small to see with the unaided eye (p. 25)

microtubule hollow tube of protein that maintains cell shape and can also serve as a "track" along which organelles are moved (p. 176)

migration periodic movement and return of animals from one place to another (p. 878)

mineral inorganic nutrient the body needs, usually in small amounts (p. 975)

mitochondrion cell organelle that releases energy from stored food molecules (p. 180)

mitosis part of eukaryotic cell division during which the cell nucleus divides (p. 245)

mixture material composed of two or more elements or compounds that are physically mixed together but not chemically combined (p. 41)

molecular clock model that uses DNA comparisons to estimate the length of time that two species have been evolving independently (p. 455)

molecule smallest unit of most compounds (p. 38)

molting process in which an arthropod sheds its exoskeleton and manufactures a larger one to take its place (p. 719)

monocot angiosperm whose seeds have one cotyledon (p. 569)

monoculture farming strategy in which large fields are cleared, plowed, and planted with a single, highly productive crop year after year (p. 142)

monomer small unit that can join together with other small units to form polymers (p. 45)

monosaccharide single sugar molecule (p. 46)

monotreme egg-laying mammal (p. 828)

multiple alleles three or more alleles of the same gene (p. 273)

muscle tissue tissue that controls the internal movement of materials in the body, as well as external movement of the entire body or body parts (p. 894)

mutation change in a DNA sequence that affects genetic information (p. 307)

mutualism symbiotic relationship in which both species benefit from the relationship (p. 93)

mycelium many hyphae tangled together into a thick mass; comprises the bodies of multicellular fungi (p. 528)

mycorrhiza symbiotic association of plant roots and fungi (p. 541)

myelin sheath insulating membrane surrounding the axon in some neurons (p. 898)

myocardium thick middle muscle layer of the heart; pumps blood through the circulatory system (p. 944)

myosin protein that makes up the thick filaments in striations in skeletal muscle cells (p. 928)

N

NAD+ (nicotinamide adenine dinucleotide) electron carrier involved in glycolysis (p. 223)

NADP+ (nicotinamide adenine dinucleotide phosphate) one of the carrier molecules that transfers high-energy electrons from chlorophyll to other molecules (p. 209)

natural selection process by which individuals that are better suited to their environment survive and reproduce most successfully; also called survival of the fittest (p. 381)

natural variation differences among individuals of a species (p. 379)

nematocyst stinging structure within each cnidocyte of a cnidarian that is used to poison or kill prey (p. 669)

nephridium excretory organ of an annelid that filters fluid in the coelom (p. 696)

nephron small independent blood-filtering unit in the renal cortex of the kidney (p. 986)

nerve net loosely organized network of nerve cells that together allow cnidarians to detect stimuli (p. 671)

nervous tissue tissue that receives messages from the body's external and internal environment, analyzes the data, and directs the response (p. 894)

neuromuscular junction point of contact between a motor neuron and a skeletal muscle cell (p. 929)

neuron cell that carries messages throughout the nervous system (p. 897)

neurotransmitter chemical used by a neuron to transmit an impulse across a synapse to another cell (p. 900)

niche full range of physical and biological conditions in which an organism lives and the way in which the organism uses those conditions (p. 91)

nicotine stimulant drug in tobacco that increases heart rate and blood pressure (p. 961)

nictitating membrane movable transparent membrane in amphibians located inside the regular eyelid; protects the surface of the eye from damage under water and keeps it moist on land (p. 787)

nitrogen fixation process of converting nitrogen gas into ammonia (pp. 78, 478)

node point on a stem where a leaf is attached (p. 589)

nondisjunction error in meiosis in which homologous chromosomes fail to separate (p. 352)

nonrenewable resource resource that cannot be replenished by natural processes (p. 144)

notochord long supporting rod that runs through a chordate's body just below the nerve cord (pp. 767, 849)

nuclear envelope double-membrane layer that surrounds the nucleus of a cell (p. 176)

nucleic acid macromolecule containing hydrogen, oxygen, nitrogen, carbon, and phosphorus (p. 47)

nucleolus small, dense region within most nuclei in which the assembly of ribosomes begins (p. 176)

nucleotide monomer of nucleic acids made up of a 5-carbon sugar, a phosphate group, and a nitrogenous base (pp. 47, 291)

nucleus the center of the atom which contains the protons and neutrons (p. 35); in cells, large structure inside some cells that contains the cell's genetic material (DNA) and controls the cell's activities (p. 171)

nutrient chemical substance that an organism requires to live (p. 76)

nymph immature form that lacks functional sex organs and other adult structures (p. 729)

observation use of one or more of the senses—sight, hearing, touch, smell, and sometimes taste—to gather information (p. 4)

omnivore organism that obtains energy by eating both plants and animals (p. 69)

oogonium specialized structure formed by hyphae that produces female nuclei (p. 519)

open circulatory system system in which blood is not always contained within a network of blood vessels (pp. 703, 754)

operant conditioning learning process in which an animal learns to behave in a certain way through repeated practice, in order to receive a reward or avoid punishment; also called trial-and-error learning (p. 875)

operational definition description of how a particular variable is to be measured or how a term is to be defined (p. 1057)

operator region of chromosome in an operon to which the repressor binds when the operon is "turned off" (p. 310)

operon group of genes operating together (p. 309)

opposable thumb thumb that enables grasping objects and using tools (p. 835)

order group of similar families (p. 449)

organ group of tissues that work together to perform closely related functions (p. 193)

organ system group of organs that work together to perform a specific function (p. 193)

organelle specialized structure that performs important cellular functions within a eukaryotic cell (p. 172)

osmosis diffusion of water through a selectively permeable membrane (p. 186)

ossification process of bone formation, during which cartilage is replaced by bone (p. 922)

ovary in plants, a flower structure that contains one or more ovules from which female gametophytes are produced (p. 612); in animals, the female gonad that produces eggs (p. 1008)

oviparous term used to refer to animals whose eggs hatch outside the mother's body (p. 778)

ovoviviparous term used to refer to animals whose young are born alive after developing in eggs inside the mother's body (p. 778)

ovulation process in which an egg is released from the ovary (p. 1013)

ovule structure in seed cones in which female gametophytes develop (p. 610)

ozone layer band of ozone, a gas made up of three oxygen atoms (p. 157)

pacemaker small group of cardiac muscle cells in the right atrium that "set the pace" for the heart as a whole; also known as the sinoatrial node (p. 946)

paleontologist scientist who studies fossils (p. 417)

palisade mesophyll layer of tall, column-shaped mesophyll cells just under the upper epidermis of a leaf (p. 596)

pancreas gland that produces hormones that regulate blood sugar; enzymes that break down carbohydrates, proteins, lipids, and nucleic acids; and sodium bicarbonate, a base that neutralizes stomach acid (p. 982)

parasite organism that lives within or on another organism and harms that organism by feeding on it (p. 658)

parasitism symbiotic relationship in which one organism lives in or on another organism and harms it (p. 93)

parenchyma type of ground-tissue cell with a thin cell wall and large central vacuole (p. 583)

pathogen disease-causing agent, such as a bacterium or fungus (pp. 479, 1029)

pedigree chart that shows the relationships within a family (p. 342)

pedipalps pair of mouthparts in chelicerates that are usually modified to grab prey (p. 722)

pellicle cell membrane in euglenas (p. 506)

penis external male reproductive organ that connects the urethra to the outside of the body (p. 1011)

peptic ulcer hole in the stomach wall (p. 981)

perennial flowering plant that lives for more than two years (p. 572)

period unit of time into which eras are subdivided (p. 422)

periosteum tough layer of connective tissue surrounding a bone (p. 922)

peristalsis rhythmic muscular contractions that squeeze food through the esophagus into the stomach (p. 980)

permafrost layer of permanently frozen subsoil in the tundra (p. 104)

permanent immunity condition in which people who have survived exposure to a disease never develop it again (p. 1038)

petal brightly-colored structure just inside the sepals; attracts insects and other pollinators to a flower (p. 612)

petiole thin stalk by which a leaf blade is attached to a stem (p. 595)

pH scale measurement system used to indicate the concentration of hydrogen ions (H^+) in solution; ranges from 0 to 14 (p. 43)

phagocyte white blood cell that engulfs and digests foreign cells (p. 952)

phagocytosis process in which extensions of cytoplasm surround and engulf large particles and take them into the cell (p. 189)

pharyngeal pouch one of a pair of structures in the throat (pharynx) region of a chordate (p. 767)

pharynx muscular tube at the end of the gastrovascular cavity, or throat, that connects the mouth with the rest of the digestive tract and serves as a passageway for air and food (pp. 684, 956)

phenotype physical characteristics of an organism (p. 268)

pheromone specific chemical messenger that affects the behavior or development of other individuals of the same species (p. 731)

phloem vascular tissue responsible for the transport of nutrients and the carbohydrates produced by photosynthesis (p. 560)

photic zone well-lit upper layer of the oceans (p. 109)

photoautotroph prokaryote that carries out photosynthesis in a manner similar to that of plants (p. 474)

photoheterotroph prokaryote that is photosynthetic but also needs organic compounds for nutrition (p. 474)

photoperiodism response of plants to periods of light and darkness (p. 641)

photosynthesis process by which plants and some other organisms use light energy to power chemical reactions that convert water and carbon dioxide into oxygen and high-energy carbohydrates such as sugars and starches (pp. 68, 204)

phototropism tendency of plants to grow toward a source of light (p. 634)

phycobilin accessory pigment found in red algae that is especially good at absorbing blue light (p. 510)

phylum group of closely related classes (p. 449)

phytochrome plant pigment responsible for photoperiodism (p. 641)

phytoplankton population of algae and other small, photosynthetic organisms found near the surface of the ocean and forming part of plankton (pp. 107, 508)

pigment light-absorbing colored molecule (p. 207)

pioneer species first species to populate an area during primary succession (p. 94)

pith parenchyma cells inside the ring of vascular tissue in dicot stems (p. 590)

pituitary gland gland in the base of the skull that secretes nine hormones that directly regulate many body functions and control the actions of several other endocrine glands (p. 1003)

placenta organ in placental mammals through which nutrients, oxygen, carbon dioxide, and wastes are exchanged between embryo and mother (pp. 829, 1018)

plankton tiny, free-floating, weakly swimming organisms that occur in aquatic environments (p. 107)

Plantae kingdom of multicellular photosynthetic autotrophs that have cell walls containing cellulose (p. 461)

plasma straw-colored fluid that makes up about 55 percent of blood; consists of about 90 percent water and about 10 percent dissolved gases, salts, nutrients, enzymes, hormones, waste products, and plasma proteins (p. 951)

plasmid circular DNA molecule found in bacteria (p. 327)

plasmodium structure with many nuclei formed by acellular slime molds (p. 518)

plastron ventral part of a turtle's or tortoise's shell (p. 805)

platelet cell fragment released by bone marrow (p. 953)

point mutation mutation that affects a single nucleotide, usually by substituting one nucleotide for another (p. 307)

polar zone cold climate zone where the sun's rays strike Earth at a very low angle (p. 188)

pollen cone cone in gymnosperms that produces male gametophytes in the form of pollen grains (p. 610)

pollen grain male gametophyte in seed plants (p. 565)

pollen tube structure grown by a pollen grain; contains two haploid sperm nuclei (p. 611)

pollination transfer of pollen from the male gametophyte to the female gametophyte (p. 565)

pollutant harmful material that can enter the biosphere through the land, air, or water (p. 148)

polygenic trait trait controlled by two or more genes (pp. 273, 343, 396)

polymer large compound formed from combinations of many monomers (p. 45)

polymerase chain reaction (PCR) technique that allows molecular biologists to make many copies of a particular gene (p. 325)

polyp usually sessile stage of the life cycle of a cnidarian that has a cylindrical body with armlike tentacles (p. 670)

polyploid having many sets of chromosomes (p. 321)

polysaccharide large macromolecule formed from monosaccharides (p. 46)

population group of individuals of the same species that live in the same area (p. 64)

population density number of individuals per unit of area (p. 119)

predation interaction in which one organism captures and feeds on another organism (p. 93)

predator-prey relationship mechanism of population control in which a population is regulated by predation (p. 126)

prehensile term used to refer to a long tail that can grasp branches (p. 835)

pressure-flow hypothesis hypothesis that considers plants in terms of where they produce and use materials from photosynthesis (p. 602)

primary growth type of plant growth that occurs at the tips of roots and shoots (p. 590)

primary productivity rate at which organic matter is created by producers in an ecosystem (p. 80)

primary succession succession that occurs on surfaces where no soil exists (p. 94)

prion infectious particle made up of protein rather than RNA or DNA (p. 487)

probability likelihood that a particular event will occur (p. 267)

producer organism that can capture energy from sunlight or chemicals and use it to produce food from inorganic compounds; also called an autotroph (p. 67)

product element or compound produced by a chemical reaction (p. 49)

proglottid one of the segments that make up most of a tapeworm's body (p. 688)

prokaryote single-celled microorganism that lacks a nucleus (pp. 172, 471)

promoter region of DNA that indicates to an enzyme where to bind to make RNA (p. 301)

prophase first and longest phase of mitosis, during which the chromosomes become visible and the centrioles separate and take up positions on the opposite sides of the nucleus (p. 246)

prosimian with few exceptions, small, nocturnal primate that has large eyes for seeing in the dark (p. 834)

prostaglandin hormonelike modified fatty acid produced by a wide range of cells; generally affects only nearby cells and tissues (p. 1000)

protein macromolecule that contains carbon, hydrogen, oxygen, and nitrogen; needed by the body for growth and repair and to make up enzymes (pp. 47, 973)

proteinoid microsphere tiny bubble, formed of large organic molecules, that has some characteristics of a cell (p. 425)

protist any eukaryote that is not a plant, an animal, or a fungus (p. 495)

Protista kingdom composed of eukaryotes that are not classified as plants, animals, or fungi (p. 460)

protonema mass of tangled green filaments in mosses that forms during germination (p. 558)

protostome animal whose mouth is formed from its blastopore (p. 661)

pseudocoelom body cavity between the endoderm and mesoderm tissues that is partially lined with mesoderm tissue (p. 689)

pseudopod projection of cytoplasm, or false foot, used by some protists for feeding or movement (p. 498)

puberty period of rapid growth and sexual maturation during which the reproductive system becomes fully functional (p. 1009)

pulmonary circulation pathway in which the right side of the heart pumps blood to the lungs (p. 944)

punctuated equilibrium pattern of evolution in which long stable periods are interrupted by brief periods of more rapid change (p. 439)

Punnett square diagram showing the gene combinations that might result from a genetic cross (p. 268)

pupa stage of metamorphosis in which an insect changes from a larva into an adult (p. 729)

pupil small opening in the middle of the iris through which light enters the eye (p. 906)

radial symmetry body plan in which body parts repeat around the center of the body; characteristic of sea anemones and sea stars (pp. 662, 748)

radioactive dating technique in which scientists calculate the age of a sample based on the amount of remaining radioactive isotopes it contains (p. 420)

radula tongue-shaped structure used for feeding by snails and slugs (p. 702)

reabsorption process by which most of the material removed from the blood at Bowman's capsule makes its way back into the blood (p. 987)

reactant element or compound that enters into a chemical reaction (p. 49)

recombinant DNA DNA produced by combining DNA from different sources (p. 324)

reflex quick automatic response to a stimulus (p. 903)

relative dating method of determining the age of a fossil by comparing its placement with that of fossils in other layers of rock (p. 419)

relative frequency number of times an allele occurs in a gene pool compared with the number of times other alleles occur (p. 394)

renewable resource resource that can regenerate quickly and that is replaceable (p. 144)

replication copying process by which a cell duplicates its DNA (p. 299)

reproductive isolation separation of species or populations so that they cannot interbreed and produce fertile offspring (p. 404)

reptile any vertebrate that has dry scaly skin, lungs, and terrestrial eggs with several protective membranes (p. 797)

resource any necessity of life, such as water, nutrients, light, food, or space (p. 92)

responding variable factor in an experiment that a scientist wants to observe, which may change in response to the manipulated variable; also known as a dependent variable (pp. 9, 1056)

response single, specific reaction to a stimulus (p. 871)

resting potential difference in electrical charge across the cell membrane of a resting neuron (p. 898)

restriction enzyme enzyme that cuts DNA at a specific sequence of nucleotides (p. 323)

retina innermost layer of the eye (p. 907)

retrovirus virus that contains RNA as its genetic information (p. 487)

rhizoid in fungi, a rootlike hypha that penetrates the surface of an object (p. 530); in mosses, a long, thin cell that anchors the moss to the ground and absorbs water and minerals from the surrounding soil (p. 557)

rhizome creeping or underground stem in ferns (p. 562)

ribonucleic acid (RNA) single-stranded nucleic acid that contains the sugar ribose (p. 47)

ribosomal RNA (rRNA) type of RNA that makes up the major part of ribosomes (p. 301)

ribosome small particle in the cell on which proteins are assembled; made of RNA and protein (p. 177)

RNA polymerase enzyme similar to DNA polymerase that binds to DNA and separates the DNA strands during transcription (p. 301)

rod photoreceptor in eye that is extremely sensitive to light (p. 907)

root underground organ in plants that absorbs water and minerals (p. 561)

root cap tough structure that protects a root as it forces its way through the soil (p. 585)

root hair tiny projection from the outer surface, or epidermis, of a root (p. 585)

rumen stomach chamber in cows and related animals in which newly swallowed plant food is stored and processed (p. 823)

S

salt marsh temperate-zone estuary dominated by salt-tolerant grasses above the low-tide line and by seagrasses under water (p. 108)

saprobe organism that obtains food from decaying organic matter (p. 537)

sapwood area in plants that surrounds heartwood and is active in fluid transport (p. 592)

science organized way of using evidence to learn about the natural world; also, the body of knowledge that scientists have built up after years of using this process (p. 3)

sclerenchyma type of ground-tissue cell with an extremely thick, rigid cell wall that makes ground tissue tough and strong (p. 583)

scolex head of an adult tapeworm; can contain suckers or hooks (p. 688)

scrotum external sac containing the testes (p. 1010)

secondary growth pattern of plant growth in which stems increase in width (p. 95)

secondary succession succession following a disturbance that destroys a community without destroying the soil (p. 95)

seed embryo of a living plant that is encased in a protective covering and surrounded by a food supply (p. 565)

seed coat structure that surrounds and protects a plant embryo and keeps it from drying out (p. 565)

seed cone cone that produces female gametophytes (p. 610)

segregation separation of alleles during gamete formation (p. 266)

selective breeding method of improving a species by allowing only those individual organisms with desired characteristics to produce the next generation (p. 319)

selective permeability property of biological membranes that allows only certain substances to pass through them (p. 186)

semicircular canal one of three structures within the inner ear that help an organism maintain balance (p. 908)

seminiferous tubule one of hundreds of tiny tubules in the testes in which sperm are produced (p. 1010)

sensory receptor neuron that reacts directly to light, sound, or other stimuli by sending impulses to other neurons and eventually to the central nervous system (p. 906)

sepal outermost circle of flower parts that encloses a bud before it opens and protects the flower while it is developing (p. 612)

septum internal wall between the segments of an annelid's body (p. 694)

seta bristle attached to the segments of many annelids (p. 694)

sex chromosome one of two chromosomes that determine an individual's sex; females have two X chromosomes; males have one X chromosome and one Y chromosome (p. 341)

sex-linked gene gene located on the X or Y chromosome (p. 350)

sexual reproduction process by which two cells from different parents unite to produce the first cell of a new organism (p. 17)

shell structure in mollusks made by glands in the mantle that secrete calcium carbonate (p. 702)

short-day plant plant that flowers when daylight is short (p. 641)

sieve tube element phloem cell that is joined end-to-end to similar cells to form a continuous sieve tube (p. 582)

single-gene trait trait controlled by a single gene (p. 395)

siphon tubelike structure through which water enters and leaves a mollusk's body (p. 703)

small intestine digestive organ in which most chemical digestion takes place (p. 981)

smog gray-brown mixture of chemicals that occurs as a haze in the atmosphere (p. 148)

society group of closely related animals of the same species that work together for the benefit of the group (p. 732)

soil erosion wearing away of surface soil by water and wind (p. 145)

solute substance that is dissolved in a solvent to make a solution (p. 42)

solution mixture of two or more substances in which the molecules of the substances are evenly distributed (p. 42)

solvent substance in which a solute is dissolved to form a solution (p. 42)

sorus cluster of sporangia on the underside of a fern frond (p. 562)

speciation formation of new species (p. 404)

species group of similar organisms that can breed and produce fertile offspring (p. 64)

species diversity number of different species in the biosphere (p. 150)

spicule spike-shaped structure that makes up the skeletons of harder sponges; made of either chalklike calcium carbonate or glasslike silica (p. 665)

spindle fanlike microtubule structure that helps separate the chromosomes during mitosis (p. 247)

spinneret organ in spiders that contains silk glands (p. 723)

spiracle small opening located along the side of the body through which air enters and leaves the body of many terrestrial arthropods (p. 717)

spirillum spiral or corkscrew-shaped prokaryote (p. 473)

spongy mesophyll loose tissue beneath the palisade layer of a leaf; has many air spaces between its cells (p. 596)

spontaneous generation hypothesis (disproven) stating that life could arise from nonliving matter (p. 8)

sporangiophore specialized hyphae where sporangia are found (p. 528)

sporangium structure in ferns and some fungi that contains spores (pp. 528, 562)

spore haploid reproductive cell (p. 514)

sporophyte diploid, or spore-producing, phase of an organism (pp. 514, 552)

stabilizing selection form of natural selection by which the center of the curve remains in its current position; occurs when individuals near the center of a distribution curve have higher fitness than individuals at either end (p. 399)

stamen male part of the flower; made up of an anther and a filament (p. 612)

stem supporting structure that connects roots and leaves and carries water and nutrients between them (p. 561)

sterilization process of destroying bacteria using great heat or chemical action (p. 481)

stigma sticky portion at the top of the style where pollen grains frequently land (p. 612)

stimulant drug that speeds up the actions regulated by the nervous system (p. 910)

stimulus any kind of detectable signal that carries information (p. 871)

stolon in fungi, a stemlike hypha that runs along the surface of an object (p. 530); in plants, a long, trailing stem that produces roots when it touches the ground (p. 622)

stoma opening in the underside of a leaf that allows carbon dioxide and oxygen to diffuse into and out of the leaf (p. 596)

stomach large muscular sac that continues the mechanical digestion of food (p. 980)

stroma region outside the thylakoid membranes in chloroplasts (p. 208)

struggle for existence competition among members of a species for food, living space, and the other necessities of life (p. 380)

style narrow stalk of the carpel in a flower (p. 612)

subcutaneous fat layer of fat cells beneath the skin (p. 822)

subsistence hunting hunting only to acquire basic necessities for survival; makes relatively few demands on the environment (p. 140)

substrate reactant of an enzyme-catalyzed reaction (p. 52)

survival of the fittest process by which individuals that are better suited to their environment survive and reproduce most successfully; also called natural selection (p. 381)

suspension mixture of water and nondissolved materials (p. 42)

sustainable use using natural resources at a rate that does not deplete them (p. 145)

swim bladder internal gas-filled organ in many bony fishes that adjusts their buoyancy (p. 777)

swimmerets flipperlike appendages used by decapods for swimming (p. 721)

symbiosis relationship in which two species live closely together (p. 93)

synapse location at which a neuron can transfer an impulse to another cell (p. 900)

systemic circulation pathway in which the left side of the heart pumps blood to all of the body except the lungs (p. 944)

taproot primary root found in some plants that grows longer and thicker than other roots (p. 584)

target cell cell affected by a particular hormone (pp. 634, 997)

taste bud sense organ that detects the flavor of a substance (p. 909)

taxon group or level of organization into which organisms are classified (p. 449)

taxonomy discipline of classifying organisms and assigning each organism a universally accepted name (p. 447)

telophase fourth and final phase of mitosis, during which the chromosomes begin to disperse into a tangle of dense material (p. 248)

temperate zone moderate climate zone between the polar zones and the tropics (p. 88)

temporal isolation form of reproductive isolation in which two populations reproduce at different times (p. 405)

tendon tough connective tissue that joins skeletal muscles to bones (p. 930)

territory specific area occupied and protected by an animal or group of animals (p. 881)

testis male gonad that produces sperm (pp. 688, 1008)

tetrad structure containing 4 chromatids that forms during meiosis (p. 276)

thalamus brain structure that receives messages from the sense organs and relays the information to the proper region of the cerebrum for further processing (p. 903)

theory well-tested explanation that unifies a broad range of observations (pp. 14, 369)

thigmotropism response of plants to touch (p. 639)

thorax body part of a crustacean that lies just behind the head and houses most of the internal organs (p. 721)

threshold minimum level of a stimulus required to activate a neuron (p. 899)

thylakoid saclike body in chloroplasts made of photosynthetic membranes that contain photosystems (p. 208)

tissue group of similar cells that perform a particular function (p. 192)

toxin poison that produces illness by disrupting bodily functions (p. 1031)

trachea windpipe; tube through which air moves (p. 956)

tracheal tube one of many branching, air-filled tubes that extend throughout the bodies of many terrestrial arthropods (p. 717)

tracheid hollow plant cell in xylem tissue with thick cell walls that resist pressure (p. 560)

trait specific characteristic that varies from one individual to another (p. 264)

transcription process in which part of the nucleotide sequence of DNA is copied into a complementary sequence in RNA (p. 301)

transfer RNA (tRNA) type of RNA molecule that transfers amino acids to ribosomes during protein synthesis (p. 301)

transformation process in which one strain of bacteria is changed by a gene or genes from another strain of bacteria (p. 288)

transgenic term used to refer to an organism that contains genes from other organisms (p. 331)

translation decoding of a mRNA message into a polypeptide chain (p. 304)

transpiration loss of water from a plant through its leaves (pp. 75, 596)

trichocyst small, bottle-shaped structures used for defense by paramecia (p. 499)

trichome tiny cellular projection on the surfaces of some leaves that helps protect the leaf and also gives it a fuzzy appearance (p. 581)

trochophore free-swimming larval stage of an aquatic mollusk (p. 701)

trophic level step in a food chain or food web (p. 70)

tropical zone warm climate zone that receives direct or nearly direct sunlight year round (p. 88)

tropism response of a plant to an environmental stimulus (p. 639)

true-breeding term used to describe organisms that produce offspring identical to themselves if allowed to self-pollinate (p. 263)

tube foot suction cup-like structure attached to radial canals of echinoderms; used to walk and to open shells (p. 735)

tumor mass of growing tissue that may form when a cell or group of cells begins to grow and divide uncontrollably (p. 1046)

tympanic membrane eardrum of amphibians inside the skull; vibrates in response to sound, allowing hearing (p. 787)

U

understory layer in a rain forest formed by shorter trees and vines (p. 100)

ureter tube that carries urine from the kidney to the urinary bladder (p. 985)

urethra tube through which urine and semen are released from the body (pp. 988, 1011)

urinary bladder saclike organ in which urine is stored before being excreted (p. 985)

uterus organ of the female reproductive system in which a fertilized egg can develop (p. 1013)

V

vaccination injection of a weakened or mild form of a pathogen to produce immunity (p. 1040)

vacuole cell organelle that stores materials such as water, salts, proteins, and carbohydrates (p. 179)

vagina canal in the human female reproductive system that leads from the uterus to the outside of the body (p. 1013)

valve flap of connective tissue between an atrium and a ventricle, or in a vein, that prevents backflow of blood (p. 945)

van der Waals forces a slight attraction that develops between the oppositely charged regions of nearby molecules (p. 39)

variable factor in an experiment that can change (p. 1056)

vas deferens tube that carries sperm from the epididymis to the urethra (p. 1010)

vascular bundle plant stem structure that contains xylem and phloem tissue (p. 590)

vascular cambium lateral meristematic tissue that produces vascular tissues and increases the thickness of the stem over time (p. 591)

vascular cylinder central region of a root that includes the vascular tissue—xylem and phloem (p. 585)

vascular tissue type of plant tissue specialized to conduct water (p. 560)

vector animal that carries disease-causing organisms from person to person (p. 1032)

vegetative reproduction method of asexual reproduction used by many flowering plants (p. 622)

vein in plants, a cluster of vascular tissue in leaves (p. 561); in animals, a blood vessel that returns blood to the heart (p. 947)

ventricle thick-walled lower chamber of the heart that pumps blood out of the heart (pp. 776, 944)

vertebra individual segment of the backbone; encloses and protects the spinal cord (p. 768)

vertebrate animal that has a vertebral column, or backbone (p. 657)

vessel element in angiosperms; xylem cell that forms part of a continuous tube through which water can move (p. 582)

vestigial organ organ that serves no useful function in an organism (p. 385)

villus folded projection that increases the surface area of the walls of the small intestine (p. 983)

virus particle made up of nucleic acid, protein, and in some cases lipids that can replicate only by infecting living cells (p. 482)

visceral mass area beneath the mantle of a mollusk that contains the internal organs (p. 702)

vitamin organic molecule that helps regulate body processes (p. 974)

viviparous term used to refer to animals that bear live young that are nourished directly by the mother's body as they develop (p. 778)

water vascular system system of internal tubes in echinoderms that carries out essential functions such as feeding, respiration, circulation, and movement (p. 735)

weather condition of Earth's atmosphere at a particular time and place (p. 87)

wetland ecosystem in which water either covers the soil, or is present at or near the surface of the soil for at least part of the year (p. 107)

xerophyte desert plant (p. 644)

xylem vascular tissue that carries water upward from the roots to every part of a plant (p. 560)

zonation prominent horizontal banding of organisms that live in a particular habitat (p. 110)

zooplankton tiny animals that form part of the plankton (p. 107)

zoosporangium spore case (p. 518)

zygospore resting spore that contains zygotes formed during the sexual phase of a mold's life cycle (p. 530)

zygote fertilized egg (p. 1016)

Credits

Staff Credits

The people who made up the *Prentice Hall Biology* team—representing design services, editorial, editorial services, market research, marketing services, online services & multimedia development, production services, project office, and publishing processes—are listed below. Bold type denotes the core team members.

Laura Baselice, Diane Braff, **Kristen Cetrulo Braghi,** Jonathan D. Cheney, Christine Cuccio, Patricia M. Dambry, Robert Danielenko, **Irene Ehrmann,** Holly Gordon, **Maureen Grassi,** Jon Greenberg, Kristan Hoskins, Anne Jones, Carol Lavis, **Ellen Levinger, Sandra McGloster,** Chris Maniatis, Natania Mlawer, Carrie O'Connor, **Steve Palme, Rachel Avenia-Prol, Maureen Raymond,** Amy Rosen, Robin Santel, Annette Simmons, **Dori Steinhauff,** Janna Wasilewski, Mike Wevrick

Additional Credits

Greg Abrom, Ernest Albanese, Robert Aleman, Diane Alimena, Gabriella Apolito, Penny Baker, Michele Bigness, Anthony Barone, Barbara Blecher, Chris Callaway, Rui Camarinha, Catherine Caradonna, John Carle, Martha Conway, Lisa Del Gatto, Paul DelSignore, Yvonne Favaro, Elizabeth Forsyth, Catalina Gavilanes, Michael Ginsberg, Evan Holstrom, Beth Hyslip, Helen Issackedes, Catherine Johnson, Susan Karpin, Vicki Lamb, Marguerite McCartney, Vickie Menanteaux, Kathleen Mercandetti, Art Mkrtchayn, LaShonda Morris, Kenneth Myett, Raymond Parenteau, Linda Punskovsky, Bruce Rolff, Laura Ross, Gerry Schrenk, Mildred Schulte, Nancy Sharkey, Lou Suffredini, Kathleen Ventura

t. = Top, b. = Bottom; l. = Left; r. = Right; m. = Middle

Art Credits

Charts and Graphs: Ernest Albanese and Studio A
Aleman, Rob **400, 440, 460** (fungi icons), **461, 610, 612, 630** Art and Science **767, 769, 770** Articulate Graphics **71, 72, 73, 109, 115, 243** (cubes; with E. Albanese), **245, 246–247, 248, 250, 251, 257, 258, 259, 266, 268** t., **269, 270, 271, 272, 276, 277, 278, 283, 284, 290, 291, 294, 295, 298, 300, 301, 302, 303, 304, 305, 306, 307, 308, 309, 310, 311, 312, 315, 316, 322, 323, 324, 325, 326, 327, 328, 329, 332, 337, 338, 342, 343, 347, 349, 350, 352, 356, 358, 360, 361, 364, 472, 483, 484, 485, 498, 499, 500, 506, 523, 661, 679, 680, 718, 852, 944, 953, 959, 999, 1035, 1037, 1038, 1044** Bechtold, Glory **264** (from Biology, The Living Science), **265** (from Biology, The Living Science), **379** (from Science Exporer), Cavallo, Tamara **514, 517, 518, 519, 527, 528, 531, 533, 534, 540, 545, 973, 974, 975** Cummings, Sally **193** r., **979, 980, 995** Dorling Kindersley Publishers **892–893, 903, 922, 933** t.r., **924, 927** t.r., **945** t.r., **955** Duray-Bito, Cecile **414, 436, 450, 450, 465, 467** Gagliano, Tom **35, 36, 38, 39, 40, 41, 42, 44, 45, 46, 47, 48, 52, 57, 92, 153, 164, 184, 185, 186, 187, 188, 189, 193** l. (from Science Explorer), **198, 202, 203, 206, 209** t., **211, 212, 217, 218, 222, 223, 225, 227, 228, 230, 652, 653, 701, 878** (turtles in map), **892–893, 897–900, 902, 907, 908, 917, 998, 1025, 1027** Imagineering **9, 11, 12, 21, 24, 25, 64, 68, 75, 77, 78, 79, 85, 87, 88, 148, 152, 159, 160, 237, 297** (with Articulate Graphics), **299** (with Articulate Graphics), **312, 369, 389, 418, 419, 422, 424, 425, 445, 566, 580** (with Patrice Rossi Calkin), **586** (leaf art), **588, 591, 597, 599, 602, 683, 763, 777, 793, 810**t.l., **811, 817, 825, 858, 859** b., **862** Iverson, Carlyn **69, 384, 501, 513, 517, 518, 685, 687, 688, 689, 694, 697, 702, 703, 711, 772, 773, 774, 776, 782, 783, 786, 803, 823, 826–827, 837, 838, 845, 859** t., **867, 868, 934** Levine, Andy **182, 209** b. Mapping Specialists **89, 91, 99, 101, 148, 153, 156, 159, 165, 348, 371, 383** (with Wendy Smith), **405, 410** (with Ernest Albanese), **700, 724, 832** (with Wendy Smith), **878, 1045** McGregor, Malcolm **423** Miller, Mark **923, 931, 947, 951, 1030, 1036, 1051** Mkrtchyan, Art **195, 460, 461, 807** (icons), **836, 869** Morales, Elizabeth **904, 1010, 1011, 1012, 1014, 1017** (from Biology, The Living Science) Oh, Steve **169, 172, 174, 175, 176, 177, 178, 180, 181, 208, 427, 551** O'Keefe, Laurie **376, 382, 390, 406, 439** (modern horse), **452, 552, 557, 558, 609, 611, 612, 634, 635, 636, 641, 662, 665, 666, 669, 670, 672, 717, 718, 721, 722, 728, 729, 732, 733, 735, 741, 784, 785, 798, 799, 801, 806, 809, 810** b., **812, 824, 849, 860, 862,**

874, 885 Phippin, Spencer **901, 902, 925, 927, 928, 945, 946, 957, 958, 968, 978, 981, 983, 986, 987, 989, 1003, 1005, 1006, 1018** Precision Graphics **111, 280, 288, 290, 334, 461, 554** b., **555, 625, 627, 640, 649, 660, 726, 747, 768, 790, 807** (icons), **850** (icons), **905, 915, 930, 964** Rossi-Calkin, Patrice **280, 511, 554** t., **563, 565, 570, 576, 580** (with Imagineering, Inc.), **581, 582, 584, 585, 587, 589, 590, 593, 595, 596, 600, 602** (with Imagineering, Inc.), **616, 621, 629, 642, 651, 671, 745, 746, 752, 753, 754, 755, 756, 757** Rothman, Michael **96, 97** Smith, Wendy **64, 68, 69, 83, 84, 383** (animals), **692, 832** Woolsey Associates, J/B **41, 209, 226, 259** Adapted from Neil A. Campbell, Jane B. Reece, and Lawrence G. Mitchell, Biology: Concepts and Connections, 3rd ed. (Menlo Park, CA: Benjamin/Cummings, 2000) **973**

Photo Credits

Photo Research: Slip Jig

Cover ©Tim Fitzharris 1996/Minden Pictures, Inc. **Title Page** ©Tim Fitzharris 1996/Minden Pictures, Inc. **ii** F. Rauschenbach/ Natural Selection Stock Photography, Inc. **iii** t. Courtesy of Ken Miller; b. Russ Lappa/PH School **vi** ©Gregory Ochocki/Photo Researchers, Inc. **vii** t. Joseph Van Os/The Image Bank; b. ©XX NCI/CNRI/Phototake NYC/Phototake **ix** Lee Rentz/Bruce Coleman, Inc. **x** t. ©Dorling Kindersley **xi** t. Courtesy of Wolfgang Kaehler; b. ©Kjell B. Sandved/Visuals Unlimited **xiv** ©George Hall/Check Six/PictureQuest **xv** t. Manny Millan/Sports Illustrated; b. ©Michael Fogden/DRK Photo **xvi** t. Pearson Education/PH School; b.l. Pearson Education/PH School; b.r. ©William Leonard/DRK Photo **xvii** t. Pearson Education/ PH School; b. Pearson Education/PH School **xviii** Runk/Schoenberger/ Grant Heilman Photography **xix** t. ©Andy Rouse/DRK Photo; b.l. ©Dan McCoy/ Rainbow; b.r. Richard Anderson/PH School **xx** b. Courtesy of Ken Miller **xxi** Russ Lappa/PH School **xxvii** t.l. ©Harold Hoffman/Photo Researchers, Inc.; t.r. ©Steve Kaufman/DRK Photo **xxii–1** ©Steve Wolper/DRK Photo **2** ©Andrew Syred/Science Photo Library/Photo Researchers, Inc. **3** 35464/13 "Creation of North Sacred Mountain" by Harrison Begay, Navajo. In the Collections of the Museum of Indian Arts and Culture/Laboratory of Anthropology, Museum of New Mexico. Photograph by Blair Clark. **4** t. ©The Stock Market/ Douglas Faulkner; b. ©The Stock Market/John Zoiner **5** ©Jim Sugar Photography/CORBIS **6** CORBISSygma **7** ©Thierry Orban/CORBIS Sygma **9** Animals Animals/©Breck P. Kent **10** ©James L. Amos/CORBIS **12** t. ©Bettmann/CORBIS; b.l. ©CORBIS; b.r. Courtesy of the National Portrait Gallery, London **13** t. ©CORBIS; b.l. ©Julia Cameron/ CORBIS; b.r. ©A. Barrington Brown/Science Source/Photo Researchers, Inc. **14** ©Frans Lanting/ Minden Pictures, Inc. **15** l. Eric and David Hosking/CORBIS; r. ©Tom McHugh/Photo Researchers, Inc. **16** t. ©Chris Bjornberg/Photo Researchers, Inc.; b. ©Marty Cordano/ DRK Photo **17** t. Animals Animals/©Robert Maier; m. ©Dwight R. Kuhn/ DRK Photo; b. ©Biophoto Associates/ Photo Researchers, Inc. **18** l–r: #1 Animals Animals/©E.R. Degginger; l–r: #2 Animals Animals/©Jennifer Loomis; l–r: #3 Animals Animals/©Patti Murray; l–r: #4 Animals Animals/ ©Patti Murray; b. Animals Animals/©Bruce Davidson **19** ©Ron Spomer/Visuals Unlimited **20** l. ©Michael Fogden/DRK Photo; r. ©Michael Fogden/DRK Photo **22** ©Zigy Kaluzny/ Stone **23** Stephff/Cartoonists & Writers Syndicate **26** t. ©Kevin and Betty Collins/Visuals Unlimited; m. ©M.I. Walker/Photo Researchers, Inc.; b. ©Oliver Meckes/Photo Researchers, Inc. **27** ©The Stock Market/Charles Gupton **28** ©Paul Chelsley/ Stone **31** Anthony Bannister; Gallo Images/CORBIS **34** Animals Animals/©Patti Murray **37** t.l. ©PhotoDisc, Inc., 2001; t.r. Richard Anderson/Pearson Education/PH School **39** t.l. Kellar Autumn & Ed Florance; t.r. ©Mark Moffett/Minden Pictures, Inc.; b. ©Mark Moffett/Minden Pictures, Inc. **40** Wood Sabold/Index Stock Photography, Inc. **41** ©Mark Moffett/Minden Pictures, Inc. **45** ©Bill Bachmann/Photo Network/PictureQuest **46** ©Ricardo Arias, Latin Stock/Science Photo Library/Photo Researchers, Inc. **49** Richard Megna/Fundamental Photographs **53** t. Thomas Steitz, Yale University; b. Thomas Steitz, Yale University **54** Pearson Education/PH School **55** Pearson Education/PH School **56** Wood Sabold/Index Stock Photography, Inc. **60–61** Corel Professional Photos CD-ROM™ **62** ©Bruce Coleman, Ltd./Natural Selection **63** ©Gerry Ellis/Minden Pictures, Inc. **65** ©Mark Moffett/Minden Pictures, Inc. **66** t.l. U.S. Department of the Interior/ U.S. Geological Survey; t.r. U.S. Department of the Interior/ U.S. Geological Survey; b. Provided by the SeaWiFS Project, NASA/Goddard Space Flight Center, and ORBIMAGE **67** ©Gregory Ochocki/Photo Researchers, Inc. **69** ©Rod Planck/Photo Researchers, Inc. **70** Pearson Education/ PH

Gulin/DRK Photo **320** t. ©Mitsuaki Iwago/Minden Pictures, Inc.; b. ©Manfred Kage/Peter Arnold, Inc. **321** Runk/Schoenberger/Grant Heilman Photography **326** Pearson Education/PH School **330** N. Cobbing. ©Still Pictures/Peter Arnold, Inc. **331** ©Keith V. Wood/Visuals Unlimited **333** "PA" News **335** Pearson Education/PH School **340** ©The Stock Market/Rob Lewine **341** ©CNRI/Science Photo Library/Photo Researchers, Inc. **343** ©Craig Farraway **344** ©The Stock Market/Charles Gupton **346** ©Simon Fraser/RVI, Newcastle-Upon Tyne/ Science Photo Library/Photo Researchers, Inc. **347** ©Omikron/ Photo Researchers, Inc. **349** Leslie Jones/CORBIS **352** ©PhotoDisc, Inc., 2001 **353** t.l. ©Lawrence Migdale; t.r. ©Dr. Dennis Kunkel/CNRI/ Phototake **354** AP/Wide World Photos **355** t. ©James King-Holmes/ Science Photo Library/ Photo Researchers, Inc.; b. AP/Wide World Photos **356** l. ©Leonard Lessin/Peter Arnold, Inc.; r. ©D. VoTrung/Phototake **357** Paul Hosefros/NYT Permissions **359** t.l. ©PhotoDisc, Inc., 2001; t.r. ©2000 Ron Caesar **362** ©CNRI/Science Photo Library/Photo Researchers, Inc. **366–367** ©1996 Jack S. Grove c/o Mira **368** Art Wolfe Incorporated **370** l. Syndics of Cambridge University Library; r. ©Joe McDonald/Bruce Coleman, Inc./PictureQuest **371** t. ©D. Cavagnaro/ DRK Photo; m. ©M. Cavagnaro/DRK Photo; b. ©D. Cavagnaro/DRK Photo **372** ©Frans Lanting/Photo Researchers, Inc. **373** ©Bibliotheque des Arts Decoratifs, Paris, France/Archives Charmet/Bridgeman Art Library **374** t. ©Tom Bean/DRK Photo; m. The Granger Collection, New York; b. Stock Montage, Inc. **375** t.l. The Granger Collection, New York; t.r. Brown Brothers; b. ©2000 North Wind Picture Archives **377** Archiv für Kunst und Geschichte, Berlin **378** Mark Downey/Index Stock Photography, Inc. **379** Pearson Education/PH School **380** ©J. Sneesby/B. Wilkins/Stone **381** ©Ron Austing/Photo Researchers, Inc. **382** Neil Fletcher/©Dorling Kindersley **385** t. Harry Taylor/©Dorling Kindersley; b.l. ©George Whiteley/Photo Researchers, Inc.; m.b. Animals Animals/©Keith Gillett; b.r. ©David Spears/ Science Photo Library/Photo Researchers, Inc. **386** ©ARCHIV/Photo Researchers, Inc. **390** t. ©M. Cavagnaro/ DRK Photo; b. ©D. Cavagnaro/DRK Photo **392** ©J. Eastcott & Y. Momatiuk/Masterfile Stock Image Library **393** ©Melanie Carr/ Zephyr Photos **395** l. ©David Young-Wolff/PhotoEdit/PictureQuest; r. ©David Young-Wolff/PhotoEdit/ PictureQuest **396** New York Public Library, (Rare Book Division or Print Collection. Miriam and Ira D. Wallach Division of Art, Prints and Photographs); Astor, Lenox and Tilden Foundations **397** ©Charlie Ott/Photo Researchers, Inc. **399** ©Melanie Carr/Zephyr Photos **401** Pearson Education/PH School **402** ©Lee F. Snyder/Photo Researchers, Inc. **403** ©David R. Frazier/Photo Researchers, Inc. **404** l. ©Harold Hoffman/ Photo Researchers, Inc.; r. ©Steve Kaufman/DRK Photo **405** t. ©Danny Lehman/CORBIS; inset: l. Animals Animals/©Breck P. Kent; inset: r. ©Tom & Pat Leeson/DRK Photo **407** t. Photograph by B.R. Grant; b. Photograph by P.R. Grant **409** Yahn Arthus-Bertrand/CORBIS **411** Pearson Education/PH School **416** Jackie Beckett/American Museum of Natural History **417** Ira Block/National Geographic Society **419** l. ©David Hanson/Stone; r. CORBIS **425** ©Sidney Fox/Visuals Unlimited **426** ©Fred Bavendam/Peter Arnold, Inc. **428** British Museum of Natural History, London **429** ©D.W. Miller **430** British Museum of Natural History, London/J. Sibbick **431** t. The Field Museum, Chicago, Il; b. Lefever/ Grushow/ Grant Heilman Photography **432** 1989 Mark Hallett **433** t. The Natural History Museum London/M. Long; b.l. ©PhotoDisc, Inc., 2001; b.r. Dan Olson/Pearson Education/PH School **434** ©Douglas Henderson **435** ©D. Van Ravenswaay/Science Photo Library/ Photo Researchers, Inc. **437** t. ©PhotoDisc, Inc., 2001; m. ©Wayne Lynch/ DRK Photo; b. Mike Bacon/Tom Stack & Associates **438** t. The Natural History Museum, London; b. ©Charles Marden Fitch **439** t-b: 2 Sean Milne/©Dorling Kindersley; t-b: 3 Sean Milne©Dorling Kindersley; t-b: 4 Sean MiIne/©Dorling Kindersley; t-b: 5 Sean Milne/©Dorling Kindersley **441** Pearson Eduction/School Division **446** Steve Winter **447** ©Jeff Lepore/Photo Researchers, Inc. **448** ©Kenneth W. Fink/Photo Researchers, Inc. **449** t. CORBIS; bl. ©Art Wolfe/Photo Researchers, Inc.; mb. Animals Animals/©Norbert Rosing; br. Daniel J. Cox/naturalexposures.com **451** t.l. Animals Animals/©Rudolf Ingo Riepl ;b.l. ©Peter Howorth/Mo Yung Productions/ www.norbertwu.com; b.r. ©Nancy Sefton/Photo Researchers, Inc. **454** t. ©Barbara Gerlach/ DRK Photo; b. ©D. Parer & E. Parer-Cook/ Auscape International Photo Library **456** t. ©Marie Selby Botanical Gardens; b. ©Marie Selby Botanical Gardens **457** l. ©Michael Abbey/ Photo Researchers, Inc.; r. ©CNRI/ Phototake **463** cw:1 Matthew Ward/©Dorling Kindersley; cw:2 ©Dorling Kindersley; cw:3 Matthew Ward/©Dorling Kindersley; cw:4 ©Dorling Kindersley; cw:5 ©Dorling Kindersley; cw:6 Matthew Ward/©Dorling Kindersley; m. Matthew Ward/©Dorling Kindersley **468–469** ©David M. Dennis **470** ©Beth

Donidow/Visuals Unlimited **471** Esther R. Angert, Harvard University **472** ©M. Wurtz/Biozentrum, University of Basel/Science Photo Library/Photo Researchers, Inc. **473** t.l. ©David Scharf/Peter Arnold, Inc.; t.r. ©Scott Camazine/Photo Researchers, Inc.; m.t. ©David M. Phillips/Visuals Unlimited; m.r. ©Biodisc/Visuals Unlimited; b. ©CNRI/Phototake **474** ©Fred McConnaughey/Science Source/Photo Researchers, Inc. **475** l. ©PhotoDisc, Inc., 2001; r. Courtesy of Elizabeth Lawton; b. ©Dr. Dennis Kunkel/ Phototake **476** t. ©Dr. Dennis Kunkel/Phototake; b. ©Dr. Dennis Kunkel/Phototake **477** ©Michael P. Gadomski/Photo Researchers, Inc. **478** l. ©Richard L. Carlton/Visuals Unlimited; m. W. J. Short; b. Hulton-Deutsch Collection/CORBIS **479** t. Brown Brothers; b. Chris Ware/Liaison Agency **480** SuperStock **482** ©Norm Thomas/Photo Researchers, Inc. **483** l. ©M. Wurtz/Biozentrum, University of Basel/Science Photo Library/Photo Researchers; m. ©Dr. O. Bradfute/Peter Arnold, Inc.; r. ©National Institute for Biological Standards and Control, England/Photo Researchers, Inc. **486** Pearson Education/PH School **487** Sinclair Stammers/Science Photo Library/ Photo Researchers, Inc. **488** ©Meckes/Ottawa/Photo Researchers, Inc. **489** Pearson Education/PH School **490** t. ©M. Wurtz/Biozentrum, University of Basel/Science Photo Library/Photo Researchers, Inc.; b. ©Dr. Dennis Kunkel/ Phototake **491** t.l. ©M. Wurtz/Biozentrum, University of Basel/Science Photo Library/Photo Researchers, Inc.; t.r. ©David M. Phillips/Visuals Unlimited; b.l. ©David Scharf/Peter Arnold, Inc.; b.r. ©Scott Camazine/Photo Researchers, Inc. **494** ©Biophoto Associates/Photo Researchers, Inc. **495** l. ©Manfred Kage/Peter Arnold, Inc.; m. ©Manfred Kage/Peter Arnold, Inc.; r. ©M.I. Walker/Photo Researchers, Inc. **496** ©T.E. Adams/Visuals Unlimited **497** l. ©Michael Abbey/Photo Researchers, Inc.; r. ©Oliver Meckes/Photo Researchers, Inc. **498** Runk/Schoenberger/ Grant Heilman Photography **499** ©Eric V. Grave/Photo Researchers, Inc. **501** ©Oliver Meckes/Photo Researchers, Inc. **502** ©Robert Brons/Biological Photo Service **503** l. ©Dr. Dennis Kunkel/ Phototake; r. ©Eric Grave/Science Source/Photo Researchers, Inc. **504** ©Garry D. McMichael 1987/Photo Researchers, Inc. **505** ©A. Flowers & L. Newman/Photo Researchers, Inc. **506** ©M. Abbey/Visuals Unlimited **507** t. ©Dr. Dennis Kunkel/Phototake; b. ©Dr. Dennis Kunkel/Phototake **509** t. ©Bill Bachman/Photo Researchers, Inc.; inset ©David M. Phillips/ Visuals Unlimited **510** ©G. Robinson/Visuals Unlimited **512** t. Biophoto Assoc./Photo Researchers, Inc.; m. ©James W. Richardson/Visuals Unlimited; b. ©Laurie Campbell/ NHPA **515** t. ©StockFood America/Eising; b. ©StockFood America/DeSanto **516** ©L. West/Photo Researchers, Inc. **517** ©Matt Meadows/Peter Arnold, Inc. **518** ©Dr. Dennis Kunkel/Phototake **520** t. The Granger Collection, New York b.l. ©E. Webber/Visuals Unlimited; b.r. ©Holt Studios Int./Photo Researchers, Inc. **521** Pearson Education/PH School **526** ©D. Cavagnaro/DRK Photo **528** t. ©Sarah J. Frankling/Stone; b. Robert & Linda Mitchell Photography **529** ©Jeff Lepore/Photo Researchers, Inc. **532** Lee Rentz/Bruce Coleman, Inc. **535** t.l. ©Jeff Lepore/Photo Researchers, Inc.; t.r. ©Laurie Campbell/ Stone; m.t. ©Robert W. Domm/Visuals Unlimited; m.b. ©Michael Fogden/DRK Photo; b.l. ©Michael Fogden/DRK Photo; b. ©Ed Reschke/Peter Arnold, Inc. **536** t. ©Jack M. Bostrack/Visuals Unlimited; b. ©David Scharf/Peter Arnold, Inc. **537** D. Redecker (B-E), R. Kodner (A); ©Science, 2000 **538** ©Stephen G. Maka/DRK Photo **539** t.l. ©Astrid & Hanns-Frieder Michler/Science Photo Library/Photo Researchers, Inc.; m.t. ©Holt Studios International/Nigel Cattlin/Photo Researchers, Inc.; t.r. ©Dr. P. Marazzi/Photo Researchers, Inc.; b. ©Michael Fogden/DRK Photo **540** t. ©Courtney Milne; m. ©Jack Dermid; b. ©L. West/Photo Researchers, Inc. **541** ©Phil Matt/Stone **542** t. ©John D. Cunningham/Visuals Unlimited; b. Runk/Schoenberger/Grant Heilman Photography **543** Pearson Education/PH School **548–549** ©Clyde H. Smith/Peter Arnold, Inc. **550** ©Frans Lanting/ Minden Pictures, Inc. **551** Runk/Schoenberger/ Grant Heilman Photography **552** ©Russell D. Curtis/Photo Researchers, Inc. **553** t. Jane Grushow/Grant Heilman Photography; b. Animals Animals/ ©Joyce & Frank Burek **554** Hans Steur, The Netherlands **555** cw: 1 ©Dorling Kindersley; cw: 2 ©Ed Reschke/Peter Arnold, Inc.; cw: 3 ©Ed Reschke/ Peter Arnold, Inc.; cw: 4 ©Pat Lynch/Photo Researchers, Inc. **556** ©Terry Donnelly/Stone **557** l. ©Alvin E. Staffan/National Audubon Society/Photo Researchers, Inc. r. Robert & Linda Mitchell Photography **559** ©Farrell Greham/Photo Researchers, Inc. **560** t. Peter Chadwick/©Dorling Kindersley; b. Photo Researchers, Inc. **561** l. ©Gary W. Carter/Visuals Unlimited; r. ©Ed Reschke/Peter Arnold, Inc. **562** t. ©Peter Chadwick/Dorling Kindersley; b.l. ©Biophoto Associates/ Photo Researchers, Inc.; b.r. ©Ed Reschke/Peter Arnold, Inc. **564** Animals Animals/©Erwin & Peggy Bauer **565** ©PhotoDisc, Inc., 2001 **566** t. Dr. E.R. Degginger; b. Peter Chadwick/©Dorling Kindersley; r. Larry Lefever/Grant Heilman Photography **573** ©Fritz Polking/Visuals Unlimited **574** ©Dorling Kindersley **575** ©Stephen G. Muka/DRK Photo **576** Brian Parker/ Tom Stack & Associates **577** ©Hans Steur, The Netherlands **578** ©Manfred Kage/Peter Arnold, Inc. **581** t.l. Ray F. Evert, University of Wisconsin; t.r. Ray F. Evert, University of Wisconsin; b. ©Andrew Syred/Science Photo Library/Photo Researchers, Inc. **582** Ray F. Evert, University of Wisconsin **583** l. ©Ed Reschke/Peter Arnold, Inc.; m. ©Ed Reschke/Peter Arnold, Inc.; r. ©George Wilder/Visuals Unlimited **585** ©Carolina Biological Supply/Phototake **590** l. ©Ed Reschke/Peter Arnold, Inc.; r. ©Ed Reschke/Peter Arnold, Inc. **592** ©Manfred Kage/Peter Arnold, Inc. **594** t.l. Barry L. Runk/Grant Heilman Photography; t.r. ©Dorling Kindersley; b.l. ©Geoff Dann/Dorling Kindersley; b.r. ©Dorling Kindersley **597** ©Dr. Jeremy Burgess/Science Photo Library/Photo Researchers, Inc. **598** l. ©Kjell B. Sandved/Visuals Unlimited; m. ©Doug Sokell/Visuals Unlimited; t.r. ©Brian P. Foss/ Visuals Unlimited; b.r. ©Kjell B. Sandved/ Visuals Unlimited **600** ©Jack M. Bostrack/Visuals Unlimited **601** Pearson Education/PH School **608** ©Carl R. Sams II/Peter Arnold, Inc. **610** t. ©Walter H. Hodge/Peter Arnold, Inc.; b.l. ©Martha Cooper/Peter Arnold, Inc.; b.r. ©Manfred Kage/Peter Arnold, Inc. **612** l. ©Nigel Cattlin/H.S.I./Photo Researchers, Inc.; r. ©Rod Planck/Photo Researchers, Inc. **613** t. Pearson Education/PH School; b.l. Geoff Dann©Dorling Kindersley; b.r. CORBIS **615**; t.r. ©Geoff Bryant/Photo Researchers, Inc. **615** b.l. Animals Animals/©Carroll W. Perkins; b.r. ©M. H. Sharp/Photo Researchers, Inc. **617** t. Florigene Limited; b. Florigene Limited **618** t.l. ©Dorling Kindersley; b.l. ©Dorling Kindersley; b.r. ©Dorling Kindersley **619** t. ©Gregory K. Scott/Photo Researchers, Inc.; b. ©Stephen J. Krasemann/Photo Researchers, Inc. **620** ©L. Linkhart /Visuals Unlimited **622** Runk/Schoenberger/Grant Heilman Photography **623** t. ©Michael P. Gadomski/Photo Researchers, Inc.; b. ©Holt Studios Int./Photo Researchers, Inc. **624** t. ©Wolfgang Kaehler/Peter Arnold, Inc.; m.l. ©PhotoDisc, Inc., 2001; m.r. SBG; b.l. ©Werner H. Muller/Peter Arnold, Inc.; b.r. ©Karen Su/CORBIS **625** t.l. ©Holt Studios Int./Nigel Cattlin/Photo Researchers, Inc.; t.r. ©David Cavagnaro/Peter Arnold, Inc.; b. ©PhotoDisc, Inc., 2001 **626** ©Michael P. Gadomski/Photo Researchers, Inc. **628** ©Walter H. Hodge/Peter Arnold, Inc. **632** ©Dr. Paul A. Zahl/Photo Researchers, Inc. **633** Animals Animals/©Dani/ Jeske **635** Dr. E.R. Degginger **637** ©Sylvan Wittwer/Visuals Unlimited **638** Courtesy of Stephen Gladfelter, Stanford University **639** ©Charles D.Winters/ Photo Researchers, Inc. **640** t. ©Ed Reschke/Peter Arnold, Inc.; b. ©Ed. Reschke/Peter Arnold, Inc. **642** ©Ed. Reschke/Peter Arnold, Inc. **643** ©Paul A. Souders/CORBIS **644** ©Doug Sokell/Visuals Unlimited **645** t. Sean Morris/©Oxford Scientific Films; b. ©Ray Pfortner/ Peter Arnold, Inc. **646** l. ©Bill Ivy/Stone; r. ©Rod Planck/Photo Researchers, Inc. **647** ©David Cavagnaro/Peter Arnold, Inc. **648** ©Jack Bostrack/ Visuals Unlimited **654–655** ©Wayne Lynch/DRK Photo **656** ©Jeff Greenberg/Photo Researchers, Inc. **657** ©Ken Highfill/Photo Researchers, Inc. **658** t.l. ©John Cancalosi/ DRK Photo; m.l. Super-Stock; b.l. ©BIOS (F. Marquez)/Peter Arnold, Inc.; b.r. ©Roger Eriksson **659** l. ©Anthony Bannister/Photo Researchers, Inc.; r. ©Kevin Schafer/Stone; b. ©Tom & Pat Leeson/Photo Researchers, Inc.; t. ©Carolina Biological Supply/Phototake **661** m. ©Carolina Biological Supply/ Phototake; b. ©Carolina Biological Supply /Phototake **663** F. Rauschenbach/Natural Selection Stock Photography, Inc. **664** l. ©Mary Beth Angelo/Photo Researchers, Inc.; r. ©Charles V. Angelo/Photo Researchers, Inc. **667** ©Fred McConnaughey/Photo Researchers, Inc. **668** ©Larry Dunmire/Photo Network/PictureQuest **671** l. Jeffrey L. Rotman; r. ©Mary Beth Angelo/Photo Researchers, Inc. **673** t.l. Copyright ©2000 Harbor Branch Oceanographic/E. Widder; t.r. Copyright ©2000 Harbor Branch Oceanographic; b. ©2001 Norbert Wu/ www.norbertwu.com **674** ©Doug Perrine/Innerspace Visions **675** ©2001 Norbert Wu/www.norbertwu.com **676** t. Pearson Education/PH School; b. ©Science Pictures Limited/CORBIS **682** ©Jeffrey L. Rotman **683** ©Fred McConnaughey/Photo Researchers, Inc. **684** ©Drs. Kessel and Shih/ Peter Arnold, Inc. **685** ©Carolina Biological Supply Company/Phototake **686** l. ©Jeffrey L. Rotman/Peter Arnold, Inc.; r. ©Brian Rogers/Visuals Unlimited **688** ©Oliver Meckes/Photo Researchers, Inc. **689** ©Cabisco/Visuals Unlimited **690** t. ©Oliver Meckes/Photo Researchers, Inc.; b. ©David Scharf/ Peter Arnold, Inc. **691** t.l. ©PhotoDisc, Inc., 2001; t.r. Jim Foster/ Pearson Education/PH School; b. ©R. Umesh Chandran, TDR, WHO/Science Photo Library/Photo Researchers, Inc. **692** ©C. James Webb/Phototake NYC **693** l. ©Sinclair Stammers/Science Photo Library/Photo Researchers, Inc.; r. ©Fernand Ivaldi/Stone **694** ©Kjell B. Sandved/Visuals Unlimited **695** t. Pearson Education/PH School; b.

Animals Animals/©Raymond A. Mendez **696** t. ©Aldo Brando/Peter Arnold, Inc.; b. Bruce Coleman, Inc. **698** t.l. ©C.P. Hickman/Visuals Unlimited; t.r. National Archives; b. ©Hal Beral/Visuals Unlimited **699** ©Robert Pickett/CORBIS **701** ©Kelvin Aitken/Peter Arnold, Inc. **704** left: 1 ©Jane Burton/Dorling Kindersley; left: 2 Jane Burton/ ©Dorling Kindersley; left: 3 ©Jane Burton/Dorling Kindersley; left: 4 ©Jane Burton/Dorling Kindersley; b. ©Fred Bavendam/Peter Arnold, Inc. **705** t.l. ©A. Flowers and L. Newman/Photo Researchers, Inc.; t.r. ©William J. Weber/Visuals Unlimited; b.r. ©Alexandra Edwards/Peter Arnold, Inc. **706** ©Fred Bavendam/Peter Arnold, Inc.; b. ©Dave B. Fleetham/ Visuals Unlimited **707** ©Frank Greenway/Dorling Kindersley **708** ©Heather R. Davidson **710** ©Jeffrey L. Rotman/Peter Arnold, Inc. **712** ©Marty Snyderman/Visuals Unlimited; b. ©T.E. Adams/Visuals Unlimited **714** ©Leroy Simon/Visuals Unlimited **715** ©Carolina Biological Supply/Phototake **716** t. ©John Cancalosi/DRK Photo; b. ©Dorling Kindersley **719** Barry L. Runk/Grant Heilman Photography **720** ©Rod Planck/Photo Researchers, Inc. **723** t. ©Franz Lanting/ Minden Pictures, Inc.; b. ©Dorling Kindersley **724** t. ©R. Calentine/Visuals Unlimited b. ©BIOS (X. Eichaker)/Peter Arnold, Inc. **725** t. ©Tom McHugh/Photo Researchers, Inc.; b. ©Michael & Patricia Fogden/ DRK Photo **726** t. Wolfgang Kaehler Photography; b.l. ©Dorling Kindersley; b.r. ©M.C. Chamberlain/DRK Photo **727** ©Dorling Kindersley **728** ©Stephen Dalton/Photo Researchers, Inc. **730** t. ©Martin Dohrn/Science Photo Library/Photo Researchers, Inc.; b.l. ©David Scharf/Peter Arnold, Inc.; b.r. ©Galen Rowell/CORBIS **731** t. ©E. R. Degginger/Photo Researchers, Inc.; b. AP/Wide World Photos/David Jennings **734** ©Glenn M. Oliver/Visuals Unlimited **736** ©Dorling Kindersley **737** t. ©Charles V. Angelo/Photo Researchers, Inc. m. Animals Animals/©Clay Wiseman b.l. ©Fred Bavendam/Peter Arnold, Inc. b.r. ©Andrew J. Martinez/Photo Researchers, Inc. **738** t. ©M.C. Chamberlain/DRK Photo; b. ©James Amos/Photo Researchers, Inc. **744** ©Doug Perrine/Innerspace Visions **746** Chip Clark/National Museum of Natural History, Smithsonian **751** ©Ray Coleman/Photo Researchers, Inc. **753** Pearson Education/PH School **757** ©Lawrence Naylor/Photo Researchers, Inc. **758** l. ©Brandon D. Cole; r. ©Kelvin Aitken/Peter Arnold, Inc. **759** Pearson Education/PH School **764–765** ©Merlin D. Tuttle/Bat Conservation International **766** ©Art Wolfe/ Stone **769** Animals Animals/©W. Gregory Brown **770** Runk/ Schoenberger/Grant Heilman Photography **771** ©Labat-Lanceau/ AUSCAPE International **773** Dr. Michael E. Williams/Cleveland Museum of Natural History **774** ©Peter David/Masterfile Stock Image Library **775** t. Pearson Education/PH School; b. Animals Animals/©A. Root **777** ©Richard T. Nowitz/Photo Researchers, Inc. **778** t. ©Natalie Fobes/Stone m. Animals Animals/©Zig Leszczynski b. ©Brian Parker/Tom Stack & Associates **779** t. Howard Hall Productions; m. Animals Animals/©Herb Segars; b. ©Stephen Frink/Stone **780** t.l. ©Fred Bavendam/Minden Pictures, Inc.; m.t. ©Fred Bavendam/ Minden Pictures, Inc.; t.r. ©Norbert Wu/DRK Photo; m.l. ©Stephen Frink/Waterhouse Stock; m.r. Howard Hall Productions; b. ©Mark Erdmann/ Innerspace Visions **781** ©Ralph A. Clevenger/CORBIS **787** Animals Animals/©Bill Beatty **788** t.l. ©William Leonard/DRK Photo; b.l. Animals Animals/©Juan Manuel Renjifo; b.r. ©Dorling Kindersley **789** Animals Animals/©Stephen Dalton **790** t. ©RogerTreadwell/Visuals Unlimited; b. Animals Animals/©M. Gibbs **791** Pearson Education/PH School **792** t. ©William Leonard/ DRK Photo; b. ©Labat-Lanceau/AUSCAPE International **796** ©Bruce Coleman, Ltd./Natural Selection **797** ©David A. Northcott/CORBIS **800** ©Joe McDonald/ Natural Selection **801** ©Michael Fogden/DRK Photo **802** t.l. ©Michael Fogden/DRK Photo; t.r. ©Michael Fogden/DRK Photo; b. ©E.R. Degginger/Photo Researchers, Inc. **803** ©K.H. Switak/Photo Researchers, Inc. **804** t.l. ©Dorling Kindersley; t.r. ©Anup Shah/DRK Photo; m. Michael & Patricia Fogden/ CORBIS; b.l. ©John Cancalosi/ Peter Arnold, Inc.; b.r. ©Gary Retherford/Photo Researchers, Inc. **805** Gerry Ellis/gerryellis.com **807** ©Sinclair Stammers/Science Photo Library/ Photo Researchers, Inc. **808** t–b:1 Steve Gettle/gerryellis.com; t–b: 2 ©Joe McDonald/DRK Photo; t–b: 3 Gerry Ellis/gerryellis.com; t–b: 4 ©Michael Fogden/DRK Photo; t–b: 5 ©Joe McDonald/ DRK Photo; t–b: 6 ©Frans Lanting/Minden Pictures, Inc. **813** cw: 1 ©Stephen J. Krasemann/DRK Photo; cw: 2 Michael Gore; Frank Lane Picture Agency/ CORBIS; cw: 3 ©Tim Davis/Photo Researchers, Inc.; cw: 4 ©M.H. Sharp/Photo Researchers, Inc.; cw: 5 ©PhotoDisc, Inc., 2001; cw: 6 Seldon Jr., W. Lynn/Omni-Photo Communications, Inc.; m. ©2000, Gail Shumway/FPG International LLC **814** ©Wayne Lankinen/DRK Photo **815** AP/Wide World Photos **816** ©Dorling Kindersley **820** Animals Animals/©Zig Leszczynski **821** ©Frans Lanting/ Minden Pictures, Inc. **822** t. Daniel J. Cox/naturalexposures.com; b. ©Flip Nicklin/Minden

Note: *Every effort has been made to locate the copyright owner of material reprinted in this book. Omissions brought to our attention will be corrected in subsequent editions.*